1966
FORD-MERCURY
SHOP MANUAL

GROU

VEHICLE IDENTIFICATION	1
BRAKES	2
SUSPENSION, STEERING, WHEELS AND TIRES	3
REAR AXLE	4
DRIVE SHAFT AND CLUTCH	5
MANUAL SHIFT TRANSMISSION	6
AUTOMATIC TRANSMISSION	7
ENGINE	8
IGNITION SYSTEM	9
FUEL SYSTEM	10
COOLING SYSTEM	11
EXHAUST SYSTEM	12
CHARGING SYSTEM	13
STARTING SYSTEM	14
LIGHTING SYSTEM, HORNS AND INSTRUMENTS	15
VENTILATING, HEATING AND ACCESSORIES	16
BODY, DOORS AND WINDOWS	17
TRIM, SEATS AND CONVERTIBLE TOP	18
MAINTENANCE SCHEDULE	19
MAINTENANCE OPERATIONS	20
LUBRICATION CHARTS AND SPECIFICATIONS	21
SCHEMATICS	22

SPECIFICATIONS AND SPECIAL SERVICE TOOLS AT END OF EACH GROUP

 SERVICE PUBLICATIONS

FIRST PRINTING—AUGUST, 1965
© 1965 FORD MOTOR COMPANY, DEARBORN, MICHIGAN

FOREWORD

This shop manual provides the Service Technician with complete information for the proper servicing of the 1966 Ford and Mercury cars.

The information is grouped according to the type of work being performed, such as diagnosis and testing, frequently performed adjustments and repairs, in-vehicle adjustments, overhaul, etc. Specifications and recommended special tools are included.

Refer to the opposite page for important vehicle identification data.

The descriptions and specifications in this manual were in effect at the time this manual was approved for printing. The Ford Motor Company reserves the right to discontinue models at any time, or change specifications or design, without notice and without incurring obligation.

 SERVICE PUBLICATIONS

VEHICLE IDENTIFICATION

GROUP 1

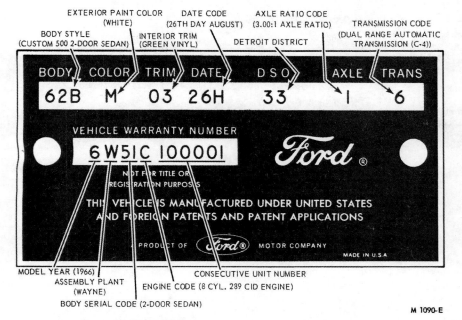

EXTERIOR PAINT COLOR (WHITE)
BODY STYLE (CUSTOM 500 2-DOOR SEDAN)
INTERIOR TRIM (GREEN VINYL)
DATE CODE (26TH DAY AUGUST)
AXLE RATIO CODE (3.00:1 AXLE RATIO)
DETROIT DISTRICT
TRANSMISSION CODE (DUAL RANGE AUTOMATIC TRANSMISSION (C-4))

BODY	COLOR	TRIM	DATE	D S O	AXLE	TRANS
62B	M	03	26H	33	1	6

VEHICLE WARRANTY NUMBER

6W51C 100001

Ford ®

NOT FOR TITLE OR REGISTRATION PURPOSES

THIS VEHICLE IS MANUFACTURED UNDER UNITED STATES AND FOREIGN PATENTS AND PATENT APPLICATIONS

A PRODUCT OF Ford ® MOTOR COMPANY

MADE IN U.S.A

MODEL YEAR (1966)
ASSEMBLY PLANT (WAYNE)
BODY SERIAL CODE (2-DOOR SEDAN)
ENGINE CODE (8 CYL. 289 CID ENGINE)
CONSECUTIVE UNIT NUMBER

M 1090-E

FIG. 1—Ford Warranty Plate

N 1319-D

FIG. 3—Ford Vehicle Identification Number Location

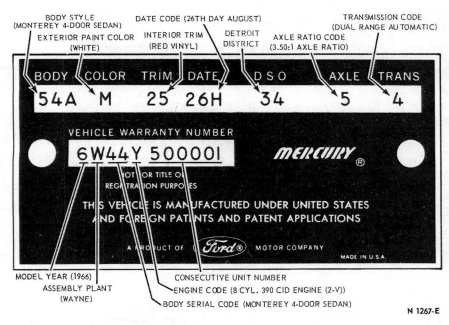

BODY STYLE (MONTEREY 4-DOOR SEDAN)
EXTERIOR PAINT COLOR (WHITE)
INTERIOR TRIM (RED VINYL)
DATE CODE (26TH DAY AUGUST)
DETROIT DISTRICT
AXLE RATIO CODE (3.50:1 AXLE RATIO)
TRANSMISSION CODE (DUAL RANGE AUTOMATIC)

BODY	COLOR	TRIM	DATE	D S O	AXLE	TRANS
54A	M	25	26H	34	5	4

VEHICLE WARRANTY NUMBER

6W44Y 500001

MERCURY ®

NOT FOR TITLE OR REGISTRATION PURPOSES

THIS VEHICLE IS MANUFACTURED UNDER UNITED STATES AND FOREIGN PATENTS AND PATENT APPLICATIONS

A PRODUCT OF Ford ® MOTOR COMPANY

MADE IN U.S.A.

MODEL YEAR (1966)
ASSEMBLY PLANT (WAYNE)
BODY SERIAL CODE (MONTEREY 4-DOOR SEDAN)
ENGINE CODE (8 CYL. 390 CID ENGINE (2-V))
CONSECUTIVE UNIT NUMBER

N 1267-E

FIG. 2—Mercury Warranty Plate

N 1268-D

FIG. 4—Mercury Vehicle Identification Number Location

VEHICLE DATA

Figures 1 and 2 illustrate the Ford and Mercury Warranty Plates. The plate is located on the rear (lock) face of the left front door.

The official Vehicle Identification Number for title and registration purposes is stamped on a tab attached to the top right side (weld flange) of the dash panel in the engine compartment (Figs. 3 and 4). Do not use the Vehicle Warranty Number which appears on the Warranty plate for title or registration purposes.

The vehicle data appears in a line across the top of the warranty plate (Figs. 1 and 2). The first two letters and a number identify the body Style. The following one or two letters identify the Exterior Paint Color. The next code consisting of two numbers, or a letter and a number, identifies the Interior Trim. The Date Code showing the date the car was manufactured, follows the Trim Code and consists of two numbers and a letter. The next code gives the district in which the car was ordered and consists of two numbers. The next to the last code is the Axle Ratio Code and is designated by a number for a conventional axle or a letter for an Equa-Lock axle. The last code in the vehicle data is the Transmission Code and consists of one number. The charts that follow, list in detail the various vehicle data codes.

VEHICLE WARRANTY NUMBER

The vehicle warranty number is the second line of numbers and letters appearing on the Warranty Plate (Figs. 1 and 2). The first number indicates the model year. The letter following the model year indicates the assembly plant at which the car was manufactured. The next two numbers designate the Body Serial Code. The letter following the Body Serial Code designates the Engine Code. The remaining numbers indicate the Consecutive Unit Number. The charts that follow, list the various Vehicle Warranty Number codes.

BODY SERIAL AND STYLE CODES

The two-digit numeral which follows the assembly plant code identifies the body series. This two-digit number is used in conjunction with the Body Style Code, in the Vehicle Data, which consists of a two-digit number with a letter suffix. The following chart lists the Body Serial Codes, Body Style Codes and the model.

MERCURY

Body Serial Code	Body Style Code	Body Type
Monterey		
42	50A	4-Door Sedan†
43	62A	2-Door Sedan
44	54A	4-Door Sedan
45	76A	2-Door Convertible
47	63A	2-Door H/T Fastback
48	57A	4-Door H/T Fastback
45	76G	2-Door Convertible*
47	63G	2-Door H/T Fastback*
Montclair		
52	50B	4-Door Sedan†
54	54B	4-Door Sedan
57	63B	2-Door H/T Fastback
58	57B	4-Door H/T Fastback
Parklane		
62	50F	4-Door Sedan†
65	76F	2-Door Convertible
65	76C	2-Door Convertible*
67	63F	2-Door H/T Fastback
67	63C	2-Door H/T Fastback*
68	57F	4-Door H/T Fastback
Commuter		
72	71B	4-Door 6 Passenger Station Wagon
72	71C	4-Door 9 Passenger Station Wagon
Colony Park		
76	71A	4-Door 9 Passenger Station Wagon
76	71E	4-Door 6 Passenger Station Wagon

†Reverse Back Window
*Bucket Seats

FORD

Body Serial Code	Body Style Code	Body Type
Ford Custom		
53	62E	2-Door Sedan
54	54E	4-Door Sedan
Ford Custom 500		
52	54B	4-Door Sedan
51	62B	2-Door Sedan
Galaxie 500		
62	54A	4-Door Sedan
64	57B	4-Door Fastback
66	63B	2-Door Fastback
65	76A	2-Door Convertible

Body Serial Code	Body Style Code	Body Type
Galaxie 500 XL		
68	63C	2-Door Fastback*
69	76B	2-Door Convertible*
Galaxie 500 7.0 Litre		
61	63D	2-Door Fastback
63	76D	2-Door Convertible
Galaxie 500 Lt'd		
60	57F	4-Door Fastback
67	63F	2-Door Fastback
Ranch Wagon		
71	71D	4-Door 6 Passenger Station Wagon
Country Sedan		
72	71B	4-Door 6 Passenger Station Wagon
74	71C	4-Door 9 Passenger Station Wagon
Country Squire		
76	71E	4-Door 6 Passenger Station Wagon
78	71A	4-Door 9 Passenger Station Wagon

*Bucket Seats

EXTERIOR PAINT COLOR CODES

A single letter code designates a solid body color and two letters denote a two-tone—the first letter, the lower color and the second letter, the upper color.

Code	M-30-J/ M-32-J#	Color
A	1724-A	Black
C	1900-A	Dk. Executive Gray Met.
F	1226-A	Lt. Blue
H	1912-A	Lt. Beige
K	1903-A	Dk. Blue Met.
M	1619-A	White
P	1910-A	Med. Palomino Met.
R	1879-A	Dk. Green Met.
T	2008-A	Red
U	1070-A	Med. Turquoise Met.
V	1921-A	Emberglo Met.
X	1632-A	Maroon Met.
Y	1269-A	Lt. Blue Met.
Z	1915-A	Med. Sage Gold Met.
2	1907-A	Dk. Turquoise Met.
4	1901-A	Med. Silver Met.
8	1955-A	Yellow

INTERIOR TRIM CODES

Code	Trim Schemes
12	Blue Cloth and Blue Vinyl
15	Red Cloth and Red Vinyl
16	Black Cloth and Black Vinyl
17	Aqua Cloth and Aqua Vinyl
19	Palomino Cloth and Palomino Vinyl
22	Blue Vinyl
25	Red Vinyl
26	Black Vinyl
31	Silver Cloth and Silver Vinyl
32	Blue Cloth and Blue Vinyl
35	Red Cloth and Red Vinyl
36	Black Cloth and Black Vinyl
37	Aqua Cloth and Aqua Vinyl
38	Ivy Gold Cloth and Ivy Gold Vinyl
39	Palomino Cloth and Palomino Vinyl
42	Blue Vinyl
45	Red Vinyl
46	Black Vinyl
47	Aqua Vinyl
48	Ivy Gold Vinyl
51	Silver Cloth and Silver Vinyl
52	Blue Cloth and Blue Vinyl
53	Burgundy Cloth and Burgundy Vinyl
55	Red Cloth and Red Vinyl
56	Black Cloth and Black Vinyl
57	Aqua Cloth and Aqua Vinyl

INTERIOR TRIM CODES (Continued)

Code	Trim Schemes
58	Ivy Gold Cloth and Ivy Gold Vinyl
62	Blue Vinyl
64	Emberglo Vinyl
65	Red Vinyl
66	Black Vinyl
67	Aqua Vinyl
68	Ivy Gold Vinyl
72	Blue Vinyl
75	Red Vinyl
76	Black Vinyl
77	Aqua Vinyl
82	Blue Vinyl
84	Emberglo Vinyl
85	Red Vinyl
86	Black Vinyl
92	Blue Vinyl
93	Burgundy Cloth and Burgundy Vinyl
94	Emberglo Vinyl
95	Red Vinyl
96	Black Vinyl
A3	Burgundy Leather
B2	Blue with Parchment Vinyl
B3	Burgundy with Parchment Vinyl
B6	Black with Parchment Vinyl
B7	Aqua with Parchment Vinyl
B8	Gold with Parchment Vinyl
B9	Palomino with Parchment Vinyl
D6	White with Black Vinyl
E6	White with Black Vinyl
F2	Blue with White Vinyl
F3	Burgundy with White Vinyl
F4	Emberglo with White Vinyl
F6	Black with White Vinyl
F7	Aqua with White Vinyl
F8	Ivy Gold with White Vinyl
F9	Palomino with White Vinyl
G2	Blue with White Vinyl
G3	Burgundy with White Vinyl
G4	Emberglo with White Vinyl
G6	Black with White Vinyl
G7	Aqua with White Vinyl
G8	Ivy Gold with White Vinyl
G9	Palomino with White Vinyl
K2	Blue Vinyl
K6	Black Vinyl
N2	Blue Vinyl
N5	Red Vinyl
O3	Green Vinyl
O4	Beige Vinyl
S2	Blue with Parchment Vinyl
X5	Red Vinyl
XD	Parchment Vinyl
Y5	Red Vinyl
Z6	Black Vinyl
ZD	Parchment Vinyl

DATE CODES

The code letters for the month are preceded by a numeral to show the day of the month when the car was completed. The second year code letters are to be used if the model production exceeds 12 months.

Month	First Model Year	Second Model Year
January	A	N
February	B	P
March	C	Q
April	D	R
May	E	S
June	F	T
July	G	U
August	H	V
September	J	W
October	K	X
November	L	Y
December	M	Z

DISTRICT CODES (DSO)

Domestic Special Orders, Foreign Special Orders, Limited Production Options and Pre-Approved Special Orders have the complete order number recorded in this space. Also to appear in this space is the two-digit code number of the District which ordered the unit. If the unit is regular production, only the District code number will appear.

FORD

Code	District	Code	District
11	Boston	45	Davenport
12	Buffalo	51	Denver
13	New York	52	Des Moines
14	Pittsburgh	53	Kansas City
15	Newark	54	Omaha
21	Atlanta	55	St. Louis
22	Charlotte	61	Dallas
23	Philadelphia	62	Houston
24	Jacksonville	63	Memphis
25	Richmond	64	New Orleans
26	Washington	65	Oklahoma City
31	Cincinnati	71	Los Angeles
32	Cleveland	72	San Jose
33	Detroit	73	Salt Lake City
34	Indianapolis	74	Seattle
35	Lansing	81	Ford of Canada
36	Louisville	83	Government
41	Chicago	84	Home Office Reserve
42	Fargo	85	American Red Cross
43	Rockford	89	Transportation Services
44	Twin Cities	90	Export

MERCURY

Code	District	Code	District
11	Boston	34	Detroit
15	New York	41	Chicago
16	Philadelphia	42	St. Louis
17	Washington	46	Twin Cities
21	Atlanta	51	Denver
22	Dallas	52	Los Angeles
23	Jacksonville	53	Oakland
26	Memphis	54	Seattle
31	Buffalo	81	Ford of Canada
32	Cincinnati	84	Home Office Reserve
33	Cleveland	90-99	Export

AXLE RATIO CODES

A number designates a conventional axle, while a letter designates an Equa-Lock axle.

Code	Ratio	Code	Ratio
1	3.00:1	A	3.00:1
4	3.25:1	E	3.25:1
5	3.50:1	F	3.50:1
8	3.89:1	H	3.89:1
9	4.11:1		

ENGINE CODES

Code	Engine
B	6 Cyl. 240 Cu. In. (1V)
C	8 Cyl. 289 Cu. In. (2V)
E	6 Cyl. 240 Cu. In. (1V) (Taxi)
H	8 Cyl. 390 Cu. In. (2V, Special)
M	8 Cyl. 410 Cu. In. (4V)
P	8 Cyl. 428 Cu. In. (4V, Police)
Q	8 Cyl. 428 Cu. In. (4V)
R	8 Cyl. 427 Cu. In. (8V, Hi-Perf.)
V	6 Cyl. 240 Cu. In. (1V)
X	8 Cyl. 352 Cu. In. (4V)
Y	8 Cyl. 390 Cu. In. (2V)
Z	8 Cyl. 390 Cu. In. (4V)
3	8 Cyl. 289 Cu. In. (2V)①
5	6 Cyl. 240 Cu. In. (1V)①
8	8 Cyl. 428 Cu. In. (4V)①

①Low Compression

MODEL YEAR CODE

The numeral 6 designates 1966

CONSECUTIVE UNIT NUMBER

Each assembly plant, with each model year, begins with consecutive unit number 100001 (Ford) or 500001 (Mercury) and continues on for each car built.

ASSEMBLY PLANT CODES

Code Letter	Assembly Plant	Code Letter	Assembly Plant
A	Atlanta	L	Michigan Truck
B	Oakville	N	Norfolk
C	Ontario	P	Twin Cities
D	Dallas	R	San Jose
E	Mahwah	S	Pilot Plant
F	Dearborn	T	Metuchen
G	Chicago	U	Louisville
H	Lorain	W	Wayne
J	Los Angeles	Y	Wixom
K	Kansas City	Z	St. Louis

TRANSMISSION CODES

Code	Type
1	3-Speed Manual Shift
2	Overdrive
4	C-6 Automatic Dual Range
5	4-Speed Manual-Shift
6	C-4 Automatic Dual Range
7	Cruis-o-matic (Ford)
8	Cruis-o-matic (Ford) Multi-Drive (Mercury)

BRAKES

GROUP 2

PART 2-1 GENERAL BRAKE SERVICE

1 DIAGNOSIS AND TESTING

PRELIMINARY TESTS

1. Check the fluid level in the master cylinder, and add Rotunda R-103-A (B7AZ-19542-A) brake fluid if required.

2. With the engine running or enough vacuum in the system for power brakes, push the brake pedal down as far as it will go while the car is standing still. If the pedal travels more than halfway between the released position and the floor, check the brake adjustment and the automatic adjusters.

To check adjuster operation, check the shoes and the adjuster components for binding or improper installation. Follow the procedure described under Brake Shoe Adjustments in Part 2-2, Section 2.

Make several reverse brake stops to ensure uniform adjustment at all wheels.

3. On cars with power brakes, with the transmission in neutral, stop the engine and apply the parking brake. Depress the service brake ped-

al several times to exhaust all vacuum in the system. Then, depress the pedal and hold it in the applied position. Start the engine. If the vacuum system is operating, the pedal will tend to fall away under foot pressure and less pressure will be required to hold the pedal in the applied position. If no action is felt, the vacuum booster system is not functioning. Follow the procedures in the Booster Diagnosis Guide. With the engine shut off, exhaust all vacuum in the system. Depress the brake pedal and hold it in the applied position. If the pedal gradually falls away under this pressure, the hydraulic system is leaking. Check all tubing hoses, and connections for leaks.

If the brake pedal movement feels spongy, bleed the hydraulic system to remove air from the lines and cylinder. See Section 2, Hydraulic System Bleeding. Also, check for leaks or insufficient fluid.

4. Should one of the brakes be locked and the car must be moved,

open the brake cylinder bleeder screw long enough to let out a few drops of brake fluid. **This bleeding operation will release the brakes, but it will not correct the cause of the trouble.**

ROAD TEST

The car should be road tested only if the brakes will safely stop the car. Apply the brakes at a speed of 25-30 mph to check for the existence of the trouble symptoms listed in Table 1, with the exception of those resolved in the preliminary tests and brake chatter. For each of the symptoms encountered, check and eliminate the causes which are also listed in Table 1. To check for brake chatter or surge, apply the brakes lightly at approximately 50 mph.

For booster removal and installation procedures, refer to Part 2-2, Section 3. For disassembly and assembly procedures, refer to Part 2-2, Section 4. For cleaning and inspection refer to Part 2-1, Section 3.

TABLE 1—Disc Brake Trouble Symptoms and Possible Causes

Possible Causes of Trouble Symptoms	Excessive Pedal Travel	Brake Roughness or Chatter (Pedal Pumping)	Excessive Pedal Effort	Pull—Uneven or Grabbing Brakes	Rattle	Heavy Brake Drag	Caliper Brake Fluid Leak	No Braking Effect When Pedal is Depressed
Shoe and Lining Knock-back after violent cornering or rough road travel	X							
Piston and Shoe and Lining Assembly Not Properly Seated or Positioned	X							X
Air Leak or Insufficient Fluid in System or Caliper	X							X
Loose Wheel Bearing Adjustment	X							
Damaged or Worn Caliper Piston Seal	X						X	X
Excessive Lateral Run-out of Rotor		X						
Rotor Excessively Out of Parallel		X						
Frozen or Seized Pistons			X	X		X		
Brake Fluid, Oil or Grease on Linings			X	X				
Shoe and Lining Worn Below Specifications			X					
Proportioning Valve Malfunction			X					
Caliper Out of Alignment with Rotor				X				
Loose Caliper Attachment				X				
Excessive Clearance Between Shoe and Caliper or Between Shoe and Splash Shield					X			
Shoe Hold-Down Clips Missing or Improperly Positioned					X			
Operator Riding Brake Pedal						X		
Scores in the Cylinder Bore							X	
Corrosion Build-up in the Cylinder Bore or on the Piston Surface							X	
Bleeder Screw Still Open								X
Improper Booster Push Rod Adjustment	X							
Shoe Out of Flat More Than 0.005"	X							
Rear Brake Auto. Adjusters Inoperative	X							
Improperly Ground Rear Brake Shoe and Lining Assemblies	X							
Booster Inoperative			X					
Leaking Booster Vacuum Check Valve			X					
Unequalized Front Tire Pressure				X				
Incorrect Front End Alignment				X				
Lining Protruding Beyond End of Shoe				X				
Incomplete Brake Pedal Return Due to Linkage Interference						X		
Faulty Booster Check Valve Holding Pressure in Hydraulic System						X		
Residual Pressure in Front Brake Hydraulic System						X		
Metal Chip in Seal Groove							X	
Air in Hydraulic System or Improper Bleeding								X

TABLE 2—Drum Brake Trouble Symptoms and Possible Causes

Possible Causes of Trouble Symptoms	Trouble Symptoms												
	One Brake Drags	All Brakes Drag	Hard Pedal	Spongy Pedal	Car Pulls to One Side	One Wheel Locks	Brakes Chatter	Excessive Pedal Travel	Pedal Gradually Goes to Floor	Brakes Uneven	Shoe Click Release	Noisy or Grabbing Brakes	Brakes Do Not Apply
Mechanical Resistance at Pedal or Shoes Damaged Linkage		X	X										
Brake Line Restricted	X	X	X		X								
Leaks or Insufficient Fluid				X				X	X				X
Improper Tire Pressure					X					X			
Improperly Adjusted or Worn Wheel Bearing	X				X								
Distorted or Improperly Adjusted Brake Shoe	X	X	X		X	X		X				X	
Faulty Retracting Spring	X				X								
Drum Out of Round	X				X	X							
Linings Glazed or Worn			X		X	X	X	X				X	X
Oil or Grease In Lining			X		X	X	X			X		X	X
Loose Carrier Plate	X					X	X						
Loose Lining						X	X						
Scored Drum										X		X	
Dirt on Drum-Lining Surface												X	
Faulty Wheel Cylinder	X				X	X						X	
Dirty Brake Fluid	X	X								X			X
Faulty Master Cylinder		X						X	X				X
Air in Hydraulic System	X			X				X					X
Self Adjusters Not Operating					X			X			X		
Insufficient Shoe-to-Carrier Plate Lubrication	X										X		
Tire Tread Worn						X							
Poor Lining to Drum Contact							X						
Loose Front Suspension							X						
"Threads" Left by Drum Turning Tool Pull Shoes Sideways											X		
Cracked Drum								X					
Sticking Booster Control Valve		X										X	

BOOSTER DIAGNOSIS GUIDE

BOOSTER INOPERATIVE— HARD PEDAL	If the preliminary tests show that the booster is inoperative or if a hard pedal condition still exists after eliminating the causes of Excessive Pedal Effort or Hard Pedal listed in Tables 1 and 2, the trouble may be caused by vacuum leakage. Disconnect the vacuum line at the booster, remove the vacuum manifold and check valve assembly, and look for a sticking or faulty check valve. Check all vacuum connections for leakage or obstruction. Check all hoses for a leaking or collapsed condition. Re-	pair or replace parts as necessary. If the foregoing procedure does not eliminate the trouble, remove the booster from the car. Separate the front shell from the rear shell, and check the valve and rod assembly reaction disc, diaphragm plate, and diaphragm assembly for damage that would cause leaks. When assembling, be sure that the diaphragm assembly is properly positioned. Improper location could cause leakage between the vacuum and atmospheric sides of the diaphragm.
BRAKES DRAG OR GRAB	If the brakes still drag or grab after eliminating the causes listed in Tables 1 and 2, the condition is probably caused by a sticking valve	plunger assembly. Remove and disassemble the booster. Clean, inspect, and replace parts as necessary.
SELF APPLICATION OF BRAKES WHEN ENGINE STARTS	Remove and disassemble the booster. Check for a leak in the rear shell. Check the diaphragm for being out of locating radii in the housing. Check for a sticking or unseated	valve poppet. Clean, inspect, and replace parts as necessary. Be sure that the diaphragm is properly located when assembling.

2 COMMON ADJUSTMENTS AND REPAIRS

PARKING BRAKE LINKAGE ADJUSTMENT

Check the parking brake cables when the brakes are fully released. If the cables are loose, adjust them as follows:

1. Fully release the parking brake pedal.

2. Depress the parking brake pedal one notch from its normal released position.

3. Raise the car.

4. Turn the adjusting nut forward against the equalizer until a moderate drag is felt when turning the rear wheels (Fig. 1).

5. Release the parking brake, and make sure that the brake shoes return to the fully released position.

POWER BRAKE MASTER CYLINDER PUSH ROD ADJUSTMENT

The push rod is provided with an adjustment screw to maintain the correct relationship between the booster control valve plunger and the master cylinder piston. Failure to maintain this relationship will prevent the master cylinder piston from completely releasing hydraulic pressure and can cause the brakes to drag.

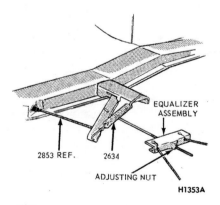

FIG. 1—Parking Brake Linkage Adjustment

To check the adjustment of the screw, fabricate a gauge of the dimensions shown in Fig. 2. On the Midland-Ross booster, remove the master cylinder and air filter assembly and push the bellows back into the booster body. Re-install the air filter directly against the booster body, and then place the gauge against the master cylinder mounting surface of the air filter assembly as shown in Fig. 3 or Fig. 4. The push rod screw should be adjusted so that

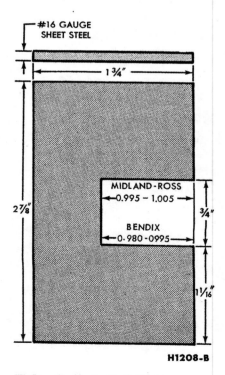

FIG. 2—Push Rod Gauge Dimensions

the end of the screw just touches the inner edge of the slot in the gauge.

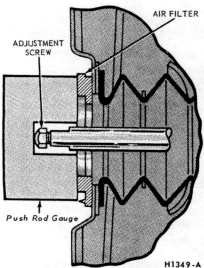

FIG. 3—Push Rod Adjustment —Midland-Ross

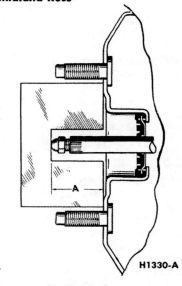

FIG. 4—Push Rod Adjustment—Bendix

Do not set up side forces on the push rod as it may break the valve plunger.

To check the Bendix-type booster, remove the master cylinder and fit the gauge against the master cylinder mounting surface as shown in Fig. 4.

This is an approximate adjustment only. To verify the adjustment, look through the make-up (rear) port of the master cylinder when installing the master cylinder to the booster. The master cylinder piston should not move more than 0.015 inch as it contacts the push rod. No movement (exact contact) is ideal.

HYDRAULIC SYSTEM BLEEDING

When any part of the hydraulic

system has been disconnected for repair or replacement, air may get into the lines and cause spongy pedal action. Bleed the hydraulic system after it has been properly connected to be sure that all air is expelled from the brake cylinders, disc brake calipers and lines.

The hydraulic system can be bled manually or with pressure bleeding equipment.

MANUAL BLEEDING

Bleed the longest lines first. Keep the master cylinder reservoir filled with new heavy-duty brake fluid during the bleeding operation. If the reservoir is not kept full, the diaphragm gasket may be sucked down to the bottom of the master cylinder.

Never use brake fluid which has been drained from the hydraulic system.

1. Position an offset ⅜-inch box wrench on the bleeder fitting on the right rear brake wheel cylinder (Fig. 5). Attach a rubber drain tube to the bleeder fitting. **The end of the tube should fit snugly around the bleeder fitting.**

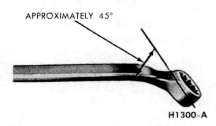

FIG. 5—Wrench for Bleeding Brake

2. Submerge the free end of the tube in a container partially filled with clean brake fluid, and loosen the bleeder fitting approximately ¾ turn.

3. Push the brake pedal down slowly thru its full travel. Close the bleeder fitting, then return the pedal to the fully-released position. Repeat this operation until air bubbles cease to appear at the submerged end of the tube.

4. When the fluid is completely free of air bubbles, tighten the bleeder fitting and remove the drain tube.

5. Repeat this procedure at each brake wheel cylinder or disc caliper in order: left rear, right front, and left front. Refill the master cylinder reservoir after each brake cylinder is bled and when the bleeding operation is completed. The fluid level should be within ⅜ inch of the top of the reservoir. The diaphragm-type gasket

should be properly positioned in the reservoir cap, before the cap is installed.

6. Be sure that the front brake pistons (on disc brakes) are returned to their normal positions and that the shoe and lining assemblies are properly seated. **Brake fluid should not be allowed to contaminate the rotors or shoe and lining assemblies.**

7. It is mandatory that the brake pedal be pumped after any disc brake repair or bleeding, in order to establish proper brake running clearance and brake pedal reserve.

PRESSURE BLEEDING

Bleed the longest lines first. **Never use brake fluid which has been drained from the hydraulic system.**

The bleeder tank should contain enough new heavy-duty Rotunda brake fluid to complete the bleeding operation, and it should be charged with 10-30 pounds of air pressure.

1. Clean all dirt from the master cylinder reservoir cap.

2. Remove the master cylinder reservoir cap, install an adapter cap on the reservoir, and attach the bleeder tank hose to the fitting on the adapter cap. Adapter cap 2162 can be used, or an adapter cap can be fabricated by cutting a hole in the center of a filler cap and soldering a fitting at the hole.

3. Position a ⅜-inch box wrench on the bleeder fitting on the right rear brake wheel cylinder (Fig. 5). Attach a rubber drain tube to the bleeder fitting. **The end of the tube should fit snugly around the bleeder fitting.**

4. Open the valve on the bleeder tank to admit pressurized brake fluid to the master cylinder reservoir.

5. Submerge the free end of the tube in a container partially filled with clean brake fluid, and loosen the bleeder fitting.

6. When air bubbles cease to appear in the fluid at the submerged end of the drain tube, close the bleeder fitting and remove the tube.

7. Repeat this procedure at each brake wheel cylinder in the following order: left rear, right front, and left front.

8. When the bleeding operation is completed, close the bleeder tank valve and remove the tank hose from the adapter fitting.

9. Remove the adapter cap, refill the master cylinder reservoir to within ⅜ inch from the top of the reservoir, and install the filler cap. The diaphragm-type gasket should be

properly positioned in the cap before it is installed on the master cylinder.

10. Be sure that the front brake pistons (disc brakes) are returned to their normal position and that the shoe and lining assemblies are properly seated. **Brake fluid should not be allowed to contaminate the rotors or shoe and lining assemblies.**

11. It is mandatory that the brake pedal be pumped after any disc brake repair or bleeding, to establish proper brake running clearance and brake pedal reserve.

3 CLEANING AND INSPECTION

DISC BRAKES

1. Remove the wheel and tire, caliper splash shield, and the shoe and lining assemblies as outlined in Part 2-2, Section 2.

2. Make three thickness measurements with a micrometer across the middle section of the shoe and lining. Take one reading at each side and one in the center. If the assembly has worn to a thickness of 0.195-inch (shoe and lining together) or 0.030-inch (lining material only) at any one of the three measuring locations, replace all (4) shoe and lining assemblies on both front wheels.

3. With the shoe and lining assemblies installed, insert a feeler gauge between the lining and rotor. If the clearance is not within 0.002-0.010-inch, check for shoe and lining assemblies not being properly seated on the caliper bridges, for a piston pushed back in the cylinder bore, for a seized piston, or for malfunction of a piston seal.

Ordinarily, the clearance should be 0.002-0.010-inch. However, if the car was stopped by a brake application just prior to checking the clearance, the brakes may drag slightly.

4. To check rotor runout, first eliminate the wheel bearing end play by tightening the adjusting nut. After tightening the nut check to see that the rotor can still be rotated.

5. Clamp a dial indicator to the caliper housing so that the stylus contacts the rotor at a point approximately 1 inch from the outer edge. Rotate the rotor and take an indicator reading. If the reading exceeds 0.002 inch total indicator runout, replace the rotor. **Do not attempt to refinish a rotor that indicates runout in excess of specification.** When the runout check is finished be sure to adjust the bearings as outlined in Group 3, in order to prevent bearing failure.

6. Check the rotor for scoring. Minor scores can be removed with a fine emery cloth. If the rotor is excessively scored, replace it.

7. Visually check the caliper. If it is cracked or if excess leakage is evident, it should be replaced. Slight leakage or seized pistons indicate removal and disassembly.

8. If upon disassembly the caliper is found to be distorted or damaged, or if the cylinder bores are scored or excessively worn, replace the assembly.

The two halves of the caliper assembly should never be separated. Damage or failure of one requires replacement of both as a unit.

DRUM BRAKES

1. Remove the wheel from the drum, and remove the drum as outlined in Part 2-2, Section 2. Wash all the parts except the brake shoes in a cleaning fluid and dry with compressed air.

2. Brush all dust from the carrier plates and interior of the brake drums.

3. Inspect the brake shoes for excessive lining wear or shoe damage. If the lining is worn within $1/32$ inch of the rivet heads or if the shoes are damaged, they must be replaced. Replace any lining that has been oil saturated. Replace lining in axle sets. Prior to replacement of lining, the drum diameter should be checked to determine if oversize linings must be installed.

4. Check the condition of brake shoes, retracting springs, hold-down springs, and drum for signs of overheating. If the shoes have a slight blue coloring, indicating overheating, replacement of the retracting and hold down springs is strongly recommended. **Overheated springs lose their pull and could cause the new lining to wear prematurely, if they are not replaced.**

5. If the car has 30,000 or more miles of operation on the brake linings or signs of overheating are present when relining brakes, the wheel cylinders should be disassembled and inspected for wear and entrance of dirt into the cylinder. The cylinder cups should be replaced, thus avoiding future problems.

6. Inspect all other brake parts and replace any that are worn or damaged.

7. Inspect the brake drums and, if necessary, refinish. Refer to Part 2-2, Section 4 for refinishing.

BOOSTER UNIT

After disassembly, immerse all metal parts in a suitable solvent. Use only alcohol on rubber parts or parts containing rubber. After the parts have been thoroughly cleaned and rinsed in cleaning solvent, the metal parts which come in contact with hydraulic brake fluid or rubber parts should be rewashed in clean alcohol before assembly. Use an air hose to blow dirt and cleaning fluid from the recesses and internal passages. When overhauling a power booster, use all parts furnished in the repair kit. **Discard all old rubber parts.**

Inspect all other parts for damage or excessive wear. Replace damaged or excessively worn parts. If the inside of the booster body is rusted or corroded, polish it with steel wool or fine emery cloth.

PART 2-2
BRAKE SYSTEM

1 DESCRIPTION AND OPERATION

OPTIONAL DISC BRAKES

Disc brakes are available as optional equipment for the front wheels. The hydraulic brake system employs single anchor, internal expanding and self-adjusting drum brake assemblies on the rear wheels of cars with disc brakes, and on the front and rear wheels of all others.

A vacuum booster is available as optional equipment.

The master cylinder converts physical force from the brake pedal (and booster if so equipped) into hydraulic pressure against the pistons in the calipers (disc brakes) or in the wheel cylinders (drum brakes). The pistons in turn convert hydraulic pressure back into physical force at the brake shoes.

HYDRAULIC SELF-ADJUSTING BRAKE SYSTEM

The standard hydraulic brake system employs single anchor, internal expanding and self adjusting brake assemblies.

The master cylinder converts physical force from the brake pedal and

booster into hydraulic pressure against the pistons in the wheel cylinders. The wheel cylinder pistons, in turn, convert hydraulic pressure back into physical force at the brake shoes.

The self-adjusting brake mechanism consists of a cable, cable guide, adjusting lever, and adjuster spring (Fig. 1). The cable is hooked over the anchor pin at the top and is connected to the lever at the bottom. The cable is connected to the secondary brake shoe by means of the cable guide. The adjuster spring is hooked to the primary brake shoe and to the lever. The automatic adjuster operates only when the brakes are applied while the car is moving rearward and only when the secondary shoe is free to move toward the drum beyond a predetermined point.

With the car moving rearward and the brakes applied, the wrap-around action of the shoes following the drum forces the upper end of the primary shoe against the anchor pin. The action of the wheel cylinder moves the upper end of the secondary shoe away from the anchor pin.

The movement of the secondary shoe causes the cable to pull the adjusting lever upward and against the end of a tooth on the adjusting screw starwheel. The upward travel of the lever increases as lining wear increases. When the lever can move upward far enough, it passes over the end of the tooth and engages the tooth. When the brakes are released, the adjusting spring pulls the lever downward causing the star-wheel to turn and expand the shoes. The star-wheel is turned one tooth at a time as the linings progressively wear.

With the car moving forward and the brakes applied, the secondary shoe is against the anchor pin and the primary shoe is moved toward the drum. Therefore, the adjuster does not operate.

The rear brake assembly is basically the same as the front brake. The conventional parking brake lever, link, and spring are used in the rear brake.

The anchor pins on all brakes are fixed and non-adjustable.

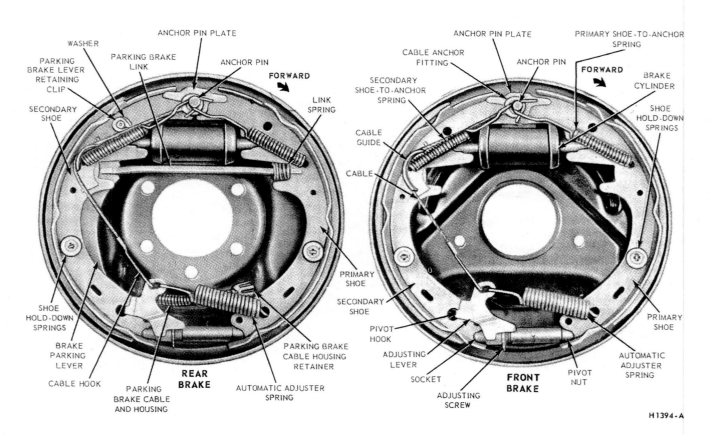

FIG. 1—Self-Adjusting Brake Assemblies

DISC BRAKE ASSEMBLIES

RELATION AND FUNCTION OF COMPONENT PARTS

The disc brake is a fixed caliper, opposed piston, non-energized, ventilated disc type, actuated by a hydraulic system (Fig. 2). There is no lateral movement of either the disc (rotor) or the caliper. The caliper assembly consists of two caliper housings bolted together with each half containing two cylinder bores of 1-15/16 inch diameter. Each cylinder bore contains a piston with an attached molded rubber dust boot to seal the cylinder bore from contamination. (Fig. 3). Square-section rubber piston seals are positioned in grooves in the cylinder bores.

The piston seals perform three important tasks:

1. They provide hydraulic sealing between the cylinders and pistons.

2. They return the pistons to released position, when hydraulic pressure is released.

3. They maintain the shoes in correct adjustment at all times (comparable to the automatic adjusters in drum-type brakes).

The cylinders are connected hy-

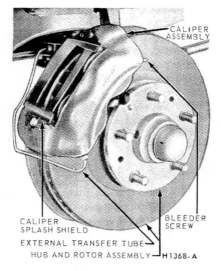

FIG. 2—Disc Brake Assembly

draulically by means of internal passages in the caliper housing and an external transfer tube between the two halves of the caliper assembly. One bleeder screw and fluid inlet fitting is provided on each caliper assembly.

The shoe and lining assemblies are located in between parallel machined abutments within the caliper, and are supported radially by tabs on the outer ends of the shoe assemblies (Fig. 2). The shoes slide axially in the caliper abutments by means of the tabs which ride on machined ledges (bridges) when hydraulic pressure is applied to the piston (Fig. 3). A shoe and lining assembly consists of friction material bonded to a metal plate called the shoe. It is replaced as a unit. Brake torque is absorbed by the mating of the shoe end against the caliper abutments (Fig. 2). A splash shield is attached to the top of the caliper to retain the shoe and lining assemblies and reduce contamination. The caliper assembly is mounted directly to the front wheel spindle to the rear of the wheel vertical centerline.

The cast iron disc is of the ventilated rotor type incorporating forty fins and is staked to, and rotates with the wheel hub. The outside diameter of the rotor is 11.875 inches and the inside diameter is 7.875 inches. This type of design increases cooling area and permits circulation of air through the rotor resulting in more rapid cooling of the brake. A splash shield bolted to the spindle is used primarily

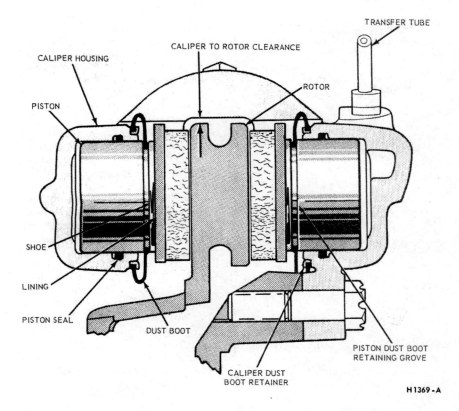

FIG. 3—Caliper Assembly—Sectional View

OPERATION

to prevent road contaminants from contacting the inboard rotor and lining surfaces (Fig. 23 Part 2-2). The wheel provides protection for the outboard surface of the rotor.

OPERATION

As the brake pedal is depressed, hydraulic pressure from the master cylinder forces the pistons out of the caliper bores against their respective shoe and lining assemblies. The force of the pistons against the shoes moves the linings against both sides of the revolving rotor to effect braking action.

During brake application, the rubber seal on each piston stretches as the piston moves against the shoe (Fig. 4). When the hydraulic pressure against the piston is released, the seal relaxes or rolls back. This roll-back action pulls the piston away from the shoe approximately 0.005 inch to relieve the force of the lining against the rotor and, thereby, provide the required running clearance. Also, inherent rotor runout contributes to the maintenance of running clearance. Automatic adjustment is accomplished by the pistons sliding in the seals outward from the cylinder bores. The piston gradually changes its position relative to the

seal as the lining wears and, thus, maintains the correct adjustment location at all times.

When the brakes are in the unapplied position, there is no hydraulic pressure to the calipers because the fluid source at the master cylinder bypasses the residual check valve.

A warning sound feature (Fig. 5) is incorporated in the design of the brake shoes. Metal tabs on the ends of the shoes create an audible metallic, scraping noise, when the linings

become worn enough to allow the tabs to contact the rotor. This metal-to-metal contact warns the driver that the shoes need replacing and is not detrimental to the function of the disc brake.

A proportioning valve located between the master cylinder and the rear brake wheel cylinders provides balanced braking action between the front and the rear brakes under a wide range of braking conditions. (Fig. 6). By regulating the hydraulic pressure applied to the rear wheel cylinders, the valve limits rear braking action when high pressures are required at the front brakes. In this manner, premature rear wheel skid is prevented. The proportioning valve is serviced as an assembly and is never adjusted or overhauled.

BOOSTER SYSTEM—BENDIX

This diaphragm type brake booster is a self contained vacuum-hydraulic braking unit mounted on the engine side of the dash panel.

Two Bendix models are used. The type supplied with disc brakes is exchanged rather than repaired when it is determined to be defective.

The vacuum power chamber consists of a front and rear shell locked together. Within the vacuum chamber are the rubber diaphragm and the integral valve hub and diaphragm plate. The rubber diaphragm fits over the plate, and the outer bead of the diaphragm is locked between the front and rear shells (Fig. 7). The diaphragm return spring is located between the diaphragm plate and the front shell.

The valve hub section of the diaphragm plate protrudes from the rear

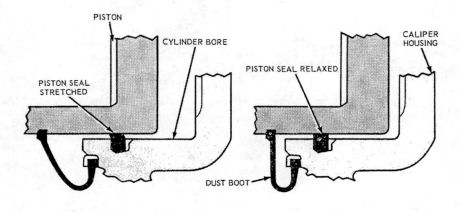

BRAKES APPLIED   **BRAKES RELEASED**   H1370-A

FIG. 4—Function of Piston Seal

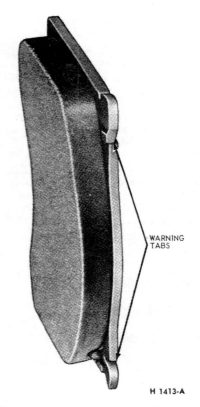

FIG. 5—Worn Lining Warning

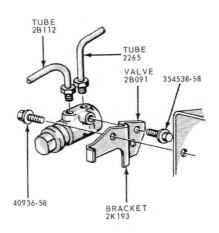

FIG. 6—Proportioning Valve

shell. A synthetic rubber seal is used between the valve hub and the rear shell. The seal and the valve hub are protected from dirt by a rubber guard connected between the air filter at the end of the hub and a flange on the rear shell. The control valve assembly fits into the hub and is connected to the brake pedal by the valve operating rod. The control valve assembly consists of a plunger, a valve body which supports a single poppet of flexible rubber, and two return springs. When the brake pedal is in the released position the valve return spring holds the valve assembly and operating rod away from the diaphragm plate. In this position, the poppet on the valve body is off the vacuum port seat which is a part of the diaphragm plate. The poppet return spring likewise holds the poppet against the atmospheric port seat which is a part of the plunger.

The hydraulic master cylinder which contains all of the components of the conventional master cylinder is bolted to the booster front shell. The hydraulic push rod forms the link between the master cylinder piston and the vacuum power diaphragm assembly. The end of the push rod, that enters the master cylinder piston, is equipped with a self-locking adjusting screw. The opposite end has a piston head which enters the diaphragm plate. A seal, located in the front shell, seals the opening between the hydraulic push rod and the shell.

Engine manifold vacuum is supplied to the booster through a vacuum check valve located in the front shell. Air is admitted through the air filter located at the end of the valve hub. The hydraulic push rod is actuated by pedal pressure assisted by the diaphragm, which derives power from the pressure differential existing between the vacuum on its front side and atmospheric pressure on its

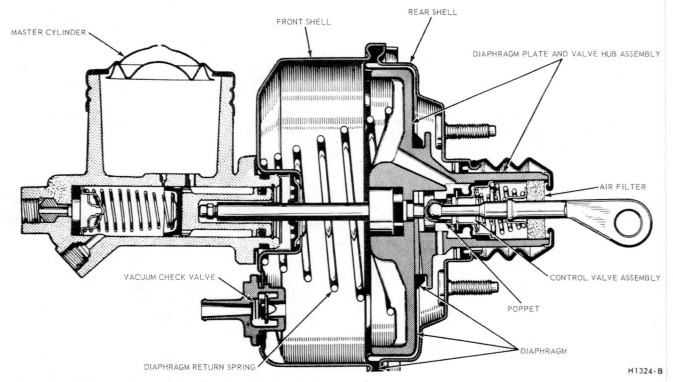

FIG. 7—Cutaway View of Bendix Vacuum Booster

rear side. A passage in the diaphragm plate permits vacuum to pass from the front to the rear side of the diaphragm when the vacuum port opens as the brakes are released.

RELEASED POSITION

With the engine running and the brakes released (Fig. 8), vacuum from the intake manifold is admitted through the check valve to the front (constant vacuum) chamber of the power unit. In the released position (no pressure applied to the brake pedal), the valve operating rod and valve *plunger* are held to the rear in the valve hub by the valve return spring to CLOSE the atmospheric port and OPEN the vacuum port. With the valve in this position, the rear (control vacuum) chamber is also open to vacuum through the porting in the diaphragm and valve hub assembly. The diaphragm is then balanced or suspended in vacuum, since vacuum is present on both sides of the power diaphragm. With the power diaphragm balanced in vacuum, the diaphragm return spring holds the diaphragm and hydraulic push rod in the fully released position. With the hydraulic push rod in this position, the hydraulic compensating port in the hydraulic master cylinder is OPEN. The open port permits brake fluid to either return from the brake system to the fluid reservoir or enter the brake system from the fluid reservoir to compensate for any gain or loss in fluid volume.

APPLIED POSITION

When the brakes are applied (Fig. 9), the valve operating rod and valve plunger move forward in the valve hub section of the diaphragm plate to compress the valve return spring and force the poppet against the vacuum valve seat in the diaphragm plate to CLOSE the vacuum port. Any additional movement of the valve operating rod in the applied direction moves the valve plunger away from the poppet valve to OPEN the atmospheric port and admit atmosphere through the air cleaner and passages in the diaphragm plate to the rear side of the power chamber. With vacuum present on the front side of the diaphragm and valve housing and atmospheric pressure present on the rear side of the diaphragm, a force is developed to move the vacuum power diaphragm assembly, hydraulic push rod and master cylinder piston forward to close the compensating port and force hydraulic fluid under pres-

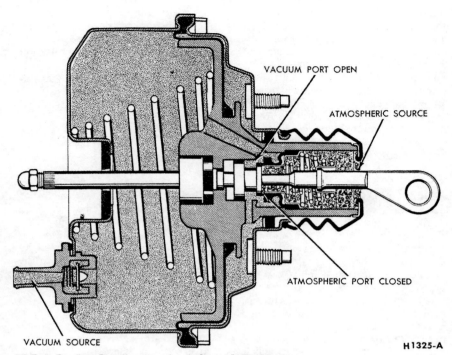

VACUUM PORT OPEN

ATMOSPHERIC SOURCE

ATMOSPHERIC PORT CLOSED

VACUUM SOURCE

H1325-A

FIG. 8—Bendix Booster in Released Position

sure through the residual check valve and brake tubes into the brake wheel cylinders. As hydraulic pressure is developed in the brake master cylinder, a counter force (to the rear) acting through the hydraulic push rod, sets up a reaction force against the power diaphragm assembly and valve plunger through the rubber reaction disc

(located at the end of the hydraulic push rod). The rubber reaction disc acts similar to a column of fluid to distribute the pressure between the vacuum power diaphragm assembly and the valve plunger in proportion to their respective contact areas. The pressure acting against the valve plunger and valve operating rod tends

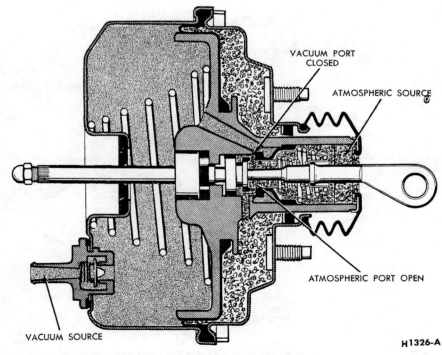

VACUUM PORT CLOSED

ATMOSPHERIC SOURCE

ATMOSPHERIC PORT OPEN

VACUUM SOURCE

H1326-A

FIG. 9—Bendix Booster in Applied Position

to move the valve plunger slightly to the rear in relation to the diaphragm and valve hub assembly to close off the atmospheric port. The driver is thus assured a "feel" of the brake, since part of the counter force reacts through the valve plunger, valve operating rod, and pedal linkage against the driver's foot. This reaction force is in direct proportion to the hydraulic pressure developed within the brake system.

HOLDING POSITION

During brake application, the reaction force which opposes the force applied by the driver, tends to close the atmospheric port. When both atmospheric and vacuum ports are CLOSED, the booster is said to be in the holding position (Fig. 10). With both valves closed, any degree of brake application attained will be held until either the atmospheric port is **reopened** by an increase in pedal pressure to further increase the brake application or by a decrease in pedal pressure to **reopen** the vacuum port to decrease the brake application. Whenever the pressure applied to the brake pedal is held constant for a moment, the valve returns to its holding position. However, upon reaching the fully applied position the force applied to the brake pedal overrules the reaction force. In this position the valve plunger and atmospheric valve seat are held away from the valve

poppet to admit maximum atmospheric pressure to the rear chamber. With the front chamber open to manifold vacuum, full power application is attained which is referred to as the run-out of the power unit. Any increase in hydraulic pressure beyond this point must be supplied by physical effort of the driver.

NO POWER CONDITION

It should be noted that in case of engine failure and consequent loss of engine vacuum, at least one full power brake application may be made from the vacuum in the booster. With the engine off and no vacuum in the power system, the brakes can be applied in the conventional manner by applying more physical effort to the brake pedal.

BOOSTER SYSTEM— MIDLAND-ROSS

The booster consists of a vacuum chamber, atmospheric valve, control valve plunger assembly, diaphragm, and an atmospheric chamber (Figs. 11, 12 and 13).

Atmospheric pressure is present at all times in the atmospheric chamber at the front side of the atmospheric valve. The air intake to the atmospheric chamber is protected by an air filter. The atmospheric chamber is separated from the vacuum chamber by the bellows assembly within the vacuum chamber.

Vacuum is present at all times in that area of the vacuum chamber forward of the diaphragm. Vacuum is supplied through a hose from the intake manifold to the vacuum manifold and check valve on the booster body. With this integral check valve and vacuum chamber, it is possible to obtain several power assisted brake applications with the engine shut off. This arrangement makes a vacuum reservoir unnecessary.

Either vacuum from the forward side of the diaphragm or air from the bellows (atmospheric chamber) can be connected to the rear side of the diaphragm through porting in the control valve hub and the plunger assembly.

APPLYING POSITION

As the brake pedal is depressed, the valve operating rod and valve plunger assembly move forward compressing the plunger return spring (Fig. 11). The initial movement of the plunger closes the porting from the vacuum chamber preventing further evacuation of the area back of the diaphragm. Further movement of the plunger forces the atmospheric valve off its seat so that atmospheric pressure from the bellows can enter the hub porting that leads to the rear side of the diaphragm.

With vacuum on the front side of the diaphragm and atmospheric pressure on the back side of the diaphragm, a force is developed to move the diaphragm, push rod and master cylinder piston forward to close the compensating port and force hydraulic fluid under pressure through the residual pressure check valve and brake tubes to the wheel brakes. As hydraulic pressure is developed in the hydraulic system, a reaction counterforce acts against the reaction lever and ring assembly. This reaction lever and ring assembly is designed to transmit the reaction forces back through the actuating control valve assembly to the brake pedal and provide the driver with a resistance that is in proportion to the brake hydraulic apply forces. This is the means of providing the proper driver feel to the power brake unit.

HOLDING POSITION

When the forward motion of the brake pedal is stopped and held, the valve operating rod ceases to move the control valve plunger forward. However, the unbalanced forces of atmospheric pressure and vacuum on

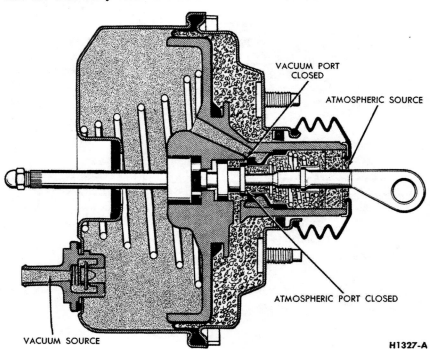

VACUUM PORT CLOSED

ATMOSPHERIC SOURCE

ATMOSPHERIC PORT CLOSED

VACUUM SOURCE

H1327-A

FIG. 10—Bendix Booster in Holding Position

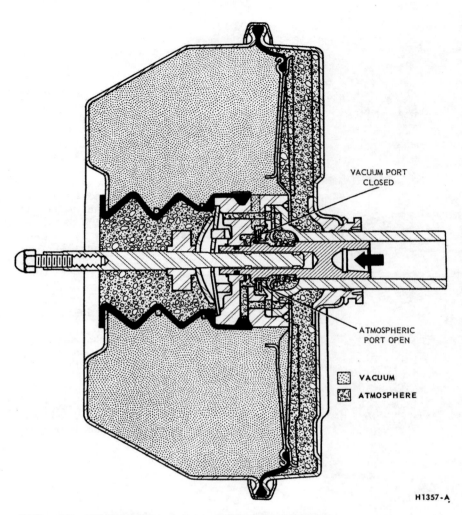

VACUUM PORT
CLOSED

ATMOSPHERIC
PORT OPEN

▢ VACUUM

▨ ATMOSPHERE

H1357-A

FIG. 11—Midland-Ross Booster in Applying Position

each side of the diaphragm will continue to move the outer sleeve of the control valve plunger forward keeping the vacuum porting closed. At the same time, the reaction force acting through the reaction ring and lever assembly will tend to move the atmospheric valve to the closed position (Fig. 12). When these combined forces balance, the porting to the vacuum supply will remain closed and the atmospheric valve will cut off any further passage of atmospheric pressure to the area behind the diaphragm. Therefore, the power assist force acting on the master cylinder piston will stabilize and the hydraulic force applying the brakes will be maintained at a constant level.

RELEASED POSITION

When the pedal pressure is released from the valve operating rod and plunger assembly, the plunger return spring moves the plunger away

from the atmospheric valve allowing the valve to seat against the hub (Fig. 13). This seating of the valve closes off the bellows chamber from the hub porting that connects to the rear side of the diaphragm. At the same time, the rearward movement of the plunger opens the porting from the vacuum chamber and draws out the air from the rear side of the power diaphragm. With vacuum on both sides of the diaphragm, the assist force against the master cylinder push rod is eliminated.

Also, a pressure differential is created by the presence of vacuum on the rear (small diameter) side of the valve hub and atmospheric (bellows) pressure on the front (large diameter) side. This pressure differential moves the valve hub and, with it, the valve plunger and diaphragm assembly back to the released position. This releasing action permits the brake shoe retracting springs, acting

through the wheel cylinder pistons and the hydraulic fluid, to return the master cylinder piston and push rod to the released position.

With the piston and push rod in the released position, the hydraulic compensating port in the master cylinder is open. The open port permits fluid to either return from the brake system to the fluid reservoir, or enter the brake system from the reservoir.

PARKING BRAKE

An independent foot-operated parking brake control actuates the rear wheel brake shoes through a cable linkage. The operating cable is routed from the parking brake control assembly to the equalizer. The rear brake cables connect the equalizer assembly to the parking brake lever at each rear secondary shoe (Fig. 1).

Two types of brake pedal control are used. The automatic (vacuum) release type (Fig. 14) is used on the Mercury Parklane. All other models use the manual release type (Fig. 29).

When the pedal is depressed (either manual or automatic release type) the secondary brake shoes are forced against the rear brake drums. The pedal is held in the applied position by the engagement of a spring-loaded pawl with a ratchet in the control assembly (Figs. 14 and 29).

Either type of parking brake control assembly is mounted to the dash panel and the cowl upper panel. The pedal, pivots on a stationary pedal mount. A spring-loaded pawl and a release lever are assembled to the pedal. A ratchet is assembled to the upper end of the pedal. The pawl contacts the ratchet at such an angle that the ratchet teeth will slide over the pawl as the pedal is depressed; however, when the applying motion stops and the pedal starts to release, the pawl engages the ratchet and thus locks the brakes in the applied position.

When the lever is pulled back on the manual release type (Fig. 29), the cam action of the lever on the pawl cam pin will disengage the pawl from the ratchet to release the brakes.

On the automatic type, the vacuum power unit will release the parking brakes automatically when the transmission selector lever is moved into any drive position with the engine running. The brakes will not release automatically, however, when the selector lever is in the neutral or park position with the engine run-

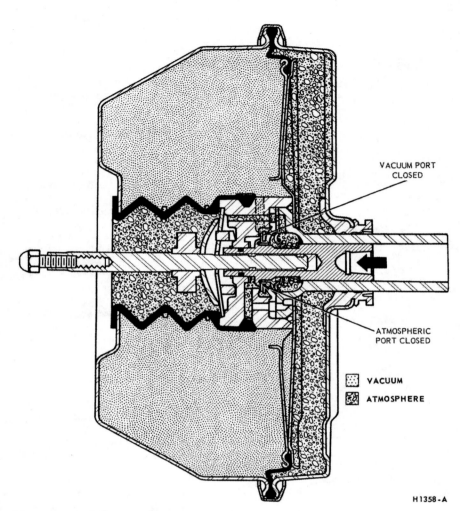

VACUUM PORT
CLOSED

ATMOSPHERIC
PORT CLOSED

▦ VACUUM

▦ ATMOSPHERE

H 1358-A

FIG. 12—Midland-Ross Booster in Holding Position

ning, or in any position with the engine off.

The power unit piston rod is attached to the release lever. Since the release lever pivots against the pawl, a slight movement of the release lever will disengage the pawl from the ratchet allowing the brakes to release. The release lever pivots on a rivet pin in the pedal mount (Fig 14).

The vacuum power unit with mounting bracket is riveted to the control assembly. The vacuum actuated piston within the unit is connected by a rod to the upper end of the release lever to move the pawl out of engagement with the ratchet (Fig. 14). The lower end of the release lever extends out for alternate manual release in the event of vacuum power failure or for optional manual release at any time.

Hoses connect the power unit and the engine manifold to a vacuum release valve in the transmission neutral safety switch (Fig. 14 and 15). Moving the transmission selector lever into any drive position with the engine running will open the release valve to connect engine manifold vacuum to one side of the actuating piston in the power unit. The pressure differential thus created will cause the piston and link to pull the release lever.

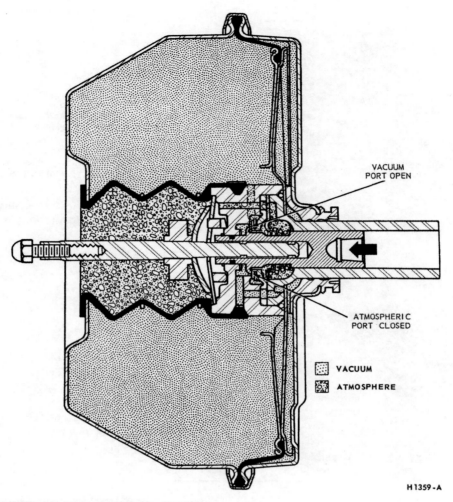

VACUUM
PORT OPEN

ATMOSPHERIC
PORT CLOSED

VACUUM

ATMOSPHERE

H1359-A

FIG. 13—Midland-Ross Booster in Released Position

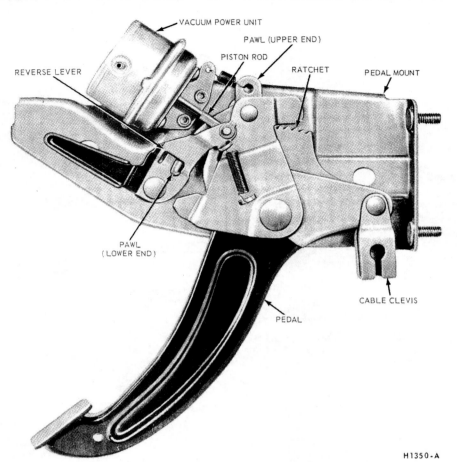

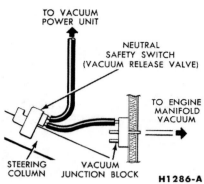

FIG. 15—Connections for Automatic Parking Brake Release

FIG. 14—Parking Brake Control Assembly with Automatic Release

2 IN-CAR ADJUSTMENTS AND REPAIRS

BRAKE SHOE ADJUSTMENTS

The hydraulic service brakes are self-adjusting and require a manual adjustment only after the brake shoes have been relined, replaced, or when the length of the adjusting screw has been changed while performing some other service operation. **The manual adjustment is performed with the drums removed, using the tool and the procedure detailed below.**

(In case a brake drum cannot be removed in the normal manner, an access knock-out slug is provided in the brake carrier plate. Knock the slug out with a punch and then release the brake shoe as detailed under **Brake Drum—Replacement.** Remove the drum and knock-out slug. Install a standard adjusting hole cover in the carrier plate when assembling.)

When adjusting the rear brake shoes, check the parking brake cables for proper adjustment. Make sure

that the equalizer operates freely.

To adjust the brake shoes:

1. Use Rotunda Tool HRE 8650, (Fig. 16) to determine the inside diameter of the drum braking surface.

FIG. 16—Measuring Drum

2. Reverse the tool as shown in Fig. 17 and adjust the brake shoe diameter to fit the gauge. Hold the automatic adjusting lever out of en-

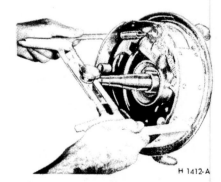

FIG. 17—Measuring Shoes

gagement while rotating the adjusting screw, to prevent burring the screw slots. Make sure the adjusting screw rotates freely. If necessary, lubricate the adjusting screw threads with a thin, uniform coating of C1AZ-19590-B Grease.

3. Rotate Tool HRE 8650 around the brake shoes to be sure of the setting.

4. Apply a small quantity of high temperature grease to the points where the shoes contact the carrier plate, being careful not to get the lubricant on the linings.

5. Install the drums.

6. Install the wheels on the drums and tighten the mounting nuts to specification. Install Tinnerman nuts and tighten securely.

7. Complete the adjustment by applying the brakes several times while backing the car.

8. After the brake shoes have been properly adjusted, check the operation of the brakes by making several stops while operating in a forward direction.

FRONT BRAKE DRUM
REMOVAL

1. Raise the car until the wheel and tire clear the floor. Remove the wheel cover or hub cap, and remove the wheel and tire from the drum.

2. Remove the drum. If the drum will not come off, knock the access slug out of the brake carrier plate, using a punch. Insert a narrow screwdriver through the slot and disengage the adjusting lever from the adjusting screw. While holding the adjusting lever away from the screw, back off the adjusting screw with the brake adjusting tool (Fig. 18). **Be very careful not to burr, chip, or damage the notches in the adjusting screw; otherwise the self-adjusting mechanism will not function properly.**

3. Remove the grease cap from the hub. Remove the cotter pin, nut lock, adjusting nut, and flat washer from the spindle. Remove the outer bearing cone and roller assembly.

4. Pull the drum off the wheel spindle.

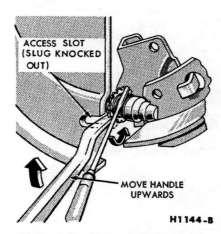

ACCESS SLOT (SLUG KNOCKED OUT)

MOVE HANDLE UPWARDS

H1144-B

FIG. 18—Backing Off Brake Adjustment

INSTALLATION

1. If the drum is being replaced, remove the protective coating from the new drum with carburetor degreaser. Install new bearings and grease retainer. Soak the new grease retainer in light engine oil at least 30 minutes before installation. Pack the wheel bearings, install the inner bearing cone and roller assembly in the inner cup, and install the new grease retainer. See Part 3-5, Section 4.

If the original drum is being installed, make sure that the grease in the hub is clean and adequate.

2. Adjust the brakes and install the drum assembly as outlined under Brake Shoe Adjustments in this section.

3. Install the outer wheel bearing, washer and adjusting nut.

4. Adjust the wheel bearing as outlined in Part 3-5, Section 2, then install the cotter pin grease cap. Install the wheel and hub cap.

REAR BRAKE DRUM
REMOVAL

1. Raise the car so that the wheel is clear of the floor.

2. Remove the hub cap and wheel. Remove the three Tinnerman nuts and remove the brake drum. If the drum will not come off, knock the access slot slug out of the brake carrier plate, using a punch. (Clean away all metal from the brake area before installing the drum). Insert a narrow screwdriver through the hole in the carrier plate, and disengage the adjusting lever from the adjusting screw. While holding the adjusting lever away from the adjusting screw, back off the adjusting screw with the brake adjusting tool (Fig. 18). **Be very careful not to burr, chip, or damage the notches in the adjusting screw; otherwise, the self-adjusting mechanism will not function properly.**

INSTALLATION

1. Remove the protective coating from a new drum with carburetor degreaser.

2. Adjust the brakes as outlined under Brake Shoe Adjustments in this section. Place the drum over the brake assembly and into position.

3. Install the three Tinnerman nuts and tighten securely. Install the wheel on the axle shaft flange studs against the drum, and tighten the attaching nuts to specifications.

BRAKE SHOES AND ADJUSTING SCREW
REMOVAL

1. With the wheel and drum removed, install a clamp over the ends of the brake cylinder as shown in Fig. 19.

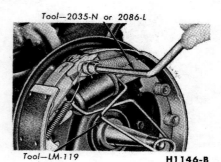

Tool—2035-N or 2086-L

Tool—LM-119   H1146-B

FIG. 19—Retracting Spring Removal

2. Remove the secondary shoe to anchor spring with the tool shown in Fig. 19. With the same tool, remove the primary shoe to anchor spring and unhook the cable eye from the anchor pin.

3. Remove the anchor pin plate.

4. Remove the shoe hold-down springs, shoes, adjusting screw, pivot nut, socket and automatic adjustment parts.

5. On rear brakes, remove the parking brake link and spring. Disconnect the parking brake cable from the parking brake lever.

6. After removing the rear brake secondary shoe, disassemble the parking brake lever from the shoe by removing the retaining clip and spring washer (Fig. 1).

INSTALLATION

1. Before installing the rear brake shoes, assemble the parking brake lever to the secondary shoe and secure with the spring washer and retaining clip.

2. Apply a light coating of high-temperature grease at the points where the brake shoes contact the carrier plate.

3. Position the brake shoes on the carrier plate and secure the assembly with the hold down springs. On the rear brake, install the parking brake link and spring. Connect the parking brake cable to the parking brake lever (Fig. 1).

4. Install the anchor pin plate on the anchor pin.

5. Place the cable eye over the anchor pin with the crimped side toward the carrier plate.

6. Install the primary shoe to anchor spring (Fig. 20).

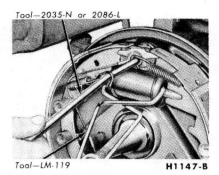

Tool—2035-N or 2086-L

Tool—LM-119   H1147-B

FIG. 20—Retracting Spring Installation

7. Install the cable guide on the secondary shoe web with the flanged hole fitted into the hole in the secondary shoe web. Thread the cable around the cable guide groove (Fig. 1).

It is imperative that the cable be positioned in this groove and not between the guide and the shoe web.

8. Install the secondary shoe to anchor spring with the tool shown in Fig. 20.

Be certain that the cable eye is not cocked or binding on the anchor pin when installed. All parts should be flat on the anchor pin. Remove the brake cylinder clamp.

9. Apply high-temperature grease to the threads and the socket end of the adjusting screw. Turn the adjusting screw into the adjusting pivot nut to the limit of the threads and then back off ½ turn.

Interchanging the brake shoe adjusting screw assemblies from one side of the car to the other would cause the brake shoes to retract rather than expand each time the automatic adjusting mechanism operated. To prevent installation on the wrong side of the car, the socket end of the adjusting screw is stamped with an R or L (Fig. 21). The adjusting pivot nuts can be distinguished by the number of grooves machined around the body of the nut. Two grooves on the nut indicate a right thread; one groove indicates a left thread.

10. Place the adjusting socket on the screw and install this assembly between the shoe ends with the adjusting screw toothed wheel nearest the secondary shoe.

11. Hook the cable hook into the hole in the adjusting lever. The ad-

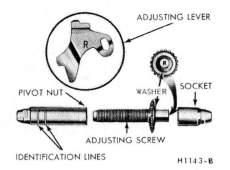

ADJUSTING LEVER

PIVOT NUT

WASHER   SOCKET

ADJUSTING SCREW

IDENTIFICATION LINES   H1143-B

FIG. 21—Adjusting Screw and Lever Identification

justing levers are stamped with an R or L to indicate their installation on a right or left brake assembly (Fig. 21).

12. Position the hooked end of the adjuster spring completely into the large hole in the primary shoe web. The last coil of the spring should be at the edge of the hole. Connect the loop end of the spring to the adjuster lever hole.

13. Pull the adjuster lever, cable and automatic adjuster spring down and toward the rear to engage the pivot hook in the large hole in the secondary shoe web (Fig. 1).

14. After installation, check the action of the adjuster by pulling the section of the cable between the cable guide and the adjusting lever toward the secondary shoe web far enough to lift the lever past a tooth on the adjusting screw wheel. The lever should snap into position behind the next tooth, and release of the cable should cause the adjuster spring to return the lever to its original position. This return action of the lever will turn the adjusting screw one tooth.

If pulling the cable does not produce the action described, or if the lever action is sluggish instead of positive and sharp, check the position of the lever on the adjusting screw toothed wheel. With the brake in a vertical position (anchor at the top), the lever should contact the adjusting wheel $3/16$ inch (plus or minus $1/32$ inch) above the centerline of the screw. If the contact point is below this centerline, the lever will not lock on the teeth in the adjusting screw wheel, and the screw will not be turned as the lever is actuated by the cable.

To determine the cause of this condition:

a. Check the cable end fittings. The cable should completely fill or

extend slightly beyond the crimped section of the fittings. If it does not meet this specification, possible damage is indicated and the cable assembly should be replaced.

b. Check the cable length. The cable should measure $11\frac{1}{8}$ inches (plus or minus $1/64$ inch) from the end of the cable anchor to the end of the cable hook.

c. Check the cable guide for damage. The cable groove should be parallel to the shoe web, and the body of the guide should lie flat against the web. Replace the guide if it shows damage.

d. Check the pivot hook on the lever. The hook surfaces should be square with the body of the lever for proper pivoting. Replace the lever if the hook shows damage.

e. See that the adjusting screw socket is properly seated in the notch in the shoe web.

DISC BRAKE SERVICE PRECAUTIONS

1. Before the vehicle is moved, after any brake service work, obtain a firm brake pedal by pumping the pedal until it reaches the proper height.

2. Grease or any other foreign material must be kept off the caliper assembly, surfaces of the rotor and external surfaces of the hub during service operations. Handling of the rotor and caliper assemblies should be done in a way to avoid deformation of the brake rotor and nicking or scratching of brake linings.

3. If the square sectioned rubber piston seals are worn or damaged, they should be replaced immediately.

4. During removal and installation of a wheel assembly, exercise care not to interfere with and damage the caliper splash shield, the bleeder screw fitting or the transfer tube.

5. Front wheel bearing end play is critical and must be within specifications.

6. Be sure the car is centered on the hoist before servicing any front end components, to avoid bending or damaging the rotor splash shield on full right or left wheel turns.

7. The bridge bolts joining the two caliper housings should not be disturbed.

8. The proportioning valve should not be disassembled or adjustments attempted on it.

9. Riding of the brake pedal (common on left foot applications) should be avoided during vehicle operation.

10. The wheel and tire must be removed separately from the brake rotor, unlike drum brakes where the wheel, tire and drum are removed as a unit.

DISC BRAKE SHOE AND LINING REPLACEMENT
REMOVAL

1. Remove the wheel and tire from the hub. **Be careful to avoid damage or interference with the caliper splash shield, bleeder screw fitting or transfer tube.**

2. Remove the two bolts that attach the caliper splash shield, and remove the shield (Fig. 23).

3. To facilitate removal and installation of the shoe and lining assemblies, the pistons must be pushed into their bores. Apply a steady inward pressure against each shoe and lining assembly toward its respective caliper housing on each side of the rotor (Fig. 3). Maintain the pressure for at least a minute. If the pistons will not go in easily, force them in with water pump pliers.

4. Grasp the metal flange on the outer end of the shoe with two pairs of pliers and pull the shoe out of the caliper (Fig. 22).

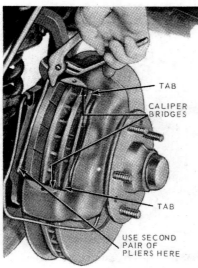

TAB

CALIPER BRIDGES

TAB

USE SECOND PAIR OF PLIERS HERE

H 1366 - A

FIG. 22—Removing Disc Brake Shoe and Lining Assembly

CLEANING AND INSPECTION

When the shoe and lining assemblies are replaced, remove the dust boots from the pistons. Check the condition of the boots, and inspect each piston surface for damage or corrosion. Thoroughly clean each dust boot and surrounding area before installing.

INSTALLATION

1. Position a new shoe and lining assembly on each side of the rotor so that the lining faces the rotor. Be sure that the tabs on the shoe flanges seat fully against the caliper bridges (Fig. 22).

2. Install the caliper splash shield and secure the shield to the caliper with two attaching bolts (Fig. 23).

3. **Pump the brake pedal several times until a firm pedal is obtained and the shoe and lining assemblies are properly seated.**

4. Install the wheel and tire on the hub.

5. Check and refill the master cylinder reservoir with specified brake fluid as required. **It should not be necessary to bleed the system after a shoe and lining replacement providing the hydraulic system has not been opened.**

6. Road test the car.

DISC BRAKE CALIPER ASSEMBLY

REMOVAL

1. Remove the wheel and tire from the hub. **Be careful to avoid damage or interference with the caliper splash shield, bleeder screw fitting or transfer tube.**

2. Disconnect the front brake flexible hose from the brake tube at the bracket on the frame (Fig. 26).

3. Remove the two bolts that attach the caliper to the spindle. **Take care to avoid loosening the bridge bolts that hold the two halves of the caliper together.**

4. Lift the caliper assembly off the rotor.

INSTALLATION

1. Position the caliper assembly on the rotor, and mate the mounting bolt holes in the caliper with those in the spindle. It may be necessary to push the caliper pistons into the cylinder bores to obtain clearance between the shoe and lining assemblies and the rotor. The shoe and lining assemblies should be seated properly on the bridges.

2. Install the caliper to spindle attaching bolts and torque them to specification. Make sure that the rotor runs squarely and centrally between the two halves of the caliper. There should be approximately 0.090-0.120 inch clearance between the caliper and the rotor outside diameter (Fig. 3).

3. Connect the front wheel brake flexible hose to the brake tube at the bracket on the frame (Fig. 26). The hose should be checked for correct routing.

4. Bleed the brake system as outlined in Section 2-1. Check the master cylinder fluid level, and add the specified brake fluid as required.

5. **Pump the brake pedal several times to actuate the piston seals and to position the shoe and lining assemblies.**

6. Install the wheel and tire.

7. Road test the car.

FRONT WHEEL HUB AND ROTOR ASSEMBLY—DISC BRAKES

REMOVAL

1. Remove the wheel and tire from the hub. (Fig. 23). **Be careful to avoid damage or interference with per splash shield, bleeder screw fitting or transfer tube.**

2. Remove the caliper assembly from the spindle and the rotor. If the caliper does not require servicing, it is not necessary to disconnect the brake hose or remove the caliper from the car. Position the caliper out of the way, and support it with a wire to avoid damaging the caliper or stretching the hose. Insert a **clean** cardboard spacer between the linings to prevent the pistons from coming out of the cylinder bores while the caliper is removed. **Handle the rotor and caliper assemblies in such a way as to avoid deformation of the rotor and nicking or scratching of the brake linings.**

3. Remove the grease cap from the hub. Remove the cotter pin, nut lock, adjusting nut, and flat washer from the spindle. Remove the outer bearing cone and roller assembly.

4. Remove the hub and rotor assembly from the spindle.

INSTALLATION

1. If the rotor is being replaced, remove the protective coating from the new rotor with carburetor degreaser. Pack a new set of bearings with specified grease (M-1C75A), and install the inner bearing cone and roller assembly in the inner cup. Pack grease lightly between the lips of a new grease retainer and install the retainer (Fig. 23).

If the original rotor is being installed, make sure that the grease in the hub is clean and adequate, that the inner bearing and grease retainer

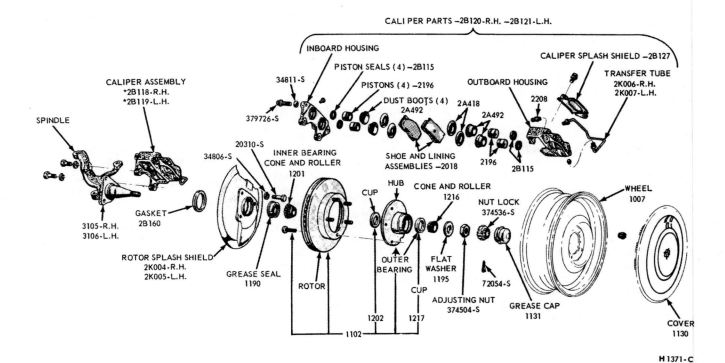

FIG. 23—Disc Brake Disassembled

are lubricated and in good condition, and that the rotor braking surfaces are clean.

2. Install the hub and rotor assembly on the spindle.

3. Lubricate and install the outer wheel bearing, washer and adjusting nut.

4. Adjust the wheel bearings to specification, and then install the nut lock, cotter pin, and grease cap. **The wheel bearing adjustment is especially important with disc brakes.**

5. Mount the caliper assembly on the mounting bracket and torque the two mounting bolts to specification. If necessary, push the caliper pistons into the cylinder bores to obtain clearance between the shoe and lining assemblies and the rotor. Be sure that the shoe and lining assemblies are seated on the bridges. Check the flexible hose for correct routing.

6. Install the wheel and tire on the hub.

DISC BRAKE ROTOR SPLASH SHIELD

REMOVAL

1. Remove the caliper and the hub and rotor assembly as outlined under Removal in the foregoing procedure (it is not necessary to disconnect hy-

draulic connections).

2. Remove the three bolts that attach the splash shield to the spindle (Fig. 23).

INSTALLATION

1. If the shield is bent, straighten it out before installation. Position the shield to the mounting bracket, install the attaching bolts nuts, and torque them to specification (Fig. 23).

2. Install the hub and rotor assembly and the caliper as outlined under Installation in the foregoing procedure.

PROPORTIONING VALVE

The proportioning valve is serviced as an assembly and is never adjusted or overhauled.

REMOVAL

1. Disconnect and remove the junction block to proportioning valve brake tube. (Fig. 24).

2. Disconnect the front to rear brake tube at the proportioning valve.

3. Remove the bolt attaching the proportioning valve to the frame and remove the valve.

INSTALLATION

1. Position the proportioning valve

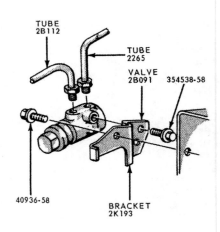

FIG. 24—Proportioning Valve

to the frame and install the attaching bolt.

2. Connect the front to rear brake tube to the valve.

3. Position and connect the junction block to proportioning valve brake tube.

4. Bleed the brake system as directed in **Part 2-1.**

STANDARD OR REAR WHEEL CYLINDER REPAIR

Wheel cylinders should not be disassembled unless they are leaking or unless new cups and boots are to be installed. It is not necessary to remove the brake cylinder from the carrier plate to disassemble, inspect, or hone and overhaul the cylinder. Removal is necessary only when the cylinder is damaged or scored beyond repair.

DISASSEMBLY

1. Remove the links and the rubber boots from the ends of the brake cylinder. Remove the pistons, cups, and return spring from the cylinder bore (Fig. 25).

2. Remove the bleeder screw from the cylinder.

the cylinder and tighten securely.

3. Insert the return spring, cups, and pistons into their respective positions in the cylinder bore (Fig. 25). Place a boot over each end of the cylinder. Bleed the brake system.

WHEEL CYLINDER REPLACEMENT

REMOVAL

1. Remove the wheel and the drum.

2. Remove the brake shoe assemblies, following procedures outlined in this section.

3. Disconnect the brake line from the brake cylinder. **On a car with a**

the cylinder is removed from the carrier plate.

4. On the rear wheel, remove the wheel cylinder attaching bolts and lock washers and remove the cylinder. On the front wheel, remove the nut and washer that attaches the cylinder to the anchor pin. Remove the cylinder from the anchor pin.

INSTALLATION

Wipe the end(s) of the hydraulic line to remove any foreign matter before making connections.

1. **To install a front cylinder:**

a. Position the cylinder on the anchor pin against the carrier plate. Install the washer and cylinder attaching nut on the anchor pin, and torque it to specification.

b. Install a new copper gasket over the hose fitting. Thread the hose assembly into the cylinder.

c. Engage the opposite end of the hose to the bracket on the frame. Install the horseshoe-type retaining clip, and connect the brake tube to the hose with the tube fitting nut. Tighten the nut to specification with tool 1112-144.

2. **To install a rear cylinder:**

a. Place the rear wheel cylinder into position. Enter the tubing into the cylinder, and start the tube fitting nut into the threads of the cylinder.

b. Secure the cylinder to the carrier plate by installing the attaching bolts and lock washers.

c. Tighten the tube fitting nut to specification with tool 1112-144.

3. Install the links in the ends of the wheel cylinder, install the shoes and adjuster assemblies, and adjust the shoes as outlined in this section.

4. Adjust the brakes (Part 2-2, Section 2). Install the brake drum and wheel. Bleed the brakes as outlined in Part 2-1, Section 2.

BRAKE CARRIER PLATE REPLACEMENT

REMOVAL

1. Remove the wheel and brake drum. Disconnect the brake line from the brake cylinder.

2. Remove the brake shoe and adjuster assemblies and the wheel cylinder as outlined in this section. On the rear wheels, disconnect the parking brake lever from the cable.

3. If the rear carrier plate is being replaced, rotate the axle shaft so that the hole in the axle shaft flange lines up with the carrier plate attaching nuts and remove the nuts. Pull the

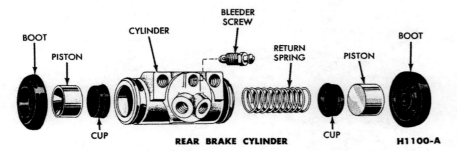

FIG. 25—Front and Rear Wheel Cylinders

INSPECTION

1. Wash all parts in clean denatured alcohol. If alcohol is not available, use specified brake fluid. Dry with compressed air.

2. Replace scored pistons. Always replace the rubber cups and dust boots.

3. Inspect the cylinder bore for score marks or rust. If either condition is present, the cylinder bore must be honed. **However, the cylinder should not be honed more than 0.003 inch beyond its original diameter.**

4. Check the bleeder hole to be sure that it is open.

ASSEMBLY

1. Apply a coating of heavy-duty brake fluid to all internal parts.

2. Thread the bleeder screw into

vacuum brake booster, be sure the engine is stopped and there is no vacuum in the booster system before disconnecting the hydraulic lines.

To disconnect the hose at a front cylinder, loosen the tube fitting that connects the opposite end of the hose to the brake tube at a bracket on the frame. Remove the horseshoe-type retaining clip from the hose and bracket, disengage the hose from the bracket, then unscrew the entire hose assembly from the front wheel cylinder.

At a rear cylinder, unscrew the tube fitting that connects the tube to the cylinder. **Do not pull the metal tube away from the cylinder. Pulling the tube out of the cylinder connection will bend the metal tube and make installation difficult.** The tube will separate from the cylinder when axle shaft out of the housing with tool-4235C and a slide hammer (Part 4-2), then remove the carrier plate.

If the front carrier plate is being replaced, remove the bolts and nuts that secure the plate to the front wheel spindle and remove the plate.

INSTALLATION

1. Position a new **rear** carrier plate and gaskets on the attaching bolts in the axle housing flange. Insert the axle shaft into the housing so that the splines engage the differential side gear with the bearing retainer sliding onto the attaching bolts and against the carrier plate. Install the attaching nuts through the access hole in the axle shaft flange.

Position a new **front** carrier plate and gasket to the wheel spindle and

install the attaching bolts and nuts.

2. Install the wheel cylinder and connect the brake line as outlined in this section.

3. Install the brake shoe and adjuster assemblies as outlined in this section. On a rear brake, connect the parking brake cable to the lever.

4. Adjust the brake shoes (Section 2), and install the brake drums and wheels. Bleed the brake system as outlined in Part 2-1, Section 2.

HYDRAULIC LINES

Steel tubing is used throughout the brake system with the exception of the flexible hoses at the front wheels and at the rear axle housing brake tube connector (Fig. 26). **Always bleed the entire system after any hose or line replacement.**

BRAKE TUBE REPLACEMENT

If a section of the brake tubing becomes damaged, the entire section should be replaced with tubing of the same type, size, shape, and length. **Copper tubing should not be used in a hydraulic system.** When bending brake tubing to fit underbody or rear axle contours, be careful not to kink or crack the tube.

All brake tubing should be flared properly to provide good leak-proof connections. Clean the brake tubing by flushing with clean denatured alcohol, before installation.

When connecting a tube to a hose, tube connector, or brake cylinder, tighten the tube fitting nut to specified torque with Milbar tool 1112-144 or equivalent.

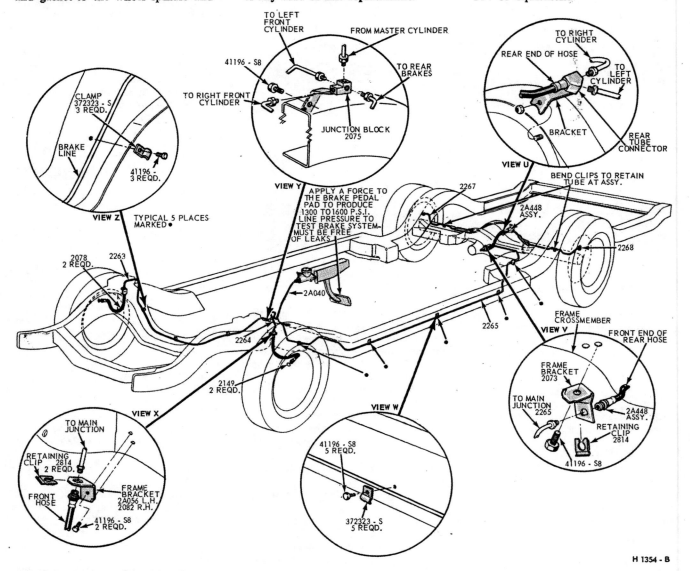

FIG. 26—Service Brake System

BRAKE HOSE REPLACEMENT

A flexible brake hose should be replaced if it shows signs of softening, cracking, or other damage.

When installing a new front brake hose, position the hose to avoid contact with other chassis parts. Place a new copper gasket over the hose fitting and thread the hose assembly into the front brake cylinder. Engage the opposite end of the hose to the bracket on the frame. Install the horseshoe-type retaining clip, and connect the tube to the hose with the tube fitting nut (Fig. 26).

A rear brake hose should be installed so that it does not touch the muffler outlet pipe or shock absorber.

Place a new gasket over the rear hose fitting and thread the hose into the rear brake tube connector. Engage the front end of the hose to the bracket on the frame. Install the horseshoe-type retaining clip, and connect the tube to the hose with the tube fitting nut.

3   REMOVAL AND INSTALLATION

MASTER CYLINDER— STANDARD BRAKES

REMOVAL

1. Disconnect the rubber boot from the rear end of the master cylinder in the passenger compartment.
2. Disconnect the brake line from the master cylinder.
3. Remove the nuts and lock washers that secure the master cylinder to the dash panel and lift the cylinder out and away from the push rod (Fig. 27). Remove the rubber boot from the push rod.

INSTALLATION

1. With the rubber boot on the push rod, guide the master cylinder over the end of the push rod, and position the cylinder on the mounting studs against the dash panel.
2. Install the lock washers and attaching nuts and torque to specification.
3. Connect the brake line to the master cylinder fitting, but leave the brake line fitting loose.
4. Fill the master cylinder reservoir with Rotunda B7A-19542-B or

C heavy-duty brake fluid to within 3/8 inch of the top. Be sure that the diaphragm is properly seated in the filler cap. Install and tighten the filler cap.
5. Bleed the master cylinder to let air escape from the cylinder at the brake line fitting. Then tighten the fitting.
6. Remove the filler cap and fill the reservoir to the level specified. Install the cap and wipe off any fluid from the cylinder.
7. Connect the rubber boot to the master cylinder.

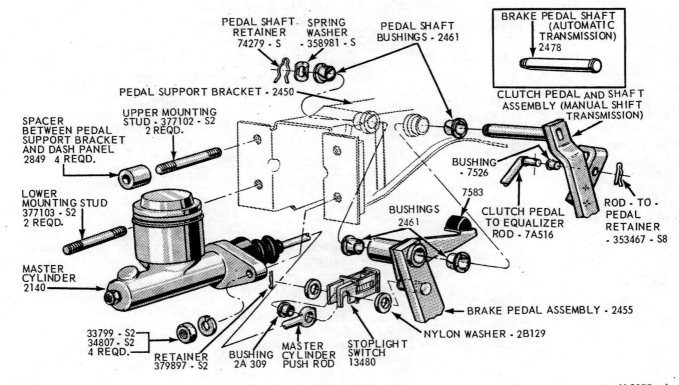

FIG. 27—Master Cylinder, Pedals and Stop Light Switch

H 1355 - A

8. Bleed the hydraulic system as directed in Hydraulic System Bleeding, Part 2-1. Fill the master cylinder within ⅜ inch of the top of the filler opening. Install the filler cap and diaphragm.

MASTER CYLINDER— POWER BRAKES

REMOVAL

1. Remove the hydraulic line outlet fitting from the master cylinder.

2. Remove the attaching nuts, lock washers, and the master cylinder from the booster unit (Fig. 28).

3. Remove the rubber seal from the outer groove at the end of the master cylinder.

3. Position the master cylinder over the push rod onto the two studs that are integral with the booster body.

4. Install the attaching nuts and lock washers and torque the nuts to specifications.

5. Install the master cylinder hydraulic line outlet fitting.

6. Bleed the hydraulic system. Fill the master cylinder within ⅜ inch from the top of the filler opening. Install the filler cap and diaphragm.

BOOSTER UNIT

REMOVAL

1. Working from inside the car below the instrument panel, discon-

washers and bushing off the brake pedal pin (Fig. 28).

2. Open the hood and remove the master cylinder from the booster. Secure it to one side without disturbing the hydraulic lines.

3. Disconnect the manifold vacuum hose from the booster unit. If the car is equipped with an automatic transmission disconnect the transmission vacuum unit hose.

4. Remove the four bracket-to-dash panel attaching nuts and washers (Fig. 28). Remove the booster and bracket assembly from the dash panel, sliding the push rod link out from the engine side of the dash panel. Remove the four spacers.

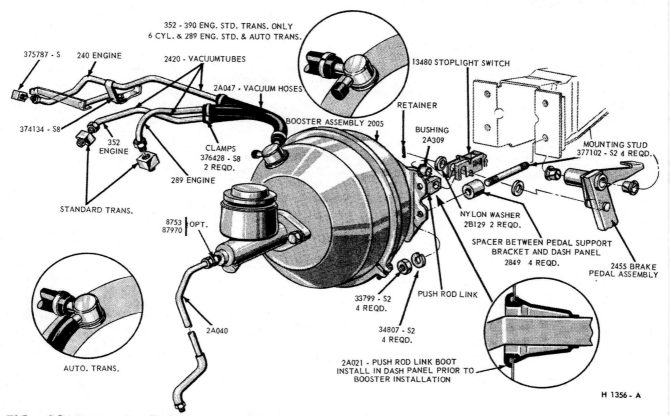

FIG. 28—Booster Installation

INSTALLATION

1. Before installing the master cylinder, check the distance from the outer end of the push rod to the master cylinder mounting surface at the end of the vacuum cylinder (Fig. 3, Part 2-1). If the push rod dimension is not correct, see Master Cylinder Push Rod Adjustment, Part 2-1, Section 2.

2. When the push rod adjustment is correct, replace the rubber seal in the groove at the end of the master cylinder.

nect the booster push rod link from the brake pedal assembly. To do this, proceed as follows:

Disconnect the stop light switch wires at the connector. Remove the hairpin retainer. Slide the stop light switch off from the brake pedal pin **just far enough for the switch outer hole to clear the pin,** and then lift the switch straight **upward** from the pin. Be careful not to damage the switch during removal. Slide the master cylinder push rod and the nylon

5. Remove the push rod link boot from the dash panel.

INSTALLATION

1. Install the push rod link boot in the hole in the dash panel as shown in Fig. 28. Install the four spacers on the mounting studs.

2. Mount the booster and bracket assembly to the dash panel by sliding the bracket onto the mounting studs and the push rod link in through the hole and boot in the dash panel. Install the bracket-to-dash panel attaching nuts and washers (Fig. 28).

3. Connect the manifold vacuum hose to the booster. If the car is equipped with an automatic transmission connect the transmission vacuum unit hose.

4. Install the master cylinder.

5. Working from inside the car below the instrument panel, connect the booster push rod link to the brake pedal assembly. To do this, proceed as follows:

Install the inner nylon washer, the master cylinder push rod, and the bushing on the brake pedal pin. Position the switch so that it straddles the push rod with the switch slot on the pedal pin and the switch outer hole just clearing the pin. Slide the switch completely onto the pin, and install the nylon washer as shown in Fig. 28. **Be careful not to bend or deform the switch.** Secure these parts to the pin with the hairpin retainer. Connect the stop light switch wires to the connector, and install the wires in the retaining clip.

BRAKE PEDAL—MANUAL SHIFT TRANSMISSION

REMOVAL

1. Disconnect the clutch pedal-to-equalizer rod at the clutch pedal by removing the hairpin type retainer and bushing (Fig. 27).

2. Disconnect the stop light switch wires at the connector.

3. Remove the hairpin retainer. Slide the stop light switch off the brake pedal pin **just far enough for the switch outer hole to clear the pin,** and then lift the switch straight **upward from the pin. Be careful not to damage the switch during removal.** Slide the master cylinder push rod and the nylon washers and bushing off the brake pedal pin (Fig. 27).

4. Remove the hairpin type retainer and spring washer from the clutch and brake pedal shaft. Remove the clutch pedal and shaft, the brake pedal, and the bushings from the pedal support bracket (Fig. 27).

INSTALLATION

1. Apply a coating of SAE 10 engine oil to the bushings and locate all bushings in their proper places on the clutch and brake pedal assemblies.

2. Position the brake pedal to the support bracket, then install the clutch pedal and shaft through the support bracket and brake pedal. Install the spring washer and retainer (Fig. 27).

3. Install the inner nylon washer,

the master cylinder push rod, and the bushing on the brake pedal pin. Position the switch so that it straddles the push rod with the switch slot on the pedal pin and the switch outer hole just clearing the pin. Slide the switch completely onto the pin, and install the nylon washer as shown in Fig. 27. **Be careful not to bend or deform the switch.** Secure these parts to the pin with the hairpin retainer.

4. Connect the stop light switch wires to the connector, and install the wires in the retaining clip.

5. Connect the clutch pedal-to-equalizer rod to the clutch pedal assembly with the bushing and hairpin retainer. Apply SAE 10 engine oil to the bushing. Adjust the clutch pedal free play to specification if required.

BRAKE PEDAL—AUTOMATIC TRANSMISSION

REMOVAL

1. Disconnect the stop light switch wires at the connector.

2. Remove the hairpin retainer. Slide the stop light switch off the brake pedal pin **just far enough for the switch outer hole to clear the pin,** and then lift the switch straight upward from the pin. **Be careful not to damage the switch during removal.** Slide the master cylinder push rod and the nylon washers and bushing off the brake pedal pin (Fig. 27).

3. Remove the hairpin type retainer and spring washer from the brake pedal shaft, then remove the shaft, the brake pedal and the bushings from the pedal support bracket.

INSTALLATION

1. Apply a coating of SAE 10 Engine oil to the bushings and locate bushings in their proper places on the pedal assembly and pedal support bracket (Fig. 27).

2. Position the brake pedal assembly to the support bracket, then install the pedal shaft through the support bracket and brake pedal assembly. Install the spring washer and retainer.

3. Install the inner nylon washer, the master cylinder push rod, and the bushing on the brake pedal pin. Position the switch so that it straddles the push rod with the switch slot on the pedal pin and the switch outer hole just clearing the pin. Slide the switch completely onto the pin, and install the nylon washer as shown in Fig. 27. **Be careful not to bend or deform the switch.** Secure these parts to the pin with the hairpin retainer.

4. Connect the stop light switch wires to the connector, and install the wires in the retaining clip.

PARKING BRAKE CONTROL ASSEMBLY

REMOVAL

1. Working from the engine compartment, remove the two nuts and washers that attach the parking brake control assembly to the dash panel (Fig. 29).

2. Working from the passenger compartment, remove the bolt and nut that attach the control assembly to the cowl upper panel.

3. Pull the control assembly from the dash panel, remove the hairpin retainer that holds the cable housing to the control assembly bracket, and disconnect the ball end of the cable from the clevis on the pedal (Fig. 30). Disconnect the hose from the vacuum power unit on an automatic release type control assembly.

INSTALLATION

1. Connect the ball end of the cable to the clevis on the pedal, and secure the cable housing to the control assembly bracket with the hairpin retainer. Connect the hose to the vacuum power unit on an automatic release type control assembly.

2. Install the two spacers on the mounting studs, and position the control assembly so that the mounting studs enter the holes in the dash panel (Fig. 30).

3. Install the bolt and nut that attaches the control assembly to the cowl upper panel. Do not tighten at this time.

4. Working from the engine compartment, install the two attaching nuts and washers on the mounting studs at the dash panel.

5. Working from the passenger compartment, tighten the bolt and nut that attaches the assembly to the cowl upper panel. Check and adjust the parking brake linkage, if necessary.

PARKING BRAKE VACUUM POWER UNIT

REMOVAL

1. Remove the parking brake control assembly from the car as described under Removal in the foregoing procedure.

2. Drill out or grind off the two rivets that attach the vacuum power unit to the parking brake control assembly.

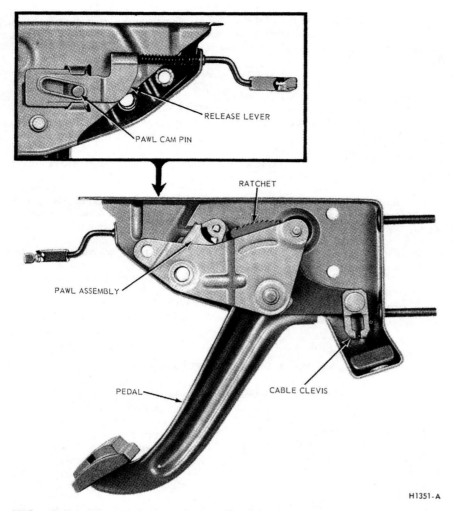

RELEASE LEVER

PAWL CAM PIN

RATCHET

PAWL ASSEMBLY

PEDAL

CABLE CLEVIS

H1351-A

FIG. 29—Parking Brake Control Assembly—Manual Release

3. Remove the retainer clip that secures the vacuum piston rod to the release lever and disconnect the rod from the lever. Remove the power unit.

INSTALLATION

1. Position the vacuum power unit on the parking brake control assembly and secure with two round head bolts and nuts.

2. Connect the vacuum piston rod to the release lever and secure with the *retainer clip.*

3. Install the parking brake control assembly in the car as described under Installation in the foregoing procedure.

4. Test the lock and automatic release operations of the parking brake control assembly with the engine running in all the transmission selector lever positions. With the engine running, the parking brake should remain engaged in Neutral or Park and should release in any drive position.

PARKING BRAKE EQUALIZER TO CONTROL CABLE

REMOVAL

1. Raise the car on a hoist. Move the parking brake equalizer lever forward and disconnect the ball end of the cable from the lever (Fig. 30).

2. Remove the hairpin retainer from the cable housing at the transmission rear support crossmember, and then pull the cable assembly forward and out of the crossmember.

3. Remove the cable housing from the retaining clip at the underside of the floor pan.

4. Lower the car. Remove the parking brake control assembly and disconnect the cable from the control as outlined in the Removal procedure under Parking Brake Control Assembly.

5. Push the cable and housing down through the hole in the floor pan and remove it from under the car.

INSTALLATION

1. Working from the underside of the car, guide the upper end of the replacement cable into the hole in the floor pan.

2. Working from inside the car, pull the new cable and housing up through the hole in the floor pan.

3. Connect the upper end of the cable to the control assembly and install the control assembly as outlined in the Installation procedure under Parking Brake Control Assembly.

4. Raise the car on a hoist. Guide the rear end of the cable assembly through the hole in the transmission rear support crossmember. Secure the cable assembly to the crossmember with the hair pin retainer (Fig. 30).

5. Engage the cable housing in the retaining clip at the underside of the floor pan.

6. Connect the cable rear end ball to the equalizer lever. Adjust the parking brake linkage as outlined in Part 2-1.

PARKING BRAKE EQUALIZER TO REAR WHEEL CABLE

REMOVAL

1. Raise the car and remove the hub cap and wheel.

2. Remove the three Tinnerman nuts that hold the brake drum in place and remove the drum.

3. Loosen the adjusting nut on the equalizer and disconnect the cable from the equalizer (Fig. 1, Part 2-1).

4. Remove the clip that attaches the cable housing to the rear suspension arm (Fig. 30).

5. Remove the hair pin retainer that holds the cable housing to the rear suspension arm mounting bracket and pull the cable and housing out of the bracket (Fig. 30).

6. Working on the wheel side of the rear brake (Fig. 1), compress the prongs on the cable retainer so that they can pass through the hole in the carrier plate. Draw the cable retainer out of the hole.

7. With the spring tension off the parking brake lever, lift the cable out of the slot in the lever and remove through the carrier plate hole.

INSTALLATION

1. Pull enough of the cable through the housing so that the end of the cable may be inserted over the slot in the parking brake lever on the rear brake shoe (Fig. 1).

2. Pulling the excess slack from the cable, insert the cable housing

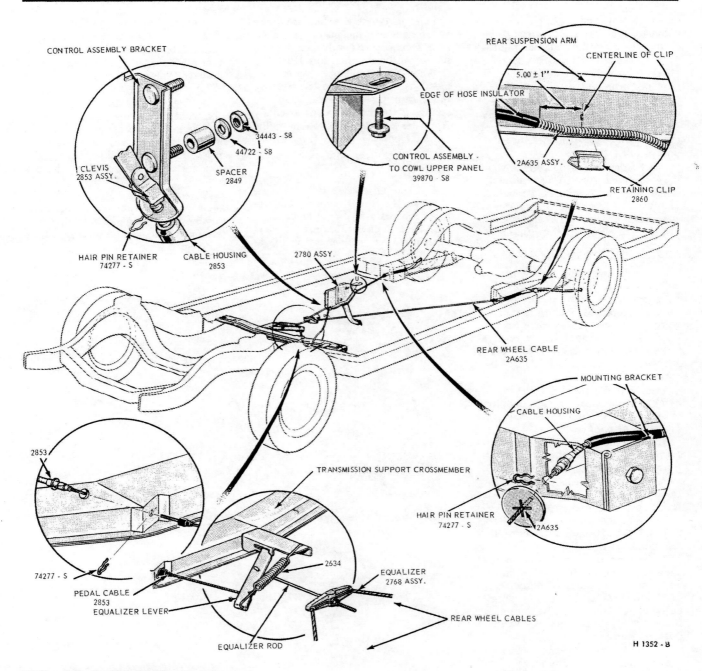

FIG. 30—Parking Brake System

into the carrier plate access hole so that the retainer prongs expand.

3. Thread the front end of the cable housing through the rear suspension arm mounting bracket and install the hair pin retainer (Fig. 30).

4. Fasten the cable housing to the rear suspension arm with the retaining clip. The clip should be installed

so that its centerline is 4-6 inches from the edge of the hose insulator as shown in Fig. 30.

5. Insert the ball end of the cable into the equalizer and tighten the adjusting nut on the equalizer end slightly (Fig. 1, Part 2-1).

6. Adjust the rear brake shoes as outlined in Section 2.

7. Install the rear drum. Tighten the three Tinnerman nuts that secure the drum, and install the wheel and hub cap.

8. Adjust the parking brake linkage as outlined in Part 2-1, Section 2.

4 MAJOR REPAIR OPERATIONS

BRAKE DRUM REFINISHING

Minor scores on a brake drum can

be removed with a fine emery cloth. A drum that is excessively scored or

shows a total indicator runout of over 0.007 inch should be turned down. Remove only enough stock to eliminate the scores and true up the drum. The refinished diameter must not exceed 0.060 inch oversize (11.090 inches).

If the drum diameter is less than 0.030 inch oversize (11.060 inches) after refinishing, standard lining may be installed. If the drum diameter is 11.060-11.090 inches, oversize linings must be installed.

After a drum is turned down, wipe the refinished surface with a cloth soaked in clean denatured alcohol. If one drum is turned down, the opposite drum on the same axle should also be cut down to the same size.

BRAKE SHOE RELINING

Brake linings that are worn to within 1/32 inch of the rivet or have been saturated with grease or oil should be replaced. Failure to replace worn linings will result in a scored drum. **When it is necessary to replace linings, they must also be replaced on the wheel on the opposite side of the car.**

Inspect brake shoes for distortion, cracks, or looseness. If this condition exists, the shoe should be discarded. **Do not repair a defective brake shoe.**

1. Wash the brake shoes thoroughly in a clean solvent. Remove all burrs or rough spots from the shoes.

2. Check the inside diameter of the brake drum. If the diameter is less than 11.060 inches, standard lining may be installed. If the diameter is 11.060-11.090 inches, oversize lining should be installed.

3. Position the new lining on the shoe. Starting in the center, insert and secure the rivets, working alternately towards each end. Install all parts supplied in the kit. **Replacement linings are ground and no further grinding is required.**

4. Check the clearance between the shoe and lining. The lining must seat tightly against the shoe with not more than 0.008 inch clearance between any two rivets.

MASTER CYLINDER

DISASSEMBLY

1. Clean the outside of the cylinder, and remove the filler cap and diaphragm. Pour out any brake fluid that may remain in the cylinder or reservoir.

2. Remove the snap ring from the bore at the rear of the cylinder with tool 33621 (Fig. 33).

3. When disassembling a master cylinder used with the standard brake system, remove the piston assembly, cup, spring, check valve, and valve seat from the cylinder bore (Fig. 31).

When disassembling a master cylinder used with a booster, remove the piston assembly, cup, and the spring and check valve assembly from the cylinder bore. Remove the O-ring from the piston (Fig. 32).

CLEANING, INSPECTION, AND REPAIR

1. Clean all master cylinder parts in clean denatured alcohol, and inspect the parts for wear or damage, replacing them as required. **When using a master cylinder repair kit, install all of the parts supplied.**

2. Check the ports and vents in the master cylinder to make sure that all are open and free of foreign matter. Check the condition of the diaphragm type gasket.

3. A leaf-type valve is riveted to the front end of the piston in a master cylinder used with the standard brake system (Fig. 31). If this valve is loose or has moved so that the piston ports are open, replace the piston.

When inspecting a master cylinder used with a booster, check the ports in the piston to make sure that they are open and free of foreign material (Fig. 32).

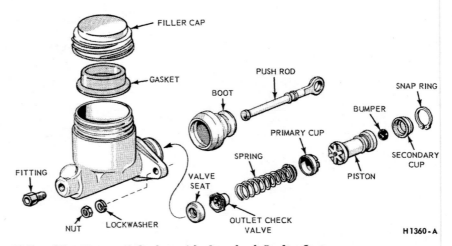

FIG. 31—Master Cylinder with Standard Brake System

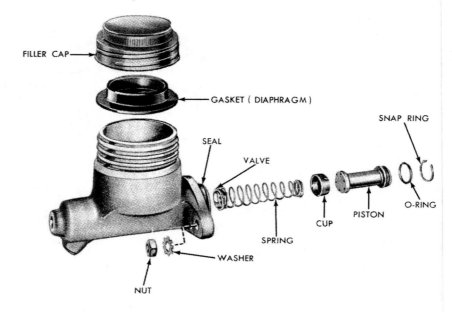

FIG. 32—Master Cylinder with Booster

4. Inspect the cylinder walls for scores or rust, and recondition them if necessary. **Hone the cylinder walls no more than necessary (0.003 inch maximum). Oversize pistons and cups are not available for excessively honed cylinders.**

5. Remove any burrs or loose metal that may have resulted from the honing operation, and clean the cylinder with denatured alcohol.

ASSEMBLY

1. Dip all parts except the master cylinder body in clean Rotunda B7A-19542-B or C heavy-duty brake fluid.

2. Install the brake line fitting on the cylinder and tighten it securely.

3. When assembling a master cylinder used with the standard brake system, install the valve seat, check valve, spring, cup, and piston assembly in the cylinder bore (Fig. 31).

When assembling a master cylinder used with a booster, install the O-ring on the piston. Install the spring and check valve assembly, cup, and piston in the cylinder bore (Fig. 32).

4. Install the snap ring in the back of the bore (Fig. 33).

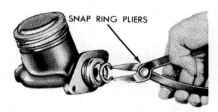

FIG. 33—Removing Snap Ring from Master Cylinder—Typical

DISASSEMBLY OF BENDIX TYPE BOOSTER

The Bendix Type booster used with disc brakes is a non-serviceable unit other than adjusting the push rod to master cylinder clearance. When the unit is known to be defective, replace it with a new booster.

REMOVAL OF EXTERNAL PARTS

1. Remove the attaching nuts and lock washers, then remove the mounting brackets from the rear shell (Fig. 38).

2. Pull the hydraulic push rod and front seal (Fig. 34) from the front shell.

3. Scribe an index mark across the front and rear shells.

4. Place the booster in a vise as shown in Fig. 35. Press downward on the rear shell and at the same time,

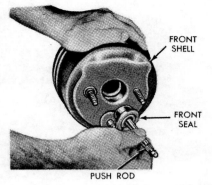

H1334-A

FIG. 34—Removing Front Seal and Push Rod (Bendix Type)

turn it counterclockwise with a flat bar to release it from the front shell. Release the pressure on the rear shell slowly to prevent the diaphragm plate return spring from flying out.

5. Separate the two shells and remove the return spring.

6. Withdraw the diaphragm plate

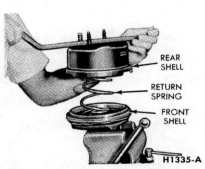

H1335-A

FIG. 35—Separating Booster Shells (Bendix Type)

and diaphragm from the rear shell. Remove the dust shield.

7. Remove the diaphragm from the diaphragm plate as shown in Fig. 36.

8. Pry the filter retainer off the diaphragm plate being careful not to chip or damage the plate.

9. Hold the diaphragm plate so that the valve retainer is facing downward. Press the valve push rod inward to release the tension on the retainer and allow it to drop out of the plate (Fig. 37).

10. Withdraw the valve and rod from the plate.

11. Press the reaction disc out of the diaphragm plate.

12. Drive the seal out of the rear shell with a punch or screwdriver. (Fig. 38). Discard the seal.

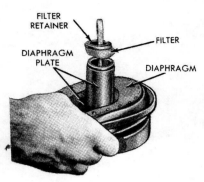

H1336-A

FIG. 36—Removing Diaphragm (Bendix Type)

13. Working from the inside of the front shell, cut the bead off the check valve grommet. Remove the check valve.

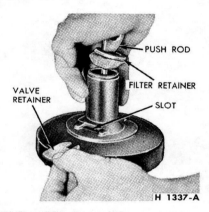

H 1337-A

FIG. 37—Removing or Installing Valve Retainer (Bendix Type)

ASSEMBLY OF BOOSTER— BENDIX TYPE

1. Place the rear shell on two wood blocks as shown in Fig. 39. Press a new seal, plastic side first, into the recess on the inside of the shell to a depth of ¼ inch.

2. Dip a new check valve grommet (Fig. 38) in alcohol and install it in the front shell making sure that the beveled edge is toward the inside. Make sure that the grommet is seated. Dip the shoulder of the check valve in alcohol and install it in the grommet. Press the check valve into the grommet until the flange contacts the grommet.

3. Apply silicone grease to the outer surface of the diaphragm plate hub and to the bearing and rubber surfaces of the valve.

4. Insert the valve and rod into

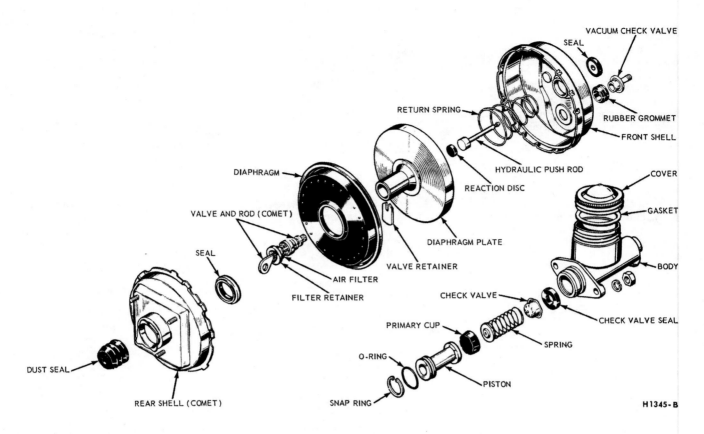

FIG. 38—Vacuum Booster Disassembled (Bendix Type)

the hub of the diaphragm plate. Push the rod inward until the retaining groove is aligned with the slot, and then slide the retainer into the groove (Fig. 37).

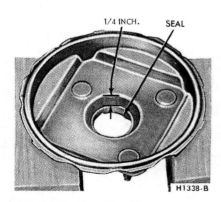

FIG. 39—Installing Rear Shell Seal

5. Tuck the filter into place in the plate hub. Press the filter retainer onto the hub being careful not to chip or damage the plastic. (Fig. 36).

6. Install the diaphragm on the diaphragm plate, making sure that the diaphragm lip is tucked in all around the recess between the hub and the plate (Fig. 36).

7. Place the rear shell in a vise. Apply silicone lubricant generously to the top outer flange of the shell. Apply silicone grease to the seal in the rear shell.

8. Carefully guide the valve rod and diaphragm plate hub through the seal in the rear shell.

9. Center the large end of the return spring on the diaphragm plate.

10. Align the index mark on the front shell with the one on the rear shell. Place a flat bar on the front shell and compress the spring until the tangs on the rear shell contact the notched section of the front shell, and then rotate it clockwise to lock it in place.

11. Apply lubricant sparingly to the stem of the hydraulic push rod keeping it away from the adjusting screw area. Apply silicone grease liberally to the piston area of the push rod and to the reaction disc.

12. Center the reaction disc on

the push rod piston. Guide the disc and push rod into the base of the diaphragm plate, and press the rod inward until the disc is bottomed (Fig. 40).

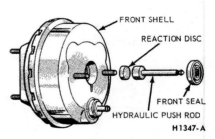

FIG. 40—Installing Reaction Disc, Push Rod and Front Seal (Bendix Type)

13. Press a new front seal into the front shell until it bottoms in the recess (Fig. 40).

14. Install a new dust seal over the push rod and onto the rear shell. Position the two mounting brackets on the rear shell studs, and install the attaching nuts and lock washers (Fig. 38).

DISASSEMBLY OF MIDLAND-ROSS TYPE BOOSTER

REMOVAL OF EXTERNAL PARTS

1. Remove the air filter assembly from the booster body. Separate the cover and retainer, and remove the air filter (Fig. 47).

2. Remove the vacuum manifold and check valve assembly and the rubber grommet from the booster body (Fig. 47).

3. Remove the retainer clip and connecting pin that connects the valve operating rod to the lever (Fig. H1362-A).

4. Remove the retainer clip and pivot pin that connects the lever to the mounting bracket and remove the lever.

5. Disconnect the push rod link from the lever.

6. Remove the attaching nuts, and disassemble the brackets from the end plate.

7. Remove the rubber boot from the valve operating rod.

SEPARATION OF MAJOR COMPONENTS

1. Scribe a line across the booster body, clamp band, and end plate.

2. Remove the clamp band screw and nut, and separate the clamp band, booster body, and end plate (Fig. 47).

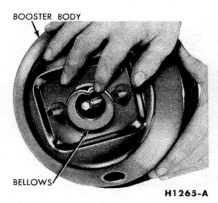

FIG. 41—Bellows to Booster Body Engagement

3. Push the bellows assembly into the vacuum chamber (Fig. 44), and separate the bellows, control valve, diaphragm assembly, and end plate from the booster body.

4. Push the valve, tail stock, and diaphragm assembly out of the end plate.

5. Remove the rear seal from the end plate (Fig. 42).

DISASSEMBLY OF BELLOWS, PUSH ROD AND VALVE ASSEMBLY FROM DIAPHRAGM

1. Remove the large bellows clamp and separate the bellows, bel-

FIG. 42—Removing or Installing Rear Seal to End Plate (Midland-Ross Type)

lows support rings, and bellows protector from the diaphragm and valve assembly (Fig. 43).

2. Remove the two support rings and the protector from the bellows.

FIG. 43—Removing or Installing the Bellows Assembly (Midland-Ross Type)

3. Remove the push rod assembly and the reaction lever assembly from the control hub (Fig. 44).

4. Remove the two plastic guides from the push rod. Remove the reaction cone retainer and the cone from the push rod (Fig. 44).

5. Hold the valve operating rod

firmly and force the plunger off the rod breaking the plastic retainer. If the plunger is to be used again, remove all the broken pieces of the plastic retainer from the groove in the plunger.

6. Turn the control hub and plunger assembly clockwise to separate it from the diaphragm, and then remove the tail stock and O-ring from the diaphragm (Fig. 45).

7. Remove the retainer that holds the plunger to the control hub (Fig. 46). Separate the control hub and plunger assembly. **It may be necessary to file the burr from the protruding end of the plunger before it can be separated from the control hub.**

DISASSEMBLY OF CONTROL VALVE PLUNGER

1. Compress the spring towards the rubber valve and remove the spring retainer.

2. Remove the spring, valve plate, rubber valve, O-ring, and fiber washer from the plunger (Fig. 47).

ASSEMBLY OF BOOSTER— (MIDLAND-ROSS TYPE)

CONTROL VALVE PLUNGER

1. Assemble the rubber valve, valve plate, spring, O-ring, and fiber washer on the plunger.

2. Compress the spring towards the rubber valve and assemble the spring retainer on the plunger with the flange towards the spring (Fig. 47).

ASSEMBLY OF VALVE ASSEMBLY, PUSH ROD, AND BELLOWS TO DIAPHRAGM

1. Assemble the control valve plunger assembly into the control hub so that the round holes in the rubber valve index with the raised projections on the hub, and the flat on the valve plate indexes with the flat projection on the hub (Fig. 48). Compress the valve spring, and install the retainer in the plunger groove to secure the control valve plunger to the control hub (Fig. 46).

2. Assemble the tail stock over the plunger with the flat on the tail stock indexing with the flat on the hub.

3. Assemble the O-ring over the tail stock and into the V-groove formed by the tail stock and hub.

4. Assemble the tail stock and the plunger and control hub assembly to the diaphragm, and turn the hub counterclockwise to secure these parts together (Fig. 45).

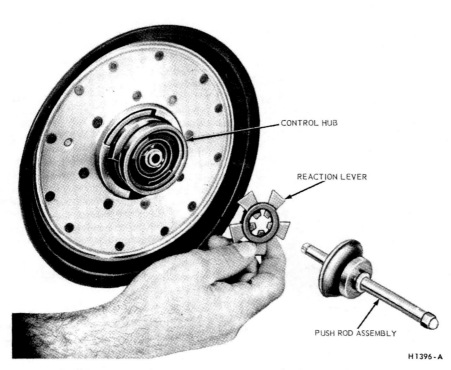

FIG. 44—Push Rod Assembly, Reaction Lever and Control Hub (Midland-Ross Type)

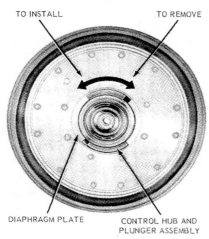

FIG. 45—Removing or Installing Control Hub and Plunger Assembly (Midland-Ross Type)

5. Install the lever assembly in the control hub with the rubber protrusions toward the hub (Fig. 44).

6. Assemble the reaction cone, retainer, and two plastic push rod guides on the push rod. Install the push rod assembly in the valve hub so that the push rod indexes in the valve plunger.

7. Install the two bellows support

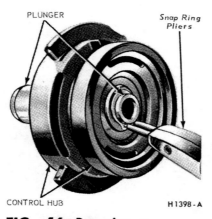

FIG. 46—Removing or Installing Plunger-to-Control Hub Retainer (Midland-Ross Type)

rings and bellows protector on the bellows. The support rings are positioned in the two larger folds of the bellows and the protector in the smaller fold.

8. Assemble the bellows on the control hub so that the lip of the bellows indexes in the groove on the hub. Secure the bellows to the hub by assembling the large bellows clamp on the diaphragm end of the bellows approximately $1/32$ inch from the end of the bellows (Fig. 43).

ASSEMBLY OF MAJOR COMPONENTS

1. Assemble the rear seal in the end plate (Fig. 45) and position the diaphragm, the control valve components, and the bellows as an assembly into the end plate.

2. Install the rubber grommet in the booster body with the large diameter side to be outside of the booster. Force the vacuum manifold and check valve assembly through the grommet (Fig. 47).

3. Assemble the booster body to the end plate. Make sure that the lip of the diaphragm is evenly positioned on the retaining radius of the end plate and the booster body. Pull the front lip of the bellows through the booster body and position it evenly around the hole in the booster body (Fig. 44).

4. Install the clamp band over the lips of the booster body and end plate. Align the scribe lines, compress the assembly together, and secure with the clamp and band bolt. Tap the clamp band with a fibre hammer around its circumference as the bolt is being tightened. Tighten to 15 in-lbs. of torque.

INSTALLATION OF EXTERNAL PARTS

1. Install the rubber boot to the valve operating rod and assemble the plastic retainer to the end of the rod. Insert the rod into the plunger so that the retainer engages the groove in the plunger. Install the lip of the boot in the groove of the rear seal (Fig. 47).

2. Connect the valve operating rod to the upper end of the lever, and connect the push rod link to the center of the lever with the connecting pins and clips.

3. Position the mounting brackets to the end plate and install the attaching nuts.

4. Connect the lever assembly to the lower end of the mounting brackets with the picot pin and clip.

5. Position the air filter in the plastic filter cover and then snap the cover and filter on the metal hub with the filter between.

6. Assemble the cover, filter, and hub assembly to the booster body with the metal hub against the booster body.

7. Adjust the push rod clearance to specifications.

8. Assemble the master cylinder to the booster body. Torque the master cylinder mounting nuts to specification.

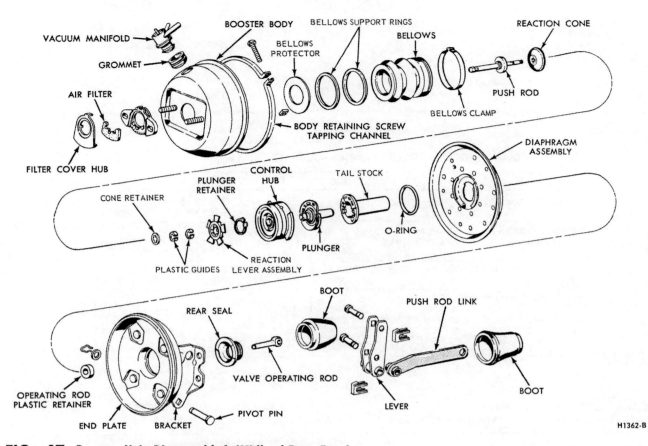

FIG. 47—Booster Unit Disassembled (Midland-Ross Type)

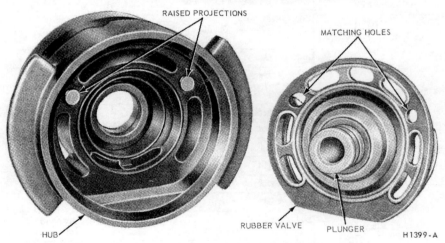

FIG. 48—Assembling Valve Plunger to Hub (Midland-Ross Type)

PART 2-3 SPECIFICATIONS

LINING DIMENSIONS—DRUM BRAKES—INCHES

Models	Position	Front	Rear	Color Code
Ford Passenger Cars	Primary Secondary	2.5 x 9.34 2.5 x 12.12	2.25 x 9.34 2.25 x 12.12	Yellow-Black Blue-Black
Ford & Mercury—All 427 CID Engine & 8 Cylinder Police—Maximum Fade Resistant	Primary Secondary	3.00 x 9.34 3.00 x 12.12	2.25 x 9.34 2.25 x 12.12	Yellow-Black Blue-Blue
Ford and Mercury Station Wagons	Primary Secondary	3.00 x 9.34 3.00 x 12.12	2.25 x 9.34 2.25 x 12.12	Silver Yellow-White
Ford and Mercury Passenger Cars (240-289 CID Engine) All Taxi and 6 Cylinder Police—Maximum Wear Resistant	Primary Secondary	3.00 x 9.34 3.00 x 12.12	2.5 x 9.34 2.5 x 12.12	Pink Red-Red
Mercury Passenger Cars	Primary Secondary	2.5 x 9.34 2.5 x 12.12	2.25 x 9.34 2.25 x 12.12	Silver Yellow-White

CHECKS AND ADJUSTMENTS —DRUM BRAKES—INCHES

Master Cylinder Bore Diameter Standard Power	 1.000 0.875
Master Cylinder Maximum Allowable Hone	0.003
Front Wheel Cylinder Bore Diameter Passenger, Police & Taxi Station Wagon	 1.094 1.062
Rear Wheel Cylinder Bore Diameter Passenger, Police & Station Wagon Taxi (Max. Wear Resistant)	 0.969 0.875
Wheel Cylinder Maximum Allowable Hone	0.003
Drum Diameter	11.030
Drum Maximum Allowable Run-Out	0.007
Drum Maximum Boring Diameter	11.090
Drum Width—Front Passenger Station Wagon, Maximum Wear & Maximum Fade Resistant	 2.50 3.00
Drum Width—Rear Passenger Taxi	 2.25 2.50
Lining Maximum Wear Limit (From Top of Rivets or Shoe Rim)	0.031
Lining Maximum Clearance to Shoe (Midway Between Rivets)	0.008
Pedal Height—Standard	8 inches
Pedal Height—Power	$5^{13}/_{16}$ inches
Power Unit	Push-Rod Adjustment—0.995-1.005 inches
Self Adjustment Cable Length End of Cable Anchor to End of Cable Hook—11⅛ inch ±¹/₆₄	

CHECKS AND ADJUSTMENTS —DISC BRAKES—INCHES

Master Cylinder Bore Diameter	1.00
Caliper Cylinder Bore Diameter	$1^{15}/_{16}$
Rotor Diameter Outside Inside	 11.87 7.875
Rotor Thickness	1.25
Rotor Maximum Allowable Runout	0.002
Lining Area (Square Inches per Segment)	10.03
Lining Thickness (Nominal)	0.436
Lining Maximum Wear Limit (From Surface of Shoe)	0.030
Lining to Rotor Clearance (Brakes Released)	0.002-0.010
Pedal Height (Top of Pedal to Floor)	5.20
Pedal Travel	4.00
Pedal Ratio	2.1:1
Lining Material	Bonded FoMoCo
Proportioning Valve	300 psi—50%

TORQUE LIMITS

Description	Ft-lbs
Master Cylinder-To-Pedal Support Bracket	18-25
Pedal Pad to Brake Pedal Nut	12-16
Control Assembly—Parking Brake to Cowl Side Bolt	15-19
Master Cylinder Fitting	6-12
Left Brake Hose—Front to Connector Bolt	12-18
Wheel Cylinder Bleeder Screw	120 in-lbs Maximum
Vacuum Connector at Engine Manifold	20-28

FRONT BRAKES

Description	Ft-lbs
Carrier Plate and Cylinder Assembly Brake Shoe Anchor Pin Nut	20-30
Anchor Pin to Spindle Bolt	80-106
Wheel-to-Hub and Drum Nuts	75-110
Front Brake Carrier Plate to Spindle Nut	25-45

TORQUE LIMITS (Cont.)
REAR BRAKES

Description	Ft-lbs
Drum to Axle Shaft Speednut	Hand Push Fit
Wheel to Axle Shaft to Drum Nuts	75-110
Brake Cylinder-to-Brake Carrier Plate Bolt	10-20
Brake Carrier Plate-to-Axle Housing	30-40*

POWER BRAKES

Description	Ft-lbs
Master Cylinder-to-Booster Body	10-13
Brake Booster-to-Pedal Support Bracket	18-25
*Models 59, 71 RPO Heavy Duty—55-65 ft-lbs	

TORQUE LIMITS—DISC BRAKES (R.P.O.)

Description	Ft-lbs
Caliper Assembly to Mounting Bracket	45-60
Mounting Bracket to Spindle	35-45
Caliper Bleeder Screw	10 (120 in.-lbs. maximum)—Must be leak proof
Caliper Splash Shield	7-9
Caliper Bridge Bolts	65-75
Rotor Splash Shield to Spindle	10-20
Hub and Rotor Assembly to Front Wheel Spindle	17-25—Rotate rotor while torquing*
Wheel Assembly to Front Wheel Hub and Rotor Assembly	75-110 ft./lbs.
Brake Tube Fitting Nuts to Proportioning Valve	70 in.-lbs.—maximum—Must be leak proof

*.0005" to .0065" maximum bearing end play with torque specification of 17-25 ft./lbs.

SERVICE TOOLS

Ford Tool No.	Former No.	Description
—	LM-119	Brake Cylinder Retaining Clamp
—	2035N 2086L	Brake Shoe Retracting Spring Remover and Installer
TOOL-4235-C	4235-C	Axle Shaft and Bearing Remover
TOOL-33621	33621	Pump Shaft Bearing Retainer and Power Brake Pliers
—	1112-144	In-Lb Torque Wrench

SUSPENSION, STEER-ING, WHEELS & TIRES

GROUP 3

PART 3-1 SUSPENSION, STEERING, WHEELS AND TIRES—GENERAL SERVICE

1 DIAGNOSIS AND TESTING

MANUAL STEERING

Table 1 lists various manual and power steering trouble symptoms and possible causes. Several of these symptoms are also common to suspension, frame, and wheel and tire troubles. For this reason, be sure that the cause of the trouble is in the steering gear or linkage before adjusting, repairing, or replacing any of the steering parts.

POWER STEERING—PRELIMINARY TESTS

The following preliminary checks should always be made before performing any trouble-shooting operations.

AIR BLEEDING

Air in the power steering system (shown by bubbles in the fluid) should be bled. After making sure that the reservoir is filled to specification (the fluid must be at normal operating temperature when the

check is made), turn the steering wheel through its full travel three or four times. **Do not hold the wheels against their stops.** Recheck the fluid level.

CHECK FLUID LEVEL

Run the engine until the fluid is at normal operating temperature. Then turn the steering wheel all the way to the left and right several times, and shut off the engine.

Check the fluid level in the power steering reservoir. The level must be at the full mark on the dipstick. On a pump with a straight filler tube the lubricant must be to the bottom of the filler tube. If the level is low, add enough automatic transmission fluid C1AZ-19582-A to raise the level to the F mark on the dip stick or to the bottom of the filler tube. **Do not overfill the reservoir.**

CHECK PUMP BELT

If the pump belt is broken, glazed, or worn, replace it with a new belt.

Use only the specified type of belt. Refer to Part 3-4 for belt adjustment.

CHECK FOR FLUID LEAKS

With the engine idling, turn the steering wheel from stop to stop several times. Check all possible leakage points. Tighten all loose fittings, and replace any damaged lines or defective seats.

CHECK TURNING EFFORT

With the front wheels properly aligned and tire pressures correct, check the effort required to turn the steering wheel.

1. With the car on dry concrete, set the parking brakes.

2. With the engine warmed up and running at idle speed, turn the steering wheel to the left and right several times to warm the fluid.

3. Attach a pull scale to the rim of the steering wheel. Measure the pull required to turn the wheel one complete revolution in each direction. The effort required to rotate the

TABLE 1 — Trouble Symptoms and Possible Causes

POSSIBLE CAUSES OF TROUBLE	Jerky Steering	Loose Steering	Hard Steering and/or Loss of Power Assist	Hard Turning When Stationary	Steering and Suspension Noises	Shimmy or Wheel Tramp	Pull to One Side	Side-to-Side Wander	Body Sway or Roll	Tire Squeal on Turns	Binding or Poor Recovery	Abnormal or Irregular Tire Wear	Sag at One Wheel	Hard or Rough Ride	Rear Suspension Misalignment (Dog-Tracking)
Incorrect Tire Pressure			X	X	X	X	X	X	X	X		X	X	X	
Tire Sizes Not Uniform			X	X		X	X	X				X	X		
Overloaded or Unevenly Loaded Vehicle								X				X	X	X	
Power Steering Fluid Level Low-Leak	X		X	X	X										
Sagging Spring					X	X	X	X	X			X	X	X	
Glazed, Loose or Broken Power Steering Pump Belt	X		X	X	X										
Bent Spindle Arm							X	X		X		X			
Bent Spindle							X	X		X		X			
Lack of Lubrication			X	X	X						X			X	
Air in Power Steering System	X		X		X	X									
Obstruction in Power Steering Lines			X	X	X										
Loose or Weak Shock Absorber					X	X			X			X		X	
Loose or Worn Suspension Arm Bushings					X	X						X		X	
Binding Front Suspension Ball Joints or Steering Linkage	X		X	X	X						X			X	
Loose, Worn, or Damaged Steering Linkage or Connections	X	X			X	X		X		X		X			
Loose Steering Gear Mountings	X	X			X	X		X	X						
Insufficient Steering Pump Pressure			X	X							X				
Incorrect Steering Gear Adjustment	X	X	X	X	X	X		X	X		X	X			
Incorrect Brake Adjustment	X				X		X					X			
Incorrect Front Wheel Bearing Adjustment	X	X			X	X	X	X				X			
Wheel Out of Balance	X				X	X						X		X	
Incorrect Front Wheel Alignment			X		X	X	X	X		X	X	X			
Out-of-Round Wheel or Brake Drum						X						X		X	
Frame or Underbody Out of Alignment							X					X			X
Bent Rear Axle Housing					X		X					X			X
Excessive Wear of Steering Pump Internal Parts					X										
Steering Gear Valve Spool Binding or Out of Adjustment			X	X							X				
Obstruction Within Steering Gear			X	X							X				

steering wheel should not exceed 5.0 pounds.

PUMP-FLUID PRESSURE TEST

A fluid pressure test will show whether the pump or some other unit in the power steering system is causing trouble in the system. Steps outlined below should be followed to determine the cause of the trouble.

1. Measure the pump belt tension. **When adjusting the belt tension on the power pump, do not pry against the pump to obtain the proper belt load.**

A half-inch cast boss has been incorporated on the front face of the pump cover plate onto which a $^{9}/_{16}$″ open end wrench can be fitted to pry the pump and obtain the proper belt tension.

2. Disconnect the pressure line hose from the pump outlet, and install a 0-2000 psi pressure gauge (Tool T56L-33610-D) and shut off valve between the end of the hose and the pump outlet (Fig. 1).

any air from the system; stop the engine. Remove the reservoir filler cap and check the fluid level in the reservoir. If necessary, add lubricant (C1AZ-19582-A) to the proper level.

6. With the engine running at **approximately 500 rpm** and no steering effort applied, and the lubricant at normal operating temperature, the pressure gauge should show a pressure of less than **50 psi**. If the pressure is higher inspect the hoses for kinks and obstructions.

7. Increase the engine speed to 1000 rpm, then slowly close the gauge shut-off valve. With the valve fully closed, the pump pressure should be 1000 to 1150 psi.

Do not close the valve for more than a few seconds (maximum 5 seconds), as this would abnormally increase the lubricant temperature and cause undue pump and/or steering gear wear. Engine rpm should not exceed fast idle during this test.

If pressure is more or less than

of the front-end parts. Refer to Section 3.

Check all the factors of front wheel alignment except the turning angle before making any adjustments. The turning angle should be checked only after caster, camber, and toe-in have been adjusted to specifications.

The front wheel alignment specifications given in Part 3-6, are correct only when the car is at Curb Load. Before checking or adjusting the alignment factors the suspension alignment spacers must be installed to obtain the curb height.

EQUIPMENT INSTALLATION

Equipment used for front wheel alignment inspection must be accurate. Whenever possible, front wheel alignment checks should be performed on stationary wheel aligning equipment. In the absence of such equipment, portable equipment may be used and the work may be performed on a level floor. The floor area should be level within ¼ inch from front to rear of the car and within ⅛ inch from side to side. Alignment height spacers (Figs. 2 and 3) are used to check caster and camber. The spacers should be omitted when checking toe-in.

1. Check the runout of each front wheel and tire using a dial indicator against the rim outer band. If the runout exceeds ⅛ inch, correction may be made by rotating the wheel on the drum. When the minimum runout has been obtained, mark the point of greatest runout so the wheels can be positioned as shown in Fig. 4 when checking the front end alignment. Hold a piece of chalk against the wheel rim or the tire sidewall while spinning the wheels. The chalk will mark the rim or tire at the point or greatest runout.

2. Drive the car in a straight line far enough to establish the straight-ahead position of the front wheels, and then mark the steering wheel hub and the steering column collar (Fig. 5). **Do not adjust the steering wheel spoke position at this time.** If the front wheels are turned at any time during the inspection, align the marks to bring the wheels back to the straight-ahead position.

3. With the car in position for the front end alignment inspection and adjustment, install the suspension alignment spacers as follows to establish the curb height.

Lift the front of the car and posi-

SHUT-OFF VALVE Tool—T 56 L-33610-D   PUMP OUTLET   PRESSURE LINE

G 1271-A

FIG. 1—Pressure Testing Tool—Typical

Be sure that the pressure gauge is between the pump and the shut off valve, all connections are tight, and the shut off valve is fully open.

3. Connect a tachometer to the engine.

4. Start the engine and operate it at idle speed for at least two (2) minutes to warm up the fluid.

5. Cycle the steering wheel from stop-to-stop several times to expel

specification, replace the pump assembly. If pressure is as specified and steering efforts are heavy, the gear and/or control valve could be at fault.

FRONT WHEEL ALIGNMENT CHECKS

Do not attempt to check and adjust front wheel alignment without first making a preliminary inspection

POWER STEERING
DIAGNOSIS GUIDE

JERKY STEERING	Low fluid level or fluid leakage. Obstruction in power steering lines or within the steering gear.	Loose steering gear mountings. Incorrect steering gear adjustment.
HARD STEERING AND/OR LOSS OF POWER ASSIST	Low fluid level or fluid leakage. Air in power steering system. Obstruction in power steering lines or within the steering gear. Insufficient power steering pump pressure.	Incorrect steering gear adjustment. Steering gear valve spool binding or out of adjustment.
HARD TURNING WHEN STATIONARY	Low fluid level or fluid leakage. Obstruction in power steering lines or within the steering gear.	Insufficient power steering pump pressure.
STEERING AND SUSPENSION NOISES	Low fluid level or fluid leakage. Air in power steering system. Obstruction in power steering lines or within the steering gear.	Loose steering gear mountings. Insufficient power steering pump pressure. Incorrect steering gear adjustment.
LOOSE STEERING SHIMMY SIDE-TO-SIDE WANDER OR WHEEL TRAMP OR	Loose steering gear mountings.	Incorrect steering gear adjustment.
BINDING OR POOR RECOVERY	Insufficient power steering pump pressure. Incorrect steering gear adjustment. Steering gear valve spool binding	or out of adjustment. Obstruction within the steering gear.
BODY SWAY OR ROLL	Incorrect steering gear adjustment.	
HARDER STEERING IN ONE DIRECTION	Steering gear valve spool binding or out of adjustment.	
ABNORMAL OR IRREGULAR TIRE WEAR	Incorrect steering gear adjustment.	

Tool—T65P-3000-B or -C

FIG. 2—Alignment Spacer Installation—Front

tion the alignment spacers between the suspension lower arm and the frame spring pocket as shown in Fig. 2. **Be sure the spacer pin is placed in the correct hole for the car being checked.** The lower end of the alignment spacers should be placed over the head of the strut front attaching bolt. Remove the bumpers

Tool—T65P-3000-B or -C

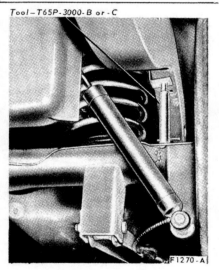

FIG. 3—Alignment Spacer Installation—Rear

from the right and left rear side rails. Position the rear alignment spacers between the rear axle and the rear side rails as shown in Fig. 3.

4. Install the wheel alignment equipment on the car. Whichever

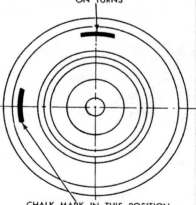

CHALK MARK IN THIS POSITION WHEN CHECKING TOE-IN AND TOE-OUT ON TURNS

CHALK MARK IN THIS POSITION WHEN CHECKING CASTER AND CAMBER

LOCATION OF POINT OF GREATEST LATERAL RUN-OUT ON FRONT WHEELS WHEN CHECKING ALIGNMENT FACTORS

F1215-A

FIG. 4—Front Wheel Position For Checking Alignment

type of equipment is used, follow

ALIGNMENT MARKS   F1267-B

FIG. 5—Straight Ahead
Position Marks—Typical

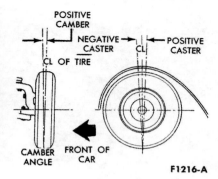

F1216-A

FIG. 6—Caster and Camber
Angles

the installation and inspection instructions provided by the equipment manufacturer.

CASTER

Check the caster angle at each front wheel.

The caster is the forward or rearward tilt of the top of the wheel spindle (Fig. 6). If the spindle tilts to the rear, caster is positive. If the spindle tilts to the front, caster is negative. The correct caster angle, or tilt, is specified in Part 3-6. The maximum difference between both front wheel caster angles should not exceed $\frac{1}{2}°$. However, a difference of

not more than $\frac{1}{4}°$ is preferred.

CAMBER

Check the camber angle at each front wheel.

Camber is the amount the front wheels are tilted at the top (Fig. 6). If a wheel tilts outward, camber is positive. If a wheel tilts inward, camber is negative. The correct camber angle, or outward (positive) tilt, is specified in Part 3-6. The maximum difference between both front wheel camber angles should not exceed $\frac{1}{2}°$. However, a difference of not more than $\frac{1}{4}°$ is preferred.

TOE-IN

Alignment height spacers should not be used to check and adjust toe-in. Toe-in should only be checked and adjusted after the caster and camber has been adjusted to specifications.

Check the toe-in with the front wheels in the straight-ahead position. Measure the distance between the extreme front and also between the extreme rear of both front wheels. The difference between these two distances is the toe-in.

Correct toe-in, or inward pointing of both front wheels at the front is specified in Part 3-6.

**FRONT WHEEL
TURNING ANGEL**

When the inside wheel is turned 20°, the turning angle of the outside wheel should be as specified in Part 3-6. The turning angle cannot be adjusted directly, because it is a result of the combination of caster, camber, and toe-in adjustments and should, therefore, be measured only after these adjustments have been made. If the turning angle does not measure to specifications, check the spindle or other suspension parts for a bent condition.

2 COMMON ADJUSTMENTS AND REPAIRS

After front wheel alignment factors have been checked, make the necessary adjustments. **Do not attempt to adjust front wheel alignment by bending the suspension or steering parts.**

**CAMBER AND CASTER
ADJUSTMENTS**

Camber and caster is adjusted by loosening the bolts that attach the upper suspension arm inner shaft to the frame side rail, and moving the inner shaft in or out in the elongated bolt holes with the tool shown in Fig. 7. The tool should be installed with the tool pins in the frame holes and the hooks over the upper arm inner shaft. Then, tighten the tool hook nuts snug before loosening the upper arm inner shaft attaching bolts.

CAMBER

To adjust the camber angle, install the tool as outlined above (Fig. 7). Loosen both inner shaft attaching

bolts and tighten or loosen the hook nuts to move the inner shaft inboard or outboard as necessary with Tool T65P-3000-D to increase or decrease camber (Table 2). The camber angle can be checked without tightening the inner shaft attaching bolts.

CASTER

To adjust the caster angle, tighten the tool front hook nut or loosen the rear hook nut (Table 2) as required to increase caster to the desired angle. To decrease caster, tighten the tool rear hook nut or loosen the front hook nut as required (Table 2). The caster angle can be checked without tightening the inner shaft attaching bolts. Check the camber adjustment to be sure it did not change during the caster adjustment and adjust if necessary. Then, tighten the upper arm inner shaft attaching bolts to specification. Remove the adjusting bar (Tool T65P-3000-D) and the alignment spacers (Tool T65P-3000-B or C).

**TOE-IN AND STEERING WHEEL
SPOKE POSITION
ADJUSTMENTS**

Check the steering wheel spoke position when the front wheels are in the straight-ahead position. If the spokes are not in their normal position, they can be properly adjusted while toe-in is being adjusted.

1. Loosen the two clamp bolts on each spindle connecting rod sleeve (Fig. 8).

2. Adjust toe-in. If the steering wheel spokes are in their normal position, lengthen or shorten both rods equally to obtain correct toe-in (Fig. 8). If the steering wheel spokes are not in their normal position, make the necessary rod adjustments to obtain correct toe-in and sterring wheel spoke alignment (Fig. 9).

3. Recheck toe-in and the steering wheel spoke position. If toe-in is correct and the steering wheel spokes are still not in their normal position, turn both connecting rod sleeves upward or downward the same number of turns to move the steering wheel spokes (Fig. 8).

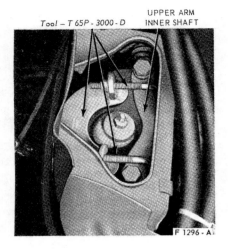

Tool – T 65P - 3000 - D
UPPER ARM INNER SHAFT

F 1296 - A

FIG. 7—Camber and Caster Adjusting Tool

4. When toe-in and the steering wheel spoke position are both correct, torque the clamp bolts on both connecting rod sleeves to specification (Part 3-6). **The sleeve position should not be changed when the clamp bolts are tightened.**

WHEEL BALANCING

See the instructions provided with the Rotunda Wheel Balancer.

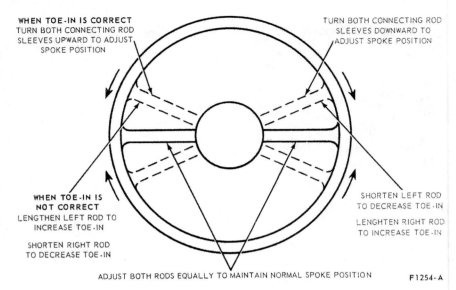

WHEN TOE-IN IS CORRECT TURN BOTH CONNECTING ROD SLEEVES UPWARD TO ADJUST SPOKE POSITION

TURN BOTH CONNECTING ROD SLEEVES DOWNWARD TO ADJUST SPOKE POSITION

WHEN TOE-IN IS NOT CORRECT LENGTHEN LEFT ROD TO INCREASE TOE-IN
SHORTEN RIGHT ROD TO DECREASE TOE-IN

SHORTEN LEFT ROD TO DECREASE TOE-IN
LENGHTEN RIGHT ROD TO INCREASE TOE-IN

ADJUST BOTH RODS EQUALLY TO MAINTAIN NORMAL SPOKE POSITION

F1254-A

FIG. 9—Toe-In and Steering Wheel Spoke Alignment Adjustment

LUBRICANT CHECKING PROCEDURE

MANUAL STEERING GEAR

1. Center the steering wheel.
2. Remove the steering gear housing filler plug.
3. Remove the lower cover-to-housing attaching bolt.

4. With a clean punch or like instrument, clean out or push inward the loose lubricant in the filler plug hole and cover to housing attaching bolt hole.

5. Slowly turn the steering wheel to the left stop, lubricant should rise within the lower cover bolt

TABLE 2—Caster and Camber Adjustments

SUSPENSION UPPER ARM MOVEMENT	CASTER CHANGE	CAMBER CHANGE
Front Bolt Outboard	**Tilt Backward** Increase Positive Caster or Decrease Negative Caster	**Tilt Outward** Increase Positive Camber or Decrease Negative Camber
Rear Bolt Outboard	**Tilt Forward** Decrease Positive Caster or Increase Negative Caster	
Front Bolt Inboard	**Tilt Forward** Decrease Positive Caster or Increase Negative Caster	**Tilt Inward** Decrease Positive Camber or Increase Negative Camber
Rear Bolt Inboard	**Tilt Backward** Increase Positive Caster or Decrease Negative Caster	

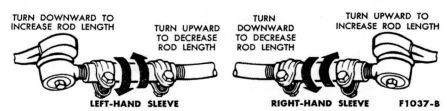

TURN DOWNWARD TO INCREASE ROD LENGTH
TURN UPWARD TO DECREASE ROD LENGTH
TURN DOWNWARD TO DECREASE ROD LENGTH
TURN UPWARD TO INCREASE ROD LENGTH

LEFT-HAND SLEEVE
RIGHT-HAND SLEEVE
F1037-B

FIG. 8—Spindle Connecting Rod Adjustments

hole; then slowly turn the steering wheel to the right stop, lubricant should rise within the filler plug hole. If lubricant does not rise in both the cover bolt hole and the filler plug hole, add lubricant until it comes out both holes during this check.

6. Install the lower cover-to-housing attaching bolt and the filler plug.

DRIVE SHAFT PINION ANGLE ADJUSTMENT

The pinion-driveshaft working angle must be checked and adjusted to specification whenever the rear axle has been removed.

Before checking the driveshaft pinion angle, the car curb loading should be as follows:

1. Full tank of fuel, radiator filled and engine crankcase filled to correct level.

2. Spare tire, wheel, jack and jack handle in design position.

3. Front seats in rearmost position.

4. All other loading removed.

5. Inflate tires to specification (cold).

CHECKING PROCEDURE

The checking and adjusting procedure must be done with the weight of the car on the front and rear suspension.

1. With the car at normal curb height, remove the axle bumper bracket from the pinion bearing retainer.

2. Hold the protractor against the machined outer surface of the pinion bearing retainer (Fig. 10), and cen-

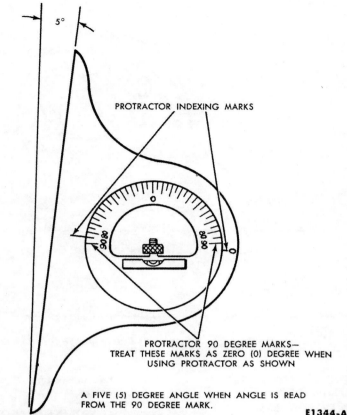

A FIVE (5) DEGREE ANGLE WHEN ANGLE IS READ FROM THE 90 DEGREE MARK.

E1344-A

FIG. 11—Reading Protractor—Vertical Position

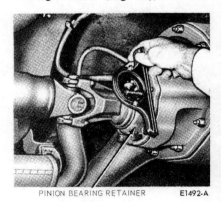

PINION BEARING RETAINER   E1492-A

FIG. 10—Measuring Pinion Angle

ter the bubble. Record the angle (Pinion Angle) indicated (Fig. 11).

3. Place the protractor against the driveshaft (above or below) and center the bubble (Fig. 12). Record the angle (drive-shaft angle) indicated (Fig. 13).

4. Add the readings obtained in steps 2 and 3 if the pinion angle is down. Subtract the readings obtained in steps 2 and 3 if the pinion angle is up. The sum of difference of these two angles should equal the required angle of 2°±½°.

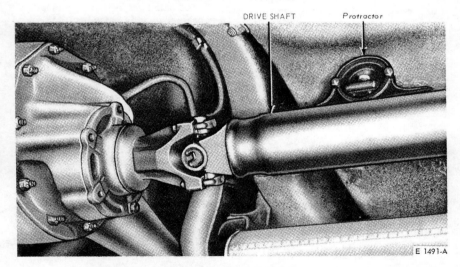

DRIVE SHAFT   Protractor

E 1491-A

FIG. 12—Measuring Drive Shaft Angle

ADJUSTMENT

If the pinion angle is not within specifications, adjust the pinion angle as follows:

The upper arm-to-axle housing bolt and two eccentric washers form an adjusting cam mechanism (Fig. 14 which will tilt the axle housing to the required angle.

1. Loosen the upper arm pivot bolt nuts.

2. If the sum of the two angles is less than specification, rotate the adjusting cam forward and recheck the two angles. If the sum of the two angles is more than specification, rotate the adjusting cam rearward and recheck the two angles.

3. When the axle housing is ad-

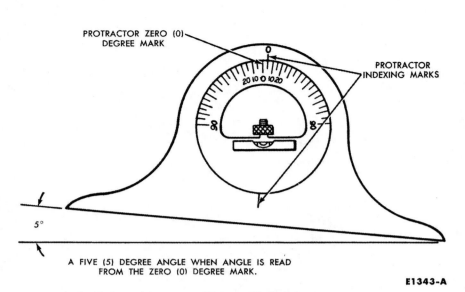

FIG. 13—Reading Protractor—Horizontal Position

A FIVE (5) DEGREE ANGLE WHEN ANGLE IS READ
FROM THE ZERO (0) DEGREE MARK.

E1343-A

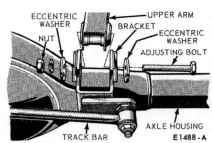

FIG. 14—Pinion Angle Adjustment

justed in such a way that the sum of the drive shaft angle reading and the pinion shaft angle reading is within specification, install new pivot bolt nuts and torque to specification (Fig. 14).

4. Lower the car and road test for proper axle operation.

3 CLEANING AND INSPECTION

FRONT END GENERAL INSPECTION

Do not check and adjust front wheel alignment without first making the following inspection for front-end maladjustment, damage, or wear.

1. Check for specified air pressures in all four tires.
2. Raise the front of the car off the floor. Shake each front wheel grasping the upper and lower surfaces of the tire. Check the front suspension ball joints and mountings for looseness, wear, and damage. Check the brake backing plate mountings. Torque all loose nuts and bolts to specification. Replace all worn parts as outlined in Part 3-2.
3. Check the steering gear mountings and all steering linkage connections for looseness. Torque all mountings to specifications. If any of the linkage is worn or bent, replace the parts as outlined in Part 3-3.
4. Check the front wheel bearings. If any in-and-out free play is noticed, adjust the bearings to specifications. Replace worn or damaged bearings as outlined in Part 3-5.
5. Spin each front wheel with a wheel spinner, and check and balance each wheel as required.
6. Check the action of the shock absorbers. If the shock absorbers are not in good condition, the car may not settle in a normal, level position,

and front wheel alignment may be affected.

WHEEL INSPECTION

Wheel hub nuts should be inspected and tightened to specification at pre-delivery. Loose wheel hub nuts may cause shimmy and vibration. Elongated stud holes in the wheels may also result from loose hub nuts.

Keep the wheels and hubs clean. Stones wedged between the wheel and drum and lumps of mud or grease can unbalance a wheel and tire.

Check for damage that would affect the runout of the wheels. Wobble or shimmy caused by a damaged wheel will eventually damage the wheel bearings. Inspect the wheel rims for dents that could permit air to leak from the tires.

UPPER BALL JOINT INSPECTION

1. Raise the car on floor jacks placed beneath the lower arms.
2. Ask an assistant to grasp the lower edge of the tire and move the wheel in and out.
3. As the wheel is being moved in and out, observe the upper end of the spindle and the upper arm.
4. Any movement between the upper end of the spindle and the upper arm indicates ball joint wear and loss of preload. If any such movement is

observed, replace the upper ball joint.

During the foregoing check, the lower ball joint will be unloaded and may move. Disregard all such movement of the lower ball joint. Also, do not mistake loose wheel bearings for a worn ball joint.

LOWER BALL JOINT INSPECTION

1. Raise the car on jacks placed under the lower arms as shown in

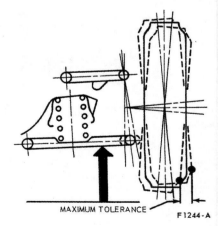

MAXIMUM TOLERANCE F1244-A

FIG. 15—Measuring Upper Ball Joint Radial Play

Fig. 15. This will unload the lower ball joints.
2. Adjust the wheel bearings as described in Part 3-5.

3. Attach a dial indicator to the lower arm. Position the indicator so that the plunger rests against the upper surface of the spindle at the lower ball joint stud.

4. With the dial indicator attached to the lower arm, position the indicator so that the plunger rests against the inner side of the wheel rim adjacent to the lower ball joint.

5. Grasp the tire at the top and bottom and slowly move the tire in and out (Fig. 15). Note the reading (radial play) on the dial indicator. If the reading exceeds specifications (Part 3-6), replace the lower ball joint.

POWER STEERING GEAR

CLEANING

Disassembly and assembly of the steering gear and the sub-assemblies must be made on a clean workbench. As in repairing any hydraulically operated unit, cleanliness is of utmost importance. The bench, tools, and parts must be kept clean at all times. Thoroughly clean the exterior of the unit with a suitable solvent and, when necessary, drain as much of the hydraulic oil as possible. Handle all parts very carefully to avoid nicks, burrs, scratches and dirt, which could make the parts unfit for use.

INSPECTION

1. Check the sector shaft bushing in the cover for wear. If worn, replace the cover.

2. Inspect the input shaft bearing for cracked races and the balls for looseness, wear, pitting, end play or other damage. Check the fit of the bearing on the input shaft. Replace the bearing, if required.

3. Inspect the valve housing for wear, scoring or burrs.

4. Inspect the tube seats in the pressure and return ports in the valve body for nicks, etc. If necessary, remove and replace.

5. Check the sector shaft bushings in the housing for wear. If worn, replace the bushings.

6. Check all fluid passages for obstruction or leakage.

7. Inspect the steering gear housing for cracks, stripped threads, and mating surfaces for burrs. Inspect the piston bore of the housing for scoring or wear. If necessary, replace the housing.

8. Check the input shaft bearing after installation to be sure that it rotates freely.

9. If the valve spool is not free in the valve housing, check for burrs at the outward edges of the working lands in the housing and remove with a hard stone. Check the valve spool for burrs and, if burrs are found, stone the valve in a **radial direction only**. Check for freedom of the valve again.

FLUSHING THE POWER STEERING SYSTEM

Should a power steering pump become inoperative, the shaft and pulley should be checked for freedom of rotation. If the pump shaft does not turn freely (binding), it is an indication that there is wear on the pump internal components and the need for flushing the steering system is required when installing a new pump.

1. Remove the power steering pump and remove the pulley as outlined in Part 3-4.

2. Install the pulley on a new pump. Install the pump and connect only the pressure hose to the pump (Part 3-4).

3. Place the oil return line in a suitable container and plug the reservoir return pipe.

4. Fill the reservoir with lubricant (C1AZ-19582-A).

5. Disconnect the coil wire to prevent the engine from starting and raise the front wheels off the ground.

6. While approximately two quarts of steering gear lubricant are being poured into the reservoir, turn the engine over using the ignition key, at the same time cycle the steering wheel from stop to stop.

7. As soon as all of the lubricant has been poured in, turn off the ignition key, and attach the coil wire.

8. Remove the plug from the reservoir return pipe, and attach the return hose to the reservoir.

9. Check the reservoir fluid level; if low, add fluid to the proper level. **Do not overfill.**

10. Lower the car.

11. Start the engine and cycle the steering from stop to stop to expel any trapped air from the system.

PART 3-2 SUSPENSION

1 DESCRIPTION AND OPERATION

FRONT SUSPENSION

Each front wheel rotates on a spindle. The upper and lower ends of the spindle are attached to upper and lower ball joints which are mounted to an upper and lower arm respectively. The upper arm pivots on a bushing and shaft assembly which is bolted to the frame. The lower arm pivots on a bolt in the front crossmember (Fig. 1). A coil spring seats between the lower arm and the top of the spring housing. A double action shock absorber is bolted to the arm and the top of the spring housing.

The swiveling action of the ball joints allows the wheel and spindle assemblies to move up and down with changes in road surfaces. The swiveling ball joints also permit the spindles and wheels to be turned to the left or right by the steering gear and linkage.

The pivoting action of the suspension arms provides an **up-and-down** movement for the spindles and wheels as required by bumps or depressions in the road surface. The coil springs and shock absorbers control this up-and-down movement. The stabilizer bar (Fig. 1) is attached to each lower arm to dampen

road shocks and minimize road sway. The struts, which are connected between the suspension lower arms and the frame crossmember prevent the suspension arms from moving forward and backward.

REAR SUSPENSION

Each rear wheel, hub, and brake drum assembly is bolted to the rear axle shaft flange. The wheel and axle shaft assembly rotates in the rear axle housing.

The rear axle housing and wheel assembly is suspended from the frame by a coil spring and shock absorber at each side of the car and by three arms (one upper and two lower) which pivot in the frame members (Fig. 2).

Each coil spring is mounted between a lower seat, which is welded to the axle housing, and an upper seat which is integral with the frame.

The upper end of the rear shock absorber is attached to the spring upper seat; the lower end is bolted to a bracket on the axle housing.

The upper suspension arm attaches to the right side of the axle housing through an eccentric pivot bolt and a bracket which is welded to the top

of the housing. The forward end of the arm is connected by a pivot bolt to the frame crossmember.

Each lower suspension arm attaches to one end of the axle housing through a pivot bolt and a bracket which is welded to the underside of the housing. The forward end of the arm is connected by a pivot bolt to the frame side member.

A track bar is connected between the upper arm bracket on the axle housing and a mounting bracket on the left frame side rail.

All of the above mentioned components work together to control the position and the movement of the rear axle housing and wheel assembly. The coil springs and shock absorbers cushion road shocks and bumps. The suspension arms prevent forward or rearward movement of the axle housing and wheel assembly with respect to the frame. The pivoting action of the suspension arms provides an **up-and-down** movement for the axle and wheel assembly as required by changes in the road surface. The track bar holds the assembly in proper alignment with the frame to prevent lateral swaying action.

F 1246 - A

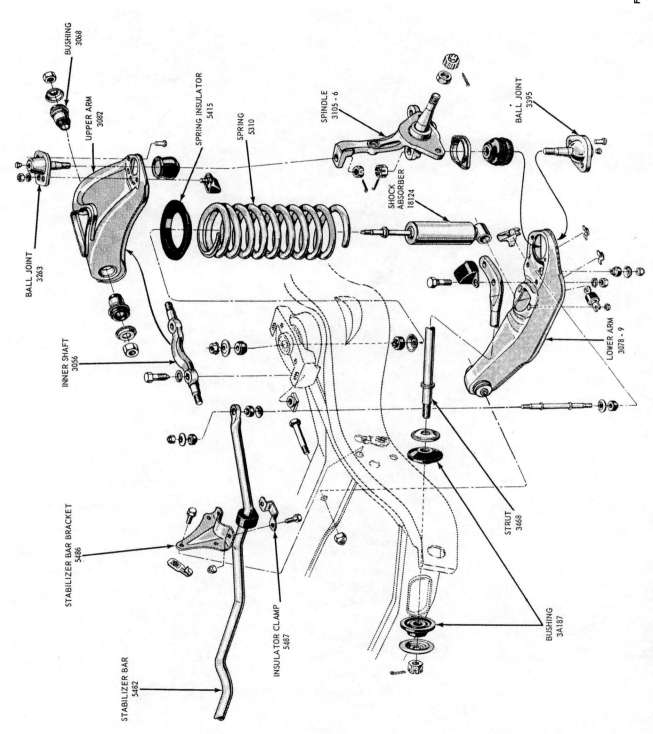

BUSHING
3068

UPPER ARM
3082

SPRING INSULATOR
5415

SPRING
5310

SPINDLE
3105 - 6

BALL JOINT
3395

SHOCK ABSORBER
18124

BALL JOINT
3263

INNER SHAFT
3056

LOWER ARM
3078 - 9

STABILIZER BAR BRACKET
5486

INSULATOR CLAMP
5487

STRUT
3468

STABILIZER BAR
5482

BUSHING
3A187

FIG. 1—Front Suspension Disassembled

F 1245 - B

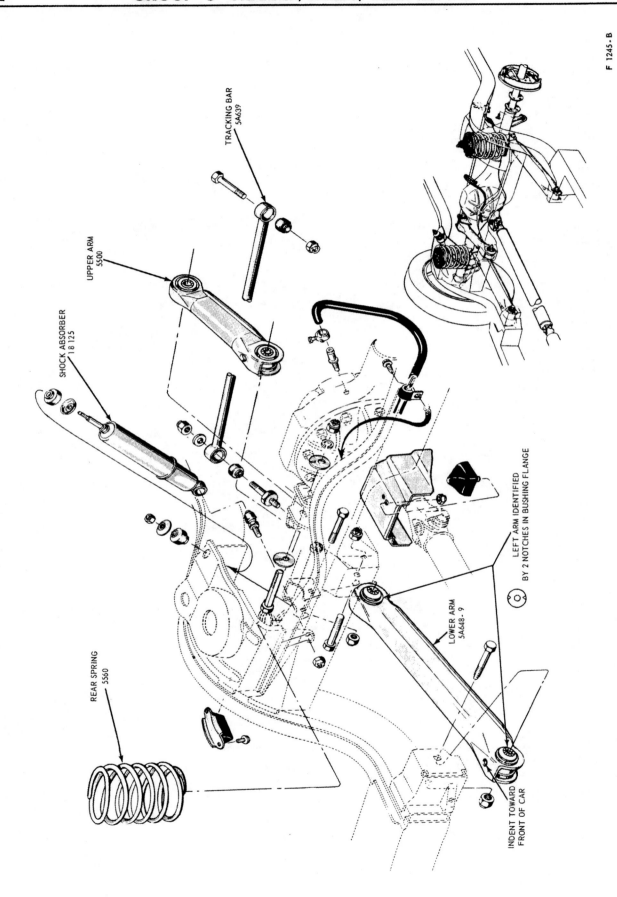

TRACKING BAR
5A639

UPPER ARM
5500

SHOCK ABSORBER
18125

REAR SPRING
5560

LOWER ARM
5A648 - 9

LEFT ARM IDENTIFIED
BY 2 NOTCHES IN BUSHING FLANGE

INDENT TOWARD
FRONT OF CAR

FIG. 2—Rear Suspension Disassembled

2 IN-CAR ADJUSTMENTS AND REPAIRS

HOISTING INSTRUCTIONS

Damage to steering linkage components and front suspension struts may occur if care is not exercised when positioning the hoist adapters of 2 post hoists prior to lifting the car.

If a 2 post hoist is used to lift the car, place the adapters under the lower arms or the No. 1 crossmember. Do not allow the adapters to contact the steering linkage. If the adapters are placed under the crossmember, a piece of wood (2x4x16 inches) should be placed on the hoist channel between the adapters. This will prevent the adapters from damaging the front suspension struts.

UPPER BALL JOINT REPLACEMENT—ARM IN CAR

1. Raise the car high enough to provide working space, and place a support under the lower arm. If a chain hoist or a jack that has a narrow contact pad is to be used on the bumper to raise the car, distribute the load along the bumper by using a steel plate 3 or 4 inches long as a contact pad to prevent damaging the bumper.

2. Remove the wheel and tire.

3. Drill a ⅛-inch hole through each upper ball joint retaining rivet. Using a large chisel, cut off the rivets.

4. Remove the upper arm suspension bumper.

5. Remove the cotter pin and nut from the upper ball joint stud.

6. Place a box wrench over the lower end of the ball joint remover tool, and position the tool as in Fig. 3. The tool should seat firmly against the ends of both studs, and not against the lower stud nut.

7. Turn the wrench until both studs are under tension, and then, with a hammer, tap the spindle near the upper stud to loosen the stud from the spindle. **Do not loosen the stud with tool pressure alone.** Remove the ball joint.

8. Clean the end of the arm, and remove all burrs from the hole edges. Check for cracks in the metal at the holes, and replace the arm if it is cracked.

9. Attach the new ball joint to the upper arm. **Use only the specified bolts, nuts, and washers. Do not rivet the new ball joints to the arm.** Torque the nuts to specification.

10. Install the upper arm suspension

Tool—T57P-3006-A

F1272-A

FIG. 3—Disconnecting the Ball Joints—Typical

sion bumper. Torque the nut to specification.

11. Position the ball joint stud in the spindle bore, and torque the retaining nut to specification. Install a new cotter pin.

12. Install the wheel and tire.

13. Remove the safety stands, and lower the car.

14. Check and, if necessary, adjust caster, camber, and toe-in. **Whenever any part of the front suspension has been removed and installed, front wheel alignment must be checked.**

LOWER BALL JOINT REPLACEMENT—ARM IN CAR

1. Raise the car high enough to provide working space, leaving the lower arm free to drop as coil spring tension is eased. If a chain hoist or a jack that has a narrow contact pad is to be used on the bumper to raise the car, distribute the load along the bumper by using a steel plate 3 or 4 inches long as a contact pad to prevent damaging the bumper.

2. If the ball joint is riveted to the arm, drill a ⅛-inch pilot hole completely through each rivet. Then drill off the rivet head through the pilot

hole with a ⅜-inch drill, and drive out both rivets.

3. Position a jack or safety stand under the lower arm, and lower the car about 6 inches to offset the coil spring tension.

4. Remove the cotter pin from the ball joint stud, and remove the nut.

5. Place a box wrench over the lower end of the tool shown in Fig. 3, and position the tool. **The tool should seat firmly against the end of both studs, and not against the upper stud nut.**

6. Turn the wrench until both studs are under tension, and then, with a hammer, tap the spindle near the lower stud to loosen the stud from the spindle. **Do not loosen the stud with tool pressure alone.** Remove the ball joint.

7. Clean the end of the arm, and remove all burrs from the hole edges. Check for cracks in the metal at the holes, and replace the arm if it is cracked.

8. Position the stud of the ball joint to the spindle bore, and install the retaining nut finger-tight.

9. Attach the ball joint to the lower arm. **Use only the specified bolts, nuts, and washers. Do not rivet the new ball joint to the arm. Torque nuts to specification.**

10. Torque the ball joint stud nut to specification, and install a new cotter pin.

11. Remove the jack.

12. Check and, if necessary, adjust caster, camber, and toe-in. **Whenever any part of the front suspension has been removed and installed, front wheel alignment must be checked.**

STABILIZER REPAIR

To replace the end bushings on each stabilizer link, use the following procedure.

1. Raise the car on a hoist.

2. Remove the link-to-stabilizer bar retaining nut, washers, and insulators, and disconnect the link from the bar (Fig. 1).

3. Remove the link-to-lower arm retaining nut, washers, and insulators, and remove the link from the arm.

4. Assemble the link and new washers and insulators to the lower arm, then install the link-to-lower arm retaining nut.

5. Connect the link to the bar with new washers and insulators and secure with the retaining nut.

6. Lower the car.

FRONT SUSPENSION LOWER ARM STRUT AND/OR BUSHING

1. Remove the cotter pin from the lower arm strut at the frame front crossmember and remove the nut, washer, and bushing from the strut.

2. Remove nuts, washers, and bolts attaching the strut and rubber bumper to the lower arm (Fig. 1).

3. Pull the strut from the frame crossmember.

4. Remove the crossmember rear side bushing and washer from the strut.

5. Place the crossmember rear side washer and bushing on the strut and position the strut to the frame and lower arm.

6. Position the rubber bumper on the strut and install the bolts, washers, and nuts attaching the strut to the lower arm. Torque the nuts and bolts to specification.

7. Install the bushing, washer, and nut on the strut at the front crossmember. Tighten the nut and install the cotter pin.

8. Check caster, camber, and toe-in and adjust if necessary.

---

3 REMOVAL AND INSTALLATION

HOISTING INSTRUCTIONS

Damage to steering linkage components and front suspension struts may occur if care is not exercised when positioning the hoist adapters of 2 post hoists prior to lifting the car.

If a 2 post hoist is used to lift the car, place the adapters under the lower arms or the No. 1 crossmember. Do not allow the adapters to contact the steering linkage. If the adapters are placed under the crossmember, a piece of wood (2x4x16 inches) should be placed on the hoist channel between the adapters. This will prevent the adapters from damaging the front suspension struts.

FRONT SUSPENSION LOWER ARM AND COIL SPRING

REMOVAL

1. Raise the front of the car and position safety stands under both sides of the frame just back of the lower arms.

2. Remove the hub cap or wheel cover.

3. If equipped with drum type brakes—Remove the wheel and tire and brake drum as an assembly. Remove the brake backing plate attaching bolts and remove the backing plate from the spindle. Wire the backing plate to the underbody to prevent damage to the brake hose.

4. If equipped with disc brakes—Remove the wheel and tire from the hub. Remove 2 bolts and washers that attach the caliper and brake hose bracket to the spindle. Remove the caliper from the rotor and wire it to the underbody to prevent damage to the brake hose. Then, remove the hub and rotor from the spindle.

5. Disconnect the lower end of the shock absorber, and push it up to the retracted position.

6. Disconnect the stabilizer bar link from the lower arm.

7. Remove the cotter pins from the upper and lower ball joint stud nuts.

8. Remove 2 bolts and nuts attaching the strut to the lower arm.

9. Loosen the lower ball joint stud nut one or two turns. **Do not remove the nut from the stud at this time.**

10. Install Tool T57P-3006-A between the upper and lower ball joint studs (Fig. 3). **The tool should be seated firmly against the ends of both studs and not against the stud nuts.**

11. With a wrench, turn the adapter screw until the tool places the stud under tension. Tap the spindle near the lower stud with a hammer to loosen the stud in the spindle. **Do not loosen the stud from the spindle with tool pressure only.**

12. Position a floor jack under the lower arm and remove the lower ball joint stud nut.

13. Lower the floor jack and remove the spring and insulator (Fig. 4).

14. Remove one nut and bolt attaching the lower control arm to the No. 2 crossmember and remove the lower arm.

INSTALLATION

1. Position the lower arm to the No. 2 crossmember and loosely install the attaching bolt and nut (Fig. 1).

2. Position the spring and insulator to the upper spring pad and lower arm. Using a floor jack, compress the spring and guide the lower ball joint stud into the spindle hole.

3. Install the ball joint stud attaching nut and torque to specification. Continue to tighten the nut until the cotter pin hole is in line with the nut slots. Install a cotter pin in the upper and lower ball joint studs.

4. Pull the shock absorber down and connect to the lower arm.

5. Position the strut and bumper

F1275-A

FIG. 4—Removing Front Spring

to the lower arm. Install the attaching bolts and nuts and torque to specification.

6. Torque the lower arm to No. 2 crossmember attaching bolt and nut to specifications.

7. Position the stabilizer bar link to the lower arm and install the attaching nuts.

8. If equipped with drum type brakes—Position the brake backing plate to the spindle and install the attaching bolts. Torque the bolts to specification. Adjust the brakes as outlined in Part 2-2. Install the wheel, tire, and drum to the spindle and adjust the wheel bearings as outlined in Part 3-5.

If equipped with disc brakes—Install the hub and rotor on the spindle. Position the caliper over the rotor and install the retaining bolts. Be sure to insert the upper bolt through the brake hose bracket. Torque the bolts to specification. Install the wheel and tire on the hub and adjust the wheel bearings as outlined in Part 3-5.

9. Install the hub cap or wheel cover.

10. Remove the safety stands and lower the car.

11. Check the caster, camber, and toe-in and adjust as required (Section 2, Part 3-1).

FRONT SUSPENSION UPPER ARM

REMOVAL

1. Raise the front of the car and position safety stands under both sides of the frame just back of the lower arm.

2. Remove the hub cap or wheel cover.

3. If equipped with drum type brakes—Remove the wheel and tire and brake drum as an assembly (Part 3-5).

4. If equipped with disc brakes—Remove the wheel and tire from the hub.

5. Remove the cotter pin from the upper ball joint stud nut.

6. Loosen the upper ball joint stud nut one or two turns. **Do not remove the nut from the stud at this time.**

7. Install tool T57P-3006-A between the upper and lower ball joint studs with the adapter screw on top (Fig. 3). **The tool should be seated firmly against the ends of both studs and not against the nuts or lower stud cotter pin.**

8. With a wrench, turn the adapter screw until the tool places the stud under tension. Tap the spindle near the upper stud with a hammer to loosen the stud in the spindle. **Do not loosen the stud from the spindle with tool pressure only.**

9. Remove the tool from between the ball joint studs and place a floor jack under the lower arm.

10. Raise the floor jack to relieve the pressure from the upper ball joint stud nut and remove the nut.

11. Remove the upper arm inner shaft attaching bolts. Remove the upper arm and inner shaft as an assembly (Fig. 1).

12. Remove the bumper from the upper arm.

INSTALLATION

1. Position the bumper to the upper arm and install the nut and washer. Torque the nut to specifications.

2. Position the upper arm inner shaft to the frame side rail and install the 2 attaching bolts and washers snug.

3. Connect the upper ball joint stud to the spindle and install the retaining nut. Torque the nut to specification and continue to tighten the nut until the cotter pin hole in the stud is in line with the nut slots. Then, install the cotter pin.

4. If equipped with drum type brakes—Adjust the brakes as outlined in Part 2-2. Install the wheel, tire, and drum to the spindle and adjust the wheel bearings as outlined in Part 3-5.

5. If equipped with disc brakes—Install the wheel and tire on the hub and adjust the wheel bearings as outlined in Part 3-5.

6. Install the hub cap or wheel cover.

7. Remove the safety stands and lower the front of the car.

8. Check caster, camber, and toe-in and adjust as required (Section 2, Part 3-1).

FRONT WHEEL SPINDLE

REMOVAL

1. Raise the car until the front wheel clears the floor, and place a support under the frame.

2. Remove the hub cap or wheel cover.

3. If equipped with drum type brakes—Remove the wheel and tire and brake drum as an assembly (Part 3-5). Remove the brake backing plate attaching bolts and remove the backing plate from the spindle. Wire the backing plate to the underbody to prevent damage to the brake hose.

4. If equipped with disc brakes—Remove the wheel and tire from the hub. Remove 2 bolts and washers retaining the caliper and brake hose bracket to the spindle. Remove the caliper from the rotor and wire it to the underbody to prevent damage to the brake hose. Then, remove the hub and rotor from the spindle (Part 3-5). Remove 3 bolts attaching the splash shield to the spindle and remove the splash shield.

5. Remove the steering connecting rod from the spindle arm with Tool OTC 462.

6. Remove the cotter pins from both ball joint stud nuts, and loosen the nuts one or two turns. **Do not remove the nuts from the studs at this time.**

7. Install the ball joint remover tool between the upper and lower ball joint studs (Fig. 3). **The tool should seat firmly against the ends**

of both studs and not against the stud nuts.

8. Turn the tool nut with a wrench until the tool places the studs under tension, and, with a hammer, tap the spindle near the studs to loosen them in the spindle. **Do not loosen the studs in the spindle with tool pressure only.**

9. Position a floor jack under the lower control arm.

10. Remove the ball joint stud nuts and lower the lower arm enough to remove the spindle.

INSTALLATION

1. Position the spindle to the lower ball joint stud and install the attaching nut. Torque the nut to specification. Continue to tighten the nut until the cotter pin hole is in line with the slots in the nut. Then, install the cotter pin.

2. Raise the lower arm and guide the upper ball joint stud into the spindle hole and install the attaching nut. Torque the nut to specification and install the cotter pin as outlined in the preceding step.

3. Remove the floor jack from under the lower arm.

4. Attach the steering connecting rod to the spindle and install the nut. Torque the nut to specification. Continue to tighten the nut until the cotter pin hole is in line with the slots in the nut. Then, install the cotter pin.

5. If equipped with drum type brakes—Position the brake backing plate to the spindle and install the attaching bolts. Torque the bolts to specification. Adjust the brakes as outlined in Part 2-2. Install the wheel, tire, and drum to the spindle and adjust the wheel bearings as outlined in Part 3-5.

6. If equipped with disc brakes—Install the splash shield on the spindle and torque the attaching bolts to specification (Part 3-6). Install the hub and rotor on the spindle. Position the caliper over the rotor and install the attaching bolts. Be sure to insert the upper bolt through the brake hose bracket. Torque the bolts to specification (Part 3-6). Install the wheel and tire on the hub and adjust the wheel bearings as outlined in Part 3-5.

7. Install the hub cap or wheel cover. Then, remove the support stand and lower the car.

8. Check caster, camber, and toe-in (Part 3-1) and adjust as necessary.

REAR SPRING

REMOVAL

1. Raise the car on a hoist with the hoist under the rear axle housing. Place jack stands under the frame side rails.

2. Disconnect the lower studs of the two rear shock absorbers from the mounting brackets on axle housing.

3. Lower the hoist and axle housing until the coil springs are released (Fig. 5).

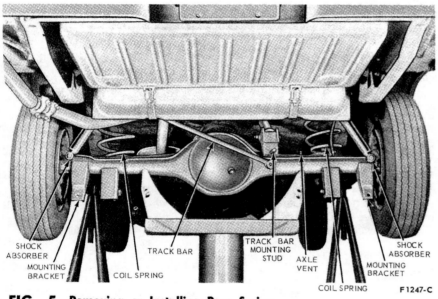

SHOCK ABSORBER
MOUNTING BRACKET
COIL SPRING
TRACK BAR
TRACK BAR MOUNTING STUD
AXLE VENT
COIL SPRING
MOUNTING BRACKET
SHOCK ABSORBER
F1247-C

FIG. 5—Removing or Installing Rear Spring

4. Remove the springs and the insulators from the car.

INSTALLATION

1. Position the spring in the upper and lower seats with an insulator between each seat and the spring.

2. Raise the hoist and axle housing with the spring in position and connect the lower studs of the rear shock absorbers to the mounting brackets on the axle housing. Install the mounting nuts, and torque to specifications.

3. Remove the jack stands and lower the car.

REAR SUSPENSION LOWER ARM

REMOVAL

1. Raise the car on a hoist and place jack stands under the frame side rails.

2. Remove the attaching nut and washer from the axle track bar mounting stud and disconnect the bar from the stud (Fig. 2).

3. Disconnect the right and left shock absorbers from the axle.

4. Lower the axle enough to relieve spring pressure.

5. Remove the lower arm pivot bolt and nut from the axle bracket. Then, disengage the lower arm from the bracket.

6. Remove the pivot bolt and nut from the frame bracket and remove the lower arm from the car.

INSTALLATION

The rear suspension lower arms are not interchangeable. The lower arm for the left side can be identified by notches in the bushing flange (Fig. 2). The right arm does not have the notches.

1. Position the lower arm in the bracket on the frame side rail. The end of the lower arm marked with a round depression on the top (Fig. 2) must be installed at the frame side rail (Front) attachment. Install a new pivot bolt and nut (Fig. 6). Do not tighten the nut at this time.

2. Position the lower arm to the axle bracket and install a new bolt and nut (Fig. 6). Do not tighten the nut at this time.

3. Raise the axle and connect the rear shock absorbers to the axle.

4. Install alignment spacers (Tool —T65P-3000-B- or C) between the rear axle and frame (Fig. 3, Part 3-1). Then, torque the lower arm pivot bolts and nuts to specification (Part 3-6).

5. Connect the track bar to the mounting stud, install the washer and attaching nut, and torque to specification (Part 3-6).

6. Remove the alignment spacers and jack stands and lower the car.

REAR SUSPENSION UPPER ARM

REMOVAL

1. Raise the car and support the frame side rails with jack stands.

2. Support the rear axle, then disconnect the track bar from the axle housing.

3. Lower the axle far enough to allow the shock absorbers to support it.

4. Remove the nut, bolt and two washers that attach the upper arm to the axle housing. Disconnect the arm from the housing.

5. Remove the nut and bolt that secures the upper arm to the crossmember and remove the arm.

INSTALLATION

The end of the upper arm marked with a round depression on the top (Fig. 2) must be installed at the frame crossmember (Front) attachment.

1. Hold the upper arm in place on the crossmember and install the attaching bolt and a new nut. Do not tighten the nut at this time.

2. Secure the upper arm to the axle housing with the attaching bolt, two washers and a new nut. Do not tighten the nut at this time.

3. Adjust the pinion angle as detailed in Part 3-1.

4. Remove jack stands and lower the car.

TRACK BAR

1. Raise the car on an axle contact hoist.

2. Remove the nut and washer retaining the track bar to the upper arm bracket and disengage the track bar from the mounting stud (Fig. 5).

3. Remove the nut and bolt attaching the track bar to the frame side rail and remove the track bar.

4. Position the track bar to the frame side rail and install a new attaching bolt and nut.

5. Position the track bar on the upper arm bracket mounting stud and install the washer and a new retaining nut. Torque the track bar attaching bolt and nuts to specification

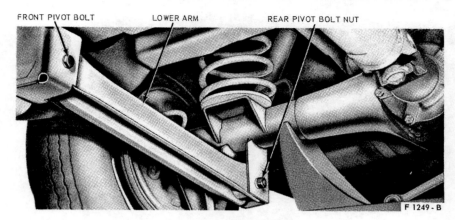

FRONT PIVOT BOLT   LOWER ARM   REAR PIVOT BOLT NUT

F 1249-B

FIG. 6—Rear Suspension Lower Arm Installed

(Part 3-6). Then, lower the car.

SHOCK ABSORBERS

Passenger cars and station wagons are equipped with hydraulic shock absorbers of the direct-acting type and are nonadjustable and nonrefillable, and cannot be repaired.

Before replacing a shock absorber, check the action of the shock absorbers by grasping the bumper and jouncing the car up and down. If the shock absorbers are in good condition the car will immediately settle to a normal position after the bumper is released.

TESTING

To check a shock absorber removed from a car proceed as follows:

1. Hold the shock absorber in the vertical position with the piston (lower end) up, and pull out the piston rod until the shock is extended to its full length.
2. With the shock absorber held in the same position, push in the piston rod until the shock is compressed to its shortest length.
3. Repeat steps 1 and 2 several times until all the air is expelled.
4. Clamp the lower end (small diameter) in a vise in a vertical position.
5. Extend the shock to its full length and then compress it to its shortest length. There should be a constant drag during the complete cycle. Any sudden loss of drag indicates air in the system or faulty internal valve operation. Replace defective shock absorbers.

FRONT SHOCK ABSORBER REPLACEMENT

1. Remove the nut, washer, and bushing from the shock absorber upper end.
2. Raise the car on a hoist and install safety stands.
3. Remove 2 bolts attaching the shock absorber to the lower arm and remove the shock absorber.
4. Place a washer and bushing on the shock absorber top stud and

position the shock absorber inside the front spring. Install the 2 lower attaching bolts and torque them to specifications.

5. Remove the safety stands and lower the car.
6. Place a bushing and washer on the shock absorber top stud and install the retaining nut. Torque to specifications.

REAR SHOCK ABSORBER REPLACEMENT

1. Raise the car on a hoist.
2. Remove the shock absorber mounting nut, washer and insulator from the upper stud at the upper side of the spring upper seat. Compress the shock absorber to clear the hole in the spring seat, and remove the inner insulator and washer from the upper mounting stud.
3. Remove the self-locking retaining nut, and disconnect the shock absorber lower stud from the mounting bracket on the rear axle housing (Fig. 2).
4. Expel all air by performing steps 1 and 2 under Testing.
5. Place the inner washer and insulator on the upper mounting stud, and position the shock absorber so that the upper mounting stud enters the hole in the spring upper seat. While holding the shock absorber in this position, install the outer insulator and washer and the nut on the upper stud from the upper side of the spring upper seat. Torque the nut to specifications.
6. Extend the shock absorber and locate the lower stud in the hole in mounting bracket on the rear axle housing. Install the self-locking retaining nut and torque to specifications.

4   MAJOR REPAIR OPERATIONS

FRONT SUSPENSION UPPER ARM BUSHINGS—ARM REMOVED

1. Remove the nuts and washers from both ends of the upper arm inner shaft.
2. Install Tool T65P-3044-A1 on the inner shaft and place Tool T65P-3044-A3 inside the upper arm around the inner shaft (Fig. 7).

3. Position the upper arm in an arbor press on Tool T65P-3044-A4 (Fig. 7), and press the lower bushing out of the upper arm.

4. Remove the bushing from the inner shaft; turn the assembly over and remove the bushing from the other side of the arm. **It may be necessary to remove Tool T65P-3044-A1 from the inner shaft and remove**

the shaft from the arm to remove the bushing from the shaft. Then, install the tool on the shaft and remove the other bushing.

5. Position the shaft and bushings to the upper arm and install the bushings and inner shaft in the upper arm as shown in Fig. 8.
6. Install a washer and new nut on each end of the inner shaft.

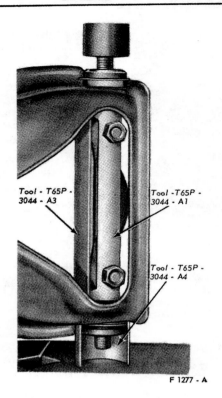

Tool - T65P - 3044 - A3

Tool - T65P - 3044 - A1

Tool - T65P - 3044 - A4

F 1277 - A

FIG. 7—Removing Upper Arm Bushings

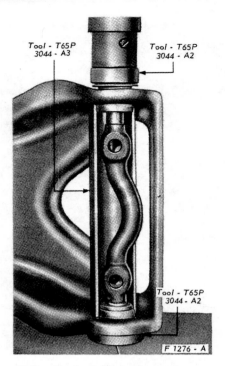

Tool - T65P 3044 - A3

Tool - T65P 3044 - A2

Tool - T65P 3044 - A2

F 1276 - A

FIG. 8—Installing Upper Arm Shaft And Bushings

PART 3-3 MANUAL STEERING

1 DESCRIPTION

The steering gear (Fig. 1) is of the worm and recirculating ball type.

The sector shaft is straddle mounted having a bushing located in the cover above the gear and a roller bearing in the housing below the gear.

The worm bearing preload is controlled by the large adjusting nut which is threaded into the housing. The sector shaft mesh load is controlled by an adjusting screw located in the housing cover.

The steering linkage consists of the Pitman arm, steering-arm-to-idler arm rod, idler arm and the spindle connecting rods (tie rods).

A steering gear identification tag is provided under one of the cover attaching bolts (Fig. 2).

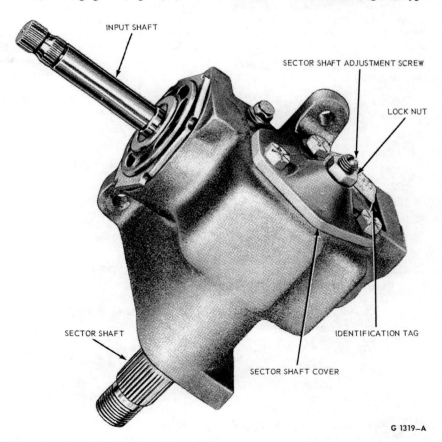

INPUT SHAFT
SECTOR SHAFT ADJUSTMENT SCREW
LOCK NUT
IDENTIFICATION TAG
SECTOR SHAFT COVER
SECTOR SHAFT

G 1319–A

FIG. 1—Manual Steering Gear

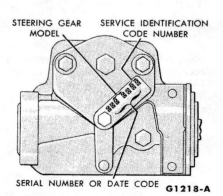

STEERING GEAR MODEL
SERVICE IDENTIFICATION CODE NUMBER
SERIAL NUMBER OR DATE CODE
G1218-A

FIG. 2—Steering Gear Identification Tag

2 IN-CAR ADJUSTMENTS AND REPAIRS

STEERING WORM AND SECTOR

GEAR ADJUSTMENTS

The ball nut assembly and the sector gear must be adjusted properly to maintain minimum steering shaft end play (a factor of preload adjustment) and minimum backlash between sector gear and ball nut. There are only two possible adjustments within the recirculating ball-type steering gear, and **these should be made in the following order to avoid damage or gear failure.**

1. Disconnect the Pitman arm from the steering arm-to-idler arm rod.

2. Loosen the nut which locks the sector adjusting screw (Fig. 1), and turn the adjusting screw counter-clockwise.

3. Measure the worm bearing preload by attaching an in-lb torque wrench to the steering wheel nut (Fig. 3). With the steering wheel

Torque Wrench (In. Lb.)   G-1270-B

FIG. 3—Checking Steering Gear Preload—Typical

off center, read the pull required to rotate the input shaft approximately 1½ turns either side of center. If the torque or preload is not within specification (Part 3-6), adjust as explained in the next step.

4. Loosen the steering shaft bearing adjuster lock nut, and tighten or back off the bearing adjuster (Fig. 1) to bring the preload within the specified limits.

5. Tighten the steering shaft bearing adjuster lock nut, and recheck the preload.

6. Turn the steering wheel slowly to either stop. **Turn gently against the stop to avoid possible damage to the ball return guides.** Then rotate the wheel 2¾ turns to center the ball nut.

7. Turn the sector adjusting screw clockwise until the specified torque (Part 3-6) is necessary to rotate the worm past its center (high spot) (Fig. 3).

8. While holding the sector adjusting screw, tighten the sector adjusting screw locknut to specification, and recheck the backlash adjustment.

9. Connect the Pitman arm to the steering arm-to-idler arm rod.

STEERING WHEEL SPOKE POSITION ADJUSTMENT

When the steering gear is on the high point, the front wheels should be in the straight-ahead position and the steering wheel spokes should be in their normal position with the Pitman arm pointing directly forward. If the spokes are not in their normal position, they can be adjusted without disturbing the toe-in adjustment (Part 3-1).

MOVABLE STEERING COLUMN ADJUSTMENT

1. Set the stop screw (Fig. 4) to

bracket. Tighten the stop screw lock nut.

2. Place the selector lever in the Park position. Lift the locking arm and move the column to the right to allow the locking arm to set on the top side of the locking bracket (nylon surface). Loosen the three locking actuator screws and move the actuator to obtain a clearance of approximately 0.060 inch at point A. If the actuator crank contacts the locking arm at this point, back the locking actuator set screw out until the crank is free of the locking arm.

3. With the selector lever still in Park position, turn the locking actuator set screw inward until the actuator crank lifts the locking arm to obtain a clearance of approximately 0.030 inch between the top of the locking bracket and the lower end of the locking arm. Tighten the actuator lever set screw lock nut. It may be necessary to place the selector lever in L position to gain access to the set screw. However the selector lever must be in the Park position when obtaining the 0.030 inch clearance between the locking bracket and locking arm.

4. Place the selector lever in the L position. Set the actuator crank adjustment screw to obtain a clearance of approximately 0.125 inch between the bottom surface of the

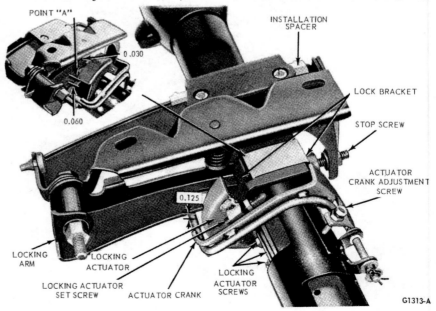

FIG. 4—Movable Column Adjustment Points

prevent column lateral movement by centering the locking arm on the lock

locking arm and the actuator crank.

5. Place the selector lever in the

Reverse position. Make sure that actuator crank does not exert pressure on the locking arm. If the actuating crank does exert a force on the locking arm, inspect the complete mechanism for damaged parts.

STEERING WHEEL REPLACEMENT

1. Disconnect the battery and remove the horn ring (or bottom) assembly and related parts.

2. Remove the nut from the end of the steering shaft, and remove the steering wheel from the shaft with Tool 3600-AA.

3. With the front wheels straight forward, position the steering wheel on the steering shaft with the spokes properly centered and the alignment marks on both parts properly aligned.

4. Install the steering wheel nut on the shaft, torque to specifications, and apply two drops of locktite to the thread and nut juncture.

5. Install the horn ring (or button) assembly and related parts.

STEERING COLUMN UPPER BEARING

STATIONARY AND MOVABLE COLUMN

Removal

1. Disconnect the steering column turn signal and horn wires at the wire connector.

2. Remove the horn button or ring and spring from the steering wheel.

3. Remove the steering wheel to steering shaft retaining nut and remove the steering wheel with Tool 3600-AA. Then, remove the tool from the steering wheel.

4. Remove the turn signal lever from the turn signal switch.

5. Remove 3 bearing retainer and turn signal attaching screws and remove the bearing retainer (Fig. 6 or 7.) Then, lift the turn signal switch from the flange. **Do not remove the wires from the steering column.**

6. Loosen 2 flange attaching nuts and lift the flange from the steering column.

7. Press the bearing and insulator from the flange and remove the insulator from the bearing.

Installation

1. Press the bearing into the insulator and insert the bearing and insulator in the recess of the flange (Fig. 6 or 7).

2. Position the flange over the steering shaft and to the steering column. Loosen the 2 flange attaching nuts (Figs. 6 or 7) until the end of the flange bolt is just below the top of the nut.

3. Press the flange down over the steering column until it bottoms. **Be sure the heads of the flange bolts are on the outside diameter of the steering column.** Then, tighten the 2 nuts to retain the flange to the steering column. **The heads of the flange bolts must slip into the slots on each side of the steering column.**

4. Position the turn signal switch and retainer in the flange and install the 3 attaching screws.

5. Apply 2 drops of Loctite sealer (C3AZ-19554-A) to the threads of the turn signal switch lever. Install the lever in the turn signal switch and **tighten finger tight.**

6. Align the steering wheel and steering shaft marks for straight ahead and position the steering wheel on the steering shaft. Install the steering wheel attaching nut and torque to specification. Then, apply 2 drops of Loctite sealer (C3AZ-19554-A) to the joint of the nut and steering shaft threads.

7. Install the horn ring and spring on the steering wheel hub.

8. Connect the horn and turn signal wires at the connector and position the wires in the clip.

TILT WHEEL COLUMN

Removal

1. Disconnect the negative (ground) cable from the battery.

2. Remove the horn ring from the steering wheel and remove the steering wheel with Tool 3600-AA.

3. Remove the turn signal switch lever and the tilt release lever.

4. Remove the turn signal cover as shown in Fig. 10.

5. Remove the turn signal switch plate and detent spring.

6. Pry out the horn contact plate from the mounting plate and remove the contact plate and wire assembly as shown in Fig. 11.

7. Pry up the tabs on the lock washer and remove the upper bearing nut, lock washer, bearing race seat, bearing race and the upper bearing.

8. Install the tilt release lever and lift it up so that the column will go to the fully up position; then, unhook the upper ends of the lock springs as shown in Fig. 13.

9. Remove the two pivot pins as shown in Fig. 14.

10. Lift the tilt release lever to disengage the upper and lower levers from the pins and remove the mounting plate.

11. Remove the turn signal switch cable from the turn signal switch plate.

12. Remove the lower bearing from the steering shaft yoke.

Installation

1. Position the lower bearing on the steering shaft yoke.

2. Thread the horn wire through the mounting plate, leaving the horn contact plate hanging from the mounting plate.

3. Install the horn wire into the triangular hole in the column and pull the wire through the exit hole.

4. Move the tilt release lever up slightly to prevent the upper and lower levers from engaging the pins; then, guide the turn signal Bowden cable through the mounting plate and install the mounting plate over the steering shaft yoke. Hold the right lock spring in position with bent wire.

5. Align the mounting plate pivot pin holes with the pin holes in the flange and install the pivot pins. Pins should go in no further than flush.

6. Raise the tilt release lever and lift the mounting plate to the maximum up position.

7. Install the upper ends of the two lock springs (Fig. 17).

8. Install the upper bearing, bearing race, seat, a new lock washer and nut. **Do not tighten the nut.**

9. Install the horn contact plate in the mounting plate. Make sure that the horn wire is completely in the slot.

10. Install the turn signal switch plate and detent spring.

11. Remove the steering shaft flex coupling from the steering shaft in the engine compartment.

12. Mount a dial indicator on the mounting plate.

13. Tighten the steering shaft nut until there is 0.010 inch end play between the two bearings. Then, tighten the nut an additional ½ turn. **Do not exceed ½ turn.**

14. Bend the lock washer tabs across the flats on the nut. If the tabs **do not** align with the flats on the nut, back the nuts off to the closest flat. **Do not tighten the nut.**

15. Remove the dial indicator from the mounting plate.

16. Remove the tilt release lever.

17. Install the turn signal cover, aligning the key in the cover into the keyway in the turn signal switch plate. Use Tool T65P-3D505-B.

18. Install the tilt and turn signal levers.

19. Install the steering wheel and

the flex coupling on the steering shaft.

20. Connect the battery ground cable to the battery.

3 REMOVAL AND INSTALLATION

STEERING GEAR

REMOVAL

1. Remove the bolt that attaches the flex coupling to the steering gear.

2. Raise the front of the car and install safety stands.

3. Disconnect the Pitman arm from the sector shaft with Tool T64P-3590-F.

4. If necessary, disconnect the muffler inlet pipe.

5. Remove the steering gear housing attaching bolts, and remove the steering gear.

INSTALLATION

1. With the steering wheel spokes aligned and the sector shaft in the center position, install the steering gear. Torque the mounting bolts to specification.

2. With the wheels straight ahead, connect the Pitman arm to the sector shaft.

3. If necessary, connect the muffler inlet pipe.

4. Remove the steering gear filler plug and housing lower cover bolt. After turning the steering wheel to the left to move the ball nut away from the filler hole, fill the steering gear with the correct lubricant. Fill the gear until lubrication comes out of the housing cover lower bolt hole. Install the filler plug and the cover bolt. Torque the bolt to specification.

STEERING COLUMN SHIFT TUBE

STATIONARY COLUMN WITH STANDARD TRANSMISSION

Removal

1. Open the hood and disconnect the shift linkage rods from the steering column shift arms.

2. Remove the clutch pedal-to-equalizer rod adjusting nut.

3. Remove 5 nuts and washers that attach the steering column bracket and lower clamp to the dash panel in the engine compartment (Fig. 5).

4. Remove the 2 bolts that attach the bracket and lower clamp to steering column and separate them from the column.

5. Loosen the flex coupling from the lower end of the steering shaft.

6. Pull the floor covering back from the steering column and remove the insulation from the dash panel in the area of the retainer.

7. Remove the clutch pedal to equalizer rod hair pin retainer and disconnect the rod from the clutch pedal.

8. Remove 3 retainer attaching screws and remove the retainer and seal from the dash panel (Fig. 5).

9. Remove the turn signal and horn wires from the clip on the steering column and disconnect the wires.

10. Remove 2 steering column to instrument panel shroud retaining screws and remove the shrouds and retainer (Fig. 5).

3600-AA. Then, remove the tool from the steering wheel.

13. Remove the shift lever from the shift lever hub (Fig. 6).

14. Remove 2 steering column clamp to support bracket (instrument panel) retaining nuts and remove the steering column.

15. Remove 3 screws that attach the shift tube bearing, shift arms, and shift tube to the lower end of the steering column (Fig. 6). Remove the shift tube bearing and shift arms from the column.

16. Remove the shift tube and steering shaft from the steering column.

17. Remove the snap ring from the upper end of the steering shaft (Fig. 6), and pull the shift tube

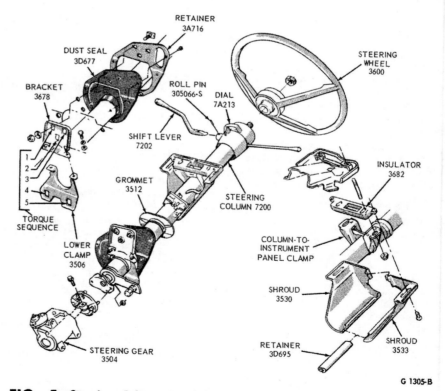

FIG. 5—Steering Column Installation—Stationary Column

11. Remove the horn ring from the steering wheel and remove the steering wheel to shaft attaching nut.

12. Remove the steering wheel from the steering shaft with Tool

from the steering shaft.

18. Remove the shift tube bearing from the steering shaft lower end (Fig. 6).

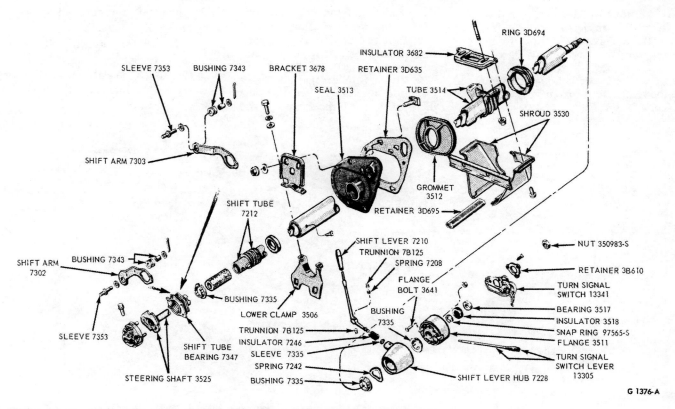

FIG. 6—Stationary Steering Column Disassembled—Standard Transmission

Installation

1. Position the shift tube bearing (Fig. 6) on the shift tube and insert the steering shaft in the shift tube.

2. Install the snap ring on the upper end of the steering shaft.

3. Insert the shift tube and steering shaft into the housing and install the 3 attaching screws.

4. Position the steering column in the car and position the flex coupling to the steering shaft (Fig. 5).

5. Position the steering column to the support bracket and start the 2 attaching nuts.

6. Install the seal and retainer to the dash panel (Fig. 5).

7. Install the flex coupling clamp bolt.

8. Position the bracket and lower clamp over the steering column in the engine compartment. Install but do not tighten the 2 bracket to lower clamp attaching bolts.

9. Position the bracket and lower clamp to the dash panel and start the 5 washers and nuts. Torque the 2 bracket to lower clamp attaching bolts to specification. Then, torque the 5 attaching nuts to specification in the sequence shown in Fig. 5.

10. Connect the shift linkage rods to the column shift arms.

11. Insert the clutch pedal to equalizer and the clutch pedal.

12. Position the insulation to the dash panel and the floor covering around the steering column.

13. Torque the steering column to support bracket (instrument panel) retaining nuts to specification.

14. Position the 2 shroud halves and the retainer to the steering column and install the 2 attaching screws.

15. Connect the horn and turn signal wires at the connector and secure the wire harness in the clip.

16. Position the steering wheel on the steering shaft. Install the steering wheel attaching nut and torque to specification. Then, apply 2 drops of Loctite sealer (C3AZ-19554-A) to the joint of the nut and steering shaft threads.

17. Install the horn ring and spring on the steering wheel hub.

18. Start the engine and check the shift operation. Adjust the shift linkage if required.

STATIONARY COLUMN WITH AUTOMATIC TRANSMISSION

Removal

1. Open the hood and disconnect the shift linkage rod from the steering column shift arm.

2. Remove 2 bolts that attach the bracket and lower clamp to the steering column in the engine compartment and separate them from the column (Fig. 5).

3. Remove 5 nuts and washers that attach the bracket and lower clamp to the dash panel.

4. Disconnect the steering column turn signal and horn wires at the multiple connectors.

5. Remove the horn ring from the steering wheel and remove the steering wheel to shaft attaching nut.

6. Remove the steering wheel from the steering shaft with Tool 3600-AA. Then, remove the tool from the steering wheel.

7. Pull the floor covering back from the steering column and remove the insulation from the dash panel in the area of the retainer.

8. Remove 3 screws that attach the seal and retainer to the dash panel and slide the seal and retainer up the steering column.

9. Remove the 2 shroud attaching screws (Fig. 5), and remove the shrouds and retainer.

10. Remove 2 steering column clamp to support bracket (instrument panel) retaining nuts. Lift the steering column off the steering shaft and remove the column from the car.

11. Remove the turn signal lever from the turn signal switch.

12. Remove the roll pin from the selector lever and remove the lever.

13. Remove one bolt attaching the shift tube to the column and remove the shift tube from the steering column (Fig. 7).

dash panel and the floor covering around the steering column.

8. Connect the steering column turn signal and horn wires at the connector.

9. Position the bracket and lower clamp to the steering column and dash panel. Install the 5 washers and

the joint of the nut and steering shaft threads.

14. Install the horn ring and spring on the steering wheel hub.

15. Adjust the shift linkage if necessary and torque the adjusting nut to specification.

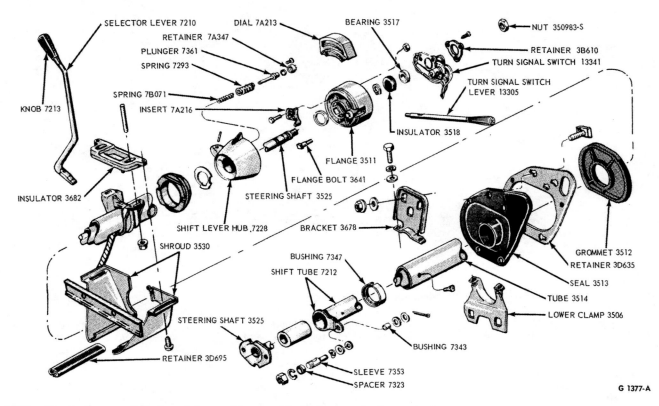

FIG. 7—Stationary Steering Column Disassembled—Automatic Transmission

14. Remove the bushing from the shift tube.

Installation

1. Position the bushing on the shift tube and position the shift tube in the steering column (Fig. 7).

2. Position the shift lever in the shift lever hub and install the roll pin.

3. Install the turn signal lever in the turn signal switch. Apply a small amount of Loctite sealer (C3AZ-19554-A) to the lever threads before installation.

4. Position the steering column over the steering shaft and slide the column through the hole in the dash panel.

5. Position the column to the support bracket (instrument panel) and start the 2 attaching nuts.

6. Position the seal and retainer to the dash panel and install the 3 retaining screws (Fig. 5).

7. Position the insulation to the

nuts to secure the bracket and clamp to the dash panel and the 2 bolts and washers that attach the bracket to the lower clamp. Torque the 2 brackets to the clamp attaching bolts to specification. Then, torque the 5 attaching nuts to specification in the sequence shown in Fig. 5.

10. Connect the shift linkage rod to the steering column shift arm.

11. Torque the 2 steering column to support bracket (instrument panel) attaching nuts to specification.

12. Position the shrouds to the instrument panel, steering column, and insulator and install the 2 attaching screws. Tighten the right screw and then the left screw. Then, install the retainer as shown in Fig. 5.

13. Position the steering wheel on the steering shaft. Install the steering wheel attaching nut and torque to specification. Then, apply 2 drops of Loctite sealer (C3AZ-19554-A) to

MOVABLE COLUMN

Removal

1. Remove the bolt that secures the flex coupling to the upper steering shaft (Fig. 8).

2. Disconnect the selector lever from the shift rod. This does not apply to 500XL Models.

3. Remove the nut that attaches the column to the pivot bracket. Remove the washer and sleeve.

4. Remove the two bolts that attach the pivot bracket to the support and remove the bracket from the column.

5. Remove the three nuts, and washers that attach the support to the dash panel and remove the support.

6. Remove the five screws that attach the retainer plate to the dash panel.

7. Disconnect the turn signal wires at the connector.

8. Disconnect the neutral safety

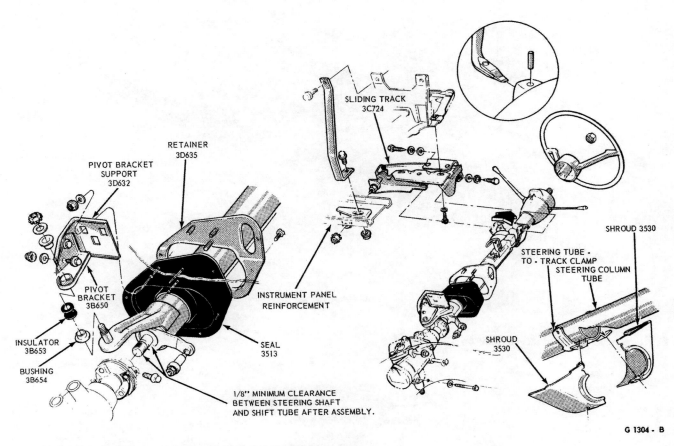

FIG. 8—Steering Column Installation—Movable Column

switch and back up light wires from the switch.

9. Slide the retainer off the shroud.

10. Remove the bolt that attaches the shroud to the movable track. Rotate the shroud off the ring and remove it.

11. Remove the two screws that attach the column to the track. Lift the column from the car.

12. Remove the 3 actuator attaching screws and remove the actuator from the shift tube (Fig. 9).

13. Remove the starter neutral switch actuator from the shift tube.

14. Remove the roll pin from the selector lever and remove the lever from the hub.

15. Remove the shift tube retaining screw from the underside of the shift lever hub and remove the shift tube from the steering column.

Installation

1. Position the shift tube in the steering column and install the shift tube to selector lever hub attaching screw.

2. Position the selector lever in

the selector lever hub and install the roll pin.

3. Install the starter neutral switch actuator on the shift tube.

4. Position the actuator to the shift tube and install the 3 attaching screws.

5. Install the locating spacer on the sliding track as shown in Fig. 8.

6. Hold the column in position with the upper steering shaft centered in the flex coupling. Install, but, do not tighten the steering column-to-track attaching bolts (Fig. 8).

7. Secure the dust seal and the retainer plate to the dash panel with the attaching screws.

8. Connect the turn signal, neutral safety switch, and the shift quadrant wires to their respective connectors.

9. Secure the pivot bracket support to the dash panel with the three attaching nuts and washers.

10. Make sure that the insulator and bushings are in place in the pivot bracket. Then, position it on the steering column pivot. Secure the bracket to the pivot with a flat washer and nut.

11. Secure the pivot bracket to

the support with the two attaching bolts.

12. Connect and adjust the manual shift rod as required.

13. Tighten the steering tube-to-track clamp attaching bolts.

14. Position the shroud halves in the shroud ring and rotate the shroud into place.

15. Secure the shroud to the track with the attaching screw.

16. Adjust the track if required.

TILT WHEEL COLUMN

Removal

1. Disconnect the negative (ground) cable from the battery.

2. Remove the cap from the center of the steering wheel.

3. Remove the steering wheel attaching nut and remove the steering wheel with Tool 3600-AA.

4. Remove the turn signal switch lever and the tilt release lever.

5. Remove the turn signal cover as shown in Fig. 10.

6. Remove the turn signal switch plate and detent spring.

7. Tie a piece of string to the

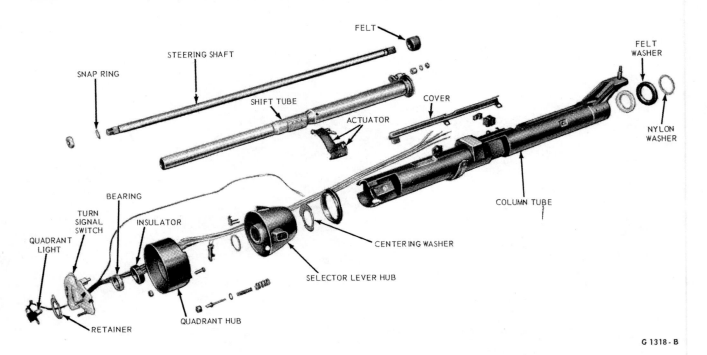

FIG. 9—Movable Steering Column Disassembled

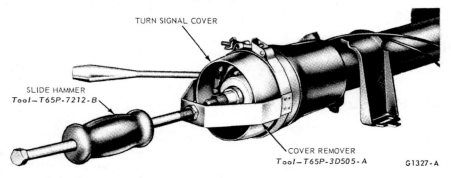

FIG. 10—Removing Turn Signal Cover

horn wire at the lower end of the steering column. Pry the horn contact plate from the mounting plate and remove the horn contact plate and wire as shown in Fig. 11.

9. Straighten the tabs on the lock washer and remove the upper bearing nut, lock washer, bearing race seat, bearing race, and the upper bearing.

FIG. 11—Removing Horn Contact Plate and Wire

8. Remove the turn signal switch cable from the turn signal switch plate and mounting plate (Fig. 12).

10. Install the tilt release lever and tilt the mounting plate up. Then, unhook the upper ends of the lock

springs from the mounting plate as shown in Fig. 13.

11. Remove the 2 pivot pins as shown in Fig. 14.

12. Lift the tilt release lever to disengage the upper and lower levers from the pins and remove the mounting plate.

13. Remove the lower bearing from the steering shaft yoke.

14. Remove the spring from between the steering shaft yoke and the U-joint bearing as follows:

a. Use care during removal of the spring to prevent losing it as it is under compression.

b. Turn the yoke slightly from the centerline of the steering shaft.

c. With a narrow blade screwdriver, compress the spring enough to remove it from the upper seat; then, remove the spring.

15. Turn the steering shaft yoke 90° from the centerline of the steering shaft so that the flats on the bearing align with the steering shaft socket; then, remove the yoke and U-joint bearing from the steering shaft socket.

16. Remove the U-joint bearing from the steering shaft yoke by rotating the bearing so that the flats on the bearing align with the yoke socket.

17. Remove the lock springs from the flange (Fig. 12).

18. Remove the 4 flange screws and remove the flange (Fig. 12) from the steering column.

G 1378-A

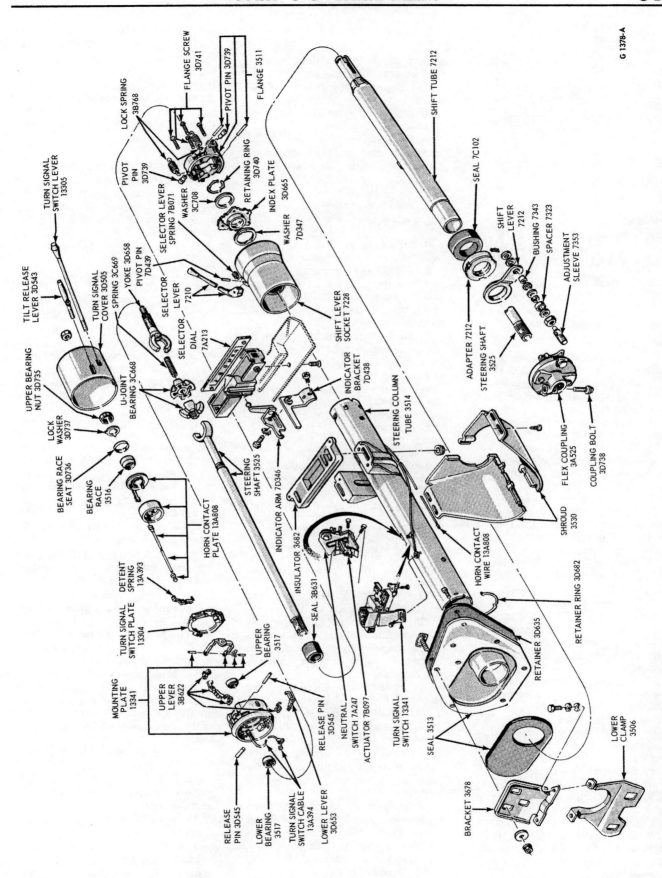

FIG. 12—Tilt Wheel Column Disassembled

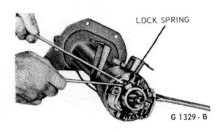

FIG. 13—Removing Lock Springs

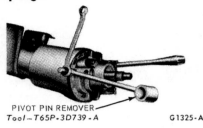

PIVOT PIN REMOVER
Tool—T65P-3D739-A   G1325-A

FIG. 14—Removing Pivot Pins

19. Remove the bolt that attaches the flex coupling to the steering shaft.

20. Lift the steering shaft from the steering column.

21. Disconnect the shift linkage from the shift lever.

22. Raise the front of the car and remove 5 nuts and 2 bolts attaching the bracket and lower clamp to the dash panel and steering column in the engine compartment (Fig. 15).

23. Pull the floor covering back from the steering column and remove the insulation from the dash panel in the area of the retainer (Fig. 15).

24. Remove 3 retainer attaching screws and remove the retainer and seal from the dash panel (Fig. 15).

25. Remove 4 steering column to instrument panel shroud attaching screws and remove the shroud.

26. Disconnect the turn signal and horn wires at the steering column connectors.

27. Remove 2 steering column clamp to instrument panel attaching nuts (Fig. 15) and remove the steering column from the car.

28. Remove the selector indicator bracket and indicator arm from the steering column (Fig. 15).

29. Remove the neutral switch actuator from the shift tube.

30. Remove the retaining ring and washer from the top end of the shift tube.

31. Remove the retainer ring from the lower end of the steering column, and remove the shift tube as shown in Fig. 16.

32. Remove seal from shift tube.

Installation

When assembling the steering column, apply a thin coat of lithium soap grease to all friction parts (Refer to Fig. 12 for parts identification).

1. Position the seal on the shift tube.

2. Position the shift tube in the steering column and tap it into place with a soft hammer. Be sure the shift tube is properly installed in the index plate.

3. Install the washer and retaining ring on the top end of the shift tube.

4. Install the retainer ring on the lower end of the steering column.

5. Install the indicator bracket and indicator arm on the shift tube.

6. Position the neutral switch actuator to the shift tube and install the attaching screw.

7. Position the steering column in the car and loosely install the 2 steering column clamp to instrument panel attaching nuts.

8. Position the seal and retainer to the dash panel and install the 3 attaching screws (Fig. 15).

9. Position the bracket and lower clamp over the steering column in the engine compartment (Fig. 15). Install but do not tighten the 2 brackets to lower clamp attaching bolts.

10. Position the bracket and lower clamp to the dash panel and start the 5 washers and nuts. Torque the 2 bracket to lower clamp attaching bolts to specification. Then, torque the 5 attaching nuts to specification in the sequence shown in Fig. 15.

11. Connect the shift linkage to the steering column shift lever.

12. Center the steering column in the instrument panel opening and torque the steering column clamp to instrument panel attaching nuts to specification.

13. Position the shroud to the steering column and instrument panel and install the attaching screws.

14. Position the insulation and carpet to the floor pan and dash panel in the area of the steering column.

15. Insert the steering shaft in the steering column and into the flex coupling.

16. Position the flange to the steering column and install the 4 flange screws. The 2 long screws go into the left hole in the flange. Torque the screws to specification (Part 3-6) —long screws first.

17. Connect the lower end of the

lock springs to the flange.

18. Place the U-joint bearing in the yoke socket.

19. Turn the bearing so that the steering shaft can be installed over the flat area of the bearing (approximately 90° from the centerline of the steering shaft). Then, install the steering shaft socket over the bearing.

20. Install the spring through the U-joint bearing into the steering shaft and into the yoke. Work the spring into position with a screwdriver from the opposite side that the spring is inserted.

21. Place the lower bearing on the yoke.

22. Install the tilt lever in the mounting plate.

23. Thread the turn signal switch cable through the mounting plate.

24. Move the tilt release lever up slightly to prevent the upper and lower levers from engaging the pins; then, install the mounting plate over the steering shaft yoke. Hold the right lock spring in position with a piece of wire.

25. Align the mounting plate pivot pin holes with the holes in the flange and install the pivot pins. The pivot pins should go in no further than flush.

26. Raise the tilt release lever and lift the mounting plate to the full up position.

27. Install the upper ends of the 2 lock springs as shown in Fig. 17.

28. Install the upper bearing, bearing race, seat, a new lock washer, and the upper bearing nut.

29. Position a dial indicator on the mounting plate. Tighten the upper bearing nut until there is 0.010 inch end play between the 2 bearings. Then, tighten the nut an additional ½ turn. **Do not exceed ½ turn.**

30. Bend the lock washer tabs across the flats on the upper bearing nut. If the tabs **do not** align with the flats on the nut, back the nut off to the closest flat. **Do not tighten the nut.**

31. Remove the dial indicator from the mounting plate.

32. Position the horn contact plate to the mounting plate and connect the wire.

33. Position the turn signal switch cable to the mounting plate and install the clamp attaching screw.

34. Install the turn signal switch plate in the mounting plate. Connect the turn signal switch cable to

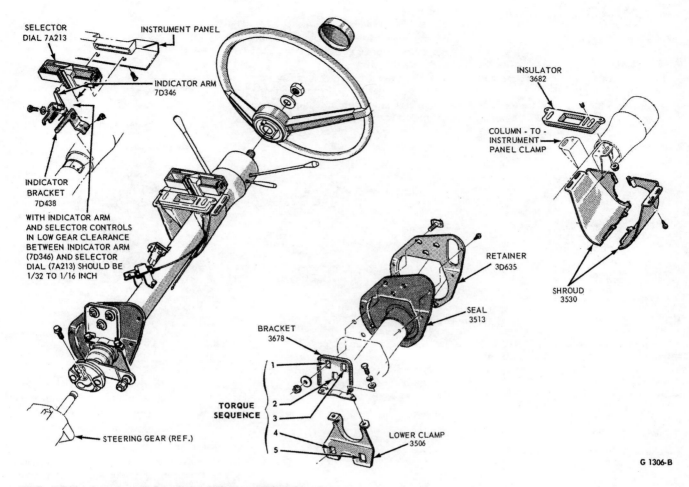

FIG. 15—Steering Column Installation—Tilt Wheel

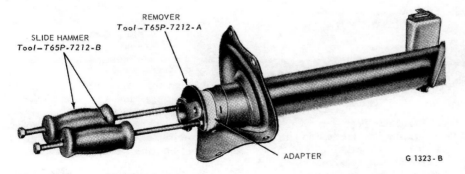

FIG. 16—Removing Shift Tube

the switch plate with the cable loop inboard.

35. Remove the tilt release lever.

36. Install the turn signal cover, aligning the key in the cover into the keyway in the turn signal switch plate. Use Tool T65P-30505-B.

37. Install the tilt release and turn signal switch levers.

38. Install the coupling bolt in the steering shaft flex coupling.

39. Install the steering wheel and steering wheel attaching nut. Torque the nut to specification and apply 2

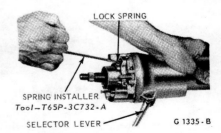

FIG. 17—Installing Lock Springs

drops of Loctite sealer (C3AZ-19554-A) to the junction of the steering shaft and attaching nut threads.

40. Install the cap in the center of the steering wheel.

41. Connect the ground cable to the battery.

4 MAJOR REPAIR OPERATIONS

STEERING GEAR

DISASSEMBLY

1. Rotate the steering shaft 3 turns from either stop.

2. After removing the sector adjusting screw locknut and the housing cover bolts (Fig. 18), remove

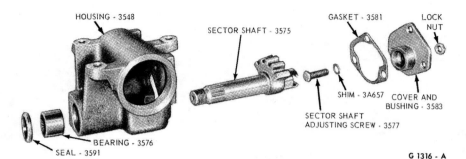

FIG. 18—Sector Shaft and Housing Disassembled

the sector shaft with the cover. Remove the cover from the shaft by turning the screw clockwise. **Keep the shim with the screw.**

3. Loosen the worm bearing adjuster nut, and remove the adjuster assembly and the steering shaft upper bearing (Fig. 19).

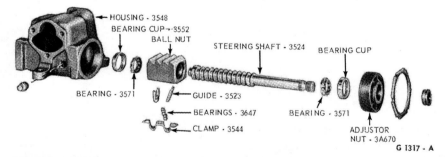

FIG. 19—Steering Shaft and Related Parts Disassembled

4. Carefully pull the steering shaft and ball nut from the housing, and remove the steering shaft lower bearing. **To avoid possible damage to the ball return guides, keep the ball nut from running down to either end of the worm.**

Disassemble the ball nut only if there is indication of binding or tightness.

5. Remove the ball return guide clamp and the ball return guides from the ball nut. **Keep the ball nut clampside up until ready to remove the balls.**

6. Turn the ball nut over, and rotate the worm shaft from side to side until all 50 balls have dropped out

of the nut into a clean pan. With the balls removed, the ball nut will slide off the worm.

7. Remove the upper bearing cup from the bearing adjuster and the lower cup from the housing. It may be necessary to tap the housing or the adjuster on a block of wood to

jar the bearing cups loose.

8. Press out both the sector shaft bearing if the preliminary inspection shows damage and the oil seal from the housing (Fig. 20).

ASSEMBLY

1. If the sector shaft bearing and

oil seal have been removed, press new bearing into the housing and install a new oil seal (Fig. 19). **Apply the recommended steering gear lubricant to the bearing and seals.**

2. Install a bearing cup in the lower end of the housing and in the adjuster.

3. If the seal in the bearing adjuster was removed, install a new seal.

4. Insert the ball guides into the holes of the ball nut, tapping them lightly with a wood handle of a screw driver if necessary to seat them.

5. Insert 25 balls into the hole in the top of each ball guide. It may be

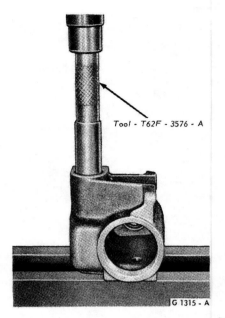

FIG. 20—Removing Oil Seal and Bearing

necessary to rotate the shaft slightly one way, then in the opposite direction to distribute the balls in the circuit.

6. After the 50 balls are installed, install the ball guide clamp. Torque the screws to specification. Check the worm shaft to make sure that it rotates freely.

7. Coat the threads of the steering shaft bearing adjuster, the housing cover bolts, and the sector adjusting screw with a suitable oil-resistant sealing compound. **Do not apply sealer to female threads and especially avoid getting any sealer on the steering shaft bearings.**

8. Coat the worm bearings, sector shaft bearings, and gear teeth with steering gear lubricant.

9. Clamp the housing in a vise, with the sector shaft axis horizontal, and position the steering shaft lower bearing in its cup.

10. Position the steering shaft and ball nut assemblies in the housing.

11. Position the steering shaft upper bearing on the top of the worm, and install the steering shaft bearing adjuster and the adjuster nut and bearing cup. Leave the nut loose.

12. Adjust the worm bearing preload, using an in-lb torque wrench (Fig. 21). See Part 3-6 for the specified preload.

13. Position the sector adjusting screw and adjuster shim, and check the end clearance which should not

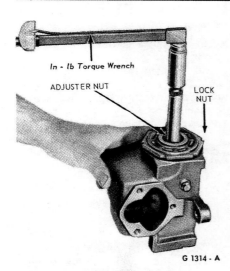

FIG. 21—Checking Steering Shaft Bearing Preload

exceed 0.002 inch between the screw head and the end of the sector shaft. If clearance is greater than 0.002 inch, add enough shims to reduce the end play to within the 0.002 inch tolerance.

14. Start the sector shaft adjusting screw into the housing cover.

15. Install a new gasket on the housing cover.

16. Rotate the steering shaft until the ball nut teeth are in position to mesh with the sector gear, tilting the housing so that the ball nut will tip toward the housing cover opening.

17. Lubricate the sector shaft journal and install the sector shaft and cover.

18. With the housing cover turned out of the way fill the gear with 0.7 lbs. ±0.7 of gear lubricant. Push the housing cover and sector shaft assemblies into place, and install the two top housing cover bolts. **Do not tighten the cover bolts until it is certain that there is some lash between ball nut and sector gear teeth.** Hold or push the cover away from the ball nut, then torque the bolts to specification.

19. After loosely installing the sector shaft adjusting screw lock nut, adjust the sector shaft mesh load. See Part 3-6 for the specified mesh load; then, tighten the adjusting screw lock nut.

TILT WHEEL HUB REPAIR

DISASSEMBLY

1. Disconnect the battery cable from the battery. Then, remove the cap from the center of the steering wheel and remove the steering wheel with Tool 3600-AA.

2. Remove the turn signal switch lever and tilt release lever.

3. Remove the turn signal switch cover as shown in Fig. 10.

4. Remove the turn signal switch plate and detent spring (Fig. 12).

5. Pry out the horn contact plate from the mounting plate and remove the contact plate and wire assembly as shown in Fig. 11. Tie a piece of string to the end of the wire to aid in wire routing during assembly.

6. Remove the turn signal switch cable from the turn signal switch plate.

7. Pry up the tabs on the lock washer and remove the nut, lock washer, bearing race seat, bearing race and upper bearing.

8. Install the tilt release lever and lift it up so that the column will go to the fully up position; then, unhook the upper ends of the lock springs as shown in Fig. 13.

9. Remove the two pivot pins as shown in Fig. 14.

10. Lift the tilt release lever to disengage the upper and lower levers from the pins and remove the mounting plate.

11. Remove the lower bearing from the steering shaft yoke.

12. Remove the spring from between the U-joint bearing in the following manner:

a. When removing the spring, use care to prevent losing it since it is under compression.

b. Turn the yoke slightly from the centerline of the steering shaft.

c. Using a narrow bladed screwdriver, compress the spring enough to remove it from the upper seat; then, remove the spring.

13. Turn the upper shaft yoke 90° from the centerline of the steering shaft and remove the shaft over the flats of the U-joint bearing.

14. Remove the U-joint bearing from the upper shaft yoke by rotating it so that the flats on the U-joint bearing align with the yoke.

15. Remove the lock springs from the flange.

16. Remove the four flange screws and remove the flange from the shift lever socket (Fig. 12).

17. Disconnect the steering gear to steering shaft flex coupling from the lower end of the steering shaft.

18. Remove the lower steering shaft from the steering column.

19. Drive the release pins from the mounting plate; then, remove the upper and lower levers and springs.

20. Remove the 2 pins retaining the lever release actuator to the

mounting plate and remove the release actuator.

ASSEMBLY

When assembling the steering column, apply a thin coat of lithium soap grease to all friction parts.

1. Position the lever release actuator to the mounting plate and install the 2 retaining pins.

2. Install the release springs on the upper and lower levers (Fig. 22).

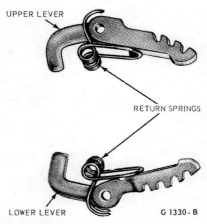

FIG. 22—Upper and Lower Levers and Springs

Install the levers in the mounting plate (Fig. 23) and secure them. The

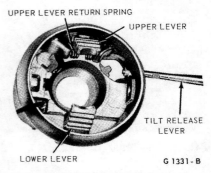

FIG. 23—Upper and Lower Levers Installed

upper lever is provided with a rubber bumper.

3. Position the lower steering shaft in the steering column and insert the lower end into the flex coupling.

4. Install the lock springs on the flange spring hangers with the loop openings of springs in the down position.

5. Install the flange (with the dog on the left side) on the upper end of the column and install the four flange screws. The two larger screws go into the left holes in the flange. Torque the screws to specification (long screw first).

6. Place the U-joint bearing in the yoke socket.

7. Turn the bearing so that the steering shaft can be installed over the flat area in the bearing (approximately 90° from the centerline of the steering shaft). Then install the steering shaft socket over the bearing.

8. Install the spring through the U-joint bearing into the steering shaft and into the yoke. Work the spring into position with a screwdriver from the opposite side that the spring is inserted.

9. Place the lower bearing on the yoke.

10. Install the tilt lever in the mounting plate.

11. Thread the turn signal switch cable through the mounting plate.

12. Move the tilt release lever up slightly to prevent the upper and lower levers from engaging the pins;

then, install the mounting plate over the steering shaft yoke. Hold the right lock spring in position with a piece of wire.

13. Align the mounting plate pivot pin holes with the holes in the flange and install the pivot pins. The pivot pins should go in no further than flush.

14. Raise the tilt release lever and lift the mounting plate to the full up position.

15. Install the upper ends of the 2 lock springs as shown in Fig. 17.

16. Install the upper bearing, bearing race, seat, a new lock washer, and nut. **Do not tighten the nut.**

17. Install the horn contact plate in the mounting plate. Make sure that the horn wire is properly routed and remove the string from the wire. Then, connect the wire to the harness. Position the turn signal switch cable to the mounting plate and install the attaching screw.

18. Install the turn signal switch

plate and detent spring (Fig. 12).

19. Mount a dial indicator on the mounting plate.

20. Tighten the steering shaft nut until there is 0.010 inch end play between the two bearings. Then, tighten the nut an additional ½ turn. **Do not exceed ½ turn.**

21. Bend the lock washer tabs across the flats on the nut. If the tabs **do not** align with the flats on the nut, back the nut off to the closest flat. **Do not tighten the nut.**

22. Remove the dial indicator from the mounting plate.

23. Remove the tilt release lever.

24. Install the turn signal cover, aligning the key in the cover into the keyway in the turn signal switch plate. Use Tool T65P-3D505-B.

25. Install the tilt and turn signal levers.

26. Install the steering wheel and the flex joint on the steering shaft.

27. Connect the battery cable to the battery.

5 STEERING LINKAGE REPAIR

The manual steering linkage (Fig. 24) consists of the Pitman arm, the

the tool shown in Fig. 25.

3. Remove the rod end from the sleeve. Discard all rod end parts that

spindle connecting rod end is replaced.

4. Thread a new end into the

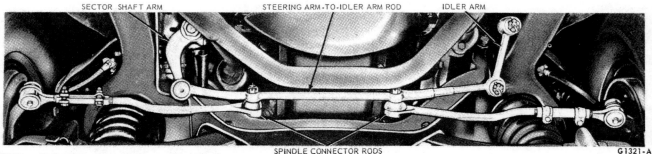

SECTOR SHAFT ARM   STEERING ARM-TO-IDLER ARM ROD   IDLER ARM

SPINDLE CONNECTOR RODS   G1321-A

FIG. 24—Steering Linkage Installed

steering arm-to-idler arm rod, the steering idler arm, and the spindle connecting rods (tie rods).

SPINDLE CONNECTING ROD END REPLACEMENT

The spindle connecting rod ends, which are threaded into the outer ends of the rod sleeves, have non-adjustable ball studs. A rod end should be replaced when excessive looseness at the ball stud is noticed.

1. Raise the end and install safety stands. Remove the cotter pin and nut from the rod end ball (Fig. 24).

2. Loosen the connecting rod sleeve clamp bolts, and remove the rod end from the spindle arm, using

were removed from the sleeve. **All new parts should be used when a new part is replaced.**

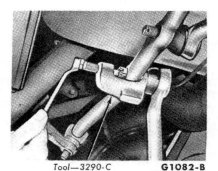

Tool—3290-C   G1082-B

FIG. 25—Removing Ball Stud

sleeve, but do not tighten the sleeve clamp bolts at this time.

5. Install the seal on the rod end ball stud, insert the stud in the spindle arm hole, and install the stud nut. Torque the nut to specification and install the cotter pin.

6. Check and, if necessary, adjust toe-in. **Be sure to tighten the sleeve clamp bolts after toe-in is checked and adjusted.** If the car has power steering, be sure that there is no interference between the sleeve bolts and the control valve.

SPINDLE CONNECTING ROD REPLACEMENT

A spindle connecting rod should be

replaced if it becomes worn or damaged. **Do not attempt to straighten a bent rod.**

1. Remove the cotter pin and nut which attach the spindle connecting rod ball stud to the steering arm to idler arm rod. Remove the ball stud from the rod, using the tool shown in Fig. 25. **Be careful not to loosen or bend any other parts on the steering arm to idler arm rod.**

2. Loosen the connecting rod sleeve clamp bolts, and remove the rod from the sleeve.

3. Thread a new connecting rod into the sleeve, but do not tighten the sleeve clamp bolts at this time.

4. With the seal properly positioned install the connecting rod ball stud in the steering arm-to-idler arm rod, and install the nut on the ball stud. Torque the nut to specification. Install a new cotter pin.

5. Check and, if necessary, adjust toe-in. **Be sure to tighten the sleeve clamp bolts after toe-in is checked and adjusted.** If the car has power steering, be sure that there is no interference between the sleeve bolts and the control valve.

STEERING ARM-TO-IDLER ARM ROD REPLACEMENT

Replace the steering arm-to-idler arm rod if it is bent. Do not try to straighten a bent rod.

1. Remove the nuts from the ball stud at the Pitman arm and from the idler arm.

2. Remove the nuts from the spindle connecting rod ball studs.

3. Remove the ball stud from the left end of the steering arm-to-idler arm rod, using the tool shown in Fig. 25. Remove the connecting rod ball studs from the rod, using the same tool. Remove the rod.

4. Position the rod on the idler arm and the Pitman arm. Torque the idler arm attaching nut and the ball stud nut at the Pitman arm to specifications. Install new cotter pins.

5. Install the spindle connecting rod ball studs, and torque the stud nuts to specification. Install new cotter pins.

6. Check and, if necessary, adjust the toe-in.

STEERING IDLER ARM BUSHING REPLACEMENT

If the idler arm bushings are worn they should be replaced.

1. Disconnect the steering arm-to-idler arm at the idler arm.

2. Remove the idler arm from the bracket.

3. Remove the bushings from the idler arm, using tool T61P-3355-A (Fig. 26).

4. Install new bushings in the idler arm, using tool T61P-3355-A.

5. Position the idler arm, and torque the retaining nuts to specification. Install new cotter pins. **When installing the idler arm, be sure that the linkage is in the straight-ahead position.**

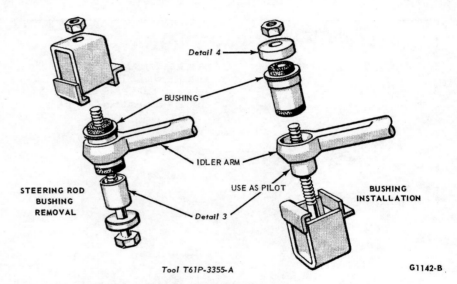

FIG. 26—Replacing Idler Arm Bushings

PART 3-4

POWER STEERING

1 DESCRIPTION AND OPERATION

STEERING GEAR

DESCRIPTION

The power steering unit (Fig. 1) is a torsion-bar type of hydraulic assisted system. This system furnishes power to reduce the amount of turning effort required at the steering wheel. It also reduces road shock and vibrations.

The torsion bar power steering unit includes a worm and one-piece rack piston, which is meshed to the gear teeth on the steering sector shaft. The unit also includes a hydraulic valve, valve actuator, input shaft and torsion bar assembly which are mounted on the end of the worm shaft and operated by the twisting action of the torsion bar.

The torsion-bar type of power steering gear is designed with the one piece rack-piston, worm and sector shaft in one housing and the valve spool in an attaching housing (Fig. 1). This makes possible internal fluid passages between the valve and cylinder, thus eliminating all external lines and hoses, except the pressure and return hoses between the pump and gear assembly.

The power cylinder is an integral part of the gear housing. The piston is double acting, in that fluid pressure may be applied to either side of the piston.

A selective metal shim, located in the valve housing of the gear is for the purpose of tailoring steering gear efforts. If efforts are not within specifications they can be changed by increasing or decreasing shim thickness as follows:

Efforts heavy to the left—Increase shim thickness.

Efforts light to the left—Decrease shim thickness.

A change of one shim size will increase or decrease steering efforts

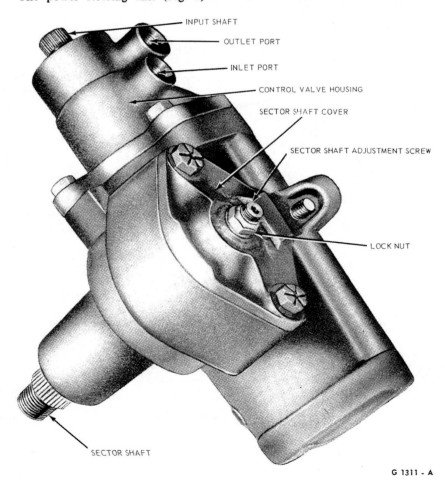

INPUT SHAFT

OUTLET PORT

INLET PORT

CONTROL VALVE HOUSING

SECTOR SHAFT COVER

SECTOR SHAFT ADJUSTMENT SCREW

LOCK NUT

SECTOR SHAFT

G 1311 - A

FIG. 1—Power Steering Gear

approximately 1½ in-lbs.

Shims are available in the following thicknesses:

0.0057-0.0063 inch
0.0077-0.0083 inch
0.0097-0.0103 inch
0.0117-0.0123 inch
0.0137-0.0143 inch

Do not use more than one shim. The operation of the hydraulic control valve spool is governed by the twisting of a torsion bar. All effort applied to the steering wheel is transmitted directly through the input shaft and torsion bar to the worm assembly and integral piston. Any resistance to the turning of the front wheels, results in twisting of the bar. The twisting of the bar increases as the front wheel turning effort increases. The control valve spool actuated by the twisting of the torsion bar, directs fluid to the side of the piston where hydraulic assist is required.

The upper end of the torsion bar is drilled and pinned to the input shaft. The lower end of the torsion bar is inserted into the worm, then drilled and pinned to the lower end of the worm, after the valve spool has been centered. The actuator is attached to the upper end of the worm by three helical splines. The valve spool is held on the actuator by a snap ring. The actuator is coarsely splined to the outside diameter of the input shaft. The coarse spline fit between the actuator and input shaft is sufficiently loose to allow upward and downward movement of the actuator and valve spool. As the torsion bar twists, its radial motion is transferred into axial motion by the three helical threads. Thus, the valve is moved off center, and fluid is directed to one side of the piston or the other.

The resistance of the torsion bar gives the driver a feel of the road, and at the same time the driver is receiving full power assist in steering.

OPERATION

Straight-Ahead Position (Neutral)

When the power unit is not assisting the steering effort, the valve spool is in the neutral (straight-ahead) position. The fluid flows from the pump through the inlet port of the steering gear to the center groove and over the lands of the valve, exhausting through holes in the outer grooves to the center of the valve and out the

exhaust port to the pump (Fig. 2). Therefore, no area of the valve spool or steering gear is under high pressure in this position. The amount of pressure in neutral position is approximately 50 psi at normal operating temperatures.

Right Turn

When the steering wheel is turned to the right, the piston on the worm resists being turned due to load on the sector shaft from the front end weight of the car. Thus, the torsion bar will start to twist.

For a right turn the valve spool moves up, allowing fluid from the pump to enter against the lower side of the power piston (Fig. 2). The fluid on the upper side of the piston is free to return through the valve to the pump. Therefore, the power assist is to the lower side of the piston, pushing it upward and providing assist in turning of the sector shaft.

Left Turn

If the steering wheel is turned to the left, it will cause a similar action but in the opposite direction. The torsion bar twists to the left moving the valve spool downward, allowing fluid from the pump to enter against the upper side of the power piston. The fluid on the lower side of the piston is free to return through the valve to the pump. Therefore, the power assist is to the upper side of the piston, pushing it downward. The instant the driver stops applying steering effort to the steering wheel the valve spool is returned to its neutral position by the unwinding of the torsion bar.

POWER STEERING PUMP

The power steering pump is a belt driven slipper type pump which is integral with the reservoir. It is constructed so that the reservoir is attached to the rear side of the pump housing front plate and the pump body is incased within the reservoir.

The pump rotor has 8 slippers and springs which rotate inside a cam insert containing two lobes 180° from each other. The cam insert and the pump port plates provide a sealed chamber within which the rotor and slippers rotate between the two lobes for pump operation.

As the rotor turns, the slippers are forced outward against the inner surface of the cam insert by a combination of centrifugal force, slipper spring force and fluid pressure acting

on the under side of the slipper. A pair of adjacent slippers, along with the surfaces of the rotor, cam and pressure plates, form a sealed chamber within the crescent-shaped void. As this sealed chamber moves through the crescent shaped void its volume changes, resulting in a pumping action.

As the rotor rotates 90° (Fig. 3), the slipper slides outward in its slot, riding on the cam and the volume of the sealed chamber increases. This creates a vacuum and sets up a suction area. With the inlet port placed in this area, the chamber will fill with fluid. As the rotor rotates from 90° to 180°, the volume of the sealed chamber decreases, thus creating a pressure area. The pressure or outlet port is located in this area. While this pumping action is going on between 0° and 180°, the same condition is occurring between 180° and 360°. This combination creates what is known as a balanced rotor pump. The two pressure and suction quadrants are diametrically opposite each other.

FLOW CONTROL VALVE

Since the pump is a constant displacement pump, the internal flow will vary directly with the pump speed. However, a power steering gear requires a relatively high constant rate of flow in the parking zone and up to approximately 2800 RPM and thereafter a lower rate of flow. This is accomplished by means of a variable orifice mechanism shown in Fig. 4.

All of the internal pump flow is ported from the pumping mechanism (rotor, slippers, and cam insert) through passage A into the flow control zone. All of the flow goes through the orifice and out into the line until the bypass port is cracked open. This is the regulation point. The oil drops in pressure in moving through the orifice. The lower pressure is then sensed through a hole drilled in the cover communicating to the rear of the spool valve. The differential in pressure thus created on the spool valve increases steadily and proportionally with increasing RPM and this moves the valve progressively back into its bore, thus increasing the opening of the bypass port.

The metering pin (Fig. 4) travels with the spool valve decreasing the net area of the orifice at higher speeds. This action reduces flow to the steering gear.

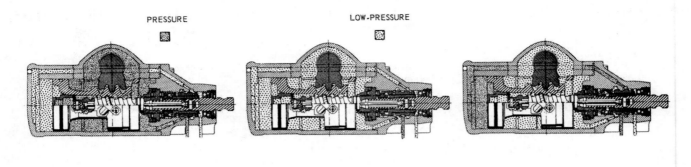

LEFT-TURN   STRAIGHT-AHEAD   RIGHT-TURN

G1275-A

FIG. 2—Power Flows

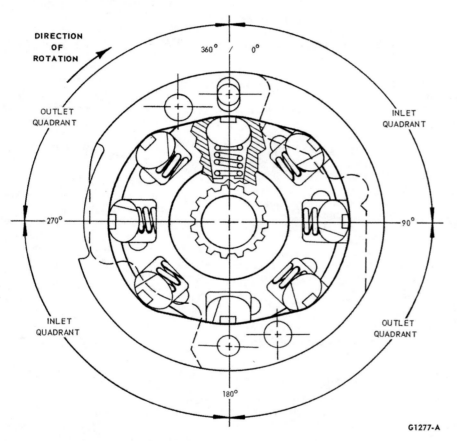

G1277-A

FIG. 3—Power Steering Pump Cycle

PRESSURE RELIEF VALVE

When the steering wheel is turned completely to the stop position in the right or left turn direction, or in the case of a road load of sufficient magnitude, the steering gear will not accept any flow from the pump, except for a very limited volume of oil due to leakage past valve seals. Because of this resistance, excessive hydraulic pressure would be developed, if it were not limited by the pressure relief valve.

When relief pressure is reached, the pressure relief ball is forced off its seat, allowing oil to pass through the spool valve and dump into the bypass port (Fig. 4). The relief valve will continue to limit oil pressure to the relief setting for the duration of the overload condition.

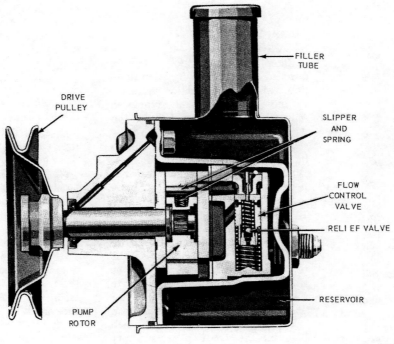

FILLER
TUBE

DRIVE
PULLEY

SLIPPER
AND
SPRING

FLOW
CONTROL
VALVE

RELIEF VALVE

RESERVOIR

PUMP
ROTOR

G1278-A

FIG. 4—Power Steering Pump—Sectional View

2 IN-CAR ADJUSTMENTS AND REPAIRS

VALVE SPOOL CENTERING CHECK

1. Install a 0-2000 psi pressure gauge Tool T56L-33610-D in the pressure line between the power steering pump outlet port and the integral steering gear inlet port.

2. **Make sure that the valve on the gauge is in the fully open position.**

3. Check the fluid level in the reservoir and fill it to the proper level with the specified fluid.

4. Start the engine and cycle the steering wheel from stop-to-stop, to bring the steering lubricant up to normal operating temperature. Stop the engine and recheck the reservoir. Add fluid if necessary.

5. With the engine running at approximately 1000 rpm and the steering wheel centered, attach an inch-pound torque wrench to the steering wheel retaining nut. Apply sufficient torque to the torque wrench in each direction, either side of center, to get a gauge reading of 250 psi.

6. The torque reading should be the same in both directions when 250 psi is reached. If the difference between the readings exceeds 4 in-lbs,

the steering gear must be removed and the valve centering shim removed from the valve housing and a thicker or thinner shim installed. Only one shim is to be used. If the steering effort is heavy to the left the shim thickness should be increased. Shim thickness should be decreased if the steering effort is light to the left.

The **out of car** procedure for valve centering check is the same as for the **In car** except the torque and simultaneous pressure reading must be made at the right and left stops instead of either side of center.

STEERING GEAR ADJUSTMENTS

During the vehicle breaking-in period, it is probable that some of the factory adjustments will change. These changes in adjustment do not necessarily affect the satisfactory operation of the steering gear assembly, and therefore ordinarily do not require readjustment unless there is excessive lash or other malfunctioning.

ADJUSTMENT IN CAR

The only adjustment which can be performed is the total over center

position load, to eliminate excessive lash between the sector and rack teeth.

1. Disconnect the pitman arm from the sector shaft.

2. Disconnect the fluid return line at the reservoir, at the same time cap the reservoir return line pipe.

3. Place the end of the return line in a clean container and cycle the steering wheel in both directions as required, to discharge the fluid from the gear.

4. Remove the ornamental cover from the steering wheel hub and turn the steering wheel to 45° from the left stop.

5. Using an inch-pound torque wrench on the steering wheel nut, determine the torque required to rotate the shaft slowly through an approximately ⅛ turn from the 45° position.

6. Turn the steering gear back to center, then determine the torque required to rotate the shaft back and forth across the center position. Loosen the adjuster nut, and turn the adjuster screw in (Fig. 5) until the reading is 8-9 in-lb greater than the torque 45° from the stop.

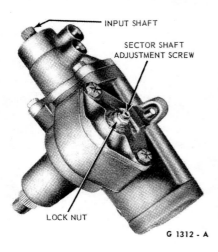

INPUT SHAFT

SECTOR SHAFT
ADJUSTMENT SCREW

LOCK NUT

G 1312 - A

FIG. 5—Adjusting Mesh Load

Tighten the lock nut while holding the screw in place.

7. Recheck the readings and replace pitman arm and steering wheel hub cover.

8. Connect the fluid return line to the reservoir and fill the reservoir

with specified lubricant to the proper level.

PUMP BELT TENSION ADJUSTMENT

Pump drive belt tension cannot be checked accurately using the thumb pressure or belt deflection methods. Correct belt adjustment is assured only with the use of a belt tension gauge.

1. Check the belt tension with a belt tension gauge tool T63L-8620-A. With a new belt, or one that has been run for less than 15 minutes, the tension should be within 120-150 lbs. With a belt that has been run for more than 15 minutes, the tension should be within 90-120 lbs.

2. To adjust the belt, loosen the mounting bolts incorporated on the front face of the pump cover plate (hub side) and one nut at the rear of the reservoir. Fix a $9/16$ inch open end wrench on the projecting $\frac{1}{2}$ inch boss on the cover plate and pry upward to correct tension.

Do not pry against the reservoir to obtain proper belt load as it can be deformed and cause a leak.

3. Recheck the belt tension. When the tension has been correctly adjusted, tighten the bolts and the nut to specification (Part 3-6).

POWER STEERING PUMP DRIVE BELT REPLACEMENT

1. Loosen the idler pulley retaining bolts and remove the compressor drive belt.

2. Loosen 3 bolts and one nut attaching the power steering pump to the pump bracket, and remove the pump drive belt.

3. Position the power steering pump drive belt on the pulleys.

4. Adjust the drive belt tension as outlined in Section 2 to specification (Part 3-6) and tighten the pump attaching bolts and one nut to specification.

5. Install the compressor drive belt and adjust to specification (Part 16-7).

3 REMOVAL AND INSTALLATION

STEERING GEAR

REMOVAL

1. Disconnect the pressure and the return lines from the steering gear. Plug the lines and the ports in the gear to prevent entry of dirt.

2. Remove the two bolts that secure the flex coupling to the steering gear and to the column.

3. Raise the car and remove the sector shaft attaching nut.

4. Remove the Pitman arm from the sector shaft with Tool T64P-3590-F. Remove the tool from the Pitman arm.

5. If working on a car equipped with a standard transmission, remove the clutch release lever retracting spring to provide clearance for removing the steering gear.

6. Support the steering gear then remove the three steering gear attaching bolts.

7. Work the steering gear free of the flex coupling and remove it from the car.

8. If the flex coupling stayed on the input shaft, lift it off the shaft at this time.

INSTALLATION

1. Slide the flex coupling into place

on the steering shaft. Turn the steering wheel so that the spokes are in the horizontal position.

2. Center the steering gear input shaft.

3. Slide the steering gear input shaft into the flex coupling and into place on the frame side rail. Install the three attaching bolts and torque them to specification.

4. Make sure that the wheels are in the straight ahead position, then install the Pitman arm on the sector shaft. Install and tighten the sector shaft attaching nut to specification.

5. Move the flex coupling into place on the input shaft and steering column shaft and install and tighten the attaching bolts to specification.

6. Connect and tighten the oil pressures and the return lines to the steering gear.

7. Fill the power steering pump and cycle the steering gear. Check for leaks and again check the fluid level. Add fluid as required.

POWER STEERING PUMP REPLACEMENT

EIGHT CYLINDER WITHOUT AIR CONDITIONER AND ALL SIX CYLINDER

1. Remove the power steering fluid

from the pump reservoir by disconnecting the fluid return hose at the reservoir, and allow the fluid to drain into a suitable container.

2. Disconnect the pressure hose from the pump.

3. Remove 3 bolts from the front of the pump and the one nut at the rear that attach the pump to the mounting bracket; disconnect the belt from the pulley and remove the pump from the car.

4. Position the pump to the mounting bracket and install the 3 bolts at the front of pump and the 1 nut at the rear. Torque to specification.

5. Place the belt on the pulley and adjust the belt tension (Section 2) with Tool T63L-8620-A and tighten the bolts and nut to specifications.

6. Torque the pressure hose fitting hex nut to specification. Then, connect the pressure hose to the fitting and torque the hose nut to specification.

7. Place a new clamp on the return hose and connect the hose to the pump. Then, tighten the clamp.

8. Fill the power steering pump reservoir with transmission fluid C1AZ-19582-A and cycle the system to remove air from the steering gear system.

9. Check for leaks and again check the fluid level. Add fluid as necessary.

EIGHT CYLINDER WITH AIR CONDITIONER

1. Remove the power steering fluid from the pump reservoir by disconnecting the fluid return hose from the reservoir and allow the fluid to drain in a suitable container.

2. Disconnect the pressure hose from the pump.

3. Remove 3 bolts from the front of the pump and the one nut at the rear that attach the pump to the mounting bracket and remove the drive belt from the pump pulley.

4. Loosen the lower pump bracket to engine attaching bolts and remove the other 2 bracket to engine attaching bolts and remove the pump.

5. Position the pump to the bracket and install the bracket to engine attaching bolts. Tighten the bolt that was loosened and the other bolts to specifications.

6. Place the belt on the pump pulley and install the pump attaching bolts and nut. Adjust the belt tension as outlined in Section 2 and tighten the bolts and nut to specification.

7. Torque the pressure hose fitting hex nut to specification. Then, connect the pressure hose to the fitting and torque the hose nut to specification.

8. Connect the return hose to the power steering pump and tighten the clamp.

9. Fill the pump with automatic transmission fluid C1AZ-19582-A. Bleed the air from the system (Part 3-1) and check for leaks and again check the fluid level. Add fluid as required.

POWER STEERING PUMP PULLEY

Other than pulley removal and reservoir replacement, the pump should not be disassembled for any repairs but replaced as a unit.

REMOVAL

1. Drain as much of the fluid as possible from the pump through filler pipe.

2. Install a ⅜-16 inch capscrew in the end of the pump shaft to prevent damage to the shaft end by the tool screw.

3. Install the pulley remover, Tool T63L-10300-B on pulley hub, and place the tool and pump in a vise as shown in Fig. 6.

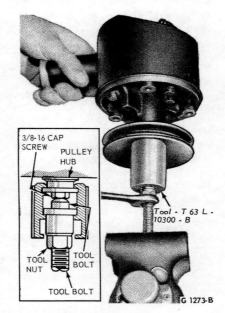

FIG. 6—Removing Power Steering Pump Pulley

4. Hold the pump and rotate the tool nut counterclockwise to remove the pulley (Fig. 6). **The pulley must**

FIG. 7—Installing Power Steering Pump Pulley

be removed without in and out pressure on the pump shaft to prevent damage to internal thrust areas.

INSTALLATION

1. Position the pulley to the pump shaft and install Tool T65P-3A733-A as shown in Fig. 7.

2. Hold the pump and rotate the tool nut clockwise to install the pulley on the shaft. The pulley face will be flush with end of pump shaft. In-

stall the pulley without in and out pressure on the shaft to prevent damage to internal thrust areas.

3. Remove the tool.

POWER STEERING PUMP RESERVOIR REPLACEMENT

Reservoir replacement must be done on a clean workbench. Cleanliness of work area and tools is extremely important when repairing any hydraulic unit. Thoroughly clean the exterior of the pump with a suitable cleaning solvent. **Do not immerse the shaft oil seal in solvent.** Plug the inlet and outlet openings with plugs or masking tape before cleaning the pump exterior or removing the reservoir.

REMOVAL

1. Position the pump in a bench mounted holding fixture, Tool T57L-500-A.

2. Rotate the pump so the pulley side is facing down and remove the outlet fitting hex nut, stud nuts, and the service identification tag.

3. Invert the pump so the pulley side is facing up and remove the reservoir by tapping around the flange with a wood block (Fig. 8).

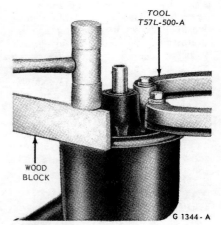

FIG. 8—Removing Pump Reservoir

4. Remove the reservoir O-ring seal, the outlet fitting gasket, and the support stud copper gasket from the pump.

INSTALLATION

1. Install a new gasket on the outlet fitting, a new copper gasket on the support stud, and a new reservoir O-ring seal on the pump housing plate (Fig. 9). **The old gaskets and seal should never be re-used.**

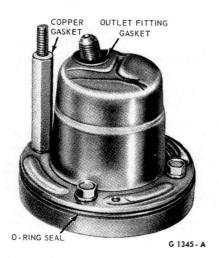

COPPER GASKET   OUTLET FITTING GASKET

O-RING SEAL

G 1345 - A

FIG. 9—Gasket Locations

2. Apply vaseline to the reservoir

O-ring seal and to the inside edge of the new reservoir flange. **Do not twist the O-ring seal.**

3. Position the reservoir over the pump and align the reservoir with the outlet fitting and the stud hole.

4. Install the reservoir on the pump and O-ring seal with a plastic or rubber hammer and a block of wood as shown in Fig. 10. **Tap at the rear of the reservoir and on the outer edges only.**

5. Inspect the assembly to be sure the reservoir is evenly seated on the pump housing plate.

6. Position the service identification tag on the outlet fitting and install the outlet fitting hex nut. Torque the nut to specification (Part 3-6). **Do not exceed specification.**

7. Install the stud nut and torque to specification.

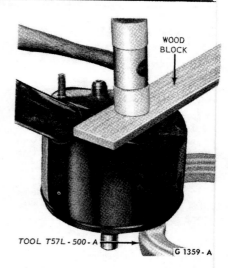

WOOD BLOCK

TOOL T57L - 500 - A

G 1359 - A

FIG. 10—Installing Reservoir on Pump

4 MAJOR REPAIR OPERATIONS

STEERING GEAR

In most cases, complete disassembly of the power steering unit will not be necessary. It is suggested that only those assemblies that are faulty be disassembled. Diassembly and reassembly of the unit and the subassemblies must be made on a clean workbench. As in repairing any hydraulically operated unit, cleanliness is of utmost importance. Therefore, the bench, tools, and parts must be kept clean at all times. Thoroughly clean the exterior of the unit with a suitable solvent and, when necessary, drain as much of the hydraulic oil as possible. Handle all parts very carefully to avoid nicks, burrs, scratches and dirt, which could make the parts unfit for use.

VALVE CENTERING SHIM REPLACEMENT

1. Hold the steering gear over a drain pan in an inverted position and cycle the input shaft six times to drain the remaining fluid from the gear.

2. Mount the gear in a soft-jawed vise.

3. Turn the input shaft to either stop then, turn it back approximately 1¾ turns to center the gear.

4. Remove the two sector shaft cover attaching screws and the identification tag.

5. Tap the lower end of the sector shaft with a soft-faced hammer to loosen it, then lift the cover and shaft

from the housing as an assembly. Discard the O-ring.

6. Remove the four valve housing attaching bolts. Lift the valve housing from the steering gear housing while holding the piston to prevent it from rotating off the worm shaft.

7. Remove the valve housing and the lube passage O-rings and discard them.

8. Place the valve housing, worm and piston assembly in the bench mounted holding fixture Tool T57L-500-A with the piston on the top.

9. Rotate the piston upward (back off) 3½ turns.

10. Insert Tool T66P-3553-C (with the arm facing away from the piston) into a bolt hole in the valve housing. Rotate the arm into position under the piston (Fig. 11).

11. Using Tool T66P-3553-B, loosen the worm bearing lock nut (Fig. 11).

12. Hold the lock nut up out of the way and loosen the attaching nut (Fig. 12).

13. Lift the piston-worm assembly from the valve housing. **During removal hold the worm to prevent it from spinning off of the shaft.**

14. Change the power steering valve centering shim.

15. Install the piston-worm assembly into the valve housing. **Hold the worm to prevent it from spinning off of the shaft.**

16. Install the valve housing at-

taching nut and torque to specification (Fig. 13).

17. Install the power steering worm bearing lock nut with Tool T66P-3553-B and torque to specification.

18. Rotate piston upward (back off) ½ turn and remove Tool T66P-3553-C.

19. Remove the valve housing, worm, and piston assembly from the holding fixture.

20. Position a new lube passage O-ring in the counterbore of the gear housing.

21. Apply vaseline to the teflon seal on the piston.

22. Place a new O-ring on the valve housing.

23. Slide the piston and valve into the gear housing being careful not to damage the teflon seal.

24. Align the lube passage in the valve housing with the one in the gear housing, and install but do not tighten the attaching bolts.

25. Rotate the ball nut so that the teeth are in the same place as the sector teeth. Tighten the four valve housing attaching bolts to specification.

26. Position the sector shaft cover O-ring in the steering gear housing. Turn the input shaft as required to center the piston.

27. Apply vaseline to the sector shaft journal; then, position the sector shaft and cover assembly in the gear housing. Install the steering

FIG. 11—Removing Worm Bearing Lock Nut

Tool—T66P-3553-C
Tool—T66P-3553-B
G1365-A

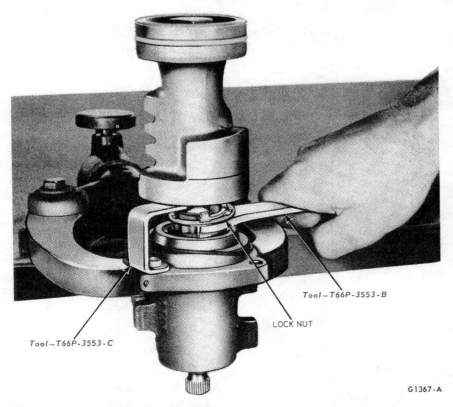

FIG. 12—Removing Valve Housing Retaining Nut

Tool—T66P-3553-C
Tool—T66P-3553-B
LOCK NUT
G1367-A

gear identification tag and air conditioner line mounting bracket, if so equipped, and the two sector shaft cover attaching bolts.

28. Position an inch-pound torque wrench on the gear input shaft and adjust the meshload to approximately 4 in-lbs. Then, torque the sector shaft cover attaching bolts to specification (Part 3-6).

29. After the cover attaching bolts have been tightened to specification, adjust the meshload to specification with an in-lb torque wrench.

STEERING GEAR DISASSEMBLY

1. Hold the steering gear over a drain pan in an inverted position and cycle the input shaft six times to drain the remaining fluid from the gear.

2. Mount the gear in a soft-jawed vise.

3. Remove the lock nut and the brass washer from the adjusting screw.

4. Turn the input shaft to either stop then, turn it back approximately 1¾ turns to center the gear.

5. Remove the two sector shaft cover attaching screws and the identification tag.

6. Tap the lower end of the sector shaft with a soft-faced hammer to loosen it, then lift the cover and shaft from the housing as an assembly. Discard the O-ring.

7. Turn the sector shaft cover counterclockwise off the adjuster screw.

8. Remove the four valve housing attaching bolts. Lift the valve housing from the steering gear housing while holding the piston to prevent it from rotating off the worm shaft. Remove the valve housing and the lube passage O-rings and discard them.

9. Stand the valve body and piston on end with the piston end down. Rotate the input shaft counterclockwise out of the piston allowing the ball bearings to drop into the piston.

10. Place a cloth over the open end of the piston and turn it upside down to remove the balls.

11. Remove the two screws that attach the ball guide clamp (Fig. 14) to the ball nut and remove the clamp and the guides.

12. Install valve body assembly in holding fixture (Do not clamp in a vise) and remove the lock nut and the retaining nut as shown in Fig. 15.

13. Carefully slide the input shaft, worm and valve assembly out of the valve housing. Due to the close diametrical clearance between the spool

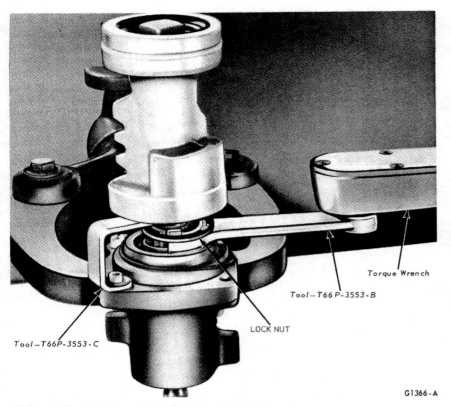

Tool—T66P-3553-C

Tool—T66P-3553-B

LOCK NUT

Torque Wrench

G1366-A

FIG. 13—Installing Valve Housing Retaining Nut

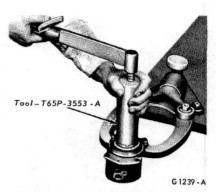

Tool—T65P-3553-A

G1239-A

FIG. 15—Removing or Installing Lock Nut

from the rear of the valve housing with Tool T59L-100-B and T58L-101-A and discard the seal.

2. Remove the snap ring from the valve housing.

3. Turn the fixture to place the valve housing in an inverted position.

4. Insert special tool in the valve body assembly, opposite the seal end and gently tap the bearing and seal out of the housing as shown in Fig. 17. Discard the seal. **Caution must be exercised when inserting and removing the tool to prevent damage to the valve bore in the housing.**

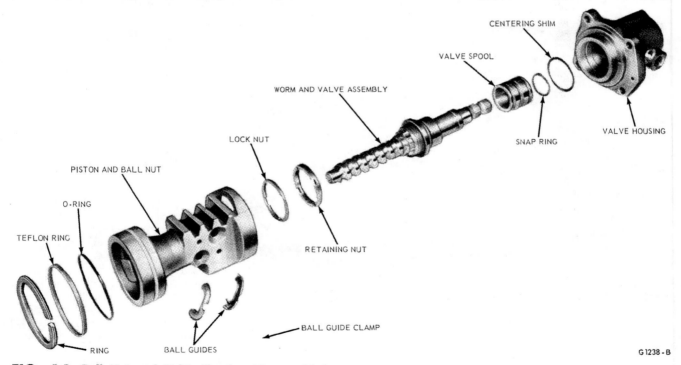

CENTERING SHIM

VALVE SPOOL

WORM AND VALVE ASSEMBLY

VALVE HOUSING

SNAP RING

LOCK NUT

PISTON AND BALL NUT

O-RING

RETAINING NUT

TEFLON RING

BALL GUIDE CLAMP

RING

BALL GUIDES

G1238-B

FIG. 14—Ball Nut and Valve Housing Disassembled

and housing, the slightest cocking of the spool may cause it to jam in the housing.

14. Remove the shim from the valve housing bore.

PARTS REPAIR OR REPLACEMENT

Valve Housing

1. Remove the dust seal (Fig. 16)

5. Remove the oil inlet and outlet tube seats with an EZ-out if they are damaged.

6. Coat the oil inlet and outlet tube seats with vaseline and position

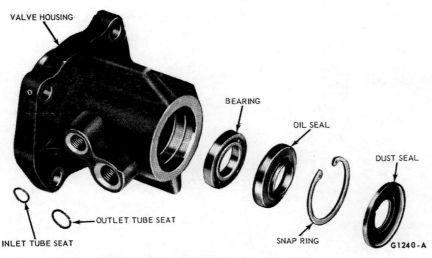

VALVE HOUSING

BEARING

OIL SEAL

DUST SEAL

SNAP RING

OUTLET TUBE SEAT

INLET TUBE SEAT

G1240-A

FIG. 16—Valve Housing Disassembled

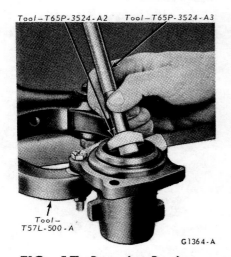

Tool—T65P-3524-A2   Tool—T65P-3524-A3

Tool—T57L-500-A

G1364-A

FIG. 17—Removing Bearing and Oil Seal

Press Ram

Tool—T65P-3524-A1

G1363-A

FIG. 18—Installing Valve Housing Bearing

Press Ram

Tool—T65P-3524-A1

G1362-A

FIG. 19—Installing Oil Seal in Valve Housing

them in the housing. Install and tighten the tube nuts to press the seats to the proper location.

7. Coat the bearing and seal surface of the housing with a film of vaseline.

8. Position the bearing in the valve housing. Seat the bearing in the housing with the tool shown in Fig. 18. Make sure that the bearing is free to rotate.

9. **Dip the new oil seal in gear lubricant;** then, place it in the housing with the metal side of the seal facing outward. Drive the seal into the housing until the outer edge of seal does not quite clear the snap ring groove (Fig. 19).

10. Place the snap ring in the housing; then, drive on the ring with the tool shown in Fig. 19 until the snap ring seats in its groove to properly locate the seal.

11. Place the dust seal in the housing with the dished side (rubber

side) facing out. Drive the dust seal into place with the tool shown in Fig. 19. The seal must be located behind the undercut in the input shaft when it is installed.

Worm and Valve

1. Remove the snap ring from the end of the actuator.

2. Slide the control valve spool (Fig. 14) off the actuator.

3. Install valve spool evenly and slowly with a slight oscillating motion into flanged end of valve housing with valve identification groove between the valve spool lands outward, checking for freedom of valve movement within housing working area. Valve spool should enter housing bore freely and fall by its own weight.

4. If valve spool is not free, check for burrs at the outward edges of the working lands in the housing and remove with a hard stone.

5. Check valve for burrs and if burrs are found, stone valve in a **radial direction only.** Check for freedom of valve again.

6. Remove valve spool from housing.

7. Slide the spool onto the actuator making sure that the groove in the spool annulus is toward the worm.

8. Install the snap ring to retain the spool.

9. Check the clearance between the spool and the snap ring. The clearance should be between 0.002-0.005 inch. If the clearance is not within these limits, select a snap ring that will allow a clearance of 0.003 inch.

Piston and Ball Nut

1. Remove the teflon ring and the O-ring (Fig. 14) from the piston and ball nut.

2. Dip a new O-ring in gear lubricant and install it on the piston and ball nut.

3. Install a new teflon ring on the piston and ball nut being careful not to stretch it any more than necessary.

Steering Gear Housing

1. Remove the snap ring and the spacer washer (Fig. 20) from the lower end of the steering gear housing.

2. Remove the lower seal from the housing as shown in Fig. 21. Lift the spacer washer from the housing.

3. Remove the upper seal in the same manner as the lower seal.

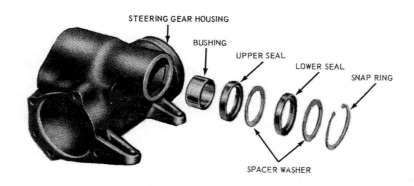

G 1309 - A

FIG. 20—Steering Gear Housing Disassembled

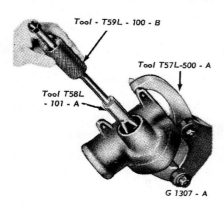

G 1307 - A

FIG. 21—Removing Lower Seal

4. Place the steering gear housing on blocks in a press as shown in Fig. 22 and press the bushing from the housing if worn or defective. Make sure that the blocks are positioned to clear the tool as it passes through the housing.

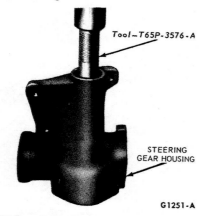

G1251-A

FIG. 22—Removing Steering Gear Housing Bushing—Typical

5. Press the bushing into place with the tools shown in Fig. 23.
6. **Dip both sector shaft seals in gear lubricant.**
7. Apply Lubricant to the sector

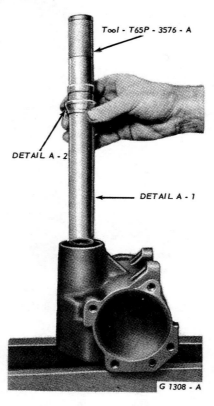

G 1308 - A

FIG. 23—Installing Bushing in Steering Gear Housing

shaft seal bore of the housing and position the sector shaft inner seal into the housing with the lip facing inward. Press the seal into place with the tool shown in Fig. 24. Place a spacer washer (0.090 inch) on top of the seal and apply more Lubricant to the housing bore.

8. Place the outer seal in the housing with the lip facing inward and press it into place as shown in Fig. 25. Then, place a 0.090 inch spacer washer on top of the seal.
9. Position the snap ring in the housing. Press the snap ring into the

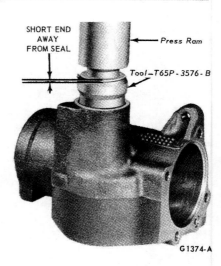

G 1374-A

FIG. 24—Installing Sector Shaft Inner Seal

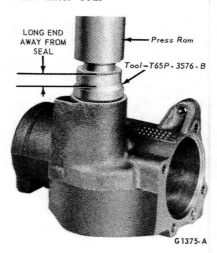

G 1375-A

FIG. 25—Installing Sector Shaft Outer Seal

housing with the tool shown in Fig. 25 to properly locate the seals and engage the snap ring in the groove.

STEERING GEAR ASSEMBLY

1. Mount the valve housing in the holding fixture with the flanged end up.
2. Place the required thickness valve spool centering shim (Fig. 14) in the housing. **Use one shim only.**
3. Carefully install the worm and valve in the housing.
4. Install the attaching nut in the housing and torque it to specification (Part 3-6) (Fig. 15).
5. Install the lock nut and torque it to specification (Part 3-6).
6. Place the piston on the bench with the ball guide holes facing up. Insert the worm shaft into the piston so that the first groove is in align-

ment with the hole nearest to the center of the piston (Fig. 26).

7. Place the ball guide in the piston. Place the 27 balls in the ball guide (Fig. 26) turning the worm in

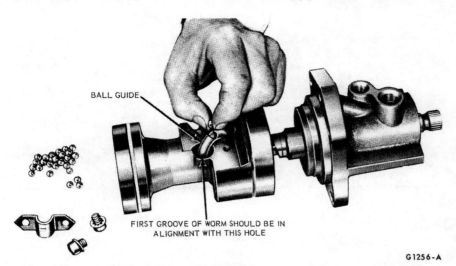

BALL GUIDE

FIRST GROOVE OF WORM SHOULD BE IN ALIGNMENT WITH THIS HOLE

G1256-A

FIG. 26—Assembling Piston on Worm Shaft

a clockwise direction as viewed from the input end of the shaft. If all of the balls have not been fed into the guide upon reaching the right stop, rotate the input shaft in one direction and then in the other while installing the balls. After the balls have been installed, do not rotate the input shaft or the piston more than 3½ turns off the right stop to prevent the balls from falling out of the circuit.

8. Secure the guides in the ball

nut with the clamp (Fig. 14).

9. Position a new lube passage O-ring in the counterbore of the gear housing.

10. Apply vaseline to the teflon seal on the piston.

11. Place a new O-ring on the valve housing.

12. Slide the piston and valve into the gear housing being careful not to damage the teflon seal.

13. Align the lube passage in the valve housing with the one in the gear housing, and install but do not tighten the attaching bolts.

14. Rotate the ball nut so that the teeth are in the same plane as the sector teeth. Tighten the four valve

housing attaching bolts to specifications.

15. Position the sector shaft cover O-ring in the steering gear housing. Turn the input shaft as required to center the piston.

16. Apply vaseline to the sector shaft journal then position the sector shaft and cover assembly in the gear housing. Install the steering identification tag and air conditioner line mounting bracket if so equipped and two sector shaft cover attaching bolts. Torque the bolts to specifications.

17. Attach an in-lb torque wrench to the input shaft. Adjust the mesh load to specifications as shown in Fig. 27.

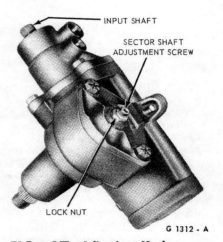

INPUT SHAFT

SECTOR SHAFT ADJUSTMENT SCREW

LOCK NUT

G 1312 - A

FIG. 27—Adjusting Mesh Load

PART 3-5 WHEELS AND TIRES

1 DESCRIPTION AND OPERATION

FRONT WHEEL ASSEMBLY

Each front wheel and tire assembly is bolted to its respective front hub and brake drum or rotor assembly. Two opposed tapered roller bearings are installed in each hub. A grease retainer is installed at the inner end of the hub to prevent lubricant from leaking into the drum or on the rotor. The entire assembly is retained to its spindle by the adjusting nut, nut lock and cotter pin (Figs. 1 and 2). The front wheel assemblies rotate freely on their respective spindles and are driven by the motion of the car.

REAR WHEEL ASSEMBLY

The rear wheel hub and brake drum assembly is retained to studs on

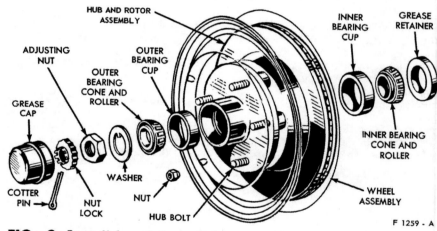

FIG. 2—Front Hub and Rotor, Bearings, and Grease Retainer

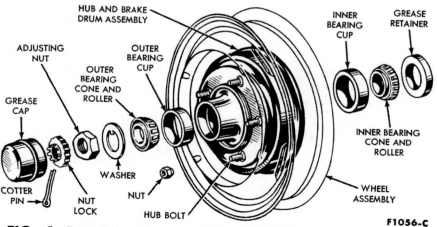

FIG. 1—Front Hub, Bearings and Grease Retainer

the rear axle shaft flange by three speed nuts (Part 3-2, Fig. 2). The wheel and tire assembly mounts on the same rear axle shaft flange studs and is held against the hub and drum by the wheel nuts. The rear wheel bearing is pressed onto the axle shaft just inside the shaft flange, and the entire assembly is retained to the rear axle housing by the bearing retainer plate which is bolted to the housing flange.

The inner end of each axle shaft is splined to the engine powered differential. The rear wheels are, therefore, driven by the engine.

2   IN-CAR ADJUSTMENTS AND REPAIRS

HOISTING INSTRUCTIONS

Damage to steering linkage components and front suspension struts may occur if care is not exercised when positioning the hoist adapters of 2 post hoists prior to lifting the car.

If a 2 post hoist is used to lift the car, place the adapters under the lower arms or the No. 1 crossmember. Do not allow the adapters to contact the steering linkage. If the adapters are placed under the crossmember, a piece of wood (2x4x16 inches) should be placed on the hoist channel between the adapters. This will prevent the adapters from damaging the front suspension struts.

FRONT WHEEL BEARING ADJUSTMENT

The front wheel bearings should be adjusted if the wheel is loose on the spindle or if the wheel does not rotate freely. The following procedures will bring the bearing adjustment to specification.

DRUM BRAKES

1. Raise the car until the wheel and tire clear the floor.
2. Pry off the hub cap or wheel cover and remove the grease cap (Fig. 1) from the hub.
3. Wipe the excess grease from the end of the spindle, and remove the cotter pin and nut lock.
4. While rotating the wheel, hub, and drum assembly, torque the adjusting nut to 17-25 ft-lbs to seat the bearings (Fig. 3).
5. Locate the nut lock on the adjusting nut so that the castellations on the lock are aligned with the cotter pin hole in the spindle.
6. Using a 1⅛-inch box wrench, back off both the adjusting nut and the nut lock together until the next castellation on the nut lock aligns

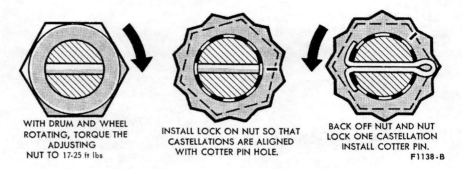

WITH DRUM AND WHEEL ROTATING, TORQUE THE ADJUSTING NUT TO 17-25 ft lbs   INSTALL LOCK ON NUT SO THAT CASTELLATIONS ARE ALIGNED WITH COTTER PIN HOLE.   BACK OFF NUT AND NUT LOCK ONE CASTELLATION INSTALL COTTER PIN.

F1138-B

FIG. 3—Front Wheel Bearing Adjustment

with cotter pin hole in the spindle.

7. Install a new cotter pin, and bend the ends of the cotter pin around the castellated flange of the nut lock.
8. Check the front wheel rotation. If the wheel rotates properly, install the grease cap and the hub cap or wheel cover. If the wheel still rotates roughly or noisily, clean, inspect or replace the bearings and cups as required.

DISC BRAKES

1. Raise the car until the wheel and tire clear the floor.
2. Pry off the wheel cover and remove the grease cap (Fig. 2) from the hub.
3. Wipe the excess grease from the end of the spindle, and remove the adjusting nut cotter pin and nut lock.
4. Loosen the bearing adjusting nut three turns. Then, rock the wheel, hub, and rotor assembly in and out several times to push the shoe and linings away from the rotor.
5. While rotating the wheel, hub,

and rotor assembly, torque the adjusting nut to 17-25 ft-lbs to seat the bearings (Fig. 3).

6. Locate the nut lock on the adjusting nut so that the castellations on the lock are aligned with the cotter pin hole in the spindle.
7. Using a 1⅛-inch box wrench, back off both the adjusting nut and the nut lock together until the next castellation on the nut lock aligns with the cotter pin hole in the spindle.
8. Install a new cotter pin, and bend the ends of the cotter pin around the castellated flange of the nut lock.
9. Check the front wheel rotation. If the wheel rotates properly, install the grease cap and the hub cap or wheel cover. If the wheel still rotates roughly or noisily, clean or replace the bearings and cups as required.
10. Before driving the car, pump the brake pedal several times to obtain normal brake lining to rotor clearance and restore normal brake pedal travel.

3   REMOVAL AND INSTALLATION

HOISTING INSTRUCTIONS

Damage to steering linkage components and front suspension struts may occur if care is not exercised when positioning the hoist adapters of 2 post hoists prior to lifting the car.

If a 2 post hoist is used to lift the car, place the adapters under the

lower arms or the No. 1 crossmember. Do not allow the adapters to contact the steering linkage. If the adapters are placed under the crossmember, a piece of wood (2x4x16 inches) should be placed on the hoist channel between the adapters. This will prevent the adapters from damaging the front suspension struts.

WHEEL AND TIRE ASSEMBLY
WHEEL AND TIRE REMOVAL

1. Pry off the wheel hub cap or cover. Loosen but do not remove the wheel hub nuts.
2. Raise the car until the wheel and tire clear the floor.
3. Remove the wheel hub nuts from the bolts, and pull the wheel and tire assembly from hub and drum.

REMOVING TIRE FROM WHEEL

The tire can be demounted on a mounting machine. **Be sure that the outer side of the wheel is positioned downward.** If tire irons are used follow the procedure given here.

1. Remove the valve cap and core, and deflate the tire completely.

2. With a bead loosening tool, break loose the tire side walls from the wheel (Fig. 4).

FIG. 4—Bead Loosening Tool

3. **Position the outer side of the wheel downward,** and insert two tire irons about eight inches apart between the tire inner bead and the back side of the wheel rim. **Use only tire irons with rounded edges or irons designed for removing tubeless tires.**

4. Leave one tire iron in position, and pry the rest of the bead over the rim with the other iron. Take small "bites" with the iron around the tire

in order to avoid damaging the sealing surface of the tire bead.

5. Stand the wheel and tire upright with the tire outer bead in the drop center well at the bottom of the wheel. Insert the tire iron between the bead and the edge of the wheel rim, and pry the wheel out of the tire.

MOUNTING TIRE TO WHEEL

1. If a used tire is being installed remove all dirt from the tire.

If a tire is being mounted to the original wheel, clean the rim with emery cloth or fine steel wool. Check the rim for dents.

If a new wheel is being installed, coat a new valve with RUGLYDE or similar rubber lubricant and position the valve to the new wheel. Use a rubber hammer or a valve replacing tool to seat the valve firmly against the inside of the rim.

2. Apply RUGLYDE or a similar rubber lubricant to the sealing surface on both tire beads. With the outer side of the wheel down, pry the beads over the wheel rim with two tire irons. **Do not use a hammer or mallet to force the beads over the rim.**

3. Align the balance mark on the tire with the valve on the wheel.

4. Hold the beads against the rim flanges by positioning a tire mounting band over the tire (Fig. 5). If a mounting band is not available, tie a tourniquet of heavy cord around the circumference of the tire. Tighten the

F1021-A

FIG. 5—Tubeless Tire Mounting Band

cord with a tire iron. Center the tire on the wheel with a rubber mallet.

5. Give the tire a few quick bursts of air to seat the beads properly, then inflate the tire to 40 psi pressure. Check to see that the bead positioning rings (outer rings near the side walls) are evenly visible just above the rim flanges all the way around the tire. If the rings are not even, deflate the tire completely and inflate it again.

6. When the rings are properly positioned, deflate the tire to the recommended pressure.

WHEEL AND TIRE INSTALLATION

1. Clean all dirt from the hub and drum.

2. Position the wheel and tire assembly on the hub and drum. Install the wheel hub nuts and tighten them alternately in order to draw the wheel evenly against the hub and drum.

3. Lower the car to the floor, and torque the hub nuts to specification.

4 MAJOR REPAIR OPERATIONS

HOISTING INSTRUCTIONS

Damage to steering linkage components and front suspension struts may occur if care is not exercised when positioning the hoist adapters of 2 post hoists prior to lifting the car.

If a 2 post hoist is used to lift the car, place the adapters under the lower arms or the No. 1 crossmember. Do not allow the *adapters to* contact the steering linkage. If the *adapters* are placed under the crossmember, a piece of wood (2x4x16 inches) should be placed on the hoist channel between the adapters. This will prevent the adapters from damaging the front suspension struts.

FRONT WHEEL GREASE SEAL AND BEARING REPLACEMENT AND/OR REPACKING

If bearing adjustment will not

eliminate looseness or rough and noisy operation, the hub and bearings should be cleaned, inspected, and repacked. If the bearing cups or the cone and roller assemblies are worn or damaged, they should be replaced.

DRUM BRAKES

1. Raise the car until the wheel and tire clear the floor.

2. Remove the wheel cover or hub cap. Remove the grease cap from the hub. Remove the cotter pin, nut lock, adjusting nut, and flat washer from the spindle. Remove the outer bearing cone and roller assembly (Fig. 1).

3. Pull the wheel, hub, and drum assembly off the wheel spindle.

4. Remove the grease retainer and the inner bearing cone and roller

assembly from the hub with tool 1175AE.

5. Clean the lubricant off the inner and outer bearing cups with solvent and inspect the cups for scratches, pits, excessive wear, and other damage. If the cups are worn or damaged, remove them with a drift.

6. Soak a new grease retainer in light engine oil at least 30 minutes before installation. Thoroughly clean the inner and outer bearing cones and rollers with solvent and dry them thoroughly. **Do not spin the bearings with compressed air.**

Inspect the cone and roller assemblies for wear or damage, and replace them if necessary. **The cone and roller assemblies and the bear-**

ing cups should be replaced as a unit if damage to either is encountered.

7. Thoroughly clean the spindle and the inside of the hub with solvent to remove all old lubricant.

Cover the spindle with a clean cloth, and brush all loose dust and dirt from the brake assembly. **To prevent getting dirt on the spindle, carefully remove the cloth from the spindle.**

8. If the inner and/or outer bearing cup(s) were removed, install the replacement cup(s) in the hub with the tool shown in Fig. 6. **Be sure to seat the cups properly in the hub.**

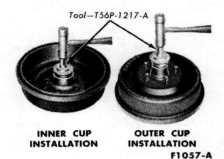

Tool—T56P-1217-A

INNER CUP INSTALLATION   OUTER CUP INSTALLATION

F1057-A

FIG. 6—Installing Front Wheel Drum Bearing Cups

9. Pack the inside of the hub with specified wheel bearing grease. Add lubricant to the hub only until the grease is flush with the inside diameter of both bearing cups (Fig. 7).

10. All old grease should be completely cleaned from the bearings before repacking them with new grease. Pack the bearing cone and roller assemblies with wheel bearing grease. A bearing packer is desirable for this operation. If a packer is not available, work as much lubricant as possible between the rollers and cages. Lubricate the cone surfaces with grease.

11. Place the inner bearing cone and roller assembly in the inner cup, and install the new grease retainer with the reverse end of the tool shown in Fig. 6. **Be sure that the retainer is properly seated.**

12. Adjust the brake shoes as outlined in Part 2.

13. Install the wheel, hub, and drum assembly on the wheel spindle. **Keep the hub centered on the spindle to prevent damage to the grease retainer or the spindle threads.**

14. Install the outer bearing cone and roller assembly and the flat washer on the spindle, then install the adjusting nut (Fig. 1).

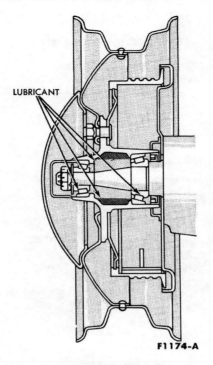

LUBRICANT

F1174-A

FIG. 7—Front Wheel Hub Lubrication

15. Adjust the wheel bearings as outlined in Section 2, and install a new cotter pin. Bend the ends of the cotter pin around the castellations of the nut lock to prevent interference with the radio static collector in the grease cap. Install the grease cap.

16. Install the hub cap or wheel cover.

DISC BRAKES

1. Raise the car until the wheel and tire clear the floor.

2. Remove the wheel cover or hub cap from the wheel.

3. Remove the wheel and tire from the hub and rotor.

4. Remove 2 bolts and washers retaining the caliper to the spindle. Remove the caliper from the rotor and wire it to the underbody to prevent damage to the brake hose.

5. Remove the grease cap from the hub. Remove the cotter pin, nut lock, adjusting nut, and flat washer from the spindle. Remove the outer bearing cone and roller assembly (Fig. 2).

6. Pull the hub and rotor assembly off the wheel spindle.

7. Remove the grease retainer, (Fig. 8) and the inner bearing cone and roller assembly from the hub.

8. Clean the lubricant off the inner and outer bearing cups with solvent and inspect the cups for

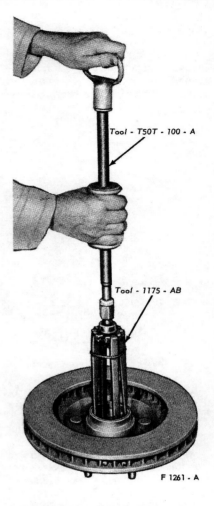

Tool - T50T - 100 - A

Tool - 1175 - AB

F 1261 - A

FIG. 8—Removing Grease Retainer

scratches, pits, excessive wear, and other damage. If the cups are worn or damaged, remove them with a drift.

9. Thoroughly clean the inner and outer bearing cones and rollers with solvent, and dry them thoroughly. Do not spin the bearings dry with compressed air.

Inspect the cones and rollers for wear or damage, and replace them if necessary. The cone and roller assemblies and the bearing cups should be replaced as a set if damage to either is encountered.

10. Thoroughly clean the spindle and the inside of the hub with solvent to remove all old lubricant.

Cover the spindle with a clean cloth, and brush all loose dust and dirt from the dust shield. **To prevent getting dirt on the spindle carefully remove the cloth from the spindle.**

11. If the inner and/or outer bearing cup(s) were removed, install the replacement cup(s) in the hub with

the tools shown in Fig. 9. **Be sure to seat the cups properly in the hub.**

12. Pack the inside of the hub with the specified wheel bearing grease. Add lubricant to the hub only until the grease is flush with the inside diameter of both bearing cups.

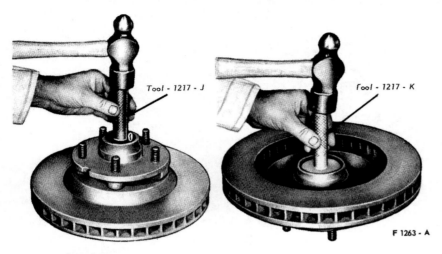

FIG. 9—Installing Front Wheel Rotor Bearing Cups

All old grease should be completely cleaned from the bearings before repacking with new grease.

13. Pack the bearing cone and roller assemblies with wheel bearing grease. A bearing packer is desirable for this operation. If a packer is not available, work as much lubricant as possible between the rollers and cages. Lubricate the cone surfaces with grease.

14. Place the inner bearing cone and roller assembly in the inner cup. Apply a light film of grease to the grease retainer and install the new grease retainer with the tool shown in Fig. 10. **Be sure the retainer is properly seated.**

15. Install the hub and rotor assembly on the wheel spindle. **Keep the hub centered on the spindle to prevent damage to the grease retainer or the spindle threads.**

16. Install the outer bearing cone and roller assembly and the flat washer on the spindle, then install the adjusting nut.

17. Adjust the wheel bearings as outlined in Section 2, and install a new cotter pin. Bend the ends of the cotter pin around the castellations of the nut lock to prevent interference with the radio static collector, in the grease cap. Install the grease cap.

18. Install the caliper to the spindle and tighten the retaining bolts to specifications. Check for the correct flexible hose routing (Part 2).

19. Install the wheel and tire on the hub.

20. Install the wheel cover.

FRONT HUB AND DRUM ASSEMBLY REPLACEMENT

When the hub and drum assembly

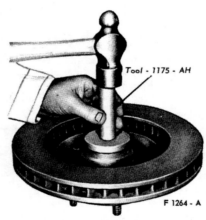

FIG. 10—Installing Grease Retainer

is replaced, new bearings, cups, and grease retainer must be installed in the new assembly. The new grease retainer should be soaked in light engine oil at least 30 minutes before installation.

1. Raise the car until the wheel and tire clears the floor. Pry off the hub cap or wheel cover, and remove the wheel and tire assembly from the hub and drum assembly.

2. Remove the grease cap from the hub. Remove the cotter pin, nut lock, adjusting nut, and flat washer from the spindle. Remove the outer bearing cone and roller assembly (Fig. 1).

3. Pull the hub and drum assembly off the wheel spindle.

4. Remove the grease retainer and the inner bearing cone and roller assembly from the hub with tool 1175AE.

5. Remove the protective coating from the new hub and drum with carburetor degreaser. Install new inner and outer bearing cups in the new hub with the tool shown in Fig. 6. **Be sure to seat the cups properly in the hub.**

6. Pack the inside of the hub with specified wheel bearing grease. Add lubricant to the hub only until the grease is flush with the inside diameter of both bearing cups (Fig. 7).

7. All old grease should be completely cleaned from the bearings before repacking them with new grease. Pack the bearing cone and roller assemblies with wheel bearing grease. A bearing packer is desirable for this operation. If a packer is not available, work as much lubricant as possible between the rollers and cages. Lubricate the cone surfaces with grease.

8. Place the inner bearing cone and roller assembly in the inner cup, and install the new grease retainer with the reverse end of the tool shown in Fig. 6. **Be sure that the retainer is properly seated.**

9. Adjust the brake shoes as outlined in Part 2.

10. Install the new hub and drum assembly on the wheel spindle. **Keep the hub centered on the spindle to prevent damage to the grease retainer.**

11. Install the outer bearing cone and roller assembly and the flat washer on the spindle; then, install the adjusting nut (Fig. 1).

12. Position the wheel and tire assembly on the new hub and drum assembly. Install the wheel hub nuts and tighten them alternately in order to draw the wheel evenly against the hub and drum.

13. Adjust the wheel bearings as outlined in Section 2, and install a new cotter pin. Bend the ends of the cotter pin around the castellations of the nut lock to prevent interference with the radio static collector in the grease cap. Install the grease cap.

14. Install the hub cap or wheel cover.

FRONT HUB AND ROTOR ASSEMBLY REPLACEMENT

When the hub and rotor assembly is replaced, new bearings, cups, and grease retainer must be installed in the new assembly.

1. Raise the car until the wheel and tire clear the floor. Pry off the hub cap or wheel cover, and remove the wheel and tire from the hub and rotor assembly.

2. Remove 2 bolts and washers that attach the caliper to the spindle. Remove the caliper from the rotor and wire it to the underbody to prevent damage to the brake hose.

3. Remove the grease cap from the hub. Remove the cotter pin, nut lock, adjusting nut, and flat washer from the spindle; then, remove the outer bearing cone and roller assembly (Fig. 2).

4. Pull the hub and rotor off the spindle.

5. Remove the protective coating from the new hub and rotor with carburetor degreaser. Install new inner and outer bearing cups in the new hub with the tool shown in Fig. 9. **Be sure to seat the cups properly in the hub.**

6. Grease and install the inner bearing cone and roller assembly in the inner bearing cup. Apply a light film of grease on the grease retainer and install the grease retainer.

7. Install the new hub and rotor assembly to the wheel spindle. **Keep the hub centered on the spindle to prevent damage to grease retainer.**

8. Install the outer bearing cone and roller assembly and the flat washer on the spindle; then, install the adjusting nut.

9. Install the caliper to the spindle and tighten the attaching bolts to specifications. Check for the correct flexible hose routing (Part 2).

10. Position the wheel and tire on the new hub and rotor. Install the wheel hub nuts and tighten them alternately in order to draw the wheel evenly against the hub and rotor.

11. Adjust the wheel bearings as outlined in Section 2, and install a new cotter pin. Bend the ends of the cotter pin around the castellations of the nut lock to prevent interference with the radio static collector in the grease cap. Install the grease cap.

12. Install the hub cap or wheel cover.

PART 3-6

SPECIFICATIONS

FRONT SUSPENSION

Wheel Alignment	Optimum Re-Setting Specifications	
	①Desired Alignment	Maximum Variation Between Wheels
Caster	$+1°\pm\frac{1}{2}°$	$\frac{1}{2}°$
Camber	$+\frac{1}{4}°\pm\frac{1}{2}°$	$\frac{1}{2}°$
Toe-In	$\frac{3}{16}$ inch $\pm\frac{1}{16}$ inch	—

①At controlled curb height—Front Alignment Spacer—$4\frac{11}{16}$ inches from frame side member to top center of strut mounting bolt. Rear Alignment Spacer—$6\frac{7}{32}$ inches from bottom of frame outer side rail to axle.

BALL JOINTS

	Radial Play (inch) Max. Allowable
Lower Ball Joint	0.250
Upper Ball Joint	**Replace if Perceptibly Loose**

FRONT SUSPENSION TORQUE LIMITS (FIG. 1)

Ref. No.	Description	Torque Ft-Lbs
1	Stabilizer Bar Mounting Bracket to Frame	10-15
2	Lower Arm to #2 Crossmember	55-75
3	Upper Arm to Frame	100-125
4	Upper Arm Bumper	15-25
5	Brake Backing Plate and Cylinder Ass. to Spindle	80-106
6	Stabilizer Bar to Lower Arm	5-10
7	Ball Joint to Spindle (Upper and Lower)	③60-90
8	Wheel Lug Nut	70-115
9	Wheel Bearing Adjusting Nut	②17-25
10	Brake Backing Plate to Spindle	25-45
11	Strut to Lower Arm	70-113
12	Stabilizer Bar to Mounting Bracket	10-15
13	Strut to Frame	③60-90
14	Shock Absorber Upper Attachment	20-28
15	Shock Absorber to Lower Arm	8-12

②Torque the adjusting nut to 17-25 ft. lb. Locate nut lock on adjusting nut so castellations are aligned with cotter pin hole in spindle. Then, back off adjusting nut and nut lock so the next castellation aligns with the cotter pin hole.
③Torque to specification; then, tighten the nut to the nearest cotter pin slot and insert the cotter pin.

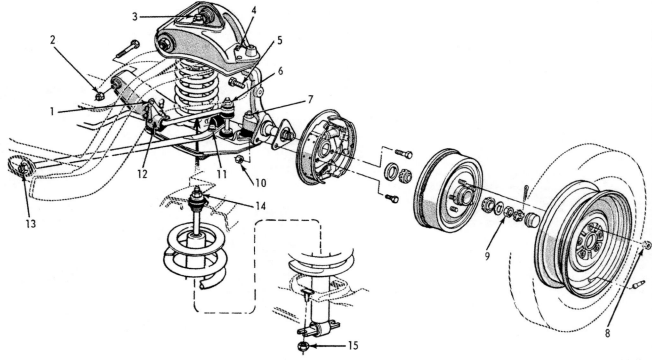

F 1283-A

FIG. 1—Front Suspension Torque Limits

REAR SUSPENSION TORQUE LIMITS (FIG. 2)

Ref. No.	Description	Torque Ft-Lbs
1	Shock Absorber to Frame (Upper Attachment)	15-25
2	Upper Arm to Axle	100-130
3	Track Bar to Axle Track Bar Stud	80-105
4	Track Bar Stud to Axle	⑥110-140
5	Track Bar to Frame (Bolt Torque)	⑤80-105
6	Track Bar to Frame (Nut Torque)	⑤60-85
7	Wheel Lug Nut	70-115
8	Brake Backing Plate and Bearing Retainer to Axle	④30-40
9	Shock Absorber to Axle (Lower Attachment)	45-65
10	Bumper Assy. to Frame	9-13
11	Lower Arm to Axle	60-85
12	*Upper Arm to Frame*	90-115
13	Lower Arm to Frame	80-105
14	Bumper Assy. to Rear Axle Differential Carrier	15-25
15	Universal Joint U Bolt Nut	12-15
④Heavy Duty Axle		50-70
⑤Torque Nut or Bolt to Torque Specified		
⑥Torque Nut or Stud		

STEERING

STANDARD STEERING GEAR	
Model	HCD-A
Type	Recirculating Ball
Ratio	24:1
Turns of Steering Wheel (Stop to Stop)⑦	6
Lubricant Part Number	C3AZ-19578-A
Lubricant Capacity (Lb.)	.7±.07
Worm Bearing Preload⑨	4-5 in-lb.
Total Preload (Worm Bearing plus Sector Mash)⑧	9-10 in-lb.

⑦Gear only—not attached to Pitman arm.
⑧Required to rotate input shaft and worm assembly past the center high point.
⑨Torque required to rotate input shaft at approximately 1½ turns either side of center (gear out of vehicle or Pitman arm disconnected).

ADJUSTMENT

Adjusting screw clearance at bottom of sector shaft T-slot 0.000-0.002 in. Sector Shaft end play—steering linkage disconnected—none.
With gear mounted in vehicle or on a suitable fixture and positioned on center, and the sector shaft retained to prevent rotation, apply a 15 in-lb. torque on the steering gear input shaft in both right and left turn directions. The total angular travel of the input shaft cannot exceed 8½ degrees, with 8 in-lb. net mesh load.

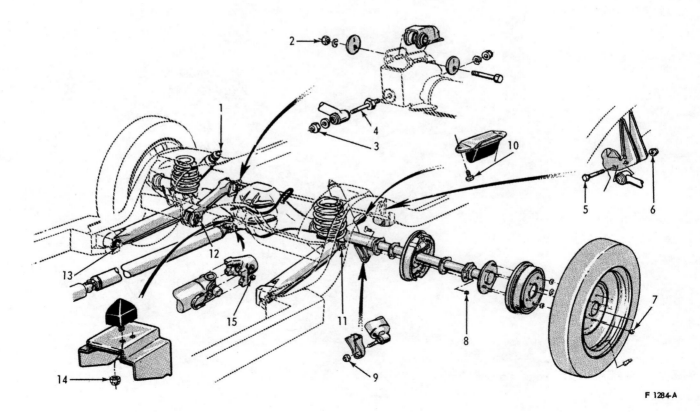

F 1284-A

FIG. 2—Rear Suspension Torque Limits

STANDARD STEERING GEAR TORQUE LIMITS

Description	Ft-lbs	In-lbs
Sector Shaft Cover Bolts	17-25	
Meshload Adjusting Screw Locknut	32-40	
Ball Return Guide Clamp Screw		18-42
Preload Adjuster Locknut	⑩60-80	

Residual torque must be 40 lbs-ft. min.

POWER STEERING GEAR TORQUE LIMITS

Description	Ft-lbs	In-lbs
Gear Cover to Gear Housing	55-65	
Valve Housing to Gear Housing	35-45	
Race Retaining Inner Nut	⑪	
Race Lock Nut	⑫	
Piston End Cap	50-75	
Guide Clamp Retaining Screw and Washer		42-70
Mesh Load Adjusting Screw Lock Nut	25-35	

⑪With Tool T65P-3553-A—Torque to 55-65 ft-lbs.
With Tool T66P-3553-B, compute the torque as follows:

$$\text{Torque} = \frac{\text{Length of Torque wrench} \times 60 \text{ ft-lbs}}{\text{Length of Torque wrench} + 5\frac{1}{2} \text{ inches}}$$

EXAMPLE—with 13 inch torque wrench

$$\frac{13 \text{ in.} \times 60 \text{ ft-lbs}}{13 \text{ in.} + 5.5 \text{ in.}} = \frac{13 \times 60 \text{ ft-lbs}}{18.5} = 0.704 \times 60 = 42 \text{ ft-lbs}$$

⑫With Tool T65P-3553-A—Torque to 20-30 ft-lbs.
With Tool T66P-3553-B, compute the torque as follows:

$$\text{Torque} = \frac{\text{Length of torque wrench} \times 25 \text{ ft-lbs}}{\text{Length of torque wrench} + 5\frac{1}{2} \text{ inches}}$$

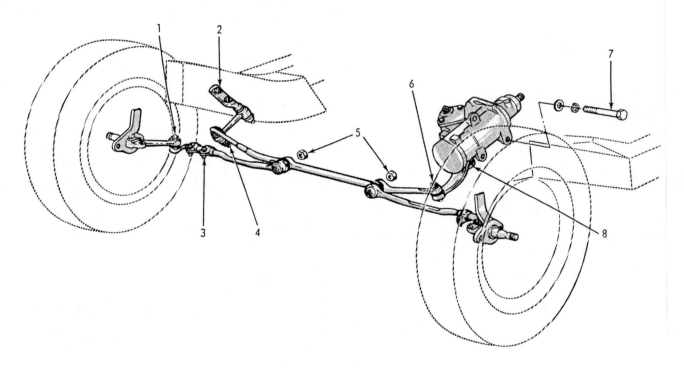

G 1369-A

FIG. 3—Steering Linkage Torque Limits

STEERING COLUMN TORQUE LIMITS

Description	Torque Ft-Lbs
Steering Wheel Retaining Nut	25-30
Bracket to Lower Clamp (under hood)	8-13
Loser Clamp and Bracket to Dash Panel (under hood)	8-13
Steering Column to Support Bracket (Instrument Panel)	8-13
Steering Column Shift Arm to Linkage Auto. Trans. .... Std. Trans.	8-13 9-15
Tilt Wheel Column Flange Screws	35-40

STEERING LINKAGE TORQUE LIMITS (FIG. 3)

Ref. No.	Description	Torque Ft-Lbs
1	Steering Spindle Arm Connecting Rod End to Spindle Arm	⑬35-47
2	Idler Arm Mounting Bracket to Frame	28-35
3	Steering Spindle Arm Connecting Rod and End Clamp to Adjusting Sleeve	8-13
4	Idler Arm to Steering Arm-to-Idler Arm Rod	⑬60-70
5	Steering Spindle Arm Connecting Rod to Steering Arm-to-Idler Arm Rod	⑬35-47
6	Pitman Arm to Steering Arm-to-Idler Arm Rod	⑬35-47
7	Steering Gear to Frame	35-50
8	Pitman Arm to Sector Shaft	150-225

⑬Torque to low end of specification; then, tighten the nut to the nearest cotter pin slot and insert the cotter pin.

POWER STEERING PUMP TORQUE LIMITS

Ref. No.	Description	Torque Ft-Lbs
1	Pump Rear Mounting Nut	14-18
2	Reservoir to Support Stud Retaining Nut	11-16
3	Outlet Fitting Hex Nut	43-47
4	Pressure Hose Nut	18-25
5	Pump Attaching Bolts	30-40
6	Bracket to Engine Attaching Bolts	30-40
7	Rear Support Bracket Retaining Nuts	30-40

TREAD WIDTH AND WHEELBASE

Front Tread Width	62 inches
Rear Tread Width	62 inches
Wheelbase—Ford	119 inches
—Mercury	123 inches

LUBRICATION

Front Wheel Bearings	Pack with C2AZ-19585-A
Front Wheel Bearing Seal	Soak in Motor Oil

TORQUE LIMITS

Wheel Nuts—all models	70-115 Ft-lbs

POWER STEERING GEAR—INTEGRAL

Type	Recirculating Ball-Torsion Bar
Gear Ratio	17.0:1
Turns of wheel for full left to right turn (within gear)	4.0
Torsion Bar Diameter	0.200 inch
Hydraulic Fluid	C1AZ-19582-A
Hydraulic Fluid Capacity	1.6 pints (Approx.)
Phosphorescent dye additive (for leak detection)	(4 oz. per quart of fluid)

Adjustment	Specification
Sector shaft mesh load—total over mechanical center position Ford and Mercury—must be 8-9 in-lbs greater than the off center torque of 2 to 7 in-lbs	14 in-lbs max.
Worm bearing preload—with the input shaft in place and 45° off of the left stop, check input torque through an approx. ⅛ turn from the 45° position.	2-7 in-lbs
Clearance between valve spool and retaining ring	0.002 inch—0.005 inch Preferably 0.003 inch
Pressure variation between right and left turns (at 250 lbs. pressure) Steering gear in car—check efforts each side of center Steering gear out of car—check efforts at right & left stops	4 in-lbs max. variation 4 in-lbs max. variation
Clearance between inner sector seal and housing	0.025 inch

SERVICE TOOLS

Tool No.	Description
T50T-100-A	Impact Slide Hammer
T59L-100-B	Impact Slide Hammer
T58L-101-A	Puller Attachment
OTC-462	Tie Rod Separator
T57L-500-A	Bench Mounting Holding Fixture
TOOL-1175-AB	Grease Seal Remover (Head Only)
TOOL-1175-AH	Grease Seal Replacer
T57P-1217-A	Front Hub Bearing Cup and Grease Seal Replacer
TOOL-1217-J	Front Hub Bearing Cup Replacer—Outer
TOOL-1217-K	Front Hub Bearing Cup Replacer—Inner
T65P-3000-A	Adjusting Bar—Caster and Camber
T65P-3000-B or C	Alignment Spacers
T57P-3006-A	Spindle Ball Joint Remover Press
T65P-3044-A	Overhaul Tool Kit—Upper Arm Bushing
TOOL-3290-C	Dist. Gear and Tie Rod Ends Remover
T61P-3355-A	Idler Arm Bushing Remover and Replacer
T65P-3D505-A	Sleeve Remover
T65P-3D505-B	Sleeve Driver

SERVICE TOOLS (Continued)

Tool No.	Description
T65P-3524-A	Input Shaft Bearing Remover and Installer
T65P-3548-A	Installer—Oil Line Connector Seal
T65P-3553-A	Worm Bearing Nut and Lock Nut Wrench
T66P-3553-B	Spanner Wrench
T66P-3553-C	Spacer
T62F-3576-A	Sector Shaft Bushing Remover and Replacer
T65P-3576-A	Sector Shaft Bushing Remover and Installer
T65P-3576-B	Sector Shaft Seals Replacer
T64P-3590-F	Steering Arm Remover
TOOL-3600-AA	Steering Wheel Remover
T65P-3C732-A	Tilt Spring Installing Hook
T65P-3A733-A	Power Steering Pump Pulley Replacer
T65P-7212-A	Shift Tube Remover
T65P-7212-B	Slide Hammer Weights
T63L-8620-A	Belt Tension Gauge
T65P-10300-B	Alternator Pulley Replacer
T56L-33610-D	Power Steering Pressure Gauge

REAR AXLE

GROUP 4

PART 4-1 GENERAL AXLE SERVICE

1 DIAGNOSIS AND TESTING

DIAGNOSIS GUIDE

Certain rear axle and drive line trouble symptoms are also common to the engine, transmission, tires, and other parts of the car. For this reason, be sure that the cause of the trouble is in the rear axle before adjusting, repairing, or replacing any of the axle parts.

REAR AXLE NOISE DIAGNOSIS

Noise characteristics in a rear axle are more difficult to diagnose and repair than mechanical failures. Slight axle noise heard only at a certain speed or under remote conditions must be considered normal. Axle noise tends to peak or be more pronounced at varying speeds and the noise is in no way a sign of trouble in the axle.

Where noise is present in an objectionable form, loud and/or at all speeds, the first efforts should be made to isolate the noise. Rear axle noise is quite often confused with other noises such as tire noise, transmission noise, driveshaft vibration and universal joint noise. Isolation of the noise in any one unit requires skill and experience. An attempt to eliminate a slight noise may baffle even the best diagnostic experts. Axle noises fall into two basic categories: gear noise and/or bearing noise.

Gear Noise. Abnormal gear noise can be recognized since it produces a cycling pitch and will be very pronounced in the speed range at which it occurs, usually under drive, float, cruise or coast conditions. Gear noise tends to peak in a narrow speed range or ranges, while bearing noise will tend to remain constant in pitch.

Bearing Noise. Defective bearings will produce a whine that is constant in pitch and varies with car speed. This fact will help distinguish between bearing and/or gear noise.

1. Pinion bearing noise can be identified as a constant grinding noise. Pinion bearings are rotating at a higher speed than differential side bearings or axle shaft bearings. The noise is most noticeable at a slight pull between 18 to 25 miles per hour.

2. Wheel bearing noise may be confused with rear axle noise. To differentiate between wheel bearings and rear axle, drive the car on a smooth road at medium low speed. With traffic permitting, turn the car sharply right and left. If noise is caused by wheel bearings, the noise will increase on the defective bearing because of side loading.

3. Side bearings will produce a constant grinding noise of a slower nature than pinion bearing, (side bearing noise cannot be determined by the wheel bearing test), but will be in the same frequency as axle shaft bearings.

Also, certain trouble symptoms are common to both the conventional and limited-slip differential axles, while still other symptoms are found

EXCESSIVE REAR AXLE NOISE (ALL REAR AXLES)	only in the limited-slip differential. To determine whether the car is equipped with a conventional or a limited-slip differential, check the car warranty plate and the axle ratio tag. Refer to CAR IDENTIFICATION at the front of this manual. Since gears are in mesh, some rear axle noise is normal. However, excessive noise often indicates the beginning of other troubles in the axle. A road test can help determine whether the noise is being caused by trouble in the rear axle or in other parts of the car. **Before road-testing the car, make sure that the tire pressures and the rear axle lubricant level are normal. Then drive the car far enough to warm the axle lubricant to its normal operating temperature.** With the car stopped and the transmission in neutral, run the engine at various speeds. If the noise still exists during this test, it probably comes from the engine or the exhaust system. To determine if the noise is being caused by the rear axle or the tires, drive the car over several different types of road surfaces. Smooth asphalt or black-top roads minimize tire noises. Tire noises may be elimi-	nated by cross-switching the tires. Snow tires often cause noises not heard with conventional tires. Noise caused by a worn or damaged wheel bearing is often loudest when the car is coasting at low speeds, and it usually stops when the brakes are gently applied. To find the noisy bearing, jack up each wheel and check each bearing for roughness while the wheel is rotating, provided that the car is equipped with a conventional differential. If all possible external sources of noise have been checked and eliminated, and the noise still exists, road-test the rear axle under all four driving conditions—drive, cruise, float, and coast. Any noise produced by the sidegears and pinions in the differential case will be most pronounced on turns. A continuous whine under a light load between 20 and 35 miles per hour indicates rough or brinnelled pinion bearings. If the tone of drive, coast and float noise differs with speed and if the noise is very rough and irregular; worn, rough or loose differential or pinion shaft bearings are indicated. Remove, disassemble, and inspect the axle.
EXCESSIVE REAR AXLE BACKLASH (ALL REAR AXLES)	Excessive backlash in the axle driving parts may be caused by worn axle shaft splines, loose axle shaft flange nuts, loose U-joint flange mountings, excessive backlash between the drive	pinion and ring gear, excessive backlash in the differential gears, or bearings which are worn or out of adjustment.
ONE WHEEL SPINS EXCESSIVELY (LIMITED-SLIP DIFFERENTIAL ONLY)	Use the procedure given under "Limited-slip Differential" for checking the differential while the carrier assembly is in the car. If the torque required to rotate one rear	wheel is less than 75 foot-pounds, the differential is not functioning properly. To repair the unit, the carrier assembly must be removed from the axle housing.
AXLE HAS A HIGH-PITCHED, CHATTERING NOISE ON TURNS (LIMITED-SLIP DIFFERENTIAL ONLY)	Drive the car in a fairly tight circle, making five circles clockwise and five counterclockwise. This will permit the lubricant to work in between the clutch plates. If the noise does not disappear during this driving test, it is probable that the axle does not have the approved Ford lubricant. The lubricant may be checked by draining two tablespoonfuls from the axle and mixing it with an equal amount of white alcohol, such as rubbing alcohol. Mix the lubricant and alcohol thoroughly and let it stand	for at least two minutes. If the sample now has a blue tint, the lubricant is approved Ford lubricant. If it has a yellow tint, it is not the correct lubricant. Drain and refill the axle with the approved lubricant. It is not necessary to flush the axle housing. After refilling the axle drive the car in fairly tight circles clockwise and counterclockwise. The chattering noise should disappear as soon as the new lubricant works in between the clutch plates.

LIMITED-SLIP DIFFERENTIAL

The limited-slip differential can be checked for proper operation without removing the carrier from the axle housing.

Jack up one rear wheel and remove the wheel cover. On a Ford model install tool T59L-4204-A on the axle shaft flange studs as shown in Fig. 1. On a Mercury model, insert tool 44211-A into the two holes in the end of the axle shaft as shown in Fig. 2.

Using a torque wrench of at least 200 ft-lbs. capacity, rotate the axle shaft. **Be sure that the transmission is in neutral gear, one rear wheel is on the floor, and the other rear wheel is raised off the floor.** The torque required to continuously rotate the shaft should be at least 75 ft-lbs. The initial breakaway torque may be higher than the continuous turning torque, but this is normal. The axle shaft should turn with even pressure throughout the check without slipping or binding.

If the torque reading is less than

75 ft-lbs., check the differential for improper assembly.

A car equipped with a limited-slip differential will always have both wheels driving. If, while the car is being serviced, only one wheel is raised off the floor and the rear axle is driven by the engine, the wheel on the floor will drive the car off the stand or jack.

GEAR TOOTH CONTACT PATTERN CHECK

When rolling a tooth pattern, use the special compound (tube) packed with each service ring gear and pinion set.

Paint the gear teeth and roll a pattern as described in Section 3. After diagnosing the tooth pattern as explained here, make the appropriate adjustments as outlined in Section 2.

In making a final gear tooth contact pattern check, it is necessary to recognize the fact that there are three different types of gear sets, hunting, non-hunting and partial non-hunting. Each type is determined by

FIG. 1—Limited-Slip Differential Check—Ford

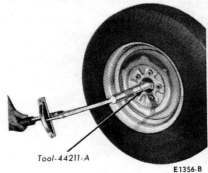

FIG. 2—Limited-Slip Differential Check—Mercury

the ratio and the number of teeth in the gears. The non-hunting and partial non-hunting types can be identified by the paint timing marks on the pinion and drive gear teeth. (Part 4-2, Fig. 46). See Part 4-3 for complete identification specifications.

THE IDEAL TOOTH PATTERN

Fig. 3 shows the ideal tooth pattern. **This pattern is not a rigid standard but merely a general norm.**

In general, desirable tooth patterns should have the following characteristics:

1. The drive pattern should be fairly well centered on the tooth.
2. The coast pattern should be centered on the tooth but may be slightly toward the toe.
3. Some clearance between the pattern and the top of the tooth is desirable.
4. There should be no hard lines where the pressure is high.

The individual gear set need not conform exactly to the ideal pattern to be acceptable. Characteristic differences between the three types of gear sets as well as differences between individual gear sets of the same type will result in patterns that are acceptable yet different from those shown in Fig. 3.

HUNTING GEAR SET

In a hunting-type gear set, any one pinion gear tooth comes into contact with all ring gear teeth. In this type, several revolutions of the ring gear are required to make all possible gear combinations.

Acceptable Pattern. The drive pattern shown in Fig. 4 was rolled on a hunting-type gear set. Since each pinion tooth came into contact with each ring gear tooth, the pattern is a result of the **combined** tooth contacts. Therefore, the pattern is uniform from tooth to tooth.

Unacceptable Pattern. An erratic tooth pattern on a hunting gear set indicates gear runout and possible need for gear replacement.

A pattern that is uniform, but off center indicates a change in shim or backlash (Fig. 9).

NON-HUNTING GEAR SET

In a non-hunting type gear set, any one pinion gear tooth comes into contact with only a few ring gear teeth. In this type, only one revolution of the ring gear is required to make all possible tooth contact combinations.

Acceptable Patterns. The drive patterns shown in Figs. 5 and 6 were rolled on two different non-hunting type gear sets. The pattern in Fig. 5 runs from the tooth center toward the toe and then back to center. The pattern in Fig. 6 runs from the tooth center toward the heel and then back to center. These patterns are not unusual for non-hunting gear sets and are acceptable. The pattern on any one ring gear tooth was formed by only **one** pinion tooth coming into contact with it. Because of this limited tooth contact, the non-hunting pattern can be more erratic than the hunting pattern and still be accept-

DRIVE SIDE

HEEL

TOE

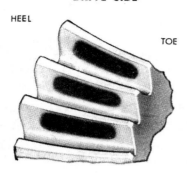

COAST SIDE

HEEL

TOE

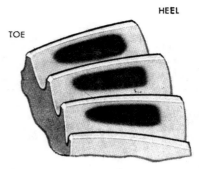

E1336-A

DESIRABLE PATTERN
CORRECT SHIM
CORRECT BACKLASH

FIG. 3—Ideal Tooth Pattern

E1337-A

FIG. 4—Acceptable Hunting
Gear Pattern

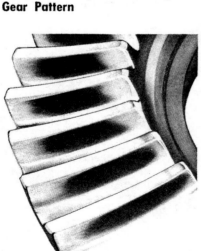

E1338-A

FIG. 5—Unacceptable
Non-Hunting Pattern—
Center-Toe-Center

able. Likewise, the coast pattern on a non-hunting gear set is usually less uniform tooth to tooth than it would

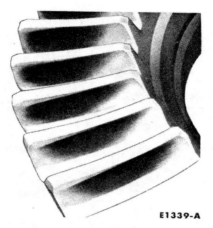

E1339-A

FIG. 6—Unacceptable
Non-Hunting Pattern—
Center-Heel-Center

be on a hunting gear set (Fig. 7).

Fig. 8 shows a pattern rolled on another gear set. In this case, the pat-

E1340-A

FIG. 7—Acceptable
Non-Hunting Gear Set
Coast Pattern

tern is fairly uniform from tooth to tooth.

Unacceptable Patterns. A non-hunting gear set should be checked

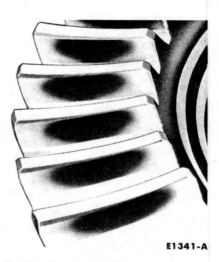

E1341-A

FIG. 8—Acceptable
Non-Hunting Pattern—Uniform

for runout and possible replacement if the pattern runs from the tooth center toward the toe and back to center on some gear teeth (Fig. 5) while on other teeth of the same gear, the pattern runs from the tooth center toward the heel and back to center (Fig. 6).

A non-hunting gear set requires a change in shimming or backlash when its pattern tends to concentrate toward the heel or toe, top or bottom of **most** teeth (Fig. 9).

PARTIAL NON-HUNTING GEAR SET

In a partial non-hunting type gear set, any one pinion tooth comes into contact with only part of the ring gear teeth, but more than one revo-

DRIVE SIDE   **COAST SIDE**

HEEL   HEEL

TOE   TOE

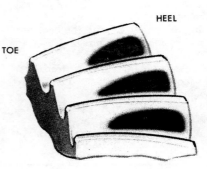

1. BACKLASH CORRECT
0.004 THICKER
SHIM REQUIRED

2. BACKLASH CORRECT
0.004 THINNER
SHIM REQUIRED

3. SHIM CORRECT
DECREASE
BACKLASH
0.004

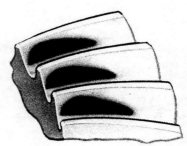

4. SHIM CORRECT
INCREASE
BACKLASH
0.004

E1342-A

FIG. 9—Typical Gear Tooth Contact Patterns Indicating Shim or Backlash Change

lution of the ring gear is required to make all possible gear tooth combinations.

Tooth to tooth pattern uniformity will usually be in between the hunting and the non-hunting patterns. Partial non-hunting gear set patterns will usually be less uniform than hunting gear set patterns, but more uniform than non-hunting gear set patterns.

SHIM AND BACKLASH CHANGES

The patterns shown in Fig. 9 are typical of gear sets that have either an incorrect backlash or an incorrect shim adjustment. Since each gear set rolls a characteristic pattern, the patterns in Fig. 9 should be considered as typical only and should be used as a guide rather than a rigid standard.

The drive pattern is rolled on the convex side of the tooth, and the coast pattern is rolled on the concave side. The movement of tooth contact patterns with changes in backlash and shimming can be summarized as follows:

1. Thicker shim with the backlash constant moves the pinion further from the ring gear:

a. Drive pattern moves toward the

top of the tooth (face contact) and toward the heel.

b. Coast pattern moves toward the top of the tooth and slightly toward the toe.

2. Thinner shim with the backlash constant moves the pinion closer to the ring gear:

a. Drive pattern moves deeper on the tooth (flank contact) and slightly toward the toe.

b. Coast pattern moves deeper on the tooth and toward the heel.

3. Decreasing backlash moves the

ring gear closer to the pinion:

a. Drive pattern moves slightly lower and toward the toe.

b. Coast pattern moves lower and toward the toe.

4. Increasing backlash moves the ring gear away from the pinion:

a. Drive pattern moves slightly higher and toward the heel.

b. Coast pattern moves higher and toward the heel.

If the patterns are not correct, make the changes as indicated. The

pinion need not be disassembled to change a shim. All that is required is to remove the pinion, bearing, and retainer assembly and install a different shim. When reinstalling the pinion and retainer assembly of a non-hunting or partial non-hunting gear set, be sure that the marked tooth on the pinion indexes between the marked teeth on the ring gear (Fig. 46, Part 4-2). Refer to Pinion and Ring Gear Tooth Contact Adjustment, Section 2.

---

2   COMMON ADJUSTMENTS AND REPAIRS

PINION AND DRIVE GEAR TOOTH CONTACT ADJUSTMENT

Two separate adjustments affect pinion and ring gear tooth contact. They are pinion location and backlash (Fig. 10).

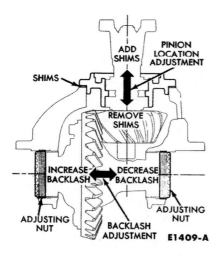

FIG. 10—Pinion and Ring Gear Tooth Contact Adjustment

Individual differences in machining the carrier housing and the gear set require a shim between the pinion retainer and the carrier housing to locate the pinion for correct contact with the ring gear. The original factory installed shim is of the correct thickness for a given original carrier and gear set assembly. In service, shims should be added or removed from the original pack only as indicated by the tooth pattern check. Adding shims moves the pinion away from the ring gear; removing shims moves the pinion toward the ring gear (Fig. 10).

The tooth pattern check also indicates whether the ring gear should be adjusted away from or toward the pinion to increase or decrease backlash between the gears.

If the tooth pattern check indicates a change in backlash only, follow the procedure under Pinion Location. ferential Bearing Preload Adjustments. If the tooth pattern indicates a change in shim thickness follow the procedure under Pinion Location.

BACKLASH AND DIFFERENTIAL BEARING PRELOAD ADJUSTMENTS

To secure a more uniform control of differential side bearing pre-load in service repairs, a dial indicator set-up such as shown in Fig. 11 is required.

1. Remove the adjusting nut locks, loosen the differential bearing cap bolts, and then torque the bolts to 25 ft-lbs.

2. The left adjusting nut is on the ring gear side of the carrier. The right nut is on the pinion side. Loosen the right nut until it is away from the cup. Tighten the left nut until the ring gear is just forced into the pinion with no backlash, then rotate the pinion several revolutions to be sure no binding is evident. (Recheck the right nut at this time to be sure that it is still loose.) **Tightening the left nut moves the ring gear into the pinion to decrease backlash, and tightening the right nut moves the ring gear away.**

3. Tighten the right nut until it first contacts the bearing cup. Rotate the ring gear several revolutions in each direction while the bearings are loaded to seat the bearings in their cups to be sure no bind is evident. **This step is important.**

4. Install the dial indicator as shown in Fig. 11.

5. Again loosen the right nut to

FIG. 11—Adjusting Side Bearing Pre-Load

release the preload. If there is any backlash between the gears, as shown by the dial indicator, tighten the left nut just enough to remove this backlash. Carefully tighten the right nut until it just contacts the cup.

6. Torque the differential cap bolts to specification. Tighten the right nut until the dial indicator (Fig. 11) shows a case spread of 0.012 inch, when new bearings are installed. If original bearings are re-used, the case spread should be 0.005 to 0.008 inch.

7. Set the dial indicator on the ring gear teeth and measure the backlash on several teeth around the ring gear. If the measurements vary more than 0.003 inch, there is excessive runout in the gears or their mountings, which must be corrected to obtain a satisfactory unit. If the backlash is out of specification, loosen one adjusting nut and tighten the opposite nut an equal amount, to move the ring gear away from or toward the pinion. **When moving the adjusting nuts, the final movement should always be made in a tightening direction. For example, if the left nut had to be loosened one notch, loosen the nut two notches, then tighten it one. This procedure makes it certain that the nut is contacting the bearing cup, and that the cup cannot shift after being put in service. After all**

such adjustments, check to be sure that the case spread (pre-load) remains at 0.012 inch. If the original bearings have been used this spread should be 0.005 to 0.008 inch.

8. Again check the tooth contact pattern. If the pattern is still incorrect, a change in pinion location (shim thickness) is indicated.

PINION LOCATION

1. Remove the retaining bolts and the pinion and bearing retainer assembly from the carrier.

2. Measure the original shim thickness with a micrometer. Increase or decrease the shim thickness as indicated by the tooth pattern check described in Section 1.

3. Replace the pinion retainer O-ring (Fig. 35, Part 4-2). Coat the O-ring with axle lubricant before installing. **Do not roll the O-ring into the groove. Snap it into position.**

4. Being careful not to pinch the O-ring, install the pinion and bearing retainer assembly in the carrier with the corrected shim pack.

Before installing the pinion and bearing retainer assembly, determine which type of gear set is being used. The **non-hunting** and **partial non-hunting** types can be identified by the paint timing marks on the gear teeth (Fig. 46, Part 4-2). Part 4-3 can also

be referred to for identification.

If the gear set is of the **non-hunting** or **partial non-hunting** type clean the teeth on both the pinion and drive gear so that the timing marks are visible. Rotate the differential case and ring gear assembly in the carrier until the marked teeth on the ring gear are opposite the pinion entry hole. Place the assembly in the carrier so that the marked tooth on the pinion indexes between the marked teeth on the ring gear (Fig. 46, Part 4-2).

In almost every case of improper assembly (gear assembled out of time), the noise level and probability of failure will be higher than they would be with properly assembled gears.

When installing the **hunting** type gear set (no timing marks), assemble the pinion and retainer assembly into the carrier without regard to the matching on any particular gear teeth.

5. Install the retainer-to-carrier mounting bolts and torque to specifications.

6. Adjust the backlash between the ring gear and pinion as outlined in the foregoing procedure.

7. Make a tooth pattern check. If the pattern is still unsatisfactory, repeat this procedure changing the shim thickness each time until a satisfactory tooth pattern is obtained.

3   CLEANING AND INSPECTION

INSPECTION BEFORE DISASSEMBLY OF CARRIER

The differential carrier should be inspected before any parts are removed from it. These inspections can help to find the cause of the trouble and to determine the corrections needed.

Mount the carrier in the holding fixture shown in Fig. 11. Wipe the lubricant from the internal working parts, and visually inspect the parts for wear or damage.

Rotate the gears to see if there is any roughness which would indicate defective bearings or chipped gears. Check the gear teeth for scoring or signs of abnormal wear.

Set up a dial indicator (Fig. 13) and check the backlash at several points around the ring gear. Backlash should be within specifications.

If no obvious defect is noted, check the gear tooth contact. Paint the gear teeth with suitable gear marking compound, such as a paste

Tool—T57L-500-A

E1181-A

FIG. 12—Bench Fixture For Carrier Overhaul

made with dry red lead and oil. A mixture that is too wet will run and smear. Too dry a mixture cannot be pressed out from between the teeth. As shown in Fig. 14, wrap a cloth or rope around the drive pinion flange to act as a brake. Rotate the ring gear back and forth (use a box

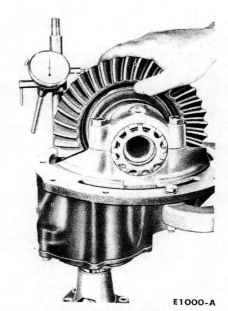

E1000-A

FIG. 13—Backlash Check

wrench on the ring gear attaching bolts for a lever) until a clear tooth

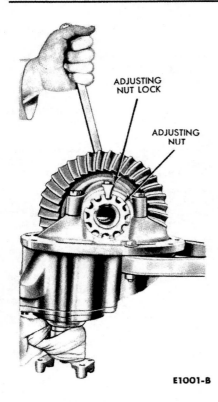

FIG. 14—Checking Gear Tooth Contact

contact pattern is obtained.

Certain types of gear tooth contact patterns on the ring gear indicate incorrect adjustment. Noise caused by incorrect adjustment can often be corrected by readjusting the gears. Typical patterns and the necessary corrections are explained under Tooth Contact Pattern Check in Section 1.

Gear tooth runout can sometimes be detected by an erratic pattern on the teeth. However, a dial indicator should be used to measure the runout of the back face of the ring gear as shown in Fig. 15. If this runout exceeds specifications, disassemble the carrier and replace necessary parts as indicated in Part 4-2, Section 4.

Loosen the differential bearing cap bolts, and then torque them to 25 ft-lbs. Remove the adjusting nut locks. Carefully loosen one of the adjusting nuts to determine if any differential bearing preload remains. If at least one notch of preload remains, the differential bearings may be re-used, provided they are not pitted or damaged.

INSPECTION AFTER DISASSEMBLY

Thoroughly clean all parts (Fig. 16). **Always use clean solvent when**

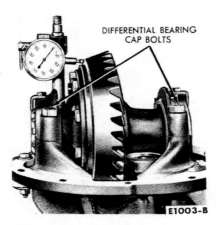

FIG. 15—Checking Ring Gear Runout

cleaning bearings. Oil the bearings immediately after cleaning to prevent rusting. Inspect the parts for defects. Clean the inside of the carrier before rebuilding it. **When a scored gear set is replaced, the axle housing should be washed thoroughly and steam cleaned.** This can only be done effectively if the axle shafts and shaft seals are removed from the housing. Inspect individual parts as outlined below.

GEARS

Examine the pinion and ring gear teeth for scoring or excessive wear. **Extreme care must be taken not to damage the pilot bearing surface of the pinion.**

The pattern taken during disassembly should be helpful in judging if gears can be re-used. Worn gears cannot be rebuilt to correct a noisy condition. Gear scoring is the result of excessive shock loading or the use of an incorrect lubricant. Scored gears cannot be re-used.

Examine the teeth and thrust surfaces of the differential gears. Wear on the hub of the differential gear can cause a chucking noise known as chuckle when the car is driven at low speeds. Wear of splines, thrust surfaces, or thrust washers, can contribute to excessive drive line backlash.

BEARING CUPS AND CONE AND ROLLER ASSEMBLIES

Check bearing cups for rings, scores, galling, or excessively worn wear patterns. Pinion cups must be solidly seated. Check by attempting to insert a 0.0015-inch feeler between these cups and the bottoms of their bores.

When operated in the cups, cone

and roller assemblies must turn without roughness. Examine the roller ends for wear. Step-wear on the roller ends indicates the bearings were not preloaded properly, or the rollers were slightly misaligned.

If inspection reveals either a defective cup or a defective cone and roller assembly **both parts** should be replaced to avoid early failure.

DIFFERENTIAL BEARING ADJUSTING NUTS

Temporarily install the bearing caps and test the fit of the adjusting nuts in their threads. The nuts should turn easily when the caps are tightened to 25 ft-lbs. The faces of the nuts that contact the bearing cups must be smooth and square. Replace the nuts or examine the threads in the carrier if their fit is not proper. Be sure that the bearing caps and adjusting nuts are on the side they were machined to fit. Observe the punch marks and scribe marks made during disassembly.

U-JOINT FLANGE

Be sure that the ears of the flange have not been damaged in removing the drive shaft or in removing the flange from the axle. The end of the flange that contacts the oil slinger as well as the flat surface of the pinion nut counterbore must be smooth. Polish these surfaces if necessary. Roughness aggravates backlash noises and causes wear of the slinger and pinion nut with a resultant loss in pinion bearing preload.

PINION RETAINER

Be sure that the pinion bearing cups are seated. Remove any chips or burrs from the mounting flange. Clean the groove for the O-ring seal and all lubricant passages. If the cups were removed, examine the bores carefully. Any nicks or burrs in these bores must be removed to permit proper seating of the cups.

CARRIER HOUSING

Make sure that the differential bearing bores are smooth and the threads are not damaged. Remove any nicks or burrs from the mounting surfaces of the carrier housing.

DIFFERENTIAL CASE

Make sure that the hubs where the bearings mount are smooth. Carefully examine the differential case bearing shoulders, which may have been damaged when the bearings were removed. The bearing assemblies will

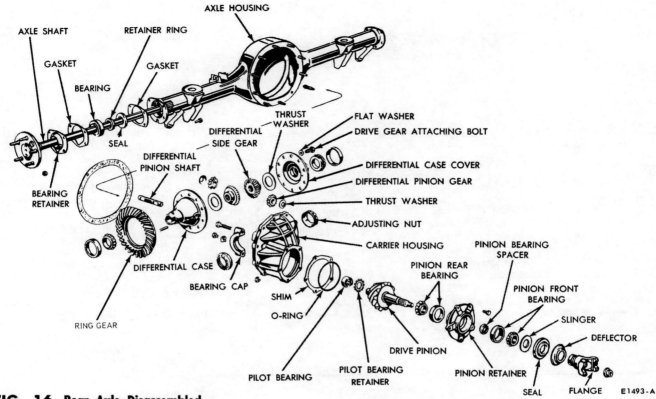

FIG. 16—Rear Axle Disassembled

fail if they do not seat firmly against the shoulders. Check the fit (free rotation) of the differential side gears in their counterbores. Be sure that the mating surfaces of the two parts of the case are smooth and free from nicks or burrs.

LIMITED-SLIP DIFFERENTIAL PARTS

Inspect the clutch plates for un-even or extreme wear. The dog-eared clutch plates must be free from burrs, nicks or scratches which could cause excessive or erratic wear to the bonding material of the internally splined clutch plates. The internally splined clutch plates should be inspected for condition of the bond, bonding material, and wear. Replace the bonded plates if their thickness is less than 0.085 inch or if the bonded material

is scored or badly worn. Inspect the bonded plate internal teeth for wear. Replace them, if excessive wear is evident. Bonded plates should be replaced as a set only.

Examine all thrust surfaces and hubs for wear. Abnormal wear on these surfaces can contribute to a noisy axle.

Inspect the Belleville spring for proper free height of ¼ inch.

PART 4-2   REAR AXLE

1 DESCRIPTION AND OPERATION

CONVENTIONAL AXLE

DESCRIPTION

The rear axle is of the banjo-housing, hypoid gear type using an 8¾, 9 or 9⅜ inch ring gear, in which the centerline of the pinion is mounted below the centerline of the ring gear (Fig. 1).

The integral pinion gear and shaft and the pinion bearings are assembled in a pinion retainer, which is bolted to the carrier. The pinion is straddle mounted; that is, it is supported by bearings both in front of and to the rear of the pinion gear. Two opposed tapered roller bearings support the pinion shaft in front of the pinion gear with a collapsible spacer for 8-¾" or 9" ring gear, and a solid spacer used with the 9-⅜" ring gear. A straight roller (pilot) bearing supports the pinion shaft at the rear of the pinion gear. Pinion and ring gear tooth contact is adjusted by adding or removing shims from between the pinion retainer and the carrier housing.

The differential assembly is mounted on two opposed tapered roller bearings, which are retained in the carrier by removable caps. The entire carrier assembly is bolted to the axle housing.

Ball bearing assemblies (rear wheel bearings) are pressed onto the outer ends of the axle shafts and set in the outer ends of the axle housing. These bearings support the semi-floating axle shafts at the outer ends. The inner ends of the shafts spline to the differential side gears. Bearing retainer plates hold the shafts in the housing. The left and right axle shafts are not interchangeable, the left shaft being shorter than the right.

A metal tag stamped with the model designation and gear ratio is secured to all Ford-produced axles under one of the carrier-to-housing bolts. The first five spaces on the top line are reserved for the model designation letters such as WDC-A, WDD-B, or WDL-G. These letters indicate a specific combination of the following factors: conventional or limited-slip axle; diameter of ring gear; size or differential bearings; size of wheel bearings; and the gear ratio. It is important, therefore, to use the model designation for obtaining the correct replacement parts.

OPERATION

The rear axle drive pinion receives its power from the engine through the transmission and drive shaft. The pinion gear rotates the differential case through engagement with the ring gear, which is bolted to the case outer flange. Inside the case, two differential pinion gears are mounted on the differential pinion shaft which is pinned to the case. These pinion gears are engaged with the side gears, to which the axle shafts are splined. Therefore, as the differential case turns, it rotates the axle shafts and rear wheels. When it is necessary for one wheel and axle shaft to rotate faster than the other, the faster turning side gear causes the pinions to roll on the slower turning side gear to allow differential action between the two axle shafts.

LIMITED-SLIP DIFFERENTIAL AXLE

DESCRIPTION

The axle assembly, except for the differential case and its internal components, is identical to the conventional axle.

A constant-friction locking differential, which employs automatic transmission-type clutch plates to *control differential action, is* available as optional equipment (Fig. 2).

Four steel clutch plates are locked into the differential cover. Three

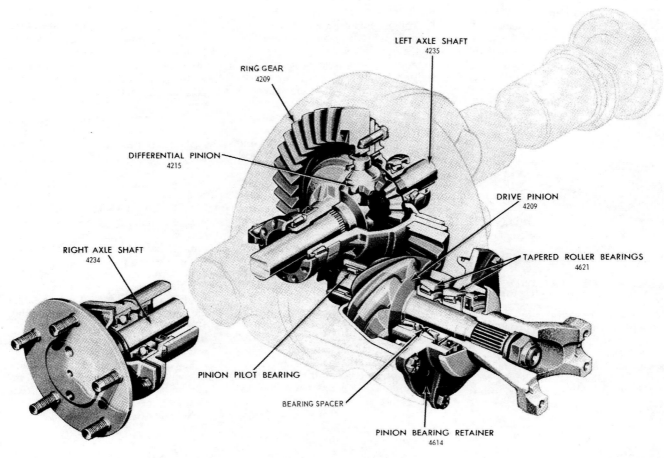

FIG. 1—Rear Axle Assembly

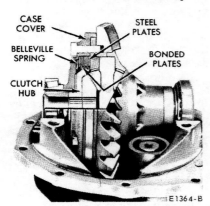

FIG. 2—Limited-Slip Differential

bronze, bonded clutch plates are splined to a clutch hub which, in turn, is splined to the left axle shaft. A Belleville spring washer maintains a constant pressure between the steel and bonded clutch plates so that the clutch is always engaged.

OPERATION

The pressure between clutch plates opposes differential action at all times. When the car turns a corner the clutch slips allowing normal differential action to take place. Under adverse weather conditions, where one or both wheels may be on a low-traction surface such as snow, ice or mud, the friction between the clutch plates will transfer a portion of the usable torque to the wheel with the most traction. Thus, the wheel that is on ice or snow will not spin, but will have a tendency to operate with the opposite wheel in a combined driving effort.

When performing the following procedures, refer to Part 4-1, Section 3 for cleaning and inspection procedures.

CARE OF AXLE

The lubricant level should be checked every 6000 miles, with the car in normal curb attitude. The lubricant level should be at the lower edge of the filler plug hole. It is unnecessary to periodically drain the axle lubricant. The factory fill should remain in the housing for the life of the car, except when repairs are made. The specified lubricant should be installed when the axle is overhauled.

2   IN-CAR ADJUSTMENTS AND REPAIRS

REAR AXLE SHAFT, WHEEL BEARING AND OIL SEAL REPLACEMENT

The rear axle shafts, wheel bearings, and oil seal can be replaced without removing the differential assembly from the axle housing.

1. Remove the wheel and tire from the brake drum.

2. Remove the nuts that secure the brake drum to the axle shaft flange, then remove the drum from flange.

3. Working through the hole provided in each axle shaft flange, remove the nuts that secure the wheel bearing retainer plate. Then pull the axle shaft assembly out of the axle housing (Fig. 3). **The brake carrier plate must not be dislodged. Install one nut to hold the plate in place after the axle shaft is removed.**

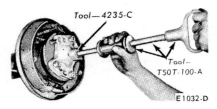

FIG. 3—Removing Axle Shaft

REMOVAL OF REAR WHEEL BEARING AND SEAL

Removal of the wheel bearings from the axle shaft makes them unfit for further use.

1. If the rear wheel bearing is to be replaced, loosen the inner retainer ring by nicking it deeply with a cold chisel in several places (Fig. 4). It will then slide off easily.

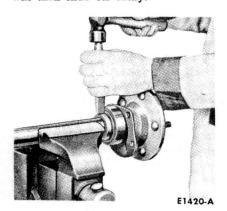

FIG. 4—Removing Rear Wheel Bearing Retainer Ring

2. On a Ford model, remove the bearing from the axle shaft with the tool shown in Fig. 5.

On a Mercury, remove the bearing from the axle shaft with the tool shown in Fig. 6.

3. **Whenever a rear axle shaft is removed, the oil seal must be replaced.** Remove the seal with tool 1175-AB and a slide hammer (Fig. 7).

INSTALLATION OF REAR WHEEL BEARING AND SEAL

1. Inspect the machined surface of

the axle shaft and the axle housing for rough spots or other irregularities which would affect the sealing action of the oil seal. Check the axle shaft splines for burrs, wear or twist. Carefully remove any burrs or rough spots. Replace worn or damaged parts.

2. Lightly coat wheel bearing bores with ball joint grease.

3. Place the retainer plate on the axle shaft, and press the new wheel bearing on the shaft with the tool shown in Fig. 5 (Ford model) or Fig. 8 (Mercury model). **Do not attempt to press on both the bearing and the inner retainer ring at the same time.**

4. Using the bearing installation tool (Ford—T60K-1225-A or Mercury—4234-4), press the bearing inner retainer ring on the shaft until the retainer seats firmly against the bearing.

5. Install the new oil seal with the tools shown in Fig. 9. **Be sure the new seal has been soaked in SAE 10 oil for ½ hour before installing it.** Wipe a small amount of oil resistant sealer on the outer edge of the seal before it is installed. **Do not put sealer on the sealing lip.**

INSTALLATION OF AXLE SHAFT

1. Place a new gasket on each side of the brake carrier plate, and then carefully slide the axle shaft into the housing so that the rough forging of the shaft will not damage the oil seal. Start the axle splines into the side gear, and push the shaft in until the bearing bottoms in the housing.

2. Install the bearing retainer plate and the nuts that secure it. Torque the nuts to specifications.

3. Install the brake drum and the drum retaining nuts.

4. Install the wheel and tire on the drum.

REMOVAL AND REPLACEMENT OF DRIVE PINION OIL SEAL

COLLAPSIBLE SPACER

The drive pinion oil seal can be replaced without removing the differential carrier assembly from the axle housing. (Soak new seals in SAE 10 oil for ½ hour before use).

1. Raise the car and install safety stands. Remove both rear wheels and brake drums.

2. Make scribe marks on the drive shaft end yoke and the axle U-joint flange to insure proper position of the drive shaft at assembly (Fig. 10).

Disconnect the drive shaft from the axle U-joint flange. **Be careful to avoid dropping the loose universal joint bearing cups.** Hold the cups on the spider with tape. Mark the cups so that they will be in their original position in relation to the flange when they are assembled. Remove the drive shaft from the transmission extension housing. Install an oil seal replacer tool in the transmission extension housing to prevent transmission fluid leakage. Refer to the transmission group for the appropriate tool.

3. Install an in-lb. torque wrench on the pinion nut. Record the torque required to maintain rotation of the pinion shaft through several revolutions.

4. Scribe the pinion shaft and the U-joint flange inner surface for assembly realignment. While holding the flange with the tool shown in Fig. 18 (Ford) or Fig. 19 (Mercury), remove the integral pinion nut and washer.

5. Clean the pinion bearing retainer around the oil seal. Place a drain pan under the seal, or raise the front of the car higher than the rear.

6. Using the tool shown in Fig. 20 (Ford) or Fig. 21 (Mercury), remove the U-joint flange.

7. Using the tool shown in Fig. 18 remove the drive pinion oil seal.

8. Clean the oil seal seat.

9. Coat the outer edge of the new seal with a small amount of oil resistant sealer. **Do not put any of the sealer on the sealing lip.** Install the seal in the retainer, using the applicable tool shown in Fig. 42.

10. Check splines on the pinion shaft to be sure they are free of burrs. If burrs are evident, remove them by using a fine crocus cloth, working in a rotational motion. Wipe the pinion shaft clean.

11. Apply a small amount of lubricant to U-joint splines.

Align scribe marks on U-joint flange and pinion shaft.

12. Install the U-joint flange using the tool shown in Fig. 41.

13. Install a new integral nut and washer on the pinion shaft. (Apply a small amount of lubricant on the washer side of the nut.)

14. Hold the flange with the tool shown in Fig. 20 or Fig. 21 while tightening nut.

15. Tighten the pinion shaft nut, rotating the pinion occasionally to insure proper bearing seating, and take frequent preload readings until the preload is at the original recorded

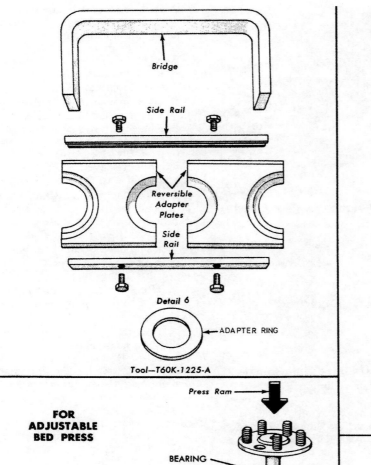

Bridge

Side Rail

Reversible Adapter Plates

Side Rail

Detail 6

ADAPTER RING

Tool—T60K-1225-A

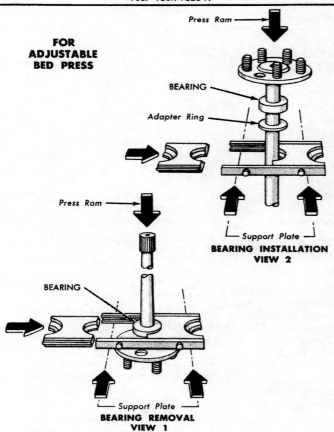

FOR ADJUSTABLE BED PRESS

Press Ram

BEARING

Adapter Ring

Support Plate

BEARING INSTALLATION VIEW 2

Press Ram

BEARING

Support Plate

BEARING REMOVAL VIEW 1

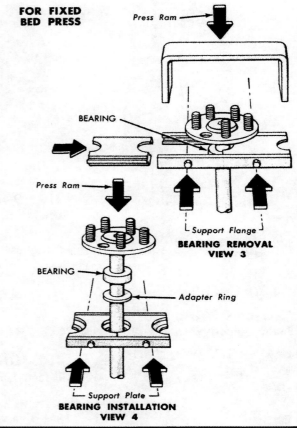

FOR FIXED BED PRESS

Press Ram

BEARING

Support Flange

BEARING REMOVAL VIEW 3

Press Ram

BEARING

Adapter Ring

Support Plate

BEARING INSTALLATION VIEW 4

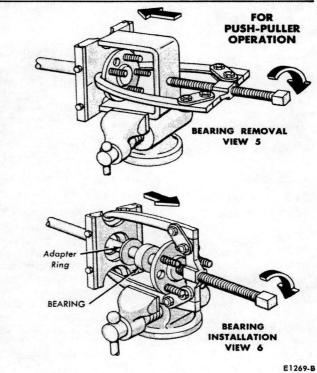

FOR PUSH-PULLER OPERATION

BEARING REMOVAL VIEW 5

Adapter Ring

BEARING

BEARING INSTALLATION VIEW 6

E1269-B

FIG. 5—Removing and Installing Wheel Bearing—Ford

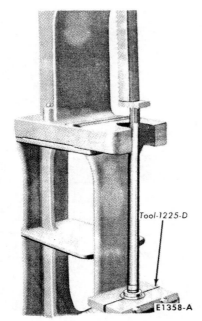

FIG. 6—Removing Wheel Bearing—Mercury

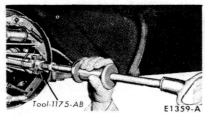

FIG. 7—Removing Rear Wheel Bearing Oil Seal

FIG. 8—Installing Wheel Bearing—Mercury

reading established in step 3.

16. After original preload has been reached, tighten the pinion nut slowly, until an additional preload of 8 to 14 in-lb over the original reading is reached. (The preload should not exceed 8 to 14 in-lb over the original reading, or bearing failure may result. Under no circumstances should the pinion nut be backed off to lessen preload. If this is done, a new pinion bearing spacer must be installed. In addition, the U-joint flange must never be hammered on, or pneumatic tools used.

FIG. 9—Installing Rear Wheel Bearing Oil Seal

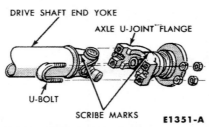

FIG. 10—Drive Shaft-To-Axle U-Joint Connection

17. Remove the oil seal replacer tool from the transmission extension housing. Install the front end of the drive shaft on the transmission output shaft.

18. Connect the rear end of the drive shaft to the axle U-joint flange, aligning the scribe marks made on the drive shaft end yoke and the axle U-joint flange (Fig. 10).

19. Check the lubricant level. Make sure the axle is in running position. Add whatever amount of specified lubricant is required to reach the lower edge of the filler plug hole.

REMOVAL AND REPLACEMENT OF DRIVE PINION OIL SEAL

SOLID SPACER

The drive pinion oil seal can be replaced without removing the differential carrier assembly from the axle housing. (Soak new seals in SAE 10 oil for ½ hour before use).

1. Make scribe marks on the drive shaft end yoke and the axle U-joint flange to insure proper position of the drive shaft at assembly (Fig. 10). Disconnect the drive shaft from the axle U-joint flange. **Be careful to avoid dropping the loose universal joint bearing cups.** Hold the cups on the spider with tape. Mark the cups so that they will be in their original position in relation to the flange when

they are assembled. Remove the drive shaft from the transmission extension housing. Install an oil seal replacer tool in the transmission extension housing to prevent transmission leakage. Refer to the transmission group for the appropriate tool.

2. Make punch marks on the end of the pinion shaft and the U-joint flange inner surface for realignment. While holding the flange with the tool shown in Fig. 18 (Ford) or Fig. 19 (Mercury), remove the integral pinion nut and washer.

3. Clean the pinion bearing retainer around the oil seal. Place a drain pan under the seal, or raise the front of the car higher than the rear.

4. Using the tool shown in Fig. 20 (Ford) or Fig. 21 (Mercury), remove the U-joint flange.

5. Using the tool shown in Fig. 18, remove the drive pinion oil seal.

6. Clean the oil seal seat.

7. Coat the outer edge of the new seal with a small amount of oil resistant sealer. **Do not put any of the sealer on the sealing lip.** Install the seal in the retainer, using the applicable tool shown in Fig. 42.

8. Check splines on the pinion shaft to be sure they are free of burrs. If burrs are evident, remove them with a fine crocus cloth, working in a rotational motion, then wipe clean. Apply a small quantity of lubricant to U-joint splines.

9. Install the U-joint flange using the tool shown in Fig. 41.

10. Install a new integral attaching nut and washer on the pinion shaft.

11. Tighten the pinion attaching nut, rotating the pinion several times to seat the bearing, then torque the pinion nut to 180-200 ft-lbs. Hold the flange with the tool shown in Fig. 18 or Fig. 19 while the nut is being tightened.

12. Remove the oil seal replacer tool from the transmission extension housing. Install the front end of the drive shaft on the transmission output shaft.

13. Connect the rear end of the drive shaft to the axle U-joint flange, aligning the scribe marks made on the drive shaft end yoke and the axle U-joint flange (Fig. 10).

14. Check the lubricant level, and add whatever amount of specified lubricant is necessary to reach the lower edge of the filler plug hole. Make sure the axle is in running position when the level is checked.

REMOVAL AND INSTALLATION OF THE ORIGINAL U-JOINT FLANGE (IN CAR)

Use procedure as outlined under Drive Pinion Oil Seal Replacement.

INSTALLATION OF A NEW UNIVERSAL JOINT FLANGE (IN CAR)

COLLAPSIBLE SPACER

1. Raise the car and install safety stands. Remove both rear wheels and brake drums.

2. Disconnect the drive shaft from the axle U-joint flange. **Be careful to avoid dropping the loose universal joint bearing cups. Hold the cups on the spider with tape.** Mark the cups so that they will be in their original position in relation to the flange when they are assembled. Remove the drive shaft from the transmission extension housing. Install an oil seal replacer tool in the transmission extension housing to prevent transmission fluid leakage. Refer to the transmission group for the appropriate tool.

3. Install an in-lb torque wrench on the pinion nut. Record the torque required to maintain rotation of the pinion shaft through several revolutions.

4. While holding the flange with the tool shown in Fig. 19 or Fig. 20, remove the integral pinion nut and washer.

5. Clean the pinion bearing retainer around the oil seal. Place a drain pan under the seal, or raise the front of the car higher than the rear.

6. Using the tool shown in Fig. 19 or Fig. 20, remove the U-joint flange.

7. Check splines on the pinion shaft to be sure they are free of burrs. If burrs are evident, remove them by using a fine crocus cloth, working in a rotational motion, then wipe clean. Apply a small amount of lubricant to U-joint splines.

8. Install the U-joint flange using the tool shown in Fig. 41.

9. Install a new integral nut and washer on the pinion shaft. (Apply a small amount of lubricant on the washer side of the nut.)

10. Hold the flange with the tool shown in Fig. 19 or Fig. 20 while the nut is being tightened.

11. Tighten the pinion shaft nut, rotating the pinion occasionally to insure proper bearing seating, and take frequent preload readings until the preload is at the original recorded reading established in step 3.

12. After original preload has been reached, tighten the pinion nut slowly, until an additional preload of 8 to 14 in-lb over the original reading is reached. (The preload should not exceed 8 to 14 in-lb over the original reading, or bearing failure may result.

Under no circumstances should the pinion nut be backed off to lessen preload. If this is done, a new pinion bearing spacer must be installed. In addition, the U-joint flange must never be hammered on, or power tools used.

13. Remove the oil seal replacer tool from the transmission extension housing. Install the front end of the drive shaft on the transmission output shaft.

14. Connect the rear end of the drive shaft to the axle U-joint flange, aligning the scribe marks made on the drive shaft end yoke and the axle U-joint flange (Fig. 10).

15. Check the lubricant level. **Make sure the axle is in running position.** Add whatever amount of specified lubricant is required to reach the lower edge of the filler plug hole.

INSTALLATION OF A NEW UNIVERSAL JOINT FLANGE (IN CAR)

SOLID SPACER

1. Disconnect the drive shaft from the axle U-joint flange. **Be careful to avoid dropping the loose universal**

joint bearing cups. Hold the cups on the spider with tape. Mark the cups so that they will be in their original position in relation to the flange when they are assembled. Remove the drive shaft from the transmission extension housing. Install an oil seal replacer tool in the transmission extension housing to prevent transmission leakage. Refer to the transmission group for the appropriate tool.

2. While holding the flange with the tool shown in Fig. 19 or Fig. 20, remove the integral pinion nut and washer.

3. Clean the pinion bearing retainer around the oil seal. Place a drain pan under the seal, or raise the front of the car higher than the rear.

4. Using the tool shown in Fig. 19 or Fig. 20, remove the U-joint flange.

5. Check splines on the pinion shaft to be sure they are free of burrs. If burrs are evident, remove them by using a fine crocus cloth, working in a rotational motion, then wipe clean. Apply a small amount of lubricant to U-joint splines.

6. Install the U-joint flange using the tool shown in Fig. 41.

7. Install integral retaining nut and washer on the pinion shaft.

8. Tighten the pinion retaining nut, rotating the pinion several times to seat the bearing, then torque the pinion retaining nut to 180-220 ft. lbs. Hold the flange with the tool shown in Fig. 19 or Fig. 20 while the nut is being tightened.

9. Remove the oil seal replacer tool from the transmission extension housing. Install the front end of the drive shaft on the transmission output shaft.

10. Connect the rear end of the drive shaft to the axle U-joint flange.

11. Check the lubricant level, and add whatever amount of specified lubricant is necessary to reach the lower edge of the filler plug hole. Make sure the axle is in running position when the level is checked.

3 REMOVAL AND INSTALLATION

CARRIER ASSEMBLY
REMOVAL

1. Raise the car on a hoist and remove the two rear wheels and tires.

2. Remove the two brake drums (3 Tinnerman nuts at each drum) from the axle shaft flange studs. If difficulty is experienced in removing the drums, remove the brake adjuster

knockout slug and back off the brake shoes.

3. Working through the hole provided in each axle shaft flange, remove the nuts that secure the rear wheel bearing retainer plate. Pull each axle shaft assembly out of the axle housing using axle shaft remover Tool 4235-C. Install a nut on one

of the brake carrier plate retaining bolts to hold the plate to the axle housing after the shaft has been removed. **Whenever a rear axle shaft is removed the wheel bearing oil seal must be replaced.** Remove both seals with tool 1175AB.

4. Make scribe marks on the drive shaft end yoke and the axle U-joint

flange to insure proper position at assembly. Disconnect the drive shaft at the rear axle U-joint. Hold the cups on the spider with tape. Mark the cups so that they will be in their original position relative to the flange when they are assembled. Remove the drive shaft from the transmission extension housing. Install an oil seal replacer tool in the housing to prevent transmission leakage. Refer to the transmission group for the appropriate tool.

5. Clean area around carrier to housing surface with a wire brush and wipe clean, to prevent dirt entry into the housing. Place a drain pan under the carrier and housing, remove the carrier retaining nuts, and drain the axle. Remove the carrier assembly from the axle housing.

INSTALLATION

1. Clean the axle housing and shafts using kerosene and swabs. To avoid contamination of the grease in the sealed ball bearings, do not allow any quantity of solvent directly on the wheel bearings. Clean the mating surfaces of the axle housing and carrier.

2. Position the differential carrier on the studs in the axle housing using a new gasket between carrier and housing. Install the carrier-to-housing retaining nuts, and torque them to specifications.

3. Remove the oil seal replacer tool from the transmission extension housing. Position the drive shaft so that the front U-joint slip yoke splines to the transmission output shaft.

4. Connect the drive shaft to the axle U-joint flange, aligning the scribe marks made on the drive shaft end yoke and the axle U-joint flange during the removal procedure (Fig. 10). Install the U-bolts and nuts and torque to specifications.

5. Soak two new rear wheel bearing oil seals in SAE 10 oil for ½ hour before installation. Wipe a small amount of an oil resistant sealer on the outer edge of each seal before it is installed. **Do not put any of the sealer on the sealing lip.** Install the oil seals in the ends of the rear axle housing with one of the tools shown in Fig. 9.

6. Install the two axle shaft assemblies in the axle housing. The shorter shaft goes into the left side of the housing.

When installing an axle shaft, place a new gasket on each side of the brake carrier plate and carefully slide the axle shaft into the housing so that

the rough forging of the shaft will not damage the oil seal. Start the axle splines into the differential side gear, and push the shaft in until the bearing bottoms in the housing.

7. Install the bearing retainers on the attaching bolts on the axle housing flanges. Install the nuts on the bolts and torque to specifications.

8. If the rear brake shoes were backed off, adjust the brakes as outlined in Part 2-1 and install rubber plugs in the adjuster slots.

9. Install the two rear brake drums and the drum Tinnerman nuts.

10. Install the rear wheels and tires.

11. Fill the rear axle with specified lubricant.

AXLE HOUSING

REMOVAL

1. Remove the carrier assembly from the axle housing as outlined in Differential Carrier Removal and Installation.

2. Position safety stands under the frame rear members, and support the axle housing with either a floor jack or hoist.

3. Disengage the brake line from the clips that retain the line to the axle housing.

4. Disconnect the vent tube from the rear axle housing.

5. Remove the brake carrier plate assemblies from the axle housing, and support them with wire. Do not disconnect the brake line.

6. Disconnect the lower studs of the two rear shock absorbers from the mounting brackets on the axle housing (Fig. 11).

7. Remove the retaining nut and washer, and disconnect the track bar from the mounting stud on the axle housing bracket.

8. Lower the axle housing until the coil springs are released. Lift out the coil springs.

9. Remove the nuts, washers and pivot bolts that connect the suspension lower arms to the axle housing. Disconnect both arms from the axle housing.

10. Disconnect the upper suspension arm from the axle housing by removing the pivot bolt, nut, lock washer and the two eccentric washers (Fig. 11).

11. Lower the axle housing and remove it from under the car.

AXLE HOUSING INSTALLATION

1. Transfer the track bar mounting stud and the axle vent from the

old to the new housing. The flat on the vent should be placed on the rear side of the axle housing.

2. Soak two new rear wheel bearing oil seals in SAE 10 oil for ½ hour before installation. Wipe a small amount of an oil resistant sealer on the outer edge of each seal before it is installed. **Do not put any of the sealer on the sealing lip.** Install the oil seals in the ends of the axle housing with one of the tools shown in Fig. 9.

3. Position the replacement axle housing under the car, and raise the axle with a hoist or floor jack. Connect the suspension lower arms to their mounting brackets on the axle housing with pivot bolts and nuts. **Do not tighten the bolts and nuts at this point.**

4. Position the suspension upper arm in its mounting bracket on the axle housing, and install the adjusting bolt, eccentric washers, lock washer and nut. **Leave the bolt and nut loose at this point.**

5. Position the brake lines to the axle housing, and secure with the retaining clips.

6. Install the brake carrier plates with new gaskets on the axle housing flanges.

7. Connect the track bar to the mounting stud, install the washer and retaining nut, and torque to specifications.

8. Position the rear coil springs in the pockets provided.

9. Connect the lower studs of the two rear shock absorbers to the mounting brackets on the axle housing. Install the attaching nuts, and torque to specifications.

10. Connect the vent tube to the vent on the housing.

11. Clean the mating surfaces of the axle housing and differential carrier. Position the carrier on the mounting studs on the housing using a new gasket between carrier and housing. Install the copper washers and the carrier-to-housing attaching nuts, and torque to specifications.

12. Make sure that both the front and rear pivot bolts of the upper and the two lower arms are loose, and then raise the axle assembly to controlled curb height (Fig. 12). Hold the axle at controlled curb height by placing blocks or pieces of steel pipe between the axle housing and the bumper rear screw on the side rail. (See specifications for dimensions)

13. With the axle at controlled curb height, torque the suspension

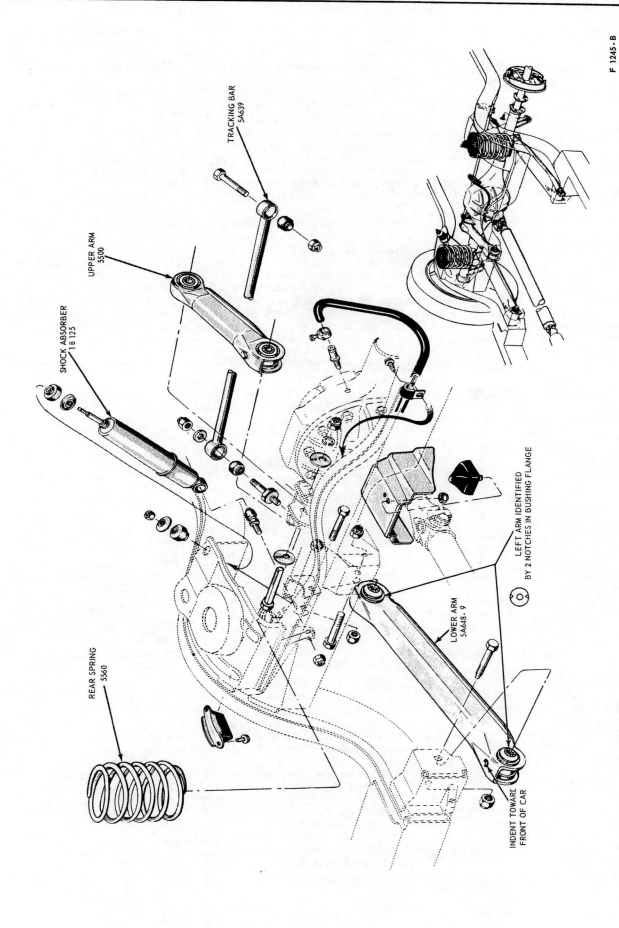

F 1245 - B

TRACKING BAR
5A639

UPPER ARM
5500

SHOCK ABSORBER
18125

LEFT ARM IDENTIFIED
BY 2 NOTCHES IN BUSHING FLANGE

LOWER ARM
5A648 - 9

REAR SPRING
5560

INDENT TOWARD
FRONT OF CAR

FIG. 11—Rear Axle Installation

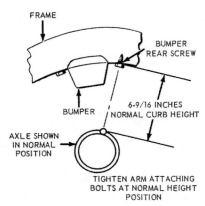

FRAME

BUMPER
REAR SCREW

BUMPER

6-9/16 INCHES
NORMAL CURB HEIGHT

AXLE SHOWN
IN NORMAL
POSITION

TIGHTEN ARM ATTACHING
BOLTS AT NORMAL HEIGHT
POSITION

E 1487-A

FIG. 12—Axle at Normal Curb Height

upper and lower arm front pivot bolts and nuts to specifications. Torque the lower arm-to-axle housing pivot bolts and nuts to specifications.

14. Remove the oil seal replacer tool from the transmission extension housing. Position the drive shaft so that the front U-joint slip yoke splines to the transmission output shaft.

15. Connect the drive shaft to the U-joint flange, aligning the scribe marks made on the drive shaft end yoke and the axle U-joint flange during the removal procedure (Fig. 10). Install the U-bolts and nuts and torque to specifications.

16. Place new gaskets on each side of the brake carrier plates and carefully slide the two axle shaft assemblies in the axle housing. The shorter shaft goes into the left side of the housing. Use care in sliding the axle shafts into the housing so that the rough forging of the shaft will not damage the oil seal. Start the axle splines into the differential side gear, and push the shaft in until the rear wheel bearing bottoms in the housing.

17. Install the rear wheel bearing retainers on the attaching bolts on the axle housing flanges. Install the nuts on the bolts and torque to specifications.

18. If the rear brake shoes were backed off, adjust the brakes as outlined in **Part 2-1**, and install rubber plugs in the adjuster slots.

19. Install the two rear brake drums and the drum attaching nuts.

20. Install the rear wheels and tires.

21. Fill the rear axle to the bottom of the filler plug hole with specified lubricant. Be sure that the axle is in operating position.

22. Road test the car to be sure that pinion and driveshaft angles are correct. Any shudder during heavy acceleration, or deceleration may require a pinion and driveshaft angle re-adjustment as detailed in **Driveshaft and Pinion Angle Adjustment, Part 3-1**.

4   MAJOR REPAIR OPERATIONS

DISASSEMBLY OF DIFFERENTIAL CARRIER

After mounting the carrier in a holding fixture, disassemble the carrier as outlined in the following procedures:

1. Mark one differential bearing cap and the mating bearing support with punch marks to help position the parts properly during assembly of the carrier. Also, mark one of the bearing adjusting nuts and the carrier with scribe marks for proper location during assembly.

2. Remove the adjusting nut locks, bearing caps, and adjusting nuts.

Then lift the differential case assembly out of the carrier. On the 9-⅜ inch ring gear differential, the bearing caps are fitted with dowel pins to prevent flexing. It is therefore necessary to pry upward on the ears located on each end of the bearing cap with a large screw driver to remove the bearing caps (Figs. 13 and 15). The 9 inch ring gear differential does not use the dowel pins under the bearing caps and may be removed by tapping the caps lightly with a soft mallet.

3. Remove the differential bearings with the tools shown in Fig. 14.

4. Mark the differential case, cover, and ring gear for assembly in the original position.

5. Remove the bolts that attach

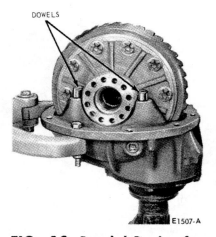

DOWELS

E1507-A

FIG. 13—Doweled Bearing Caps

the ring gear to the differential case. Press the gear from the case or tap it off with a soft-faced hammer.

6. With a drift, drive out the differential pinion shaft lock pin (Fig. 16), and separate the 2-piece differential case.

7. Drive out the pinion shaft with a brass drift (Fig. 17).

8. Remove the gears and thrust washers (Fig. 43).

REMOVAL AND DISASSEMBLY OF LIMITED-SLIP DIFFERENTIAL CASE

1. Remove the differential case

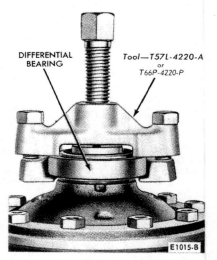

DIFFERENTIAL
BEARING

Tool—T57L-4220-A
or
T66P-4220-P

E1015-B

FIG. 14—Removing Differential Bearing—Ford

from the carrier and remove the bearings from the differential case in the same manner as the conventional differential case.

2. Place the differential case in a hydraulic press, and apply about one ton pressure across the case bearing hubs while removing the ring gear attaching bolts. Applying pressure will contain the spring pressure between the differential case and cover until after the bolts are removed, and thereby prevent stripping of the

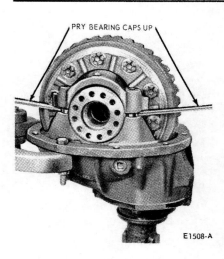

FIG. 15—Removing Doweled Bearing Caps

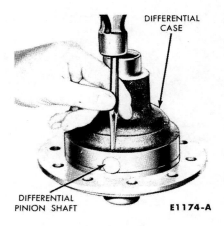

FIG. 16—Removing Differential Pinion Shaft Lock Pin

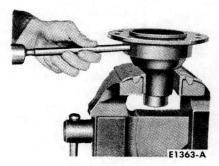

FIG. 17—Driving Out Differential Pinion Shaft

threads.

3. Release the hydraulic press ram, and remove differential case cover.

4. Remove the Belleville spring (Fig. 48).

5. Remove the steel and the bonded clutch plates.

6. Remove the differential clutch hub, side gear, and thrust washer.

7. Remove the ring gear from the differential case.

8. Drive out the differential pinion shaft lock pin.

9. With a brass drift, drive out the differential pinion shaft. Then remove the pinion gears, the other side gear, and thrust washers.

REMOVAL AND DISASSEMBLY OF DRIVE PINION AND BEARING RETAINER

1. Turn the carrier assembly upright and remove the pinion shaft nut (Fig. 18). On a Ford model, use the tool shown in Fig. 18. On a Mercury, leave the carrier mounted in the fixture as shown in Fig. 18, but use the tool shown in Fig. 19.

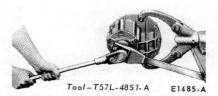

FIG. 18—Removing Pinion Shaft Nut—Ford

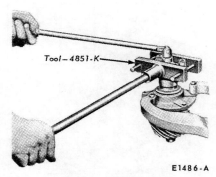

FIG. 19—U-Joint Flange Holding Tool—Mercury

2. Remove the U-joint flange from the pinion shaft (Fig. 20). On a Ford model, use the tool shown in Fig. 25. On a Mercury, leave the case mounted in the fixture as shown in Fig. 20, but use the tool shown in Fig. 21.

3. Remove the pinion seal (Fig. 27) and the slinger.

4. Remove the pinion, bearing, and retainer assembly from the carrier housing (Fig. 37). Measure the shim

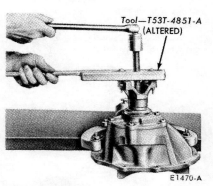

FIG. 20—Removing U-Joint Flange

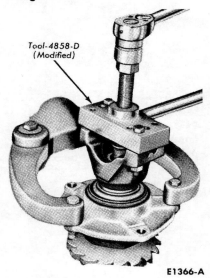

FIG. 21—Flange Removal Tool —Mercury

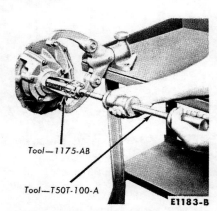

FIG. 22—Removing Pinion Seal

thickness with a micrometer. Record this original shim thickness. If a new gear set is installed during assembly, a new shim will have to be installed. The original shim thickness is one of the factors necessary in calculating the new shim thickness. **Extreme care must be taken not to damage the**

mounting surfaces of the retainer and carrier.

5. Place a protective sleeve (hose) on the pinion pilot bearing surface.

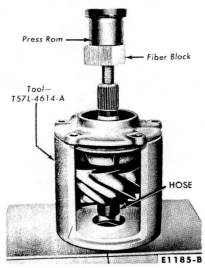

FIG. 23—Removing Pinion Front Bearing

Press the pinion shaft out of the pinion front bearing cone with the tool shown in Fig. 23.

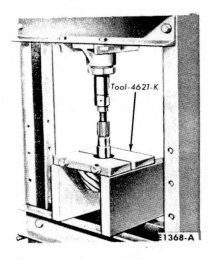

FIG. 24—Removing Pinion Rear Bearing Cone

6. Press the pinion shaft out of the pinion rear bearing cone and roller (Fig. 24).

PILOT BEARING

1. Remove the pilot bearing as shown in Fig. 25. Drive out the pilot bearing and the bearing retainer together.

PINION BEARING CUPS

Do not remove the pinion bearing cups from the retainer unless the cups are worn or damaged. The flange and pilot of the retainer are machined

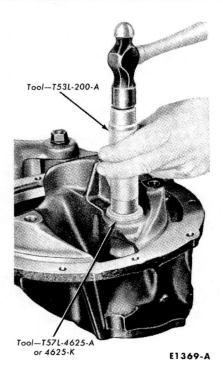

FIG. 25—Removing Pilot Bearing

during manufacture by locating on these cups after they are installed in their bores. If the cups are worn or damaged, they should be replaced.

Remove the bearing cups as shown in Figs. 26, 27 and 28. Install the cups as shown in Figs. 29 and 30.

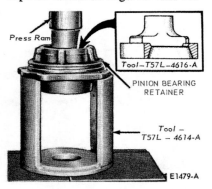

FIG. 26—Removing Pinion Front Bearing Cup—Ford

After the new cups are installed, make sure they are seated in the retainer by trying to insert a 0.0015-inch feeler gauge between the cup and the bottom of the bore.

Whenever the cups are replaced, the cone and roller assemblies should also be replaced.

DRIVE PINION AND RING GEAR SET

When replacing a ring gear and pinion, note that the original factory

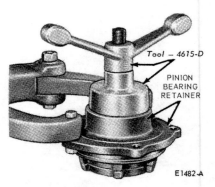

FIG. 27—Removing Pinion Front Bearing Cup—Mercury

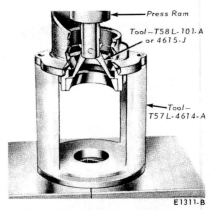

FIG. 28—Removing Pinion Rear Bearing Cup

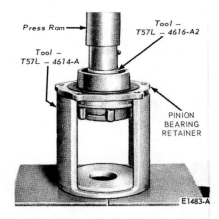

FIG. 29—Installing Pinion Front Bearing Cup

installed shim is of the correct thickness to adjust for individual variations in both the carrier housing dimension and in the original gear set dimension. Therefore, to select the correct shim thickness for the new gear set to be installed, follow these steps:

1. Measure the thickness of the **original shim** with a micrometer.

2. Note the shim adjustment num-

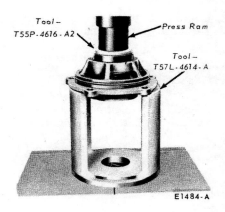

FIG. 30—Installing Pinion Rear Bearing Cup

ber on both the old pinion and the new pinion. Each pinion gear is marked with an adjustment number such as the +1 marking in Fig. 31.

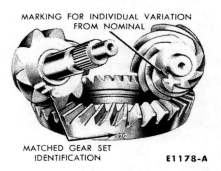

MARKING FOR INDIVIDUAL VARIATION FROM NOMINAL

MATCHED GEAR SET IDENTIFICATION

E1178-A

FIG. 31—Pinion and Ring Gear Markings

3. Refer to Part 4-3 to determine the correct amount of shim thickness change. The amount shown in the table under the old pinion shim adjustment number and in line with the new pinion number is the amount of **change** that should be made to the **original** shim thickness.

If the old pinion is marked +4, for example, and the new pinion is marked −2, the table indicates that 0.006 inch of shim stock should be removed from the **original** shim pack.

If the **original** shim pack was lost or if a new carrier housing is being installed, substitute a **nominal** (0.015 inch) shim for the **original** and follow the foregoing procedure for a trial build-up. If any further shim change is necessary, it will be indicated in the tooth pattern check.

A new ring gear and pinion should always be installed in an axle as a matched set (never separately). **Be sure that the same matching number**

appears on both the drive pinion and the ring gear. Note the number 170 in Fig. 31.

4. After determining the correct shim thickness as explained in the foregoing steps, install the new pinion and ring gear as outlined under Assembly.

DIFFERENTIAL CASE, BEARINGS AND RING GEAR

If the ring gear runout check (before disassembly) exceeded specifications, the condition may be caused by a warped gear, a defective case, or excessively worn differential bearings.

To determine the cause of excessive runout proceed as follows:

1. Assemble the two halves of the differential case together **without** the ring gear, and press the two differential side bearings on the case hubs.

2. Place the cups on the bearings and set the differential case in the carrier.

3. Install the bearing caps and adjusting nuts as outlined in steps 11 thru 14 under Assembly and Installation of Conventional Differential Case in this section.

4. Tighten the right nut two notches beyond the position where it first contacts the bearing cup. Rotate the differential case several revolutions in each direction while the bearings are loaded to seat the bearings in their cups. **This step is important.**

5. Again loosen the right nut to release the preload. Check to see that the left nut contacts the bearing cup. Using the dial indicator set-up shown in Fig. 11, Part 4-1, adjust the preload to 0.012 case spread for new bearings or 0.005 to 0.008 for the original bearings, if re-used.

6. Check the runout of the differential case flange with a dial indicator. If the runout does **not now** exceed specifications, install a new ring gear. If the runout still exceeds specifications, the ring gear is true and the trouble is due to either a defective case or worn bearings.

7. Remove the differential case from the carrier and remove the side bearings from the case.

8. Install **new** bearings on the case hubs, and again install the differential assembly in the carrier **without** the ring gear.

9. Check the case runout again with the new bearings. If the runout is **now** within limits, the old bearings were excessively worn. Use the new

bearings for assembly. If the runout is still excessive, the case is defective and should be replaced.

ASSEMBLY OF DIFFERENTIAL CARRIER

PILOT BEARING INSTALLATION

1. Drive the new pilot bearing inward until it bottoms, as shown in Fig. 32.

2. Using the same tool indicated in Fig. 32, install the new pilot bearing retainer with the concave side up.

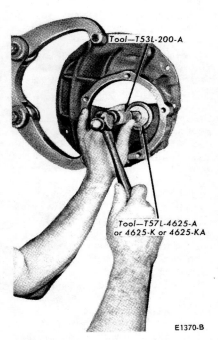

FIG. 32—Installing Pilot Bearing

AXLE WITH COLLAPSIBLE PINION BEARING SPACER

1. Install the drive pinion rear bearing cone and roller on the pinion shaft. On a Ford model, use the tools shown in Fig. 33. On a Mercury, use the tool shown in Fig. 34. Place a new spacer on the pinion shaft (Fig. 35).

2. Place the bearing retainer on the pinion shaft, and install the front bearing cone and roller. Press the front bearing cone and roller into position as shown in Fig. 36. Be careful not to crush the bearing spacer.

3. Lubricate the O-ring with axle lubricant and install it in its groove in the pinion retainer. Be careful not to twist it. Snap the O-ring into position.

4. Place the proper shim on the carrier housing and install the pinion and retainer assembly, being careful not to pinch the O-ring (Fig. 37).

5. Install the pinion retainer bolts. Torque the bolts to specification.

6. Place the slinger over the pinion shaft and against the front bearing.

7. Coat the outside edge of a new oil seal with a small amount of an oil resistant sealer. **Do not put any of the sealer on the sealing lip.** Install the seal in the bearing retainer (Fig. 42). New seals should be soaked in SAE 10 oil for ½ hour before use.

8. Install the U-joint flange (Fig. 44).

9. Start a new integral nut and washer on the pinion shaft.

10. Hold the flange with the tool shown in Fig. 18 (Ford) or Fig. 19 (Mercury), and torque the pinion shaft nut to 175 ft-lbs. **Do not exceed 175 ft-lbs at this time.**

11. Check the pinion bearing preload as shown in Fig. 38. If an inch-pound torque wrench is not available, tool 4209-C may be used in combination with tool 4209-C12. Correct preload will be obtained when the torque required to rotate the pinion in the retainer is as specified in Part 4-3. If the torque required to rotate the pinion is less than specified, tighten the pinion shaft nut a little at a time until the proper preload is established. **Do not overtighten the nut.** If excessive preload is obtained as a result of overtightening, replace the collapsible bearing spacer.

Do not back off the pinion shaft nut to establish pinion bearing preload. If the torque on the pinion shaft nut is less than 175 ft-lbs. after bearing preload is established, a new collapsible spacer must be used.

AXLE WITH SOLID PINION BEARING SPACER

(See Specifications, 4-3). The axle, used on a car equipped with a 427 CID engine, or on a car with a 390 CID engine and standard or overdrive transmission, employs a solid spacer between the pinion bearings. The spacer is serviced in fifteen sizes listed in Part 4-3. The manner of selecting the size spacer required for obtaining correct preload is included in the following assembly procedure.

1. Install the drive pinion rear bearing cone and roller assembly on the pinion shaft as shown in Figs. 33 or 34.

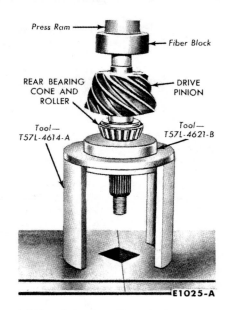

FIG. 33—Installing Pinion Rear Bearing Cone—Ford

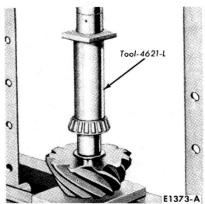

FIG. 34—Installing Pinion Rear Bearing Cone Mercury

2. Select a new solid spacer of the largest size (0.485 inch thick), and slide it over the pinion shaft against the rear bearing.

The pinion bearing preload can be accurately measured only when the pinion shaft nut is torqued to 180-220 ft-lbs. If a spacer smaller than required were used, the specified 180-220 ft-lbs torque would damage the bearings. For this reason, the largest spacer should be tried first. Then, if the bearings are too loose, the size of the spacer can be decreased until the correct preload is obtained.

3. Position the bearing retainer and cup assembly on the pinion shaft and install the front bearing cone and roller. Press the front cone and roller assembly into position, as shown in Fig. 36.

4. Mount the retainer in a holding

fixture as shown in Fig. 19, and place the slinger over the pinion shaft and against the front bearing.

5. Install the U-joint flange with the tool shown in Fig. 41.

6. Hold the flange with the tool shown in Fig. 20 or 19, and install the old pinion shaft nut. Using a ft-lb torque wrench, torque the nut to 180-220 ft-lbs. While tightening the nut, rotate the bearing retainer to determine the existence of any bearing preload which will be indicated by a slight drag in the rotation of the retainer.

DETERMINING SPACER SIZE FROM PRELOAD READING

1. If bearing drag indicates a preload condition exists, apply an in-lb torque wrench to the pinion nut as shown in Fig. 38 and read the torque required to turn the shaft. Effort should be 12-½ to 32-½ in-lbs.

2. If preload is the correct value, proceed with assembly procedure given in Final Assembly of Pinion and Retainer.

3. If preload exists, but is below specification, select the correct spacer from Table 1 and install, completing assembly as shown in Final Assembly of Pinion and Retainer.

DETERMINING SPACER SIZE FROM ENDPLAY READING

1. If no perceptible preload is felt when rotating the pinion shaft, install a dial indicator as shown in Fig. 39, so that the indicator point is resting on the end of the pinion gear shaft (companion flange end).

2. Use both hands to squeeze the pinion shaft and the bearing retainer together (Fig. 40). Record the endplay reading shown on the dial indicator.

3. Disassemble the pinion shaft and retainer and install the correct spacer as shown in Table 1.

4. Proceed with assembly of the pinion shaft and retainer as directed in **Final Assembly of Pinion and Retainer.**

FINAL ASSEMBLY OF PINION AND RETAINER

1. Install the drive pinion rear bearing cone and roller assembly on the pinion shaft as shown in Figs. 33 and 34.

2. Slide the correct spacer over the pinion shaft against the rear bearing.

3. Position the bearing retainer and cup assembly on the pinion shaft and install the front bearing cone and

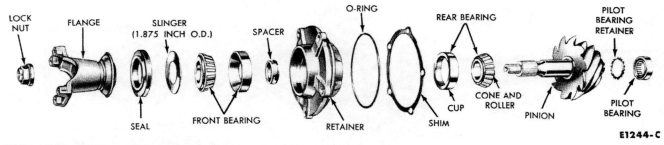

FIG. 35—Pinion and Bearing Retainer

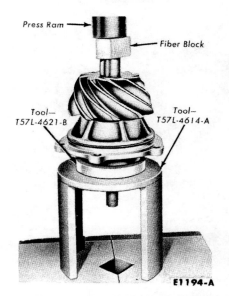

FIG. 36—Installing Pinion Front Bearing

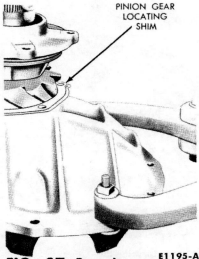

FIG. 37—Removing or Installing Pinion and Retainer Assembly

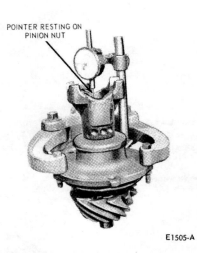

FIG. 39—End Play Indicator Installation

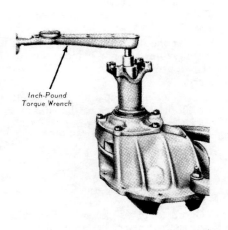

FIG. 38—Checking Pinion Bearing Preload

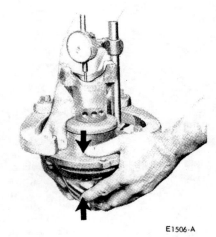

FIG. 40—Checking Pinion End Play

roller. Press the front cone and roller into position, as shown in Fig. 36.

4. Lubricate a new O-ring with axle lubricant and install it in the groove provided in the pinion retainer. Be careful not to twist the O-ring. Install it by snapping it into place.

5. Place the proper shim on the carrier housing and install the pinion and retainer assembly, being careful not to pinch the O-ring (Fig. 37).

6. Install the pinion retainer bolts. Torque the bolts to specification.

7. Place the slinger over the pinion shaft and against the front bearing.

8. Coat the outside edge of a new oil seal with a small amount of an oil-resistant sealer. Do not put any of the sealer on the sealing lip. Install the seal in the bearing retainer. (Fig. 42). (New seals should be soaked in SAE 10 oil for ½ hour before use).

9. Start a new integral nut and washer on the pinion shaft.

10. Hold the companion flange

with the tool shown in Fig. 19 or Fig. 20 and torque the pinion nut to specifications (200 ft-lbs).

11. With a new seal installed, pinion bearing preload should now read 17 to 32 in-lbs for new pinion bearings and new seal, or 8 to 14 in-lbs

for original bearings and a new seal.

ASSEMBLY AND INSTALLATION OF CONVENTIONAL DIFFERENTIAL CASE

1. Place a side gear and thrust washer in the differential case bore (Fig. 43). **Lubricate all differential**

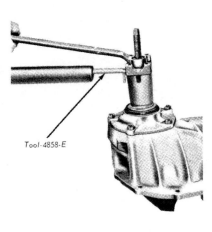

E1197-C

FIG. 41—Installing U-Joint Flange

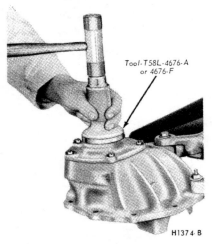

Tool-T58L-4676-A
or 4676-F

H1374-B

FIG. 42—Installing Oil Seal

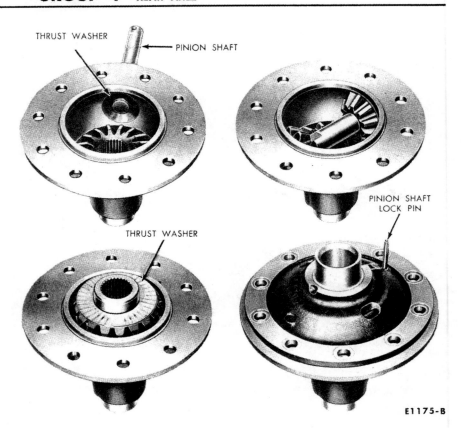

E1175-B

FIG. 43—Assembling of Differential Case

parts liberally with axle lubricant during assembly.

2. With a soft-faced hammer, drive the differential pinion shaft into the case only far enough to retain a pinion thrust washer and pinion gear.

3. Place the second pinion and thrust washer in position, and drive the pinion shaft into place. **Carefully line up the pinion shaft lock pin holes.**

4. Place the second side gear and thrust washer in position (Fig. 43), and install the cover on the differential case. Install the pinion shaft lock pin. A pinion or axle shaft spline can be inserted in the side gear spline to check for free rotation of the differential gears.

5. Insert two $7/16$ (N.F.) bolts two inches long through the differential case flange, and thread them three or

four turns into the ring gear as a guide in aligning the ring gear bolt holes. Press or tap the ring gear into position.

6. Install and tighten the ring gear bolts and washers evenly, and torque them alternately across the gear to specification.

7. If the differential bearings have been removed, press them on as shown in Fig. 44 (Ford) or 45 (Mercury).

8. Wipe a thin coating of lubricant on the bearing bores so that the differential bearing cups will move easily.

9. Place the cups on the bearings. If the gear set is on the **non-hunting** or **partial non-hunting** type, assemble the differential case and ring gear assembly in the carrier so that the marked tooth on the pinion indexes between the marked teeth on the ring gear as shown in Fig. 46.

In almost every case of improper assembly (gears assembled out of time), the noise level and probability of failure will be higher than they would be with properly assembled gears.

When installing the **hunting** type gear set (no timing marks), assemble the differential case and ring gear assembly in the carrier without regard

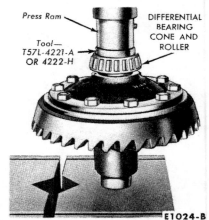

Press Ram

Tool—
T57L-4221-A
OR 4222-H

DIFFERENTIAL
BEARING
CONE AND
ROLLER

E1024-B

FIG. 44—Installing Differential Bearing—Ford

to the matching of any particular gear teeth.

10. Slide the assembly along the bores until a slight amount of backlash is felt between the gear teeth.

11. Set the adjusting nuts in the bores so that they just contact the bearing cups. The nuts should be engaged about the same number of threads on each side.

12. Carefully position the bearing caps on the carrier. Match the marks made when the caps were removed.

13. Install the bearing cap bolts and alternately torque them. The $9\frac{3}{8}$

Tool-4222-K

E1376-A

FIG. 45—Installing Differential Bearing—Mercury

PAINT MARKING INDICATES POSITION IN WHICH GEARS WERE LAPPED   E1335-A

FIG. 46—Gear Set Timing Marks

inch ring gear size axle requires 60-70 ft-lbs. The 8¾ inch and 9 inch ring gear size axles require 70-85 ft-lbs.

14. If the adjusting nuts do not turn freely as the cap bolts are tightened, remove the bearing caps and again inspect for damaged threads or incorrectly positioned caps. Tightening the bolts to the specified torque is done to be sure that the cups and adjusting nuts are seated. Loosen the cap bolts, and torque them to only 25 ft-lbs before making adjustments.

15. Adjust the backlash between the ring gear and pinion as outlined in Part 4-1, Section 2.

16. Be sure to make a final tooth pattern check before installing the carrier assembly in the axle housing.

ASSEMBLY AND INSTALLATION OF LIMITED-SLIP DIFFERENTIAL CASE

1. Place the inner side gear and thrust washer in the differential case (Fig. 47). **Lubricate all parts liberally with axle lubricant during assembly.**

2. With a soft-faced hammer, drive the pinion shaft into the case only far enough to retain a pinion thrust washer and pinion gear.

3. Place the second pinion and thrust washer in position, and drive the pinion shaft into place. **Carefully line up the pinion shaft lock pin**

holes.

4. Install the pinion shaft lock pin. **The lock pin must not extend beyond the surface of the case.**

5. Insert two 2-inch ⁷/₁₆ (N.F.) bolts through the differential case flange, and thread them three or four turns into the ring gear as a guide in aligning the ring gear bolt holes. Press or tap the ring gear into position.

6. Clamp the differential case in a soft-jawed vise. Install the differential outer side gear on the differential pinion gears. Place the clutch hub on the side gear. Place the thrust washer on the hub (Fig. 48).

7. To align the clutch plates during assembly, insert two ³/₁₆ x 2 inch dowel pins into the differential case. Place a steel plate on the differential

case so that the slots in the ears straddle the dowel pin (Fig. 48). **Lubricate all the Limited-slip differential parts with axle lubricant so that an accurate torque check can be made.**

8. Place a bonded plate on the steel plate. Make sure the bonded plate inner spline teeth properly engage the hub spline. Assemble the remaining plates: a steel plate, a bonded plate, a steel plate, a bonded plate, and lastly a steel plate.

9. Place the Belleville spring on the top steel plate. The Belleville spring is assembled with concave side down (Fig. 49). Carefully center the Belleville spring so that it will fit into the cover.

10. Place the differential case cover on the case (Fig. 50), position the case in a hydraulic press, and apply

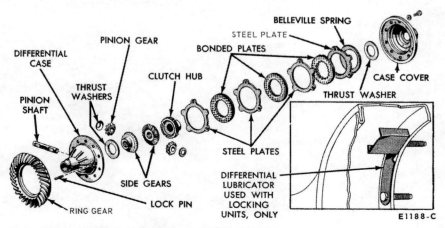

BELLEVILLE SPRING
PINION GEAR
STEEL PLATE
DIFFERENTIAL CASE
BONDED PLATES
CLUTCH HUB
CASE COVER
THRUST WASHERS
PINION SHAFT
THRUST WASHER
STEEL PLATES
SIDE GEARS
DIFFERENTIAL LUBRICATOR USED WITH LOCKING UNITS, ONLY
RING GEAR
LOCK PIN

E1188-C

FIG. 47—Limited Slip Differential Assembly

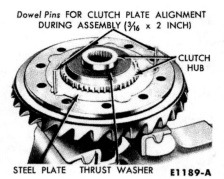

FIG. 48—Installing Clutch Plate

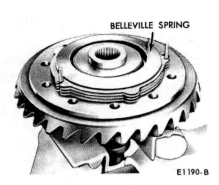

FIG. 49—Installing Belleville Spring

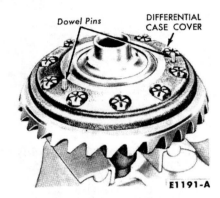

FIG. 50—Installing Differential Cover

FIG. 51—Checking Differential Torque

about one ton pressure across the case bearing hubs. As the pressure is applied, the Belleville spring is compressed and the differential case and cover are pulled together.

11. Install the case-to-ring gear bolts.

12. Remove the dowel pins.

13. Torque the case-to-ring gear bolts to specifications.

14. Check the torque required to rotate one side gear while the other side gear is held (Fig. 51). Ignore the torque required to start the side gear turning. The torque required to keep it moving steadily should be between 155 and 195 ft-lbs, if new clutch plates were installed. The torque

should be over 75 ft-lbs, if the original clutch plates were installed. If the required torque is not within these limits, check for improper assembly.

15. Install the side bearings on the differential case, and install the case in the carrier as described in steps 7 through 16 under Assembly and Installation of Conventional Differential Case. Adjust and check backlash between the ring gear and pinion as directed under Differential Bearing Pre-load Adjustments.

PART 4-3

SPECIFICATIONS

REAR AXLE ADJUSTMENTS

Description	Inches
Backlash Between Ring Gear and Pinion	0.008-0.012
Maximum Backlash Variation Between Teeth	0.003
Maximum Runout of Backface of Ring Gear as Assembled	0.003
Differential Side Gear Thrust Washer Thickness	0.030-0.032
Differential Pinion Gear Thrust Washer Thickness	0.030-0.032
Nominal Pinion Locating Shim	0.020
Available Pinion Shims (In steps of 0.001 inch)	0.010-0.29

DRIVE PINION BEARING SOLID SPACERS Used With 9⅜ Inch Ring Gear		
6 Spacers in increments of 0.002 inch	0.466 inch through	0.476 inch
9 Spacers in increments of 0.001 inch	0.477 inch through	0.485 inch

LUBRICANTS

Ring Gear Size	Ford Specification	Ford Part No.	Capacity (Pints)
8¾-9 inch Conventional	M2C57-A	CIAZ-19580E or F	5.0
8¾-9 inch Limited-Slip	M2C50A①	COLY-19A508-B	4.5①
9⅜ inch Conventional	M2C80A	CIA2-19580E or F	5.5
9⅜ inch Limited-Slip	M2C50A①	CIAZ-19580E or F	5.25①

①For all cars equipped with Equa-Lock axles, regardless of engine size, use M-2C50-A, plus 4 ounces of M-2C58-A (C1AA-19B546-A) additive per refill of M-2C50-A. SAE 90 grade lubricants are recommended for all temperatures above —25° F. For temperatures below —25°F, the same type of lubricant, but of an SAE 80 grade, should be used.

REAR AXLE RATIOS, GEAR AND CODE IDENTIFICATION

Identification Tag	Ring Gear Diameter (Inches)	Type of Differential	Axle Ratio	No. of Teeth	
				Ring Gear	Pinion
WDC-AS	8¾	Conventional	3.25:1	39	12
AT	9	Conventional	3.00:1	39	13
AU	9	Conventional	3.25:1	39	12
AV	8¾	Conventional	3.00:1	39	13
BS	9	Conventional	3.00:1	39	13
BT	9	Conventional	3.00:1	39	13
BU	8¾	Conventional	3.50:1	35	10
BV	8¾	Conventional	3.50:1	35	10
WDD-K	8¾	Conventional	3.50:1	35	10
L	8¾	Conventional	3.00:1	39	13
T	8¾	Conventional	3.00:1	39	13
U	8¾	Conventional	3.25:1	39	12
WDL-M	8¾	Limited-Slip	3.25:1	39	12
N	9	Limited-Slip	3.00:1	39	13
P	8¾	Limited-Slip	3.50:1	35	10
WDT-G	9⅜	Conventional	3.00:1	39	13
H	9⅜	Limited-Slip	3.00:1	39	13
J	9⅜	Conventional	3.25:1	39	12
L	9⅜	Conventional	3.50:1	35	10

DRIVE PINION ADJUSTING SHIM THICKNESS CHANGES (Inches)

New Pinion Marking	Old Pinion Marking								
	−4	−3	−2	−1	0	+1	+2	+3	+4
+4	+0.008	+0.007	+0.006	+0.005	+0.004	+0.003	+0.002	+0.001	0
+3	+0.007	+0.006	+0.005	+0.004	+0.003	+0.002	+0.001	0	−0.001
+2	+0.006	+0.005	+0.004	+0.003	+0.002	+0.001	0	−0.001	−0.002
+1	+0.005	+0.004	+0.003	+0.002	+0.001	0	−0.001	−0.002	−0.003
0	+0.004	+0.003	+0.002	+0.001	0	−0.001	−0.002	−0.003	−0.004
−1	+0.003	+0.002	+0.001	0	−0.001	−0.002	−0.003	−0.004	−0.005
−2	+0.002	+0.001	0	−0.001	−0.002	−0.003	−0.004	−0.005	−0.006
−3	+0.001	0	−0.001	−0.002	−0.003	−0.004	−0.005	−0.006	−0.007
−4	0	−0.001	−0.002	−0.003	−0.004	−0.005	−0.006	−0.007	−0.008

TORQUE LIMITS (Ft-Lbs)

Differential Bearing Cap Bolts (Doweled—9⅜" Gear)	60-70
Differential Bearing Cap Bolts (8¾-9" Gear)	70-85
Differential Bearing Adjusting Nut Lock Bolts	12-25
Carrier to Housing Stud Nuts	30-40
Pinion Retainer to Carrier Bolts	30-45*
Ring Gear Attaching Bolts	65-80
Rear Axle Shaft Bearing Retainer Bolts	55-65
Rear Shock Absorber to Rear Spring Clip Plate Assembly Nuts	15-25
Pinion Flange U-Bolt Nuts	15-20
Spring Clip Nuts (Rear Springs to Axle Housing)	30-45
Minimum Torque Required to Tighten Pinion Nut to Obtain Correct Pinion Bearing Preload (9⅜" Ring Gear)	180-220

Pinion Bearing Preload (Collapsible Spacer)	New Bearings	22-32 in-lbs
	Used Bearings	10-14 in-lbs
Pinion Bearing Preload (Solid Spacer)	Without Seal	12½-32½ in-lbs
	Seal in Place	15-35 in-lbs
Differential Bearing Preload Case Spread	(New Brgs)	0.012
	(Original Bearings)	0.005-0.008

*Torque 3 pinion bumper bolts 25-40

REAR AXLES WITH LIMITED-SLIP DIFFERENTIAL

TORQUE CHECK		
Minimum Torque required to turn Axle Shaft and Side Gear with One Wheel on the Ground		75 ft-lbs
Bench Check After Assembly	With New Clutch Plates	155-195 ft-lbs
	With Original Clutch Plates	75 ft-lbs minimum

SPECIAL TOOLS

Ford Tool No.	Former No.	Description
T59L-4204-A	42211 or 42211-A	Limited-Slip Differential Check
T57L-500-A	6005-M 6005-MS	Bench Fixture
T50T-100-A	B-160	Impact Hammer
TOOL-4235-C	4235C	Axle Shaft Remover
T60K-1225-A	1225-B, C, D	Rear Wheel Bearing Remover and Installer
TOOL-1225-D	—	Rear Wheel Bearing Remover
TOOL-4234-4	4234-A	Rear Wheel Bearing Installer
TOOL-1177	4245-B	Rear Wheel Bearing Oil Seal Installer
TOOL-1175-AB	1175-AB	Rear Wheel Bearing Oil Seal Remover
T57L-4220-A		Differential Bearing Remover
TOOL-4221-AE TOOL-4221-AF T66P-4220-P	4221-AF	Differential Bearing Remover
TOOL-4851-K	T57L-4851-A 4851-K	U-Joint Flange Holder
T53T-4851-A	4851-A, D	U-Joint Flange Remover
TOOL-4858-D	—	U-Joint Flange Remover
T57L-4614-A	4614	Drive Pinion Retainer Support
TOOL-4621-K	4621-K	Pinion Rear Bearing Cone Remover
T53L-200-A	—	Handle Adapter
T57L-4625-A or TOOL-4625-K	4625-K	Pinion Pilot Bearing Remover and Installer
T57L-4616-A or TOOL-4615-D	—	Pinion Front Bearing Cup Remover and Replacer
T58L-101-A	—	Puller Attachment—For Bearing Cup Removal
T55P-4616-A2	—	Pinion Rear Bearing Cup Remover and Replacer
T57L-4621-B or TOOL-4621-L	—	Pinion Rear Bearing Cone Installer
T58L-4676-A	4676-F	Drive Pinion Oil Seal Replacer
TOOL-4858-E	4858-E	U-Joint Flange and Pinion Bearing Replacer
T57L-4221-A or TOOL-4222-K	4222-H	Differential Bearing Installer

DRIVE SHAFT AND CLUTCH

GROUP 5

PART 5-1   DRIVE SHAFT

1 TROUBLE DIAGNOSIS

DRIVE SHAFT TROUBLE DIAGNOSIS AND POSSIBLE CAUSES

DRIVE SHAFT VIBRATION	Undercoating or other foreign material on shaft. Universal joint U-bolts loose. Universal joints worn, or lack of lubricant. Drive shaft mis-aligned (drive line angle). Drive shaft and universal joints	180° out of phase. Broken rear spring center bolt. Broken rear spring. Rear springs not matched (sagged to one side). Drive shaft damaged (bent) or out of balance (missing balance weights).
U-JOINT NOISE	Universal joint U-bolts loose. Lack of lubrication.	Worn U-bolts. Worn needle bearings.

2 DESCRIPTION AND OPERATION

The drive shaft is the means of transferring power from the engine, through the transmission, to the differential in the rear axle, and then to the rear wheels. The drive shaft incorporates two universal joints and a slip yoke. The universal joints (Fig. 1) are provided with a threaded plug which can be removed to lubricate them when necessary. The splines in the yoke and on the transmission output shaft permit the drive shaft to move forward and rearward as the axle moves up and down.

All drive shafts are balanced. If the car is to be undercoated, cover the drive shaft and universal joints to prevent application of the undercoating material.

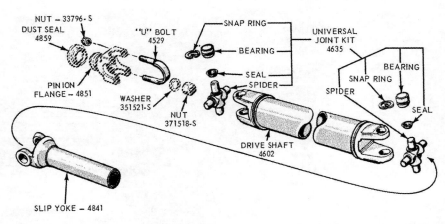

FIG. 1—Drive Shaft and Universal Joints Disassembled

3 REPLACEMENT

REMOVAL

1. To maintain drive line balance, mark the relationship of the rear drive shaft yoke and the drive pinion flange of the axle (if the yellow alignment marks are not visible) with the shaft so that they may be installed in their original positions.

2. Disconnect the rear U-joint from the axle drive pinion flange. Wrap tape around the loose bearing caps to prevent them from falling off the spider. Pull the drive shaft toward the rear of the car until the slip yoke clears the transmission extension housing and the seal. Install the appropriate tool in the extension housing to prevent lubricant leakage.

3. Place the drive shaft in a vise being careful not to damage it.

4. Remove the snap rings that retain the bearings in the slip yoke and in the drive shaft.

5. Position the tool shown in Fig. 2 on the shaft and press the bearing out of the slip yoke. If the bearing cannot be pressed all the way out of the yoke, remove it with vise grip or channel lock pliers.

6. Reposition the tool to press on the spider to remove the bearing from the opposite side of the yoke.

7. Remove the yoke from the spider.

8. Remove the bearings and spider from the drive shaft in the same manner.

9. Clean all foreign matter from the yoke area at each end of the drive shaft.

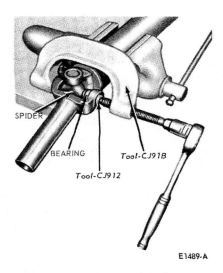

FIG. 2—Removing Universal Joint Bearing

INSTALLATION

1. Start a new bearing into the yoke at the rear of the drive shaft.

2. Position the spider in the rear yoke and press the bearing ¼ inch below the surface (Fig. 3).

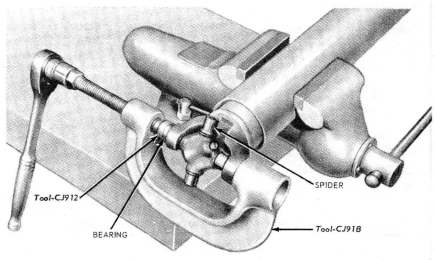

FIG. 3—Installing Universal Joint Bearing

3. Remove the tool and install a new snap ring.

4. Start a new bearing into the opposite side of the yoke.

5. Install the tool and press on the bearing until the opposite bearing contacts the snap ring.

6. Remove the tool and install a new snap ring. It may be necessary to grind the surface of the snap ring to permit easier entry.

7. Reposition the drive shaft and install the new spider and two new bearings in the same manner as the rear yoke.

8. Position the slip yoke on the spider and install two new bearings

and snap rings.

9. Check the joint for freedom of movement. If a bind has resulted from misalignment during the foregoing procedures, a sharp rap on the yokes with a brass hammer will seat the bearing needles and usually provide freedom of movement. Care must be taken to support the shaft end during this operation, as well as preventing blows to the bearings themselves. Do not install the drive shaft unless the universal joints are free of bind.

10. If either the rubber seal on the output shaft or the seal in the end of the transmission extension housing is damaged in any manner, replace the seal or seals as required. Also, if the lugs on the axle pinion flange are shaved or distorted so that the bearings slide, replace the flange.

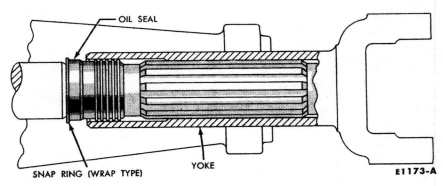

FIG. 4—Output Shaft Spline Seal

11. Lubricate the yoke spline with B8A-19589-A lubricant. This spline is sealed so that the transmission fluid does not "wash" away the spline lubricant (Fig. 4). Remove the tool from the extension housing. Install the yoke on the transmission output shaft.

Install the drive shaft so that the index marks or the yellow mark (if visible) on the yoke is in line with the yellow mark on the axle pinion flange. This prevents vibration which occurs when the balance of the shaft and balance of the axle pinion flange become additive instead of neutraliz-

ing. If a vibration exists, the drive shaft should be disconnected from the axle, rotated 180° and reinstalled.

12. Install the U-bolts and nuts that attach the U-joint to the drive pinion flange. Torque the U-bolt nuts to 12-15 ft.-lbs.

PART 5-2 GENERAL CLUTCH SERVICE

1 DIAGNOSIS AND TESTING

DIAGNOSIS GUIDE—CLUTCH

TROUBLE SYMPTOMS	POSSIBLE CAUSES	CORRECTION
LOSS OF OR EXCESSIVE CLUTCH PEDAL FREE PLAY AND/OR INADEQUATE RESERVE	1. Clutch linkage out of adjustment. 2. Worn clutch disc. 3. Bent or cracked equalizer bar.	1. Adjust clutch linkage. 2-3. Replace worn or defective parts.
CLUTCH PEDAL HANG UP OR EXCESSIVE CLUTCH PEDAL EFFORT	**CLUTCH** 1. Incorrect assist spring over center adjustment. 2. Assist spring not positioned properly. 3. Binding at pedal support bracket, or equalizer rod at firewall. **RELEASE BEARING** 1. Lack of lube on transmission input shaft bearing retainer.	1. Adjust over center spring and clutch total travel. 2. Install correctly. 3. Lubricate with engine oil or replace support bracket bushing if defective. 1. Clean and lubricate retainer with thin coat of Lithium base grease (no Polyethylene).
CLUTCH NOISY WHEN PEDAL FREE TRAVEL IS TAKEN OUT, ENGINE RUNNING	1. Release bearing failure due to: A. improper travel adjustment B. bearing cocked on hub C. release lever out of plane D. flywheel housing misalignment E. excessive crankshaft end play	1. A. Adjust travel to specification. B. Install correctly. C. Check fulcrum plate and return spring. Install correctly. D. Align to specification. E. Repair to specifications.
CLUTCH NOISY WITH ENGINE OFF	1. Insufficient lubricant on assist spring seats. 2. Clutch assist spring clunking. 3. Binding at pedal support bracket or equalizer rod at fire wall.	1. Lubricate linkage and/or spring seats. 2. Lubricate spring ends. 3. Lubricate with engine oil or replace support bracket bushing if defective.

DIAGNOSIS GUIDE—CLUTCH (Continued)

TROUBLE SYMPTOMS	POSSIBLE CAUSES	CORRECTION

CLUTCH SLIPS OR CHATTERS	1. Incorrect pedal free travel.
	 2. Worn or contaminated clutch lining.
	 3. Grease or oil on clutch facings from:
	   A. release bearing
	   B. engine
	   C. release lever
	   D. pilot bearing
	   E. transmission
		1. Adjust travel to specification.
		 2-3. Replace defective parts. (If grease or oil is causing the clutch to slip, replace the disc. Remove the grease or oil from the pressure plate and re-use if it is not burned or scored).

THUD	1. Excessive engine crankshaft end play.	1. Repair to specification.
CLUTCH PEDAL SCRUBBING—ENGINE OFF	1. Pedal push rod rubbing on firewall felt and insulator. 2. Pedal shaft binding at support bracket. 3. Lack of lube on transmission input shaft bearing retainer.	1. Lubricate and check clearance. 2. Lubricate with engine oil or replace support bracket bushing if defective. 3. Clean and lubricate retainer with a thin coat of Lithium base grease (no Polyethylene).

2 FLYWHEEL HOUSING ALIGNMENT

Alignment of the flywheel housing bore and rear face with the engine should be checked as a possible cause of any of the following troubles: excessive transmission gear wear, transmission jumping out of gear, especially third gear, drive line vibration, excessive pilot bushing wear, noisy release bearing, or excessive clutch spin time.

INSPECTION

1. With the clutch release bearing removed, install the indicator pilot tool shown in Fig. 1.
2. Clean the faces of the flywheel housing bolt bosses, and remove all burrs, nicks, and paint from the mounting face of the housing.
3. Install the dial indicator on the pilot and adjust the holder so the button will contact a circumference just inside of the transmission mounting holes.
4. Push the flywheel forward to remove crankshaft end play. Set the dial indicator face to read zero.
5. Remove the spark plugs to alleviate compression.
6. Pull the engine crankshaft

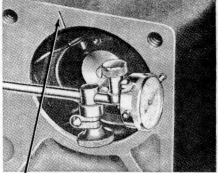
MAXIMUM FACE RUN OUT + 0.009 INCH

MAXIMUM NEGATIVE BORE RUN OUT 0.015 INCH   C1017-C

FIG. 1—Flywheel Housing Alignment Check

through one revolution. The crankshaft must be held in the forward position while rotating it.

7. Note the indicator reading and mark the maximum point of runout on the face of the housing (Fig. 1).
8. Position the dial indicator to check bore alignment (Fig. 1). The bore must be clean and free of burrs, nicks and paint.
9. Pull the crankshaft through one revolution. Note the indicator reading and mark the maximum point of

runout on the face of the housing as shown in Fig. 1.

10. Remove the dial indicator from the crankshaft and the housing.
11. Select the Dia-L-Igner pilot (Fig. 3) which will fit snugly in the bore of the flywheel housing.
12. Press the pilot into place on the locator on the back of the dial.
13. Position the Dia-L-Igner on the face of the housing (Fig. 2) with the pilot in the bore.
14. Rotate the face runout arrow

to the positive face runout mark on the housing.

15. Without moving the face runout arrow, rotate arrow **A** until it is at the negative bore reading.

16. Slide arrow **A** to register the amount of bore runout on the—.010—line of the white scale. Use the scale No. to coincide with the pilot being used.

17. Rotate arrow **B** until it points in the direction of the face runout arrow and its center line is parallel to the center line of the face runout arrow.

18. Determine the amount of the face runout on the **B** arrow scale.

19. The value of the circular line beneath the amount of face runout will be the desired reading. If the reading is in excess of 0.014 inch the housing alignment is unacceptable.

20. Remove the Dial-L-Igner gauge from the flywheel housing.

21. Install the spark plugs and connect the wires.

CORRECTION

ENGINE IN CAR

Since any change in face alignment will change bore alignment, it may be possible to correct bore alignment by changing face alignment. Face alignment can be changed by

shimming between the flywheel housing and engine. Fig. 4 shows the type of shim which can be fabricated.

Not more than 0.010 inch thickness shims may be used between the the flywheel housing and engine. If a 0.010-inch shim will not bring face and bore alignment within limits, replace the flywheel housing.

The shim required is one half the maximum (−) indicator reading, and should be located at the point of maximum minus (−) indicator reading.

If both the bore and face alignment are out of limits, shim between the flywheel housing and engine to bring face alignment within limits. Check the bore alignment.

If the bore alignment is out of limits and the face alignment is within limits, shim the flywheel housing to the limit of face misalignment and check the bore alignment. If it is not within limits, replace the housing.

ENGINE OUT OF CAR

The same procedure to correct alignment may be used with the engine out of the car or in the car, up to the point of replacing the flywheel housing. If the bore alignment

cannot be brought within limits by shimming, follow this procedure:

1. Remove the flywheel housing from the engine and remove the dowel pins. Install the flywheel housing and tighten the attaching bolts.

2. Install the dial indicator (Fig. 1). Check the face alignment, and shim as required to bring face alignment within limits.

3. Position the indicator to check the bore alignment. If the bore alignment is not within limits, reduce the tension on the flywheel housing attaching bolts so that the housing can be moved by striking it with a lead hammer or a block of wood and a steel hammer.

4. The lateral alignment should be brought within limits so that an indicator reading is within limits between the 9 o'clock and 3 o'clock positions on the bore circle. When the lateral alignment is within limits, the housing usually can be moved straight up or down without disturbing the lateral alignment. When alignment is within limits, torque the housing bolts and recheck bore alignment.

5. If the flywheel housing cannot be moved enough to bring the alignment within limits, mark the holes restricting movement, and then remove the housing and drill the marked bolt holes $\frac{1}{32}$ inch larger.

6. When the flywheel housing bore alignment is within limits and the attaching bolts are at normal torque, hand ream the dowel pin holes $\frac{1}{32}$ inch larger. Use a straight reamer and ream from the flywheel housing side. Oversize dowel pins can be made from drill rod stock.

7. Remove the flywheel housing and then install the oversize dowel pins in the cylinder block. Complete the assembly in the usual way.

8. Recheck the flywheel housing with the Dia-L-Igner gauge to make sure that the housing is within the specified limits.

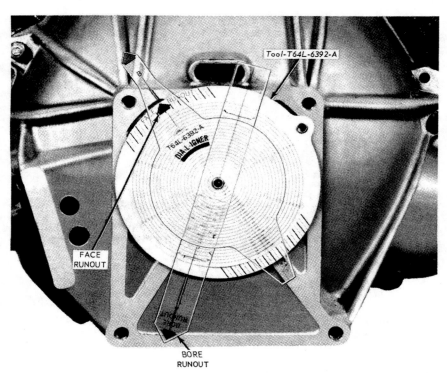

FIG. 2—Dia-L-Igner Gauge Installed

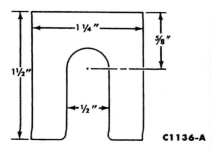

FIG. 4—Fabricated Flywheel Housing Shim

C1467-A

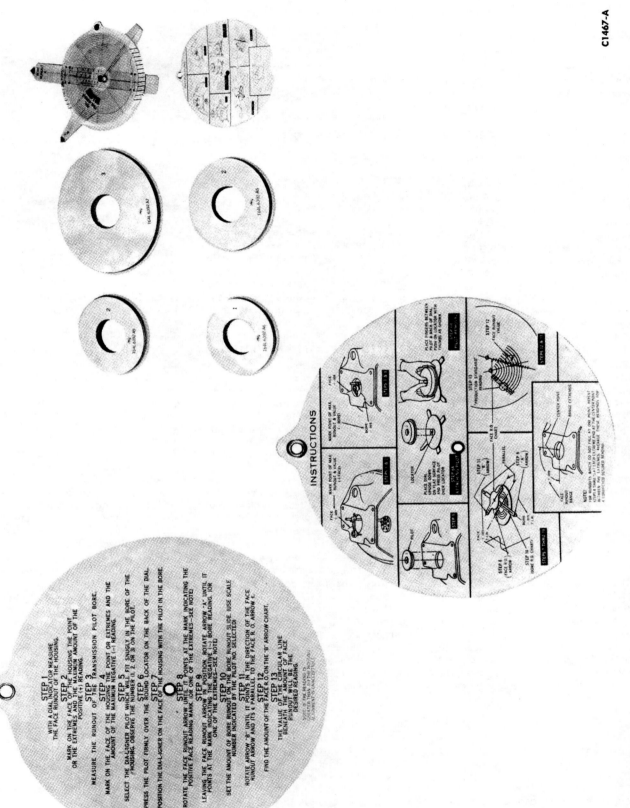

FIG. 3—Dia-L-Igner Gauge

3 CLEANING AND INSPECTION

RELEASE BEARING

Wipe all oil and dirt off the release bearing. **The bearing is pre-lubricated and should not be cleaned with solvent.**

Inspect the bearing retainer for loose spring clips and rivets.

Inspect the release bearing assembly for burrs which may cause the assembly to drag on the transmission bearing retainer. Any such burrs should be cleaned up with fine crocus cloth. If burrs are found, inspect the transmission input shaft bearing retainer for evidence of scoring. Any scoring should be polished out with crocus cloth. Coat the bearing retainer with a thin film of lithium-base grease (C3VY-195 86-A). Prior to release bearing installation, apply a light film of Lubriplate on both sides of the release lever fork where it contacts the release bearing hub and retaining springs. Apply a light film of Lubriplate to the release bearing surface that contacts the pressure plate fingers. Care must be exercised when applying lubricants to the release bearing, release bearing hub and the release lever fork to avoid excessive grease from contaminating the clutch disc.

Hold the bearing inner race and rotate the outer race while applying pressure to it. If the bearing rotation is rough or noisy, replace the bearing.

Most release bearing failures are caused by improper clutch pedal adjustments. If the clutch linkage does not have enough free travel, the release bearing will constantly touch the release fingers and will spin whenever the engine is running.

When installing a release bearing, use the tool shown in Fig. 5.

Release bearing failure can be caused by the release lever contact points being out of plane. Check the wear on the release bearing assembly where the release lever contacts it.

If one side of the assembly shows more wear than the other, the release lever is bent out of plane, or is not centering on the bracket on the flywheel housing.

Misalignment between the engine and transmission can cause release

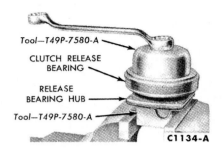

FIG. 5—Installing Clutch Disc-Typical

bearing failure. Other symptoms of misalignment are: transmission jumping out of gear, especially third gear, drive line vibration; excessive wear in the pilot bushing, excessive clutch disc spin time resulting in gear clash, and excessive transmission gear wear.

PRESSURE PLATE AND COVER

Inspect the surface of the pressure plate for burn marks, scores, or ridges. Generally, pressure plate resurfacing is not recommended. However, minor burn marks, scores, or ridges may be removed. During the resurfacing process, the flatness of the pressure plate must be maintained. If the pressure plate is badly heat-checked or deeply scored, replace the pressure plate and cover assembly. Clean pressure plate and flywheel surfaces with a suitable solvent, such as carbon tetrachloride, to be sure the surfaces are free from any oil film. **Do not use cleaners with petroleum base, and do not immerse the pressure plate in the solvent.**

Place the plate on the floor, being careful not to score or scratch the surface. Force each individual finger down, then release quickly. If the finger does not return quickly, a binding condition is indicated, and the pressure plate should be replaced.

The pressure plate should be lubricated with a lithium-base grease between the driving lugs and the edges of the pressure plate openings as shown in Fig. 6. Depress the pressure plate fingers fully, apply the lubricant, and then move the fingers up and down until the lubricant is

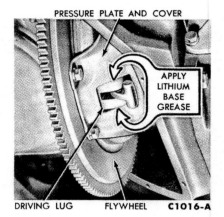

FIG. 6—Pressure Plate Lubrication Points

worked in. **Do not apply excessive lubricant.**

CLUTCH DISC

Inspect the clutch disc facings for oil or grease. **Eliminate the source of any oil or grease before replacing the disc.** An excessive amount of grease in the pilot bushing or release bearing hub will find its way to the disc facings. Too much lubricant in the transmission or a plugged transmission vent will force the transmission lubricant out the input shaft and onto the disc facings.

Inspect the clutch disc for worn or loose facings. Check the disc for distortion and for loose rivets at the hub. Check for broken springs. **Springs loose enough to rattle will not cause noise when the car is operating.** Replace the disc assembly if any of these defects are present. **Be especially careful when installing a new disc to avoid dropping it or contaminating it with oil or grease.**

PILOT BUSHING

Check the fit of the clutch pilot bushing in the bore of the crankshaft.

The bushing is pressed into the crankshaft and should not be loose. Inspect the inner surface of the bushing for wear or a bell-mouthed condition. If the bushing is worn or damaged, replace the bushing with a new service bearing. Refer to the applicable engine for the replacement procedure.

PART 5-3 CLUTCH

1 DESCRIPTION AND OPERATION

DESCRIPTION

The clutch is of the centrifugal single dry disc type and consists of the clutch disc, pressure plate and the clutch release bearing (Fig. 1).

OPERATION

The clutch is actuated by a clutch pedal and a series of mechanical linkage.

When the clutch pedal is in the engaged position, the clutch disc facings are clamped between the friction surface of the engine flywheel and the face of the clutch pressure plate, thereby connecting engine power to the transmission. Depressing the clutch pedal actuates the clutch release shaft fork which moves the clutch release bearing against the clutch fingers. This, in turn, moves the pressure plate away from the clutch disc. Since the disc is splined to the transmission input shaft, the clutch disc and transmission input shaft will stop when the clutch is disengaged, thereby disconnecting engine power from the transmission.

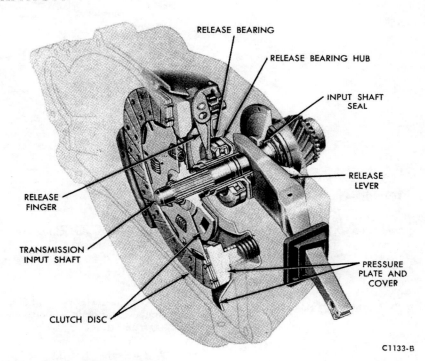

FIG. 1—Clutch Assembly

2 IN-CAR ADJUSTMENTS AND REPAIRS

CLUTCH PEDAL ADJUSTMENTS

Adjust the clutch pedal free travel whenever the clutch does not disengage properly, or when new clutch parts are installed. **Improper adjustment of the clutch pedal is one of the most frequent causes of clutch failure and can be a contributing** factor in some transmission failures. The over-center assist spring will not normally require adjustment and should not be disturbed; however, if the assist for clutch engagements or disengagements (pedal efforts) is not correct or pedal return action is erratic, an adjustment may be necessary. Also, if the linkage is removed or replaced, the adjustment should be checked.

ASSIST SPRING

1. With the clutch pedal against its bumper (pedal released), measure the distance between the assist spring bracket and the equalizer upper lever. (Fig. 2). The distance

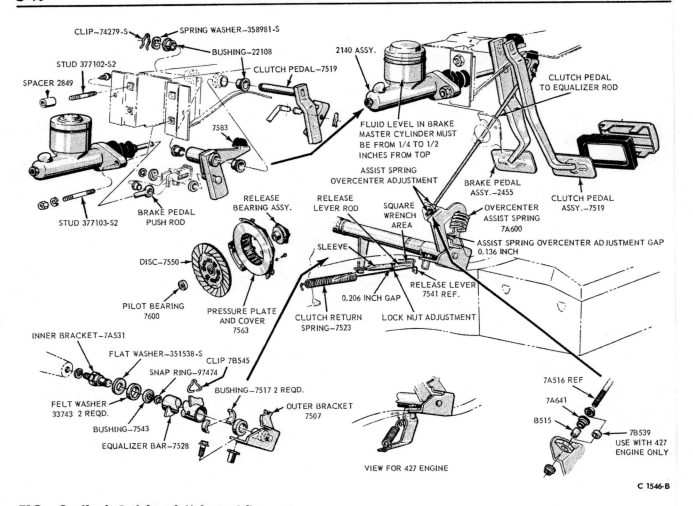

FIG. 2—Clutch Pedal and Linkage Adjustments

between the bracket and upper lever should be 0.136 inch. It may be necessary to depress the clutch pedal to insert the feeler gauge.

2. To decrease the gap, loosen the rearward nut and tighten the front nut.

3. To increase the gap, loosen the forward nut and tighten the rearward nut.

4. After a gap of 0.136 inch has been established, tighten the nuts to specification being careful not to change the adjustment.

5. Remove the feeler gauge.

FREE TRAVEL

1. Disconnect the clutch return spring from the release lever.

2. Loosen the release lever rod locknut (Fig. 2) approximately three or four turns.

3. If there is no free travel, shorten the rod (by turning at square wrench area) until it is free of the clutch release lever.

4. Move the clutch release lever

rearward until the release bearing lightly contacts the clutch pressure plate release fingers.

5. Adjust the rod length until the rod just contacts its seat in the release lever.

6. Using a feeler gauge, adjust the locknut to obtain approximately 0.206 inch clearance between the nut and the rod sleeve end.

7. Turn the rod at the square wrench area until the nut just contacts the rod sleeve end.

8. Tighten the locknut against the sleeve while holding the rod with a wrench.

9. Install the clutch return spring.

10. Check the free travel at the pedal for conformance to specification. Re-adjust if necessary. As a final check, measure the free travel with the engine idling. This dimension should not be less than ½ inch.

11. Without disturbing the assist spring, lubricate each spring seat with C3VY-19586-A grease.

12. As a final check, measure the

pedal free travel with the transmission in neutral and the engine running at about 3000 rpm. If the free travel at this speed is not a minimum of ½ inch, readjust the clutch pedal free travel. Otherwise, the release fingers may contact the release bearing continuously, resulting in premature bearing and clutch failure. **Free travel must be exactly to specification.**

INTERLOCK (OVERDRIVE MODELS ONLY)

Be sure that the clutch linkage is correctly adjusted before adjusting the interlock (Fig. 3).

1. Place the gearshift lever in the neutral position.

2. Loosen the adjustment lock nut on the interlock rod.

3. Disconnect the rod from the interlock lever.

4. *Loosen the interlock plate attaching screws. Move the interlock lever forward as far as possible to seat the interlock plate on the first*

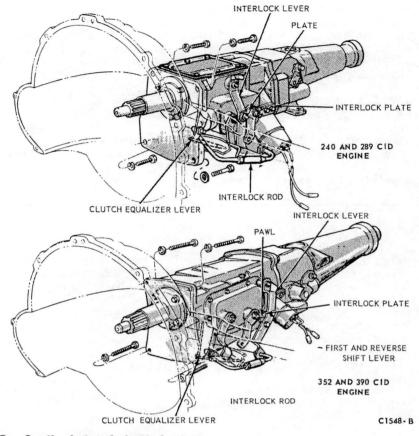

FIG. 3—Clutch Interlock Mechanisms

and reverse-speed shift lever pawl. Tighten the two attaching screws.

5. Adjust the length of the interlock rod so that it can be connected to the interlock lever while being held in the forward position. Connect the rod to the lever.

6. Shift the transmission into low and into neutral to check operation of the interlock. Readjust the interlock plate for snug fit if necessary.

7. Use COAZ-19584-A lubricant as required for the interlock linkage.

CLUTCH PEDAL AND/OR BUSHING REPLACEMENT

REMOVAL

1. Depress the clutch pedal and insert a ¼ inch spacer in the assist spring adjustment gap.

2. Remove the retainer that secures the clutch pedal to equalizer rod to the clutch pedal (Fig. 2). Disconnect the rod from the clutch pedal.

3. Disconnect the brake pedal push rod from the brake pedal.

4. Remove the retaining clip, spring washer, and flat washer from the clutch pedal shaft. Then remove

the shaft, bushings clutch pedal and the brake pedal from the support.

5. Remove the bushings from the pedal shaft, and transfer the pedal pad.

INSTALLATION

1. After lubricating all pedal shaft bushings, position them on the shafts. Then position the brake pedal and the clutch pedal in the pedal support.

2. Install the flat washer, spring washer, and retaining clip on the clutch pedal shaft.

3. Connect the clutch pedal-to-equalizer rod to the clutch pedal. Depress the pedal and remove the ¼ inch spacer.

4. Check the assist spring adjustment and the clutch pedal free travel and adjust as required.

EQUALIZER BAR AND/OR BUSHING REPLACEMENT

1. Disconnect the clutch pedal to equalizer rod at the pedal, and then disconnect the rod from the equalizer bar (Fig. 2).

2. Raise the car and disconnect the return spring at the release lever. Disconnect the release lever rod from the equalizer lever. Position the tool shown in Fig. 4 on the lever. Hold the tool firmly and move it rearward

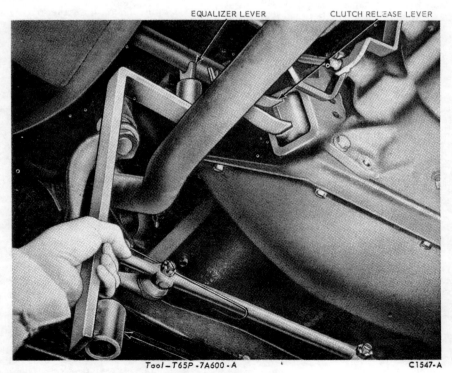

FIG. 4—Removing or Installing Assist Spring

to release the assist spring tension. Remove the assist spring.

3. Remove the equalizer bar frame bracket two bushing halves and the felt washer.

4. Lift the equalizer bar from the pivot on the flywheel housing.

5. Remove the snap ring, bushing, felt washer, and flat washer from the inner pivot.

6. Position the flat washer, felt washer and bushing on the pivot. Secure these parts with the snap ring.

7. Position the equalizer bar on the inner pivot.

8. After positioning, the equalizer bar install the frame bracket, felt washer and split bushing (Fig. 2). Torque the bracket attaching bolts to specifications.

9. Lubricate the assist spring seats with C3VY-19586-A grease. Place the assist spring in position with the lower open end of the spring facing toward the engine.

10. Make certain that the flat section at each end of the spring is seated in the lever and in the bracket, as shown in Fig. 4.

11. Install the tool on the equalizer lever. Grasp the tool firmly and move it toward the front of the car until the spring is seated in the bracket.

12. Install the clutch release rod and return spring.

13. Install the clutch pedal to equalizer rod.

14. Adjust the clutch free travel, assist spring, and the interlock adjustments. The clutch interlock is used only on cars equipped with an overdrive transmission.

---

3 REMOVAL AND INSTALLATION

CLUTCH REMOVAL

1. Raise the car on a hoist.

2. Disconnect the drive shaft from the rear U-joint flange. Then, slide the drive shaft off the transmission output shaft. Insert the appropriate tool over the output shaft and into the extension housing oil seal.

3. Disconnect the speedometer cable from the extension housing.

4. Disconnect the gear shift rods from the transmission. If the car is equipped with a four-speed transmission, remove the bolts that secure the shift control bracket to the extension housing and position it out of the way.

5. If the car is equipped with an overdrive transmission, disconnect the interlock rod from the overdrive. Disconnect the solenoid and governor wires at their connections; disconnect the overdrive control cable, and then remove the wiring harness and the solenoid from the transmission.

6. Disconnect the parking brake cable, and support the rear of the engine with a transmission jack.

7. Remove the extension housing-to-engine rear support attaching bolts.

8. Raise the rear of the engine high enough to remove the weight from the crossmember. Remove the crossmember attaching bolts. Remove the crossmember from the frame side supports and allow it to hang by the front brake cable. If the car is equipped with a four-speed transmission, disconnect the front brake cable from the crossmember and remove the crossmember from the car.

9. Remove the bolts that attach the transmission to the flywheel housing.

10. Move the transmission rearward until the input shaft clears the flywheel housing, then remove it from the car.

11. If removing a clutch from a car with an aluminum flywheel housing, remove the starter. Remove the bolts that attach the housing to the cylinder block.

12. Move the housing back just far enough to clear the pressure plate, then move it to the right to free the pivot from the clutch equalizer bar. Be careful not to lose the bushing or disturb the linkage and assist spring.

13. Remove the flywheel housing cover (cast iron housings only).

14. Remove the release lever return spring. Then, slide the release bearing and hub off the release lever. This applies only to cast iron flywheel housings.

15. Loosen the six pressure plate cover attaching bolts evenly to release the spring tension. **If the same pressure plate and cover is to be installed after the clutch is overhauled, mark the cover and flywheel so that the pressure plate can be installed in the same position.**

16. Remove the pressure plate and the clutch disc from the flywheel.

CLUTCH INSTALLATION

1. Install the clutch release lever if it was removed.

2. Place the clutch disc, and pressure plate assembly in position on the flywheel. Start the cover attaching bolts to hold the pieces in place, but do not tighten them. **Avoid dropping the parts or contaminating them with oil or grease.**

3. Align the clutch disc with the tool shown in Fig. 5, and torque the six pressure plate cover attaching bolts evenly to specification. Then, remove the tool.

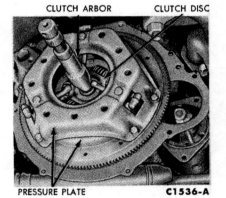

CLUTCH ARBOR CLUTCH DISC

PRESSURE PLATE C1536-A

FIG. 5—Installing Clutch Release Bearing on Hub

4. apply a light film of grease (C3VY-19586-A) to the outside diameter of the transmission front bearing retainer. Apply a light film of grease (COAZ-19584-A) to both sides of the release lever fork where it contacts the release bearing hub and spring clips. Apply a light film of grease to the release bearing surface that contacts the pressure plate release fingers. Care must be exercised to avoid excessive grease from contaminating the clutch disc. Place the release bearing and hub on the release lever.

5. If working on an engine with an aluminum flywheel housing, make sure that the mounting surfaces are clean. Position the felt washer and bushing on the pivot in the flywheel housing. Slip the pivot into the clutch equalizer shaft being careful not to disturb the linkage or trip the assist spring and at the same time position the housing on the dowels in the *cylinder block. Install and torque the attaching bolts to specification.*

6. Install the starting motor if

working on a car with an alumimum flywheel housing.

7. The mounting surfaces of the transmission and the flywheel housing must be free of dirt, paint, and burrs. Install two guide pins in the flywheel housing lower mounting bolt holes. Move the transmission forward on the guide pins until it is tightly positioned against the flywheel housing.

8. Install the two upper mounting bolts. Then, remove the guide pins and install the two lower mounting bolts. Torque all the bolts to specification.

9. Raise the rear of the engine

and install the crossmember. Install and torque the crossmember attaching bolts to specifications, then lower the engine.

10. Install the extension housing-to-engine rear support attaching bolts. Torque the bolts to specification.

11. Remove the transmission jack and connect the parking brake cable.

12. If the car is equipped with overdrive, install the solenoid and the wiring harness on the transmission; connect the overdrive control cable, and connect the solenoid and governor wires at their connectors. Connect and adjust the clutch inter-

lock rod to the overdrive shift lever.

13. If the car is equipped with a four-speed transmission, connect the gear shift linkage control bracket to the extension housing.

14. Connect the gear shift rods to the transmission. Adjust the shift linkage as required.

15. Connect the release lever return spring. Install the flywheel housing cover (cast iron housing only).

16. Remove the tool from the transmission output shaft and install the drive shaft.

17. Check the clutch pedal free travel and the assist spring control gap and adjust as required.

PART 5-4
SPECIFICATIONS AND SPECIAL TOOLS

CLUTCH

CLUTCH ADJUSTMENTS

Description	Inches
Clutch Pedal Free Travel (Engine Idling)	7/8-1 1/8
Clutch Pedal Total Travel	6 3/4
Assist Spring (Overcenter) Control Gap	0.136
Release Lever Rod Lock Nut-to-Rod Sleeve End (to obtain free travel adjustment)	0.206
Clutch Housing Alignment If Dia-L-Igner reading is greater than that indicated the clutch housing alignment is unacceptable	0.014
Maximum Shim to Correct Alignment	0.010

TORQUE SPECIFICATIONS

	Foot Pounds
Lower Access Clutch Cover Plate to Flywheel Housing Bolts (Iron Housings Only)	17-20
Flywheel Housing to Block Bolts 6-cyl. / 8-cyl.	23-33 / 40-50
Pressure Plate and Cover Plate Assembly Retaining Bolts	23-28
Clutch Release Equalizer Frame Bracket Bolts	25-30
Clutch Pedal Free Travel Adjustment Nut	17-25

LUBRICATION

Description	Lubricant	Part No.
Clutch Release Bearing	Lithium Base Grease (No Polyethylene)	C3VY-19586-A
Transmission Front Bearing Retainer		
Clutch Linkage		
Assist Spring Seats		
Pressure Plate Lugs	Lithium Base Grease	C4AZ-19590-A
Pressure Plate Fingers		
Release Fork Tips—Both Sides	Lubriplate	COAZ-19584-A
Interlock Linkage (Overdrive Transmissions)		
Equalizer Bar, Pivot, Bracket and Bushings	SAE-10W-Engine Oil	——

SPECIAL TOOLS

Tool No.	Description
A-37 H	Clutch Disc Aligner-Universal
T61L-7657-A or B T57L-7657-A T64P-7657-A	Transmission Extension Housing Oil Seal Replacer
CJ91B	Universal Joint Bearing Replacer
T64L-6392-A	Dia-L-Igner Gauge
T49P-7580-A	Clutch Release Bearing Replacer
T65P-7A600-A	Wrench—Clutch Assist Spring Remover and Replacer

CLUTCH IDENTIFICATION

Engine Cubic Inch Displacement	Pressure Plate Diameter (Inches)	Number of Springs	Color Identification Paint Daub	Disc Number of Springs	Spring Color
240 6 Cyl.	9 1/2	6	Aluminum	5 / 5	Yellow—Small / No Color—Large
240 6 Cyl.	11①	9①	Pressure Plate—Bronze* Cover Plate—Bronze*	4 / 4	Aluminum① / Pink①
289 V-8	10.4	9	Pressure Plate—White Cover Plate—Pink	4 / 6	Orange—Small / Orange—Large
352 V-8	11	9	Pressure Plate—Aluminum Cover Plate—Pink and Orange	6 / 6	Blue—Small / Yellow—Large
390 V-8	11	9	Pressure Plate—Purple Cover Plate—Green and Yellow	5 / 5	
427 V-8	11 1/2	12	Pressure Plate—Bronze and White Cover Plate—White	5 / 5	No Color
410 V-8	11 1/2	12		5 / 5	
428 V-8	11 1/2	12		5 / 5	

①Heavy-Duty Clutch

MANUAL SHIFT TRANSMISSION

GROUP 6

PART 6-1 GENERAL TRANSMISSION SERVICE

1 DIAGNOSIS AND TESTING

The problems related to the transmission usually are: excessive amount of noise, hard shifting efforts, transmission jumps out of gear, gears clash when transmission is shifted from one gear ratio to another, and lubricant leakage.

The car should be road tested, if possible, to determine or confirm complaint. Under normal operating conditions, a large percentage of transmission complaints are due to maladjusted or faulty components outside of the transmission, such as, clutch, clutch linkage, steering columns and shift linkage. Before and during the road test, make sure that the clutch is functioning properly, the shift linkage is properly adjusted, the steering column is properly aligned and, that the transmission is filled to proper level with lubricant.

The following diagnosis procedure is compiled as a guide in correcting problems related to manual transmissions. Trouble symptoms, possible causes and corrective measures are listed in the order they should be checked to eliminate all possibility of maladjustment or faulty components outside of the transmission prior to any transmission removal and disassembly. If the transmission was removed, repaired and reinstalled, make certain the clutch and all the gear shift linkage is adjusted to specifications. Road test the vehicle to be sure that the problem has been completely corrected.

DIAGNOSIS GUIDE—TRANSMISSIONS

To eliminate all possibility of maladjustments or faulty components in the clutch and/or clutch linkage, refer to Clutch Diagnosis and Testing, Group 5 (Driveshaft and Clutch), of the shop manual.

TROUBLE SYMPTOMS	POSSIBLE CAUSES	CORRECTION
RATTLE OR BUZZ IN FLOOR SHIFT LEVER	Some floor shift transmissions are subject to shift lever buzz or rattle. No transmission overhaul should be attempted to correct this problem as it is often mistaken for a grating noise in the transmission.	

CONTINUED ON NEXT PAGE

DIAGNOSIS GUIDE—TRANSMISSIONS (Continued)

TROUBLE SYMPTOMS	POSSIBLE CAUSES	CORRECTION
RATTLE OR BUZZ IN FLOOR SHIFT LEVER (Continued)	1. Loose nuts at transmission levers and shift rods. If the nuts are loose, check for bell-mouthing of slots. 2. Bent transmission shift rods or linkage interference. 3. Lack of lubrication of shift linkage, trunnions and external shift mechanism (floor shift). 4. Improperly located console and excessive boot compression (floor shift). 5. Grommets damaged allowing hold down bolts and/or hold down washers to ground out against lever (floor shift).	1. Adjust levers and shift rods to proper crossover, torque nuts to specification. Replace bell-mouthed rods or levers. 2. Replace bent rods or levers. 3. Clean and lubricate with Lithium base grease (no Polyethylene). 4. Install correctly. 5. Replace defective parts. Install correctly.
GEAR CLASH	**CLUTCH LINKAGE** 1. Lack of clutch pedal reserve, free play and total travel. 2. Lost motion in clutch release arm at fulcrum plate (pivot point). 3. Bottoming of clutch release arm in window of clutch housing. 4. Bent or cracked equalizer bar.	1. Adjust to specification. 2-3. Adjust clutch overcenter spring gap. If adjustment is correct, grind opening in clutch housing or release arm to provide clearance. 4. Replace defective parts.
	SHIFT LINKAGE 1. Improper crossover. 2. Loose nuts at transmission levers and shift rods. If the nuts are loose, check for bell-mouthing of slots. 3. Bent transmission shift rods or linkage interference. 4. Lack of lubrication of shift linkage, trunnions and external shift mechanism (floor shift).	1-2. Adjust levers and shift rods to proper crossover, torque nuts to specification. Replace bell-mouthed rods or levers. 3. Replace bent rods. 4. Clean and lubricate with Lithium base grease (no Polyethylene).
	CLUTCH 1. Excessive engine idle speed. 2. Inadequate clutch pedal reserve resulting in excessive spin time. 3. Incorrect pedal free travel. 4. Disc binding on transmission input shaft. 5. Excessive disc runout. 6. Flywheel housing misalignment. 7. Oil or grease on clutch facings from: A. release bearing B. engine C. release lever D. pilot bearing E. transmission 8. Damaged or contaminated clutch lining.	1. Adjust engine idle rpm. 2. Adjust clutch linkage to specification. Check for damaged input shaft pilot bearing or excessive clutch disc runout—replace defective parts. 3. Adjust to specification. 4. Check for burrs on splines, replace if necessary. 5-7-8. Replace clutch disc. 6. Align to specification.

CONTINUED ON NEXT PAGE

DIAGNOSIS GUIDE—TRANSMISSIONS (Continued)

TROUBLE SYMPTOMS	POSSIBLE CAUSES	CORRECTION

GEAR CLASH (Continued)	**TRANSMISSION**
	  1. Forward Gear Clash
	    A. Weak or broken insert springs in the synchronizer assembly.
	    B. Worn blocking rings and/or cone surfaces.
	    C. Broken blocking rings.
	    D. Excessive output shaft end play.
	    E. Shifter fork loose on shift rails.
	    F. Binding input shaft pilot bearing (non-synchronized low gear transmission only).
	    G. Worn shifter forks or sleeves.
		1. **A-B-C-D-F-G** Replace worn or defective parts.
		
		E. Torque shifter fork set screws to specification.

	2. Reverse Gear Clash (Allow approximately three-four seconds after the clutch pedal has been depressed before shifting into reverse gear).
	    A. If gear clash continues after allowing proper time for the clutch plate to stop, check the clutch adjustments to make sure that they are within specifications.
	    B. Excessive engine idle speed.
	    C. Binding input shaft pilot bearing.
	    D. Worn or damaged clutch disc.
		2. A. Adjust clutch to specification—See possible causes under Clutch for gear clash trouble symptoms.
		
		B. Adjust engine idler rpm.
		C-D. Replace defective parts.

HARD SHIFTING	**SHIFT LINKAGE**
	  1. Improper crossover.
	  2. Loose nuts at transmission levers and shift rods. If the nuts are loose, check for bell-mouthing of slots.
	  3. Bent transmission shift rods or linkage interference.
	  4. Lack of lubrication of shift linkage, trunnions and external shift mechanism (floor shift).
	  5. Improperly located console and excessive boot compression (floor shift).
		1-2. Adjust levers and rods to proper crossover, torque nuts to specification. Replace bell-mouthed rods or levers.
		
		3. Replace bent rods or levers.
		
		4. Clean and lubricate with Lithium base grease (no Polyethylene).
		
		5. Install correctly.

	STEERING COLUMNS
	  1. Improper column alignment, looseness, binding and worn surfaces. Make certain the toe plate at the base of the column is fastened securely to the firewall.
	  2. Worn shift key or broken weld securing shift key to top or bottom of shift tube.
	  3. Loose shift lever pin in die cast selector lever hub.
		1. Align column properly, replace defective column parts and fasten toe plate to firewall securely.
		
		2-3-4. Replace defective parts.

CONTINUED ON NEXT PAGE

DIAGNOSIS GUIDE—TRANSMISSIONS (Continued)

TROUBLE SYMPTOMS	POSSIBLE CAUSES	CORRECTION
HARD SHIFTING (Continued)	**4.** Keyway in die cast selector lever hub pounded out. **5.** Alignment of column to steering gear pilot bushing. **6.** Loose screws securing die casting to bottom of tube. Excessive radial movement in the column linkage. (If the vehicle has high mileage or is subjected to hard use, even though the crossover has been properly set, the column may have deteriorated to a point where proper crossover engagement will not occur due to excessive radial movement in the column linkage (lost motion). **7.** Lack of lubrication at column lower plate.	**5.** Align properly. **6.** Replace defective parts. Tighten screws securely. **7.** Clean and lubricate with Lithium base grease (no Polyethylene).
	CLUTCH LINKAGE **1.** Lost motion in clutch release arm at fulcrum plate (pivot point). **2.** Loss of clutch pedal reserve, free play and total travel.	**1.** Adjust over center spring gap. **2.** Adjust to specification.
	TRANSMISSION **1.** Excessive shift effort **A.** Shift side cover loose or damaged (Dagenham, Warner Gear four speed overdrive transmission only). **B.** Shift levers, shafts or forks worn or bent. **C.** Synchronizer worn or broken. **D.** Shift rail components not functioning properly. **E.** Worn shifter forks or sleeves.	**1. A.** Torque screws to specification. Replace damaged cover. **B-C-E.** Replace worn or defective parts. **D.** Install correctly, replace defective parts, if necessary.
	2. Sticking in Gear **A.** Low lubricant level. **B.** Corroded transmission levers (shaft). **C.** Defective (tight) input shaft pilot bearing. **D.** Stuck detent plug. **E.** Burred or battered teeth on synchronizer sleeve and/or input shaft. **F.** Shifter fork loose on shift rails.	**2. A.** Fill to bottom of filler plug hole. **B-D.** Free-up and clean parts, replace if necessary. **C-E.** Replace defective parts. **F.** Torque shifter fork set screw to specification.
GEAR JUMPOUT	**SHIFT LINKAGE** **1.** Improper crossover. **2.** Loose nuts at transmission levers and shift rods. If the nuts are loose, check for bell-mouthing of slots.	**1-2.** Adjust levers and rods to proper crossover. Torque nuts to specification. Replace bell-mouthed rods or levers.

CONTINUED ON NEXT PAGE

DIAGNOSIS GUIDE—TRANSMISSIONS (Continued)

TROUBLE SYMPTOMS	POSSIBLE CAUSES	CORRECTION
GEAR JUMPOUT (Continued)	3. Bent transmission shift rods or linkage interference. 4. Lack of lubrication of shift linkage, trunnions and external shift mechanism (floor shift). 5. Improperly located console and excessive boot compression (floor shift).	3. Replace bent rods or levers. 4. Clean and lubricate with Lithium base grease (no Polyethylene). 5. Install correctly.
	STEERING COLUMNS 1. Improper column alignment looseness, binding and worn surfaces. Make certain the toe plate at the base of the column is fastened securely to the firewall. 2. Alignment of column to steering gear pilot bushing. 3. Worn shift key or broken weld securing shift key to top or bottom of shift tube. 4. Keyway in die cast selector lever hub pounded out. 5. Loose screws securing die casting to bottom of tube. Excessive radial movement in the column linkage. (If the vehicle has high mileage or is subjected to hard use, even though the crossover has been properly set, the column may have deteriorated to a point where proper crossover engagement will not occur due to excessive radial movement in the column linkage (lost motion).	1. Align column properly, replace defective column parts and fasten toe plate to firewall securely. 2. Align properly. 3-4. Replace defective parts. 5. Replace defective parts. Tighten screws securely.
	TRANSMISSION 1. Transmission misaligned or loose. 2. Bent or worn shift fork, lever and/or shaft. 3. Worn input shaft pilot bearing. 4. End play in input shaft (bearing retainer loose or broken, loose or worn bearings on input and output shafts). 5. Detent springs broken. 6. Detent notches worn. 7. Worn clutch teeth on the respective gear and/or worn clutch teeth on synchronizer sleeve. 8. Shift side cover loose or damaged (Dagenham and Warner Gear four speed and overdrive transmission only). 9. Shifter forks loose on shift rails.	1. Align to specification. Torque transmission-to-flywheel housing bolts and flywheel housing-to-engine bolts to specifications. 2-3-5-6-7. Replace worn or defective parts. 4. Torque retainer bolts to specification. Replace worn or defective parts. 8. Torque screws to specification. Replace damaged cover. 9. Torque shifter fork set screw to specification.

DIAGNOSIS GUIDE—TRANSMISSIONS (Continued)

TROUBLE SYMPTOMS	POSSIBLE CAUSES	CORRECTION
LOCKED IN GEAR When a complaint of momentary lockout is encountered in transmissions with non-synchronized low-gear, determine whether or not a normal "blockout" condition exists. If a "blockout" condition does exist, the customer should be informed that the transmission gears cannot be pulled into mesh because of gear tooth to tooth abutment which can be eliminated by releasing and depressing the clutch pedal again (thus spinning the clutch disc). This will re-index the drive and driven gear teeth and allow the gears to mesh.	**SHIFT LINKAGE** 1. Improper crossover. 2. Loose nuts at transmission levers and shift rods. If the nuts are loose, check for bell-mouthing of slots. 3. Bent transmission shift rods or linkage interference.	1-2. Adjust levers and rods to proper crossover. Torque nuts to specification. Replace bell-mouthed rods and levers. 3. Replace bent rods or levers.
	STEERING COLUMN 1. Tricking of shift linkage. Make certain that when slowly shifting out of low gear, the low gear shift lever at the transmission is completely out of low gear detent prior to the column shift lever dropping through neutral crossover. If the transmission shift lever is not completely out of low gear detent, the shift interlock in the transmission will prevent engagement of second gear and a lockup condition occurs. 2. Improper column alignment, looseness, binding and worn surfaces. Make certain the toe plate at the base of the column is fastened securely to the firewall. 3. Alignment of column to steering gear pilot bushing. 4. Worn shift key or broken weld securing shift key to top or bottom of shift tube. 5. Loose shift lever pin in die cast selector lever hub. 6. Keyway in die cast selector lever hub pounded out. 7. Loose screws securing die casting to bottom of tube. Excessive radial movement in the column linkage. (If the vehicle has high mileage or is subjected to hard use even though the crossover has been properly set, the column may have deteriorated to a point where proper crossover engagement will not occur due to excessive radial movement in the column linkage (lost motion). Lack of lubrication at column lower plate.	1-2. Adjust column properly, replace defective parts and fasten toe plate to firewall securely. 3. Align properly. 4-5-6. Replace defective parts. 7. Replace defective parts. Tighten screws securely. Clean and lubricate with Lithium base grease (no Polyethylene).
	TRANSMISSION 1. Shift rail components not functioning properly. 2. Gear seizure. 3. Synchronizer inserts out of position.	1-3. Install correctly, replace defective parts. *2. Replace defective parts.*

CONTINUED ON NEXT PAGE

DIAGNOSIS GUIDE—TRANSMISSIONS (Continued)

TROUBLE SYMPTOMS	POSSIBLE CAUSES	CORRECTION
NOISY IN FORWARD SPEEDS	1. Low lubricant level. 2. Transmission misaligned or loose. 3. Input shaft bearings worn or damaged. 4. Output shaft bearing worn or damaged. 5. Mainshaft gears worn or damaged. (In any case of scored or broken gears, the mating gears should be checked.) 6. Countershaft gear or bearings worn or damaged. 7. Failure of the operator to fully engage the gears on every shift before engaging the clutch and applying engine power. Gear roll-over noise, inherent in manual transmissions, is caused by the constant mesh gears turning at engine idle speed, while the clutch is engaged and the transmission in neutral; and throwout bearing rub are sometimes mistaken for **mainshaft bearing noise.** Gear roll-over noise will disappear when the clutch is disengaged or when the transmission is engaged in gear. Throwout bearing rub will disappear when the clutch is engaged. In the event that a bearing is defective, the noise is more pronounced while engaged in gear under load or coast than in neutral. When complaints of this nature are encountered, it will be necessary to road test the vehicle to determine if bearing noise exists. **Under no circumstances should any transmission rework be attempted to eliminate gear roll-over noise, or throwout bearing rub.**	1. Fill to bottom of filler plug hole. 2. Align to specification. Torque transmission-to-flywheel housing bolts and flywheel housing-to-engine bolts to specifications. 3-4-5-6-7. Replace worn or defective parts.
NOISY IN REVERSE	1. Reverse idler gear or shaft, worn or damaged. 2. Reverse sliding gear worn or broken.	1-2. Replace worn or defective parts.
LUBRICANT LEAKS	1. Excessive lubricant. 2. Vent plugged. 3. Input shaft bearing retainer loose or cracked, seal or gasket damaged. 4. Worn or damaged extension housing seal.	1. Drain to bottom of filler plug hole. 2. Free up. 3. Add sealer and torque retainer bolts to specifications. Replace defective parts. 4-5-9. Replace defective parts.

CONTINUED ON NEXT PAGE

DIAGNOSIS GUIDE—TRANSMISSIONS (Continued)

TROUBLE SYMPTOMS	POSSIBLE CAUSES	CORRECTION
LUBRICANT LEAKS (continued)	**5.** Worn shifter shaft seals. **6.** Shift side cover bolts not sealed. (Dagenham and Warner Gear four speed and overdrive transmission only.) **7.** Shift side cover loose or gasket damaged. (Dagenham and Warner Gear four speed and overdrive transmission only.) **8.** Extension housing bolts not sealed. **9.** Expansion plug at front of case not seated properly. **10.** Access cover loose or gasket damaged.	**6-7-8-10.** Add sealer to bolts, and torque to specifications. Replace defective parts.

2 COMMON ADJUSTMENTS AND REPAIRS

REAR SEAL REPLACEMENT

1. Remove the drive shaft.
2. Remove the seal from the extension housing with the tool shown in Fig. 1.

FIG. 2—Installing Extension Housing Seal

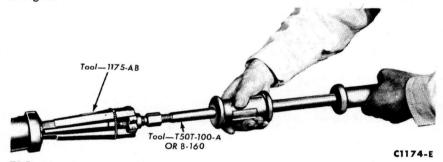

FIG. 1—Removing Extension Housing Seal

3. Install the new seal in the extension housing with the tool shown in Fig. 2.
4. Install the drive shaft.

REAR BUSHING AND SEAL REPLACEMENT

1. Remove the drive shaft from the car.
2. Insert the tool shown in Fig. 3, into the extension housing until it grips on the front side of the bushing.
3. Turn the screw clockwise until

the seal and the bushing are free of the housing.
4. Drive a new bushing into the extension housing with the tool shown in Fig. 4.
5. Install a new seal in the housing as shown in Fig. 2.
6. Install the drive shaft.

LUBRICATION

Lubricant level should be even with the bottom of the filler hole at the right side of the transmission case.

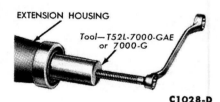

FIG. 3—Removing Extension Housing Bushing and Seal

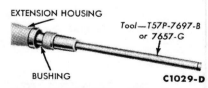

FIG. 4—Installing Extension Housing Bushing

3 CLEANING AND INSPECTION

CLEANING

1. Wash all parts, except the ball bearings, in a suitable cleaning sol-

vent. Brush or scrape all foreign matter from the parts. Be careful not to damage any parts with the scraper.

Dry all parts with compressed air.
2. Rotate the ball bearings in a cleaning solvent until all lubricant is

removed. Hold the bearing assembly to prevent it from rotating and dry it with compressed air.

3. Lubricate the bearings with approved transmission lubricant and wrap them in a clean, lint-free cloth or paper until ready for use.

INSPECTION

1. Inspect the transmission case for being cracked, worn or damaged bearing bores, damaged threads or any other damage that could affect the operation of the transmission.

2. Inspect the front face of the case for small nicks or burrs that could cause misalignment of the transmission with the flywheel housing. Remove all small nicks or burrs with a fine stone.

3. Replace a cover that is bent or distorted. Make sure that the vent hole in the cover is open.

4. Check the condition of the shift levers, forks, shift rails and the lever and shafts.

5. Examine the ball bearing races for being cracked, worn or rough. Inspect the balls for looseness, wear, end play or other damage. Check the bearings for looseness in the bores. If any of these conditions exist, replace the bearings.

6. Replace roller bearings that are broken, worn or rough.

7. Replace the countershaft (cluster) gear if the teeth are chipped, broken or worn. Replace the countershaft if it is bent, scored or worn.

8. Replace the reverse idler gear or sliding gear if the teeth are chipped, worn or broken. Replace the idler gear shaft if bent, worn or scored.

9. Replace the input shaft and gear if the splines are damaged or if the teeth are chipped, worn or broken. If the roller bearing surface in the bore of the gear is worn or rough, or if the cone surface is damaged, replace the gear and the gear rollers.

10. Replace all other gears that are chipped, broken or worn.

11. Check the synchronizer sleeves for free movement on their hubs. Make sure that the alignment marks (etched marks) are properly indexed.

12. Inspect the synchronizer blocking rings for widened index slots, rounded clutch teeth and smooth internal surfaces (must have machined grooves). With the blocker ring on the cone, the distance between the face of the blocker ring and the clutch teeth on the gear must not be less than 0.010 inches.

13. Replace the speedometer drive gear if the teeth are stripped or damaged. Make certain to install the correct size replacement gear.

14. Replace the output shaft if there is any evidence of wear or if any of the splines are damaged.

15. Inspect the bushing and the seal in the extension housing. Replace them if they are worn or damaged. The bushing and/or seal should be replaced after the extension housing has been installed on the transmission.

16. Replace the seal in the input shaft bearing retainer.

17. Replace the seals on the cam and shafts.

PART 6-2   MODEL 3.03
THREE-SPEED TRANSMISSION

1   DESCRIPTION AND OPERATION

DESCRIPTION

The 3.03 HEF and HEG Model three-speed transmissions (Fig. 1) are

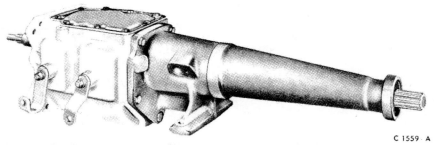

FIG. 1—Three-Speed Transmission

C 1559 A

used on all Ford and Mercury models having 240, 289, 352, 390, and 410 C.I.D. engines. The specifications of this section, Part 6-5, lists the transmission model numbers and vehicles in which they are used.

A transmission service identification tag is located on the right side of the case at the front. The first line on the tag will show the transmission model and service identification code when required. The second line will show the transmission serial number.

The three-speed transmission will be designated by the numeral, on the vehicle warranty plate.

The designation 3.03 is the actual distance between the centerline of the countershaft and the centerline of the input shaft.

This transmission is of the fully synchronized type, with all gears except the reverse gear and sleeve being in constant mesh. All forward-speed changes are accomplished with syn-

chronizer sleeves (Fig. 2). The synchronizers permit quicker shifts, greatly reduce gear clash, and permit

down-shifting from high to intermediate between 40-20 mph and from intermediate to low below 20 mph.

The forward-speed gears are helical-cut and are in constant mesh (Fig. 2). Gears used in the reverse gear train are spur-cut and are not synchronized.

Ball bearings support the input shaft and gear and the center of the output shaft (Figs. 12 and 14). Roller bearings in the input shaft bore support the front of the output shaft. The countershaft gear (cluster) runs on two rows of roller bearings. Two bronze bushings are used in the reverse idler gear (Fig. 11). A bushing located at the rear of the extension housing supports the rear of the output shaft.

Synchronizers and blocking rings are the conventional tapered ring and straight clutch gear type (Figs. 16 and 17).

The shift forks, shift rails, detent

mechanism and related parts are provided in the transmission case (Fig. 8).

OPERATION

When the first-speed gear is selected, the shift lever moves the reverse gear and sleeve forward and forces the synchronizer blocking ring conical surface against the matching cone on the constant mesh first gear located on the output shaft. If the car is moving, the internal teeth of the reverse gear and sleeve and blocking ring will not index until the constant-mesh first gear is brought up or down to the speed of the reverse gear and sleeve which is rotating at output shaft speed.

The reverse gear and sleeve has internal splines that, with further movement, will slide over the blocking ring and engage external clutch teeth on the constant mesh first gear. Since first gear is now locked to the output shaft and is always meshed with the countershaft (cluster) gear, the power flow is from the input gear, through the countershaft gear, to the constant mesh first gear, through the reverse gear and sleeve to the output shaft and out the rear of the transmission.

Engagement of second and third gears is the same as first except for ratio. In third gear, the input gear and shaft is locked directly to the output shaft by the second and third *speed synchronizer to provide a ratio of 1:1.

Spur teeth are cut on the outside of the reverse gear and sleeve which,

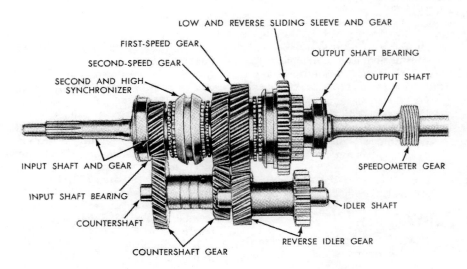

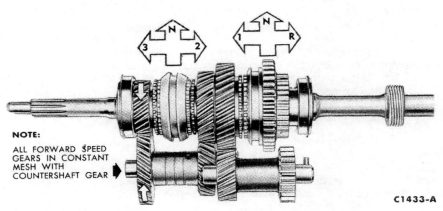

FIG. 2—Power Flow—Three-Speed Transmission

like the hub, are always locked to the output shaft. Reverse gear is engaged by sliding the reverse gear and sleeve into mesh with the spur gear at the rear of the idler gear. The drive is then from the input gear, through the countershaft gear, to and through the reverse idler gear to the output shaft reverse gear and sleeve. The gears in this position will rotate the output shaft in a reverse direction.

A system of interlocks and detents in the transmission case prevents the selection of more than one gear speed at a time and helps to hold any gear in the selected position.

2   IN-CAR ADJUSTMENTS AND REPAIRS

GEAR SHIFT LINKAGE ADJUSTMENT

1. Place the gear shift lever in the neutral position.

2. Loosen the two gear shift rod adjustment nuts (Fig. 3).

3. Check shift levers on transmission to be in neutral position.

4. Insert a 3/16-inch diameter alignment tool through the first and reverse gear shift lever, the second and third gear shift lever and both holes in the lower casting. It may be necessary to align the levers to insert the tool.

5. Tighten the two gear shift rod adjustment nuts.

6. Remove the alignment tool from the levers.

7. Start the engine and shift the selector lever to each position to make sure it operates freely.

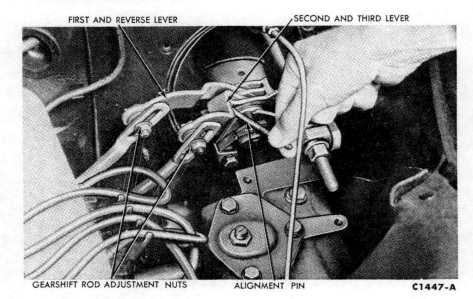

FIG. 3—Gearshift Linkage Adjustment—Typical

3 REMOVAL AND INSTALLATION

REMOVAL

1. Raise the car on a hoist.

2. Mark the drive shaft so that it may be installed in the same relative position. Disconnect the drive shaft from the rear U-joint flange.

3. Slide the front of the drive shaft out of the extension housing and off the output shaft. Insert the tool shown in Fig. 2, Part 6-1, into the extension housing to prevent the lubricant from leaking out of the transmission.

4. Remove the cap screw and lock washer that secures the speedometer cable retainer to the extension housing. Pull the speedometer cable out of the extension housing.

5. Remove the cotter pin, flat washer, and spring washer that secures the first and reverse shift rod to the shift lever.

6. Remove the nut, lock washer and flat washer securing the second and third shift lever to the transmission. Pry the lever away from the transmission and allow it to hang.

7. Disconnect the parking brake cable from the equalizer lever and separate the lever from the crossmember.

8. Remove the two bolts that secure the extension housing to the engine rear support.

9. Raise the rear of the engine high enough to remove the weight from the crossmember. Remove the crossmember attaching bolts. Remove the crossmember from the frame side supports and allow it to hang by the front brake cable.

10. Support the transmission with a transmission jack and remove the four flywheel housing-to-transmission case attaching bolts and lock washers.

11. Move the transmission and jack rearward until the input shaft is clear of the flywheel housing.

12. Remove the transmission from the jack and mount it in a holding fixture.

Do not depress the clutch pedal while the transmission is removed.

INSTALLATION

1. Make certain that the machined surfaces of the transmission case and the flywheel housing are free of dirt, paint, and burrs.

2. Install a guide pin in each lower mounting bolt hole.

3. Start the input shaft through the release bearing. Align the splines on the input shaft with the splines in the clutch disc. Move the transmission forward on the guide pins until the input shaft pilot enters the bearing or bushing in the crankshaft. If the transmission front bearing retainer binds up on the clutch release bearing hub, work the release bearing lever until the hub slides onto the transmission front bearing retainer. Install the two transmission-to-flywheel housing upper mounting bolts and lockwashers. Remove the two guide pins and install the lower mounting bolts and lock washers. Torque the four mounting bolts to specifications.

4. Raise the rear of the engine high enough to provide clearance for installing the crossmember. Bolt the

crossmember assembly to the frame side supports.

5. Lower the engine until the extension housing just contacts the rear support. Align the bolt holes in the extension housing with those in the support. Then lower the engine and remove the jack. Install the two extension housing-to-support attaching bolts and lock washers.

6. Insert the parking brake front cable in the equalizer and install the equalizer in the bracket on the crossmember. Secure the parking brake rear cable to the equalizer.

7. Position the second and third shift lever to the transmission and secure with the flat washer, lock washer and nut.

8. Connect the first and reverse shift rod to the shift lever on the transmission with a spring washer, flat washer, and cotter pin.

9. Insert the speedometer cable and driven gear in the extension housing and secure it with a cap screw and lock washer.

10. Remove the tool shown in Fig. 2, Part 6-1, from the extension housing. Align the reference marks and slide the front universal joint yoke onto the output shaft and into the extension housing. Connect the rear universal joint to the axle pinion flange and torque the nuts to specifications.

11. Fill the transmission to the proper level with the approved lubricant.

12. Adjust the clutch pedal free travel and the shift linkage as required.

4 MAJOR REPAIR OPERATIONS

DISASSEMBLY

1. Mount the transmission in a holding fixture and drain the lubricant.

2. Remove the cap screws that attach the cover to the case. Remove the cover and the gasket (Fig. 4) from the case.

3. Remove the cap screws and lock washers that attach the extension housing to the case. Remove extension and gasket from the case.

4. Remove the cap screws and lock washers that attach the front bearing retainer to the case. Remove the retainer and gasket from the case.

5. Remove the lubricant filler plug from the right side of the case. Working through the plug opening, drive the roll pin out of the case and countershaft with a ¼-inch punch (Fig. 5).

6. Hold the countershaft gear with a hook and with the tool shown in Fig. 6, push the countershaft out the rear of the case.
The countershaft (cluster) gear and thrust washers (Fig. 10) can be lowered to the bottom of the case. Remove the countershaft from the rear of the case.

7. Remove the snap ring that se-

cures the speedometer drive gear on the output shaft. Slide the speedometer drive gear off the shaft. Remove the speedometer drive gear lock ball from the shaft.

8. Remove the snap ring that retains the output shaft bearing on the shaft. Remove the bearing from the case and shaft as shown in Figure 7.

9. Place both shift levers in the neutral (center) position.

10. Remove the set screw (Fig. 8) that retains the detent springs and plugs in the case. Remove the detent spring and plug from the case.

11. Remove the set screw that se-

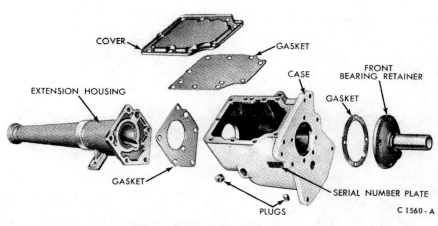

FIG. 4—Transmission Case and Related Parts

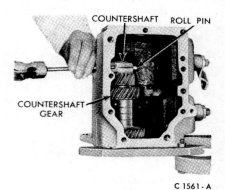

FIG. 5—Removing Countershaft Roll Pin

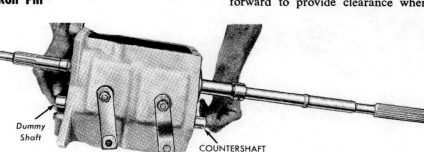

Tool—T63P-7111-A (352, 390 AND 410 V-8)
Tool—T63P-7111-B (240, SIX AND 289 V-8)

C 1562-A

FIG. 6—Removing Countershaft

cures the first and reverse shift fork to the shift rail. Slide the first and reverse shift rail out through the rear of the case.

12. Slide the first and reverse synchronizer forward as far as possible, and rotate the first and reverse shift fork upward. Then lift it from the case.

13. Move the second and third-speed shift fork to the second-speed position to gain access to the set screw. Remove the set screw from the

fork. Rotate the shift rail 90° as shown in Fig. 9.

14. Lift the interlock plug (Fig. 8) from the case with a magnet.

15. Tap on the inner end of the second and third-speed shift rail to remove the expansion plug (Fig. 8) from the front of the case. Remove the shift rail.

16. Remove the second and third-speed shift rail detent plug and spring from the detent bore.

17. Pull the input gear and shaft forward until the gear contacts the case, and then remove the large snap ring. It is necessary to move the gear forward to provide clearance when

removing the output shaft assembly from HEG model transmissions. On all other models, the input shaft and gear is removed from the front of the case at this time.

18. Rotate the second and third-speed shift fork upward, and lift it from the case.

19. Carefully lift the output shaft assembly out through the top of the case.

20. On an HEG model, work the input shaft bearing and gear back

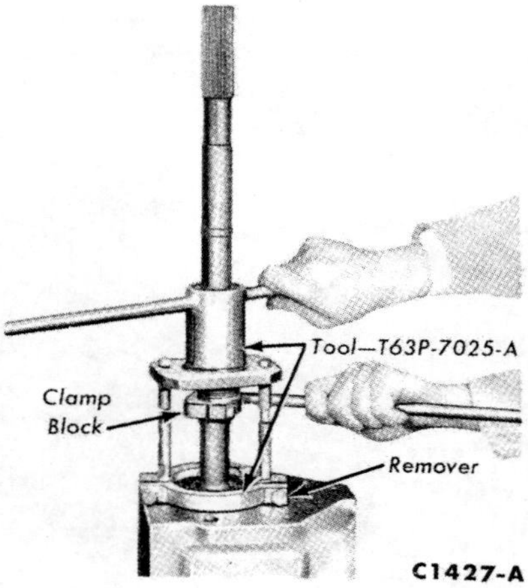

FIG. 7—Removing Output Shaft Bearing

through the bore in the case and out through the top. Remove idler gear shaft, driving from the front of the case.

21. Lift the reverse idler gear and two thrust washers (Fig. 11) from the case. Lift the countershaft gear, thrust washers, and dummy shaft from the case.

22. Remove the snap ring from the front of the output shaft, and slide the synchronizer and the second-speed gear (Fig. 12) off the shaft.

23. Remove the next snap ring and tabbed thrust washer from the output shaft. Then slide the first gear and blocking ring off the shaft.

24. Remove the next snap ring from the output shaft. Then slide the reverse gear and sleeve off the shaft.

PARTS REPAIR OR REPLACEMENT

SHIFT LEVERS AND SEALS

1. Remove the nut, lock washer, and flat washer that secure each shift lever (Fig. 13) to the lever and shaft in the transmission case. Lift the levers off the shaft. Slide each lever and shaft out of the case. Discard the "O" ring from each shaft.

2. Lubricate the new seals with transmission lubricant and install them on the shafts.

3. Install the lever and shafts in the case.

4. Position a shift lever on each shaft and secure them with a flat washer, lock washer, and nut.

INPUT SHAFT BEARING

1. Remove the snap ring securing the input shaft bearing (Fig. 14), and

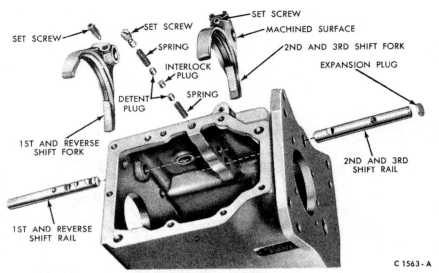

FIG. 8—Shift Rails and Forks Disassembled

FIG. 9—Rotating Second and Third-Speed Shift Rail

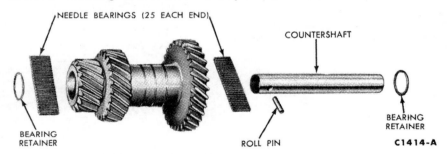

FIG. 10—Countershaft Gear Disassembled

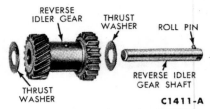

FIG. 11—Reverse Idler Shaft Disassembled

press the input shaft out of the bearing.

2. Press the input shaft bearing onto the input shaft with the tool shown in Fig. 15, and install the snap ring on the shaft.

SYNCHRONIZERS

1. Push the synchronizer hub from each synchronizer sleeve.

2. Separate the inserts and insert springs from the hubs. Do not mix the parts from the second and third-speed synchronizer with the first and reverse synchronizer (Figs. 16 and 17).

3. Install the rear insert spring (Fig. 18) in the groove of the first and reverse synchronizer hub. Make sure that the spring covers all insert

grooves. Start the hub in the sleeve making sure that the alignment marks are properly indexed. Position the three inserts in the hub making sure that the small end is over the spring and that the shoulder is on the inside of the hub. Slide the sleeve and reverse gear onto the hub until the detent is engaged. Install the front insert spring in the hub to hold the inserts against the hub.

4. Install one insert spring (Fig. 17) into a groove of the second and third speed synchronizer hub, making sure that all three insert slots are fully covered. With the alignment marks on the hub and sleeve aligned, start the hub into the sleeve. Place the three inserts on top of the retaining spring and push the assembly together. Install the remaining insert spring so that the spring ends cover the same slots as does the other spring. Do not stagger the springs. Place a synchronizer blocking ring on each end of the synchronizer sleeve.

COUNTERSHAFT GEAR BEARINGS

1. Remove the dummy shaft, fifty roller bearings, and the two bearing retainer washers from the countershaft gear (Fig. 10).

2. Coat the bore in each end of the countershaft gear with grease.

3. Hold the dummy shaft in the gear and install the twenty-five roller bearings and a retainer washer in each end of the gear.

4. Position the countershaft gear, dummy shaft, and roller bearings in the case.

5. Place the case in a vertical position. Align the gear bore and the thrust washers with the bores in the case and install the countershaft.

6. Place the case in a horizontal position and check the countershaft gear end play with a feeler gauge. The end play should be 0.004-0.018 inch. If not within these limits, replace the thrust washers.

7. After establishing the correct end play, install the dummy shaft in

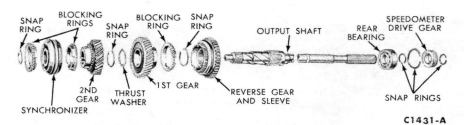

FIG. 12—Output Shaft Disassembled

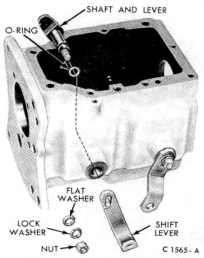

FIG. 13—Shift Lever and Shaft Disassembled

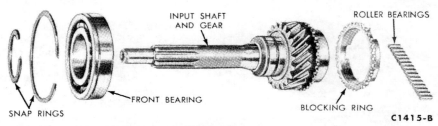

FIG. 14—Input Shaft Gear Disassembled

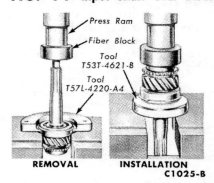

FIG. 15—Replacing Input Shaft Bearing

the countershaft gear and allow the gear to remain at the bottom of the case until the output and input shafts have been installed.

ASSEMBLY

1. Coat the reverse idler gear thrust surfaces in the case with a thin film of lubricant and position the two thrust washers in place.

2. Position the reverse idler gear and dummy shaft in place. Align the gear bore and thrust washers with the case bores and install the reverse idler shaft.

3. Measure the reverse idler gear end play with a feeler gauge. End play should be 0.004-0.018 inch. If the end play is not within limits, replace the thrust washers. If the end play is within limits, leave the reverse idler gear installed.

4. Lubricate the output shaft splines and machined surfaces with transmission lubricant.

5. Slide the first and reverse gear and sleeve (Fig. 12) onto the output shaft with the teeth end of the gear facing toward the rear of the shaft. Secure it in place with the snap ring.

6. Place the blocking ring on the tapered machined surface of the first gear.

7. Slide the first gear onto the output shaft with the blocking ring toward the rear of the shaft. Rotate the gear as necessary to engage the three notches in the blocking ring with the synchronizer inserts. Secure the first gear with the thrust washer and snap ring.

8. Slide the blocking ring onto the tapered machined surface of the second gear. Slide the second gear with blocking ring and the second and third gear synchronizer onto the mainshaft. The tapered machined surface of the second gear must be toward the front of the shaft. Make sure that the notches in the blocking ring engage the synchronizer inserts. Secure the synchronizer with a snap ring.

9. Coat the bore of the input shaft and gear with a **thin** film of grease. **A thick film of grease will plug the lubricant holes and prevent lubrication to the bearings.** Install the 15 bearings (Fig. 14) in the bore.

10. If working on an HEG model transmission, install the input gear and bearing through the top of the case and through the bore in front of the case. On HEF models, the input shaft is installed through the front of the transmission. Install the snap ring in the bearing groove.

11. Position the output shaft assembly in the case. Position the second and third-speed shift fork on the second and third-speed synchronizer.

12. Place a detent plug spring and a plug in the case (Fig. 8). Place the second and third-speed synchronizer in the second speed position (toward rear of transmission). Align the fork and install the second and third-speed shift rail. It will be necessary to depress the detent plug to enter the rail in the bore. Move the rail inward until the detent plug engages the forward notch (second-speed position).

13. Secure the fork to the shaft with the set screw. Move the synchronizer to the neutral position.

14. Install the interlock plug in the case. If the second and third-speed shift rail is in the neutral position, the top of the interlock will be slightly lower than the surface of the first and reverse shift rail bore.

15. Move the first and reverse synchronizer forward to the first-speed position. Place the first and reverse shift fork in the groove of the first and reverse synchronizer. Rotate the fork into position and install the first and reverse shift rail. Move the rail inward until the center notch (neutral) is aligned with the detent bore. Secure the fork to the shaft with the set screw. Install the remaining detent plug and spring. Secure the detent spring with the slotted head set screw. Turn the set screw in until the head is flush to 0.020 inch below the top of the case.

16. Install a new shift rail expansion plug in the front of the case.

17. Hold the input shaft and blocking ring in position. Then move the output shaft forward to seat the pilot in the roller bearings of the input gear.

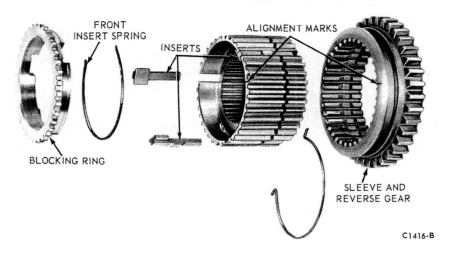

FIG. 16—First and Reverse Synchronizer Disassembled

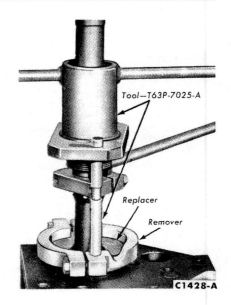

FIG. 19—Installing Output Shaft Rear Bearing

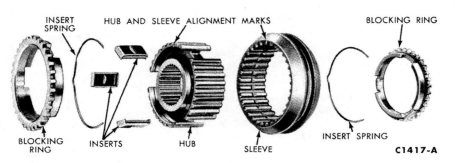

FIG. 17—Second and Third Synchronizer Disassembled

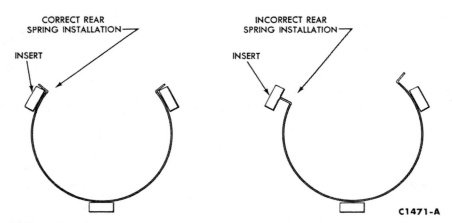

FIG. 18—First and Reverse Speed Synchronizer Insert Spring Installation

18. Tap the input gear bearing into place in the case while holding the output shaft to prevent the roller bearings from dropping. Install the front bearing retainer and new gasket making sure that the oil return slot is at the bottom of the case. Install and torque the attaching screws to 30-36 ft-lbs.

19. Install the large snap ring on the rear bearing. Place the bearing on the output shaft with the snap ring end toward the rear of the shaft. Press the bearing into place with the tool shown in Fig. 19. Secure the bearing to the shaft with a snap ring.

20. Hold the speedometer drive gear lock ball in the detent and slide

the speedometer drive gear into place. Secure the gear with a snap ring.

21. Place the transmission in the vertical position. Working through the drain hole in the bottom of the case, align the bore of the countershaft gear and the thrust washers with the bore of the case with a screwdriver.

22. Working from the rear of the case, push the dummy shaft out of the countershaft gear with the countershaft. Before the countershaft is completely inserted in the bore, make sure that the hole that accommodates the roll pin is aligned with the hole in the case. Drive the shaft into place and install the roll pin.

23. Coat a new extension housing gasket with sealer and position it on the case.

24. Install lock washers on the five attaching screws. Dip the threads of the cap screws in sealer. Secure the housing to the case and torque the cap screws to 42-50 ft-lbs.

25. Install the filler and drain plugs in the case. Make sure that the magnetic plug is installed in the bottom of the case.

26. Place the transmission in gear. Pour lubricant over the entire gear train while rotating the input or output shaft.

27. Coat a new cover gasket (Fig. 4) with sealer. Secure the cover with cap screws. Torque the screws to 14-19 ft-lbs.

28. Check the operation of the transmission in all of the gear positions.

PART 6-3 FORD DESIGN FOUR-SPEED TRANSMISSION

1 DESCRIPTION AND OPERATION

DESCRIPTION

The Ford designed 4-speed transmission (Fig. 1) is of the fully synchronized type with all gears except the reverse sliding gear being in constant mesh. All forward-speed changes are accomplished with synchronizer sleeves. The synchronizers will enable quicker shifts, greatly reduce gear clash, and permit downshifting into any forward-speed gear while the car is moving.

The shift linkage is mounted directly on the transmission extension housing (Fig. 1) and enters the driver's compartment through an opening in the floor pan. A flexible rubber dust boot is provided to seal the driver's compartment from the exterior.

The shift pattern is shown on the top of the gear shift lever knob. A finger-operated release lever is provided on the shift lever to prevent the transmission from being accidentally shifted into reverse gear. All forward-speed gears in the transmission are helical-type, however, the reverse sliding gear and the exterior of the first-and second-speed synchronizer sleeve are spur-type gears. The specifications of this section Part 6-6 lists the transmission model numbers and vehicles in which they are used.

A transmission service identification tag is located on the right side of the case at the front. The first line on the tag will show the transmission model and service identification code when required. The second line will show the transmission serial number.

The four-speed transmission will be designated by the numeral 5 on the vehicle warranty plate.

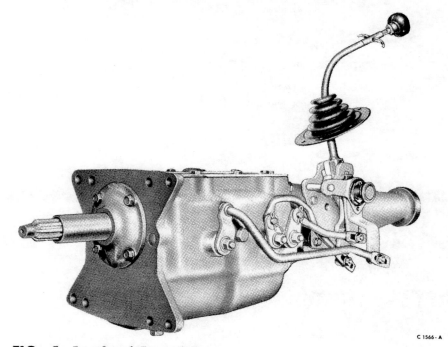

C 1566 - A

FIG. 1—Four-Speed Transmission

OPERATION

In first-speed (Fig. 2), the first- and second-speed synchronizer sleeve is moved rearward by the shift fork. The sleeve engages the first-speed blocking ring, which acts as a cone clutch applied to the free-wheeling first-speed gear. This action speeds up or slows down the first-speed gear to match the speed of the output shaft. Further movement of the sleeve locks the first- and second-speed synchronizer hub to the first-speed gear by means of internal splines. On engagement of the clutch, power flows through the input shaft and gear to the meshed countershaft gear and thence to the first-speed gear. This gear transmits the power through the locked synchronizer hub to the transmission output shaft. All the other forward-speed gears are in idler motion, as they are all driven by the countershaft (cluster) gear, but they do not transmit power because they are not locked to the output shaft. All the forward-speed shifts are made in the same manner as the first-speed shift, due to the constant-mesh features.

Reverse gear is engaged by moving the reverse sliding gear forward on the reverse idler gear until it meshes with the external teeth (spur-type) of the first- and second-speed synchronizer sleeve. Movement of the sliding gear is accomplished by the center shaft lever. With all forward-speed synchronizer sleeves in neutral, power flow in reverse is through the input shaft to the constant-mesh countershaft (cluster) gear, thence to the constant mesh reverse idler. Splines then carry the power through the reverse sliding gear to the first- and second-speed synchronizer sleeve which is locked to the output shaft. As the reverse sliding gear is meshed with the synchronizer sleeve, power is transmitted to the output shaft, rotating it in a reverse direction.

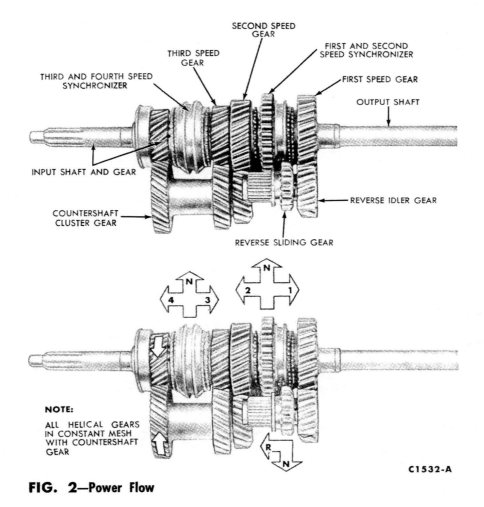

FIG. 2—Power Flow

C1532-A

2 IN-CAR ADJUSTMENTS AND REPAIRS

SHIFT LINKAGE ADJUSTMENT

1. Loosen the three shift linkage adjustment nuts. Install a ¼ inch diameter alignment tool through the control bracket and levers as shown in Fig. 3.

An alignment tool can be made from ¼″ diameter drill rod bent to an "L" shape. The extensions should be 1½″ and 3¾″ from the elbow. Short end of alignment pin should be *inserted into* control bracket and linkage holes until it bottoms.

2. Tighten the three linkage adjustment nuts and then remove the alignment pin.

3. Check the gear shift lever for a smooth crossover.

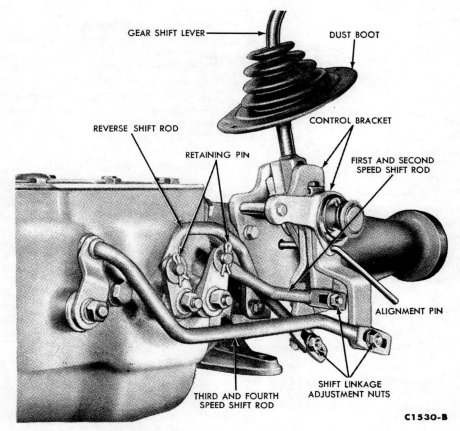

FIG. 3—Adjusting Shift Linkage

3 REMOVAL AND INSTALLATION

REMOVAL

1. Raise the car on a hoist.

2. Disconnect the drive shaft from the rear U-joint flange. Slide the drive shaft off the transmission output shaft and install the extension housing seal installation tool into the extension housing to prevent lubricant leakage. See Fig. 2, Part 6-1.

3. Disconnect the speedometer cable from the extension housing.

4. Disconnect the parking brake cable from the equalizer lever and separate the lever from the crossmember.

5. Remove the hairpin retainer securing the cable to the transmission rear support crossmember, and then pull the cable assembly forward and out of the crossmember.

6. Remove the retaining clip, flat washer, and spring washer that secures the shift rods to the shift levers.

7. Remove the bolts that attach the shift linkage control bracket to the extension housing and position the assembly out of the way.

8. Support the engine with a transmission jack and remove the extension housing-to-engine rear support attaching bolts.

9. Raise the rear of the engine high enough to remove the weight from the crossmember. Remove the bolts retaining the crossmember to the frame side supports and remove the crossmember.

10. Support the transmission on a jack and remove the bolts that attach the transmission to the flywheel housing.

11. Move the transmission and jack rearward until the transmission input shaft clears the flywheel housing. If necessary, lower the engine enough to obtain clearance for transmission removal.

Do not depress the clutch pedal

while the transmission is removed.

INSTALLATION

1. Make sure that the mounting surface of the transmission and the flywheel housing are free of dirt, paint, and burrs. Install two guide pins in the flywheel housing lower mounting bolt holes. Move the transmission forward on the guide pins until the input shaft splines enter the clutch hub splines and the case is positioned against the flywheel housing.

2. Install the two upper transmission to flywheel housing, mounting bolts snug, and then remove the two guide pins. Install the two lower mounting bolts. Torque all mounting bolts to specifications.

3. Raise the rear of the engine and install the crossmember. Install and torque the crossmember attaching bolts to specifications, then lower the engine.

4. With the transmission extension housing resting on the engine rear support, install the transmission extension housing attaching bolts. Torque the bolts to specifications.

5. Position the shift linkage control bracket to the extension housing and install the attaching bolts.

6. Secure each shift rod to its respective lever with the spring washer, flat washer, and retaining pin.

7. Guide the parking brake cable assembly through the hole in the transmission rear support crossmember. Secure the cable assembly to the crossmember with the hair pin retainer.

8. Insert the parking brake front cable in the equalizer and install the equalizer in the bracket on the crossmember. Secure the parking brake rear cable to the equalizer.

9. Connect the speedometer cable to the extension housing.

10. Remove the extension housing installation tool and slide the forward end of the drive shaft over the transmission output shaft. Connect the drive shaft to the rear U-joint flange.

11. Place both forward gear shift levers and the reverse shift lever in the neutral position and insert a ¼ inch diameter alignment tool in the shift linkage alignment hole (Fig. 3). It may be necessary to loosen the adjustment nuts to install the alignment tool. Adjust the linkage as necessary and tighten the adjustment nuts to specifications. Remove the alignment tool.

12. Fill the transmission to the proper level with the specified lubricant.

13. Lower the car. Check the shift and crossover motion for full shift engagement and smooth crossover operation.

---

4 MAJOR REPAIR OPERATIONS

DISASSEMBLY

1. Mount the transmission in a holding fixture and drain the lubricant.

2. Remove the cover attaching screws from the case. Lift the cover and gasket from the case.

3. Remove the extension housing attaching screws and lock washers. Remove the housing and the gasket.

4. Remove the input shaft bearing retainer attaching screws. Slide the retainer off the input shaft.

5. Support the countershaft gear with a wire hook. Working from the front of the case, push the countershaft out the rear of the case as shown in Fig. 4. Lower the countershaft to the bottom of the case with the wire hook. Remove the hook.

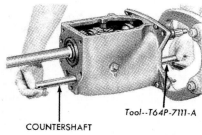

COUNTERSHAFT

Tool--T64P-7111-A

C 1567 - A

FIG. 4—Removing Countershaft From Case

6. Place the first- and second-speed gear shift lever and the reverse shift lever in the neutral position. Place the third- and fourth-speed gear shift lever in the third-speed position.

7. Remove the bolt that retains the third- and fourth-speed shift rail detent spring and the plug in the left side of the case as shown in Fig. 5.

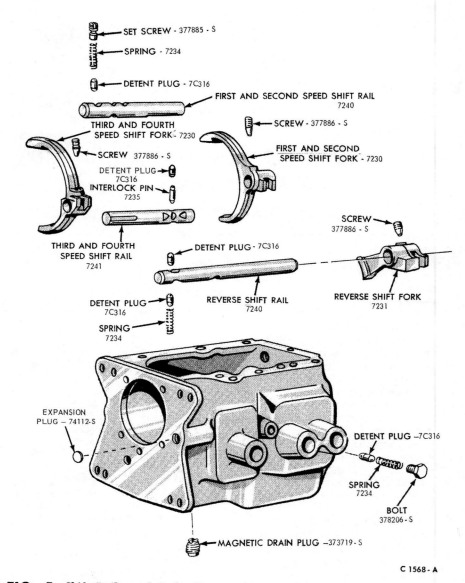

SET SCREW - 377885 - S

SPRING - 7234

DETENT PLUG - 7C316

FIRST AND SECOND SPEED SHIFT RAIL 7240

THIRD AND FOURTH SPEED SHIFT FORK - 7230

SCREW - 377886 - S

SCREW 377886 - S

FIRST AND SECOND SPEED SHIFT FORK - 7230

DETENT PLUG - 7C316

INTERLOCK PIN 7235

THIRD AND FOURTH SPEED SHIFT RAIL 7241

DETENT PLUG - 7C316

SCREW 377886 - S

REVERSE SHIFT FORK 7231

DETENT PLUG 7C316

SPRING 7234

REVERSE SHIFT RAIL 7240

EXPANSION PLUG - 74112-S

DETENT PLUG - 7C316

SPRING 7234

BOLT 378206 - S

MAGNETIC DRAIN PLUG - 373719 - S

C 1568 - A

FIG. 5—Shift Rails and Forks Disassembled

Remove the spring and the plug with a magnet.

8. Remove the detent mechanism set screw from the top of the case. Remove the detent spring and plug with a small magnet.

9. Remove the attaching screw from the third- and fourth-speed shift fork. Tap on the inner end of the shift rail to unseal the expansion plug from the front of the case. Then withdraw the third- and fourth-speed shift rail from the front of the case. Do not lose the interlock pin from the shift rail.

10. Remove the set screw from the first- and second-speed shift fork. Slide the first- and second-speed shift rail out the rear of the case.

11. Remove the interlock plug and the detent plug from the top of the case (Fig. 5) with a magnet.

12. Remove the snap ring that secures the speedometer drive gear to the output shaft. Slide the gear off the shaft, then remove the speedometer gear drive ball.

13. Remove the snap ring that secures the output shaft bearing to the shaft.

14. Remove the output shaft bearing as shown in Fig. 6.

15. Remove the input shaft and bearing and the blocking ring from the front of the case.

16. Move the output shaft to the right side of the case to provide clearance for the shift forks. Rotate the forks as shown in Fig. 7, then

lift them from the case.

17. Support the thrust washer and first-speed gear to prevent them from sliding off the shaft, then lift the output shaft assembly from the case as shown in Fig. 8.

18. Remove the reverse gear shift fork set screw. Rotate the reverse shift rail 90° as shown in Fig. 9. Slide the shift rail out the rear of the case. Lift the reverse shift fork from the case.

19. Remove the reverse detent plug and spring from the case with a magnet.

20. Remove the reverse idler gear shaft from the case as shown in Fig. 10.

21. Lift the reverse idler gear and the thrust washers from the case. Be careful not to drop the bearings and the dummy shaft from the gear.

22. Lift the countershaft gear and the thrust washers from the case. Be careful not to drop the bearings or the dummy shaft from the countershaft gear.

23. Remove the snap ring from the front of the output shaft. Slide the third- and fourth-speed synchronizer (Fig. 11) blocking ring and the third-speed gear off the shaft.

24. Remove the next snap ring and the second-speed gear thrust washer from the shaft. Slide the second-speed gear and the blocking ring off the shaft.

25. Remove the next snap ring, then slide the first- and second-speed

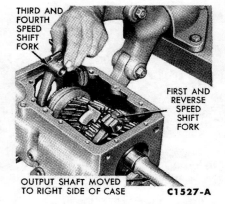

FIG. 7—Removing Shift Forks From Case

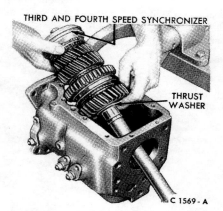

FIG. 8—Removing Output Shaft Assembly

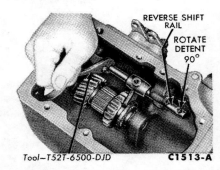

FIG. 9—Rotating Reverse Shift Rail

synchronizer, blocking ring and the first-speed gear off the shaft.

26. Remove the thrust washer from the rear of the shaft.

PARTS REPAIR OR REPLACEMENT

GEAR SHIFT LEVER

1. Remove the snap ring from the end of the selector shaft with pointed snap ring pliers (Fig. 12).

2. Remove the flat washer and spring.

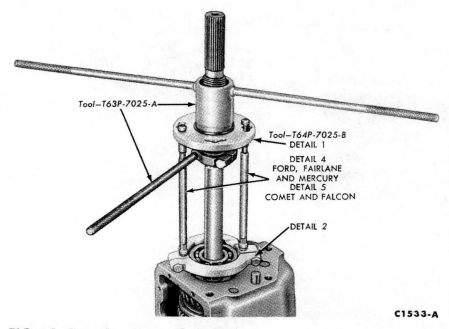

FIG. 6—Removing Output Shaft Bearing

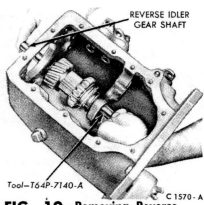

REVERSE IDLER
GEAR SHAFT

Tool–T64P-7140-A

C 1570 - A

FIG. 10—Removing Reverse Idler Gear Shaft

3. After removing two bolts, pull the retainer, selector levers, and bracket from the shaft.

4. Drive the short selector lever pin from the shaft with a large pin punch.

5. Drive the long trunnion pin from the shaft and remove the trunnion and shaft.

6. If necessary to remove the studs from the selector levers, remove the cotter pins, flat washers, wave washers and studs.

7. Lubricate all mating friction surfaces with Lubriplate before assembly.

8. Install the shaft in the bracket. Position the trunnion and drive the long straight pin through the trunnion and into the shaft until an equal length of the pin is exposed on both sides of the shaft.

9. Drive the short pin into the shaft until the pin is centered in the shaft.

10. Install the levers and the neutral index bracket on the shaft as shown in Fig. 12.

11. Position the retainer and start the bolts. Before tightening the bolts be sure that the retainer is not interfering with free movement of the shaft. Tighten the bolts.

12. Install the spring, flat washer and snap ring.

13. Install the lever studs if they were removed.

CAM AND SHAFT SEALS

1. Remove the attaching nut, lock washer and the flat washer from each shift lever and remove the three levers.

2. Remove the three cam and

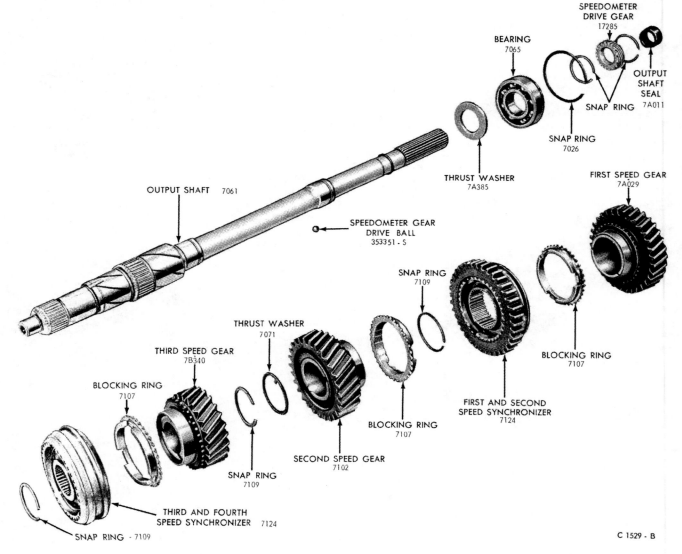

SPEEDOMETER
DRIVE GEAR
17285

BEARING
7065

OUTPUT
SHAFT
SEAL
7A011

SNAP RING

THRUST WASHER
7A385

SNAP RING
7026

FIRST SPEED GEAR
7A029

OUTPUT SHAFT   7061

SPEEDOMETER GEAR
DRIVE BALL
353351 - S

SNAP RING
7109

BLOCKING RING
7107

THRUST WASHER
7071

FIRST AND SECOND
SPEED SYNCHRONIZER
7124

THIRD SPEED GEAR
7B340

BLOCKING RING
7107

SECOND SPEED GEAR
7102

BLOCKING RING
7107

BLOCKING RING
7107

SNAP RING
7109

THIRD AND FOURTH
SPEED SYNCHRONIZER   7124

SNAP RING - 7109

C 1529 - B

FIG. 11—Output Shaft Disassembled

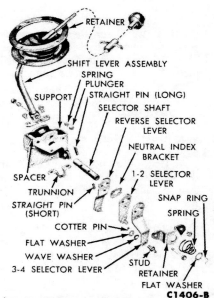

FIG. 12—Gear Shift Lever Disassembled—Typical

shafts from inside the case.

3. Remove and discard the O-ring from each cam and shaft (Fig. 13).

4. Dip the new O-rings in gear lubricant and install them on the cam and shafts.

5. Slide each cam and shaft into its respective bore in the transmission case.

6. Secure each shift lever with a flat washer, lock washer and nut.

INPUT SHAFT BEARING

1. Remove the snap ring that secures the bearing to the shaft (Fig. 14).

2. Press the input shaft gear out of the bearing as shown in Fig. 15.

3. Press a new bearing onto the input shaft with the tool shown in Fig. 15.

4. Secure the bearing with a snap ring.

SYNCHRONIZERS

1. Push the synchronizer hub from each synchronizer sleeve (Fig. 16).

2. Separate the inserts and insert springs from the hubs. Do not mix the parts of the first- and second-speed synchronizer with the third- and fourth-speed synchronizer.

3. Position the hub in the sleeve, making sure that the alignment marks are properly indexed.

4. Place the three inserts into place on the hub. Install the insert springs making sure that the irregular surface (hump) is seated in one of the inserts. Do not stagger the springs.

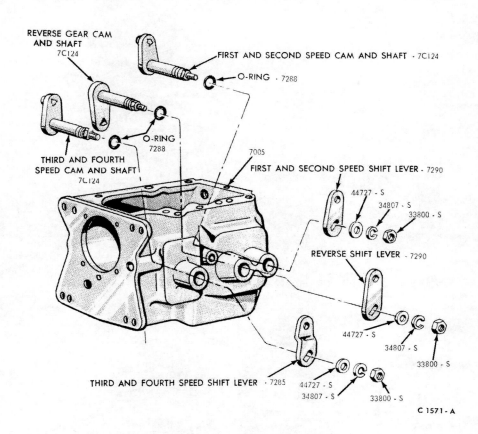

FIG. 13—Cam and Shafts and Shift Levers Disassembled

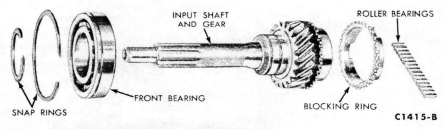

FIG. 14—Input Shaft Gear Disassembled

COUNTERSHAFT GEAR BEARINGS

1. Remove the dummy shaft, two bearing retainer washers, and the 21 roller bearings (Fig. 17) from each end of the countershaft gear.

2. Coat the bore in each end of the countershaft gear with grease.

3. Hold the dummy shaft in the gear and install the 21 roller bearings and a retainer washer in each end of the gear.

REVERSE IDLER GEAR BEARINGS

1. Slip the reverse idler sliding gear off of the reverse idler gear (Fig. 18).

2. Remove the dummy shaft, two bearing retainer washers and the 44 roller bearings from the reverse idler gear.

3. Coat the bore in each end of the reverse idler gear with grease.

4. Hold the dummy shaft in the gear and install the 22 roller bearings and the retainer washer in each end of the gear.

5. Install the reverse idler sliding gear on the reverse idler gear making sure that the shift fork groove is toward the front (Fig. 18).

INPUT SHAFT SEAL

1. Remove the seal from the input

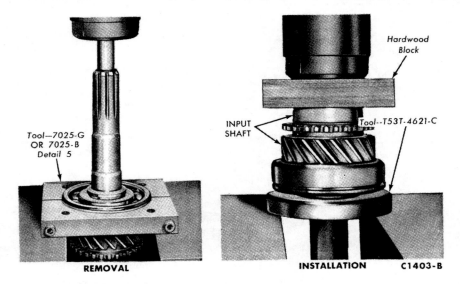

FIG. 15—Replacing Input Shaft Bearing

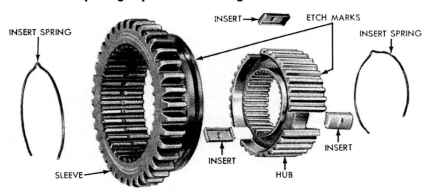

FIRST AND SECOND SPEED SYNCHRONIZER

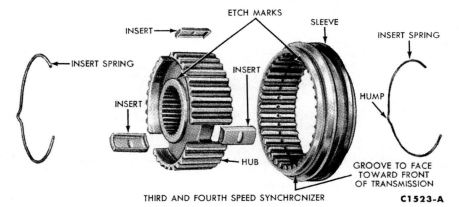

THIRD AND FOURTH SPEED SYNCHRONIZER

C1523-A

FIG. 16—Synchronizers Disassembled

shaft bearing retainer as shown in Fig. 19.

2. Coat the sealing surface with lubricant.

3. Install the seal as shown in Fig. 20.

ASSEMBLY

1. Coat the countershaft gear thrust surfaces in the case with a thin film of lubricant and position a thrust washer (Fig. 17) at each end of the case.

2. Position the countershaft gear, dummy shaft, and roller bearings in the case.

3. Place the case in a vertical position. Align the gear bore and the thrust washers with the bores in the case and install the countershaft.

4. Place the case in a horizontal position and check the countershaft gear end play with a feeler gauge. The end play should be 0.004-0.018 inch. If not within these limits, replace the thrust washers.

5. After establishing the correct end play, install the dummy shaft in the countershaft gear and allow the gear to remain at the bottom of the case.

6. Coat the reverse idler gear thrust surfaces in the case with a thin film of lubricant and position the two thrust washers (Fig. 18) in place.

7. Position the reverse idler gear, sliding gear, dummy shaft and the roller bearings in place making sure that the shift fork groove in the sliding gear is toward the front of the case.

8. Align the gear bore and thrust washers with the case bores and install the reverse idler shaft.

9. Measure the reverse idler gear end play with a feeler gauge. End play should be 0.004-0.018 inch. If the end play is not within limits, replace the thrust washers. If the end play is within limits, leave the reverse idler gear installed.

10. Position the reverse gear shift rail detent spring and detent plug in the case. Hold the reverse shift fork in place on the reverse idler sliding gear and install the shift rail from the rear of the case. Secure the fork to the rail with the Allen head set screw.

11. Install the first- and second-speed synchronizer onto the front of the output shaft (Fig. 11) making sure that the shift fork groove is toward the rear of the shaft.

12. Position the blocking ring on the second-speed gear.

13. Slide the second-speed gear onto the front of the shaft, making sure that the inserts in the synchronizer engage the notches in the blocker ring.

14. Install the second-speed gear thrust washer and snap ring.

15. Slide the third-speed gear onto the shaft with the synchronizer coned surface toward the front.

16. Place a blocking ring on the third-speed gear.

17. Slide the third- and fourth-speed gear synchronizer onto the shaft making sure that the inserts in the synchronizer engage the notches in the blocking ring.

18. Install the snap ring on the

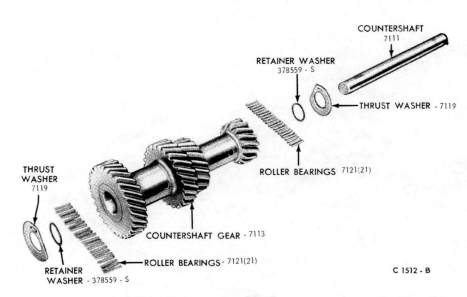

FIG. 17—Countershaft Bearing Disassembled

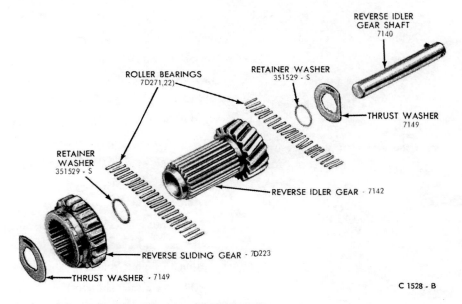

FIG. 18—Reverse Idler Gear Disassembled

front of the output shaft.

19. Position the blocking ring on the first-speed gear.

20. Slide the first-speed gear onto the rear of the output shaft making sure that the notches in the blocking ring engage the synchronizer inserts.

21. Install the heavy thrust washer on the rear of the output shaft.

22. Support the thrust washer and first-speed gear to prevent them from

sliding off the shaft and carefully lower the output shaft assembly into the case as shown in Fig. 8.

23. Position the first- and second-speed shift fork and the third- and fourth-speed shift fork in place on their respective gears and rotate them into place.

24. Place a detent plug (Fig. 5) in the detent bore. Place the reverse shift rail into neutral position.

25. Coat the third- and fourth-speed shift rail interlock pin with grease and position it in the shift rail.

26. Align the third- and fourth-speed shift fork with the shift rail bores and slide the shift rail into place making sure that the three detents are facing toward the outside of the case. Place the front synchronizer into third-speed position and install the set screw in the third- and fourth-speed shift fork. Move the synchronizer to the neutral position. Install the third- and fourth-speed shift rail detent plug, spring and bolt in the left side of the transmission case (Fig. 5). Place the interlock plug (tapered ends) in the detent case.

27. Align the first- and second-speed shift fork with the case bores and slide the shift rail into place. Secure the fork with the set screw. Install the detent plug and spring in the detent bore. Thread the set screw into the case until the head is flush to 0.020 inch below the surface of the case.

28. Coat the input gear bore with a thin film of grease, then install the 15 roller bearings in the bore. **A thick film of grease could plug the lubricant holes and restrict lubrication of the bearings.**

29. Position the front blocking ring in the third- and fourth-speed synchronizer.

Place the input shaft gear in the transmission case making sure that the output shaft pilot enters the roller bearings in the input gear.

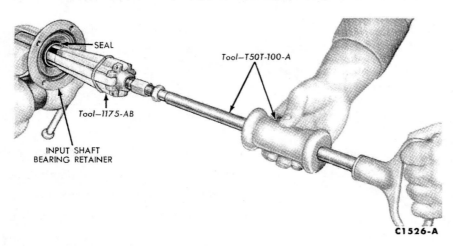

C1526-A

FIG. 19—Removing Input Shaft Seal

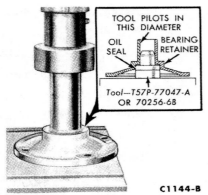

C1144-B

FIG. 20—Installing Input Shaft Seal

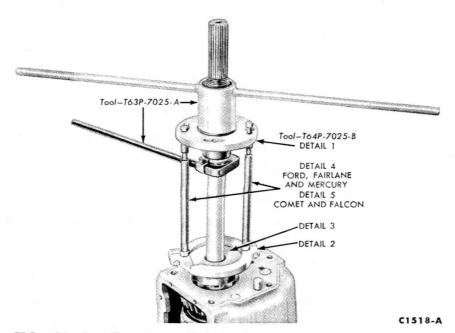

C1518-A

FIG. 21—Installing Output Shaft Bearing

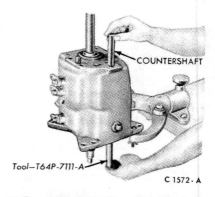

C1572-A

FIG. 22—Installing Countershaft

30. Place a new gasket on the input shaft bearing retainer. Dip the attaching bolts in sealer and install and tighten them to specifications.

31. Install the output shaft bearing as shown in Fig. 21. Install the snap ring to retain the bearing.

32. Position the speedometer gear drive ball in the output shaft and slide the gear into place. Secure the gear with the snap ring.

33. Place the transmission in a vertical position as shown in Fig. 22. Align the countershaft gear bore and thrust washers with the bore in the case. Install the countershaft.

34. Use a new gasket and secure the extension housing to the case with the attaching screws. Use a sealer on the extension housing attaching screws. Torque the screws to specifications.

35. Install the filler and drain plugs in the case if they were removed. Make sure that the magnetic plug is installed in the bottom of the case.

36. Pour the specified lubricant over the entire gear train while rotating the input shaft.

37. Place each shift fork in all positions to make sure that they operate properly.

38. Use a new cover gasket and install the cover. Coat the cover attaching screws with sealer and install and tighten them to specifications.

39. Coat the third- and fourth-speed shift rail plug bore with a sealer and install a new expansion plug.

40. If the extension housing bushing and seal are to be replaced, refer to Section 4.

PART 6-4

OVERDRIVE TRANSMISSION

1 DIAGNOSIS AND TESTING

When trouble occurs in the overdrive unit, check the mechanical operation of the unit before checking the operation of the overdrive electrical control system.

MECHANICAL CHECKS

OVERDRIVE CONTROL HANDLE CLEARANCE CHECK

Check the specified clearance between the overdrive control handle shank and the bezel on the instrument panel.

OVERDRIVE CONTROL LEVER POSITION CHECK

Raise the car and check the position of the overdrive control lever at the overdrive unit housing. The lever should rest firmly against its stop at the rear. If the lever is not all the way back the overdrive shift rail may be locking the pawl and preventing it from engaging the balk ring gear.

With the engine stopped and the clutch engaged, shift the transmission to third or second gear and shift the overdrive control lever to the automatic (rearward) position. The drive shaft should then turn freely in a clockwise direction (when viewed from the front), but should lock up when turned counterclockwise.

With the transmission remaining in third or second gear, shift the overdrive control lever to the locked-out (forward) position. The drive shaft should lock up when turned either clockwise or counterclockwise.

PAWL ENGAGEMENT CHECK

Check the mechanical engagement of the pawl with the balk ring gear, using the following procedure:

1. Turn the ignition switch to the ON position and raise the car.

2. Shift the overdrive control lever to the locked-out (forward) position, and shift the transmission to neutral.

3. Turn the drive shaft clockwise and, at the same time ground the governor white wire with a jumper. The solenoid will click, indicating that it is energized.

4. Keep the solenoid energized, and shift the transmission to third or second gear to lock the transmission output shaft against rotation. Shift the overdrive control lever to the automatic (rearward) position.

5. Turn the drive shaft clockwise. At less than 1/4 turn of the driveshaft, the pawl will engage the balk ring gear and lock the drive shaft against rotation in both directions.

If the pawl does not engage the balk ring gear, replace the solenoid and repeat the test. If the pawl still does not engage, remove the overdrive unit from the car for inspection and repair.

ELECTRICAL CHECKS

GOVERNOR CIRCUIT CHECK

1. Turn the ignition switch ON and OFF, and listen for the relay or solenoid to click. If either clicks as soon as the ignition switch is turned ON, the governor circuit (Fig. 1) is grounded or the relay is defective.

2. To determine which condition is present, remove the wire from the TH-SW terminal on the relay and turn the ignition switch ON. If the relay clicks, the relay is defective. If it does not click, the governor circuit is grounded.

3. To check the governor operation when the relay does not click as the ignition switch is turned ON, disconnect the wire at the TH-SW terminal.

4. Raise the rear wheels off the floor.

5. Connect a test lamp between the battery and the wire removed from the TH-SW terminal.

6. Start the engine and, with the transmission in third-speed, bring the speedometer reading up through 28 mph. The lamp should light at or about this speed.

7. Throttle the engine down through 22 mph and at or about this speed the lamp should go out. If the lamp lights, and goes out at or about these speeds, the governor and governor circuit are working properly.

8. Turn the ignition switch ON

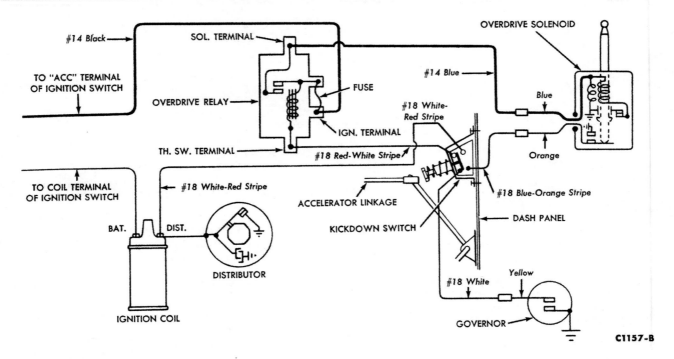

FIG. 1—Overdrive Electrical System

and raise the car. Disconnect the yellow wire from the white wire at the governor connector.

9. Ground the white wire on the transmission case. If the relay and solenoid click, the governor circuit is working properly from the TH-SW terminal to the connector (Fig. 1), and the trouble is in the yellow wire or the governor. If the relay and solenoid do not click when the white wire is grounded, the trouble is between the TH-SW terminal and the connector (Fig. 1).

SOLENOID CIRCUIT CHECK

1. With the engine stopped and the ignition switch ON, ground the TH-SW terminal on the relay. If the relay and solenoid click as the ground is made and broken, the solenoid circuit is working properly. If the relay does not click as the TH-SW terminal is grounded, check the relay IGN terminal with a test lamp.

2. With the ignition switch ON, the test lamp should light when it is connected between the IGN terminal on the relay and at a ground. If it *does not*, the trouble is between the ignition switch and the IGN terminal.

3. Connect the test lamp at the other end of the fuse and at a ground. If the lamp lit at the IGN end and not at the other, replace the fuse. **Sometimes the fuse will "open" under the fuse end caps where the "open" cannot be seen.**

4. With current at both ends of the fuse, connect the test lamp between the solenoid terminal and at a ground. Ground the TH-SW terminal. The lamp should light. If it does not, replace the relay.

5. With the relay working properly, the solenoid should click when the TH-SW terminal is grounded. If it does not, connect a jumper from the SOLENOID relay terminal to the short blue wire separated from its connector near the solenoid. If the solenoid does not click when the relay closes with the jumper wire connected, replace the solenoid. If it does click, replace the wire from the SOLENOID relay terminal to the connector.

INTERRUPTOR CIRCUIT CHECK

If the interruptor circuit does not ground the engine ignition momentarily when the driver depresses the accelerator pedal to the floor, the overdrive unit cannot shift from overdrive to direct.

1. The first check of the ignition interruptor circuit is at the ignition coil. The black wire which runs from the ignition coil to the kickdown switch must be connected to the DIST terminal on the coil. Sometimes this wire is improperly connected to BAT terminal during ignition work.

2. Disconnect the blue wire with an orange band (Fig. 1) from its connector near the solenoid, and ground it to the transmission case with a jumper.

3. With the engine running at fast idle, push the kickdown switch stem in until it bottoms (Fig. 2). When the stem bottoms, the engine should stop.

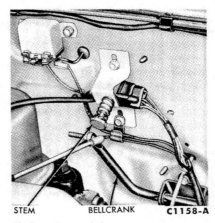

FIG. 2—Kickdown Switch Installation

If it does not stop, the circuit is open between the DIST terminal and the connector.

4. To check the ignition grounding contacts inside the solenoid, disconnect the jumper and remove the solenoid from the overdrive unit.

5. Attach the solenoid to an

adapter so that the stem can extend fully when the solenoid is energized. Make sure the solenoid is grounded.

6. Connect both solenoid wires at their connectors.

7. Ground the governor wire with a jumper.

8. With the engine running at fast idle, press in on the kickdown switch stem until it bottoms. The engine should stop. If it does not, replace the solenoid.

2 CLEANING AND INSPECTION

CLEANING

Clean and inspect the transmission unit parts in the same manner as for the conventional transmission. Clean all overdrive parts thoroughly.

INSPECTION

Check the balk ring tension, as shown in Fig. 3 for a pull of 3½-5½ pounds. Read the spring scale while the balk ring is turning, because the initial effort required to start the ring turning may be considerably higher than the specified pull. Replace the assembly if the tension is not within specifications.

Check the inner surface of the free-wheel clutch outer race. If the surface is worn or "chattered," the overdrive output shaft must be replaced.

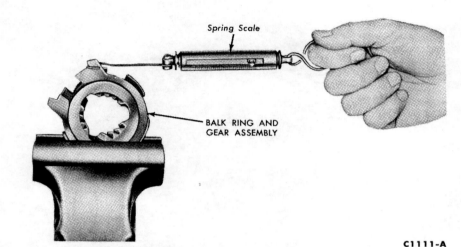

Spring Scale

BALK RING AND
GEAR ASSEMBLY

C1111-A

FIG. 3—Checking Balk Ring Tension

Check the clutch rollers for cracks and wear. Replace the complete set of 12 rollers if any are cracked or worn.

3 DESCRIPTION AND OPERATION

DESCRIPTION

The Overdrive transmission is used on all Ford models having 240, 289 or 390 C.I.D. engines. A transmission service identification tag is attached to the upper right extension to case attaching bolt. The tag will show the transmission model and service identification code when required.

The Overdrive transmission will be designated by the numeral 2 on the vehicle warranty plate.

The overdrive unit is basically an automatic planetary transmission attached to the rear of a conventional three-speed transmission (Fig. 4) to provide four forward speeds instead of three. The overdrive can be mechanically locked out by a control cable located on the instrument panel.

The electrical system which controls the operation of the overdrive when the control cable is pushed in, consists of a relay, a manual kickdown switch, solenoid, governor, and the circuit wiring.

OPERATION

MECHANICAL OPERATION

Direct, Free-Wheeling Drive

When the control handle is pushed in, the drive through the overdrive unit from start to approximately 28 mph is direct (1.00:1) and free-wheeling.

The power flow is from the transmission output shaft, through the overrunning clutch (free-wheel unit), to the overdrive main shaft (Fig. 5).

This drive is said to be free-wheeling because the overrunning clutch permits the transmission output shaft to drive the overdrive main shaft, but it does not permit the drive to reverse. **In a free-wheeling drive, the engine can drive the rear wheels, but the rear wheels cannot drive the engine.**

In direct, free-wheeling drive, the planetary gearing is in neutral, because the sun gear can run free. It can rotate clockwise (from the front), counterclockwise, or stand still, depending on the relative speeds of the planet carrier (transmission output shaft), and the internal ring gear (overdrive main shaft). At a 0.70:1 ratio, the sun gear will stand still. At a higher ratio, the sun gear will turn clockwise (from the front). At a lower ratio than 0.70:1, it will turn counterclockwise.

Overdrive

To shift the overdrive unit from direct (1.00:1) to overdrive (0.70:1) the sun gear is held against rotation (Fig. 5).

This is accomplished by engaging a pawl in the balk ring gear which is splined to the sun gear.

In overdrive, the power flow is from the transmission output shaft to the planet carrier splined to it, through the planet gears and then to the sun gear. With the sun gear held against rotation, the planet gears are forced to "walk around" the sun gear and drive the internal ring gear. The transmission output shaft will then

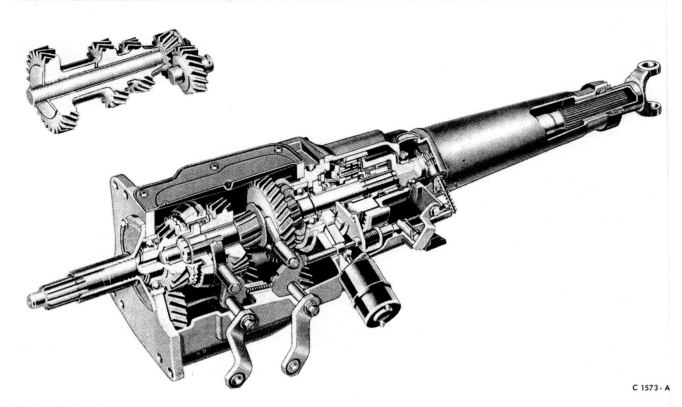

C 1573- A

FIG. 4—Overdrive Transmission

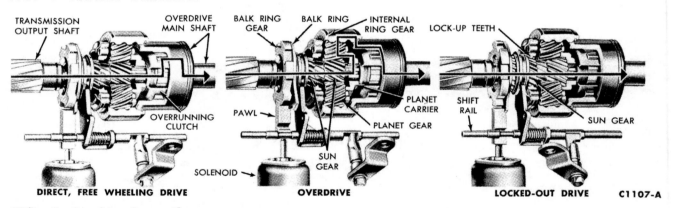

DIRECT, FREE WHEELING DRIVE   OVERDRIVE   LOCKED-OUT DRIVE   C1107-A

FIG. 5—Overdrive Power Flow

drive the overdrive main shaft at a ratio of 0.70:1.

In overdrive, the overrunning clutch is uncoupled because the outer race (overdrive main shaft) is turning faster than the clutch cam (transmission output shaft). Overdrive is a two-way drive; the engine can drive the rear wheels and the rear wheels can drive the engine.

To shift from overdrive back to direct, the pawl is disengaged from the balk ring gear, permitting the sun gear to run free. The overdrive gearing is now in neutral. As soon as the speed of the transmission output shaft comes up to the speed of the overdrive main shaft, the overrun-

ning clutch automatically locks up and direct drive is restored.

Locked-Out Drive

When the control handle is pulled out, the overdrive unit cannot function at any car speed. This lockout is accomplished by the shift rail moving the sun gear into engagement with the lock-up teeth on the planet carrier (Fig. 5).

When the sun gear is locked to the planet carrier, the planetary gearing is locked as one mechanical unit and the transmission output shaft is locked to the overdrive main shaft. This lock-up is necessary in reverse, because the transmission output shaft

reverses its rotation and therefore cannot drive the overdrive main shaft through the overrunning (one-way) clutch. The lockup in reverse is accomplished by the low and reverse position. This locked-up drive is also necessary when the car is pushed to start the engine, since the overrunning clutch will not transmit power from the overdrive main shaft to the transmission output shaft.

ELECTRICAL SYSTEM OPERATION

The overdrive electrical system, which engages and disengages the pawl, consists of a relay, a manual kick-down switch, a solenoid, a centrifugal governor and the circuit wiring.

There are three separate circuits (Section 1, Fig. 1) in the electrical system: a governor circuit which opens and closes the relay, a solenoid circuit which supplies current through the relay to energize the solenoid, and an ignition interruptor circuit, which momentarily grounds the engine ignition for full-throttle down-shift (kickdown).

Pawl Engagement

The electrical system does not operate until car speed reaches approximately 28 mph. At this speed, the governor contacts close, permitting current to flow from the battery through the relay to the solenoid.

There are two coils in the solenoid, usually referred to as the "pull-in" and "hold-in" coils. The pull-in coil is energized only while the solenoid plunger is being pulled in. As soon as the plunger is in, a set of points inside the solenoid opens the pull-in circuit.

As the plunger is pulled in, an engaging spring and a return spring are engaged.

Under pressure from the pawl engaging spring, the pawl is pushed in

until it strikes the balk ring.

The usual position of the balk ring when the solenoid engaging spring pushes the pawl against it is shown in the left view of Fig. 6. When the transmission output shaft is driving the overdrive main shaft through the overrunning clutch, all elements of the planetary gearing are revolving as a unit, and in a counterclockwise (from the rear) direction. This rotates the balk ring against the pawl.

When the driver releases the throttle, the overdrive main shaft overruns the transmission output shaft. When this overrun exceeds the ratio of 0.70:1, the sun gear and balk ring reverse, releasing the pawl to engage the balk ring gear.

The position of the balk ring, should the solenoid be energized when the car is coasting (engine idling) up through 28 mph, is shown in the right view of Fig. 6. Under this condition the sun gear will be rotating clockwise (from the rear) and the pawl will be blocked.

The pawl engages when the engine speeds up, and brings the transmission output shaft up through the 0.70:1 ratio with the overdrive main shaft. This action will cause the sun gear to reverse its clockwise (from

the rear) rotation and release the pawl to engage the balk ring gear.

Pawl Disengagement

The pawl disengages under two conditions. First, when the car speed drops below approximately 22 mph, the governor opens the circuit through the relay and de-energizes the solenoid, permitting the return spring to pull out the pawl. Second, the driver may shift the overdrive back to direct drive at any road speed, by pressing the accelerator pedal to the floor so that it depresses the kickdown switch stem.

When this happens, the kickdown switch opens the governor circuit through the relay, and de-energizes the solenoid, permitting the return spring to try to pull out the pawl.

Also, it closes the interruptor circuit and grounds the ignition long enough for the return spring to pull out the pawl.

Normal ignition is restored as soon as the pawl comes out, and the solenoid stem opens the ignition grounding contacts. The actual time of ignition interruption is equal to that required for one revolution of the crankshaft.

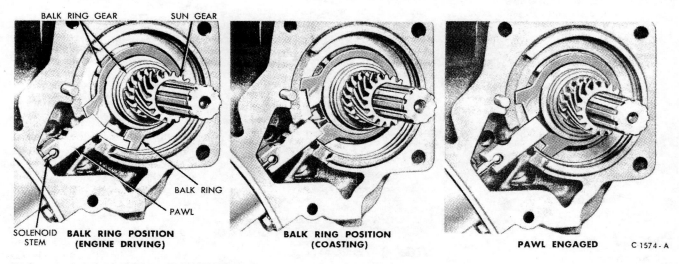

BALK RING GEAR   SUN GEAR

BALK RING

PAWL

SOLENOID STEM   **BALK RING POSITION (ENGINE DRIVING)**   **BALK RING POSITION (COASTING)**   **PAWL ENGAGED**   C 1574-A

FIG. 6—Pawl and Balk Ring Positions

4 IN-CAR ADJUSTMENTS AND REPAIRS

OVERDRIVE CONTROL CABLE ADJUSTMENT

1. Loosen the overdrive cable lock nut at the overdrive control lever.
2. Position the overdrive cable un-

til there is ¼ inch clearance between the cable control handle and bezel.

3. Move the overdrive control lever to the rear against the stop.

When moving the lever, be careful not to move the cable out of position.

4. Tighten the control cable lock nut on the overdrive.

5 TRANSMISSION REMOVAL AND INSTALLATION

REMOVAL

The overdrive unit cannot be removed from the car as a separate assembly. Remove the transmission and overdrive unit together, following the steps detailed below:

1. Disconnect the solenoid and governor wires from the connectors near the solenoid.

2. Remove the overdrive wiring harness from its clip on the transmission.

3. Disconnect the overdrive control cable from the lever on the side of the overdrive unit and from the clamp at the solenoid.

4. Remove the overdrive transmission from the car, following the procedure given in Part 6-2 for removing the 3-speed Conventional Drive transmission.

Do not depress the clutch pedal while the transmission is removed.

INSTALLATION

The overdrive unit must be assembled and installed on the transmission before the transmission is installed in the car.

1. Install the overdrive transmission in the car, following the procedure given in Part 6-2 for installing the 3-speed Conventional Drive transmission.

2. Connect the overdrive control cable to the lever on the side of the overdrive unit. With the cable connected, there must be ¼ inch clearance between the control handle shank and the bezel when the lever at the overdrive housing is against its rear stop.

3. Connect the solenoid and governor to the connectors near the solenoid.

4. Install the overdrive wiring harness in its clip on the transmission.

6 MAJOR REPAIR OPERATIONS

DISASSEMBLY (OVERDRIVE USED WITH 240 AND 289 CID ENGINES)

1. Mount the transmission in a holding fixture. Then drain the transmission and the overdrive unit.

2. Remove the solenoid retaining screw, and then rotate the solenoid about ¼ turn to remove it.

3. Remove the governor.

4. Remove the transmission cover and gasket.

5. With a sharp punch, pierce the snap ring hole cover (Fig. 7), and remove the cover from the top of the overdrive housing.

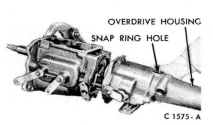

FIG. 7—Removing Overdrive Housing

6. Remove the four overdrive housing-to-transmission case bolts, and the overdrive control shaft pin.

7. Pull the overdrive control lever and shaft out as far as possible. Spread the snap ring that retains the overdrive output shaft bearing and then remove the overdrive housing (Fig. 7).

It may be necessary to tap the overdrive output shaft with a soft-faced hammer to free the output

shaft bearing from the housing.

8. Remove the overdrive output shaft from the assembly. Catch any of the free-wheel unit rollers that drop out. Remove the rest of the rollers.

9. Remove the speedometer gear retaining snap ring. Remove the gear and drive ball.

10. If the overdrive output shaft bearing is to be replaced, use the tools shown in Fig. 8.

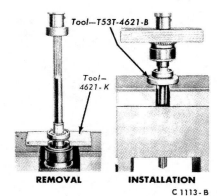

FIG. 8—Replacing Output Shaft Bearing

11. Remove the free-wheel unit retainers (Fig. 9). Then remove the clutch, planet carrier, sun gear, and shift rail.

12. Remove the snap ring from the adapter, and then remove the plate and trough, balk ring gear and pawl.

13. Remove the input shaft bearing retainer and gasket (Fig. 10). Replace the input shaft seal with

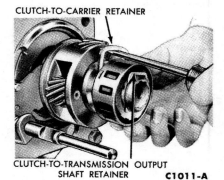

FIG. 9—Removing Free Wheel Unit Retainer

the same tools that are used on the conventional 3-speed transmission.

14. Rotate the overdrive adapter to expose the countershaft lock, and remove the lock.

15. With a drift, drive the countershaft toward the rear until it just clears the hole at the front of the case. Support the countershaft gear with a hook, then push the countershaft out of the rear with the tool shown in Fig. 11.

16. Lower the countershaft gear to the bottom of the case to provide clearance for removal of the input shaft and bearing. Tap the input shaft and bearing out of the front of the case.

17. Remove the shift lever shaft retaining pins (Fig. 12).

18. Pull the low and reverse shift lever out as far it will go; then remove the low and reverse fork.

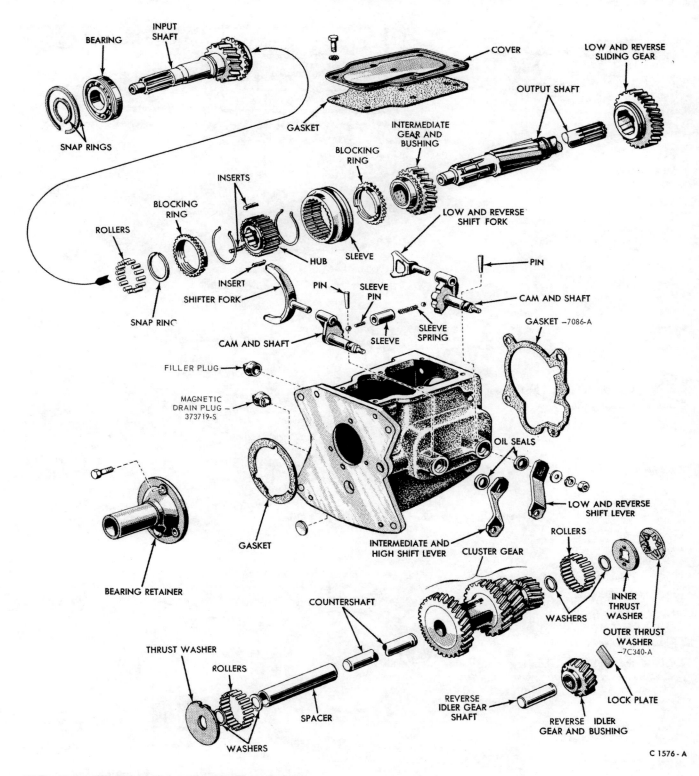

FIG. 10—Overdrive Transmission Disassembled

19. Remove the overdrive adapter and transmission output shaft as an assembly (Fig. 13).

20. Remove the snap ring at the front of the transmission output shaft, and then slide the synchronizer inter-mediate gear, and the sliding low and reverse gear off the shaft.

21. Lift the countershaft gear, thrust washers, and dummy shaft from the case.

22. Drive the reverse idler gear shaft out of the rear of the case with a brass drift and a hammer, and re-move the idler gear from the case.

23. Remove the lock plunger, spring, pin, and detent balls from the case (Fig. 14).

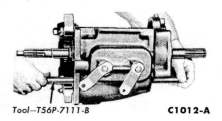

Tool—T56P-7111-B   C1012-A

FIG. 11—Removing Countershaft

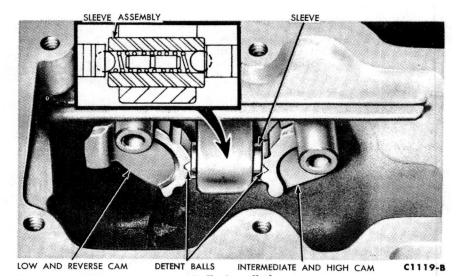

LOW AND REVERSE CAM   DETENT BALLS   INTERMEDIATE AND HIGH CAM   C1119-B

FIG. 14—Cams and Detent Balls Installed

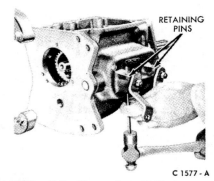

RETAINING PINS

C 1577 - A

FIG. 12—Removing Shift Lever Shaft Retaining Pin

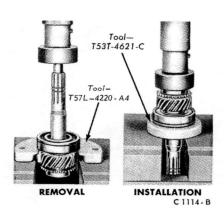

Tool— T53T-4621-C

Tool— T57L-4220-A4

REMOVAL   INSTALLATION
C 1114-B

FIG. 15—Replacing Input Shaft Bearing

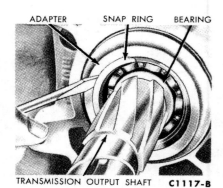

ADAPTER   SNAP RING   BEARING

TRANSMISSION OUTPUT SHAFT   C1117-B

FIG. 17—Removing Output Shaft Bearing Snap Ring

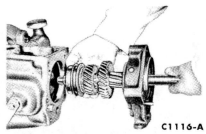

C1116-A

FIG. 13—Removing Output Shaft and Adapter

PARTS REPAIR OR REPLACEMENT

INPUT SHAFT

1. If the input shaft bearing is to be replaced, remove the snap ring that retains the bearing, and press the bearing and baffle off the shaft (Fig. 15).

2. Press a new bearing into place on the gear and shaft.

SYNCHRONIZER

1. Disassemble the synchronizer unit (Fig. 10) by sliding the intermediate and high sleeve off the hub. Remove the three inserts and two springs from the hub.

2. Assemble the synchronizer unit by installing the two springs on the

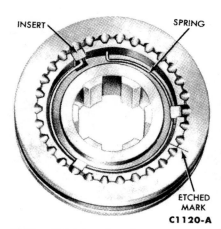

INSERT   SPRING

ETCHED MARK

C1120-A

FIG. 16—Synchronizer

hub and placing the three inserts in the hub. Hook one spring end in an insert as shown in Fig. 16.

3. After lining up the etched marks on the sleeve and hub splines,

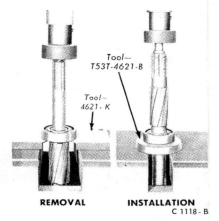

Tool— T53T-4621-B

Tool— 4621-K

REMOVAL   INSTALLATION
C 1118-B

FIG. 18—Replacing Output Shaft Bearing

slide the sleeve into place on the hub.

OUTPUT SHAFT BEARING

1. Remove the snap ring which re-

tains the output shaft in the adapter (Fig. 17), and tap the bearing out of the adapter. Remove the baffle from the adapter.

2. Remove the snap ring and press the old bearing off and the new bearing on with the tools shown in Fig. 18.

Install the snap ring to retain the bearing.

3. Position the baffle in the adapter (Fig. 17). Tap the bearing and shaft into place in the adapter.

4. Install the snap ring to retain *the bearing.*

CAM AND SHAFT SEALS

1. Remove the nuts and lock washers that secure the levers on the cam and shaft units, and remove the levers from the shafts and cams.

2. Remove the cams and shafts, detent balls, pin, spring, and sleeve (Fig. 10) from the case.

3. Remove the seals with a suitable puller. Discard the seals.

4. Install the new seals with a suitable driver.

5. Install the intermediate and high cam and shaft assembly in the case.

6. Insert a detent ball, sleeve, spring, and pin in the bore of the case. Move the cam and shaft so that the detent ball seats in the neutral (center) notch.

7. Install the low and reverse cam and shaft assembly, and then install the levers on the shafts with nuts and lock washers.

8. Install a detent ball in the sleeve at the low and reverse end. Then push the low and reverse cam toward the detent ball far enough to hold the ball in place in the neutral notch. The ball must seat in the notch of the cam.

9. Install the shift lever shaft retaining pins (Fig. 12).

10. In order to assure positive shifting, and eliminate the possibility of engaging more than one set of gears at the same time, the clearance between the ramp of one cam and the sleeve must be checked.

COUNTERSHAFT ROLLERS

1. Remove the thrust washers from each end of the countershaft.

2. Remove the dummy shaft, retainer washers, rollers, and spacer from the countershaft gear.

3. Position the spacer and the dummy shaft in the countershaft.

4. Place a retainer washer in each end of the countershaft gear.

5. Coat the bore in each end of the countershaft with grease. Hold the dummy shaft in the gear and install the roller bearings and a retainer washer in each end of the gear.

6. Apply grease to the two remaining retainer washers and to the contact surface of the thrust washers. Install the retainer washers and the thrust washers on each end of the gear.

ASSEMBLY

Always use new gaskets and gasket sealer during assembly. To provide initial lubrication, apply a thin coating of lubricant on all parts before installation.

1. Position the countershaft gear, dummy shaft, and roller bearings in the case.

2. Place the case in a vertical position. Align the gear bore and the thrust washers with the bores in the case and install the countershaft.

3. Place the case in a horizontal position and check the countershaft gear end play with a feeler gauge. The end play should be 0.004-0.018 inch. If not within these limits, replace the thrust washers.

4. After establishing the correct end play, install the dummy shaft in the countershaft gear and allow the gear to remain at the bottom of the case.

5. Install the reverse idler gear in the case, with the chamfered gear teeth ends toward the front.

6. Drive the reverse idler shaft into the case, with the locking notch aligned with the countershaft hole.

7. Install the low and reverse sliding gear on the output shaft, with the shifter fork groove toward the front.

8. Install the intermediate gear on the output shaft, with the clutch teeth toward the front.

9. Place a blocking ring on the intermediate gear, and install the synchronizer assembly on the transmission output shaft, with the hub thrust surface toward the rear (Fig. 10). Rotate the intermediate gear as necessary to line up the notches in the blocker ring with the synchronizer inserts. Install the snap ring that retains the synchronizer.

10. Install the shift forks in the cams inside the transmission case. **The offset in the low and reverse fork goes toward the front.**

11. Install a new solenoid seal in the overdrive adapter.

12. Place a new gasket on the overdrive adapter and hold it in place with gasket sealer.

13. Install the overdrive adapter and transmission output shaft assembly in the transmission.

14. Engage the shift forks with the high and intermediate sleeve, and with the low and reverse sliding gear.

15. Seat the overdrive adapter squarely against the transmission case, and secure with a cap screw.

16. Coat the bore of the input shaft with a thin film of grease and install the pilot roller bearings.

17. Place the blocking ring on the input shaft gear. Hold the input shaft and blocking ring in position. Move the input shaft forward to seat the output shaft pilot in the roller bearings of the input shaft.

18. Tap the input shaft and bearing into the case with a soft hammer, and at the same time line up the slots in the blocking ring with the synchronizer inserts.

19. Place a new gasket on the input shaft bearing retainer, and hold it in place with gasket sealer.

20. Install the input shaft bearing retainer to the transmission case.

21. Swing the transmission to an inverted position in the fixture.

22. Remove the cap screw holding the adapter in place. Pull the adapter outward approximately ¼ inch, and rotate it to expose the countershaft hole.

23. Work the countershaft gear into normal position by rotating the input and output shafts.

PAWL   BALK RING GEAR

INSTALL WITH MACHINED RECESS IN THIS POSITION   C1013-A

FIG. 19—Plate and Trough Installed

24. Push the countershaft into the case from the rear.

25. Align the slots in the countershaft with the slot in the reverse idler shaft and install the lock plate.

26. Rotate the adapter to its normal position and set it squarely against the transmission case. Check

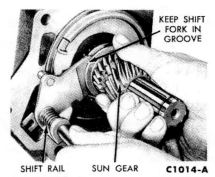

KEEP SHIFT FORK IN GROOVE

SHIFT RAIL   SUN GEAR   C1014-A

FIG. 20—Sun Gear and Shift Rail Installation

the blocking rings to make sure the slots are aligned with the synchronizer inserts.

27. Swing the transmission so that the input shaft is pointing down.

28. Place the balk ring gear assembly and pawl in the adapter (Fig. 19).

29. Place the plate and trough assembly in the adapter and install its snap ring.

30. Install the sun gear and shift rail (Fig. 20).

31. Install the planet carrier and the clutch cam. Install the retainers.

32. Install the 12 clutch rollers and hold them in position with a strong rubber band.

33. Rotate the roller cage counterclockwise (from the rear) until the rollers are off the cam surfaces. The rubber band will hold them there.

34. Slide the overdrive output shaft carefully over the clutch rollers. The rubber band will not affect operation of the overdrive.

35. Align the shift rail spring with the holes in the overdrive housing.

36. Place a new gasket on the overdrive adapter, and hold it in place with gasket sealer. (Fig. 25).

37. Install the overdrive housing over the overdrive output shaft and shift rail.

38. If the overdrive output shaft bearing snap ring does not drop into its groove when the housing is seated squarely on the adapter, pry the overdrive output shaft bearing toward the rear, working through the snap ring hole. Install the four bolts.

39. Engage the overdrive shaft lever by pushing it inward. The lever is correctly engaged when a spring load is apparent as the lever is pushed forward.

40. Install the retaining pin in the overdrive housing to hold the control shaft in place.

41. If the overdrive housing bush-

ing and seal are to be replaced, use the same tools which are used on conventional transmissions.

42. Thread the governor into the overdrive housing.

43. Position the solenoid in the adapter. Rotate the solenoid ¼ turn from normal position so that the half ball on the solenoid stem can engage the pawl.

If the solenoid stem is properly engaged, the solenoid cannot be removed from the overdrive in its normal position. Any attempt to pull it out will merely compress the engaging spring in the solenoid. Install the two solenoid attaching screws.

44. Use a new cover gasket and install the transmission cover. Coat the cover attaching screws with sealer and torque to specification.

45. Install the drain plugs in the transmission case and in the overdrive housing. Make sure that the magnetic plugs are installed in the bottom of the case.

46. Check the transmission gear operation in all positions.

DISASSEMBLY (OVERDRIVE USED WITH 390 CID ENGINE)

1. Mount the transmission in a holding fixture. Then drain the transmission and the overdrive unit.

2. Remove the gear shift cover and the shift forks from the transmission case. Discard the gear shift cover gasket.

3. Remove the solenoid retaining screws, and then rotate the solenoid about ¼ turn to remove it.

4. Remove the governor.

5. With a sharp punch, pierce the snap ring hole cover, and remove the cover from the top of the overdrive housing.

6. From the bottom, drive out the overdrive manual control shaft lock pin. Pull the manual control lever and shaft out as far as possible.

7. Remove the overdrive housing attaching bolts.

8. Insert snap ring pliers in the overdrive housing snap ring hole, and spread the snap ring that retains the main shaft bearing.

9. Remove the overdrive housing. To free the output shaft bearing from the housing, it may be necessary to tap on the shaft with a soft-faced hammer.

10. Remove the overdrive main shaft from the assembly. Catch any of the clutch rollers that drop out. Remove the rest of the rollers.

11. After removing the snap ring from the end of the transmission output shaft, remove the overrunning clutch and planet carrier. Remove the snap ring at the rear of the sun gear.

12. Remove the sun gear and the shift rail and fork assembly together.

13. Remove the snap ring that retains the plate and trough assembly in the adapter. Lift the plate and trough, balk ring gear, and pawl from the adapter.

14. Remove the input shaft bearing retainer and gasket. Discard the gasket.

15. Replace the input shaft seal with the tools that are used for the conventional transmission.

16. Tap the input shaft forward as far as it will go.

17. Remove the overdrive adapter and transmission output shaft assembly from the case (Fig. 21).

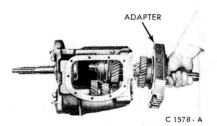

ADAPTER

C 1578-A

FIG. 21—Removing Adapter and Output Shaft

18. With a drift, drive the countershaft from the front of the case and toward the rear until the countershaft clears the front hole. Remove the Woodruff key from the rear of the countershaft as soon as the key clears the case.

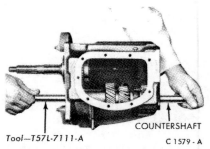

Tool—T57L-7111-A   COUNTERSHAFT   C 1579-A

FIG. 22—Removing Countershaft

19. Support the countershaft gear with a hook and push the countershaft from the countershaft gear with the dummy shaft (Fig. 22).

Lower the gear to the bottom of the case. Remove the countershaft from the case.

20. Remove the snap ring from the input shaft bearing outer race. With a soft-faced hammer, drive the input shaft and bearing toward the rear until the bearing clears the case.

21. Remove the input shaft and bearing through the gear shift cover opening.

22. Remove the countershaft (cluster) gear from the case.

23. Drive the reverse idler shaft out through the rear of the case. Remove the Woodruff key from the shaft as soon as it clears the case. Remove the idler gear.

24. Remove the snap ring that retains the synchronizer assembly to the transmission output shaft. Slide the synchronizer, blocking ring, intermediate gear, and low and reverse sliding gear from the transmission output shaft.

25. Remove the snap ring that retains the output shaft bearing in the

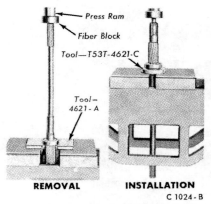

FIG. 23—Output Shaft Bearing Replacement

adapter. Tap the bearing and shaft out of the adapter. Remove the oil baffle from the adapter.

26. If the transmission output shaft or overdrive output shaft bearings are to be replaced, use the tools shown in Fig. 23.

27. The input shaft bearing should be replaced, with the tools shown in Fig. 15.

28. The synchronizer can be disassembled by sliding the high and intermediate sleeve from the hub.

29. Remove and replace the seals on the cam and shaft units in the gear shift cover and overdrive housing assembly.

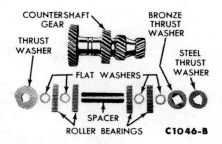

FIG. 24—Countershaft Gear Disassembled

ASSEMBLY

Always use new gaskets and gasket sealer during assembly. To provide initial lubrication, apply a thin coating of lubricant on all parts before installation.

1. Coat the bore in each end of the countershaft (cluster) gear with grease. Place the dummy shaft (Fig. 22) in the countershaft (cluster) gear. Slide the spacer over the bearing retainer tool. Install a row of needle bearings, a flat washer, a second row of needle bearings, and a second flat washer at each end of the countershaft gear. Place the thrust washers (front and rear) on the gear, and keep them in place with grease (Fig. 24). Position the countershaft gear, dummy shaft, and roller bearings in the case.

2. Install the countershaft and check end play with a feeler gauge. The end play should be 0.004-0.018 inch. If not within these limits, replace the thrust washers. After establishing the correct end play, install the dummy shaft in the countershaft gear and allow the gear to remain in the bottom of the case. The tab on the front thrust washer must enter the slot in the case. The tab on the steel washer at the rear must be at the top.

3. Place the reverse idler gear in position in the case, with the chamfered gear teeth ends toward the front. Install the reverse idler shaft and Woodruff key.

4. Coat the bore of the input shaft with a thin film of grease and assemble the pilot rollers. Install input shaft and bearing through the side of the case and tap into place with a soft-faced hammer. Install the snap ring on the input shaft bearing outer race. Place a new gasket on the bearing retainer and install it.

5. Turn the transmission upside down and work the countershaft (cluster) gear into position. Start the countershaft from the rear of

the case, and push the dummy shaft out of the front of the case. Install the Woodruff key and drive the countershaft until flush with the rear face of the transmission case.

6. Slide the oil baffle onto the transmission output shaft, with the dished side next to the bearing.

7. Install the transmission output shaft and bearing in the overdrive adapter. Install the selective-fit snap ring which secures the bearing in the adapter (Fig. 25).

8. Install the low and reverse sliding gear on the output shaft with the shift fork groove toward the front.

9. Place a blocking ring on the intermediate gear and install the intermediate and high gear on the output shaft, with the clutch teeth toward the front.

10. Assemble the synchronizer by placing the three inserts in position on the hub. Place a spring at each end of the hub, and hook one spring end in an insert (Fig. 16). Align the etched marks on the sleeve and hub splines, and slide the sleeve over the hub with the shifter fork groove toward the rear.

11. Slide the synchronizer onto the output shaft, with the hub thrust surface toward the rear. Rotate the intermediate gear as necessary to line up the notches in the blocker ring with the synchronizer inserts. Install the synchronizer snap ring.

12. Place the pilot roller bearing flat washer on the output shaft journal, and retain with grease.

13. Install a new solenoid seal in the adapter.

14. Place a new gasket on the front side of the adapter and retain with gasket sealer.

15. Place a blocker ring on the input shaft gear. Install the output shaft assembly and adapter in the case (Fig. 21), seating the pilot in the roller bearings of the input shaft. Secure the adapter in place with a bolt.

16. Place the balk ring in the adapter with the balk ring side out.

17. Install the pawl with the machined recess in line with the shift rail hole, and then install the plate and trough assembly. Install the snap ring.

18. Install the overdrive shift rail and fork assembly and sun gear at the same time (Fig. 20). Install the snap ring in the transmission output shaft groove at the rear of the sun gear.

19. Slide the planet carrier and

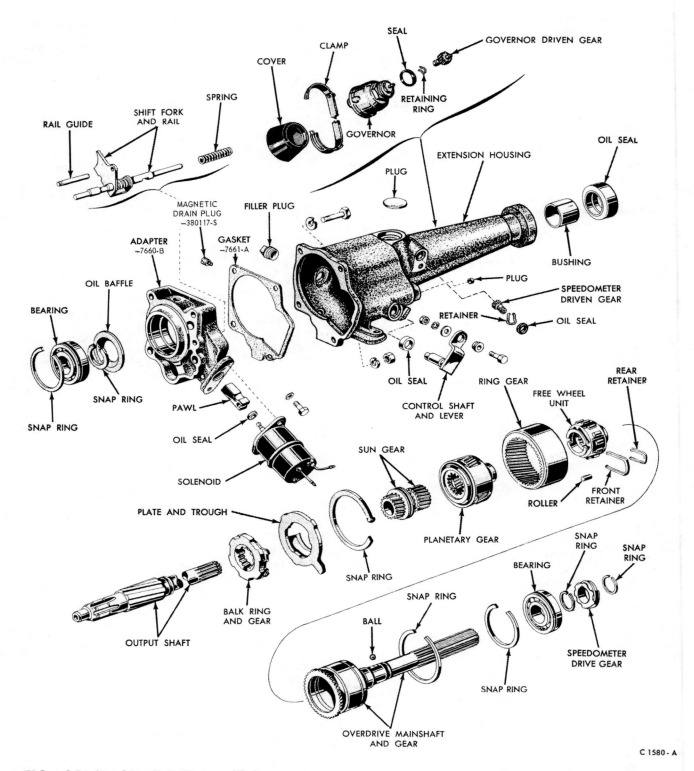

FIG. 25—Overdrive Unit Disassembled

clutch cam onto the output shaft, and install the snap ring.

20. Install the clutch rollers and hold in place with a strong rubber band. Slide the overdrive main shaft carefully over the clutch rollers.

21. Align the overdrive shift rail spring with the holes in the housing.

22. Place a new gasket (Fig. 25) on the adapter and retain in place with gasket sealer.

23. Install the overdrive housing over the main shaft and shift rail, and start the bolts. Install the overdrive main shaft bearing snap ring. Install a new snap ring hole cover.

24. Tighten the overdrive housing attaching bolts.

25. Engage the overdrive shaft lever by pushing it inward. Install the retaining pin.

26. If replacement of the overdrive housing bushing and/or seal is necessary, use the tools shown in Part 6-1.

27. Install the governor.

28. Position the solenoid in the adapter. Rotate the solenoid ¼ turn from normal position so that the half ball on the solenoid stem can engage the pawl. If the solenoid stem is properly engaged, the solenoid cannot be removed from the overdrive in its normal position. Any attempt to pull it will merely compress the engaging spring in the solenoid. Install the cap screws.

29. Place a new gear shift-housing gasket on the transmission case and retain in place with gasket sealer.

30. Shift the high and intermediate synchronizer sleeve and the low and reverse sliding gear to their neutral positions. Shift the shifter forks into their neutral positions.

31. Install the gear shift housing assembly on the case. Coat the cover attaching screws with sealer and torque to specification.

32. Install the drain plugs in the transmission case and overdrive housing. Make sure that the magnetic plugs are installed in the bottom of the case.

33. Check the transmission operation in all gear positions.

PART 6-5   SPECIFICATIONS

THREE-SPEED TRANSMISSION MODEL 3.03

GEAR RATIOS

| Car Usage | Transmission Model | Engine C.I.D. | Ratio | | | |
			First Speed	Second Speed	Third Speed	Reverse
Ford	HEF-BG	240-1V 289-2V	2.99	1.75	1.00:1	3.17
Ford	HEG-V	352-4V 390-2V-4V	2.42	1.61	1.00:1	2.33
Mercury	HEG-V	390-2V-4V 410-4V	2.42	1.61	1.00:1	2.33

LUBRICANTS & SEALERS

Application	Material
Transmission	Mild EP Gear Oil C3RZ 19547-B
Main Shaft Roller Bearing Countershaft Gear Roller Bearing	Lube Grease M-4659
Bolts and Gaskets	Sealer M-4G91-B
Steering Column Lower Plate	Lithium Base Grease (No Polyethylene) C3VY-19586-A

LUBRICANT REFILL CAPACITIES

Application	Pints (Approximate)
All Models	3.5

TRANSMISSION COMPONENT END PLAY

Component	End Play
Countershaft Gear to Case	0.004-0.018
Reverse Idler Gear to Case	0.004-0.018

TORQUE LIMITS

Description	Foot Pounds
Input shaft bearing retainer to transmission case	30-36
Transmission to flywheel housing bolts	37-42
Extension housing to transmission case	42-50
Access cover to transmission case	14-19
Gear shift control levers to cam and shaft	18-23
Shift fork to shift rail	10-18
Filler plug to case	10-20
Drain plug to case	20-30
Detent set screw (special) Flush to 0.020 inches below top of case	

FOUR-SPEED TRANSMISSION FORD DESIGN

GEAR RATIOS

| Car Usage | Transmission Model | Engine C.I.D. | Ratios | | | | |
			1st	2nd	3rd	4th	Rev.
Ford	HEH-CC	390-4V	2.32	1.69	1.29	1.00:1	2.32
Mercury	HEH-CC	390-4V	2.32	1.69	1.29	1.00:1	2.32
Ford	HEH-AM	427-8V 428-4V-8V	2.32	1.69	1.29	1.00:1	2.32
Mercury	HEH-AM	410-4V-8V 428-4V-8V	2.32	1.69	1.29	1.00:1	2.32

CONTINUED ON NEXT PAGE

FOUR-SPEED TRANSMISSION FORD DESIGN (Continued)

LUBRICANTS & SEALERS

Application	Material
Transmission	Mild EP Gear Oil C3RZ 19547-B
Main Shaft Roller Bearing Countershaft Gear Roller Bearing	Lube Grease M-4659
Bolts and Gaskets	Sealer M-4G91-B
Shift Linkage, Trunnions and External Shift Mechanism Steering Column Lower Plate	Lithium Base Grease (No Polyethylene) C3VY-19586-A

TRANSMISSION COMPONENT END PLAY

Component	End Play
Countershaft Gear to Case	0.004-0.018
Reverse Idler Gear to Case	0.004-0.018

LUBRICANT REFILL CAPACITIES

Application	Pints (Approximate)
All Models	4

TORQUES

Application	Part Name	Ft-Lbs
Input shaft bearing retainer to transmission case	Bolt-$5/16$-18 x $3/4$ Hex Head	19-25
Transmission to flywheel housing bolts	Bolt-$7/16$-14	37-42
Extension housing to transmission case	Bolt-$7/16$-14 x $1 1/4$ Hex Head	42-50
Access cover to transmission case	Screw-$5/16$-18 x $5/8$ Hex Head Screw-$5/16$-18 x 1 Hex Head	14-19
Gear shift lever to cam and shaft	Nut—$3/8$-24 Hex	18-23
Shift fork to shift rail	Screw-$5/16$-24 x .92 Set Locking	10-18
Filler plug to case	Plug—$1/2$-14	10-20
Drain plug to case	Plug—$1/2$-14 (Magnetic)	20-30
Detent Set Screw (Special)	Screw—$3/8$-16 x .88 Set	Flush to 0.020" below surface
Third and Fourth Shift Rail Detent Bolt	Bolt-$3/8$-16 x .38 Hex Head	10-18

OVERDRIVE TRANSMISSION

GEAR RATIOS

Trans Model	Vehicle Usage	Engine C.I.D.	1st Gear		2nd Gear		3rd Gear		Reverse Gear
			Conventional Drive	Overdrive	Conventional Drive	Overdrive	Conventional Drive	Overdrive	Conventional Drive
HEK-T	Ford	240-1V	3.20	2.80	1.86	1.69	1.00:1	0.70	3.80
HEK-T	Ford	289-2V	3.20	2.80	1.86	1.69	1.00:1	0.70	3.80
HEK-N	Ford (Ex. 3.25 Axle)	390-2V-4V	2.37	2.59	1.51	1.60	1.00:1	0.722	3.33
HEK-Y	Ford (3.25 Axle)	390-2V-4V	2.37	2.59	1.51	1.60	1.00:1	0.722	3.33

CONTINUED ON NEXT PAGE

OVERDRIVE TRANSMISSION (Continued)

TORQUE SPECIFICATIONS

Description	Ft-lbs
Input Shaft Bearing Retainer to Transmission Case Bolt	12-15
Transmission to Flywheel Housing Bolts	37-42
Gearshift Housing to Transmission Case Bolts	12-15
Transmission Extension Housing to Case Bolts or Nuts	42-50
Gearshift Control Levers to Cam and Shaft Assembly Nuts	20-25
Overdrive Assembly to Transmission Case Nuts	37-42
Engine Rear Support to Extension Housing Bolts	35-40
Access Cover to Transmission Case	15-20
Filler Plug to Case	10-20
Drain Plug to Case (Magnetic)	20-30
Side Cover to Transmission Case Bolts	15-26

TRANSMISSION COMPONENT END PLAY

Component	End Play
Crankshaft Gear to Case	0.004-0.018
Cam Ramp to Interlock Shift Sleeve Clearance	0.001-0.007

LUBRICANT REFILL CAPACITIES

Trans Model	Application	Pints (Approximate)
HEK-T	Engines 240 or 289 C.I.D.	3.7 pints
HEK-N	Engine 390 C.I.D.	4.5 pints

LUBRICANTS & SEALERS

Application	Material
Transmission	Mild EP Gear Oil C3RZ-19547-B
Main Shaft Roller Bearing / Countershaft Gear Roller Bearing	Lube Grease M-4659
Bolts and Gaskets	Sealer M-4G91-B
Steering Column Lower Plate	Lithium Base Grease (No Polyethylene) C3VY-19586-A

SPECIAL TOOLS

Tool Numbers	Description
T50T-100A	Impact Hammer—Long
T59L-100B	Impact Hammer—Short
T58L-101A	Puller Attachment
1175AB	Grease Seal Remover
T57L-4220-A	Differential Bearing Assembly Remover
T53T-4621-B or (4621-F)	Drive Pinion Bearing Cone Replacer Front & Rear
T53T-4621-C	Drive Pinion Bearing Cone Replacer
T-4621-K	Drive Pinion Bearing Cone Replacer
T57L-4220-A4	Differential Side Bearing Cone Replacer or Input Shaft Bearing Remover
6135-G	Piston Pin Remover & Replacer
T52T-6500-DJD (6500-D)	Solid Tappet Remover or Reverse Shift Rail Pliers
T52L-7000-GAE	Extension Housing Bushing and Seal Remover
T52L-7000-HAE	Extension Housing Bushing Installer
T57-7003-A	Transmatic Drive Bushing Replacer
T63P-7025-A	Output Shaft Bearing Remover & Replacer
T64P-7025-B	Output Shaft Bearing Remover & Replacer

SPECIAL TOOLS (Continued)

Tool Numbers	Description
T-7025-B	Rear Main Shaft Bearing Remover
T-7025-G	Main Shaft Bearing Remover & Replacer
T57L-7111-A	Cluster Gear Roller Retainer Shaft
T60K-7111-A	Cluster Gear Roller Retainer Shaft
T62K-7111-A	Cluster Gear Roller Retainer Shaft
T64P-7111-A	Cluster Gear Roller Retainer Shaft
T56P-7111-B	Cluster Gear Roller Retainer Shaft
T63P-7111-B	Cluster Gear Roller Retainer Shaft
T64P-7140-A	Reverse Idler Shaft Remover
T57L-7657-A	Transmission Extension Housing Oil Seal Replacer
T64P-7657-A	Transmission Extension Housing Oil Seal Replacer
760K-7657-B (7657-G)	Transmission Extension Housing Oil Seal Replacer
T7688	Lockout Lever Oil Seal Replacer
T60K-7697-A	Transmission Extension Housing Bushing Remover
T57P-77047-A	Transmission Input Shaft Oil Seal Replacer—Std. Trans.
T60K-77047-A	Transmission Input Shaft Oil Seal Replacer—Std. Trans.

AUTOMATIC TRANSMISSION

GROUP 7

PART 7-1 GENERAL TRANSMISSION SERVICE

Three different Dual Range three-speed transmissions are used. The C4 Automatic, C6 Automatic and the Cruise-O-Matic—used on Ford cars or Merc-O-Matic used on Mercury cars. The Cruise-O-Matic and Merc-O-Matic are the same type of automatic transmissions. Part 7-1 covers diagnosis and testing, common adjustments and repairs, and cleaning and inspection for the three types of transmissions. Where there are differences in procedures or specifications, the type of transmission affected will be designated.

1 DIAGNOSIS AND TESTING

When diagnosing transmission problems, first refer to the diagnosis guide for the detailed information on the items that could be causing the problem.

The following preliminary checks should be made before proceeding with other diagnosis checks.

TRANSMISSION FLUID LEVEL CHECK

A fluid level that is too high will cause the fluid to become aerated. Aerated fluid will cause low control pressure, and the aerated fluid may be forced out the vent.

Check the transmission fluid level. Low fluid level can affect the operation of the transmission, and may indicate fluid leaks that could cause transmission damage.

TRANSMISSION FLUID LEAKAGE CHECKS

Check the speedometer cable connection at the transmission. Replace the rubber seal if necessary.

Leakage at the oil pan gasket often can be stopped by tightening the attaching bolts to the proper torque. If necessary, replace the gasket.

Check the fluid filler tube connection at the transmission. If leakage is found here, install a new O-ring on a C6 transmission, or tighten the fitting on a Cruise-O-Matic, Merc-O-Matic or C4 transmission to the specified torque.

Check the fluid lines and fittings between the transmission and the cooler in the radiator tank for looseness, wear, or damage. If leakage cannot be stopped by tightening a fitting, replace the defective parts.

Check the engine coolant in the radiator. If transmission fluid is present in the coolant, the cooler in the radiator is probably leaking.

The cooler can be further checked for leaks by disconnecting the lines from the cooler fittings and applying 5 psi air pressure to the fittings. Remove the radiator cap to relieve the pressure build at the exterior of the oil cooler tank. If the cooler is leaking and will not hold this pressure, the radiator must be replaced. **The cooler cannot be replaced separately.**

If leakage is found at either the downshift control lever shaft or the manual lever shaft, replace either or both seals.

Inspect the pipe plug on the left side of the transmission case at the front. If the plug shows leakage, torque the plug to specification. If tightening does not stop the leaks, replace the plug. On a C6 transmission, a TV pressure plug is also provided on the right rear side of the case.

When converter drain plugs leak, remove drain plugs with a six-point wrench. Coat the threads with FoMoCo Perfect Seal Sealing Compound or its equivalent, and install the plugs. Torque the drain plugs to specification. **Fluid leakage from the converter housing may be caused by engine oil leaking past the rear main bearing or from oil gallery plugs, or power steering oil leakage from steering system. Be sure to determine the exact cause of the leak before repair procedures are started.**

Oil-soluble aniline or fluorescent dyes premixed at the rate of ½ teaspoon of dye powder to ½ pint of transmission fluid have proved helpful in locating the source of the fluid leakage. Such dyes may be used to determine whether an engine oil or transmission fluid leak is present, or if the fluid in the oil cooler leaks into the engine coolant system. A black light, however, must be used with the fluorescent dye solution.

FLUID LEAKAGE IN CONVERTER AREA

In diagnosing and correcting fluid leaks in the front pump and converter area, use the following procedures

to facilitate locating the exact cause of the leakage. Leakage at the front of the transmission, as evidenced by fluid around the converter housing, may have several sources. By careful observation, it is possible, in many instances, to pinpoint the source of the leak before removing the transmission from the car. The paths which the fluid takes to reach the bottom of the converter housing are shown in Fig. 1.

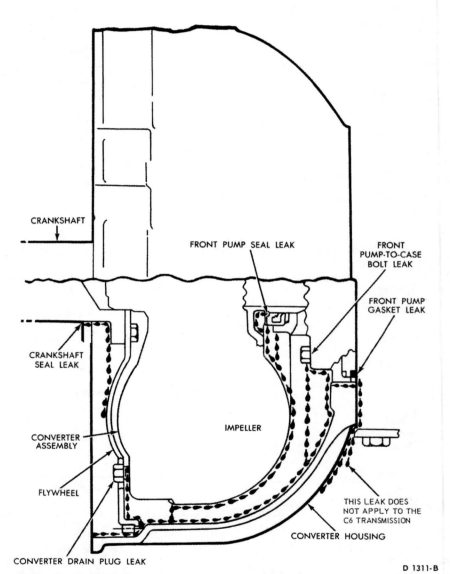

CRANKSHAFT

FRONT PUMP SEAL LEAK

FRONT PUMP-TO-CASE BOLT LEAK

FRONT PUMP GASKET LEAK

CRANKSHAFT SEAL LEAK

CONVERTER ASSEMBLY

IMPELLER

FLYWHEEL

THIS LEAK DOES NOT APPLY TO THE C6 TRANSMISSION

CONVERTER HOUSING

CONVERTER DRAIN PLUG LEAK

D 1311-B

FIG. 1—Typical Converter Area Leakage Checks

1. Fluid leaking by the front pump seal lip will tend to move along the drive hub and onto the back of the impeller housing. Except in the case of a total seal failure, fluid leakage by the lip of the seal will be deposited on the inside of the

converter housing only, near the outside diameter of the housing.

2. Fluid leakage by the outside diameter of the seal and front pump body will follow the same path which leaks by the front pump seal.

3. Fluid that leaks by a front pump to case bolt will be deposited on the inside of the converter housing only. Fluid will not be deposited on the back of the converter.

4. Leakage by the front pump to

case gasket may cause fluid to be deposited inside the converter housing, or it may seep down between the front of the case and converter housing. Fluid on the front of the case, above the pan gasket, is evidence that the front pump to case gasket or seal could be leaking.

5. Fluid leakage from the converter drain plugs will appear at the outside diameter of the converter on the back face of the flywheel, and in the converter housing only near the flywheel.

Engine oil leaks are sometimes improperly diagnosed as transmission front pump seal leaks. The following areas of possible leakage should also be checked to determine if engine oil leakage is causing the problem.

1. Leakage at the rocker arm cover (valley cover) may allow oil to flow over the converter housing or seep down between the converter housing and cylinder block causing oil to be present in or at the bottom of the converter housing.

2. Oil gallery plug leaks will allow oil to flow down the rear face of the block to the bottom of the converter housing.

3. Leakage by the crankshaft seal will work back to the flywheel, and then into the converter housing.

Fluid leakage from other areas, such as the power steering system forward of the transmission, could cause fluid to be present around the converter housing due to blow back or road draft.

The following procedures should be used to determine the cause of the leakage before any repairs are made.

1. Remove the transmission dipstick and note the color of the fluid. Original factory fill fluid is dyed red to aid in determining if leakage is from the engine or transmission. Unless a considerable amount of makeup fluid has been added or the fluid has been changed, the red color should assist in pinpointing the leak. Fluid used in the power steering system is a yellowish green dye. Since road draft may cause leaking power steering fluid to be present on the transmission, this leakage, if present, should be eliminated before checking the transmission for oil leakage.

2. Remove the converter housing cover. Clean off any fluid from the top and bottom of the converter housing, front of the transmission case, and rear face of the engine and engine oil pan. Clean the converter area by washing with carbon tetrachloride or other suitable non-flammable solvent, and blow dry with compressed air.

3. Wash out the converter housing, the front of the flywheel, and the converter drain plugs. The converter housing may be washed out using cleaning solvent and a squirt-type oil can. Blow all washed areas dry with compressed air.

4. Start and run the engine until the transmission reaches its normal operating temperature. Observe the back of the block and top of the converter housing for evidence of fluid leakage. Raise the car on a hoist and run the engine at fast idle, then at engine idle, occasionally shifting to the drive and reverse ranges to increase pressures within the transmission. Observe the front of the flywheel, back of the block (in as far as possible), and inside the converter housing and front of the transmission case. Run the engine until fluid leakage is evident and the probable source of leakage can be determined.

CONVERTER LEAKAGE CHECK

During the above fluid leakage checks, if there are indications that the welds on the torque converter are leaking, the converter will have to be removed and the following check made before the unit is replaced.

A leak checking tool (Fig. 2) can be made from standard parts. The tool can be used to check all converters.

1. Install the plug in the converter (Fig. 3) and expand it by tightening

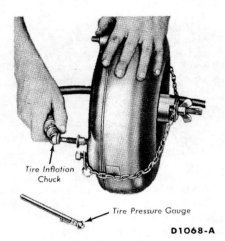

Tire Inflation Chuck

Tire Pressure Gauge

D1068-A

FIG. 3—Converter Leak Checking Tool Installation

the wing nut. Attach the safety chains.

2. Install the air valve in one of the drain plug holes.

3. Introduce air pressure into the converter. Check the pressure with a tire gauge and adjust it to 20 psi.

4. Place the converter in a tank of water. Observe the weld areas for bubbles. If no bubbles are observed, it may be assumed that the welds are not leaking.

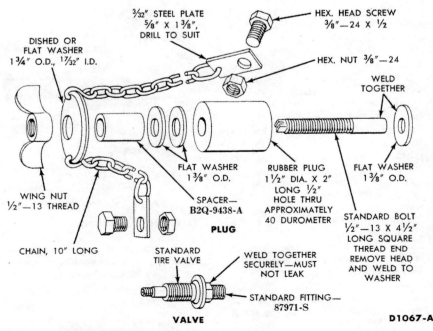

FIG. 2—Converter Leak Checking Tool

ENGINE IDLE SPEED CHECK

Check and, if necessary, adjust the engine idle speed, using the procedure given in Group 10.

If the idle speed is too low, the engine will run roughly. An idle speed that is too high will cause the car to creep when the transmission is shifted into gear and will cause rough transmission engagement.

ANTI-STALL DASHPOT CLEARANCE CHECK

After the engine idle speed has been properly adjusted, check the anti-stall dashpot clearance. Follow the procedure given in Group 10 for checking and adjusting this clearance.

MANUAL LINKAGE CHECKS

Correct manual linkage adjustment is necessary to position the manual valve for proper fluid pressure direction to the different transmission components. Improperly adjusted manual linkage may cause cross-leakage and subsequent transmission failure. Refer to Linkage Adjustments in Part 7-2, or 7-3 for detailed manual linkage adjustment procedures.

CONTROL PRESSURE AND VACUUM DIAPHRAGM UNIT CHECK

When the vacuum diaphragm unit (Fig. 4) is operating properly and the downshift linkage is adjusted properly, all the transmission shifts (automatic and kickdown) should occur within the road speed limits specified in Part 7-5.

If the shifts do not occur within limits or the transmission slips during shift points, the following procedure is suggested to determine engine, transmission, linkage, vacuum diaphragm unit or valve body problems.

1. Attach a tachometer to the engine and a vacuum gauge to the transmission vacuum line at the vacuum unit (Fig. 5).

2. Attach a pressure gauge to the control pressure outlet at the transmission.

3. Firmly apply the parking brake and start the engine.

4. Adjust the engine idle speed to the specified rpm. If the engine idle speed cannot be brought within limits by adjustment at the carburetor idle adjustment screw, check the throttle and downshift linkage for a binding condition. If the linkage is satisfactory, check for vacuum leaks

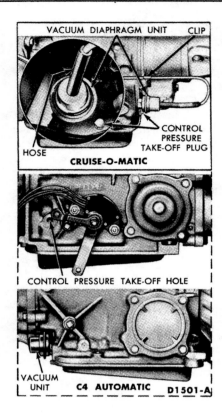

FIG. 4—Typical Vacuum Diaphragm and Control Pressure Connecting Point

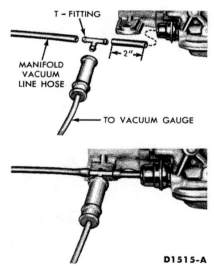

FIG. 5—Typical Vacuum Test Line Connections

in the transmission diaphragm unit (Fig. 6) and its connecting tubes and hoses. Check all other vacuum operated units (such as the power brake) for vacuum leaks.

VACUUM UNIT CHECK

To check the vacuum unit for dia-

FIG. 6—Testing Transmission Vacuum Unit for Leakage

phragm leakage, remove the unit from the transmission. Use a distributor tester equipped with a vacuum pump (Fig. 6). Set the regulator knob so that the vacuum gauge reads 18 inches with the end of the vacuum hose blocked off.

Then connect the vacuum hose to the transmission vacuum unit. If the gauge still reads 18 inches, the vacuum unit diaphragm **is not leaking.** As the hose is removed from the transmission vacuum unit, hold a finger over the end of the control rod. When the hose is removed, the internal spring of the vacuum unit should push the control rod outward.

TESTING—C4 OR C6 AUTOMATIC TRANSMISSION

The test results of the following checks should agree with the specifications given in Tables 1 and 2. When performing control pressure tests, make certain that the service brake pedal is held in the applied position. When the transmission detent position of D1 is used, position the selector lever at the large dot on the quadrant. The small dot is used for the D2 position.

TEST NUMBER—1 CONTROL PRESSURE CHECK—AT ENGINE IDLE

1. With the transmission in neutral, and the engine at the correct idle speed, the vacuum gauge should show a minimum of 18 inches. If the vacuum reading is lower than 18 inches, an engine problem is indicated or there is leakage in the vacuum line. Make necessary repairs to obtain a minimum vacuum reading of 18 inches.

At different altitudes above sea level, it may not be possible to obtain 18 inches vacuum at engine idle. At these altitudes, with idle vacuum of less than 18 inches, refer to the following specifications to determine idle speed control pressure in forward driving ranges.

C4 TRANSMISSION

Engine Vacuum (At Idle)	Control Pressure psi
17 Inches	55-62
16 Inches	55-68
15 Inches	55-74
14 Inches	55-80
13 Inches	55-87
12 Inches	55-93
11 Inches	55-99

C6 TRANSMISSION—Non-Altitude-Compensating Diaphragm Only

Engine Vacuum (At Idle)	Control Pressure (psi)	Throttle Pressure (psi)
17″	51-66	12-14
16″	51-72	16-18
15″	51-78	20-22
14″	51-84	24-26
13″	51-90	28-31
12″	51-97	32-35
11″	51-103	36-39

2. At engine idle, depress and release the accelerator pedal quickly and observe the vacuum gauge. The amount of vacuum should decrease and increase with the changes in throttle openings. If the vacuum response to changes in throttle opening is too slow the vacuum line to the diaphragm unit could be restricted. **Make the necessary repairs before completing the test.**

3. At engine idle, check the transmission control pressure gauge at all selector lever positions. Transmission control pressures should agree with the specifications as outlined in Tables 1 and 2.

TEST NUMBER—2 CONTROL PRESSURE INCREASE CHECK

The control pressure increase should be checked in all ranges except Park and Neutral. Shift the transmission into each drive range and into reverse and check control pressure increase in each range. With the correct control pressure at engine idle, advance the throttle until the engine vacuum reading falls to approximately 17.0 inches for a C4 transmission or 15 inches for the C6 transmission. As the vacuum gauge reading decreases into these specifications, **the control pressure should start to increase.**

Control pressure increase may be noted immediately when the throttle is opened due to the increased pump output, resulting from increased engine rpm. When this happens, the

TABLE 1—C4 Automatic Transmission

CONTROL PRESSURE AT ZERO OUTPUT SHAFT SPEED

Test No.	Engine Speed or Manifold Vacuum	Throttle Position	Selector Lever Position	[1]Control (Line) Pressure (psi)
1	Idle—Above 18 Inches of Vacuum	Closed	P,N,D1,D2,L	55-62
			R	55-100
2	17.0 Inches of Vacuum Approx.	As Required	D1,D2,L,R	Start Build Up
3	10 Inches of Vacuum	As Required	D1,D2,L	96-105
4	3 Inches of Vacuum	As Required	D1,D2,L	138-148
			R	215-227

[1]Transmission oil fluid at normal operating temperature.

TABLE 2—C6 Automatic Transmission—Non-Altitude-Compensating Diaphragm Only

CONTROL PRESSURE AT ZERO OUTPUT SHAFT SPEED

Test No.	Engine Speed or Manifold Vacuum	Throttle Position	Selector Lever Position	TV (Throttle Valve) Pressure (psi)	[1]Control (Line) Pressure (psi)
1	Idle—Above 17 inches of Vacuum	Closed	P,N,D1,D2,L	0-13	51-66
			R	0-13	62-98
2	15 inches of Vacuum	As Required	D1,D2,L	20-22	70-78
3	10 inches of Vacuum	As Required	D1,D2,L	40-44	98-109
4	Under 1.0 inch of Vacuum	Open	D1,D2,L	77-84	157-172
			R	77-84	230-252

[1]Transmission fluid at normal operating temperature

pressure increase point can be checked by using a **distributor vacuum tester.** Install the distributor tester vacuum line on the diaphragm assembly. Adjust the tester to provide over 18 inches of vacuum. Increase the engine speed to 600-700 rpm. Reduce the tester vacuum reading to approximately 17.0 inches and observe the transmission pressure gauge for the pressure increase.

TEST NUMBER—3 CONTROL PRESSURE CHECK AT 10 INCHES OF VACUUM

A control pressure check should be made at 10 inches of vacuum in all forward drive ranges.

Advance the throttle until the engine vacuum reading is 10 inches and check the control pressure regulation. Control pressure should be as shown in Tables 1 and 2.

TEST NUMBER—4 CONTROL PRESSURE CHECK AT 3 OR AT 1.0 INCHES OF VACUUM

Check control pressure at 3 inches of vacuum (C4 transmission) or 1.0 inch or less of vacuum (C6 transmission) in all forward drive ranges. The control pressure should be as shown in Tables 1 and 2. Then move the selector lever to R. With the vacuum at 3 inches (C4 transmission) or 1.0 inch or less (C6 transmission) the control pressure should be as shown in Tables 1 and 2.

While making this pressure test, do not hold the throttle open for more than five seconds in each detent position. Between each test move the selector lever to neutral and run the engine at 1000 rpm for fifteen seconds to cool the converter.

If the vacuum and pressure gauge readings are within specifications, the diaphragm unit and transmission control pressure regulating system are operating properly.

If transmission control pressure is too low, too high, fails to increase with throttle opening, or in extremely *erratic, use the procedure given un-der the following appropriate heading to resolve the problem.*

Control Pressure is Low at Engine Idle (Test No. 1)

If control pressure at engine idle is low in all selector lever positions, trouble other than the diaphragm unit is indicated. When control pressure at engine idle is low in all ranges, check for excessive leakage in the front oil pump, case, and control

valve body, or a sticking control pressure regulator valve.

Control Pressure is High at Engine Idle (Test No. 1)

If transmission control pressure at engine idle is too high in all ranges, the trouble may be in the diaphragm unit or its connecting vacuum tubes and hoses, throttle valve, or control rod.

With the engine idling, disconnect the hose from the diaphragm unit and check the engine manifold vacuum. Hold a thumb over the end of the hose and check for vacuum. If the engine speeds up when the hose is disconnected and slows down as the thumb is held against the end of the hose, the vacuum source is satisfactory.

Stop the engine, and remove the diaphragm unit and the diaphragm unit control rod. Inspect the control rod for a **bent** condition and for corrosion. Check the diaphragm unit for leakage with the distributor tester (Fig. 6).

Control Pressure Does Not Increase With Vacuum at Approximately 17.0 Inches (C4 Transmission) or 15 Inches (C6 Transmission) (Test No. 2)

When the control pressure is within specification at engine idle, but does not increase, as the vacuum is decreased to the specified limits, first check the control rod between the vacuum unit and throttle valve for proper engagement. If the control rod is not assembled into the end of the throttle valve or vacuum unit, the valve cannot regulate throttle pressure to increase control pressure.

Next check for a stuck primary throttle valve, pressure booster valve, or a stuck control pressure regulator valve.

If control pressure increases before or after vacuum is decreased to approximately 17.0 inches, (C4 transmission) or 15 inches (C6 transmission), check for a leaking diaphragm assembly, bent diaphragm can, or worn or bent control rod to the throttle valve.

Control Pressure Not Within Limits at 10 or 3 Inches of Vacuum (C4 Transmission) or 10 or 1.0 (C6 Transmission) (Test No. 3 or 4)

If idle pressure and pressure point increase are within specifications but

pressures at 10 or 3 inches of vacuum (C4 transmission) or 10 or 1.0 inch (C6 transmission) are not within specification in all ranges, excessive leakage, low pump capacity, or a restricted oil pan screen is indicated.

If pressures are not within specifications for specific selector lever positions only, this indicates excessive leakage in the clutch or servo circuits used in those ranges.

When the control pressure is within specifications at engine idle, **but not within specifications** at the pressure rise point of 17.0 inches of vacuum, at 10 inches of vacuum, or at 3 inches of vacuum for a C4 transmission or 15, 10 or 1.0 for a C6 transmission, the vacuum diaphragm unit may need adjustment.

HYDRAULIC CONTROL SYSTEM TESTS—C6 TRANSMISSION

In general, diagnosis and test procedures which apply to the C4 and Cruise-O-Matic transmissions will also apply to the C6. One of the most important aspects of diagnosis is understanding the correct and proper functioning of the transmission, so that when improper operation occurs, the cause can be quickly isolated. For example, in the hydraulic control system (Fig. 7, Part 7-4) the following test procedures can be applied to isolate certain valves in the C6 transmission which may be suspected of improper operation.

PRIMARY THROTTLE VALVE AND REGULATOR VALVE

With pressure gauge installed to line pressure outlet, and vacuum gauge installed in T at diaphragm, check line pressure readings against specifications. If readings are consistent and fall within specifications, it can be assumed that the diaphragm, throttle valve, and regulator valve are functioning properly. If control pressures do not fall within the specified ranges, are erratic or proper pressures cannot be obtained by a diaphragm adjustment, the pressure regulator valve can be isolated by checking primary TV pressure. Install the pressure gauge to the primary TV pressure outlet and check TV pressure vs. vacuum as shown in specifications; if TV pressures are within specification, or can be brought within specification with a diaphragm adjustment it can be assumed that the primary throttle valve, its circuit and the vacuum diaphragm are operating properly.

If TV pressures cannot be brought

within specifications, or are erratic, the problem could be in the regulator valve (due to its inability to supply sufficient pressure to the throttle valve) or in the throttle valve, diaphragm or vacuum lines. In these circumstances diagnostic and test procedures for the diaphragm, lines, etc. should be applied.

CUTBACK CONTROL VALVE, COASTING BOOST VALVE AND GOVERNOR VALVES

A series of tests can be applied which will determine if the cutback control valve, coasting boost valve and governor valves are functioning.

With a pressure gauge connected to read line pressure, the vehicle should be driven and the shift points checked. If the transmission shifts at the specified road speeds, it can be assumed that the governor is working properly. If the governor is working properly but line pressure cutback is delayed or does not occur, the cutback control valve is at fault. If the cutback control valve is sticking in the closed (up) position, primary TV pressure is being delivered to both the end and the first valley of the pressure booster valve, and no cutback will occur. Line cutback should occur at or shortly before the 1-2 shift. If the valve is sticking in the closed (down) position, the primary TV pressure passages to the pressure booster valve are open to exhaust, and there will be no boost in line pressure. The start of boost in line pressure should occur between 17 and 15 inches manifold vacuum. This condition would also result in low stall pressures.

The coasting boost valve operation can be checked as follows: with the vehicle coasting at a speed above 55 MPH, the selector lever should be moved to the L position; if the coasting boost valve is operating properly, an increase in line pressure will be noted. As speed drops below approximately 55 MPH, a drop in line pressure should be noted, indicating that the boost valve and governor are operating properly. If line pressure does not respond as described, either the governor or the coasting boost valve is at fault. If shift points indicate that the governor is operating correctly and other control pressures check out to specification then the problem is due to a sticking or inoperating coasting boost valve.

VACUUM DIAPHRAGM ADJUSTMENT—NON-ALTITUDE COMPENSATING-TYPE

The vacuum diaphragm assembly has an adjusting screw in the vacuum hose connecting tube (Fig. 7).

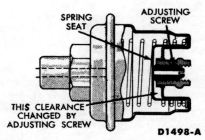

FIG. 7—C4 or C6 Automatic Transmission Vacuum Unit

The inner end of the screw bears against a plate which in turn bears against the vacuum diaphragm spring.

All readings slightly high or all readings slightly low may indicate the vacuum unit needs adjustment to correct a particular shift condition.

For example, on a C4 transmission, if the pressure at 10 inches of vacuum was 120 psi and the pressure at 3 inches of vacuum was 170 psi, and upshifts and downshifts were harsh, a diaphragm adjustment to reduce the diaphragm assembly spring force would be required.

If the pressure readings are low, and control pressure does not start to build up until vacuum drops to 15 inches, an adjustment to increase diaphragm spring force is required.

To increase control pressure, turn the adjusting screw in clockwise. To reduce control pressure, back the adjusting screw out by turning it counterclockwise. **One complete turn** of the adjusting screw (360°) will change idle line control pressure approximately 2-3 psi. After the adjustment is made, install the vacuum line and make all the pressure checks

as outlined in Tables 1 and 2.

The diaphragm should not be adjusted to provide pressure below the ranges in Tables 1 and 2, in order to change shift feel. To do so could result in soft or slipping shift points and damage to the transmission.

VACUUM DIAPHRAGM ADJUSTMENT—ALTITUDE COMPENSATING-TYPE

An adjustable altitude compensating type vacuum diaphragm has been released for service with the C6 transmission used in Ford and Mercury cars.

This diaphragm is adjusted essentially in the same manner as the non-altitude diaphragm, through the vacuum port, in conjunction with a vacuum gauge.

This type of vacuum diaphragm is conscious of barometric pressure, therefore when an adjustment is necessary, the current observed barometric pressure must be noted and allowed for. In general, barometric pressure varies with altitude in proportion to 1 inch of Hg drop in barometric pressure for each 1000 ft. of elevation. However, normal barometric pressure at any elevation may vary by as much as 1 inch Hg from the figures shown in Table 3. Therefore, barometric pressure rather than elevation should be used whenever possible in determining the pressures that should be obtained.

The current barometric pressure can be obtained either by referring to a barometer, or by checking with the local airport or U.S. Weather Bureau. The pressures referred to are actual **observed** barometric pressure (not corrected to sea level).

It may not be possible to obtain an engine vacuum reading of 15 inches Hg or better at higher elevations when checking control or TV pressures. Under this condition, control and TV pressure should coincide with the figures shown in the following chart:

Engine Vacuum At Idle	At 29.5 Inches Hg Observed Barometric Pressure		At 24.5 Inches Hg Observed Barometric Pressure	
	TV Pressure (psi)	Control Pressure (psi)	TV Pressure (psi)	Control Pressure (psi)
17 inches	12-14	51-66	0	51-59
16 inches	16-18	51-72	3-5	51-59
15 inches	20-22	51-78	7-9	51-60
14 inches	24-26	51-84	11-13	51-66
13 inches	28-31	51-90	15-17	51-72
12 inches	32-35	51-97	20-22	51-79
11 inches	36-39	51-103	24-26	51-85

TABLE 3—C6 Automatic Transmission—Altitude-Compensating Type Vacuum Diaphragm Only

CONTROL PRESSURE AT ZERO OUTPUT SHAFT SPEED

Engine Speed			Idle			As Required		As Required		As Required		
Throttle			Closed			As Required		As Required		Open Through Detent		
Manifold Vacuum (Inches Hg)			Above 17			15		10		Below 1.0		
Range			Control Pressure (psi)		TV Pressure (psi)	Control Pressure (psi)	TV Pressure (psi)	Control Pressure (psi)	TV Pressure (psi)	Control Pressure (psi)		TV Pressure (psi)
			P,N,D1,D2,L	R		D1,D2,L		D1,D2,L		D1,D2,L	R	
Psi @ Barometric Pressure	Barometric Pressure in Inches HG	Nominal Altitude (Feet)										
	29.5	Sea Level	51-66	72-108	0-13	70-78	20-22	98-109	40-44	157-172	230-252	80-84
	28.5	1000	51-59	72-104	0-11	67-75	18-20	94-105	38-41	149-163	220-242	77-81
	27.5	2000	51-59	72-99	0-8	63-71	15-17	91-101	36-38	145-159	215-236	74-78
	26.5	3000	51-59	72-99	0-5	59-67	12-14	87-97	33-36	142-157	211-231	72-76
	25.5	4000	51-59	72-92	0-3	57-64	10-12	85-94	31-33	139-154	207-227	70-74
	24.5	5000	51-59	72-83	0	51-60	7-9	81-90	28-31	136-151	202-222	67-72
	23.5	6000	51-59	72-83	0	51-60	5-7	78-87	26-28	132-147	198-217	64-68

If it is impossible to obtain vacuum readings of eleven inches at engine idle, pressure checks at 10 inches and 1.0 inches vacuum may be considered sufficient to check out the control pressure and TV pressure.

STALL TEST

Start the engine to allow it to reach its normal temperature. Apply both the parking and service brakes while making tests.

The stall test is made in D2 (small dot), D1 (large dot), L, or R, at full throttle to check engine performance, converter clutch operation or installation, and the holding ability of the forward clutch, reverse-high clutch and low-reverse or intermediate band and the gear train one-way clutch. **While making this test, do not hold the throttle open for more than five seconds at a time.** Then move the selector lever to Neutral and run the engine at 1000 rpm for about 15 seconds to cool the converter before making the next test. If the engine speed as recorded by the tachometer exceeds the maximum limits specified in Tables 4 and 5, release the accelerator immediately because clutch or band slippage is indicated.

STALL SPEED TOO HIGH

If stall speed exceeds specifications, band or clutch slippage is indicated, depending on transmission selector lever position. Excessive engine rpm only in D1, D2, and L indicates forward clutch slippage as shown in Tables 4 and 5. Excessive engine rpm only in R indicates either reverse-high clutch or low-reverse band slippage. Excessive engine rpm only in D1 indicates gear train one-way clutch slippage.

STALL SPEED TOO LOW

When the stall test speeds are low and the engine is properly tuned, converter stator clutch problems are indicated. A road test must be performed to determine the exact cause of the trouble.

If the stall test speeds are 300 to 400 rpm below the specifications shown in Tables 4 and 5, and the car cruises properly but has very poor acceleration, the converter stator clutch is slipping.

If the stall test speeds are 300 to 400 rpm below the specified values, and the car drags at cruising speeds and acceleration is poor, the stator clutch could be installed backwards. Remove the converter and check the

TABLE 4—Stall Speeds—C4 Automatic Transmission

Selector Lever Position	Clutch Applied	Band Applied	Engine Speed (rpm)	
			240-Six	289-V-8
D2	Forward	Intermediate		
D1	Forward	One-Way Clutch	1300-1500	1450-1650
L	Forward	①Low-Reverse		
R	Reverse-High	Low-Reverse		

①If band fails, one-way clutch can hold gear train.

stator clutch as described in Cleaning and Inspection.

When the stall test shows normal speeds, the acceleration is good, but the car drags at cruising speeds, the difficulty is due to a seized stator assembly. If the stator is defective, replace the converter.

INITIAL ENGAGEMENT CHECKS

Initial engagement checks are made to determine if initial band and clutch engagements are smooth.

Run the engine until its normal operating temperature is reached. With the engine at the correct idle speed,

shift the selector lever from N to D2, D1, L, and R. Observe the initial band and clutch engagements. Band and clutch engagements should be smooth in all positions. Rough band and clutch engagements in D1, D2, L, or R are caused by high engine idle speed or high control pressures.

SHIFT POINT CHECKS

Check the minimum throttle up-shifts in D1. The transmission should start in first gear, shift to second, and then shift to third, within the shift points specified in Tables 6, 7 and 8.

While the transmission is in third gear, depress the accelerator pedal through the detent (to the floor). The transmission should shift from third to second or third to first, depending on the car speed.

Check the closed throttle downshift from third to first by coasting down from about 30 mph in third gear.

TABLE 5—Stall Speeds—C6 Automatic Transmission

Position Selector Lever	Band Applied	Reverse-High Clutch Applied	Forward Clutch Applied	Reverse Clutch Applied	One-Way Clutch Applied	Engine Speed (rpm)			
						390-2V	390-4V	410-4V	428-4V
D2	X		X						
D1			X		X	1750-1950	1800-2000	1550-1750② 1850-2050③	1550-1750
R			X	X	X				
L	X			X					

①If clutch fails, one-way clutch can hold gear train.
②Dual Exhaust.
③Single Exhaust.

TABLE 6—C4 Automatic Transmission—6 Cylinder Engine

SHIFT SPEEDS (APPROXIMATE)

	Range	Shift	1	2	3	4	5	6	7	8
Minimum Throttle	D1	1—2	7—9	7—9	7—9	8—10	8—10	8—11	9—11	9—11
	D1	2—3	10—17	10—18	11—19	11—20	11—20	12—21	12—22	13—23
	D2	3—2	9	9	9	10	10	11	11	11
	D1	3—1	9	9	9	10	10	11	11	11
	L	2—1	17	18	19	20	20	21	22	23
Maximum Throttle	D1	1—2	24—32	24—32	26—39	27—36	28—37	29—39	30—40	33—42
	D1, D2	2—3	44—57	45—59	48—61	50—66	52—68	54—70	56—73	60—75
	D1, D2	3—2	58	59	62	66	68	71	74	77
	D1	2—1 or 3—1	27	28	29	31	32	33	34	36

Vehicle	Engine Displacement	Axle Ratio	Tire Size	Use Column No.
Ford	247—1V	3.89:1	7.35 x 15	1
			7.75 x 15 or 8.15 x 15	2
		3.50:1	7.35 x 15	3
			7.75 x 15 or 8.15 x 15	4
		3.25:1	7.35 x 15	5
			7.75 x 15 or 8.15 x 15	6
		3.00:1	7.35 x 15	7
			7.75 x 15 or 8.15 x 15	8

TABLE 7—C4 Automatic Transmission—8 Cylinder Engine

SHIFT SPEEDS (APPROXIMATE)

	Range	Shift	1	2	3	4	5	6	7	8
Minimum Throttle	D1	1—2	7—9	7—9	7—9	8—10	8—10	8—11	9—11	9—11
	D1	2—3	10—17	10—18	11—19	11—20	11—20	12—21	12—22	13—23
	D2	3—2	9	9	9	10	10	11	11	11
	D1	3—1	9	9	9	10	10	11	11	11
	L	2—1	17	18	19	20	20	21	22	23
Maximum Throttle	D1	1—2	26—34	26—35	28—37	30—38	30—40	32—41	33—43	34—44
	D1, D2	2—3	48—60	48—62	51—66	54—68	55—71	58—74	60—77	63—79
	D1, D2	3—2	58	59	63	66	68	71	74	76
	D1	2—1 or 3—1	27	28	29	31	32	33	34	35

Vehicle	Engine Displacement	Axle Ratio	Tire Size	Use Column No.
Ford	289-2V	3.89:1	7.35 x 15	1
			7.75 x 15 or 8.15 x 15	2
		3.50:1	7.35 x 15	3
			7.75 x 15 or 8.15 x 15	4
		3.25:1	7.35 x 15	5
			7.75 x 15 or 8.15 x 15	6
		3.00:1	7.35 x 15	7
			7.75 x 15 or 8.15 x 15	8

TABLE 8—C6 Automatic Transmission

SHIFT SPEEDS (APPROXIMATE)

	Range	Shift	1	2	3	4
Minimum Throttle	D1	1—2	7—13	7—12	7—14	7—12
	D1	2—3	12—21	11—20	12—22	11—20
	D2	3—2	7—9	7—8	7—9	7—9
	D1	3—1	7—9	7—9	7—9	7—8
	L	2—1	7—9	7—8	7—9	7—8
Maximum Throttle	D1	1—2	38—45	35—42	40—46	36—43
	D1, D2	2—2	73—83	67—76	75—84	70—77
	D1, D2	3—2	65—74	60—68	67—75	62—69
	D1	2—1 or 3—1	27—34	25—31	27—34	25—32

Car	Engine Displacement	Axle Ratio	Tire Size	Use Column No.
Ford	390—2V 390—4V	3.00:1	7.35 x 15	1
	428—4V	3.25:1	7.35 x 15	2
Mercury	410—4V	3.00:1	8.15 x 15	3
	428—4V	3.25:1		4

The shift should occur within the limits specified in Tables 6, 7 and 8.

When the selector lever is at D2, the transmission can operate only in second and third gears. Shift points for *second to third* and *third to second* are the same in both D2 and D1.

With the transmission in third gear and road speed over 30 mph, the transmission should shift to second gear when the selector lever is moved from D2 or D1 to L. When the same manual shift is made below about 20 mph, the transmission will shift from second or third to first. **This check will determine if the governor pressure and shift control valves are functioning properly.**

During the shift point check operation, if the transmission does not shift within specifications or certain gear ratios cannot be obtained, refer to the diagnosis guide to resolve the problem.

AIR PRESSURE CHECKS

A NO DRIVE condition can exist, even with correct transmission fluid pressure, because of inoperative clutches or bands. The inoperative units can be located through a series of checks by substituting air pressure for the fluid pressure to determine the location of the malfunction.

When the selector lever is at D2, a NO DRIVE condition may be caused by an inoperative forward clutch. A NO DRIVE condition at D1 may be caused by an inoperative forward clutch or one-way clutch. When there is no drive in L, the difficulty could be caused by improper functioning of the forward clutch or low-reverse band and the one-way clutch. Failure to drive in reverse range could be caused by a malfunction of the reverse-high clutch or low-reverse band. Erratic shifts could be caused by a stuck governor valve.

To make the air pressure checks, loosen the oil pan bolts and lower one edge of the oil pan to drain the transmission fluid. Remove the oil pan and the control valve body assembly. The inoperative units can be located by introducing air pressure into the transmission case passages leading to the clutches, servos, and governor (Fig. 8 or 9).

FORWARD CLUTCH

Apply air pressure to the transmission case forward clutch passage (Fig. 8 or 9). A dull thud can be heard when the clutch piston is applied. If no noise is heard, place the finger tips on the input shell and again apply air pressure to the forward clutch passage. Movement of the piston can be felt as the clutch is applied.

GOVERNOR

Apply air pressure to the control pressure to governor passage (Fig. 8 or 9) and listen for a sharp clicking

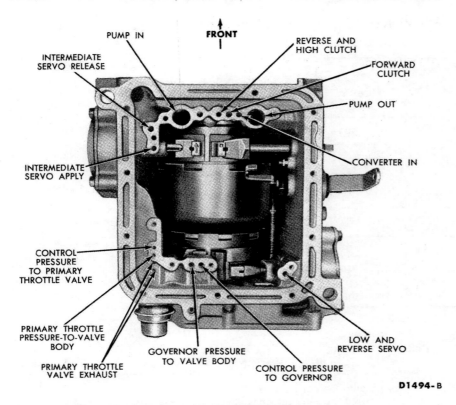

FIG. 8—Case Oil Passage Hole Identification—C4 Automatic

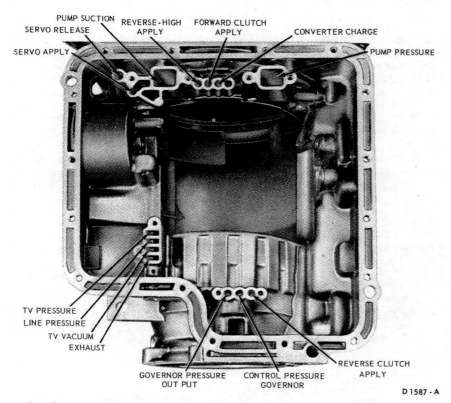

FIG. 9—Case Oil Passage Hole Identification—C6 Automatic

or whistling noise. The noise indicates governor valve movement.

high clutch passage (Fig. 8 or 9). A dull thud indicates that the reverse-high clutch piston has moved to the applied position. If no noise is heard, place the finger tips on the clutch drum and again apply air pressure to detect movement of the piston.

INTERMEDIATE SERVO

Hold the air nozzle in the intermediate servo apply passage (Fig. 8 or 9). Operation of the servo is indicated by a tightening of the intermediate band around the drum. Continue to apply air pressure to the intermediate servo apply passage, and introduce air pressure into the intermediate servo release passage. The intermediate servo should release the band against the apply pressure.

LOW-REVERSE C4 ONLY

Apply air pressure to the low-reverse apply passage (Fig. 8). The low-reverse band should tighten around the drum if the servo is operating properly.

If the servos do not operate, disassemble, clean, and inspect them to locate the source of the trouble.

If air pressure applied to either of the clutch passages fails to operate a clutch or operates both clutches at once, remove and, with air pressure, check the fluid passages in the case and front pump to detect obstructions.

LOW-REVERSE C6 ONLY

Apply air pressure to the reverse clutch apply passage (Fig. 9). A dull thud should be heard if the clutch is operating properly.

If the passages are clear, remove the clutch assemblies, and clean and inspect the malfunctioning clutch to locate the trouble.

TESTING—CRUISE-O-MATIC OR MERC-O-MATIC TRANSMISSION

The test results of the following checks should agree with the specifications given in Table 9.

TEST NUMBER—1 CONTROL PRESSURE CHECK— AT ENGINE IDLE

1. With the transmission in neutral, and the engine at the correct idle speed, the vacuum gauge should show a minimum of 18 inches. If the vacuum reading is lower than 18 inches, an engine problem is indicated or there is leakage in the vacuum line. Make necessary repairs to

REVERSE-HIGH CLUTCH

Apply air pressure to the reverse-

TABLE 9—Cruise-O-Matic or Merc-O-Matic Transmission

CONTROL PRESSURE AT ZERO OUTPUT SHAFT SPEED

Test No.	Engine Speed and Manifold Vacuum	Throttle Position	Selector Lever Position	①Control Line Pressure	
				PCE-BK, BL and PCD-Z	PCT-J-3
1	Engine Idle-Vacuum above 16 inches	Closed	P, N, D2, D1, L	57-77	57-72
	Engine Idle-Vacuum above 16 inches	Closed	R	71-106	64-105
2	Engine rpm as required for 16-13.7 inches of manifold vacuum	As Required	L, D2, D1	Line Pressure Increase	Line Pressure Increase
3	Engine rpm as required for 10 inches of manifold vacuum	As Required	D1, D2, L	97-113	105-137
4	Engine rpm—STALL Vacuum below 1.5 inches	To and thru Detent	L, D2, D1	151-176	145-170
	Engine rpm—STALL Vacuum below 1.5 inches	To and thru	R	201-213	196-213

①Transmission fluid at Normal Operating Temperature

obtain a minimum vacuum reading of 18 inches.

2. At engine idle, depress and release the accelerator pedal quickly and observe the vacuum gauge. The amount of vacuum should decrease and increase with the changes in throttle openings. If the vacuum response to changes in throttle opening is too slow, the vacuum line to the diaphragm unit could be restricted. **Make the necessary repairs before completing the test.**

3. At engine idle, check the transmission control pressure gauge at all selector lever positions. The transmission control pressure test should agree with Table 9, for control pressure at engine idle.

**TEST NUMBER—2
CONTROL PRESSURE
INCREASE CHECK**

Control pressure increase should be checked in all ranges except Park and Neutral.

Shift the transmission into D1, D2, L, and R and check control pressure rise in each range. Advance the throttle until the engine vacuum reading falls between 16-13.7 inches. As the vacuum gauge reading decreases into these specifications, **the control pressure should start to rise as outlined in Table 9.**

**TEST NUMBER—3
CONTROL PRESSURE CHECK
AT STALL SPEED**

Check control pressure at stall speed (throttle advanced to and

through detent) in R, D1, D2, L. Pressure at stall in the various ranges should agree with the control pressures as outlined in Table 9. If the engine speed exceeds the maximum limits, release the accelerator immediately because band or clutch slippage is indicated. **While making the stall pressure test, do not hold the throttle open for more than five seconds in each detent position.** Between each test move the selector lever to neutral and run engine at 1000 rpm for fifteen seconds, to cool the converter.

If the vacuum and pressure gauge readings are within specifications, the diaphragm unit and transmission control pressure regulating system are operating properly.

If transmission control pressure is too low, too high, fails to rise with throttle opening, or is extremely erratic, use the procedure given under the following appropriate heading to resolve the problem.

Control Pressure is Low at Engine Idle (Test No. 1)

If control pressure at engine idle is low in all selector lever positions, trouble other than the diaphragm unit is indicated. When control pressure at engine idle is low in all ranges, check for excessive leakage in the front oil pump, case, and control valve body, or a sticking control pressure regulator valve.

Control Pressure is High at Engine Idle (Test No. 1)

If transmission control pressure at

engine idle is too high in all ranges, the trouble may be in the diaphragm unit or its connecting vacuum tubes and hoses, throttle valve, or control rod.

With the engine idling, disconnect the hose from the diaphragm unit and check the engine manifold vacuum. Hold a thumb over the end of the hose and check for vacuum. If the engine speeds up when the hose is disconnected and slows down as the thumb is held against the end of the hose, the vacuum source is satisfactory.

Stop the engine, and remove the diaphragm unit and the diaphragm unit push rod. Inspect the control rod for a **bent** condition and for corrosion. Install the diaphragm unit in the case to prevent fluid loss, but leave the push rod out. With the push rod removed, the diaphragm unit cannot affect transmission control pressure.

Start the engine and check control pressure at engine idle in all selector lever positions. If control pressure is still too high, the trouble is in the transmission pressure regulating control system. If the pressure is now within limits, the diaphragm unit was not operating properly and should be checked with the distributor tester (Fig. 6).

Control Pressure Does Not Increase With Throttle Opening (Test No. 2)

When the control pressure is within specification at engine idle, but does not rise, as the vacuum is decreased to the specified limits, first check the control rod between the vacuum unit and throttle valve for proper engagement. If the control rod is not assembled into the end of the throttle valve or vacuum unit, the valve cannot regulate throttle pressure to increase control pressure. Next check for a stuck throttle valve, compensator valve or control pressure regulator valve.

If control pressure increases before or after vacuum is decreased to the specified limits check for the proper operation of the diaphragm assembly, bent diaphragm can, or worn or bent control rod.

Control Pressure Not Within Limits—Stall Test (Test No. 3)

If idle pressure and pressure point increase are within specifications but stall pressures are not within specification in all ranges, excessive leakage, low pump capacity or restricted oil pan screen is indicated.

If stall pressures are not within specifications for specific ranges only, this indicates excessive leakage in the clutch or servo circuits used in those ranges. Table 10 gives the clutch or band application for each selector lever position.

ADJUSTING CONTROL PRESSURE

An adjustable diaphragm has been provided to correct transmission problems causing a soft or harsh automatic shift condition. The diaphragm is preset and no attempt should be made to adjust it until a pressure and vacuum check has been made to insure that pressures are within specification and that the cause of the problem is not due to other items within the transmission or vacuum connecting lines. The adjustment screw is located in the vacuum connecting tube (Fig. 7). By turning the screw the control pressure can be increased or decreased to correct the shift condition.

CHECKING CONTROL PRESSURE

1. With engine idling (throttle closed), manifold vacuum should be above 16 inches at sea level. Select each range and note pressure gauge reading. Pressure should be within specifications as outlined in Table 9.

2. Position selector lever in Drive range with engine idling. Open throttle gradually while observing pressure gauge. Pressure should remain within idle limits until vacuum drops to between 16.7 and 13.7 inches and then the pressure should start to increase.

3. Place selector in Drive range (D1, D2, or L), open throttle until vacuum reading is 10 inches, and note transmission control pressure.

4. Open throttle until vacuum reading is below 1.5 inches and note pressure gauge reading.

5. Shift transmission to reverse and open throttle until vacuum reading is below 1.5 inches and note pressure gauge reading.

If shifts are harsh, an adjustment should be made to reduce line pressure. If shifts are soft, an adjustment should be made to increase line pressure. To increase control pressure, turn the adjusting screw in (clockwise). To decrease control line pressure, back the adjusting screw out (counterclockwise).

After the vacuum unit has been adjusted recheck the control pressure as outlined in Table 9. All tests must be within specifications. The adjustable vacuum unit can not be used to allow for adjusting control pressures that are out of specifications.

STALL TEST

Start the engine to allow it to reach its normal temperature. Apply both the parking and service brakes while making these tests.

The stall test is made in D2, (small dot), D1 (circle) L, or R, at full throttle to check engine performance, converter clutch operation or installation, and front clutch, rear clutch and rear band operation.

While making this test, do not hold the throttle open for more than five seconds at a time. Then move the selector lever to Neutral and run the engine at 1000 rpm for about 15 seconds to cool the converter before making the next test. If the engine speed, as recorded by the tachometer, exceeds the maximum limits specified in Table 10, release the accelerator immediately because clutch or band slippage is indicated.

Stall Speed Too High

If stall speed exceeds specifications, band or clutch slippage is indicated, depending on transmission selector lever position. Excessive engine rpm in D1, D2, and L indicates front clutch slippage. Excessive rpm in D1 only indicates one-way clutch slippage. Excessive engine rpm in R indicates either rear clutch or rear band slippage.

Stall Speed Too Low

When the stall test speeds are low and the engine is properly tuned, converter stator clutch problems are indicated. A road test must be performed to determine the exact cause of the trouble.

If the stall test speeds are 300 to 400 rpm below the specifications shown in Table 10, the car cruises properly but has very poor acceleration, the converter stator clutch is slipping.

Remove the converter and check the stator clutch as described in Cleaning and Inspection.

If the stall test speeds are 300 to 400 rpm below the specified values, and the car drags at cruising speeds and acceleration is poor, the stator clutch is installed backwards.

When the stall test shows normal speeds, the acceleration is good, but the car drags at cruising speeds, the difficulty is due to a seized stator assembly. If the stator is defective replace the converter.

INITIAL ENGAGEMENT CHECKS

Initial engagement checks are made to determine if initial band and clutch engagements are smooth.

Run the engine until its normal operating temperature is reached. With the engine at the correct idle speed, shift the selector lever from N to D2, D1, L, and R. Observe the initial band and clutch engagements. Band and clutch engagements should be smooth in all positions. Rough initial engagements in D1, D2, L, or R are caused by high engine idle speed or high control pressures.

SHIFT POINT CHECKS

Check the light throttle upshifts in D1. The transmission should start in first gear, shift to second and then shift to third, within the shift points specified in Table 11.

While the transmission is in third gear, depress the accelerator pedal through the detent (to the floor). The transmission should shift from third to second or third to first, depending on the car speed.

Check the closed throttle downshift from third to first by coasting down from about 30 mph in third gear. The shift should occur within the limits specified in Table 11.

When the selector lever is at D2,

TABLE 10—Stall Speeds—Cruise-O-Matic or Merc-O-Matic Transmissions

Selector Lever Position	Clutch Applied	Band Applied	Engine Speed (rpm)		
			289-2V	352 V-8	390 V-8
D2	Front	Front	1450-1650	1600-1800	390-4V 1800-2000
D1	Front	One-Way Clutch			390-2V 1750-1950
L	Front	Rear			
R	Rear	Rear			

TABLE 11—Cruise-O-Matic or Merc-O-Matic Transmission

SHIFT SPEED (APPROXIMATE)

Transmission Model	Automatic Shift Speeds (mph)								Manual Shift Speeds (mph)
	D1		D1 or D2		D1	D1 or D2	D1	D2	L
	1-2 Minimum Throttle	1-2 Maximum Throttle	2-3 Minimum Throttle	2-3 Maximum Throttle	3-1 Minimum Throttle	3-2 Maximum Throttle	2-1 or 3-1 Maximum Throttle	3-2 Minimum Throttle	2-1 Minimum Throttle
PCT	7-9	34-41	9-21	57-66	6-8	53-61	24-33	5-10	17-23
PCD	9-11	40-49	14-24	63-76	8-10	57-69	27-36	6-10	18-27
PCE	9-11	40-50	14-24	63-76	8-10	57-69	27-36	6-10	18-27

the transmission can operate only in second and third gears. Shift points for second to third and third to second are the same in both D2 and D1.

With the transmission in third gear and road speed over 30 mph, the transmission should shift to second gear when the selector lever is moved from D2 or D1 to L. When the same manual shift is made below approximately 25 mph, the transmission will shift from second or third to first. **This check will determine if the governor pressure and shift control valves are functioning properly.**

During the shift check operation, if the transmission does not shift within specifications or certain gear ratios cannot be obtained, refer to the diagnosis guide to resolve the problem.

AIR PRESSURE CHECKS

A NO DRIVE condition can exist, even with correct transmission fluid pressure, because of inoperative clutches, bands or a defective converter. The inoperative units except the converter, can be located through a series of checks by substituting air pressure for the fluid pressure to determine the location of the malfunction.

When the selector lever is at D2 (small dot) and D1 (circle) and L, a NO DRIVE condition may be caused by an inoperative front clutch. A NO DRIVE condition at D1 may be caused by an inoperative one-way clutch. When there is no drive in L, the difficulty could be caused by improper functioning of the front clutch, the rear band or the one-way clutch. Failure to drive in reverse range could be caused by a malfunction of the rear clutch or rear band. Erratic shifts could be caused by a stuck governor valve.

To make the air pressure checks, drain the transmission fluid, and then remove the oil pan and the control valve. The inoperative units can be located by introducing air pressure into the transmission case passages leading to the clutches, servos, and governor.

Front Clutch

Apply air pressure to the transmission case front clutch passage (Fig. 10). A dull thud can be heard when the clutch piston is applied. If no noise is heard, place the finger tips on the drum and again apply air pressure to the front clutch passage.

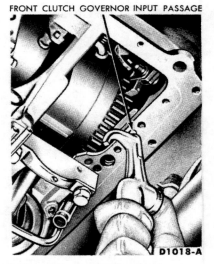

FRONT CLUTCH GOVERNOR INPUT PASSAGE

D1018-A

FIG. 10—Front Clutch Air Check—Typical

Movement of the piston can be felt as the clutch is applied.

Governor

Apply air pressure to the front clutch passage, listen for a sharp click which will indicate that the governor weight movement indicates correct governor valve operation. To observe governor operation, it will be necessary to remove the extension housing (Fig. 11).

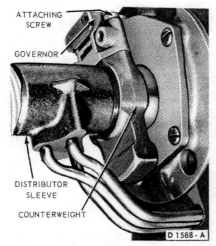

FIG. 11—Governor Valve

Rear Clutch

Apply air pressure to the rear clutch passage (Fig. 12). A dull thud

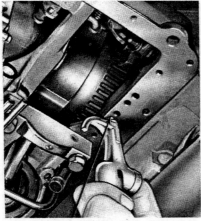

REAR CLUTCH INPUT PASSAGE   D1020-A

FIG. 12—Rear Clutch Air Check—Typical

indicates that the rear clutch piston has moved to the applied position. If no noise is heard, place the finger tips on the rear drum and again apply air pressure to detect movement of the piston.

Front Servo

Hold the air nozzle in the front servo apply tube. Operation of the front servo is indicated by a tightening of the front band around the drum. Continue to apply air pressure to the front servo apply tube and introduce air pressure into the front

servo release tube. **Hold a cloth over the release tube while applying the servo to catch the spray from the release tube.** The front servo should release the band against the apply pressure.

Rear Servo

Apply air pressure to the rear servo apply passage (Fig. 13). The

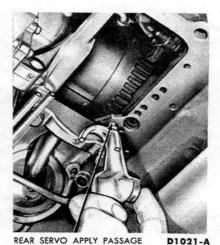

REAR SERVO APPLY PASSAGE   D1021-A

FIG. 13—Rear Servo Air Check—Typical

rear band should tighten around the drum if the rear servo is operating properly.

If either servo is inoperative, remove the inoperative unit and apply air pressure directly to its passages. Proper operation of the servos indicates that the trouble is in the case passages. If the servo does not operate, disassemble, clean, and inspect it to locate the source of trouble.

If air pressure applied to either of the clutch passages fails to operate a clutch or operates both clutches at once, remove and, with air pressure,

check the fluid passages at the output shaft aluminum sleeve for correct indexing with the shaft holes. Check the primary sun gear shaft assembly passages with air pressure to detect obstructions (Fig. 14).

If the output shaft and primary sun gear shaft passages are clear, remove the clutch assemblies, and clean and inspect the malfunctioning clutch to locate the trouble.

HYDRAULIC SYSTEM BENCH TESTS (CRUISE-O-MATIC OR MERC-O-MATIC)

After the transmission has been assembled and is ready for installation in the car, check the hydraulic system to make sure it is operating properly. These hydraulic tests can be made on the bench so that most malfunctions of the system can be corrected before the transmission is installed in the car.

Testing Tool Installation

1. Install a plug in the filler tube hole in the oil pan, and pour about four quarts of clean transmission fluid into the transmission through the speedometer gear opening.

2. Remove the vacuum diaphragm unit and the diaphragm unit control rod, and reinstall the vacuum unit if these parts had been previously installed.

3. Install the bench testing tool on the transmission.

4. Remove the 1/8-inch pipe plug at the transmission case. Turn the front pump in a clockwise direction at 75-100 rpm until a regular flow of transmission fluid leaves the hole in the transmission case. This operation bleeds the air from the pump.

5. Install the pressure gauge (77820 or T57L-77820-A) as shown in Fig. 15.

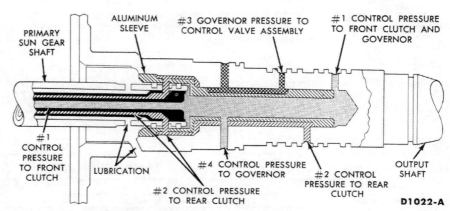

FIG. 14—Output and Primary Sun Gear Fluid Passages

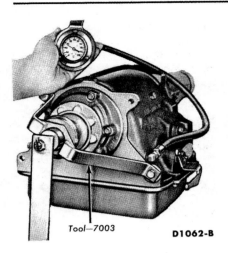

Tool—7003   D1062-B

FIG. 15—Bench Testing Tool Installation—Typical

Pressure Tests

Turn the front pump at 75-100 rpm and note the gauge readings. The pressure readings on the bench test must be within the limits as outlined in Table 9, for the engine idle check.

If pressure gauge readings are within limits in all selector lever positions, install the vacuum diaphragm control rod unit.

DIAGNOSIS GUIDE

The Diagnosis Guide lists the most common trouble symptoms that may be found and gives the items that should be checked to find the cause of the trouble. There are three diagnosis guides, one for each type transmission.

The items to check are arranged in a logical sequence which should be followed for quickest results. The letter symbols for each item are explained in the key. If items A, B, C, K, and the stall tests have already been checked during preliminary checks and adjustments, they need not be repeated.

C4 AUTOMATIC DUAL RANGE DIAGNOSIS GUIDE

Trouble Symptoms	ITEMS TO CHECK (In the order indicated) See detailed possible causes below.	
	Transmission in Car	Transmission Out of Car
Rough Initial Engagement in D1 or D2	K B W F E	a
1-2 or 2-3 Shift Points Incorrect or Erratic	A B L C D W E R	
Rough 1-2 Upshifts	B J G W E F	
Rough 2-3 Shifts	B J W F G E R	b r
Dragged Out 1-2 Shift	A B J W G E F R	c
Engine Overspeeds on 2-3 Shift	C A B J W E F G	b r
No 1-2 or 2-3 Shift	C L B D W E G J	b c
No 3-1 Shift in D1 or 3-2 Shift in D2	D E	
No Forced Downshifts	L E B	
Runaway Engine on Forced 3-2 Downshift	W J G F E B	c
Rough 3-2 or 3-1 Shift at Closed Throttle	K B J E F	
Shifts 1-3 in D1 and D2	G J B E D R	
No Engine Braking in First Gear—Manual Lo Range	C H I E D R	
Creeps Excessively	K	
Slips or Chatters in First Gear, D1	A B W F E	a c i
Slips or Chatters in Second Gear	A B J G W F E R	a c
Slips or Chatters in R	A B H W I F E R	b c r
No Drive in D1 Only	A C W E R	i
No Drive in D2 Only	A C W J E R	c i
No Drive in L Only	A C W E I R	c i
No Drive in R Only	A C H W I E R	b c r
No Drive in Any Selector Lever Position	A C W F E R	c d
Lockup in D1 Only		b g c
Lockup in D2 Only	H I	b g c i
Lockup in L Only	G J	b g c
Lockup in R Only	G J	a g c
Parking Lock Binds or Does Not Hold	C	g
Transmission Overheats	O F B W	n
Maximum Speed Too Low, Poor Acceleration	Y Z	n
Transmission Noisy in N and P	A F	d h
Transmission Noisy in First, Second, Third or Reverse Gear	A F	h a d i
Fluid Leak	A M N O P Q S U X B I J	j m p
Car moves Forward in N	C	a

Probable Trouble Sources

A.	Fluid Level	S.	Extension Housing-to-Case Gaskets & Lockwashers
B.	Vacuum Diaphragm Unit or Tubes Restricted—Leaking—Adjustment	U.	Extension Housing Rear Oil Seal
C.	Manual Linkage	W.	Perform Control Pressure Check

C4 AUTOMATIC DUAL RANGE DIAGNOSIS GUIDE (Con't)

D.	Governor	X.	Speedometer Driven Gear Adapter Seal
E.	Valve Body	Y.	Engine Performance
F.	Pressure Regulator	Z.	Vehicle Brakes
G.	Intermediate Band	a.	Forward Clutch
H.	Reverse Band	b.	Reverse-High Clutch
I.	Reverse Servo	c.	Leakage in Hydraulic System
J.	Intermediate Servo	d.	Front Pump
K.	Engine Idle Speed	g.	Parking Linkage
L.	Downshift Linkage—Including Inner Lever Position	h.	Planetary Assembly
M.	Converter Drain Plugs	i.	Planetary One-Way Clutch
N.	Oil Pan Gasket, Filler Tube or Seal	j.	Engine Rear Oil Seal
O.	Oil Cooler and Connections	m.	Front Pump Oil Seal
P.	Manual or Downshift Lever Shaft Seal	n.	Converter One-Way Clutch
Q.	⅛ inch Pipe Plug in Side of Case	p.	Front Pump to Case Gasket or Seal
R.	Perform Air Pressure Check	r.	Reverse-High Clutch Piston Air Bleed Valve

C6 AUTOMATIC DUAL RANGE DIAGNOSIS GUIDE

Trouble Symptoms	ITEMS TO CHECK (In the order indicated) See detailed possible causes below.	
	Transmission in Car	Transmission Out of Car
No Drive in D1, D2 and L	C W E R	a c
Rough Initial Engagement in D1 or D2	K B W F E	a
1-2 or 2-3 Shift Points Incorrect or Erratic	A B L C D W E R	
Rough 1-2 Upshifts	B J G W E F	
Rough 2-3 Shifts	B J W F G E R	b r
Dragged Out 1-2 Shift	A B J W G E F R	c
Engine Overspeeds on 2-3 Shift	C A B J W E F G	b r
No 1-2 or 2-3 Shift	C L B D W E G J	b c
No 3-1 Shift in D1 or 3-2 Shift in D2	D E	
No Forced Downshifts	L E B	
Runaway Engine on Forced 3-2 Downshift	W J G F E B	c
Rough 3-2 or 3-1 Shift at Closed Throttle	K B J E F	
Shifts 1-3 in D1 and D2	G J B E D R	
No Engine Braking in First Gear—Manual Lo Range	C H E D R	
Creeps Excessively	K	
Slips or Chatters in First Gear, D1	A B W F E	a c i
Slips or Chatters in Second Gear	A B J G W F E R	a c
Slips or Chatters in R	A B H W F E R	b c r
No Drive in D1 Only	C W E	i
No Drive in D2 Only	A C W J E R	c
No Drive in L Only	A C W E R	c
No Drive in R Only	A C H W E R	b c r
No Drive in Any Selector Lever Position	A C W F E R	c d
Lockup in D1 Only		g c
Lockup in D2 Only	H	b g c i
Lockup in L Only		g c
Lockup in R Only		a g c
Parking Lock Binds or Does Not Hold	C	g
Transmission Overheats	O F B W	n s
Maximum Speed Too Low, Poor Acceleration	Y Z	n
Transmission Noisy in N and P	A F	d
Transmission Noisy in First, Second, Third or Reverse Gear	A F	h a d i
Fluid Leak	A M N O P Q S U X B J	j m p
Car Moves Forward in N	C	a

Probable Trouble Sources

A.	Fluid Level	U.	Extension Housing Rear Oil Seal
B.	Vacuum Diaphragm Unit or Tubes Restricted—Leaking—Adjustment	W.	Perform Control Pressure Check
C.	Manual Linkage	X.	Speedometer Driven Gear Adapter Seal
D.	Governor	Y.	Engine Performance

C6 AUTOMATIC DUAL RANGE DIAGNOSIS GUIDE (Con't)

E.	Valve Body	Z.	Vehicle Brakes
F.	Pressure Regulator	a.	Forward Clutch
G.	Intermediate Band	b.	Reverse-High Clutch
H.	Low-Reverse Clutch	c.	Leakage in Hydraulic System
J.	Intermediate Servo	d.	Front Pump
K.	Engine Idle Speed	g.	Parking Linkage
L.	Downshift Linkage—Including Inner Lever Position	h.	Planetary Assembly
M.	Converter Drain Plugs	i.	Planetary One-Way Clutch
N.	Oil Pan Gasket, Filler Tube or Seal	j.	Engine Rear Oil Seal
O.	Oil Cooler and Connections	m.	Front Pump Oil Seal
P.	Manual or Downshift Lever Shaft Seal	n.	Converter One-Way Clutch
Q.	⅛ Inch Pipe Plugs in Case	p.	Front Pump to Case Gasket or Seal
R.	Perform Air Pressure Check	r.	Reverse-High Clutch Piston Air Bleed Valve
S.	Extension Housing-to-Case Gasket	s.	Converter Pressure Check Valves

CRUISE-O-MATIC OR MERC-O-MATIC DUAL RANGE DIAGNOSIS GUIDE

Trouble Symptom	Items to Check		Probable Trouble Sources	
	Transmission in Car	Transmission Out of Car		
Rough Initial Engagement in D1 or D2	K B W F E G		A.	Fluid Level
1-2 or 2-3 Shift Points Incorrect	A B C D W E L		B.	Vacuum Diaphragm Unit or Tubes
Rough 2-3 Shift	B G F E J		C.	Manual Linkage
Engine Overspeeds on 2-3 Shift	B G E F	r	D.	Governor
No 1-2 or 2-3 Shift	D E C G J	b c f	E.	Valve Body
No 3-1 Shift	K B E		F.	Pressure Regulator
No Forced Downshifts	L W E		G.	Front Band
Runaway Engine Forced Downshift	G F E J B	c	H.	Rear Band
Rough 3-2 or 3-1 Shift at Closed Throttle	K B E		I.	Rear Servo
Creeps Excessively in D1 or D2	K		J.	Front Servo
Slips or Chatters in First Gear, D1	A B W F E	a c f i	K.	Engine Idle Speed
Slips or Chatters in Second Gear	A B G W F E J	a c	L.	Downshift Linkage
Slips or chatters in R	A H W F E I B	b c f	M.	Converter Drain Plugs
No Drive in D1	C E	i	N.	Oil Pan Gasket, Drain Plug or Tube
No Drive in D2	E R C	a c f	O.	Oil Cooler and Connections
No Drive in L	C E R	a c f	P.	Manual or Throttle Lever Shaft Seal
No Drive in R	H I E R C	b c f	Q.	⅛-inch Pipe Plug in Side of Case
No Drive in Any Selector Lever Position	A C W F E R	c	R.	Perform Air-Pressure Check
Lockup in D1	C I J	b g c	S.	Extension Housing to Case Gaskets and Lockwashers
Lockup in D2	C H I	b g c i	T.	Center Support Bolt Lockwashers
Lockup in L	G J E	b g c	U.	Extension Housing Rear Oil Seal
Lockup in R	G J	a g c	W.	Perform Control Pressure Check
Parking Lock Binds or Does Not Hold	C	g	X.	Speedometer Driven Gear Adapter Seal
Engine Does Not Start By Pushing Car	A C F E	e c	a.	Front Clutch
Transmission Overheats	O F	n	b.	Rear Clutch
Maximum Speed Too Low, Poor Acceleration		n	c.	Leakage in Hydraulic System
Transmission Noisy in N	F	a d	d.	Front Pump
Transmission Noisy in First, Second, Third, or Reverse Gear	F	h a b d	e.	Rear Pump
Transmission Noisy in P	F	d	f.	Fluid Distributor Sleeve in Output Shaft
			g.	Parking Linkage
			h.	Planetary Assembly
			i.	Planetary One-Way Clutch
			j.	Engine Rear Oil Seal
			m.	Front Pump Oil Seal

Transmission Noisy During Coast at 30-20 mph in N, Engine Stopped		e	n. Converter One-Way Clutch
			p. Front Pump to Case Gasket
Fluid Leak	M N O P Q S T U X	j m p	r. Rear Clutch Piston Air Bleed Valve

2   COMMON ADJUSTMENTS AND REPAIRS

TRANSMISSION FLUID LEVEL CHECK

The transmission fluid level should be checked using the following procedure.

1. Make sure that the car is standing level; then firmly apply the parking brake.

2. Run the engine at normal idle speed. If the transmission fluid is cold, run the engine at fast idle speed (about 1200 rpm) until the fluid reaches its normal operating temperature. When the fluid is warm, slow the engine down to normal idle speed.

3. Shift the selector lever through all positions, and place the lever at **P. Do not turn off the engine during the fluid level checks.**

4. Clean all dirt from the transmission fluid dipstick cap before removing the dipstick from the filler tube.

5. Pull the dipstick out of the tube, wipe it clean, and push it all the way back into the tube.

6. Pull the dipstick out of the tube again, and check the fluid level. If necessary, add enough fluid to the transmission through the filler tube to raise the fluid level to the F (full) mark on the dipstick. **Do not overfill the transmission.**

TRANSMISSION FLUID DRAIN AND REFILL

Normal maintenance and lubrication requirements do not necessitate periodic automatic transmission fluid changes.

If a major failure, such as a clutch, band, bearing, etc., has occurred in the transmission, it will have to be removed for service. At this time the converter must be thoroughly flushed to remove any dirt.

When filling a dry transmission and converter, install five quarts of fluid. Start the engine, shift the selector lever as in step 7 below, and check and add fluid as necessary.

Following are the procedures for partial drain and refill due to in-car repair operation.

CRUISE-O-MATIC, MERC-O-MATIC OR C4 TRANSMISSION

1. Disconnect the fluid filler tube from the transmission oil pan.

2. When the fluid has stopped draining from the transmission, remove and thoroughly clean the oil pan and the screen. Discard the oil pan gasket.

3. Place a new gasket on the oil pan, and install the pan on the transmission.

4. Connect the filler tube to the oil pan, and tighten the fitting securely.

5. Add three quarts of fluid to the transmission through the filler tube.

6. Run the engine at idle speed for about two minutes, and then run it at fast idle speed (about 1200 rpm) until it reaches its normal operating temperature. **Do not race the engine.**

7. Shift the selector lever through all the positions, place it at P, and check the fluid level. If necessary, add enough fluid to the transmission to raise the level to the F (full) mark on the dipstick. **Do not overfill the transmission.**

C6 TRANSMISSION

1. Raise the car on a hoist or jack stands.

2. Place a drain pan under the transmission.

3. Loosen the pan attaching bolts to drain the fluid from the transmission.

4. After the fluid has drained to the level of the pan flange, remove the rest of the pan bolts working from the rear and both sides of the pan to allow it to drop and drain slowly.

5. When the fluid has stopped draining from the transmission, remove and thoroughly clean the oil pan and the screen. Discard the oil pan gasket.

6. Place a new gasket on the oil pan, and install the pan on the transmission.

7. Add three quarts of fluid to the transmission through the filler tube.

8. Run the engine at idle speed for about two minutes, and then run it at fast idle speed (about 1200 rpm) until it reaches its normal operating temperature. **Do not race the engine.**

9. Shift the selector lever through all the positions, place it at P, and check the fluid level. If necessary, add enough fluid to the transmission to raise the level to the F (full) mark on the dipstick. **Do not overfill the transmission.**

THROTTLE AND DOWNSHIFT LINKAGE

Lubricate the throttle linkage with 10W engine oil. Lubricate the lower pivot point of the downshift rod with C1AZ-19590-A moly lube (ball joint grease).

OIL COOLER FLUSHING PROCEDURE

When a clutch or band failure or other internal trouble has occurred in the transmission, any metal particles or clutch plate or band material that may have been carried into the cooler should be removed from the system by flushing the cooler and lines before the transmission is put back into service. In no case should an automatic transmission having a clutch or band failure or other internal trouble resulting in fluid contamination, be put back into service without first flushing the transmission oil cooler.

1. After installing a new or rebuilt automatic transmission and converter assembly in the car, **do not connect the cooler return line to the transmission.** Place the transmission selector lever in the P (park) position and connect the cooler inlet (converter out) line to the transmission. Place a pan under the end of the cooler return line that will hold transmission fluid. **Do not start the engine.**

2. On those Cruise-O-Matic Transmissions which do not have a cooler return check valve in the case, install a temporary plug in the **cooler return line fitting at the trans-**

mission case to prevent the possibility of transmission fluid from draining out of the transmission case.

3. Install 5 quarts of automatic transmission fluid meeting Ford Specification.

4. Start the engine and allow it to run at normal idle speed for 3 minutes with the selector lever in P (park) position. Stop the engine and add additional transmission fluid required to complete total fill. Start the engine and allow it to run at normal idle speed.

5. Allow approximately two quarts of transmission fluid to drain into the pan placed under the end of the cooler return line.

6. If the fluid does not run clean after draining two quarts of it

through the cooler, shut off the engine and add **two additional quarts** of transmission fluid.

7. Repeat steps 4 through 6 until the transmission fluid flowing out of the cooler return line is clean.

8. If there is no fluid flow or the fluid does not flow freely, shut off the engine and disconnect both cooler lines from the transmission and cooler.

9. Use an air hose with not more than 100 psi. air pressure to reverse flush the cooler lines and the cooler. After reverse flushing, connect both lines at the cooler and the cooler inlet line (converter out) to the transmission.

10. Start the engine and check the fluid flow. If the transmission fluid

flows freely, proceed with steps 4 through 7. If there is no fluid flow, check for pinched cooler lines. If the flow is restricted, replace cooler lines and/or the radiator.

11. Shut off engine, remove the temporary plug from the cooler return line fitting on the transmission case and connect the cooler return line to the transmission. Check the transmission fluid level as indicated under heading Transmission Fluid Level Check. Add or remove transmission fluid as required until the proper fluid level is obtained on the dipstick. DO NOT OVERFILL THE TRANSMISSION.

12. **Do not attempt to correct cooler or cooler line leaks by closing off the lines.**

3 CLEANING AND INSPECTION

Clean the parts with suitable solvent and use moisture-free air to dry off all the parts and clean out oil passages.

The composition clutch plates and bands should not be cleaned in a vapor degreaser or with any type of detergent solution. To clean these parts, wipe them off with a lint-free cloth. New clutch plates or bands should be soaked in transmission oil for fifteen minutes before the plates or bands are assembled.

CLEANING

CONVERTER CLEANING

The converter cannot be disassembled for cleaning. If there is reason to believe that the converter has an excessive amount of foreign material in it, the following cleaning procedure should be used:

1. With the converter on the bench, remove both drain plugs and tilt the converter in all directions to drain as much fluid as possible.

2. Install the drain plug and fill the converter through the pump drive hub with a light-body oil such as kerosene, or a cleaning solvent suitable for transmission cleaning.

3. Install the tool shown in Fig. 16 in the converter. Expand the bushing in the turbine spline. Rotate the tool to circulate the fluid in the converter.

4. Remove both drain plugs and thoroughly drain the converter. Remove the tool and install the drain

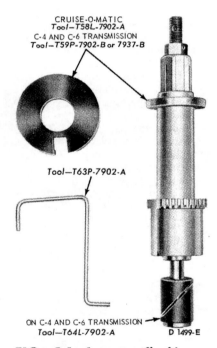

CRUISE-O-MATIC
Tool—T58L-7902-A
C-4 AND C-6 TRANSMISSION
Tool—T59P-7902-B or 7937-B

Tool—T63P-7902-A

ON C-4 AND C-6 TRANSMISSION
Tool—T64L-7902-A   D 1499-E

FIG. 16—Converter Checking Tool

plugs. Torque the plugs to specification.

INSPECTION

TURBINE AND STATOR END PLAY CHECK

1. Insert the tool into the converter pump drive hub until it bottoms.

2. Install the guide over the converter pump drive hub.

3. Expand the split fiber bushing in the turbine spline by tightening the adjusting nut. Tighten the adjusting nut until the tool is securely locked into the spline.

4. Attach a dial indicator to the tool (Fig. 17 or Fig. 18). Position the indicator button on a converter pump drive hub, and set the dial face at 0 (zero).

5. Lift the tool upward as far as it will go and note the indicator reading. The indicator reading is the total end play which the turbine and stator share. If the total end play exceeds the limits specified in Part 7-5, replace the converter unit.

STATOR ONE-WAY CLUTCH CHECK

1. Loosen the adjusting nut to free the split bushing, and then remove the tool from the converter.

2. Install the stator outer race holding tool in one of the four holes provided in the stator (Fig. 17 or Fig. 18).

3. Insert the tool in the converter pump drive hub. As the tool enters the converter, the pins will engage the stator clutch inner race spline.

4. Place a torque wrench on the tool (Fig. 17 or Fig. 18). The tool (and stator inner race) should turn freely clockwise (from the pump drive hub inside the converter). It should lock up and hold a 10 ft-lb *pull when the wrench is turned counterclockwise.* Try the clutch for lockup and hold in at least five different locations around the convert-

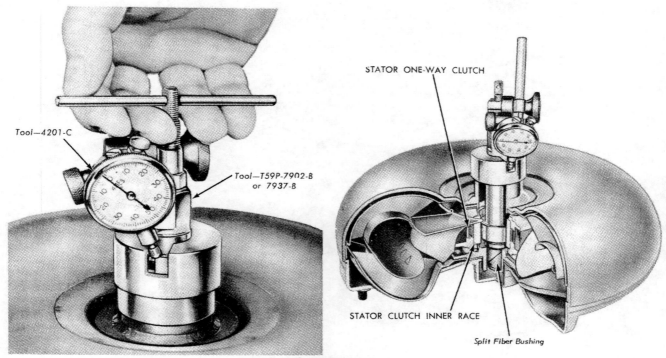

END PLAY CHECK

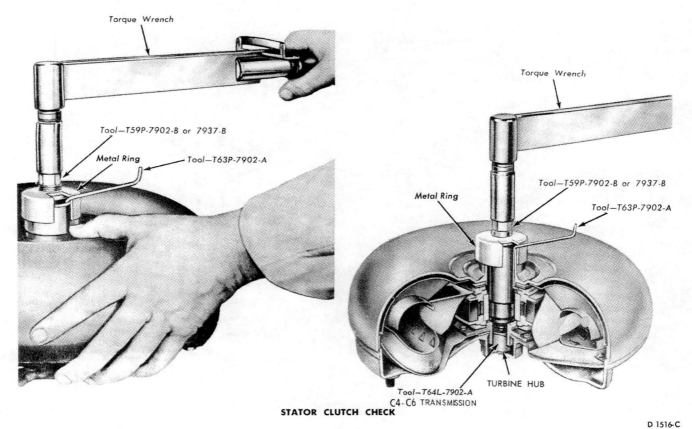

STATOR CLUTCH CHECK

D 1516-C

FIG. 17—Typical Converter Checking Tool—C4 and C6 Automatic

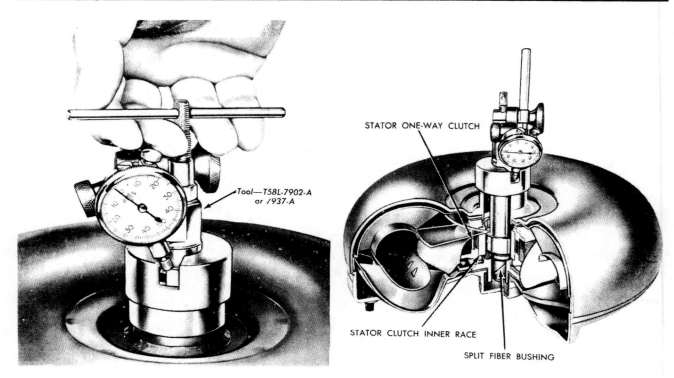

Tool—T58L-7902-A
or 7937-A

STATOR ONE-WAY CLUTCH

STATOR CLUTCH INNER RACE

SPLIT FIBER BUSHING

END PLAY CHECK

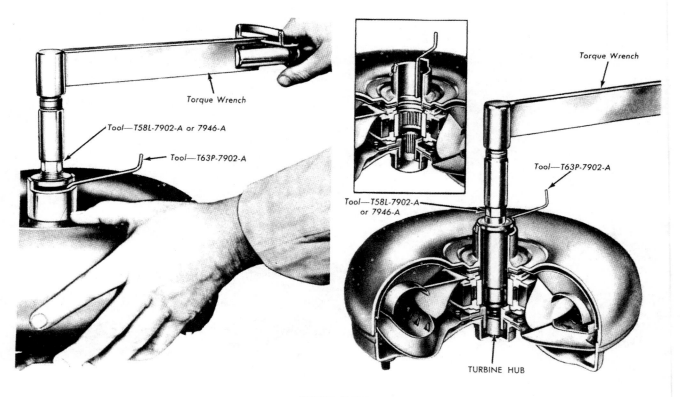

Torque Wrench

Tool—T58L-7902-A or 7946-A

Tool—T63P-7902-A

Torque Wrench

Tool—T63P-7902-A

Tool—T58L-7902-A
or 7946-A

TURBINE HUB

STATOR CLUTCH CHECK

D1064-B

FIG. 18—Typical Converter Checking Tool—Cruise-O-Matic

er. On the C4 or C6 Automatics, the metal ring holding the locking tool will have to be held by hand during this check.

5. If the clutch fails to lock up and hold a 10 ft-lb torque, replace the converter unit.

STATOR TO IMPELLER INTERFERENCE CHECK

1. Position the front pump assembly on a bench with the spline end of the stator shaft pointing up (Fig. 19).

FIG. 19—Stator to Impeller Interference Check

2. Mount a converter on the pump so that the splines on the one-way clutch inner race engage the mating splines of the stator support, and the converter hub engages the pump drive gear.

3. While holding the pump stationary, try to rotate the converter counterclockwise. The converter should rotate freely without any signs of interference or scraping within the converter assembly.

4. If there is an indication of scraping, the trailing edges of the stator blades may be interfering with the leading edges of the impeller blades. In such cases, replace the converter.

STATOR TO TURBINE INTERFERENCE CHECK

1. Position the converter on the bench front side down.

2. Install a front pump assembly to engage the mating splines of the stator support and stator, and pump drive gear lugs.

3. Install the input shaft, engaging the splines with the turbine hub (Fig. 20).

4. While holding the pump stationary, attempt to rotate the turbine with the input shaft. The turbine

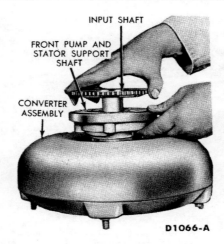

FIG. 20—Stator to Turbine Interference Check

should rotate freely in both directions without any signs of interference or scraping noise.

5. If interference exists, the stator front thrust washer may be worn, allowing the stator to hit the turbine. In such cases, the converter must be replaced.

The converter crankshaft pilot should be checked for nicks or damaged surfaces that could cause interference when installing the converter into the crankshaft. Check the converter front pump drive hub for nicks or sharp edges that would damage the pump seal.

OUTPUT SHAFT AND PRIMARY SUN GEAR SHAFT (CRUISE-O-MATIC OR MERC-O-MATIC)

1. Inspect the thrust surfaces and journals for scores. Inspect the internal gear for broken or worn teeth.

2. Inspect the aluminum sleeve for scores or leakage. Inspect the ring grooves for burrs.

3. Inspect the keyway and drive ball pocket for wear, and inspect the splines for burrs, twist or wear.

4. Inspect the output shaft sleeve for alignment with the governor drive ball (Fig. 21).

5. Inspect the external parking gear teeth for damage and the speedometer drive gear teeth for burrs.

6. If either the output shaft or ring gear has been replaced, place the assembled unit with the gear face down on the bench, push the shaft downward, and check the clearance between the top of the snap ring and its groove (Fig. 22). If this clearance exceeds 0.002 inch, replace the snap ring with a thicker ring to reduce the clearance to less than 0.002

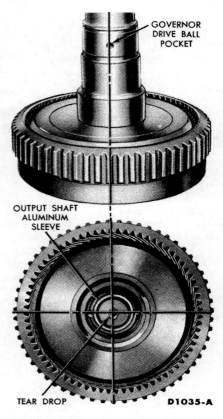

FIG. 21—Correct Position of Output Shaft Aluminum Sleeve

FIG. 22—Checking Output Shaft Snap Ring Clearance

inch. Selective snap rings are available in several thicknesses for this purpose.

7. Inspect the rubber seal and stop ring at the front of the output shaft spline. If wear or damage is evident, replace the parts.

8. Inspect the primary sun gear for broken or worn teeth. Inspect all thrust surfaces and journals for scores. Check all fluid passages (Fig. 23) for obstructions and leakage. Inspect the seal ring grooves for burrs.

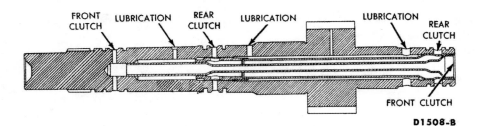

FIG. 23—Primary Sun Gear Shaft—Cross Sectional View

9. Inspect the sun gear shaft splines for burrs and wear.

10. Check the fit of the seal rings in the grooves of the shaft. The rings should enter the grooves freely without bind.

11. Check the fit of the seal rings in their respective bores. A clearance of 0.002-0.009 inch should exist between the ends of the rings.

12. Install the seal rings on the shaft, and check for free movement in the grooves.

DISTRIBUTOR SLEEVE (CRUISE-O-MATIC OR MERC-O-MATIC)

1. Inspect the distributor sleeve for scores or excessive ring wear. Inspect the distributor sleeve passages for obstructions.

2. Check the fit of the fluid tubes in the distributor.

PINION CARRIER, ONE-WAY CLUTCH AND CENTER SUPPORT (CRUISE-O-MATIC OR MERC-O-MATIC)

1. Inspect the clutch outer race, inner race, band surface, pinion gears, bearings, and thrust washer (Fig. 24) for roughness.

PINION CARRIERS—C4 or C6 TRANSMISSIONS

Individual parts of the planet carriers are not serviceable.

1. The pins and shafts in the planet assemblies should be checked for loose fit and/or complete disengagement. Use a new planet assembly if either condition exists. Before installing a planet assembly, the shaft retaining pins should be checked for adequate staking. If staking does not appear adequate, the pins should be restaked before installation. When restaking, the retaining pins must not be driven into the carrier any further than 0.040 inch below the surface of the carrier.

2. Inspect the pinion gears for damaged or excessively worn teeth.

3. Check for free rotation of the pinion gears.

EXTENSION HOUSING

1. Inspect the housing for cracks. Inspect the gasket surface for burrs or warpage.

2. Inspect the bushing for scores or wear.

3. Inspect the rear seal for hardness, cracks, or wear. If the seal

shows wear or deterioration, replace the seal.

4. Inspect the seal counterbore and remove all burrs and scores with crocus cloth.

REAR CLUTCH (MERC-O-MATIC OR CRUISE-O-MATIC) AND REVERSE-HIGH CLUTCH (C4 AND C6 AUTOMATIC)

1. Inspect the drum band surface, the bushing, and thrust surfaces for scores. Minor scores may be removed with crocus cloth. **Badly scored parts must be replaced.**

Inspect the clutch piston bore and the piston inner and outer bearing surfaces for scores. Check the air bleed ball valve in the clutch piston for free movement. Check the orifice to make sure it is not plugged.

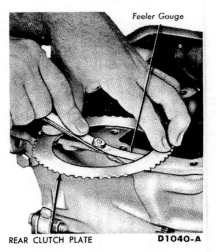

Feeler Gauge

REAR CLUTCH PLATE   D1040-A

FIG. 25—Checking Rear Clutch Steel Plate Coning

2. Check the fluid passages for obstructions. All fluid passages must be clean and free of obstructions.

3. Inspect the clutch plates for wear and scoring and check the plates for fit on the clutch hub serrations. Replace all plates that are badly scored, worn or do not fit freely in the hub serrations.

4. Inspect the clutch pressure plate for scores on the clutch plate bearing surface. Check the clutch release spring(s) for distortion.

5. On a Cruise-O-Matic or Merc-O-Matic transmission, inspect the needle bearing for worm rollers; on the PCE model, position the steel plates on a flat surface. Check the coning with a feeler gauge (Fig. 25). The plates are coned 0.010 inch.

FRONT CLUTCH (MERC-O-MATIC OR CRUISE-O-MATIC) AND FORWARD CLUTCH (C4 OR C6 AUTOMATIC)

1. Inspect the clutch cylinder thrust surfaces, piston bore, and

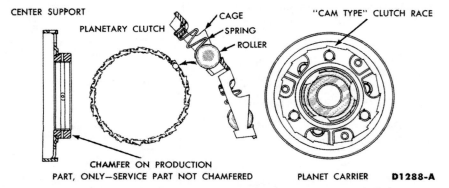

CENTER SUPPORT
PLANETARY CLUTCH
CAGE
SPRING
ROLLER
"CAM TYPE" CLUTCH RACE
CHAMFER ON PRODUCTION PART, ONLY—SERVICE PART NOT CHAMFERED
PLANET CARRIER   D1288-A

FIG. 24—Roller Type Planetary Clutch, Carrier and Center Support

2. Inspect the center support bushing for roughness.

3. Inspect the one-way clutch cage rollers and springs for excessive wear or damage.

clutch plate serrations for scores or burrs. Minor scores or burrs may be removed with crocus cloth. Replace the clutch cylinder if it is badly scored or damaged.

2. Check the fluid passage in the clutch cylinder for obstructions. Clean out all fluid passages. Inspect the clutch piston for scores and replace if necessary. Inspect the piston check ball for freedom of movement and proper seating (Fig. 26).

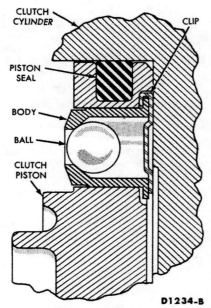

FIG. 26—Clutch Piston Check Valve

3. Check the clutch release spring for distortion and cracks. Replace the spring if it is distorted or cracked.

4. Inspect the composition and the steel clutch plates and the clutch pressure plate for worn or scored bearing surfaces. Replace all parts that are deeply scored.

5. Check the clutch plates for flatness and fit on the clutch hub serrations. Discard any plate that does not slide freely on the serrations or that is not flat.

6. Check the clutch hub thrust surfaces for scores and the clutch hub splines for wear.

7. On a Cruise-O-Matic or Merc-O-Matic transmission, inspect the turbine shaft bearing surfaces for scores. If excessive clearance or scores are found, discard the unit.

Check the splines on the turbine shaft for wear and replace the shaft if the splines are excessively worn. Inspect the bushing in the turbine

shaft for scores. On a C4 or C6 Automatic transmission, check the input shaft for damaged or worn splines.

FRONT PUMP AND STATOR SUPPORT

1. Inspect the mating surfaces of the pump body and cover for burrs.

2. Inspect the drive and driven gear bearing surface for scores, and check the gear teeth for burrs. Inspect the stator support splines for burrs and wear.

3. Check the fluid passages for obstructions.

4. If any parts other than the stator support are found defective, replace the pump as a unit. Minor burrs and scores may be removed with crocus cloth. The stator support is serviced separately.

5. On a C4 or C6 Automatic transmission, check the oil ring grooves in the stator support for nicks, burrs or damaged edges. Check the large O-ring groove of the pump body for damage. Check the gasket mating surface of the pump body for damage.

REAR PUMP (CRUISE-O-MATIC OR MERC-O-MATIC)

1. Remove the drive and driven gears from the pump body.

2. Inspect the gear pockets and the crescent of the pump body for scores or pitting.

3. Inspect the inner bushing and the drive and driven gear bearing surfaces for scores.

4. Check all fluid passages for obstructions, and check mating surfaces and gasket surfaces of the pump body and cover for burrs.

5. Inspect the pump cover bearing surface for scores. Minor burrs or scores may be removed with crocus cloth.

6. If any pump parts, other than the pump cover, are defective, replace the pump as a unit. The pump cover can be replaced separately.

PRESSURE REGULATOR (CRUISE-O-MATIC OR MERC-O-MATIC)

1. Inspect the regulator body and cover mating surface for burrs.

2. Check all fluid passages for obstructions.

3. Inspect the control pressure and converter pressure valves and bores for burrs and scores. Remove all burrs carefully with crocus cloth.

4. Check free movement of the valves in their bores. The valves

should fall freely into the bores when both the valve and bore are dry.

5. Inspect the valve springs and spacers for distortion.

VALVE BODY

1. Clean all parts thoroughly in clean solvent, and then blow them dry with moisture-free compressed air.

2. Inspect all valve and plug bores for scores. Check all fluid passages for obstructions. Inspect the check valve for free movement. Inspect all mating surfaces for burrs or distortion. Inspect all plugs and valves for burrs and scores. **Crocus cloth can be used to polish valves and plugs if care is taken to avoid rounding the sharp edges of the valves and plugs.**

3. Inspect all springs for distortion. Check all valves and plugs for free movement in their respective bores. Valves and plugs, when dry, must fall from their own weight in their respective bores.

4. Roll the manual valve on a flat surface to check it for a bent condition.

GOVERNOR

1. Inspect the governor valves and bores for scores. Minor scores may be removed from the valves with crocus cloth. Replace the governor if the valves or body is deeply scored.

2. Check for free movement of the valves in the bores. The valves should slide freely of their own weight in the bores when dry. Inspect fluid passages in the valve body and counterweight for obstructions. **All fluid passages must be clean.**

3. Inspect the mating surfaces of the governor body and governor distributor (C4 or C6 Automatic) for burrs and distortion. Mating surfaces must be smooth and flat.

4. Check the mating surface of the governor valve and the counterweight on Cruise-O-Matic or Merc-O-Matic transmissions for burrs or scratches.

FRONT SERVO (MERC-O-MATIC OR CRUISE-O-MATIC AND INTERMEDIATE SERVO (C4 AND C6 AUTOMATIC)

1. Inspect the servo bore for cracks and the piston bore and the servo piston stem for scores. Check fluid passages for obstructions. Replace seals that are damaged.

2. On Cruise-O-Matic or Merc-O-

Matic transmissions, check the actuating lever for free movement, and inspect it for wear. If necessary to replace the actuating lever or shaft, remove the retaining pin and push the shaft out of the bracket.

Inspect the adjusting screw threads and the threads in the lever.

3. Check the servo spring and servo band strut(s) for distortion.

4. Inspect the cover seal and gasket cover sealing surface for defects.

REAR SERVO (MERC-O-MATIC OR CRUISE-O-MATIC) AND LOW-REVERSE SERVO (C4 AUTOMATIC)

1. Inspect the servo body for cracks and the piston bore for scores.

2. Check the fluid passages for obstructions.

3. Inspect the band and the struts for distortion. Inspect the band ends for cracks.

4. Inspect the servo spring for distortion.

5. Inspect the band lining for ex-cessive wear and bonding to the metal band.

6. On a Cruise-O-Matic or Merc-O-Matic transmission, check the servo body to case mating surface for burrs. Check the accumulator piston and check valve for freedom of movement. Check the actuating lever socket for scores.

7. Replace seals that are damaged.

CASE

Inspect the case for cracks and stripped threads. Inspect the gasket surfaces and mating surfaces for burrs. Check the vent for obstructions, and check all fluid passages for obstructions and leakage (Figs. 8, 9, and 27).

Inspect the case bushing for scores. Check all parking linkage parts for wear or damage.

ONE-WAY CLUTCH

1. Inspect the outer and inner for scores or damaged surface area where the rollers contact the races. If the outer race on the C6 trans-

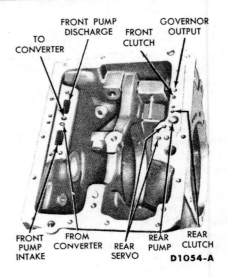

FRONT PUMP DISCHARGE   GOVERNOR OUTPUT   TO CONVERTER   FRONT CLUTCH   FRONT PUMP INTAKE   FROM CONVERTER   REAR SERVO   REAR PUMP   REAR CLUTCH

D1054-A

FIG. 27—Cruise-O-Matic Transmission Case Fluid Passages

mission is damaged the low-reverse clutch hub must be replaced.

2. Inspect the rollers and springs for excessive wear or damage.

3. Inspect the spring and roller case for bent or damaged spring retainers.

PART 7-2 C4 AUTOMATIC DUAL RANGE TRANSMISSION

1 DESCRIPTION AND OPERATION

DESCRIPTION

Figure 1 shows the location of the converter, front pump, clutches, gear train and most of the internal parts used in the C4 transmission. The identification tag (Fig. 2), attached by the low-reverse servo cover bolt, includes the model prefix and suffix, a service identification number, and a build date code. The service identification number indicates changes to service details which affect interchangeability **when the transmission model is not changed.** For interpretation of this number, see the Master Parts Catalog. Table 1 shows the engine and transmission model application.

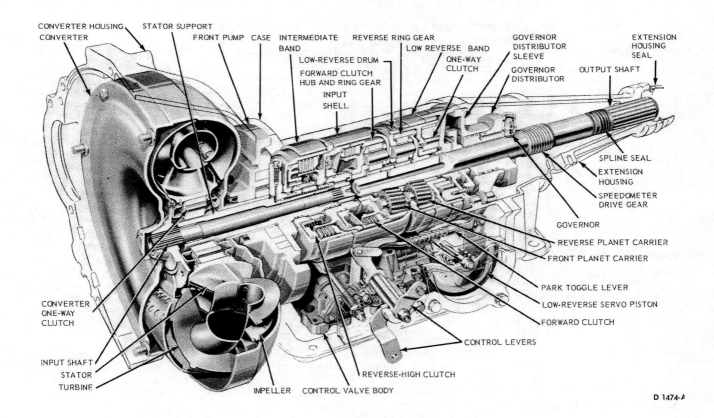

FIG. 1—C4 Automatic Transmission

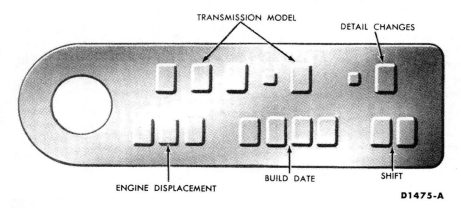

FIG. 2—Identification Tag

TABLE 1—Engine and Transmission Application

Engine Model	Transmission Prefix
240-1V	PCV-E-Column Shift
289-2V	PCW-AW-Column Shift
289-2V	PCW-AV-Floor Shift
240-1V Taxi	PDA-D Column Shift
289-2V Police	

OPERATION

TORQUE CONVERTER

The hydraulic torque converter (Fig. 3) consists of an impeller

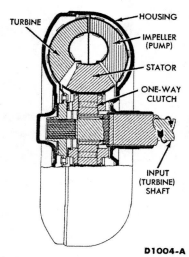

FIG. 3—Sectional View of Typical Torque Converter

(pump), a turbine, and a stator. All these parts are enclosed and operate in a fluid-filled housing.

When the engine is running, the fluid in the torque converter flows from the impeller to the turbine and back to the impeller through the stator. This flow produces a maximum torque increase of about 2 to 1 when the turbine is stalled. When enough torque is developed by the impeller, the turbine begins to rotate, turning the turbine shaft (input shaft).

The converter torque multiplication gradually tapers off as turbine speed approaches impeller speed, and it becomes 1 to 1 when the turbine is being driven at $9/10$ impeller speed. This is known as the coupling point.

When the turbine is rotating at less that $9/10$ impeller speed the converter is multiplying torque. The fluid leaving the turbine blades strikes the front face of the stator blades. These blades are held stationary by the action of a one-way clutch (Fig. 3) as long as the fluid is directed against the front face of the blades.

When the turbine rotates faster than $9/10$ impeller speed the converter no longer multiplies torque. The fluid is directed against the back face of the stator blades. As the one-way clutch permits the stator to rotate only in the direction of impeller rotation, the stator begins to turn with the impeller and turbine. The con-

verter operates as an efficient fluid coupling as long as the turbine speed remains greater than $9/10$ impeller speed.

A constant flow of fluid into and out of the converter is maintained. The fluid coming out of the converter is forced through a cooler located in the radiator tank.

PLANETARY GEAR TRAIN, CLUTCHES, BANDS, AND SERVOS

Planetary Gear Train

The gear train consists of an input shaft that is splined to the turbine of the converter and the forward clutch cylinder (Fig. 4). The forward clutch cylinder rotates the steel internal clutch plates of the forward clutch and the composition clutch plates of the reverse-high clutch. When the reverse-high clutch is applied, the external area of the clutch hub is splined to and drives the input shell to rotate the sun gear. When the forward clutch is applied, the composition clutch plates drive the forward clutch hub and ring gear. The ring gear rotates the forward planet gears.

When applied, the intermediate band holds the reverse-high clutch drum, input shell and sun gear from rotating.

The sun gear, which is driven by the input shell, is meshed with the forward and reverse planet gears. The reverse planet carrier and low-reverse drum are locked together with external splines. The low-reverse drum can be held from rotating by the low-reverse band. The low-reverse drum is also held from rotating by a roller type one-way clutch.

The forward planet carrier, reverse ring gear hub, park gear and governor distributor are all splined to the output shaft.

Forward Clutch

The input shaft is splined to and drives the forward clutch cylinder (Fig. 4). Rotation of the cylinder drives the steel clutch plates in the forward clutch and the composition clutch plates of the reverse-high clutch.

When the forward clutch piston is applied by hydraulic pressure, the movement of the piston against the disc spring locks the steel and composition clutch plates together to

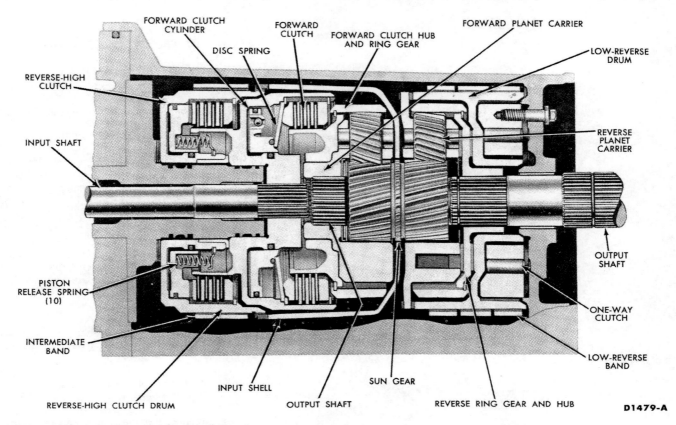

FIG. 4—Gear Train, Clutches and Bands

drive the forward clutch hub and ring gear.

When hydraulic pressure is released from the piston, the disc spring moves the piston to the released position. As the disc spring moves, the steel and composition clutch plates are released. This stops the rotation of the forward clutch hub and ring gear (Fig. 4). The forward clutch is applied in all forward drive gear ratios.

Reverse-High Clutch

When hydraulic pressure is directed to the clutch piston, the piston moves against the release springs (Fig. 4). The piston movement locks the steel and rotating composition clutch plates together. The steel clutch plates drive the reverse-high clutch drum which is splined to the input shell. Rotation of the input shell drives the sun gear which is splined to the input shell.

To release the reverse-high clutch, hydraulic pressure is exhausted from the apply side of the piston. The return springs move the piston to the released position. The steel and composition clutch plates are now released to stop rotation of the re-

verse-high clutch drum, input shell, and sun gear.

Intermediate Servo And Band

The intermediate servo is machined into the transmission case and the band has an **external** adjustment screw (Fig. 5). To apply the servo, hydraulic pressure is directed from the control valve body, through a hole in the case to the hole in the servo piston stem. The pressure passes through the center of the piston stem and then to the apply side of the piston. The piston moves against the return spring to tighten the intermediate band around the reverse-high clutch drum.

To release the servo piston, hydraulic pressure is directed to the release side of the piston. The release pressure is assisted by the compressed return spring to move the servo piston and intermediate band to the off position. The intermediate servo and band are applied only during the intermediate gear operation.

Low-Reverse Servo And Band

The low-reverse servo is machined into the transmission case and the band has an **external** adjustment screw (Fig. 6). To apply the servo,

hydraulic pressure is directed from the control valve body through a hole in the case to a hole in the piston stem. The pressure then passes through the center of the piston stem to the apply area of the servo piston. The apply pressure force moves the piston against the piston return spring to tighten the low-reverse band around the low-reverse drum.

To release the low-reverse servo piston and band, the hydraulic pressure is exhausted from the apply side of the piston. The compressed return spring expands to release the piston and the low-reverse band.

Power Flow

Table 2 shows the gear ratios obtained in the different selector lever positions. **All gear rotations are viewed from the front of transmission.**

Power Flow Neutral

In neutral (Fig. 7), the clutches or bands are not applied therefore no power is transmitted to the output shaft.

Power Flow First Gear

In low gear (Fig. 7), the forward

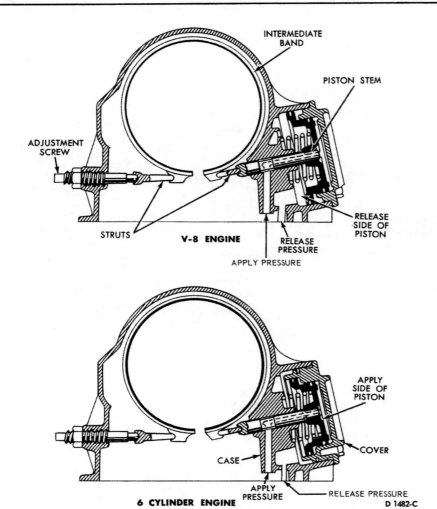

FIG. 5—Intermediate Servo and Band

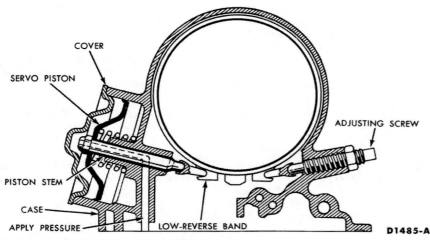

FIG. 6—Low-Reverse Servo and Band

clutch is applied, and the planet one-way clutch or low-reverse band is holding the low-reverse drum and reverse planet carrier from rotating. The power flow is through the input shaft and into the forward clutch. The input shaft is splined to and drives the forward clutch cylinder. Rotation of the forward clutch drives the forward clutch hub and ring

gear. The ring gear rotates the forward planet gears clockwise to cause the sun gear to rotate counterclockwise.

Counterclockwise rotation of the sun gear turns the reverse planet gears clockwise. The reverse planet carrier being splined to the low-reverse drum is held from rotating by the one-way clutch or low-reverse band.

With the reverse planet carrier held stationary, the clockwise rotation of the reverse planet gears rotates the reverse ring gear and hub clockwise. The hub of the reverse ring gear is splined to the output shaft and rotates the output shaft clockwise.

The output shaft rotation is at a reduced speed, compared to the input shaft rotation, but at an increased torque.

The output shaft rotation at a reduced speed is caused by the fact that the forward carrier rotates at the same speed of the output shaft and in the same direction since the carrier is splined to the output shaft. The forward ring gear and planet assembly are rotating in the same direction but the planet carrier is rotating at a slower speed than the ring gear. Therefore, the low gear ratio (torque multiplication) is a combination of the ratios provided by the forward and reverse planet assemblies.

Power Flow Intermediate Gear

In intermediate gear (Fig. 7), the forward clutch is applied and the intermediate band is holding the reverse-high clutch drum, input shell and sun gear from turning.

The power flow is through the input shaft into the forward clutch and forward planet assembly ring gear. The sun gear is held from rotating by the intermediate band. This causes the forward planet pinions to rotate (walk) around the sun gear, carrying the forward planet carrier with them. The forward planet carrier, being splined to the output shaft, causes clockwise rotation of the output shaft at a reduction in speed compared to the speed of the input shaft, and at an increase in torque.

Clockwise rotation of the output shaft causes clockwise rotation of the output shaft ring gear, causing the reverse planet pinions to also rotate (walk) around the sun gear in a clockwise direction. The reverse

TABLE 2—Gear Ratios

Transmission Selector Position	Gear	Gear Ratios	Forward Clutch	Reverse High Clutch	Intermediate Band	Low Reverse Band	One-Way Clutch
N or P	Neutral	—	Off	Off	Off	Off	Off
L	Low	2.46:1	On	Off	Off	On	Holding
D1	Low	2.46:1	On	Off	Off	Off	Holding
D1 or D2	Intermediate	1.46:1	On	Off	On	Off	Over-running
D1 or D2	High	1.00:1	On	On	Off	Off	Over-running
R	Reverse	2.20:1	Off	On	Off	On	Not affected

planet carrier will also rotate clockwise and the one-way clutch inner race, being splined to the reverse planet carrier, will overrun.

Power Flow High Gear

In high gear (Fig. 7), the forward and reverse-high clutches are applied. The power flow is through the input shaft into the forward clutch cylinder. The forward clutch cylinder rotates the steel clutch plates of the forward clutch and the composition clutch plates of the reverse-high clutch. The forward clutch directs the power flow through the forward clutch hub and ring gear to the forward planet carrier.

The reverse-high clutch directs the power flow through the input shell to the sun gear. With the sun gear and the forward clutch hub ring gear driven at the same speed, the front planet assembly (that is splined to the output shaft) is forced to rotate the output shaft at the same speed and direction to provide high gear.

Power Flow Reverse

In reverse (Fig. 7), the reverse-high clutch and low-reverse band are applied. The power flow is through the input shaft, reverse-high clutch, input shell, and to the sun gear. Clockwise rotation of the sun gear causes counterclockwise rotation of the reverse planet gears.

The low-reverse band, holding the low-reverse drum and reverse planet carrier from turning, causes the reverse planet gears to rotate counterclockwise.

This rotates the reverse ring gear and hub counterclockwise. The hub splined to the output shaft rotates the output shaft counterclockwise at a reduction in speed and at an increase in torque for reverse gear.

HYDRAULIC CONTROL SYSTEM

The hydraulic control system described below (Fig. 8) includes all models having a C4 automatic transmission.

Front Pump

Fluid for operation of the hydraulic control system is supplied by one gear type pump mounted on the front of the transmission case. Pump intake is through a screen which is part of the main control assembly, into the case casting and pump. Discharge is through the case into the main control assembly. Fluid from the front pump is directed to the following valves in the main control assembly.

Main Oil Pressure Regulator Valve

Throttle Booster Valve

Manual Valve

In addition, fluid is also directed to the primary throttle valve, which is located in the rear of the case. Fluid delivered to these valves is at a pressure controlled by the main oil pressure regulator valve.

Main Oil Pressure Regulator

The main regulator valve assembly consists of the main oil pressure regulator valve and spring, retainer, main oil pressure booster valve, spring and sleeve, located in one bore in the main control assembly (Fig. 8).

Fluid is delivered to three valleys of the main regulator valve, from the front pump. The difference in diameter between the end land and the second land provides an area differential for regulation. Fluid pressure in this area tends to move the valve against spring force. Spring force is such that at approximately 60 psi front pump pressure, the main valve

will move so that the third land uncovers the converter feed port, allowing additional pump volume to be used to charge the converter. If volume supplied by the front pump is greater than that required to maintain 60 psi line pressure, and converter and lube requirements, the valve will move further allowing the fourth land to uncover the port which allows excess pump volume to be discharged into the sump.

Pressures over 60 psi which are required under various operating conditions are obtained by delivering fluid under pressure to the pressure booster valve, where it will cause the pressure booster valve to assist the main regulator valve spring in increasing regulated line pressure.

Source of these pressures which cause variations in control pressure are discussed later.

Manual Valve

Two passages deliver control pressure to the manual valve. The valve is positioned by the manual linkage according to mode of operation desired, to direct fluid out of two or more of the line passages which lead from the manual valve. The five passages leading from the manual valve (Fig. 8) (from left to right) are:

1. D2
2. D1
3. D
4. L-R
5. R

The D2 passage is charged in D2 range only.

The D1 passage is charged in D2 and D1 ranges.

The D passage is charged in all forward ranges, (including manual low).

The LR passage is charged in L and R ranges.

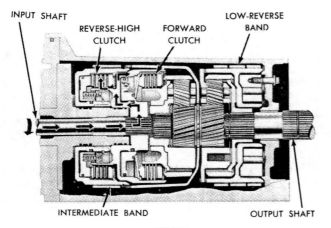

NEUTRAL

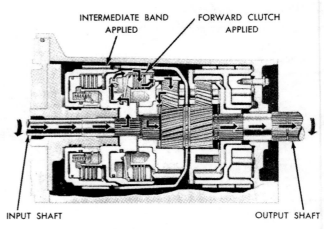

SECOND GEAR

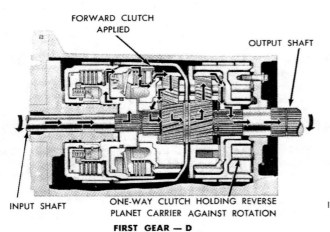

FIRST GEAR — D

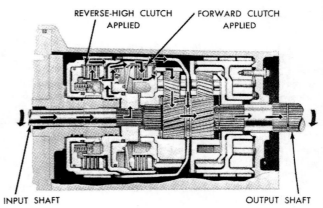

HIGH GEAR

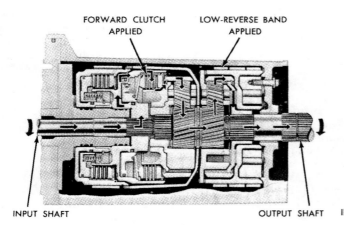

FIRST GEAR — MANUAL LOW

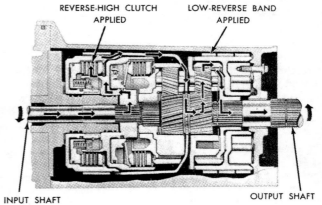

REVERSE

D1476-A

FIG. 7—Power Flow

The R passage is charged in reverse range only.

In Park and Neutral the valve blocks the flow of control pressure and exhausts the five passages leading from the manual valve.

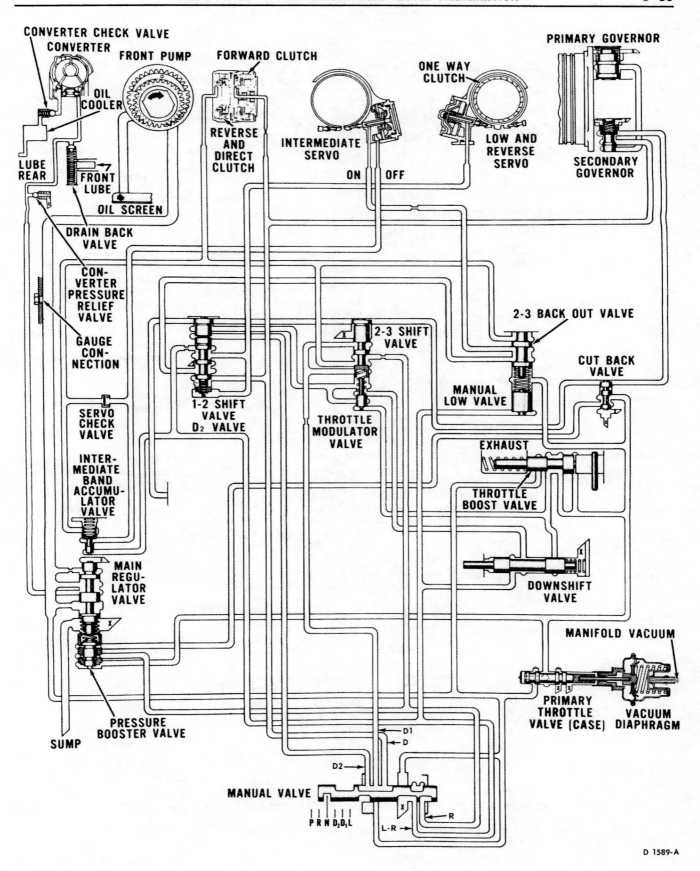

FIG. 8—Hydraulic Control System

The D passage supplies fluid pressure to the governor secondary valve, D2 valve and forward clutch.

The D2 passage supplies fluid to the adjoining ends of the D2 and 1-2 shift valves.

The D1 passage supplies fluid to the 2-3 shift valve.

L and R passage supplies fluid to the lower end of the intermediate band accumulator valve, end of the manual low valve, through the downshift valve, to and through the throttle modulator valve bore, under the 2-3 shift valve and to the underside of the first land of the 1-2 shift valve.

In addition, oil is supplied to the D2 valve and through the valve when it is in the closed (up) position, to the Low and Reverse Servo, applying the low and reverse band. The same fluid is also directed to the spring end (opposite governor) of the D2 valve.

The R passage supplies fluid to the middle valley of the pressure booster valve, through the 2-3 shift valve to the reverse and direct clutch, applying it, and to the release side of the intermediate servo. Fluid is also supplied to the end of the 2-3 back-out valve, and to the intermediate band accumulator valve.

Primary Throttle Valve

The primary throttle valve is actuated by changes in manifold vacuum. Primary throttle pressure starts at 20 inches (nominal) of mercury vacuum. Primary throttle pressure is delivered to the:

1. End of the pressure booster valve.
2. Upper valley of pressure booster valve (through cutback valve).
3. Downshift valve and throttle modulator valve (through throttle booster valve).
4. End of the throttle booster valve.
5. Spring end of the 2-3 back-out valve and manual low valve.

Figure 9 shows how primary throttle pressure varies with engine vacuum.

Pressure Booster Valve

TV pressure is delivered to the upper valley of the pressure booster valve and to the end of the pressure booster valve. When force created on the booster valve by TV pressures in these two areas exceeds pressure booster valve spring force, the force will be added to the main

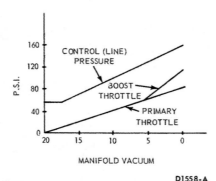

FIG. 9—Throttle Pressure Regulation

regulator valve spring force transmitted to the main regulator valve. This will provide increased control pressures required to compensate for increased throttle openings and engine torque output. Figure 9 shows how control pressure varies with engine vacuum at O output shaft RPM.

Governor

At Rest (O mph). Control pressure (line) is fed to the secondary governor valve through the center passage in the valve body. Because of the differential in area of the inner and outer lands of the valve, the valve will be forced inward, shutting off line pressure feed to the governor passage and allowing this passage to be opened to exhaust, at the inner end of the valve. At the same time, line pressure will pass by two flats on the outer end of the valve, pressurizing the line leakage passage leading to the primary governor valve. At rest, the spring on the outer end of the primary governor valve holds the primary governor valve inward, blocking further flow of the fluid in the line leakage passage. This causes pressure in the line leakage passage to build to the same value as line pressure. As a consequence, the secondary governor valve is held in and there is no pressure in the governor circuit.

Above 10 mph. When vehicle speed reaches approximately 10 mph, centrifugal force on the primary governor valve overcomes spring force, and the valve moves outward, opening the line leakage passage to exhaust. This action reduces the pressure on the end of the secondary governor valve to zero (0), allowing the secondary valve to also move outward, due to spring force and centrifugal force. When

the secondary valve moves outward, it closes the governor exhaust passage, and allows line pressure to enter the governor passage. As pressure builds in the governor passage it will create a force on the secondary governor valve due to the differential in areas of the inner and outer lands of the valve. This force tends to move the valve inward. When the force on the valve created by pressure in the governor passage exceeds the centrifugal force plus spring force, the valve will move inward, allowing governor pressure to exhaust, and close the passage between line pressure and governor pressure. When governor pressure is reduced, the secondary valve will again move outward, closing the governor exhaust port and opening the line pressure to governor passage. Above 10 mph, governor pressure is regulated in this manner, and will vary with vehicle speeds.

If vehicle speed drops below 10 mph, the primary valve spring will move the primary governor valve in, closing the line leakage exhaust port at the primary valve. Pressure in the line leakage passage will become equal to line pressure, forcing the secondary governor valve in. This action shuts off line pressure feed to the governor passage and exhausts the governor circuit.

When the secondary governor valve is regulating, governor pressure will be delivered to the cutback valve, end of the 2-3 shift valve and the 1-2 shift valve. Figure 10 shows the relationship between

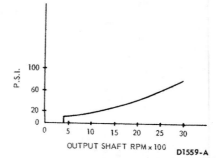

FIG. 10—Governor Pressure Regulation

governor pressure and output shaft RPM.

Throttle Booster Valve

Throttle plate openings above 50° provide very little change in engine vacuum as compared to throttle plate openings below 50°. The throttle booster valve is provided to boost throttle pressure and provide the necessary shift delay for engine throttle plate openings above 50°.

Below approximately 60 PSI primary TV pressure flows to and through the throttle boost valve unaffected, working on the end of the boost valve and on the area differential on the spring side of the boost valve. As a consequence, TV pressure passes through the throttle boost valve unaffected.

When TV pressure increases above 60 psi, the force created by TV pressure acting on the end of the throttle boost valve, minus the force of TV pressure acting on the area differential on the spring side, will exceed the force of the spring. This causes the valve to move against the spring, closing off primary TV pressure to the area differential on the spring side and permitting this area to be fed from line pressure, causing a boost in the pressure used for shift delay only. Because the area of the end of the throttle boost valve exceeds the area differential on the spring side by 2½ to 1, throttle boost pressure above 60 psi primary TV pressure will increase 2.5 psi, per 1 psi primary TV.

TV pressure from the throttle booster valve is delivered to the downshift valve and throttle modulator valve.

Figure 9 shows the relationship between primary TV and boosted throttle pressure.

Throttle Modulator Valve

The throttle modulator valve, located in the end of the 2-3 shift valve bore reduces throttle pressure which acts on the ends of the 2-3 shift valve and on the area differential of the 1-2 shift valve. Modulated throttle pressure in these areas provides shift delay in relation to throttle opening.

Cut Back Valve

Increased line pressure is required to prevent clutch and band slippage under stall conditions. Dependent upon vehicle speed, the requirements for increased line pressure are considerably reduced. When governor pressure acting on the end of the cut-back valve exceeds the force of TV pressure acting on its area opposing governor, the cutback valve will move cutting off primary TV pressure being fed to the upper valley of the pressure booster valve.

This action reduces the assist that the pressure booster valve provides to the main regulator valve spring. The cutback valve movement will therefore vary with engine throttle opening and vehicle speed. Figure 11 shows how line pressure varies with output shaft rpm at consistent vacuum values.

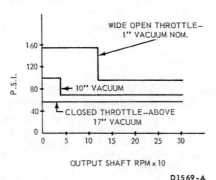

D1569-A

FIG. 11—Control Pressure Regulation

1-2 Shift Valve Train

The 1-2 shift valve train is composed of the 1-2 shift valve, the D2 valve, and the 1-2 shift valve spring.

D-1 Range. In D1 range the 1-2 shift valve is held closed (up) by modulated throttle pressure acting on the differential area between the two lands of the 1-2 shift valve, by D oil pressure acting on the differential in area between the two lands at the spring end of the D2 valve, and by the 1-2 shift valve spring. Governor pressure tends to move the 1-2 shift valve train against these forces. When force created by governor pressure exceeds the forces holding the 1-2 shift valve train closed, the 1-2 shift valve and D2 valve will be opened (moved downward), closing the exhaust port and allowing D fluid to pass through the D2 valve to accomplish the 1-2 shift. When the D2 valve is moved downward D fluid is exhausted from the differential in areas provided by the lower two lands of the D2 valve. This action eliminates the force created by D fluid which tends to hold the 1-2 shift valve train closed.

If governor pressure is reduced to the point where spring force and modulated throttle pressure force exceeds governor pressure force, the 1-2 shift valve train will move up (close) cutting off the flow of D oil through the valve and opening the exhaust port allowing a downshift to low gear.

If the throttle is open to the point

where modulated throttle pressure acting on the 1-2 shift valve plus the 1-2 shift valve spring force creates a force greater than that provided by governor pressure, the 1-2 shift valve train will be closed, providing a torque demand downshift to low.

If the throttle is open through detent, the downshift valve moves to allow boosted throttle pressure to enter the modulated throttle pressure passage at the 1-2 shift valve to provide a forced 2-1 downshift.

L Range. In L range L-R fluid enters the modulated throttle pressure passage to provide a manual low downshift to first gear. Once the transmission is in low gear L-R fluid, which is directed to the D2 valve, passes through the D2 valve and is delivered to the spring end of the D2 valve, preventing an upshift. L-R fluid which passes through the D2 fluid which passes through the D2 valve also applies the reverse and low servo.

(D2 Range). In D2 range, D2 oil is introduced between the 1-2 shift and D2 valves. This action opens the D2 valve and holds it open, providing a second gear start and preventing a 2-1 downshift.

2-3 Shift Valve

The 2-3 shift valve is held closed by throttle modulator valve spring force, modulated throttle pressure force, and by D1 fluid pressure force acting on the differential in area of the lands of the valve to which it is delivered.

Governor pressure tends to open the 2-3 shift valve. When force created by governor pressure exceeds the forces holding the valve closed, the valve will move downward (open) closing the exhaust passage (through the manual valve) and opening the D1 passage to allow D1 fluid to apply the direct clutch and release the intermediate servo.

With the shift valve open (down) the throttle modulator valve is held down cutting off modulated throttle pressure to the 2-3 shift valve and 1-2 shift valve. In addition, the port which delivered D1 fluid to the differential in area of the shift valve lands, is closed.

The shift valve will be reopened (moved up) causing a downshift under one or more of the following conditions:

(Governor Pressure Reduced). If governor pressure is reduced to the point where it can no longer hold the shift valve down against spring force and TV pressure force, the valve will move up causing a downshift. Under closed throttle conditions, the 2-3 shift valve will close at approximately 10 mph (speed at which governor pressure is cut off). Since governor pressure is cut off at this speed the 1-2 shift valve train also closes at the same time. This will provide a 3-1 downshift when coasting in D1 range.

Throttle Pressure Increase. If throttle pressure is increased sufficiently, it will move the throttle modulator valve and consequently the 2-3 shift valve up, causing a 3-2 torque demand downshift.

Throttle Pressure Introduced Below 2-3 Shift Valve. If the downshift valve is moved through detent, boosted throttle pressure is directed to the undersize of the 2-3 shift valve, forcing the valve up and causing a forced 3-2 downshift. Maximum 3-2 forced downshift speed is controlled by governor pressure.

Exhausting D1 Fluid Feed to the 2-3 Shift Valve. If manual valve is moved to L range, the D1 passage which feeds fluid to the 2-3 shift valve will be opened to exhaust allowing direct clutch apply-intermediate servo release fluid to exhaust, permitting the intermediate band to apply, causing a 3-2 downshift.

2-3 Back-Out Valve

The purpose of the 2-3 back-out valve is to provide smooth upshifts, when the throttle is suddenly closed while accelerating in second gear. Operation is as follows:

Normal Throttle-on 2-3 Upshifts. When the 2-3 shift valve moves to cause a 2-3 upshift, D1 fluid passes through the valve to apply the direct clutch and release the intermediate servo. This same fluid is also directed to the end of the 2-3 back-out valve. However, with throttle open, primary throttle pressure on the opposite end of the 2-3 back-out valve, assists spring force in holding

the valve up, so that there will be no valve movement until after the 2-3 shift has been completed.

Back-Out 2-3 Upshifts. When the throttle is closed during a 2-3 upshift, and before the shift is completed, there may be enough pressure in the direct clutch cylinder to apply the clutch at the reduced engine torque input, but not enough pressure to release the intermediate servo. This condition could cause a harsh 2-3 shift. However, if the throttle is closed during a 2-3 shift, primary throttle pressure will be reduced to zero (0), and reverse and direct clutch apply pressure on the end of the 2-3 back-out valve will move the valve down against spring force. This action immediately connects the clutch apply circuit to the intermediate servo apply circuit, reducing the pressure on apply side of the servo to the same value as in the direct clutch (and also on the release side of the intermediate servo). When this happens, the intermediate band is released, to provide a smooth 2-3 shift.

Manual Low Valve

The manual low valve insures that the 2-3 back-out valve will be moved up the instant that pressure drops in the direct clutch apply-intermediate servo release circuit when a shift to manual low range is made or a forced downshift is made, from high gear. This is accomplished by directing control pressure to the end of the manual low valve, when L range is selected or, by directing TV pressure to the end of the manual low valve, when the downshift valve is moved to the downshift position.

Intermediate Band Accumulator Valve

The intermediate band accumulator valve train is composed of the intermediate band accumulator valve and spring. The intermediate band

accumulator valve train in conjunction with the intermediate servo check valve controls intermediate servo apply force on all applications of the intermediate band, under all operating conditions, in D1 and D2 ranges. In low range the intermediate servo accumulator valve provides no control on the application of the intermediate band on 3-2 downshifts. Operation is as follows:

D1 and D2 Ranges, 1-2 Up-Shift and 3-2 Downshifts. Fluid pressure from the D2 valve acting on the apply side of the intermediate servo piston tending to apply the servo, causes the fluid which is trapped in the intermediate servo release passage to be pressurized. This pressure acting on the area differential of the intermediate servo accumulator valve will cause the accumulator valve to move against its spring to exhaust, to maintain a certain level of pressure on the release side of the intermediate servo until it has completely stroked, applying the band. Force created by this pressure on the release side of the servo, plus spring force, is subtracted from the force of control pressure acting on the apply side of the servo, thereby controlling the servo apply force during any condition requiring the intermediate band to be on in D1 or D2 ranges.

Low Range, 3-2 Down-shift. Low and reverse pressure acting on the end of the intermediate servo accumulator valve will move the valve against the accumulator valve spring to insure that the fluid in the release side of the intermediate servo can exhaust freely.

D1 and D2 Ranges, 2-3 Up-shifts. During a 2-3 upshift, D1 fluid from the 2-3 shift valve will unseat the intermediate servo check valve, bypassing the intermediate servo accumulator valve, allowing the release side of intermediate servo to be pressurized at the same pressure level as the reverse-high clutch.

---

2   IN-CAR-ADJUSTMENTS AND REPAIRS

CONTROL LINKAGE ADJUSTMENTS

The transmission control linkage adjustments should be performed in the order in which they appear in this section of the manual.

THROTTLE AND DOWNSHIFT LINKAGE ADJUSTMENTS

1. Apply the parking brake, and place the selector lever at N.

2. Run the engine at normal idle speed. If the engine is cold, run the

engine at fast idle speed (about 1200 rpm) until it reaches normal operating temperature. When the engine is warm, slow it down to normal idle speed.

3. Connect a tachometer to the engine.

4. Adjust engine idle speed to the specified rpms with the transmission selector lever at D1 (large dot) or D2 (circle) the drive position.

5. The carburetor throttle lever must be against the hot idle speed adjusting screw at specified idle speed in D1 (circle) or D2 (small dot). To make sure that the carburetor throttle lever is against the adjusting screw, refer to Group 10 for the carburetor adjusting procedures.

6. With the engine stopped, disconnect the carburetor return spring (Figs. 12 and 13) from the throttle lever.

7. Loosen the accelerator cable conduit attaching clamp.

8. With the accelerator pedal to the floor and the throttle lever held to the wide open position, slide the cable conduit to the rear (to the left on 6-cylinder engine) to remove the slack from the cable. Tighten the cable conduit attaching clamp.

9. Disconnect the downshift lever return spring (Figs. 12 and 13).

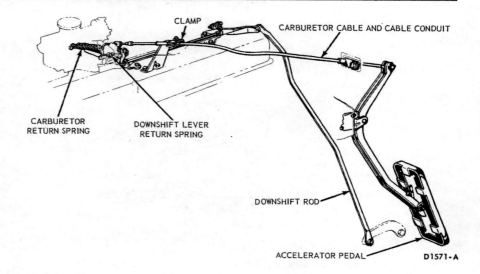

FIG. 13—Throttle Linkage—6-Cylinder Engine

D1 (circle) position tight against the D stop.

2. Loosen the nut at point A enough to permit column shift lever to slide on the shift rod (Fig. 14).

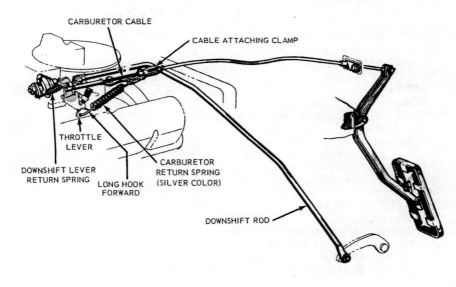

FIG. 12—Throttle Linkage—V-8 Engine

10. Hold the throttle lever at the wide open position and depress the downshift rod to the through detent stop. Set the downshift lever (at carburetor) adjusting screw against the throttle lever.

11. Connect both return springs to their respective levers.

MANUAL LINKAGE ADJUSTMENT

Column Shift

1. Place the selector lever in the

3. Shift the manual lever at the transmission into the D1 detent position, second from the rear.

4. Make sure that the selector lever has not moved from the D1 stop; then, tighten the nut at point A.

5. Check the pointer alignment and the transmission operation for all selector lever detent positions.

Floor Shift

1. Position the transmission selec-

tor lever in D1 (circle) position.

2. Raise the car and loosen the manual lever control rod retaining nut. Move the transmission manual lever to the D1 position, second detent position from the back of the transmission. The last detent position is manual low.

3. With the transmission selector lever and manual lever in the D1 positions, torque the attaching nut 20 to 25 ft-lbs.

4. Check the operation of the transmission in each selector lever position.

NEUTRAL START SWITCH ADJUSTMENT

1. With the manual linkage properly adjusted, loosen the two switch bolts (Fig. 15). Position the transmission manual lever in neutral detent position.

2. Rotate the switch and insert the shank end of the gauge pin (No. 43 drill) into the gauge pin holes of the switch. **The gauge pin has to be inserted a full 31/64 inch into the 3 holes of the switch (Fig. 15).**

3. Torque the two switch attaching bolts to specification. Remove the gauge pin tool from the switch.

4. Check the operation of the switch. The engine should start only with the transmission selector lever in N (neutral) or P (park).

NEUTRAL START SWITCH REPLACEMENT

1. Apply penetrating oil to the outer lever attaching nut to prevent breaking the inner lever shaft. Remove the transmission downshift outer lever attaching nut and lever.

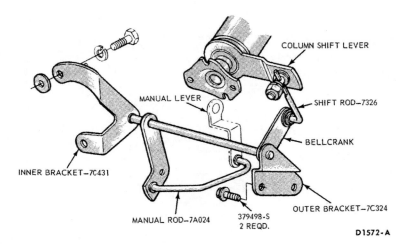

FIG. 14—Manual Linkage—Column Shift

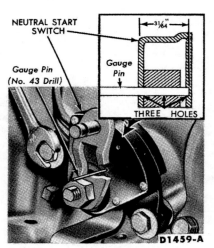

FIG. 15—Neutral Start Switch

2. Remove the two neutral start switch attaching bolts.

3. Disconnect the two multiple wire connectors. Remove the neutral start switch from the transmission.

4. Install the neutral start switch on the transmission. Install the two attaching bolts.

5. With the transmission manual lever in neutral, check the location of the switch with the gauge pin and adjust the switch if necessary.

6. Tighten the switch attaching bolts to specifications and remove the gauge pin.

7. Install the outer downshift lever and attaching nut, and torque the nut to specification. Install the downshift linkage rod to the downshift lever.

8. Install the switch wires, **red to red and blue to blue.** Connect the wire multiple connectors. Check the operation of the switch in each de-

tent position. The engine should start only with the transmission selector lever in N (neutral) and P (park).

When the engine will not start in neutral or park, check the multiple connectors to make sure the red wire is connected to the red wire and the blue wire is connected to the blue wire.

SELECTOR LEVER REMOVAL ADJUSTMENT AND INSTALLATION

Removal

1. Raise the car and disconnect the link (Fig. 16) from the shift lever.

2. Lower the car. Place the selector lever in the neutral position and remove the selector lever handle attaching screw. Lift the handle off the selector lever.

3. Remove the chrome trim panel from the console.

4. Remove the three screws that attach the quadrant to the selector lever housing. Lift the quadrant from the housing. Disconnect the bulb socket.

5. Remove the four screws that attach the selector lever housing to the console.

6. Lift the selector lever and housing from the console.

Detent Pawl Adjustment

1. Install the handle to make the detent pawl adjustment.

2. Move the selector lever to the D1-D2 range.

3. Place a 0.010-inch feeler gauge between the detent pawl and plate.

4. Loosen the cable lock nut and turn the screw clockwise to decrease the clearance or counterclockwise to

increase the clearance as shown in Fig. 17. Tighten the lock nut after a clearance of 0.010-inch has been established.

5. Remove the handle from the selector lever.

Installation

1. Position the selector lever and housing assembly in the console.

2. Install the four attaching screws to secure it in place.

3. Connect the bulb socket to the quadrant. Position the quadrant and secure it with the three attaching screws.

4. Raise the car and install the link on the shift lever (Fig. 16). Adjust the manual linkage and then the neutral switch as required. Lower the car.

5. Install the chrome trim cover on the console.

6. Place the selector lever handle on the lever with the attaching screw tapped hole facing toward the right side of the console. Install and tighten the handle attaching screw.

BAND ADJUSTMENT

INTERMEDIATE BAND

1. Clean all the dirt from the band adjusting screw area. Loosen the lock nut several turns.

2. With the tool shown in Fig. 18, tighten the adjusting screw until the tool handle clicks. The tool is a pre-set torque wrench which clicks and overruns when the torque on the adjusting screw reaches 10 ft-lbs.

3. Back off the adjusting screw exactly 1¾ turns.

4. Hold the adjusting screw from turning and torque the lock nut to specification.

LOW-REVERSE BAND

1. Clean all the dirt from the band adjusting screw area. Loosen the lock nut several turns.

2. With the tools shown in Fig. 19, tighten the adjusting screw until the tool handle clicks. The tool is a pre-set torque wrench which clicks and overruns when the torque on the adjusting screw reaches 10 ft-lbs.

3. Back off the adjusting screw exactly 3 full turns.

4. Hold the adjusting screw from turning and torque the lock nut to specification.

OIL PAN AND CONTROL VALVE BODY REPLACEMENT

1. Raise the car so the transmission oil pan is accessible.

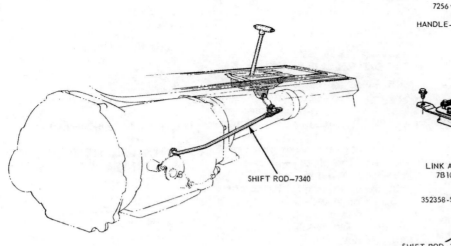

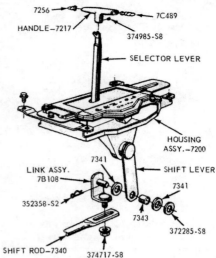

D1577-A

FIG. 16—Manual Linkage—Floor Shift

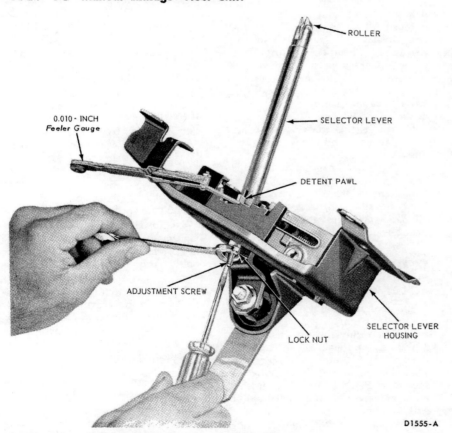

D1555-A

FIG. 17—Adjusting Selector Lever Detent Pawl

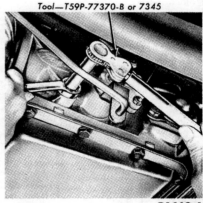

D1460-A

FIG. 18—Adjusting Intermediate Band

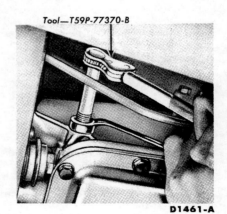

D1461-A

FIG. 19—Adjusting Low-Reverse Band

2. Remove the fluid filler tube from the oil pan, to drain the transmission oil. **If the same fluid is to be used again, filter the fluid through a 100 mesh screen. Re-use the fluid** only if it is in good condition.

3. Remove the transmission oil pan attaching bolts, oil pan and gasket.

4. Remove the valve body-to-case

attaching bolts (Fig. 31). Remove the valve body from the case and the transmission inner control levers.

5. Refer to the Major Repair Operation for control valve body repair operation.

6. Thoroughly clean and remove all the gasket material from the oil pan and the oil pan mounting face of the case. Install the valve body to the case, engaging the transmission inner control levers with the valve body manual and downshift valves.

7. Install the eight valve body to case attaching bolts. Torque the bolts to specification. **Operate the external manual and downshift levers to check for proper travel of the valve body manual and downshift valves.**

8. Place a new gasket on the oil pan. Install the oil pan and 11 attaching bolts. Torque the bolts to specification. Install the oil filler tube. Torque the attaching nut to specifications.

9. Lower the car and fill the transmission with fluid. Check the transmission oil pan area for fluid leakage.

INTERMEDIATE SERVO REPLACEMENT

1. Raise the car and remove the four servo cover-to-case attaching bolts.

2. Remove the servo cover, gasket, piston, and piston return spring. Remove the piston from the cover (Fig. 51).

3. Remove the piston seals and cover gasket.

4. Install new piston seals on the piston. Lubricate the piston seals with clean transmission fluid. Install the servo piston in the cover.

5. Install the piston return spring in the case. Place a new gasket on the cover. Install the piston and cover into the transmission case. Use two $5/16$—18x1¼ bolts, 180° apart to position the cover against the case.

6. Install the two servo cover attaching bolts. Remove the two 1¼-inch bolts and install two attaching bolts. Torque the bolts to specification.

7. Adjust the intermediate band. Lower the car and check the transmission fluid level.

8. If the band can not be adjusted properly, the struts are not in position. Remove the oil pan and valve body. Install the struts, valve body, oil pan, and adjust the band. Refill the transmission with fluid.

LOW-REVERSE SERVO PISTON REPLACEMENT

1. Raise the car and remove the four servo cover to case attaching bolts. Remove the identification tag and vent tube retaining clip. Remove the servo cover from the case.

2. Remove the servo piston from the case. **The piston seal cannot be replaced without replacing the piston. The seal is bonded to the piston.**

3. To remove the piston from the stem, insert a small screw driver in the hole of the piston (Fig. 50). Remove the piston attaching nut.

4. Make sure the spacer (Fig. 49) is positioned on the piston stem. Install a new piston on the piston retaining shaft. Install the attaching nut. Torque the nut to specification.

5. Install the piston into the case. Install a new seal on the cover. Install the cover by using two $5/16$—18 bolts, 1¼ inch long, at 180° apart to position the servo cover on the case. Install the vent tube retaining clip and identification tag. Install two cover attaching bolts. Remove the two installing bolts and install the last two attaching bolts. Torque the cover-to-case attaching bolts to specification.

6. Adjust the low-reverse band. Lower the car and check the transmission fluid level.

7. If the band can not be adjusted properly, the struts are not in position. Remove the oil pan and valve body. Install the struts, valve body, oil pan, and adjust the band. Refill the transmission with fluid.

EXTENSION HOUSING BUSHING AND REAR SEAL REPLACEMENT

1. Disconnect the drive shaft from the transmission.

2. When only the rear seal needs replacing, carefully remove it with a tapered chisel or the tools shown in Fig. 20. Remove the bushing as shown in Fig. 21. **Use the bushing remover carefully so that the spline seal is not damaged.**

3. When installing a new bushing use the special tool shown in Fig. 22.

4. Before installing a new seal, inspect the sealing surface of the universal joint yoke for scores. If scores are found, replace the yoke.

5. Inspect the counterbore of the housing for burrs with crocus cloth.

6. Install the seal into the housing with the tool shown in Fig. 23. The seal should be firmly seated in the bore. Coat the inside diameter of the fiber portion of the seal with B8A-19589-A lubricant.

7. Coat the front universal joint spline with B8A-19589-A lubricant and install the drive shaft.

EXTENSION HOUSING AND GOVERNOR REPLACEMENT

1. Raise the car on the hoist.

2. Remove the drive shaft. Position the transmission jack to support the transmission.

3. Remove the speedometer cable from the extension housing.

4. Remove the extension housing to crossmember mount attaching bolts. Raise the transmission and remove the mounting pad between the extension housing and the crossmember.

5. Loosen the extension housing attaching bolts to drain the transmission fluid. Disconnect the exhaust inlet pipes at the manifold and lower the inlet pipes.

6. Remove the six extension housing-to-case attaching bolts and remove the extension housing.

7. Remove the governor housing to governor distributor attaching bolts (Fig. 24). Remove the governor housing from the distributor.

8. Refer to Major Repair Operations for governor repair operations.

9. Install the governor housing on the governor distributor (Fig. 24). Install the attaching bolts and torque the bolts to specification.

10. Install a new extension housing gasket on the case. Install the extension housing and 6 attaching bolts. Torque the bolts to specification.

11. Install the transmission mounting pad on the crossmember. Lower the transmission and install the extension housing to crossmember attaching bolts. Torque the bolts to specification. Remove the transmission jack.

12. Install the speedometer cable in the extension housing. Install the drive shaft.

13. Install the inlet pipes on the manifold.

14. *Lower the car and fill the transmission with fluid.*

15. Check the extension housing area for fluid leakage.

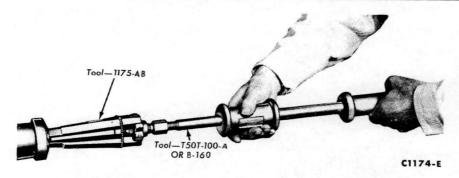

Tool—1175-AB

Tool—T50T-100-A
OR B-160

C1174-E

FIG. 20—Removing Extension Housing Seal

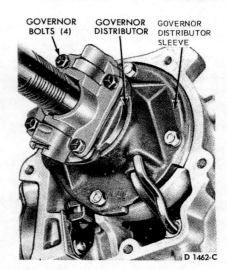

GOVERNOR BOLTS (4)   GOVERNOR DISTRIBUTOR   GOVERNOR DISTRIBUTOR SLEEVE

D 1462-C

FIG. 24—Governor Location

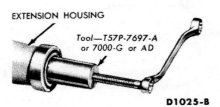

EXTENSION HOUSING

Tool—T57P-7697-A or 7000-G or AD

D1025-B

FIG. 21—Removing Extension Housing Bushing

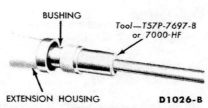

BUSHING

Tool—T57P-7697-B or 7000-HF

EXTENSION HOUSING   D1026-B

FIG. 22—Installing Extension Housing Bushing

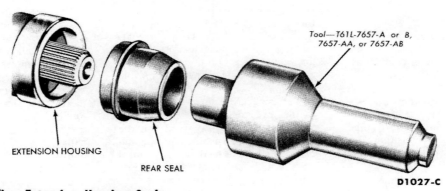

Tool—T61L-7657-A or B, 7657-AA, or 7657-AB

EXTENSION HOUSING

REAR SEAL

D1027-C

FIG. 23—Installing Extension Housing Seal

3   REMOVAL AND INSTALLATION

REMOVAL

1. Before the car is raised, disconnect the neutral start switch wires located in the engine compartment area (Fig. 25). Raise the car and remove the three converter cover attaching bolts, at the lower front side of the converter housing. Remove the cover.

2. Remove the two converter drain plugs (Fig. 26). Drain the fluid from the converter. Install the two converter drain plugs.

3. Remove the drive shaft and install the extension housing seal replacer tool in the extension housing.

4. Remove the vacuum line hose from the transmission vacuum unit.

Disconnect the vacuum line from the attaching clip.

5. Remove the two extension housing-to-crossmember attaching bolts.

6. Remove the speedometer cable from the extension housing.

7. Disconnect the exhaust pipe flange from the manifolds.

8. Remove the parking brake cable from the equalizer lever.

9. Remove the fluid filler tube from the oil pan and drain the transmission fluid.

10. Disconnect the fluid cooler lines from the transmission case.

11. Remove the manual and kickdown linkage rods from the transmission control levers.

12. Disconnect the neutral start switch wires from the retaining clips.

13. Disconnect the starter cable. Remove the starter attaching bolts and remove the starter from the converter housing.

14. Remove the four converter-to-flywheel attaching nuts.

15. Position the transmission jack to support the transmission and secure the transmission to the jack with a safety chain.

16. Remove the four crossmember attaching bolts and lower the crossmember.

17. Remove the five converter housing-to-engine attaching bolts. Lower the transmission (Fig. 27) and remove it from under the car.

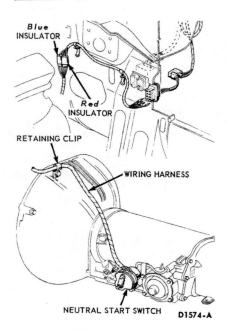

FIG. 25—Neutral Start
Switch Wiring Connection—
Ford

INSTALLATION

1. With the converter properly installed, place the transmission on the jack (Fig. 27). Secure the transmission to the jack with the safety chain.

2. Raise the transmission into position and install the five converter housing-to-engine attaching bolts. Torque the bolts to specification. Remove the safety chain from the transmission.

3. Position the crossmember and install the four attaching bolts.

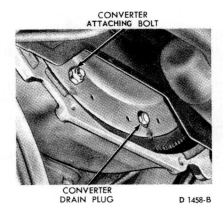

FIG. 26—Converter Drain
Plug Location

Torque the bolts to specifications.

4. Lower the transmission and install the extension housing and crossmember attaching bolts. Torque the bolts to specification.

5. Install the four flywheel to converter attaching nuts. Torque the nuts to specification.

6. Remove the transmission jack. Install the fluid filler tube in the transmission oil pan. Torque the attaching nut to specification. Install the vacuum hose on the transmission vacuum unit. Install the vacuum line retaining clip.

7. Connect the fluid cooling lines to the transmission case.

8. Install the linkage rods on the transmission downshift and manual control levers. Position the neutral start switch wires in the retaining clips.

9. Connect the speedometer ca-

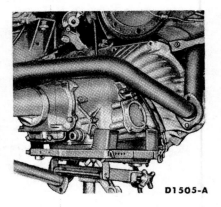

FIG. 27—Transmission
Mounted on Jack

ble to the extension housing.

10. Connect the exhaust inlet pipes to the manifolds.

11. Install and adjust the parking brake cable at the equalizer lever.

12. Install the converter housing cover and torque the attaching bolts to specification.

13. Install the starter and torque the attaching bolts to specification. Connect the starter cable.

14. Install the drive shaft. Torque the companion flange U-bolts attaching nuts to specification.

15. Lower the car and connect the neutral start switch wires at the multiple connectors (Fig. 25). Fill the transmission to the proper level with the specified fluid. Adjust the manual and downshift linkage.

16. Check the operation of the neutral start switch. If required adjust the switch as shown in Fig. 15.

4 MAJOR REPAIR OPERATIONS

Before removing any of the subassemblies, thoroughly clean the outside of the transmission to prevent dirt from entering the mechanical parts. During the repair operations, refer to Part 7-1 for common adjustments and repairs or cleaning and inspection procedures.

During the transmission disassembly or assembly operations, ten thrust washers located between the sub-assemblies must be removed and installed. It is important that each thrust washer be in the correct position during the assembly operation. To properly locate and identify the thrust washers, the various positions of the thrust washers are shown in

the illustrations and are numbered 1 through 10. No. 1 is at the first thrust washer located at the front pump. The last thrust washer, No. 10, is located at the parking pawl ring gear.

DISASSEMBLY OF TRANSMISSION

1. Remove the converter from the transmission front pump and converter housing.

2. Remove the transmission vacuum unit with the tool shown in Fig. 28.

Remove the vacuum unit gasket and the control rod.

3. Remove the primary throttle valve (Fig. 29) from the opening at the rear of the case.

4. Remove the two extension housing-to-case bolts shown in Fig. 30 and mount the transmission in the holding fixture.

5. Remove the oil pan attaching bolts, oil pan and gasket.

6. Remove the control valve body attaching bolts (Fig. 31). Remove the control valve body from the case.

7. Loosen the intermediate band adjusting screw (Fig. 32) and remove the intermediate band struts from the case. Loosen the low-reverse band adjusting screw and remove the low-reverse band struts.

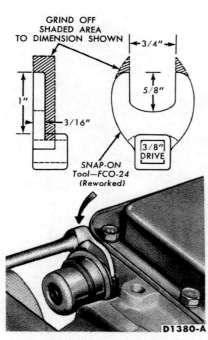

FIG. 28—Removing Vacuum Unit

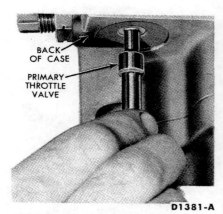

FIG. 29—Removing or Installing Primary Throttle Valve

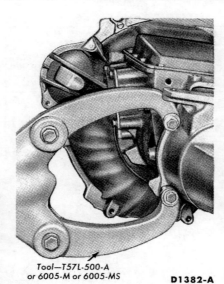

FIG. 30—Transmission Mounted in Holding Fixture

FIG. 31—Control Valve Body Attaching Bolts

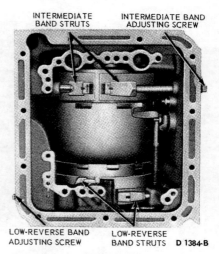

FIG. 32—Band Adjusting Screws and Struts—Typical

FIG. 33—Checking End Play

TRANSMISSION END PLAY CHECK

1. To keep the output shaft in alignment during the end play check, install the extension housing oil seal replacer tool or a front universal joint yoke in the extension housing.

2. Remove one of the converter housing-to-case attaching bolts and mount the dial indicator as shown in Fig. 33.

3. **The input shaft is a loose part and has to be properly engaged with the spline of the forward clutch hub during the end play checking procedure.** Move the input shaft and gear

train toward the rear of the transmission case.

4. With the dial indicator contacting the end of the input shaft, set the indicator at zero (Fig. 33).

5. Insert a screwdriver behind the input shell (Fig. 33). Move the input shell and the front part of the gear train forward.

6. Record the dial indicator reading. The end play should be 0.008 to 0.042 inch. If the end play is not within specification, the selective thrust washer (Fig. 34) must be replaced as required. The selective thrust washers can be replaced individually to obtain the specified end play.

7. Remove the dial indicator and remove the input shaft from the

front pump stator support (Fig. 33).

REMOVAL OF CASE AND EXTENSION HOUSING PARTS

1. Rotate the holding fixture to put the transmission in a vertical position with the converter housing up.

2. Remove the five converter housing-to-case attaching bolts (Fig. 35). Remove the converter housing from the transmission case.

3. Remove the seven front pump attaching bolts. Remove the front pump by inserting a screwdriver behind the input shell (Fig. 36). Move the input shell forward until the front pump seal is above the edge of the case.

Remove the front pump and gasket from the case. If the selective thrust washer No. 1 did not come out with

SELECTIVE THRUST WASHERS *

WASHER NO. 1 (FIBER)		WASHER NO. 2 (STEEL-BACK BRONZE)	
THICKNESS (INCHES)	IDENTIFICATION (DYE-COLOR)	THICKNESS (INCHES)	IDENTIFICATION (STAMPED NO.)
0.038-.042	GREEN	0.041-.043	1
0.053-.057	TAN	0.053-.056	2
0.070-.074	BLACK	0.073-.075	3
0.087-.091	YELLOW	0.090-.092	4
0.104-.108	BLUE	0.107-.109	5
0.121-0.125	RED		
0.138-0.142	PURPLE		

* SELECTION IN PAIRS NOT APPLICABLE

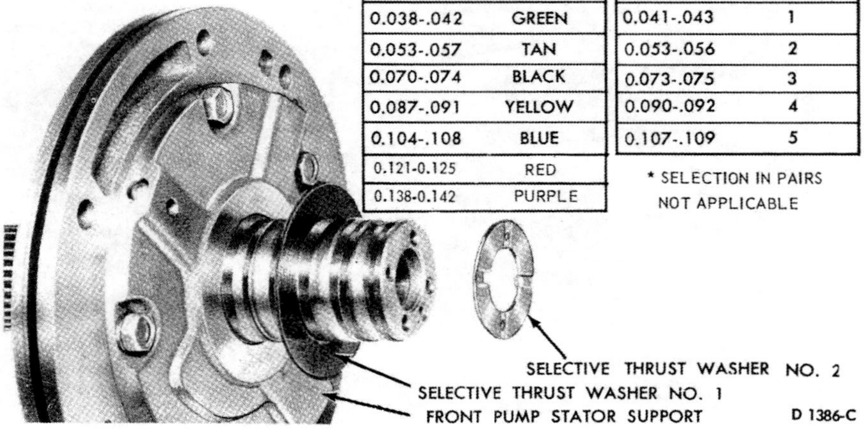

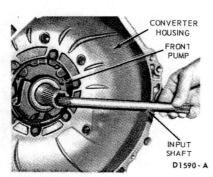

SELECTIVE THRUST WASHER NO. 2
SELECTIVE THRUST WASHER NO. 1
FRONT PUMP STATOR SUPPORT   D 1386-C

FIG. 34—Selective Thrust Washer Locations

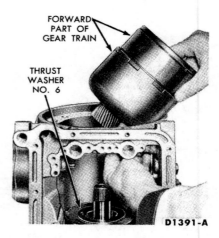

FORWARD PART OF GEAR TRAIN

THRUST WASHER NO. 6

D1391-A

FIG. 39—Removing or Installing Forward Part of Gear Train

6. Place the forward part of the gear train in the holding fixture shown in Fig. 40.

CONVERTER HOUSING
FRONT PUMP
INPUT SHAFT
D1590-A

FIG. 35—Removing or Installing Input Shaft

the clearance hole in the case (Fig. 37). Remove the intermediate band from the case.

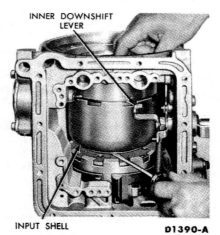

INTERMEDIATE BAND CLEARANCE HOLE IN CASE   D1389-A

FIG. 37—Position of Intermediate Band for Removal or Installation

5. Using a screwdriver between the input shell and rear planet carrier (Fig. 38), lift the input shell upward and remove the forward part

FORWARD GEAR TRAIN ASSEMBLY

Holding Fixture Tool—77530-A   D1392-A

FIG. 40—Forward Part of Gear Train Positioned in Holding Fixture

7. From the gear train in the holding fixture, remove the reverse-high clutch and drum from the forward clutch (Fig. 41).

8. If thrust washer No. 2 (Fig. 34) did not come out with the front pump, remove the thrust washer from the forward clutch cylinder. Remove the forward clutch from the forward clutch hub and ring gear (Fig. 41)

9. If thrust washer No. 3 (Fig. 41) did not come out with the forward clutch, remove the thrust washer from the forward clutch hub.

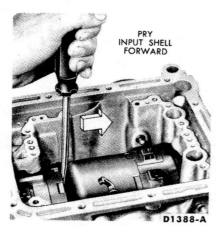

PRY INPUT SHELL FORWARD

D1388-A

FIG. 36—Removing Front Pump

the front pump, remove it from the top of the reverse-high clutch.

4. Remove the intermediate and low-reverse band adjusting screws from the case. Rotate the intermediate band to align the band ends with

of the gear train as an assembly (Fig. 39).

INNER DOWNSHIFT LEVER

INPUT SHELL   D1390-A

FIG. 38—Lifting Input Shell and Gear Train

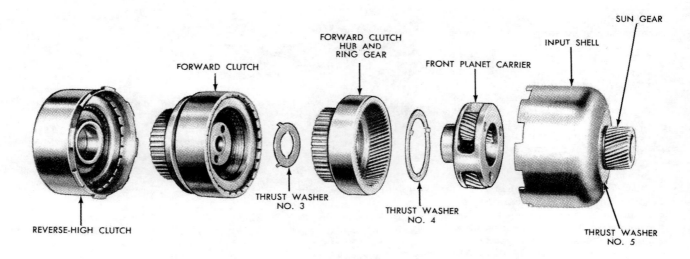

FORWARD CLUTCH

FORWARD CLUTCH HUB AND RING GEAR

FRONT PLANET CARRIER

INPUT SHELL

SUN GEAR

REVERSE-HIGH CLUTCH

THRUST WASHER NO. 3

THRUST WASHER NO. 4

THRUST WASHER NO. 5

D1393-A

FIG. 41—Forward Part of Gear Train Disassembled

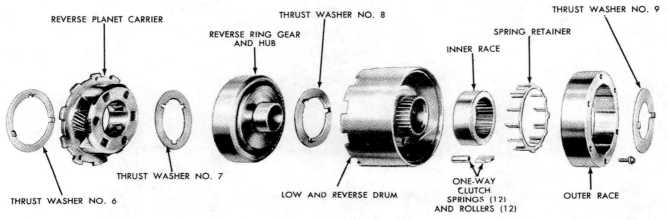

REVERSE PLANET CARRIER

THRUST WASHER NO. 8

THRUST WASHER NO. 9

REVERSE RING GEAR AND HUB

SPRING RETAINER

INNER RACE

THRUST WASHER NO. 7

THRUST WASHER NO. 6

LOW AND REVERSE DRUM

ONE-WAY CLUTCH SPRINGS (12) AND ROLLERS (12)

OUTER RACE

D1394-A

FIG. 42—Lower Part of Gear Train Disassembled

10. Remove the forward clutch hub and ring gear from the front planet carrier (Fig. 41).

11. Remove thrust washer No. 4 and the front planet carrier from the input shell.

12. Remove the input shell, sun gear and thrust washer No. 5 from the holding fixture.

13. From inside the transmission case (Fig. 39) remove thrust washer No. 6 from the top of the reverse planet carrier.

14. Remove the reverse planet carrier and thrust washer No. 7 from the reverse ring gear and hub (Fig. 42).

15. Move the output shaft forward and with the tool shown in Fig. 43, remove the reverse ring

REVERSE RING GEAR HUB RETAINING RING

D1395-A

FIG. 43—Removing or Installing Reverse Ring Gear Hub Retaining Ring

gear hub-to-output shaft retaining ring.

16. Remove the reverse ring gear and hub from the output shaft. Remove thrust washer No. 8 from the low and reverse drum.

17. Remove the low-reverse band from the case (Fig. 44).

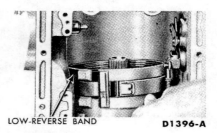

LOW-REVERSE BAND

D1396-A

FIG. 44—Removing or Installing Low-Reverse Band

18. Remove the low-reverse drum

from the one-way clutch inner race (Fig. 42).

19. Remove the one-way clutch inner race by rotating the race clockwise as it is removed.

20. Remove the 12 one-way clutch rollers, springs and the spring retainer from the outer race (Fig. 42). **Do not lose or damage any of the 12 springs or rollers. The outer race of the one-way clutch cannot be removed from the case until the extension housing, output shaft and governor distributor sleeve are removed.**

21. Remove the transmission from the holding fixture. Position the transmission on the bench in a vertical position with the extension housing up. Remove the four extension housing-to-case attaching bolts. Remove the extension housing and gasket from the case.

22. Pull outward on the output shaft and remove the output shaft and governor distributor assembly from the governor distributor sleeve (Fig. 45).

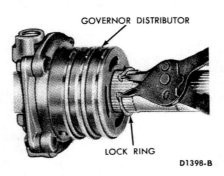

FIG. 46—Removing or Installing Governor Distributor Snap Ring

24. Remove the four distributor sleeve-to-case attaching bolts. Remove the distributor sleeve from the case. **Do not bend or distort the oil tubes as the tubes are removed from the case with the distributor sleeve.**

25. Remove the parking pawl return spring, pawl, and pawl retaining pin from the case (Fig. 47).

FIG. 48—Removing One-Way Clutch Outer Race Attaching Bolts

semblies, certain general instructions which apply to all units of the transmissions must be followed. These instructions are given here to avoid

FIG. 45—Removing or Installing Output Shaft and Governor Distributor

23. Remove the governor distributor lock ring from the output shaft (Fig. 46). Remove the governor distributor from the output shaft.

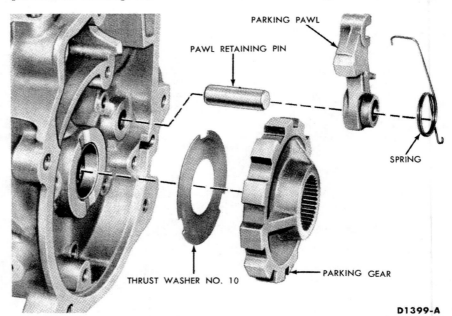

FIG. 47—Parking Pawl, Return Spring Retaining Pin and Gear

26. Remove the parking gear and thrust washer No. 10 from the case.

27. Remove the six one-way clutch outer race-to-case attaching bolts with the tool shown in Fig. 48. As the bolts are removed, hold the outer race located inside the case in position. Remove the outer race and thrust washer No. 9 from the case (Fig. 42).

PARTS REPAIR OR REPLACEMENT

During the repair of the sub-as-

unnecessary repetition.

Handle all transmission parts carefully to avoid nicking or burring the bearing or mating surfaces.

Lubricate all internal parts of the transmission before assembly with clean automatic transmission fluid. **Do not use any other lubricants except on gaskets and thrust washers which may be coated with vaseline to facilitate assembly.** Always install new gaskets when assembling the transmission.

Tighten all bolts and screws to the

recommended torque as outlined in the Specification Section.

TRANSMISSION CASE AND LINKAGE REPAIR

Low-Reverse Servo

1. Remove the four servo cover-to-case attaching bolts. Remove the transmission identification tag, vent tube and retaining clip from the case.

2. Remove the servo cover, cover seal, servo piston and piston return spring from the case (Fig. 49).

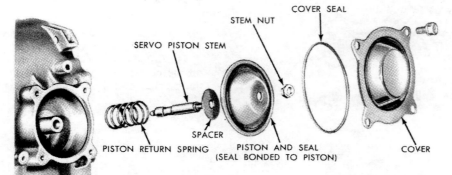

FIG. 49—Low-Reverse Servo

3. The servo piston seal is bonded to the piston. If the seal has to be replaced, replace the piston assembly which includes the seal. Disassemble the servo piston from the piston rod by inserting a small screwdriver in the hole of the piston rod and removing the piston attaching nut (Fig. 50).

FIG. 50—Removing or Installing Low-Reverse Servo Piston

Position the spacer (Fig. 49) on the stem. Install the new servo piston and attaching nut on the stem, torque the nut to specification.

4. Place the piston return spring

in the servo bore of the case. Lubricate the piston seal with clean transmission fluid and install the servo piston into the bore of the case.

5. Place a new cover seal on the cover and install the servo cover. Install the identification tag and the vent tube and retaining clip. Install the four cover attaching bolts. Torque the cover-to-case retaining bolts to specifications.

Intermediate Servo

1. Remove the four servo cover to case attaching bolts.

2. Remove the servo cover, gasket, servo piston, and piston return spring from the case (Fig. 51).

3. On a transmission used with a six-cylinder engine remove the intermediate servo piston from the cover by inserting air pressure into the pressure hole in the cover (Fig. 52).

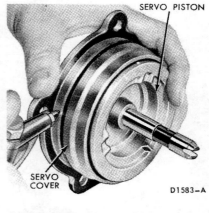

FIG. 52—Removing Intermediate Servo Piston 6-Cylinder Engine

4. Remove the seal rings from the servo piston and cover.

5. Install a new seal on the cover and servo piston. Figure 53 shows the correct servo piston and cover for each transmission model. Lubricate the seals with clean transmission fluid. Install the piston into the cover. Be careful not to damage the piston seal.

6. Install the piston return spring in the servo bore of the case.

7. Place a new gasket on the servo cover. Position the servo piston and cover assembly into the case

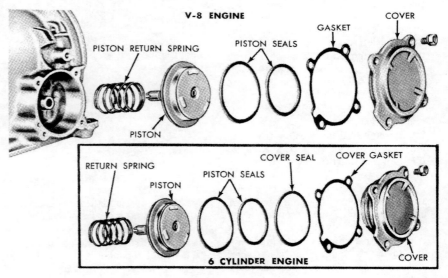

FIG. 51—Intermediate Servo Disassembled

with the piston stem slot in a horizontal position to engage the strut. Use two $5/16$-18 bolts, $1\frac{1}{4}$ inch long, 180° apart, to position the cover against the case. Install two cover attaching bolts. Remove the two $1\frac{1}{4}$

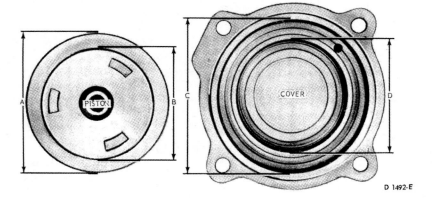

MAKE OF CAR	ENGINE	TRANSMISSION MODEL	SERVO PISTON		SERVO COVER	
			DIAMETER A	DIAMETER B	DIAMETER C	DIAMETER D
FORD	240-1V	PCV-E	3.7875	2.7065	NOT APPLICABLE	2.720
FORD	289-2V	PCW-AV: &AW	3.7875	2.8265	NOT APPLICABLE	2.840
FORD-POLICE & TAXI	289-2V & 240-1V	PDA-D	3.7875	3.1175	NOT APPLICABLE	3.131

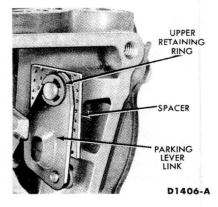

FIG. 55—Parking Pawl Link

gle rod and link assembly into the case (Fig. 56).

11. Install the parking pawl link on the case retaining pin. Install the flat washer and link retaining ring (Fig. 55).

FIG. 53—Intermediate Servo Piston and Cover Identification

inch bolts and install the other two cover attaching bolts. Torque the bolts to specification.

Downshift and Manual Linkage

1. Apply penetrating oil to the outer lever attaching nut to prevent breaking the inner lever shaft. Remove the downshift outer lever nut. Remove the downshift outer and inner levers. Remove the switch by placing a screwdriver behind the switch and carefully prying the switch off the lever. From inside the transmission case, remove the upper retaining ring and flat washer from the manual lever link (Fig. 54). Remove the upper end of the lever link from the case retaining pin.

2. From the back of the transmission case, remove the upper retaining ring and flat washer from the parking pawl link (Fig. 55). Remove the pawl link from the case retaining pin.

3. From the back of the transmission case, remove the parking pawl link, toggle rod, and manual lever link as an assembly (Fig. 56).

4. Remove the rear parking pawl link lower *retaining ring*, flat washer and link from the toggle rod (Fig. 57).

5. Remove the manual lever link, lower retaining ring, flat washer, and link from the toggle rod.

6. Install the manual and parking pawl links, flat washers and retaining rings to the toggle rods.

7. Remove the inner manual lever

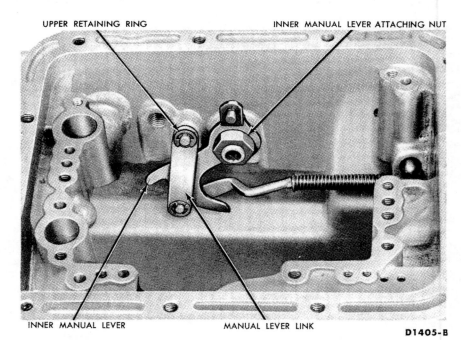

FIG. 54—Case Internal Linkage

attaching nut and lever. Remove the outer manual lever from the case.

8. To remove the manual lever seal, use the tools shown in Fig. 58. To install the new seal, use a driver that fits the ID of the seal.

9. Install the outer manual lever in the case. Install the inner manual lever and attaching nut with the chamfer facing toward the lever (Fig. 54). Torque the nut to specification.

10. From the back of the transmission case, install the parking tog-

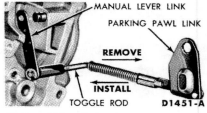

FIG. 56—Removing or Installing Parking Pawl Link

12. Position the inner manual lever behind the manual lever link,

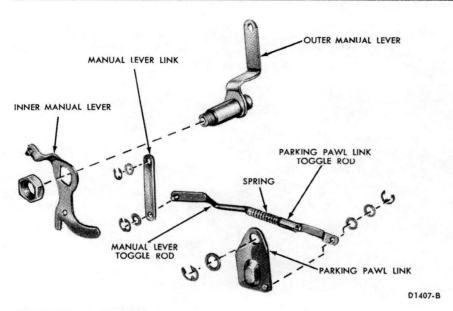

FIG. 57—Case Linkage

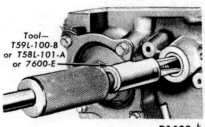

FIG. 58—Removing Manual Lever Seal

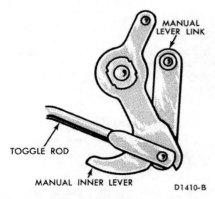

FIG. 59—Inner Manual Lever Location—As Viewed from the Control Lever Side of Case

13. Install the upper end of the manual lever link on the case retaining pin. Install the flat washer and retaining ring.

14. Operate the manual lever and check for correct linkage operation.

15. Install the neutral start switch.

Adjust the neutral safety switch after the main control valve body has been installed.

16. Install the inner and outer downshift levers. Torque the attaching nut to specification.

Thread Repair-Case

Thread service kits may be purchased from local jobbers or the Heli-Coil Corporation. To repair a damaged thread, the following procedures should be carefully followed.

1. Drill out the damaged threads, **using the same drill size as the thread OD.** For example, use a $5/16$-inch drill for a $5/16$-18 thread.

2. Select the proper **special** tap and tap the drilled hole. The tap is marked for the size of the thread being repaired. Thus, the special tap marked $5/16$-18 will not cut the same thread as a standard $5/16$-18 tap. It does cut a thread large enough to accommodate the insert, and after the insert is installed the original thread size ($5/16$-18) is restored.

3. Select the proper coil inserting tool. These tools are marked with the thread size being repaired. Place the insert on the tool and adjust the sleeve to the length of the insert being used.

Press the insert against the face of the tapped hole. Turn the tool clockwise and wind the insert into the hole until the insert is $1/2$ turn below the face.

4. Working through the insert, bend the insert tang straight up and down until it breaks off at the notch.

5. If the inserts are not properly

installed, they can be removed with the extractor tool. Place the extractor tool in the insert so that the blade rests against the top coil $1/4$ to $1/2$ turn away from the end of the coil. Tap the tool sharply with a hammer so that the blade cuts into the insert. Exert downward pressure on the tool and turn it counterclockwise until the insert is removed.

CONTROL VALVE BODY

Disassembly

1. Remove the screws that attach the oil screen to the body and remove the screen (Fig. 60).

2. Remove the attaching screws from the underside of the lower valve body. Separate the lower valve body, gasket, separator plate and hold-down plates (Fig. 61) from the upper valve body.

3. Depress the manual valve detent spring with the tool shown in Fig. 62. Remove the spring retaining pin (roll pin) from the upper valve body. Remove the spring and detent plunger.

4. Slide the manual valve out of the body.

5. Remove the cut-back and the back-out valve cover plate from the valve body (Fig. 63).

6. Remove the cut-back valve from the body.

7. Remove the 2-3 back-out valve, spring and the manual low valve from the body.

8. Remove the 1-2 shift valve and the 2-3 shift valve cover plate from the valve body.

9. Remove the 2-3 shift valve and the throttle modulator valve from the body.

10. Remove the 1-2 shift valve, D2 valve and the spring from the body.

11. Remove the intermediate band accumulator valve cover plate from the valve body.

12. Remove the spring and the intermediate band accumulator valve.

13. Remove the pressure booster valve cover plate (Fig. 63).

14. Remove the pressure booster valve, sleeve, washer, springs and the main regulator valve.

15. Carefully pry the downshift valve retainer from the body, then remove the spring and valve.

16. Hold the upper valve body as shown in Fig. 64 and depress the throttle booster valve plug to release the retaining pin. Remove the plug, valve and the spring.

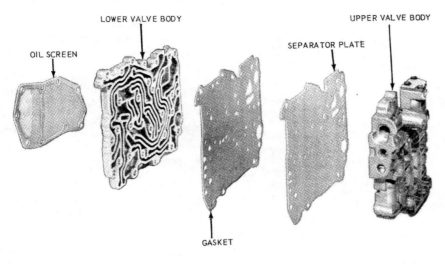

FIG. 60—Upper and Lower Valve Bodies Disassembled

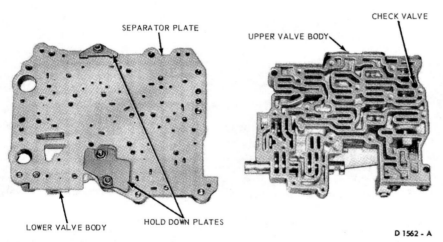

FIG. 61—Separating Upper and Lower Valve Bodies

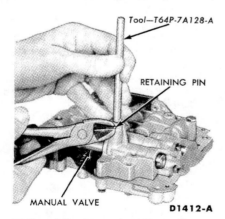

FIG. 62—Removing Manual Valve

17. Remove the two hold-down plates and the separator plate from the lower valve body.

Assembly

1. Position the separator plate and the two hold-down plates on the lower valve body and install the four attaching screws and torque them to specification.

2. Place the throttle booster valve spring, valve (long end into spring) and the plug (Fig. 64). Depress the plug and install the retaining pin.

3. Insert the downshift valve into the body with the large diameter facing inward. Install the downshift valve spring and the retainer (Fig. 63).

4. Place the main regulator valve in the body (Fig. 63) with the large diameter facing inward. Install the two springs, spacer, pressure booster valve and the sleeve.

5. Hold the pressure booster valve and the cover plate in place and in-

stall the three attaching screws and torque them to specification.

6. Position the intermediate band accumulator valve and spring in the body. Secure the cover to the body with the attaching screw. Torque the screw to specifications.

7. Position the spring, D2 valve and the 1-2 shift valve in the body.

8. Place the throttle modulator valve, spring, and 2-3 shift valve in the body.

9. Secure the 1-2 shift valve and the 2-3 valve cover plate to the body and torque the screws to specifications.

10. Place the manual low valve, spring, and the 2-3 back-out valve in the body.

11. Place the cut-back valve in the body.

12. Secure the cut-back and the back-out cover plate to the body with two screws. Torque the screws to specifications.

13. Slide the manual valve into the body making sure that the notch for the manual lever is toward the inside and that the detent notches are facing upward.

14. Place the detent plunger and spring in the body. Depress the spring and install a new roll pin.

15. Position a new rubber check valve in the upper valve body (Fig. 61).

16. Place a new gasket, separator plate and the lower valve body in place on the upper valve body and secure them with the attaching screws. Torque the screws to specifications.

17. Secure the oil screen to the body with the attaching screws. Torque the screws to specifications.

FRONT PUMP

Disassembly

1. Remove the four seal rings from stator support and the O-ring seal from the pump housing.

2. Remove the five bolts that attach the stator support to the front pump housing. Remove the stator support from the pump housing (Fig. 65).

3. Remove the drive and driven gears from the front pump housing.

Assembly

1. Install the drive and driven gears in the pump housing. Each gear has an identification mark on the side of the gear teeth that are chamfered. **The chamfered side with the identification mark has to be po-**

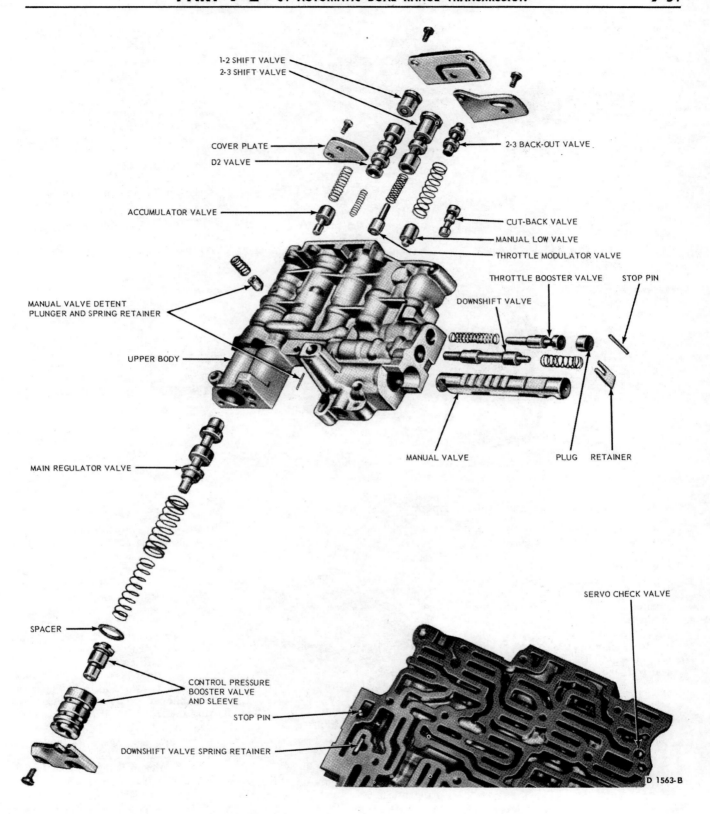

FIG. 63 —Upper Valve Body Disassembled

sitioned **downward against the face of the pump housing.**

2. Place the stator support in the

pump housing and install the five attaching bolts. Torque the bolts to specifications.

3. Install the four seal rings on the stator support. The two large oil rings are assembled first in the oil

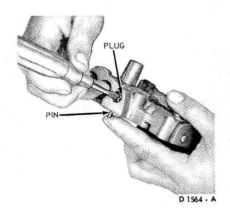

FIG. 64—Removing or Installing Throttle Booster Valve

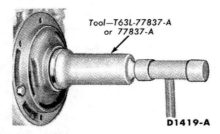

FIG. 67—Installing Front Pump Seal

REVERSE-HIGH CLUTCH

Disassembly

1. Remove the pressure plate retaining snap ring (Fig. 68).

2. Remove the pressure plate, and

tools shown in Fig. 70, compress the piston return springs and remove the snap ring. When the arbor press ram is released, guide the spring retainer to clear the snap ring groove of the drum.

4. Remove the spring retainer and 10 piston return springs.

5. Remove the piston by inserting air pressure in the piston apply hole of the clutch hub (Fig. 71).

6. Remove the piston outer seal from the piston and the piston inner seal from the clutch drum (Fig. 69).

Assembly

1. Install a new inner seal in the clutch drum and a new outer seal on the clutch piston. Lubricate the

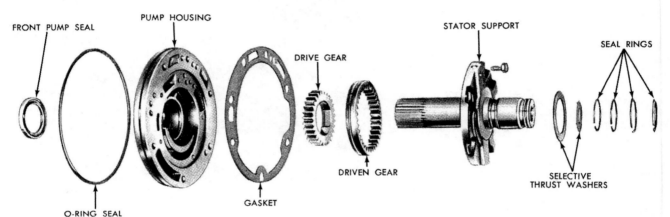

FIG. 65—Front Pump and Stator Support Disassembled

ring grooves toward the front of the stator support. Install the O-ring seal on the pump housing.

4. Check the pump gears for free rotation by placing the pump on the converter drive hub in its normal running position and turning the pump housing.

5. If the front pump seal must be replaced, mount the pump in the transmission case and remove the seal with the tool shown in Fig. 66.

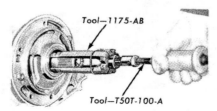

FIG. 66—Removing Front Pump Seal

To install the new seal, use the tool shown in Fig. 67.

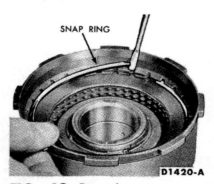

FIG. 68—Removing or Installing Reverse-High Pressure Plate Snap Ring

the drive and driven clutch plates (Fig. 69). If the composition clutch plates are to be reused, do not clean them in a vapor degreaser or with a detergent solution. Wipe the plates with a lint-free cloth.

3. To remove the piston spring retainer snap ring, place the clutch hub in the arbor press. With the

seals with clean transmission fluid and install the piston into the clutch drum.

2. Place the 10 clutch piston springs into position on the clutch piston. Place the spring retainer on top of the springs. To install the snap ring use the tools shown in Fig. 70.

As the press ram is moved downward, make sure the spring retainer is centered to clear the drum. Install the snap ring. **Before the press ram is released make sure the snap ring is positioned inside of the four snap ring guides on the spring retainer.**

3. When new composition clutch plates are used, soak the plates in transmission fluid for fifteen minutes before installing them. Install the clutch plates alternately starting with a steel plate, then a non-metallic plate (Fig. 69). The last plate installed is the pressure plate. For the correct number of clutch plates required for each transmission model, refer to Part 7-5.

4. Install the pressure plate re-

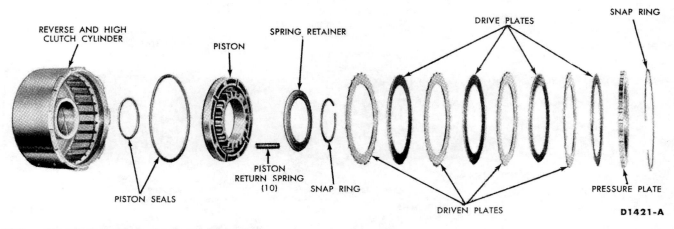

FIG. 69—Reverse-High Clutch Disassembled

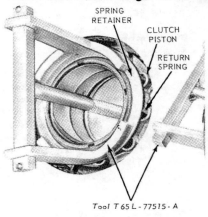

FIG. 70—Removing or Installing Reverse-High Clutch Piston Spring Snap Ring

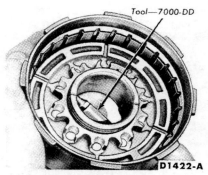

FIG. 71—Removing Reverse-High Clutch Piston

taining snap ring (Fig. 69). Make sure the snap ring is fully seated in the snap ring groove of the clutch hub.

5. With a feeler gauge, check the clearance between the snap ring and the pressure plate (Fig. 72).

6. The pressure plate should be held downward as the clearance is

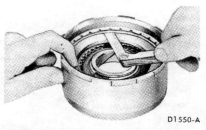

FIG. 72—Checking Reverse-High Clutch Snap Ring Clearance

checked. The clearance should be 0.050 to 0.066 inch. If the clearance is not within specifications, selective thickness snap rings are available in these thicknesses, 0.088-0.092, 0.074-0.078, 0.060-0.064 and 0.102-0.106 inch. Install the correct size snap ring and recheck the clearance.

FORWARD CLUTCH

Disassembly

1. Remove the clutch pressure plate retaining snap ring (Fig. 73).

2. Remove the pressure plate, and the drive and driven clutch plates from the clutch hub (Fig. 74).

3. Remove the disc spring retaining snap ring (Fig. 75).

4. Apply air pressure at the clutch piston pressure hole (Fig. 76) to remove the piston from the clutch hub.

5. Remove the clutch piston outer seal and the inner seal from the clutch hub (Fig. 74).

6. Install new clutch piston seals on the clutch piston and drum. Lubricate the seals with clean transmission fluid.

7. Install the clutch piston into the clutch hub. Install the disc

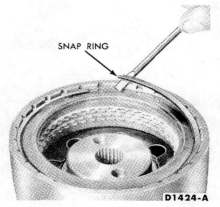

FIG. 73—Removing or Installing Forward Clutch Pressure Plate Snap Ring

spring and retaining snap ring (Fig. 74).

8. **Install the lower pressure plate with the flat side up and radius side downward.** Install one non-metallic clutch plate and alternately install the drive and driven plates. The last plate installed will be the upper pressure plate. Refer to Part 7-5 for the correct number of clutch plates for the applicable model transmission.

9. Install the pressure plate retaining snap ring (Fig. 74). Make sure the snap ring is fully seated in the ring groove of the clutch hub.

10. With a feeler gauge, check the clearance between the snap ring and the pressure plate (Fig. 77). Downward pressure on the plate should be used when making this check. The clearance should be 0.028 to 0.050 inch.

11. If the clearance is not within specifications, selective snap rings are available in these thicknesses: 0.088-0.092, 0.074-0.078, 0.060-

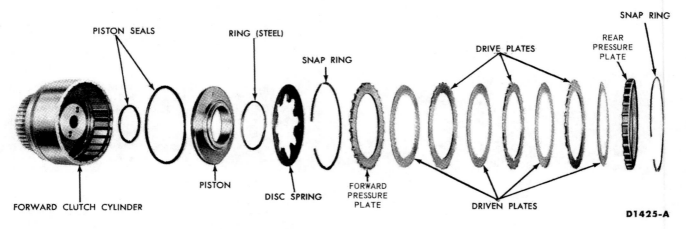

FIG. 74—Forward Clutch Disassembled

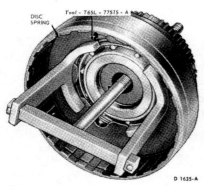

FIG. 75—Removing Disc Spring

FIG. 76—Removing Forward Clutch Piston

0.064 and 0.102-0.106 inch. Insert the correct size snap ring and re-check the clearance.

FORWARD CLUTCH HUB AND RING GEAR

Disassembly

1. Remove the forward clutch hub retaining snap ring (Fig. 78).

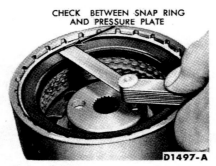

FIG. 77—Checking Forward Clutch Snap Ring Clearance

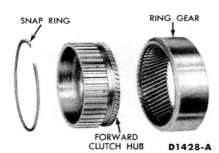

FIG. 78—Forward Clutch Hub and Ring Gear Disassembled

2. Remove the forward clutch hub from the ring gear.

Assembly

1. Install the forward clutch hub in the ring gear. Make sure the hub is bottomed in the groove of the ring gear.

2. Install the front clutch hub retaining snap ring. Make sure the snap ring is fully seated in the snap ring groove of the ring gear.

INPUT SHELL AND SUN GEAR

Disassembly

1. Remove the external snap ring from the sun gear (Fig. 79).

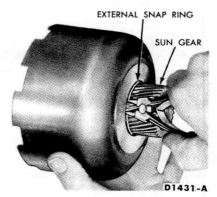

FIG. 79—Removing or Installing Sun Gear External Snap Ring

2. Remove thrust washer No. 5 from the input shell and sun gear (Fig. 80).

3. From inside the input shell, remove the sun gear. Remove the internal snap ring from the sun gear.

Assembly

1. Install the internal snap ring on the sun gear. Install the sun gear in the input shell.

2. Install thrust washer No. 5 on the sun gear and input shell (Fig. 80).

3. Install the external snap ring on the sun gear (Fig. 79).

REVERSE RING GEAR AND HUB

Disassembly

1. Remove the hub retaining snap ring from the reverse ring gear.

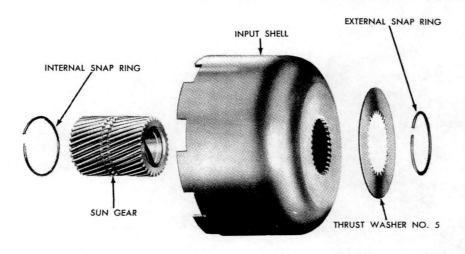

FIG. 80—Input Shell and Sun Gear Disassembled

2. Remove the hub from the reverse ring gear (Fig. 81).

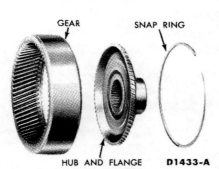

FIG. 81—Reverse Ring Gear and Hub Disassembled

Assembly

1. Install the hub in the reverse ring gear. Make sure the hub is fully seated in the groove of the ring gear.

2. Install the snap ring in the reverse ring gear. Make sure the snap ring is fully seated in the snap ring groove of the ring gear.

GOVERNOR AND OIL DISTRIBUTOR

Disassembly

1. Remove the oil rings from the governor oil distributor (Fig. 82).

2. Remove the governor housing-to-distributor attaching bolts. Remove the governor from the oil distributor.

3. Remove the primary governor valve retaining ring (Fig. 83). Remove the washer, spring, and primary governor valve from the housing.

4. Remove the secondary gov-

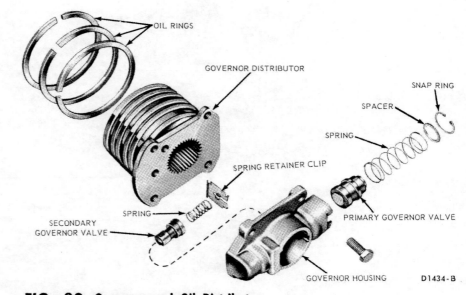

FIG. 82—Governor and Oil Distributor

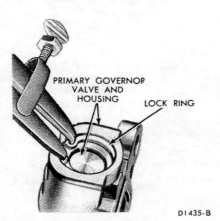

FIG. 83—Removing or Installing Retaining Ring

ernor valve spring retaining clip, spring, and governor valve from the housing.

5. Install the secondary governor valve in the housing. Install the spring and retaining clip. **Make sure the clip is installed with the small concaved area facing downward, to hold the spring in the correct position.**

Assembly

1. Install the primary governor valve in the housing. Install the spring, washer and retaining ring. **Make sure the washer is centered in the housing on top of the spring and the retaining ring is fully seated in the ring groove of the housing.**

2. Install the governor assembly on the oil distributor and torque the attaching bolts to specification.

3. Install the oil rings on the distributor. Check the oil rings for free rotation in the ring grooves of the oil distributor.

ASSEMBLY OF TRANSMISSION

When assembling the transmission sub-assemblies (Fig. 84), make sure that the correct thrust washer is used between certain sub-assemblies. Lubricate all mating surfaces with transmission fluid. Vaseline should be used to hold the thrust washers in their proper location. If the end play is not within specifications after the transmission is assembled, either the wrong selective thrust washers were

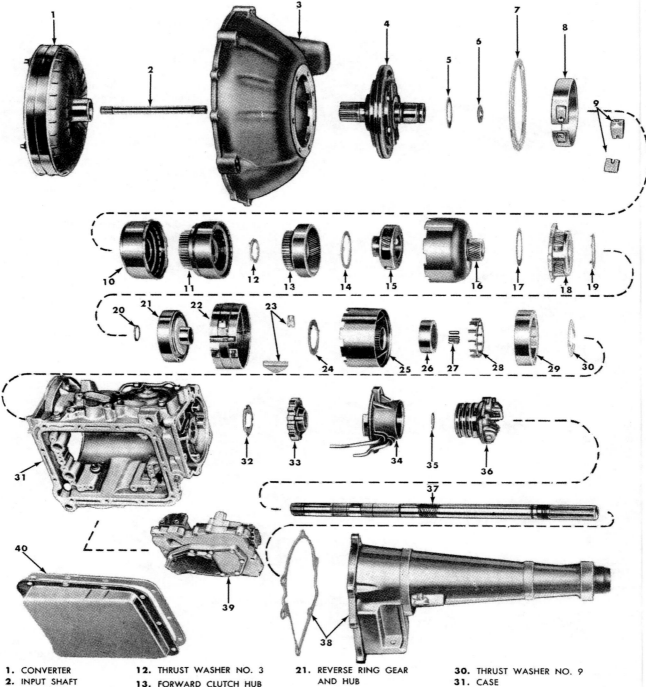

1. CONVERTER
2. INPUT SHAFT
3. CONVERTER HOUSING
4. FRONT PUMP
5. THRUST WASHER NO. 1
6. THRUST WASHER NO. 2
7. FRONT PUMP GASKET
8. INTERMEDIATE BAND
9. BAND STRUTS
10. REVERSE AND HIGH CLUTCH DRUM
11. FORWARD CLUTCH AND CYLINDER
12. THRUST WASHER NO. 3
13. FORWARD CLUTCH HUB AND RING GEAR
14. THRUST WASHER NO. 4
15. FRONT PLANET CARRIER
16. INPUT SHELL, SUN GEAR AND THRUST WASHER NO. 5
17. THRUST WASHER NO. 6
18. REVERSE PLANET CARRIER
19. THRUST WASHER NO. 7
20. SNAP RING
21. REVERSE RING GEAR AND HUB
22. LOW AND REVERSE BAND
23. BAND STRUTS
24. THRUST WASHER NO. 8
25. LOW AND REVERSE DRUM
26. ONE-WAY CLUTCH INNER RACE
27. ROLLER (12) AND SPRING (12)
28. SPRING AND ROLLER CAGE
29. ONE-WAY CLUTCH OUTER RACE
30. THRUST WASHER NO. 9
31. CASE
32. THRUST WASHER NO. 10
33. PARKING GEAR
34. GOVERNOR DISTRIBUTOR SLEEVE
35. SNAP RING
36. GOVERNOR VALVES & DISTRIBUTOR
37. OUTPUT SHAFT
38. EXTENSION HOUSING AND GASKET
39. CONTROL VALVE BODY
40. OIL PAN AND GASKET

D 1378-B

FIG. 84—Transmission Sub-Assemblies

used, or a thrust washer came out of position during the transmission assembly operation.

1. Install thrust washer No. 9 inside the transmission case (Fig. 85).

FIG. 85—Number 9 Thrust Washer Location

2. Place the one-way clutch outer race inside the case. From the back of the case install the six outer race-to-case attaching bolts. **Torque the bolts to specification with the tools shown in Fig. 86.**

FIG. 86—Installing One-Way Clutch Outer Race Attaching Bolts

3. Place the transmission case in a vertical position with the back face of the case upward. Install the parking pawl retaining pin in the case (Fig. 87).

4. Install the parking pawl on the case retaining pin. Install the parking pawl return spring as shown in Fig. 87.

5. Install thrust washer No. 10 on the parking gear (Fig. 88). Place

FIG. 87—Parking Pawl and Gear

FIG. 88—Number 10 Thrust Washer Location

the gear and thrust washer on the back face of the case (Fig. 87).

6. Place the two distributor tubes in the governor distributor sleeve. Install the distributor sleeve on the case. As the distributor sleeve is installed, the tubes have to be inserted in the two holes in the case and the parking pawl retaining pin has to be inserted in the alignment hole in the distributor sleeve.

7. Install the four governor distributor sleeve-to-case attaching bolts and torque the bolts to specification.

8. Install the governor distributor assembly on the output shaft. Install the distributor retaining snap ring (Fig. 46). Figure 89 shows the correct snap ring to be used.

9. Check the rings in the governor distributor, making sure the rings

FIG. 89—Governor and Reverse Ring Hub-Retaining Snap Ring Identification

are fully inserted in the ring grooves and will rotate freely. Install the output shaft and governor distributor assembly in the distributor sleeve (Fig. 45).

10. Place a new extension housing gasket on the case. Install the extension housing vacuum tube clip, and the extension housing-to-case attaching bolts. Torque the bolts to specification.

11. Place the transmission in the holding fixture with the front pump mounting face of the case up. **Make sure thrust washer No. 9 is still located at the bottom of the transmission case (Fig. 84).**

12. Install the one-way clutch spring retainer into the outer race (Fig. 90).

13. Install the inner race inside of the spring retainer.

14. Install the individual springs between the inner and outer race as shown in Figure 90.

15. Starting at the back of the transmission case, install the one-way clutch rollers by slightly compressing each spring and positioning the roller between the spring and the spring retainer.

16. After the one-way clutch has been assembled, rotate the inner race clockwise to center the rollers and springs. Install the low and reverse drum (Fig. 84). The splines of the

STEP-1

INSTALL SPRING RETAINER INTO OUTER RACE

STEP-2

INSTALL INNER RACE

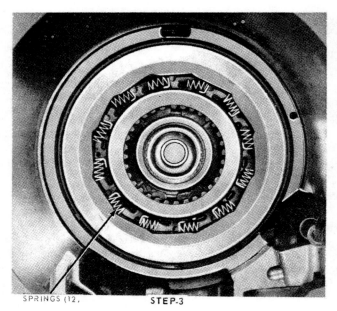

STEP-3

INSTALL 12 SPRINGS

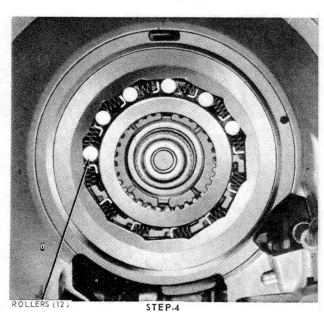

STEP-4

INSTALL 12 ROLLERS

D1551-A

FIG. 90—One-way Clutch Installation

drum have to engage with the splines of the *one-way clutch* inner race. Check the one-way clutch operation by rotating the low and reverse drum. The drum should rotate clockwise but should not rotate counterclockwise.

17. Install thrust washer No. 8 on top of the low and reverse drum (Fig. 91). Install the low-reverse band in the case, with the end of the band for the small strut to-

ward the low-reverse servo (Fig. 44).

18. Install the reverse ring gear and hub on the output shaft.

19. Move the output shaft forward and install the reverse ring gear hub-to-output shaft retaining ring (Fig. 43).

20. Place thrust washers Nos. 6 and 7 on the reverse planet carrier (Fig. 92).

21. Install the planet carrier in

the reverse ring gear and engage the tabs of the carrier with the slots in the low-reverse drum.

22. On the bench, install the forward clutch in the reverse-high clutch by rotating the units to mesh the reverse-high clutch plates with the *splines of the forward clutch* (Fig. 93).

23. Using the end play check reading that was obtained during the transmission disassembly to deter-

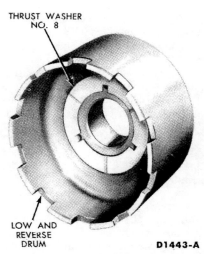

FIG. 91—Number 8 Thrust Washer Location

tween the stator support and the intermediate brake drum thrust surfaces and still maintain a slight clearance. Do not select a washer that must be forced between the stator support and intermediate brake drum.

e. Remove the intermediate brake drum and forward clutch unit from the stator support.

f. Install the selected Nos. 1 and 2 thrustwashers on the front pump stator support (Fig. 34) using enough vaseline to hold the thrust washers in position during the front pump installation.

24. Install thrust washer No. 3 on the forward clutch (Fig. 94).

25. Install the forward clutch hub and ring in the forward clutch by rotating the units to mesh the for-

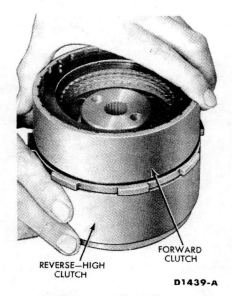

FIG. 93—Installing Clutch Units

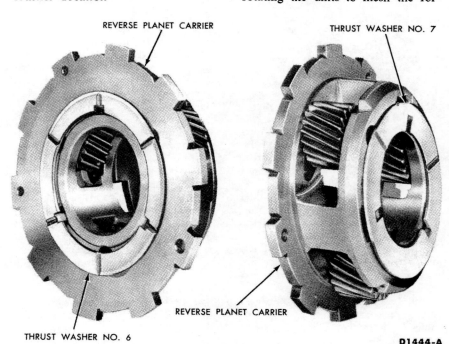

FIG. 92—Number 6 and 7 Thrust Washer Location

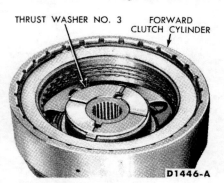

FIG. 94—Number 3 Thrust Washer Location

FIG. 95—Installing Forward Clutch Hub and Ring Gear

mine which No. 2 steel backed thrust washer is required, proceed as follows:

a. Position the stator support vertically on the work bench and install the correct No. 2 thrustwasher to bring the end play within specifications.

b. Install the reverse-high clutch and the forward clutch on the stator support.

c. Invert the complete unit making sure that the intermediate brake drum bushing is seated on the forward clutch mating surface.

d. Select the thickest fiber washer (No. 1) that can be inserted be-

ward clutch plates with the splines on the forward clutch hub (Fig. 95).

26. Install thrust washer No. 4 on the front planet carrier (Fig. 96). Install the front planet carrier into the forward clutch hub and ring gear. **Check the forward thrust bearing race inside the planet carrier for proper location against the thrust bearing. Make sure the race is centered for alignment with the sun gear on the input shell (Fig. 97).**

27. Install the input shell and sun gear on the gear train (Fig. 98). Rotate the input shell to engage the drive lugs of the reverse-high clutch. If the drive lugs will not engage,

FIG. 96—Number 4 Thrust Washer Location

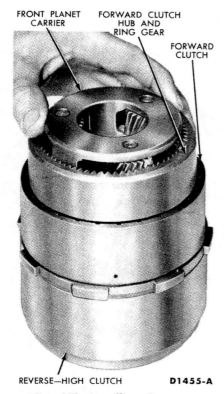

FIG. 97—Installing Front Planet Carrier

the outer race inside the forward planet carrier is not centered to engage the end of the sun gear inside the input shell. Center the thrust bearing race and install the input shell.

28. Hold the gear train together and install the forward part of the gear train assembly in the case (Fig. 39).

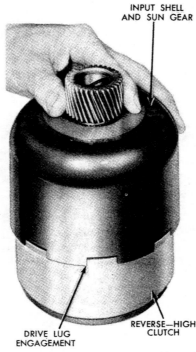

FIG. 98—Installing Input Shell

The input shell sun gear must mesh with the reverse pinion gears. The front planet carrier internal splines must mesh with the splines on the output shaft.

29. A new band should be soaked in transmission fluid for fifteen minutes before it is installed. Install the intermediate band through the front of the case (Fig. 37) so that the arrow on the band end forging points toward the front of the transmission.

30. Install a new front pump gasket on the case. Line up the bolt holes in the gasket with the holes in the case.

31. Lubricate a new front pump O-ring seal with transmission fluid and install it on the pump. Install the front pump stator support into the reverse-high clutch. Align the pump-to-case attaching bolt holes. Install the front pump-to-case attaching bolts and torque them to specification.

32. Install the input shaft (Fig. 35).

Rotate the holding fixture to place the transmission in a horizontal position. Check the transmission end play as shown in Fig. 33. If the end play is not within specification, either the wrong selective thrust washers (Fig. 34) were used, or one of the 10 thrust washers (Fig. 84) is not properly positioned.

33. Remove the dial indicator

used for checking the end play and install the one front pump-to-case attaching bolt. Torque the bolt to specification.

34. Place the converter housing on the transmission case. Install the five converter housing-to-case attaching bolts. Torque the bolts to specification.

35. Install the intermediate and low-reverse band adjusting screws in the case. Install the struts for each band (Fig. 32).

36. Adjust the intermediate and low-reverse band. Refer to In-Car Adjustments and Repair for band adjusting procedures.

37. Install a universal joint yoke on the output shaft. Rotate the input and output shafts in both directions to check for free rotation of the gear train.

38. Install the control valve body (Fig. 31). As the valve body is installed engage the manual and downshift valves with the inner control levers. Torque the control valve body-to-case attaching bolts to specification.

39. Place a new oil pan gasket on the case and install the oil pan and oil pan-to-case attaching bolts. Torque the attaching bolts to specification.

40. Remove the transmission from the holding fixture. Install the two extension housing-to-case attaching bolts. Torque the bolts to specification.

41. Install the primary throttle valve in the transmission case (Fig. 29).

42. Install the vacuum unit, gasket, and control rod in the case. Using the tools shown in Fig. 99, torque the vacuum unit to 15-23 ft-lbs.

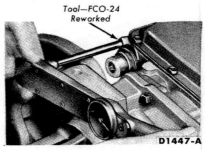

FIG. 99—Installing Vacuum Unit

43. Make sure the input shaft is properly installed in the front pump stator support and gear train. Install the converter in the front pump and the converter housing.

PART 7-3 CRUISE-O-MATIC OR MERC-O-MATIC DUAL RANGE TRANSMISSION

1 DESCRIPTION AND OPERATION

DESCRIPTION

Figure 1 shows the location of the converter, front pump, clutches, bands, gear train and most of the internal parts used in the Cruise-O-Matic or Merc-O-Matic Transmission.

The identification tag (Fig. 2) includes the model prefix and suffix, a service identification number, and a build date code. The service identification number indicates changes to

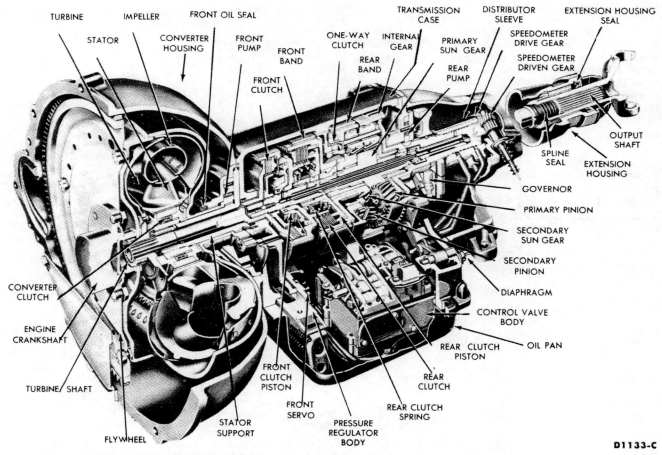

FIG. 1—Typical Cruise-O-Matic Transmission

D1133-C

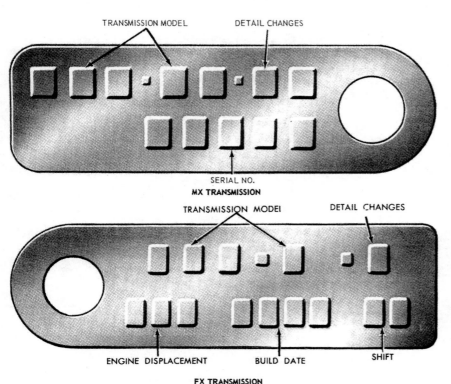

FIG. 2—Identification Tags

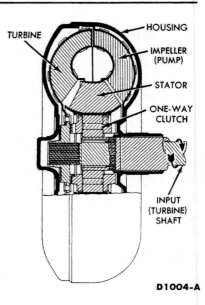

FIG. 3—Sectional View of Typical Torque Converter

service details which affect interchangeability **when the transmission model is not changed.** For interpretation of this number, see the Master Parts Catalog.

The tag must be kept with the individual transmission it was originally installed on. If the tag was removed during disassembly, reinstall it on the same unit.

Table 1 shows the engine and transmission model applications.

When the engine is running, the fluid in the torque converter flows from the impeller to the turbine and back to the impeller through the stator. This flow produces a maximum torque increase of about 2 to 1 when the turbine is stalled. When enough torque is developed by the impeller, the turbine begins to rotate, turning the turbine shaft.

The converter torque multiplication gradually tapers off as turbine

ing the turbine blades strikes the front face of the stator blades. These blades are held stationary by the action of a one-way clutch (Fig. 3) as long as the fluid is directed against the front face of the blades.

When the turbine rotates faster than $9/10$ impeller speed the converter no longer multiplies torque. The fluid is directed against the back face of the stator blades. As the one-way clutch permits the stator to rotate only in the direction of impeller rotation, the stator begins to turn with the impeller and turbine. The converter operates as an efficient fluid coupling as long as the turbine speed remains greater than $9/10$ impeller speed.

A constant flow of fluid into and out of the converter is maintained. Some of the fluid coming out of the converter is forced through a cooler located in the radiator tank.

PLANETARY GEAR TRAIN, CLUTCHES, BANDS AND SERVOS

Planetary Gear Train

The planetary gear train consists of a primary sun gear, secondary sun gear, primary and secondary pinions which are held in a common carrier, and an internal gear to which the transmission output shaft is attached (Fig. 4).

Front Clutch

The front clutch drive plates (Fig. 5) are connected to the turbine shaft through the front clutch drum. The

TABLE 1—Engine and Transmission Application

Car Line	Engine Model	Trans. Prefix	Application
Ford	289-2V	PCT-J-3	Column Shift
Ford, Mercury	390-2V	PCE-BK	Column Shift
Ford	390-4V	PCE-BK	Column Shift
Mercury	390-2V	PCE-BL	Floor Shift

OPERATION

TORQUE CONVERTER

The hydraulic torque converter (Fig. 3) consists of an impeller (pump), a turbine, and a stator. All these parts are enclosed and operate in a fluid-filled housing.

speed approaches impeller speed, and it becomes 1 to 1 when the turbine is being driven at $9/10$ impeller speed. This is known as the coupling point.

When the turbine is rotating at less than $9/10$ impeller speed, the converter is multiplying torque. The fluid leav-

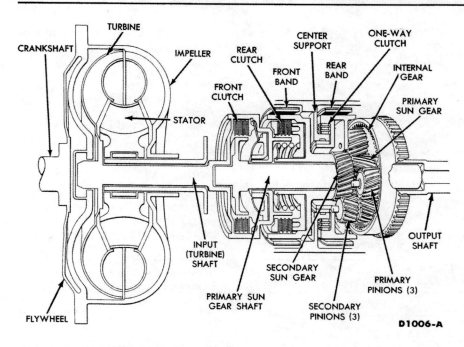

FIG. 4—Planetary Gear Train

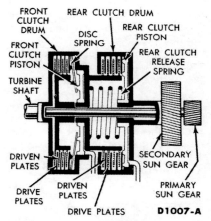

FIG. 5—Front and Rear Clutches

driven plates are connected to the primary sun gear shaft.

The front clutch is operated by fluid pressure against the clutch piston. The piston moves against a disc spring which acts as a lever to lock the drive and driven plates together. When the clutch is applied, the primary sun gear is locked to and driven by the turbine shaft. The piston is returned to the release position by the disc spring when the fluid pressure is removed (Fig. 5). A check ball is installed in the front clutch piston to permit fluid exhaust, when the piston is in its released position.

In neutral, the front clutch drum and steel plates are being driven while the bronze plates are stationary. In reverse, the clutch is not ap-

plied, since the steel and bronze plates must rotate in opposite directions.

Rear Clutch

The rear clutch (Fig. 5) is operated by fluid pressure against the clutch piston. Movement of the piston compresses the release spring and locks the multiple-disc clutch. The rear clutch drive plates are splined to the front clutch drum and the driven plates are connected to the rear clutch drum and secondary sun gear. When the rear clutch is applied (in the reverse and third gear ratios) the secondary sun gear is driven. The piston is returned to the released position by the release spring (Fig. 5).

In neutral, the rear clutch bronze plates are being driven while the steel plates are free. In second gear, the bronze plates are driven, but the steel plates are held stationary. In first gear, the bronze plates are driven clockwise at engine speed while the steel plates are driven counterclockwise.

Front Band and Servo

One end of the front band, which encircles the rear clutch drum, is anchored to the transmission case, and the other end is connected to the front servo (Fig. 6).

Fluid pressure moves the front servo piston against the inner end of the front servo actuating lever. Force

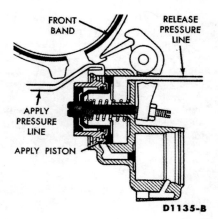

FIG. 6—Typical Front Servo

is transmitted through a strut between the outer end of the lever and the end of the band to tighten the band around the rear clutch drum. Under certain conditions, the servo is released by directing fluid pressure to the opposite side of the piston, assisted by release spring force.

Rear Band and Servo

The rear band fits around the planetary gear drum. One end of the band contacts the end of the band adjusting screw, and the other end connects to the rear servo.

Two rear servo pistons apply the rear band (Fig. 7). The small (fast-

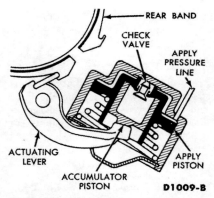

FIG. 7—Typical Rear Band and Servo

acting) piston, which is in direct contact with the servo lever, is located inside the large piston.

Fluid pressure against the large piston flows through a check valve to work against the small piston, which has low pressure resistance from the spring force of the rear band and whatever friction is in the servo lever and band struts. At a low apply pressure and small volume of fluid flow.

the small piston moves and tightens the rear band on the pinion carrier.

When the apply pressure builds up to about 10 psi, the large piston moves against its return spring, allowing the check valve to close. When the check valve closes, the fluid in the small piston is trapped, and the apply force of the large piston is added to that of the small piston.

POWER FLOWS

Table 2 lists the ratios obtained through the various power flows.

TABLE 2—Cruise-O-Matic or Merc-O-Matic Gear Ratios

Gear	Selector Lever Position	Clutch Applied	Band Applied	Gear Ratio
Neutral	N	None	None	—
First	D1 or L	Front	Rear①	2.40:1
Second	D1 or D2	Front	Front	1.47:1
Third	D1 or D2	Front and Rear	None	1.00:1
Reverse	R	Rear	Rear	2.00:1

①In first gear D1, the planet carrier is held against rotation by the one-way clutch.

Power Flow—Neutral

When the transmission is in neutral (Fig. 8), no gears are held or driven, and no power is transmitted to the output shaft.

Power Flow—First Gear, L

In first gear when the selector lever is at L, the primary sun gear is driven and the pinion carrier is held by the rear band (Fig. 8). Power is transmitted to the primary pinions, the secondary pinions, and the internal gear, driving the internal gear in the same direction as the primary sun gear. The secondary sun gear turns free in the reverse direction and has no effect on the gear train.

Power Flow—First Gear, D1

In first gear at the D1 selector lever position (large dot on selector indicator), the pinion carrier is held against rotation by the one-way clutch instead of by the rear band (Fig. 8). First gear in D1 is the only gear that uses the one-way clutch.

Power Flow—Second Gear

Second gear ratio is obtained by driving the primary sun gear and holding the secondary sun gear (Fig. 8). The primary pinions drive the secondary pinions, causing them to

walk around the secondary sun gear and to carry the internal gear and output shaft around with them.

Power Flow—Third Gear

In third gear, the primary and secondary sun gears are locked together and driven as a unit (Fig. 8). Therefore, the pinions cannot rotate and the entire planetary train revolves as a unit, which causes the output shaft to rotate at the same speed as the turbine shaft.

Power Flow—Reverse

Reverse gear is obtained by driving the secondary sun gear and holding the pinion carrier (Fig. 8). The secondary pinions drive the internal gear in the reverse direction. The primary sun gear and the primary pinions rotate freely and have no effect on the gear train.

Power Flow—Park Position

When the selector lever is in the P (park) position, the parking pawl engages the external teeth on the internal gear to lock the internal gear and output shaft to the case. This locks the rear wheels to prevent movement of the car.

THROTTLE PRESSURE

Throttle pressure adjusts the transmission operation to engine torque. Throttle pressure is produced from control pressure by the throttle valve. The throttle valve is controlled by a spring-loaded vacuum diaphragm unit mounted on the rear of the transmission case (Fig. 9).

The vacuum diaphragm is actuated by the engine intake manifold vacuum working against spring pressure. When the vacuum is higher than 16 inches the diaphragm moves against spring pressure and moves

the push rod away from the throttle valve to cut off the throttle pressure regulation. As the engine throttle is advanced, manifold vacuum will fall below 16 inches. As the vacuum drops, the spring-loaded diaphragm moves the push rod to open the throttle valve and increase the throttle pressure.

THROTTLE PRESSURE BOOST VALVE

To compensate for the slight manifold vacuum changes with throttle movements beyond about 50° carburetor valve opening, a throttle pressure boost valve comes into operation. At 51 psi throttle pressure, the spring-loaded boost valve (Fig. 9) comes into balance. Throttle pressure below 51 psi cannot move the boost valve against spring force plus throttle pressure force acting at the boost valve plug. Below 51 psi, therefore, throttle pressure will flow through the boost valve without interference.

Throttle pressure above 51 psi will move the boost valve to the left (Fig. 9). This movement will first cut off throttle pressure flow to the shift valves and the coasting control valve, and it will then open a passage to permit the new boosted throttle pressure to flow to the shift valves and the coasting control valve. Throttle pressure will continue to work against the right end of the boost valve. For each pound of increase in throttle pressure (above 51 psi), the boosted throttle pressure will increase about three pounds.

GOVERNOR PRESSURE

Governor pressure is produced from front clutch control pressure by the valve in the governor body which rotates at output shaft speed.

The governor valve is a balanced valve. It is balanced between centrifugal force acting on the governor valve plus governor spring force and governor pressure force (Fig. 9). Governor pressure is, therefore, proportional to road speed.

TRANSITION VALVE

The transition valve controls the front servo apply pressure flow.

In the D1 range, the transition valve blocks front servo apply pressure flow until the 1-2 valve is closed by governor pressure.

In the D2 range (small dot to the right of N), the transition valve permits front servo apply pressure to flow through it at all times.

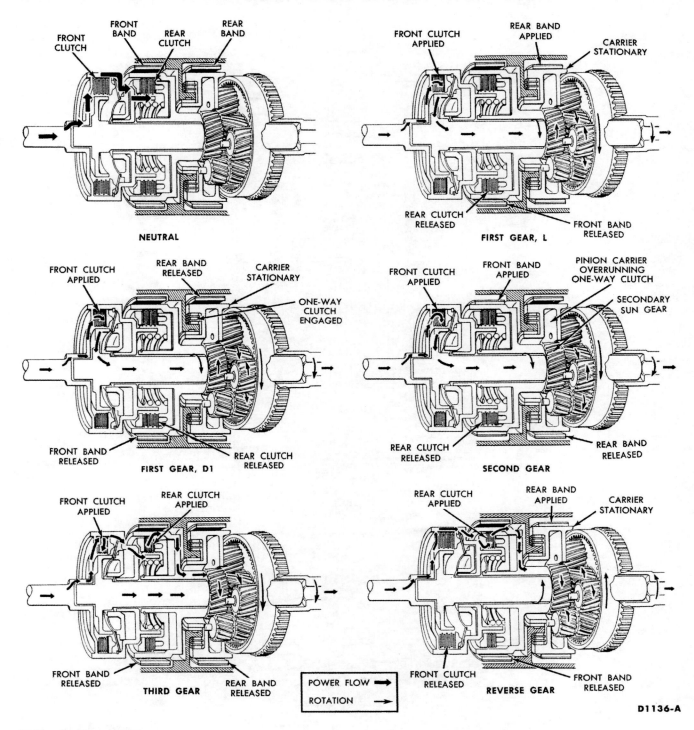

FIG. 8—Power Flow

1-2 SHIFT VALVE

The 1-2 shift valve controls the 1-2 upshift in the D1 range. On the 2-1 downshift, either manual (shift to L) or kickdown, the 1-2 shift valve controls the shift only within the road speed range permitted by the inhibitor valve.

The 1-2 valve is held in its rest (open) position by a spring. It is closed by governor pressure. Under various driving conditions, governor pressure is opposed by spring force plus reduced throttle and reduced boosted throttle pressures, and control pressure.

REAR SERVO LOCKOUT VALVE

The rear servo lockout valve blocks control pressure flow to the rear servo (rear servo apply pressure) in the D1 and D2 ranges.

THROTTLE REDUCING VALVE

Before throttle pressure or boosted throttle pressure is admitted to the front face of the 2-3 shift valve, plug and 1-2 shift valve, it must open a passage past the spring-loaded throt-

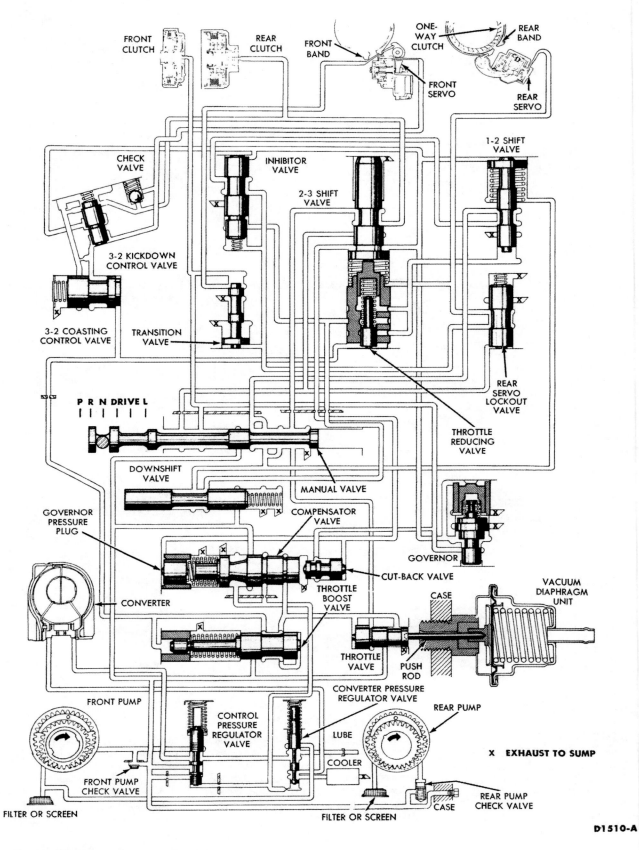

FIG. 9—Hydraulic Control System—Neutral

tle reducing valve.

Approximately 20 psi throttle pressure is required to move the valve against its spring far enough to open the passage. Once past the valve, throttle pressure will work on the spring end of the valve and exert a force to cut off throttle pressure flow past the valve. In this case, the valve becomes a balanced valve, wherein the valve is balanced between throttle pressure force on the one end and spring force plus throttle pressure force on the other end. The pressure past the valve will, therefore, be reduced.

2-3 SHIFT VALVE

The 2-3 shift valve controls the 2-3 upshift and the 3-2 downshift. The valve is held in its rest (closed) position by springs. It is opened by governor pressure. Under various driving conditions, governor pressure is opposed by spring force plus throttle or boosted throttle pressures, and control pressure.

INHIBITOR VALVE

The inhibitor valve prevents a 2-1 downshift, either manual or kickdown, at excessive road speeds.

The inhibitor valve is held in its rest (open) position by a spring. It is closed by governor pressure. Under various driving conditions, governor pressure is opposed by spring force plus control pressure.

3-2 COASTING CONTROL VALVE

The 3-2 coasting control valve operates in the front servo release passage.

During a 3-2 closed-throttle downshift in D2 range, the valve is positioned by its spring so that front servo release pressure must exhaust slowly through an orifice. This slow exhaust of release pressure provides a slow front band application.

During a partial-to-full-throttle 3-2 downshift, the 3-2 coasting control valve is positioned by throttle pressure or boosted throttle pressure so that front servo release pressure can exhaust rapidly to provide a rapid front band application.

DOWNSHIFT VALVE

The downshift valve is in the control valve upper body. The inner downshift lever contacts one end of the spring-loaded downshift valve.

Control pressure is directed to a land of the valve. Linkage is connected between the accelerator pedal and downshift lever. The downshift valve is moved to open a passage to direct control pressure to the shift valves and the inhibitor valve, when the accelerator pedal is depressed through the detent (Fig. 9).

3-2 DOWNSHIFT CONTROL VALVE

The 3-2 downshift control valve operates in the front servo release pressure passage between the 2-3 valve and the front servo. A check valve is installed parallel with the downshift valve in the same passage so that release pressure flow to the servo by-passes it.

The downshift valve controls the rate of front servo release pressure exhaust (flow from the servo), and thereby the rate of front band application.

The 3-2 downshift control valve eliminates the possibility of a runaway condition in the transmission during a 3-2 kickdown at low car speeds (about 25 mph). It also eliminates the possibility of a tie-up during the same shift at higher speeds (50 mph and more).

HYDRAULIC CONTROL SYSTEM—NEUTRAL

The manual valve at N selector lever position blocks the fluid flow to both clutches and both bands (Fig. 9). With no fluid pressure in the clutches or servos, the clutches and bands are released by spring pressure, preventing power being transmitted to the transmission output shaft.

Neutral operation of the transmission keeps control pressure up to its proper value, maintains a full torque converter, lubricates the transmission, and maintains a flow of fluid through the cooling system.

HYDRAULIC CONTROL SYSTEM—D1, FIRST GEAR

When the selector lever is moved from N to D1, the manual valve opens three passages to control pressure. From left to right, the first passage admits control pressure to supply the 2-3 valve and close the rear servo lockout valve. The second passage admits control pressure to apply the front clutch and supply the governor and transition valve. The third passage admits control pressure to flow through the 1-2 and inhibitor valves and close the transition valve.

With the front clutch applied, the

primary sun gear tries to drive the pinion carrier in a counterclockwise direction. Counterclockwise rotation at the pinion carrier is prevented by the one-way clutch. With the front clutch applied and the pinion carrier held, the transmission is in first gear.

HYDRAULIC CONTROL SYSTEM—D1, SECOND GEAR

The 1-2 shift occurs when governor pressure force on the 1-2 shift valve overcomes shift plug pressure and spring forces. The 1-2 valve moves inward, exhausting the fluid which holds the transition valve closed. The transition valve opens and admits control pressure to apply the front band.

The front clutch remains on, and the front band applies to put the transmission in second gear.

HYDRAULIC CONTROL SYSTEM—D1, THIRD GEAR

The 2-3 shift occurs when governor pressure force overcomes spring and shift plug pressure force at the 2-3 shift valve. When the shift valve opens, control pressure flows through it to apply the rear clutch and release the front band. With both clutches applied, the transmission is in third gear.

HYDRAULIC CONTROL SYSTEM—D2, SECOND GEAR

When the manual valve is at the D2 selector lever position, control pressure to the 1-2 shift valve is cut off. This condition permits control pressure to flow through the transition valve to apply the front band.

With the front clutch and the front band applied, the transmission operates in second gear.

HYDRAULIC CONTROL SYSTEM—D2, THIRD GEAR

Operation in D2 range, third gear is the same as in D1 range, third gear except that the closed throttle downshift is from third to second in D2 instead of from third to first as in D1.

HYDRAULIC CONTROL SYSTEM—D1 AND D2 RANGES, 3-2 KICKDOWN

When the accelerator pedal is depressed through the detent, the downshift valve opens a passage that admits control pressure behind the 2-3 shift plug to oppose governor pressure. If the transmission is in high and road speed is below 47-69 mph, the 2-3 valve will be forced closed against governor pressure. When the 2-3 valve closes, control pressure which has been applying the rear clutch and releasing the front band is exhausted. The apply pressure that was in the front servo in third gear is now free to apply the front band. As soon as the front band applies, the transmission is in second gear.

HYDRAULIC CONTROL SYSTEM—L, FIRST GEAR

In L range, first gear, control pressure is directed by the manual valve to apply the front clutch and rear band. Control pressure is also directed by the manual valve to lock the 1-2 and 2-3 shift valves in their closed positions. Since neither shift valve can move, the transmission will stay in first gear regardless of throttle position or road speed.

HYDRAULIC CONTROL SYSTEM—REVERSE

When the manual valve is shifted into reverse, control pressure is directed to apply the rear clutch and rear band. Governor supply pressure is cut off by the manual valve; hence, the transmission cannot shift automatically. Rear clutch pressure is also directed to the throttle valve to regulate throttle pressure to obtain the correct line pressure for the reverse circuit.

HYDRAULIC CONTROL SYSTEM OPERATION

PRESSURE PUMPS

The front pump (Fig. 9), driven by the converter impeller, delivers fluid pressure to the hydraulic control system whenever the engine runs. The rear pump, driven by the transmission output shaft, delivers fluid pressure to the control system when the car moves forward.

Both pumps deliver fluid pressure to the control pressure regulator and control valve body. A regulated control pressure is available at the control valve body whenever the engine is running.

CONTROL PRESSURE AND COMPENSATOR PRESSURE

Control pressure is regulated by

the spring-loaded control pressure regulator valve (Fig. 9). It is adjusted to engine torque, road speed, and selector lever position.

To accomplish this, compensator pressure under various conditions is adjusted by throttle pressure (engine torque), governor pressure (road speed), or selector lever position. Compensator pressure, in turn, adjusts control pressure.

CONVERTER PRESSURE

Like control pressure, converter pressure is regulated by the converter pressure regulator valve spring and is adjusted to driving conditions by compensator pressure and selector lever positions.

OIL COOLING AND LUBRICATING SYSTEM

Figure 10 shows the transmission series cooling circuit that is used with a 390 CID engine. The converter out circuit is directed through the oil cooler, then the cooled oil is used in the transmission lubricating circuit. Compensator pressure is replaced by converter out pressure at the end of the converter pressure regulator valve.

A spring-loaded check valve is used in the circuit to maintain approximately 3-5 psi in the converter out circuit. When the converter out circuit exceeds 3-5 psi, the check ball opens against spring pressure and cooled oil is directed to lubricate the various parts of the transmission gear train.

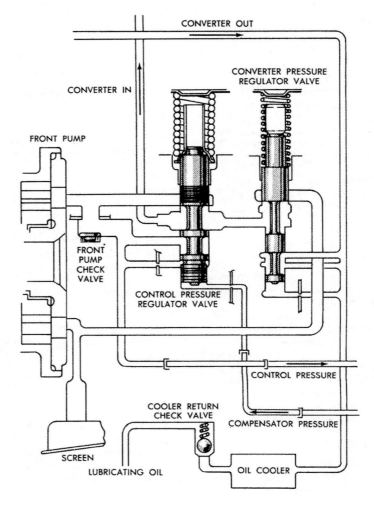

D1316-A

FIG. 10—Series Cooling Pressure Regulator Circuit—390 CID Engine

2 IN-CAR ADJUSTMENTS AND REPAIRS

CONTROL LINKAGE ADJUSTMENTS

The transmission control linkage adjustments should be performed in the order in which they appear in this section of the manual.

THROTTLE AND DOWNSHIFT LINKAGE ADJUSTMENTS

1. Apply the parking brake and place the selector lever at N. If the car is equipped with a vacuum release parking brake, make certain that the service brake is applied when making or checking the engine idle speed adjustments.

2. Run the engine at normal idle speed. If the engine is cold, run the engine at fast idle speed (about 1200 rpm) until it reaches normal operating temperature. When the engine is warm, slow it down to normal idle speed.

3. Connect a tachometer to the engine.

4. Adjust engine idle speed to the specified rpm with the transmission selector lever at D1 (circle) or D2 (small dot) the drive position.

5. The carburetor throttle lever must be against the hot idle speed adjusting screw at specified idle speed in D1 (circle) or D2 (small dot). To make sure that the carburetor throttle lever is against the adjusting screw, refer to Group 10 for the carburetor adjusting procedures.

6. With the engine stopped, disconnect the carburetor return spring (Fig. 11) from the throttle lever.

7. Loosen the accelerator cable conduit attaching clamp.

8. With the accelerator pedal to the floor and the throttle lever held to the wide open position, slide the cable conduit to the rear to remove the slack from the cable. Tighten the cable conduit attaching clamp.

9. Disconnect the downshift lever return spring (Fig. 11).

10. Hold the throttle lever at the wide open position and depress the downshift rod to the through detent stop. Set the downshift lever (at carburetor) adjusting screw against the throttle lever.

11. Connect both return springs to their respective levers.

MANUAL LINKAGE ADJUSTMENT

Column Shift

1. Place the selector lever in the

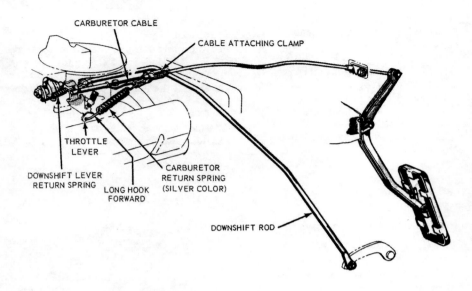

FIG. 11 — Throttle Linkage — V-8 Engine

D1 (circle) position tight against the D stop.

2. Loosen the nut at point A enough to permit column shift lever to slide on the shift rod (Fig. 12).

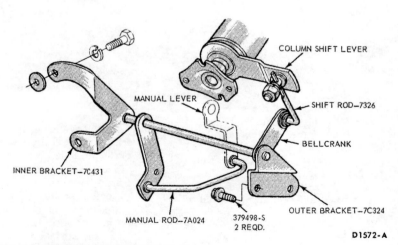

FIG. 12 — Column Shift Manual Linkage

3. Shift the manual lever at the transmission into the D1 detent position, second from the rear.

4. Make sure that the selector lever has not moved from the D1 stop, then tighten the nut at point A.

5. Check the pointer alignment and the transmission operation for all selector lever detent positions.

Floor Shift

1. Position the transmission selec-

tor lever in D1 (circle) position.

2. Raise the car and loosen the manual lever control rod retaining nut. Move the transmission manual lever to the D1 position, second detent position from the back of the transmission. The last detent position is manual low.

3. With the transmission selector lever and manual lever in the D1 positions, torque the retaining nut 20 to 25 ft-lbs.

4. Check the operation of the transmission in each selector lever position.

STARTER NEUTRAL SWITCH ADJUSTMENT

COLUMN SHIFT

1. With the manual linkage properly adjusted, check the starter engagement circuit in all transmission selector lever positions. The circuit must be open in all drive positions and closed only in park and neutral. The starter should engage only in park or neutral.

2. To adjust the switch, loosen the retaining screws that locate the switch on the steering column (Fig. 13).

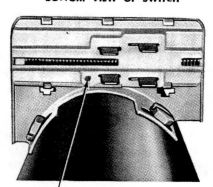

BOTTOM VIEW OF SWITCH

Gauge Pin HOLE

D1506-A

FIG. 13—Starter Neutral Switch—Column Shift

3. Place the transmission selector lever firmly against the stop of the neutral detent position.

4. Rotate the switch actuating lever until the gauge pin (No. 43 drill) can be inserted into the gauge pin holes (Fig. 13).

5. Tighten the two switch retaining screws and remove the gauge pin.

6. Check the operation of the switch in each selector lever position. The starter should engage in only the neutral and park detent positions. Whenever the manual linkage is adjusted the starter neutral switch should be checked and if necessary adjusted.

CONSOLE SHIFT

1. With the manual linkage properly adjusted, check the starter engagement circuit in all positions. The circuit must be open in all drive positions and closed only in park and neutral.

2. Remove the selector lever handle from the lever.

3. Remove the chrome trim panel from the top of the console.

4. Place the lever in the neutral position and remove the three quadrant attaching screws. Remove the indicator light from the quadrant base. Lift the quadrant from the console.

5. Loosen the two combination starter neutral and back-up light switch attaching screws (Fig. 14).

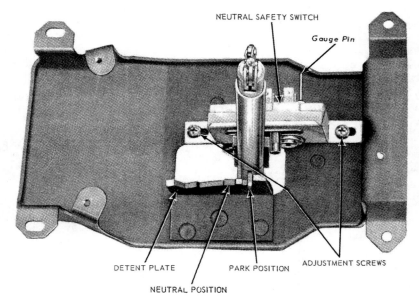

NEUTRAL SAFETY SWITCH

Gauge Pin

DETENT PLATE   PARK POSITION   ADJUSTMENT SCREWS

NEUTRAL POSITION

D1556-A

FIG. 14—Starter Neutral Switch—Console Shift

6. Move the selector lever back and forth until the gauge pin (No. 43 drill) can be fully inserted into the gauge pin holes.

7. Place the transmission selector lever firmly against the stop of the neutral detent position.

8. Slide the combination starter neutral and back-up light switch forward or rearward as required, until the switch actuating lever contacts the selector lever.

9. Tighten the switch attaching screws and check for starting in the park position.

10. Turn the ignition key to the ACC position and place the selector lever in the reverse position and check the operation of the back-up lights. Turn the key off.

11. Place the selector lever *in* park. Position the quadrant on the housing and install the bulb and socket in the quadrant base. Align the

quadrant with the pointer and install the three attaching screws.

12. Install the chrome trim panel on the top of the console. Install the selector lever handle.

SELECTOR LEVER REMOVAL ADJUSTMENT AND INSTALLATION

REMOVAL

1. Raise the car and disconnect the link (Fig. 15) from the shift lever.

2. Lower the car. Place the selector lever in the neutral position and remove the selector lever handle attaching screw. Lift the handle off the selector lever.

3. Remove the chrome trim panel from the console.

4. Remove the three screws that attach the quadrant to the selector lever housing. Lift the quadrant from the housing. Disconnect the bulb socket.

5. If the car is equipped with a vacuum release parking brake, disconnect the vacuum hose from the starter neutral switch.

6. Remove the four screws that attach the selector lever housing to the console.

7. Lift the selector lever and *housing from the console.*

DETENT PAWL ADJUSTMENT

1. Install the handle to make the

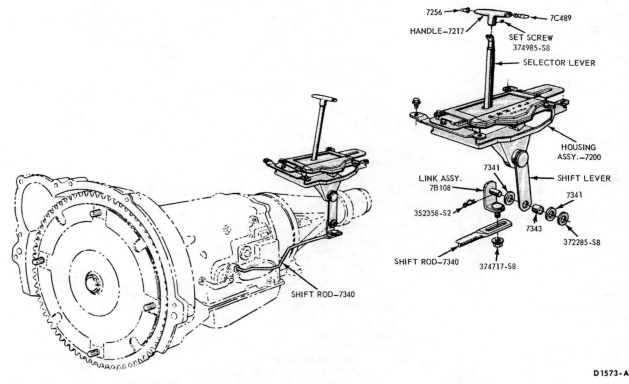

FIG. 15—Console Shift Linkage—Typical

detent pawl adjustment.

2. Move the selector lever to the D1-D2 range.

3. Place a 0.010-inch feeler gauge between the detent pawl and plate.

4. Loosen the cable lock nut and turn the screw clockwise to decrease the clearance or counterclockwise to increase the clearance as shown in Fig. 16. Tighten the lock nut after a clearance of 0.010 inch has been established.

5. Remove the handle from the selector lever.

INSTALLATION

1. Position the selector lever and housing assembly in the console.

2. Install the four attaching screws to secure it in place.

3. If the car is equipped with a vacuum release parking brake, connect the vacuum hose to the starter neutral switch.

4. Connect the bulb socket to the quadrant. Position the quadrant and secure with the three attaching screws.

5. Raise the car and install the link on the shift lever (Fig. 15). Adjust the manual linkage and then the neutral switch as required. Lower the car.

6. Install the chrome trim cover on the console.

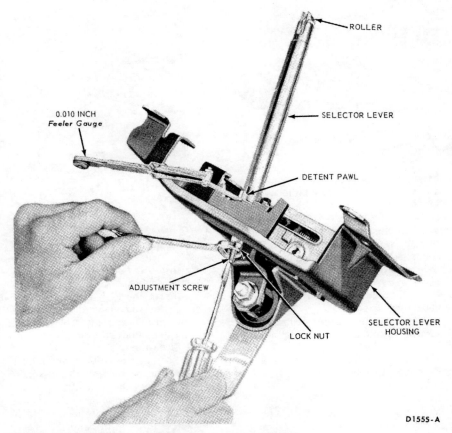

FIG. 16—Adjusting Selector Lever Detent Pawl

7. Place the selector lever handle on the lever with the attaching screw tapped hole facing toward the right side of the console. Install and tighten the handle attaching screw.

BAND ADJUSTMENTS

FRONT BAND ADJUSTMENT

1. Drain the fluid from the transmission by removing the oil filler tube. Use a clean drain can equipped with a 100-mesh screen if the fluid is to be reused.

2. Remove the oil pan, then remove the oil screen and clip from the transmission. Clean the inside of the oil pan. Remove all gasket material from the oil pan and pan mounting face of the case.

3. Loosen the front servo adjusting screw lock nut two full turns.

4. Pull back on the actuating rod, then insert the gauge block of the front band adjusting tool (Fig. 17),

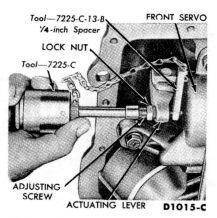

Tool—7225-C-13-B
¼-inch Spacer
FRONT SERVO
LOCK NUT
Tool—7225-C
ADJUSTING SCREW
ACTUATING LEVER
D1015-C

FIG. 17—Adjusting Front Band—Typical

between the servo piston stem and adjusting screw. Tighten the adjusting screw until the wrench overruns. Back off the adjusting screw **exactly one complete turn,** then hold the adjusting screw stationary and tighten the lock nut to specifications. Remove the gauge block. **Severe damage may result if the adjusting screw is not backed off exactly one complete turn.**

5. Install the transmission fluid screen. Install the pan using a new gasket.

6. Connect the transmission fluid filler tube to the oil pan.

7. Refill the transmission to the **FULL** mark on the dipstick.

8. Start the engine and engage the transmission in each drive range to fill all fluid passages, then place the

selector lever in the **P** position. Check the fluid level and add enough fluid to bring the level up to the **FULL** mark on the dipstick.

ALTERNATE FRONT BAND ADJUSTMENT PROCEDURE

1. Disconnect the fluid filler tube from the oil pan, and drain the fluid from the transmission. **If the same fluid is to be used again in the transmission after the band adjustment, filter the fluid through a 100-mesh screen as it drains from the transmission. Re-use the fluid only if it is in good condition.**

2. Remove and thoroughly clean the oil pan and screen. Discard the oil pan gasket.

3. Loosen the front servo adjusting screw locknut two full turns with a $9/16$-inch wrench. Check the adjusting screw for free rotation in the actuating lever after the lock nut is loosened, and free the screw if necessary.

4. Pull the adjusting screw end of the actuating lever away from the servo body, and insert the adjusting tool gauge block (Fig. 18) between the servo piston stem and the adjusting screw.

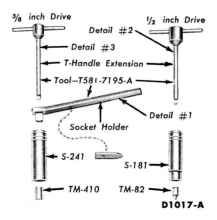

⅜ inch Drive
Detail #2
½ inch Drive
Detail #3
T-Handle Extension
Tool—T581-7195-A
Detail #1
Socket Holder
S-241
S-181
TM-410
TM-82
D1017-A

FIG. 18—Front and Rear Band Adjusting Tools

5. Install the socket handle on the $9/16$-inch socket.

6. Insert the T-handle extension through the socket handle and socket, and install the screwdriver socket on the T-handle extension.

7. Place the tool on the adjusting screw so that the screwdriver socket engages the screw and the $9/16$-inch socket engages the lock nut.

8. With a torque wrench on the T-handle extension, torque the adjusting screw to 10 in-lbs, and then back off the screw exactly one full turn.

Severe damage may result to the transmission if the adjusting screw is not backed off exactly one full turn.

9. Hold the adjusting screw stationary, and torque the lock nut to specification.

10. Remove the gauge block from the transmission.

11. Place a new gasket on the oil pan, and install the screen and pan on the transmission.

12. Connect the filler tube to the oil pan and tighten the fitting securely.

13. Fill the transmission with fluid.

REAR BAND ADJUSTMENT

1. Fold back the floor mat to expose the right side of the floor pan.

2. Remove the access hole cover from the floor pan. Remove all dirt from the adjusting screw threads, then oil the threads.

3. Loosen the rear band adjusting screw lock nut with the tool shown in Fig. 19. Using the T-handle portion of the tool, tighten the adjusting screw until the wrench overruns.

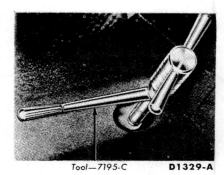

Tool—7195-C
D1329-A

FIG. 19—Adjusting Rear Band

If the screw is found to be tighter than wrench capacity (10 ft-lbs torque), loosen the screw and tighten until the wrench overruns.

4. Back off the adjusting screw 1½ turns. Hold the adjusting screw stationary, and tighten the adjusting screw lock nut to specifications.

Severe damage may result if the adjusting screw is not backed off exactly 1½ turns.

ALTERNATE REAR BAND ADJUSTMENT PROCEDURE

The tool shown in Fig. 18 may be used to adjust the rear band.

1. Place the socket holder on the ¾-inch socket (Fig. 18). Insert the T-handle extension through the handle and socket.

2. Place the $5/16$-inch 8-point

socket on the extension. Place a torque wrench on the T-handle extension.

3. Insert the assembled tool in the access hole so that it engages the adjusting screw and the lock nut.

4. Loosen the adjusting screw lock nut.

5. Torque the adjusting screw to 10 ft-lbs.

6. Remove the torque wrench from the T-handle extension and back off the adjusting screw exactly 1½ turns. **Severe damage may result to the transmission if the adjusting screw is not backed off exactly 1½ turns.**

7. Hold the adjusting screw stationary and tighten the lock nut securely.

REAR BAND ADJUSTMENT WITH CONSOLE

It is necessary to remove the console to gain access to the rear band adjustment screw.

1. Raise the car on a hoist. Disconnect the link from the shift lever (Fig. 15).

2. Lower the car. Remove the chrome trim panel attaching screws. Lift the panel slightly and turn it ¼ turn to allow the panel to be lifted over the selector lever handle.

3. Remove the four screws that attach the selector lever housing to the console. Disconnect the bulb socket and remove the selector lever assembly.

4. Move the carpet away from each side of the console. Remove the three attaching screws from each side of the console. Move the console to the left side of the car to gain access to the band adjustment screw.

5. Remove the plastic plug from the rear band adjustment screw access hole.

6. Clean the rear band adjustment screw threads and apply oil to them.

7. Use tool T58L-7195-A to loosen the rear band adjustment screw lock nut. Tighten the rear band adjustment screw to 10 in-lbs, then back the adjustment screw off 1½ turns. Tighten the lock nut to specifications while holding the adjustment screw from turning.

8. Install the plastic plug in the rear band adjustment screw access hole.

9. Position the console and install the six attaching screws (Fig. 20). Position the floor mat up to the console.

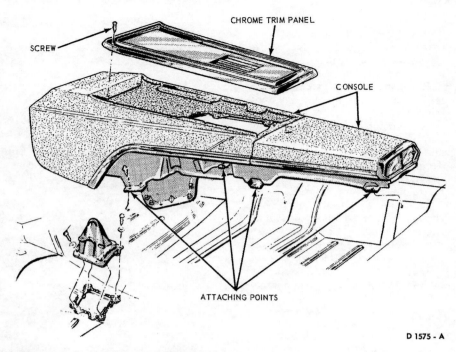

D 1575 - A

FIG. 20—Console Disassembled

10. Connect the wiring and bulb to the selector assembly. Secure the selector housing to the console with the four attaching screws.

11. Place the chrome trim panel over the selector lever handle and rotate it into position on the console. secure with the attaching screws.

12. Raise the car on a hoist. Secure the link (Fig. 15) to the shift lever.

GOVERNOR REPLACEMENT

1. Raise the car so that the transmission extension housing is accessible.

2. Drain the fluid from the transmission.

3. Disconnect the drive shaft from the rear axle and slide the front yoke out of the extension housing.

4. Disconnect the speedometer cable from the extension housing.

5. Remove the two bolts that secure the extension housing to the engine rear support.

6. Remove the nut and bolt that secures the engine rear support to the crossmember.

7. Raise the transmission high enough to provide clearance for the rear mount.

8. Lift the engine rear support from the crossmember.

9. Lower the jack until the extension housing just clears the crossmember to remove all weight from the housing.

10. Loosen the parking brake cable adjustment nut enough to disconnect the cables from the equalizer.

11. Remove the extension housing attaching bolts. Slide the housing off the output shaft and remove the gasket.

12. Remove the governor to counterweight attaching bolts. Lift the governor from the counterweight (Fig. 21).

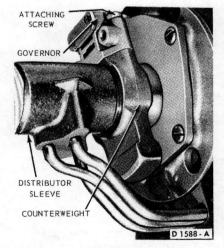

D 1588 - A

FIG. 21—Governor Installed

13. Lubricate the governor valve parts with clean transmission fluid. **Make certain that the valve moves freely in the valve body bore.**

14. Position the governor valve body on the counterweight with the cover facing toward the rear of the car. Install and tighten the two attaching bolts to the specified torque.

15. Position a new extension housing gasket on the rear of the transmission case.

16. Slide the extension housing into place and secure it to the transmission case with the attaching bolts. Torque the bolts to specification.

17. Connect the speedometer cable to the extension housing.

18. Raise the transmission high enough with a jack to position the engine rear support on the crossmember. Secure the support to the crossmember with the attaching bolt.

19. Lower the transmission and remove the jack. Secure the extension housing to the rear support with the two attaching bolts.

20. Connect the parking brake cables to the equalizer and adjust the cables as required.

21. Install the driveshaft.

22. Fill the transmission to the correct level with the specified fluid.

OIL PAN AND CONTROL VALVE BODY REPLACEMENT

1. Raise the car so that the transmission oil pan is accessible.

2. Disconnect the fluid filler tube from the oil pan, and drain the fluid from the transmission. **If the same fluid is to be used again in the transmission, filter the fluid through a 100-mesh screen before installing it in the transmission. Re-use the fluid only if it is in good condition.**

3. Disconnect the hose from the vacuum diaphragm unit. Remove the diaphragm unit using tool FCO-24. **Do not use any tools on the diaphragm housing, such as pliers, pipe wrenches, etc. Do not allow solvents to enter the diaphragm unit.** Remove the push rod.

4. Remove the oil pan and gasket, and discard the gasket.

5. Remove the fluid screen retaining clip and the screen.

6. Remove the two tubes which connect to the pressure regulator and the control valve body. **The regulator lubrication tube (Fig. 22) does not have to be removed.**

7. Loosen the front servo attaching bolts three turns.

8. Remove the three control valve body attaching bolts, and lower the valve body while pulling it off the front servo tubes. **Be careful not to**

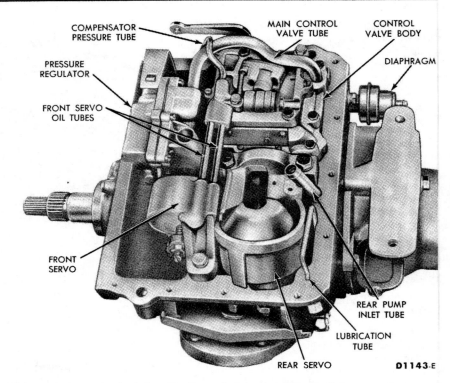

FIG. 22—Typical Hydraulic Control System—PCE Model

damage the valve body or the tubes.

9. Before installing the control valve body, check for a bent manual valve by rolling it on a flat surface.

10. Install the control valve body by aligning the front servo tubes with the holes in the valve body. Shift the manual lever to the L detent, and place the inner downshift lever between the downshift lever stop and the downshift valve. **The manual valve must engage the actuating pin in the manual detent lever.**

11. Install, but do not tighten, the control valve body attaching bolts.

12. Install the tubes to the pressure regulator and the control valve body.

13. Move the control valve body toward the center of the case as far as the attaching bolts will permit. This movement is made to take up clearance between the manual valve and the actuating pin on the manual detent lever

14. Torque the attaching bolts to specification.

15. Turn the manual valve one full turn in each manual lever detent position. If the manual valve binds against the actuating pin in any detent position, loosen the valve body attaching bolts and move the body away from the center of the case. Move the valve body only enough to relieve the binding. Torque the attaching bolts and recheck the manual

valve for binding.

16. Position the push rod in the bore of the vacuum diaphragm unit. Using the diaphragm unit as a guide, insert the push rod into the threaded opening of the case. Torque the diaphragm unit to specification. Connect the vacuum hose.

17. Torque the front servo attaching bolts to specification

18. Adjust the front band.

19. Install the fluid screen and the screen retaining clip.

20. Position a new oil pan gasket on the bottom of the transmission case, and install the oil pan. Torque the oil pan screws to specification.

21. Connect the fluid filler tube to the oil pan, and tighten the fitting securely.

22. Adjust the rear band.

23. Fill the transmission with fluid. **If the fluid that was drained from the transmission is to be used again, filter the fluid through a 100-mesh screen as it is poured back into the transmission. Re-use the fluid only if it is in good condition.**

24. If the control valve body was replaced, adjust the transmission control linkage.

PRESSURE REGULATOR REPLACEMENT

1. Drain the fluid from the transmission, and remove the oil pan and fluid screen.

2. On all models except PCE, remove the pressure regulator lubrication tube.

3. Remove the small compensator pressure tube and the large control pressure tube from the control valve body and the pressure regulator.

4. Remove the pressure regulator spring retainer, springs, and spacer. **Maintain pressure on the retainer to prevent the springs from flying out.**

5. Remove the pressure regulator attaching bolts and washers, and remove the regulator.

6. Position the replacement regulator body on the transmission case and install the two attaching bolts. Torque the bolts to specification.

7. Check the converter pressure and control pressure valves to be sure the valves operate freely in the bores.

8. Install the valve springs, spacer, and retainer.

9. Install the large control pressure tube, and the small compensator pressure tube, and the pressure regulator lubrication tube.

10. Install the fluid screen and the oil pan, and fill the transmission to the correct level with the specified fluid.

FRONT SERVO REPLACEMENT

1. Drain the fluid from the transmission, and remove the oil pan and fluid screen.

2. Remove the vacuum diaphragm unit.

3. On all models except PCE, remove the pressure regulator lubrication tube.

4. Loosen the three control valve body attaching bolts.

5. Remove the attaching bolts from the front servo (Fig. 23), hold the strut with the fingers, and remove the servo.

6. To install the front servo, position the front band forward in the case with the end of the band facing downward. Align the large end of the servo strut with the servo actuating lever, and align the small end with the band end.

7. Rotate the band, strut, and servo to align the anchor end of the band with the anchor in the case.
Push the servo body onto the control valve body tubes.

8. Install the attaching bolts and torque to specification.

9. Torque the control valve body attaching bolts to specification.
Check the clearance between the manual valve and the manual lever actuating pin as given in Oil Pan

and Control Valve Body Replacement.

10. On all models except PCE, install the pressure regulator lubrication tube.

11. Adjust the front band.

12. Install the vacuum diaphragm unit and rod.

13. Install the fluid screen and oil pan, and fill the transmission with fluid.

14. Adjust the downshift and manual linkage.

REAR SERVO REPLACEMENT

1. Drain the fluid from the transmission, and remove the oil pan and fluid screen.

2. Remove the vacuum diaphragm unit.

3. On all models except PCE, remove the pressure regulator lubrication tube.

4. Remove the control valve body and the two front servo oil tubes.

5. Remove the attaching bolts from the rear servo, hold the actuating and anchor struts with the fingers, and remove the servo.

6. To install the rear servo, position the servo anchor strut on the servo band, and rotate the band to engage the strut.

7. Hold the servo anchor strut in position with the fingers, position the actuating lever strut, and install the servo.

8. Install the servo attaching bolts, and torque them to specification. **The longer bolt must be installed in the inner bolt hole.**

9. Install the two front servo tubes and the control valve body.
Check the clearance between the manual valve and the manual lever actuating pin as given above in Oil Pan and Control Valve Body Replacement.

10. Install the pressure regulator lubrication tube.

11. Adjust the rear band

12. Install the fluid screen and oil

pan, and fill the transmission with fluid.

EXTENSION HOUSING BUSHING AND REAR SEAL REPLACEMENT

1. Disconnect the drive shaft from the transmission.

2. Carefully remove the seal with the tool shown in Fig. 23.

3. Remove the bushing as shown in Fig. 24. **Use the bushing remover carefully so that the spline seal is not damaged.**

4. When installing a new bushing use the special tool shown in Fig. 25.

5. Before installing a new seal, inspect the sealing surface of the universal joint yoke for scores. If scores are found, replace the yoke.

6. Inspect the counterbore of the housing for burrs. Polish off all burrs with crocus cloth.

7. Install the seal into the housing with the tool shown in Fig. 26. The seal should be firmly seated in the bore.

PARKING PAWL REPLACEMENT

1. On all models except the console shift, loosen the right front scuff plate and lift the carpet back until the rear band adjusting stud access hole is accessible. On console shift transmissions, remove the necessary console parts to gain access to the rear band adjusting screw.

2. Remove the access hole plug and, with Tool 7195-C or Tool T58L-7195-A, loosen the adjusting stud lock nut. Turn the adjusting stud in until the tool handle overruns. **This will tighten the rear band around the planet carrier and will hold the planet carrier and clutch assemblies in position during the parking pawl repair operation.**

3. Raise the car and drain the fluid from the transmission.

4. Place the adjustable support stand under the rear of the engine.

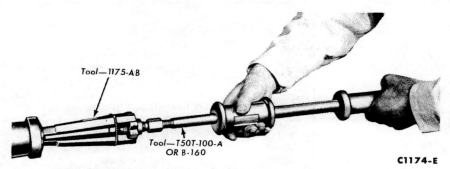

Tool—1175-AB

Tool—T50T-100-A OR B-160

C1174-E

FIG. 23—Removing Extension Housing Seal

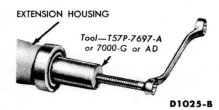

FIG. 24 —Removing Extension Housing Bushing

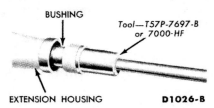

FIG. 25 —Installing Extension Housing Bushing

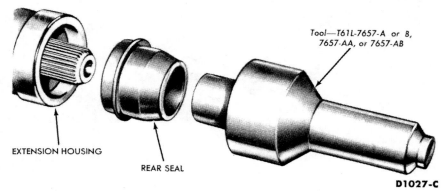

FIG. 26 —Installing Extension Housing Seal

5. Remove the drive shaft.

6. Disconnect the parking brake cables from the crossmember and equalizer bracket.

7. Remove the engine rear support-to-extension housing bolts.

8. Remove the bolt that secures the engine rear support to the crossmember. Raise the engine with the adjustable support stand just high enough to provide clearance for re-

moving the support.

9. Lower the jack until the extension housing just clears the crossmember to remove all weight from the housing.

10. Disconnect the speedometer cable from the transmission.

11. Remove the transmission oil pan and oil screen.

12. Remove the vacuum control diaphragm unit and control rod.

13. Remove the main control valve assembly retaining bolts and valve assembly.

14. Remove the tubes that go from the case into the rear pump.

15. Remove the extension housing attaching bolts and housing.

16. Remove the output shaft and rear pump assembly from the case.

17. Remove the parking pawl pin from the case with a magnet.

18. Working from inside of the case, drive on the shoulder of the toggle lever (Fig. 52) pin with a small punch to move the retaining plug part way out of the case. Remove the plug with a pair of pliers.

19. To remove the toggle lever pin, slide the toggle lever toward the front of the case. Cock the lever to one side to apply pressure on the pin, then move the toggle to the rear of

the case to move the pin outward. Repeat this procedure until the pin can be removed from the case. Lift the pawl and toggle from the case as an assembly.

20. Remove the pawl and toggle lever as an assembly.

21. Position the new parking pawl and link assembly, then install the toggle lever pin and the plug.

22. Secure the pawl to the case with the pawl pin.

23. Position a new gasket on the front of the pump and at the rear. Hold them in place with transmission fluid.

24. Make sure that the thrust washer is in place, then position the pump and output shaft in place making sure that the distributor sleeve tubes are entered in the case

25. Install the rear pump discharge tube and new O-ring.

26. Secure the extension housing to the case with the attaching bolts.

27. Install the main control valve assembly.

28. Adjust the front band.

29. Position the vacuum control rod in the case. Install the vacuum diaphragm unit.

30. Install the screen, oil pan and a new gasket.

31. Connect the speedometer cable to the extension housing.

32. Raise the transmission high enough to position the engine rear support on the crossmember. Secure the support with the attaching bolt.

33. Lower the transmission and remove the jack. Install the two extension housing-to-engine rear support attaching bolts.

34. Connect the parking brake cables to the equalizer.

35. Install the driveshaft, then lower the car.

36. Adjust the rear band.

37. Fill the transmission to the correct level with the specified fluid.

---

3 REMOVAL AND INSTALLATION

TRANSMISSION AND CONVERTER REPLACEMENT

REMOVAL

1. Drive the car on a hoist, **but do not raise it at this time.**

2. Remove the two upper bolts and lock washers which attach the converter housing to the engine.

3. Raise the car, and remove the cover from the lower front side of

the converter housing.

4. Remove one of the converter drain plugs. Then rotate the converter 180° and remove the other plug. **Do not attempt to turn the converter with a wrench on the converter stud nuts.** If desired, the converter may be drained after the unit has been removed from the car.

5. Disconnect the fluid filler tube from the transmission oil pan. Dis-

connect the vacuum hose from the vacuum diaphragm unit and the tube from the extension housing clip.

6. When the fluid has stopped draining from the transmission and converter, remove the flywheel to converter nuts and flat washers. Install the drain plugs in the converter and torque to specifications. Install the converter housing front plate to hold the converter in place when the

transmission is removed.

7. Disconnect the starter cables from the starter and remove the starter.

8. Disconnect the oil cooler lines from the transmission. Remove the transmission vent tube.

9. Disconnect the manual and downshift linkage from the transmission.

10. Disconnect the speedometer cable from the extension housing, and remove the drive shaft.

11. Support the transmission on a stand. Remove the engine rear support to transmission bolts, and raise the transmission slightly to take the weight off the cross member. Remove the cross member. Support the rear part of the engine.

12. Remove the remaining converter housing to engine attaching bolts. Move the assembly to the rear and down to remove it.

INSTALLATION

1. If the converter has been removed from the converter housing, carefully position the converter in the housing, and then install the housing lower front cover plate to prevent the converter from slipping out of the housing.

2. Install the transmission vent tube. Rotate the converter until the studs adjacent to the drain plugs are in a vertical position.

3. Rotate the flywheel as required to align the drain plug holes with the drainplugs in the converter. With the transmission mounted on a support stand, move the converter and transmission assembly forward into position, using care not to damage the flywheel and the converter pilot.

4. Install the converter lower housing-to-engine bolts, then torque the bolts to specification.

5. Install the cross member.

6. Lower the transmission until the extension housing rests on the cross member, and then install the extension housing-to-cross member bolts.

7. **The converter must rest squarely against the flywheel. This indicates that the converter pilot is not binding in the engine crankshaft.**

8. Install the converter attaching nuts and flat washers. Install the access plates.

9. Connect the oil cooler inlet and outlet lines to the transmission case.

10. Coat the front universal joint yoke seal and spline with B8A-

19589-A lubricant, and install the drive shaft.

11. Connect the speedometer cable at the transmission.

12. Connect the manual linkage at the transmission manual lever.

13. Connect the downshift linkage and bushing at the transmission throttle lever.

14. Install the starter motor.

15. Connect the fluid filler tube to the oil pan. Connect the vacuum hose to the vacuum diaphragm unit and the tube to its clip.

16. Lower the transmission support stand. Then install the upper two converter housing-to-engine bolts and tighten them to specification.

17. Fill the transmission with transmission fluid, following the recommended procedure.

18. Check the transmission, converter assembly, and fluid cooler lines for fluid leaks, and then adjust the manual and downshift linkages.

TRANSMISSION REPLACEMENT WITHOUT CONVERTER

The frame construction of the convertible will not permit the transmission to be moved rearward enough to clear the turbine shaft from the converter. For this reason, the converter and transmission must be removed as a unit from this model.

REMOVAL

1. Raise the car on a hoist.

2. Disconnect the hose from the vacuum diaphragm unit and the tube from its clip. Disconnect the fluid filler tube from the oil pan, and drain the fluid.

3. Remove the cover from the lower front side of the converter housing.

4. Remove one of the converter drain plugs. Then rotate the converter 180° and remove the other plug. **Do not attempt to turn the converter with a wrench on the converter stud nuts.**

5. Disconnect the drive shaft from the rear axle, and remove the drive shaft.

6. Disconnect the fluid cooler lines from the transmission. Remove the vent tube.

7. Disconnect the manual and downshift linkage at the transmission.

8. Disconnect the speedometer cable at the extension housing.

9. Remove the two engine rear support to transmission bolts.

10. Position a transmission jack under the transmission and raise it

slightly to take the weight off the cross member.

11. Remove the cross member bolts and cross member. With the transmission jack in position, remove the four transmission to converter housing bolts.

12. Support the engine. Tilt the rear of the transmission assembly slightly upward, and with the jack move the assembly toward the rear until it is clear of the turbine shaft. Lower the assembly and remove it from the car.

INSTALLATION

1. Install guide pins in the two top transmission to converter housing attaching bolt holes.

2. Mount the transmission on the jack. **Be sure to align the turbine shaft splines with the turbine splines and the converter impeller lugs with the slots in the front pump drive gear.**

3. Raise the transmission, move it toward the front of the car, and position it on the converter housing.

4. Install the transmission to converter housing lower attaching bolts. Remove the two guide pins and install the two upper attaching bolts. Torque the bolts to specification.

5. Install the frame cross member and bolts.

6. Lower the transmission onto the cross member, and install the engine rear support to transmission bolts.

7. Connect the oil cooler to transmission oil inlet and outlet lines to the transmission. Tighten the fittings securely. Install the vent tube

8. **Lubricate the front universal slip yoke seal and spline with B8A-19589-A lubricant.** Slide the universal joint yoke onto the output shaft, and then connect the drive shaft at the rear axle.

9. Connect the speedometer cable to the extension housing.

10. Connect the manual and downshift linkage at the transmission.

11. Adjust the linkage.

12. Check the operation of the starter neutral switch. Adjust if necessary.

13. Connect the fluid filler tube to the oil pan. Tighten the fittings securely. Connect the hose to the vacuum diaphragm unit and the tube to the clip.

14. Lower the car to the floor and fill the transmission with the specified transmission fluid. Check the fluid level with the transmission at normal operating temperature.

4 MAJOR REPAIR OPERATIONS

DISASSEMBLY OF TRANSMISSION

1. Before removing any of the transmission sub-assemblies, thoroughly clean the outside of the transmission case to prevent dirt from getting inside the mechanism.

2. After the transmission has been removed from the car, place the assembly in the transmission holder shown in Fig. 27.

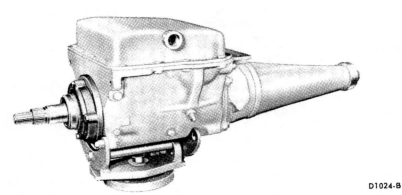

FIG. 27 —Transmission Mounted on Bench

3. Remove the oil pan, gasket, and screen clip.

4. Lift the screen off the forward tube, and then lift it off the rear tube.

5. Remove the spring seat from the pressure regulator. **Maintain constant pressure on the spring seat to prevent distortion of the spring seat and the sudden release of the springs.** Remove the pressure regulator springs and pilots, but do not remove the valves.

6. Loosen, **but do not remove,** the regulator body attaching bolts. Remove the lubrication tube. If necessary, tap the tube with a soft-faced hammer. **Be careful not to bend or distort the tube.**

7. Lift the rear pump intake tube out of the bore in the transmission case. **Be careful not to bend the tube.**

8. Remove the small compensator pressure tube. Then remove the large control pressure tube from the pressure regulator and the control valve body. If necessary, tap the tubes with a soft-faced hammer but do not distort them.

9. Loosen the front and rear servo band adjusting screws five turns. Loosen the front servo attaching bolts three turns.

10. Remove the vacuum diaphragm unit and push rod.

11. Remove the control valve body attaching bolts. Align the levers to permit removal of the valve body. Then lift the valve body clear of the transmission case. Pull the body off the servo tubes and remove it from the case.

12. Remove the regulator body from the case. **Keep the control pressure valve and the converter pressure regulator valve in the pressure regulator to avoid damage to the valves.**

13. Remove the front servo apply and release tubes by twisting and pulling at the same time. Remove the front servo attaching bolts. Hold the front servo strut with the fingers, and lift the servo from the case.

14. Remove the rear servo attaching bolts. Hold the actuating and anchor struts with the fingers, and lift the servo from the case.

TRANSMISSION END PLAY CHECK

1. Remove one of the front pump attaching bolts. Mount the dial indicator support tool in the front pump bolt hole. Mount a dial indicator on the support so that the contact rests on the end of the turbine shaft as shown in Fig. 28.

2. Install the extension housing seal replacer on the output shaft to provide support for the shaft.

3. Pry the front clutch cylinder to the rear of the transmission with a large screwdriver (Fig. 28). Set the dial indicator at zero while maintaining a slight pressure on the screwdriver.

4. Remove the screwdriver and pry the units toward the front of the transmission by inserting the screwdriver between the large internal gear and the transmission case (Fig. 28).

5. Record the indicator reading for use during transmission assembly. End play should be 0.010-0.029

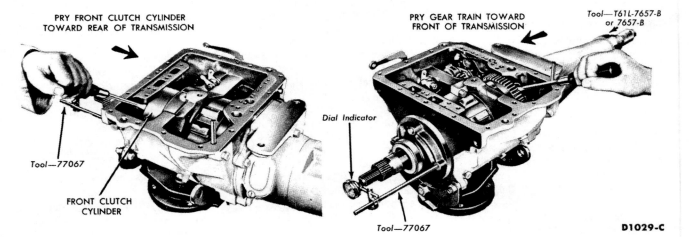

FIG. 28 —Checking Transmission End Play

inch (minimum end play is preferred). If end play is not within specifications a new selective thrust washer must be used when the transmission is assembled.

6. Remove the indicator support, and then remove the seal replacer from the output shaft.

REMOVAL OF CASE AND EXTENSION HOUSING PARTS

1. Remove the remaining front pump attaching bolts. Then remove the front pump and gasket. **If necessary, tap the screw bosses with a soft-faced hammer to loosen the pump from the case.**

2. Remove the lubrication tube from the case. Remove the five transmission to extension housing bolts. These bolts also attach the rear pump to the case. Remove the extension housing. Install the discharge tube extractor tool in the rear pump discharge tube (Fig. 29) and remove the tube.

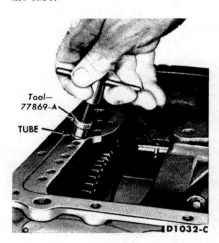

FIG. 29—Removing Rear Pump Discharge Tube

3. Remove the output shaft assembly (Fig. 30). Be careful not to bend the pressure tubes between the distributor sleeve and case as the tubes are removed from the case.

4. A nylon speedometer drive gear is used on the output shaft and is a 0.004-0.010 inch shrink fit. If gear replacement is necessary, the old type steel gear may be used.

5. To remove the nylon drive gear, place the output shaft assembly on the bench and remove the oil distributor tubes from the sleeve. Remove the speedometer drive gear snap ring from the shaft. Pry the oil delivery sleeve toward the rear of the shaft with a hammer handle. Make

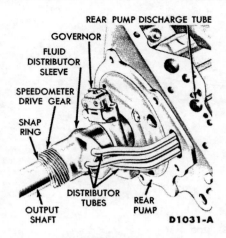

FIG. 30—Rear Pump and Output Shaft Installed

certain to apply pressure on the governor counterweight, and not against the governor valve body (Fig. 31).

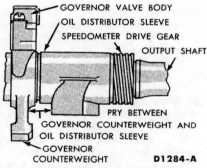

FIG. 31—Pressure Apply Area for Removing Speedometer Gear

6. Slide the oil delivery sleeve toward the front of the transmission.

7. Using a hammer and a small brass drift, tap the gear evenly and alternately (Fig. 32) to prevent cock-

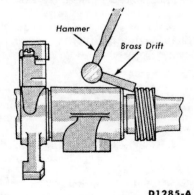

FIG. 32—Removing Speedometer Drive Gear

ing it on the shaft. Tap the gear gently to prevent damaging it.

8. If the drive gear ball does not fall out as the speedometer gear is removed, remove the ball from the seat in the output shaft.

9. Remove the distributor sleeve. Remove the four seal rings from the output shaft with the fingers to prevent breaking the rings.

10. Remove the governor snap ring from the output shaft. Slide the governor assembly off the output shaft. Then remove the governor drive ball. Remove the rear pump, extension housing and pump gaskets. On PCE models, remove the rear pump thrust washer and race (Fig. 33).

11. Remove the rear pump drive key from the output shaft. Then remove the bronze thrust washer from the output shaft.

12. Remove the selective thrust washer from the rear of the pinion carrier.

13. Remove the two seal rings from the primary sun gear shaft. Remove the pinion carrier.

14. Remove the primary sun gear rear thrust bearing and races from the pinion carrier.

15. Note the rear band position for reference in assembly. The end of the band next to the adjusting screw has a depression (dimple) in the center of the boss. Squeeze the ends of the rear band together, tilt the band to the rear, and remove the rear band from the case.

16. Remove the two center support outer bolts (one each side) from the transmission case.

17. Exert enough pressure on the end of the input shaft to hold the clutch units together. Then remove the center support and the front and rear clutch assemblies as a unit (Fig. 34).

18. Install the clutch assemblies in the bench fixture (Fig. 35).

19. Remove the thrust washer from the front of the input shaft.

20. Remove the front band from the case. Lift the front clutch assembly from the primary sun gear shaft.

21. Remove the bronze and the steel thrust washers from the rear clutch assembly. Wire the thrust washers together to assure correct installation.

22. Remove the front clutch seal rings from the primary sun gear shaft.

23. Lift the rear clutch assembly from the primary sun gear shaft.

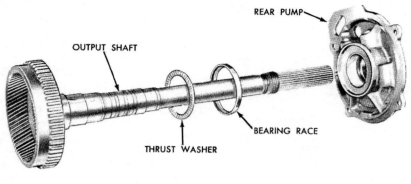

D1289-A

FIG. 33—Rear Pump Thrust Washer and Race

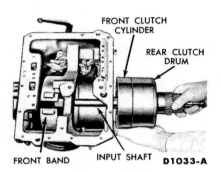

D1033-A

FIG. 34—Removing or Installing Input Shaft and Clutch

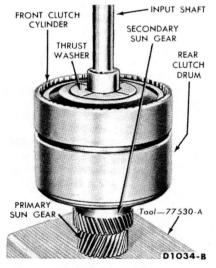

Tool—77530-A

D1034-B

FIG. 35—Input Shaft and Clutch in Holding Fixture

24. Remove the rear clutch seal rings from the primary sun gear shaft. **Do not break the seal rings.**

25. Remove the primary sun gear front thrust washer.

PARTS REPAIR AND REPLACEMENT

During the repair of the sub-assemblies, certain general instructions which apply to all units of the transmission must be followed. These instructions are given here to avoid unnecessary repetition.

Handle all transmission parts carefully to avoid nicking or burring the bearing or mating surfaces.

Lubricate all internal parts of the transmission with transmission fluid before assembly. **Do not use any other lubricants except on gaskets and thrust washers which may be coated with vaseline to facilitate assembly. Always install new gaskets when assembling parts of the transmission.**

Tighten all bolts and screws to the recommended torque. For detail cleaning and inspection operations refer to Part 7-1.

PRIMARY SUN GEAR SHAFT

1. Position the primary sun gear shaft in the clutch bench fixture.

2. Check the fit of the seal rings in their respective bores. A clearance of 0.002-0.009 inch should exist between the ends of the rings.

3. Install the seal rings on the shaft, and check for free movement in the grooves.

REAR CLUTCH

1. Remove the clutch pressure plate snap ring, and remove the pressure plate from the drum. Remove the bronze and steel plates.

2. Compress the spring with the tools shown in Fig. 36 and remove the snap ring.

3. Guide the spring retainer while releasing the pressure to prevent the retainer from locking in the snap ring groove.

4. Position the primary sun gear

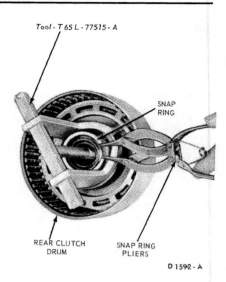

Tool - T 65 L - 77515 - A

D 1592 - A

FIG. 36—Removing Rear Clutch Spring Snap Ring

shaft in the rear clutch. Place an air hose nozzle in one of the holes in the shaft, and place one finger over the other hole. Then force the clutch piston out of the clutch drum with air pressure. **Hold one hand over the piston to prevent damage.**

5. Remove the clutch piston inner seal ring from the clutch drum. Remove the clutch piston outer seal ring from the groove in the piston.

6. Lubricate all parts to facilitate assembly. Install the clutch piston inner seal ring in the groove in the drum. Install a new outer seal ring on the piston, and install the piston in the clutch drum.

7. Install the clutch release spring, and position the retainer on the spring.

8. Install the tool on the spring retainer as shown in Fig. 36. Compress the clutch spring, and install the snap ring. **While compressing the spring, guide the retainer to avoid interference of the retainer with the snap ring groove. Make sure the snap ring is fully seated in the groove.** On all models except PCE, when new composition clutch plates are used, soak the plates in automatic transmission fluid for 15 minutes before they are assembled.

9. Install the composition and the steel clutch plates alternately, starting with a steel plate.

10. Install the clutch pressure plate with the bearing surface down. Then install the clutch pressure plate snap ring. Make sure the snap ring is fully seated in the groove.

11. Install the thrust washer on

the primary sun gear shaft. Lubricate all parts with automatic transmission fluid or petroleum jelly. Install the two center seal rings.

12. Install the rear clutch on the primary sun gear shaft. **Be sure all of the needles are in the hub if the unit is equipped with loose needle bearings.** Assemble two seal rings in the front grooves.

13. Install the steel and the bronze thrust washers on the front of the secondary sun gear assembly. If the steel washer is chamfered, place the chamfered side down.

FRONT CLUTCH

1. Remove the clutch cover snap ring with a screwdriver, and remove the input shaft from the clutch drum.

2. Remove the thrust washer from the thrust surface of the clutch hub. Insert one finger in the clutch hub, and lift the hub straight up to remove the hub from the clutch drum.

3. Remove the composition and the steel clutch plates, and then remove the pressure plate from the clutch drum.

4. Place the front clutch spring compressor on the release spring, position the clutch drum on the bed of an arbor press, and compress the release spring with the arbor press until the release spring snap ring can be removed (Fig. 37).

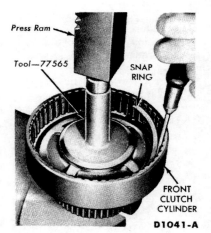

FIG. 37—Removing Front Clutch Snap Ring

5. Remove the clutch release spring from the clutch drum.

6. Install the special nozzle shown in Fig. 38 on an air hose. Place the nozzle against the clutch apply hole in the front clutch housing, and force the piston out of the housing.

7. Remove the piston inner seal

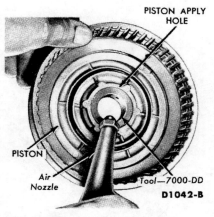

FIG. 38—Removing Front Clutch Piston

from the clutch housing. Remove the piston outer seal from the groove in the piston.

8. Lubricate all parts with transmission fluid. Install a new piston inner seal ring in the clutch cylinder. Install a new piston outer seal in the groove in the piston.

9. Install the piston in the clutch housing. **Make sure the steel bearing ring is in place on the piston.**

10. Position the release spring in the clutch cylinder with the concave side up. Place the release spring compressor on the spring, and compress the spring with an arbor press. Then install the snap ring as shown in Fig. 37. **Make sure the snap ring is fully seated in the groove.**

11. Install the front clutch housing on the primary sun gear shaft by rotating the clutch units to mesh the rear clutch plates with the serrations on the clutch hub. **Do not break the seal rings.**

12. Install the clutch hub in the clutch cylinder with the deep counterbore down (Fig. 39). Install the thrust washer on the clutch hub.

13. Install the pressure plate in the clutch cylinder with the bearing surface up (Fig. 40). Install the bronze composition and the steel clutch plates alternately, starting with a bronze plate (Fig. 41). Lubricate the plates as they are installed.

14. Install the turbine shaft in the clutch cylinder, and then install the snap ring. **Make sure the snap ring is fully seated in the groove.**

15. Install the thrust washer on the turbine shaft.

FRONT PUMP

1. Remove the stator support attaching screws and remove the

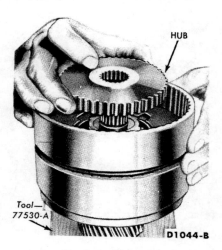

FIG. 39—Installing Clutch Hub

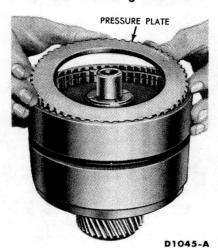

FIG. 40—Installing Pressure Plate

FIG. 41—Installing Clutch Plate

stator support. Mark the top surface of the pump driven gear with Prussian blue to assure correct assembly. **Do not scratch the pump gears.**

2. Remove the drive and driven gears from the pump body.

3. Refer to Fig. 42 for a disassembled view of the front pump. Inspect the pump body housing, drive gear

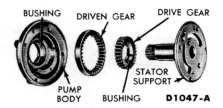

FIG. 42—Front Pump Disassembled

bushing, gear pockets, and crescent for scores.

4. If any parts other than the stator support are found defective, replace the pump as a unit. Minor burrs and scores may be removed with crocus cloth. The stator support is serviced separately.

5. Bolt the front pump to the transmission case with capscrews.

6. Install the oil seal remover shown in Fig. 43. Then pull the front seal from the pump body.

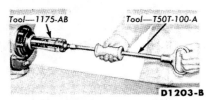

FIG. 43—Removing Front Pump Seal

7. Clean the pump body counterbore. Then inspect the bore for rough spots. Smooth up the counterbore with crocus cloth.

8. Remove the pump body from the transmission case.

9. Coat the outer diameter of a new seal with FoMoCo Sealing Compound, or its equivalent. Then position the seal in the pump body. Drive the seal into the pump body with the tool shown in Fig. 44 until the seal is firmly seated in the body. Tool 77837 may be reworked (Fig. 45) to install the latest typeseal.

10. Place the pump driven gear in the pump body with the mark on the gear facing upward. Install the drive gear in the pump body.

11. Install the stator support and attaching screws. Check the pump gears for free rotation.

REAR PUMP

1. Remove the screws and lock washers which secure the pump cover to the pump body, and remove the cover. Mark the top face of the pump drive and driven gear with Prussian blue to assure correct installation of gears at assembly (Fig.

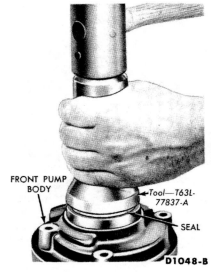

FIG. 44—Installing Front Pump Seal

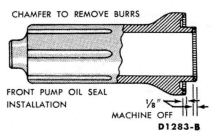

FIG. 45—Front Pump Seal Installing Tool Modification Drawing

46). Do not scratch or make punch marks on the pump gears.

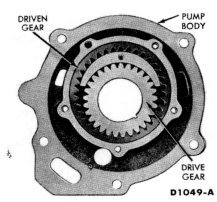

FIG. 46—Rear Pump Gears

2. Remove the drive and driven gears from the pump body.

3. Place the pump drive gear in the pump body with the mark (placed on the gear at disassembly) facing upward.

4. Install the drive gear in the pump body with the mark facing up-

ward. Install the pump cover, attaching screws, and lock washers. Torque the screws to specification.

5. Check the pump for free rotation of the gears.

PRESSURE REGULATOR

1. Remove the valves from the regulator body.

2. Remove the regulator body cover attaching screws, and remove the cover (Fig. 47).

3. Remove the separator plate. Then remove the front pump check valve and spring from the regulator cover.

4. Wash all parts thoroughly in clean solvent and blow dry with moisture-free compressed air.

5. Inspect the regulator body and cover mating surfaces for burrs.

6. Check all fluid passages for obstructions.

7. Inspect the control pressure and converter pressure valves and bores for burrs and scores. Remove all burrs carefully with crocus cloth.

8. Check the free movement of the valve in their bores. Each valve should fall freely into its bore when both the valve and bore are dry.

9. Inspect the valve springs for distortion.

10. Position the check valve spring and valve in the regulator cover.

11. Position the separator plate on the regulator cover.

12. Position the regulator cover and separator plate on the regulator body, and install the attaching screws. Torque the screws to specification.

13. Insert the valves in the pressure regulator body (Fig. 47).

CONTROL VALVE BODY

During the disassembly of the control valve assembly, avoid damage to valve parts and keep the valve parts clean. Place the valve assembly on a clean shop towel while performing the disassembly operation. **Do not separate the upper and lower valve bodies and cover until after the valves have been removed.**

Disassembly

1. Remove the manual valve (Fig. 48).

2. Remove the throttle valve body and the separator plate. Remove the throttle valve and retainer.

3. Remove one screw attaching the separator plate to the lower valve body. Remove the upper body

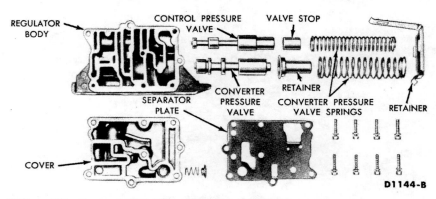

REGULATOR BODY — CONTROL PRESSURE VALVE — VALVE STOP — SEPARATOR PLATE — CONVERTER PRESSURE VALVE — RETAINER — CONVERTER PRESSURE VALVE SPRINGS — RETAINER — COVER

D1144-B

FIG. 47—Pressure Regulator Disassembled

front plate. **The plate is spring-loaded. Apply pressure to the plate while removing the attaching screws.**

4. Remove the compensator sleeve and plug, and remove the compensator valve springs. Remove the compensator valve.

5. Remove the throttle boost short valve and sleeve. Remove the throttle boost valve spring and valve.

6. Remove the downshift valve and spring.

7. Remove the upper valve body rear plate.

8. Remove the compensator cut back valve.

9. Remove the lower body side plate (Fig. 48). **The plate is spring-loaded. Apply pressure to the plate while removing the attaching screws.**

10. Remove the 1-2 shift valve and spring. Remove the inhibitor valve and spring.

11. Remove the two screws attaching the separator plate to the cover. Remove the lower body end plate. **The end plate is spring-loaded. Apply pressure to the plate while removing the attaching screws.**

12. Remove the rear servo lockout valve and spring.

13. Remove the 2-3 delay and throttle reducing valve sleeve, the throttle reducing valve, spring, and the 2-3 shift delay valve. Remove the 2-3 shift valve spring and valve.

14. Remove the transition valve.

15. Remove the plate (Fig. 48) from the valve body cover.

16. Remove the check ball spring and check ball. Remove the 3-2 kickdown control valve spring and valve.

17. Remove the 3-2 coasting control valve spring retainer from the cover. Remove the spring and valve.

18. Remove the through bolts and screws. Then separate the bodies.

19. Inspect the rear pump check valve for freedom of movement.

This valve seat in the lower body is staked for a firm fit and should not be removed unless a new one is to be installed.

Assembly

1. Arrange all parts in their correct positions (Fig. 48). Rotate the valves and plugs when inserting them in their bores to avoid shearing of soft body castings.

2. Position the separator plate on the upper body.

3. Be sure that the rear pump check valve spring, valve, and seat in the lower body are correctly installed. Position the lower body on the upper body, and start **but do not tighten** the attaching screws.

4. Position the cover and separator plate on the lower body and start the four through bolts.

5. Align the separator with the upper and lower valve body attaching bolt holes. Install and torque the four valve body bolts to specification. **Excessive tightening of these bolts may distort the valve bodies, causing valves or plugs to stick.**

6. Install the 3-2 kickdown control valve and spring and the check ball and spring in the cover. Install the plate.

7. Install the 3-2 coasting control valve, spring, and spring retainer in the cover.

8. Install the transition valve in the lower body.

9. Install the 2-3 shift valve and spring. Install the 2-3 shift delay valve and the spring and throttle reducing valve in the sleeve. Slide the sleeve and valve into position in the lower body.

10. Install the rear servo lockout valve spring and valve. Install the lower body end plate.

11. Install the inhibitor valve spring and valve in the lower body.

12. Install the 1-2 shift valve

spring and valve. Install the lower body side plate.

13. Install the compensator cut-back valve in the upper body. Install the upper body rear plate.

14. Install the downshift valve spring and valve.

15. Install the throttle boost valve and spring. Install the throttle boost short valve and sleeve.

16. Install the compensator valve, inner and outer compensator springs, and the compensator sleeve and plug.

17. Position the front plate. Apply pressure to the plate while installing the two attaching screws.

18. Install the throttle valve and retainer in the throttle valve body. Position the separator on the upper body and install the throttle valve body. Install the three attaching screws.

19. Install four screws attaching the cover to the lower body, two screws attaching the separator plate to the upper body, and one screw attaching the separator plate to lower body. Torque the cover and body screws to specification.

20. Install the manual valve.

GOVERNOR

1. Remove the governor valve body cover.

2. Remove the valve body from the counterweight.

3. Remove the plug, sleeve, and the valve and spring from the body (Fig. 49).

4. Install the governor valve and spring assembly in the bore of the valve body. Install the sleeve, and plug.

5. Install the body on the counterweight. **Make sure the fluid passages in the body and the counterweight are aligned.**

6. Position the valve body cover on the body, and install the screws.

FRONT SERVO

1. Remove the servo piston retainer snap ring (Fig. 50). The servo piston is spring-loaded. **Apply pressure to the piston when removing the snap ring.**

2. Remove the servo piston retainer, servo piston, and the return piston from the servo body. It may be necessary to tap the piston stem lightly with a soft-faced hammer to separate the piston retainer from the servo body.

3. Remove the screw and washer

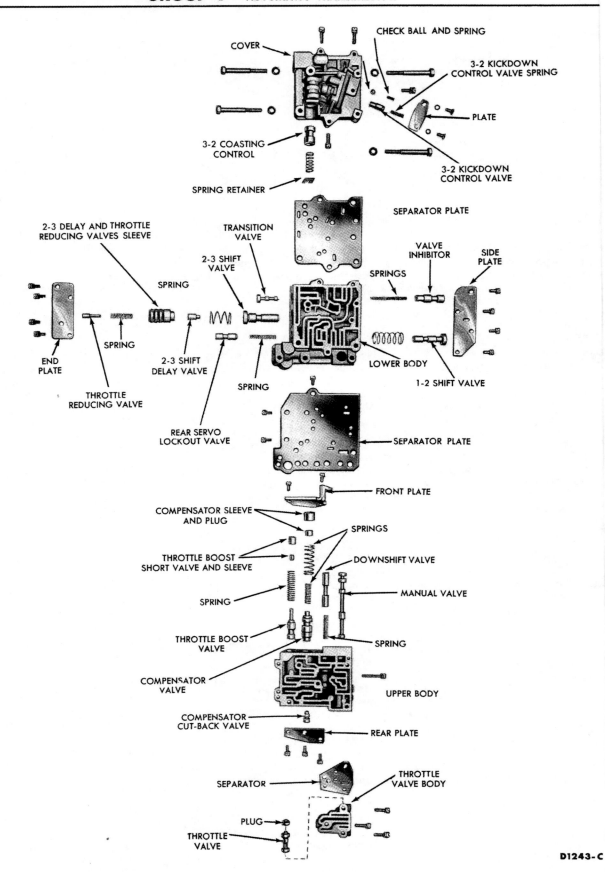

FIG. 48—Control Valve Disassembled

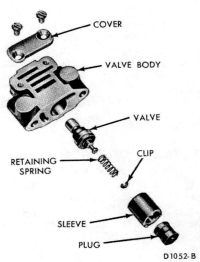

FIG. 49—Governor Disassembled

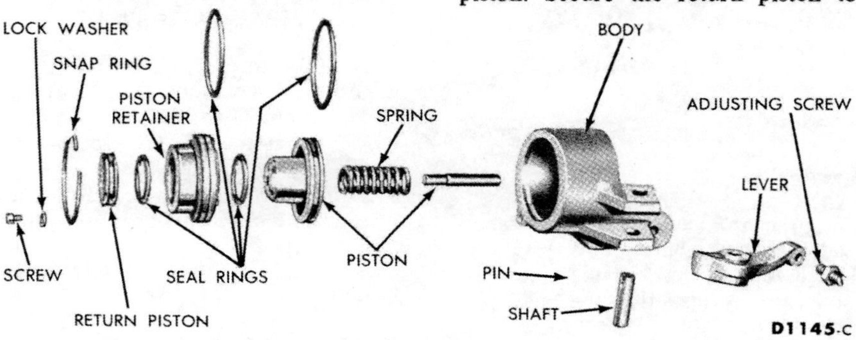

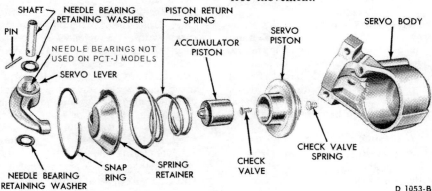

FIG. 50—Front Servo—Disassembled

from the end of the piston stem, and separate the piston retainer, return piston, and servo piston.

4. Remove all the seal rings, and remove the spring from the servo body.

5. Inspect the servo body for cracks and the piston bore and the servo piston stem for scores (Fig. 50).

Check fluid passages for obstructions.

6. Check the actuating lever for free movement, and inspect it for wear. If it is necessary to replace the actuating lever or shaft, remove the retaining pin and push the shaft out of the bracket. If the shaft is not retained by a pin, it is retained in the body by serrations on one end of the shaft. These serrations cause a press fit at that end. To remove the shaft, press on the end opposite the serrations.

Inspect the adjusting screw threads and the threads in the lever.

7. Check the servo spring and servo band strut for distortion.

8. Inspect the servo band lining

for excessive wear and bonding to the metal. **The band should be replaced if worn to a point where the grooves are not clearly evident.**

9. Inspect the band ends for cracks and check the band for distortion.

10. Lubricate all parts of the front servo with transmission fluid to facilitate assembly.

11. Install the inner and outer O-rings on the piston retainer. Install a new O-ring on the return piston and on the servo piston.

12. Tap the piston stem into the servo piston (Fig. 50). Insert the servo piston in the piston retainer. Tap the return piston onto the piston stem and into the piston retainer. Make certain that the dished side of the return piston is toward the servo piston. Secure the return piston to

the stem with a screw and plain washer.

13. Position the servo piston release spring in the servo body. Install the servo piston, retainer, and return piston in the servo body as an assembly. Compress the assembly into the body, and secure it with the snap ring. **Make sure the snap ring is fully seated in the groove.**

14. Install the adjusting screw and

locknut in the actuating lever if they were previously removed.

REAR SERVO

1. Remove the servo actuating lever shaft retaining pin with a 1/8-inch punch. Remove the shaft and actuating lever needle bearings and thrust washers. The servo used on model PCT-J-3 transmissions is not provided with needle bearings.

2. Press down on the servo spring retainer, and remove the snap ring. **Release the pressure on the retainer slowly to prevent the spring from flying out.**

3. Remove the retainer and servo spring (Fig. 51).

4. Force the piston out of the servo body with air pressure. Hold one hand over the piston to prevent damage.

5. Remove the piston seal ring. Remove the accumulator piston from the servo piston.

6. Install the accumulator piston in the servo piston.

7. Install a new seal ring on the servo piston.

8. Install the piston in the servo body. **Lubricate the parts to facilitate assembly.** Install the servo spring with the small coiled end against the servo piston.

9. Install the spring retainer. Compress the spring with a C-clamp. Then install the snap ring. **The snap ring must be fully seated in the groove.**

10. Install the needle bearings in the actuating lever. Install the actuating lever and thrust washers with the socket in the lever bearing on the piston stem. Install the actuating lever shaft, aligning the retaining pin holes, and install the pin.

11. Check the actuating lever for free movement.

FIG. 51—Rear Servo—Disassembled

TRANSMISSION CASE AND LINKAGE REPAIR

Disassembly

1. Remove the inner downshift lever shaft nut (Fig. 52). Then remove the inner downshift lever.

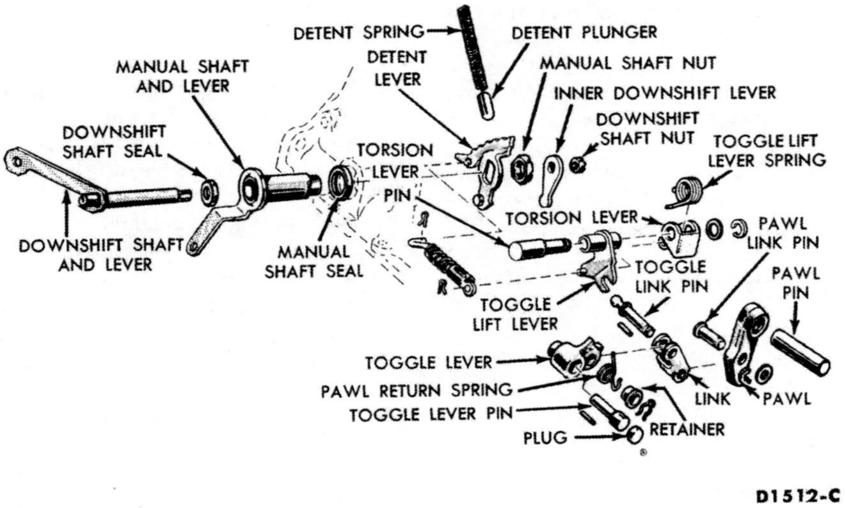

FIG. 52—Transmission Case Control Linkage

2. Remove the outer downshift lever and shaft. Remove the downshift shaft seal from the counterbore in the manual lever shaft.

3. Remove the cotter pin from the parking pawl toggle operating rod and remove the clip from the parking pawl operating lever. Remove the parking pawl operating rod.

4. Rotate the manual shaft until the detent lever clears the detent plunger. Then remove the detent plunger and spring. **Do not allow the detent plunger to fly out of the case.**

5. Remove the manual lever shaft nut, and remove the detent lever. Remove the outer manual lever and shaft from the transmission case.

6. Tap the toggle lever sharply toward the rear of the case to remove the plug and pin.

7. Remove the pawl pin by working the pawl back and forth. Remove the pawl and toggle lever assembly, and then disassemble.

8. Remove the manual shaft seal and case vent tube. On PCE models remove the oil cooler return check valve from the back of the case.

Assembly

1. Coat the outer diameter of a new manual shaft seal with sealer, then install the seal in the case with a driver.

2. Install the vent tube in the transmission case.

3. Assemble the link to the pawl with the pawl link pin, washer, and pawl return spring. Assemble the toggle lever to the link with the toggle link pin. Position the pawl return spring over the toggle link pin, and secure it in place with the washer and the small retainer clip (Fig. 52). Install the assembly in the transmission case by installing the pawl pin and the toggle lever pin. Install the torsion lever assembly. Position the spring on the torsion lever with a screwdriver. Make certain that the short side of toggle does not extend beyond the largest diameter of the ball on the toggle lever pin (Fig. 52). Tap the toggle lever in or out as necessary to center the toggle lever on the ball.

4. Install the manual lever and shaft in the transmission case. Position the detent lever on the shaft, and secure it with a nut. Tighten the nut to 35-40 ft-lbs torque. Rotate the manual lever to the rear of the case. Position the detent spring in the case. Hold the detent plug on the spring with a 3/16-inch socket wrench, then depress the spring until the plug is flush with the case. Carefully rotate the manual lever to the front of the case to secure the plug. **A piece of thin walled tubing may be used to depress the plug if a small socket wrench is not available.**

5. Position the ends of the parking pawl operating rod in the detent lever and toggle lift lever, and secure with the two small retaining pins.

6. Install a new seal on the downshift lever shaft, then install the lever and shaft in the case. Position the inner downshift lever on the inner end of the shaft with the mark O facing toward the center of the case. Install the lock washer and nut, then tighten the nut to 35-40 ft-lbs torque.

7. Check the operation of the linkage. The linkage should operate freely without binding.

ASSEMBLY OF TRANSMISSION

Do not use force to assemble mating parts. If the parts do not assemble freely, examine them for the cause of the difficulty. **Always use new gaskets and seals during the assembly operations.**

CLUTCH ASSEMBLIES

1. Install the front band in the transmission case so that the anchor end is aligned with the anchor in the case.

2. Make sure the thrust washer is in place on the input shaft. Lift the clutch assemblies out of the holding block. **Do not allow the clutches to separate.**

3. Install the clutch sub-assemblies in the transmission case while positioning the servo band on the drum. Hold the units together while installing them (Fig. 34).

CENTER SUPPORT, ONE-WAY CLUTCH, PINION CARRIER, AND OUTPUT SHAFT

The production center supports are chamfered at the edge of the race (Fig. 53). The service center supports are not chamfered. The following assembly procedures cover both types of center supports.

INSTALLATION—CENTER SUPPORT WITH CHAMFERED EDGE

1 Install the center support and the rear band in the case.

2 Install the primary sun gear rear thrust bearing race, needle bearing, and front thrust bearing race if used in the planet carrier using petroleum jelly to retain them in place.

3. Lubricate the bearing surface on the center support, the rollers of the planetary clutch, and the cam race in the carrier with petroleum jelly.

4. Install the planetary clutch in the carrier (Fig. 54).

5. Carefully position the planet carrier on the center support. Move the carrier forward until the clutch rollers are felt to contact the bear-

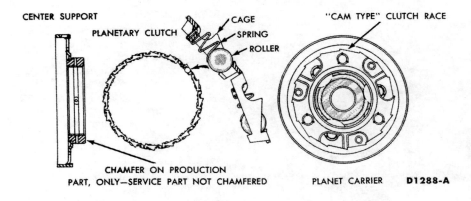

FIG. 53—Planetary Clutch, Planet Carrier and Center Support

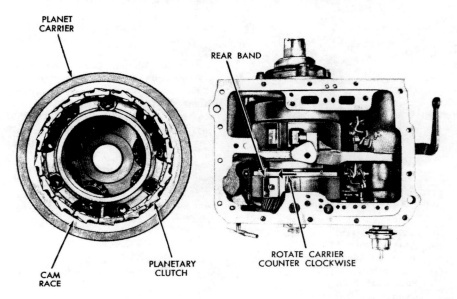

FIG. 54—Planetary Clutch Installation in Carrier—Chamfered Center Support

ing surface of the center support.

6. While applying forward pressure on the planet carrier, rotate it counterclockwise, as viewed from the rear (Fig. 54). This will cause the clutch rollers to roll toward the large opening end of the cams in the race, compressing the springs slightly, so that the rollers will ride up the chamfer on the planetary support and onto the inner race.

7. Push the planet carrier all the way forward.

8. Check the operation of the planetary clutch by rotating the carrier counterclockwise. It should rotate counterclockwise (viewed from the rear) with a slight drag, and it should lock up when attempting to rotate it in a clockwise direction.

INSTALLATION—CENTER SUPPORT NOT CHAMFERED

1. Install the center support and the rear band in the case.

2. Install the primary sun gear, rear thrust bearing race, needle bearing and front thrust bearing race if used in the planet carrier using petroleum jelly to retain them in place.

3. Lubricate the bearing surface of the center support, the rollers of the planetary clutch, and the cam race in the carrier with vaseline.

4. Install the planetary clutch on the center support with the saw teeth of the clutch cage pointing in the clockwise direction as viewed from the rear (Fig. 55). Make sure that all rollers are in the cage.

5. Position the planet carrier on the support so that the cams in the

carrier engage the saw teeth on the clutch cage.

6. Push the planet carrier forward until the rollers are felt to contact the surface of the cam race.

7. While applying forward pressure on the carrier, rotate it counterclockwise as viewed from the rear. This will cause the rollers to roll toward the large opening end of the cams in the race, compressing the springs slightly, so that the rollers will enter the cams.

8. Some rollers may become cocked preventing their entry into the outer race. These rollers must be positioned individually with a small screwdriver by pushing the rear of the rollers toward the transmission and into the cam race (Fig. 55). Keep pressure applied to the carrier at all times.

9. After all of the rollers have been started into the cam race, rotate the carrier counterclockwise while pushing it forward. Again, straighten any rollers which still may be in a cocked position and prevent the carrier from sliding onto the support.

10. Make sure that all springs are entered in the cam race before attempting to push the carrier on the support. Push the carrier all the way forward and check the operation of the clutch by rotating it in a counterclockwise direction. The carrier should rotate counterclockwise with a slight drag and should lock up when attempting to rotate it in a clockwise direction.

11. Install the selective thrust washer on the pinion carrier rear pilot. **If the end play was not within specifications when checked prior to disassembly, replace the washer with one of proper thickness.** Refer to the Specification Section of Group 7 for selective thrust washer thickness.

12. Install the output shaft, carefully meshing the internal gear with the pinions.

REAR PUMP

1. Position the rear pump drive key in the keyway on the output shaft.

2. Position new front and rear gaskets on the pump body. Retain the gaskets with transmission fluid.

3. On PCE models, or when the rear pump housing has been replaced, install the thrust washer and race in the rear pump (Fig. 33). Then install the rear pump. **Be sure the drive key is aligned with the keyway in the pump drive gear.**

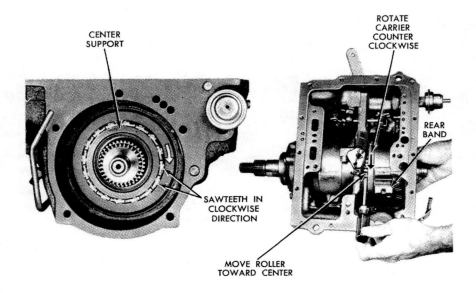

D1291-C

FIG. 55—Planetary Clutch Installation in Carrier—Center Support Not Chamfered

GOVERNOR

1. Position the governor drive ball in the pocket in the output shaft. Retain the ball with transmission fluid.

2. Install the governor assembly, aligning the groove with the ball in the output shaft.

3. **Install the governor with the governor body plate toward the rear of the output shaft.** Install the governor snap ring.

DISTRIBUTOR

1. Place the four seal rings in the distributor sleeve, and check the ring gap.

2. Check the fit of the seal rings in the grooves of the output shaft. The rings should rotate freely. Install the rings in the grooves on the output shaft.

3. Install the three tubes in the distributor sleeve.

4. Install the distributor sleeve on the output shaft, chamfer forward. Lubricate the parts to facilitate assembly. Slide the sleeve forward over the four rings and at the same time start the tubes into the case. The distributor sleeve is located between the governor snap ring and speedometer drive gear.

5. Install a new seal on the rear pump outlet tube and install the tube in the transmission case and rear pump body.

SPEEDOMETER DRIVE GEAR

1. Position the speedometer drive gear ball in the pocket of the output shaft. Retain it with fluid.

2. If a new speedometer gear is used, the steel gear will slip on to the output shaft. When the nylon gear is re-used dip it in transmission fluid and place it on an illuminated 100-watt light bulb.

3. Allow the gear to remain on the bulb for five minutes, then turn it over and heat the other side for five minutes. This will heat the gear to approximately 180°F.

4. Make sure the lock ball is in place on the shaft, then quickly slide the gear into place.

5. Install the speedometer drive gear snap ring on the output shaft.

EXTENSION HOUSING

1. Insert the extension housing oil seal replacer and pilot in the housing, and install the extension housing on the transmission case. Coat the bolt threads with B5A-19554-A sealer and install the extension housing attaching bolts, breather tube clip, vacuum tube clip, and external tooth lock washers. **The lock washers must be installed with the rolled edge toward the transmission case to insure a tight seal.**

2. Torque the extension housing attaching bolts to specification.

FRONT PUMP

1. Position a new front pump gasket in the counterbore of the transmission case.

2. Install the front pump, aligning the pump bolt holes with the holes in the case. Install three of the front pump attaching bolts and torque them to specification.

TRANSMISSION END PLAY CHECK

1. Mount the dial indicator support in a front pump bolt hole. Mount a dial indicator on the support so that the contact rests on the end of the turbine shaft (Fig. 28).

2. Use a large screwdriver to pry the front of the clutch drum toward the rear of the transmission (Fig. 28). Set the dial indicator at zero.

3. Remove the screwdriver and pry the units toward the front of the transmission by inserting a screwdriver between the large internal gear and the transmission case (Fig. 28). Note the indicator reading. End play should be 0.010-0.029 inch (minimum end play is preferred).

4. Remove the indicator and the tool from the extension housing.

5. Install the one remaining front pump attaching bolt and torque it to specification.

FRONT SERVO

1. Position the front band forward in the case with the band ends up.

2. Position the servo strut with the slotted end aligned with the servo actuating lever, and with the small end aligned with the band end. Rotate the band, strut, and servo into position engaging the anchor end of the band with the anchor pin in the case.

3. Locate the servo on the case, and install the attaching bolts. **Tighten the attaching bolts only two or three threads.**

4. Install the servo tubes.

REAR SERVO

1. Position the servo anchor strut, and rotate the rear band to engage the strut.

2. Position the servo actuating lever strut with a finger, and then install the servo and attaching bolts. Torque the bolts to specification.

PRESSURE REGULATOR BODY

1. Install the pressure regulator body and attaching bolts, and torque the bolts to specifications.

2. Install the control and converter valve guides and springs. Install the spring retainer.

3. Install a new seal ring on the rear pump intake tube, and install the tube in the case.

CONTROL VALVE BODY

1. Install the control valve assembly, carefully aligning the servo tubes with the control valve. Align the inner downshift lever between the stop and the downshift valve. Shift the manual lever to the L position. **Align the manual valve with the actuating pin in the manual detent lever. Do not tighten the attaching bolts.**

2. Install the large control pressure tube in the valve body and regulator.

3. Install the small control pressure compensator tube in the valve body and regulator.

4. Move the control valve body toward the center of the case as far as the attaching bolts will permit. This movement is made to take up clearance between the manual valve and the actuating pin on the manual detent lever.

5. Torque the attaching bolts to specification.

6. Turn the manual valve one full turn in each manual lever detent position. If the manual valve binds against the actuating pin in any detent position, loosen the valve body attaching bolts and move the body away from the center of the case. Move the body only enough to relieve the binding. Torque the attaching bolts and check the manual valve for binding.

7. Install the lubrication tube, and torque the front servo attaching bolts to specification.

FRONT BAND ADJUSTMENT

1. Loosen the front servo adjusting screw lock nut, and back off the nut three turns.

2. Loosen the adjusting screw five turns.

3. Using the front band adjusting wrench shown in Fig. 18, adjust the front band.

REAR BAND ADJUSTMENT

1. Loosen the adjusting screw lock nut three turns with the ¾-inch socket of the rear band adjusting wrench.

2. Back off the adjusting screw until free travel is obtained.

3. Use the special tools shown in Fig. 18 to adjust the rear band.

VACUUM DIAPHRAGM UNIT

1. Position the control rod in the bore of the vacuum diaphragm unit and install the diaphragm unit. Make sure the control rod enters the throttle valve as the vacuum unit is installed.

2. Torque the diaphragm unit to specification.

FLUID SCREEN AND PAN

1. Position the fluid screen over the rear pump inlet tube, and then over the front pump inlet tube. Press the screen down firmly. Install the screen retaining clip.

2. Place a new gasket on the transmission case and install the pan. Install the attaching bolts and lock washers and torque the bolts to specification.

If the converter and converter housing were removed from the transmission, install these components. Position the transmission assembly on the transmission jack, and refer to Transmission Installation Procedures for installing the transmission.

PART 7-4

C6 AUTOMATIC DUAL RANGE TRANSMISSION

1 DESCRIPTION AND OPERATION

DESCRIPTION

Figure 1 shows the location of the number, and serial number. The service identification number indi-

The C6 transmission is a three speed dual range unit capable of

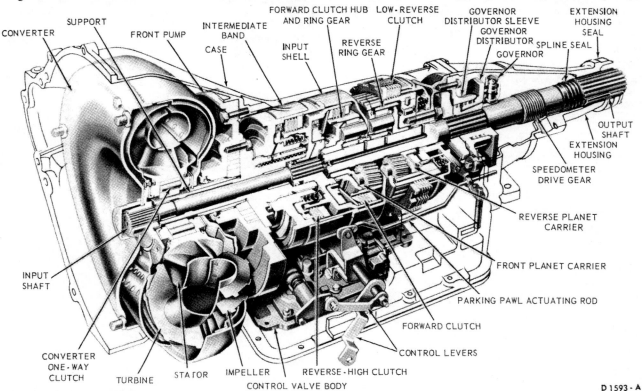

FIG. 1—Automatic Transmission

D 1593-A

converter, front pump, clutches, gear train and most of the internal parts used in the C6 transmission. The identification tag (Fig. 2), attached to the intermediate servo lower front cover bolt, includes the model prefix and suffix, a service identification

cates changes to service details which affect interchangeability **when the transmission model is not changed.** For interpretation of this number, see the Master Parts Catalog. Table 1 shows the engine and transmission model application.

transmitting the higher torque output of the new improved engines. *The converter housing and the fixed splines which engage the splined OD of the low-reverse clutch steel plates, are both cast integrally into the case.* Only one (intermediate) band is

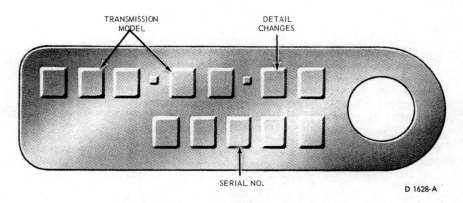

FIG. 2—Identification Tag

TABLE 1—Engine and Transmission Application

Engine Model		Transmission Prefix	Car Make
390-2V		PDD-B Column Shift	Ford
390-2V		PDD-W Floor Shift	Ford
390-4V		PDD-C Column Shift	Ford
390-4V		PDD-K Floor Shift	Ford
410-4V	Dual Exhaust	PDD-D Column Shift	Mercury
410-4V	Dual Exhaust	PDD-L Floor Shift	Mercury
410-4V	Single Exhaust	PDD-U Floor Shift	Mercury
410-4V	Single Exhaust	PDD-T Column Shift	Mercury
428-4V		PDD-H Column Shift	Ford——Mercury
428-4V		PDD-N Floor Shift	Ford——Mercury

used in the C6 transmission. This along with the forward clutch is used to obtain intermediate gear.

The only adjustments on the transmission proper are for the intermediate band and the neutral safety switch.

The fluid is drained from the transmission by loosening the pan bolts and allowing it to drain. Finally, to allow the pan to drain more thoroughly, remove all bolts except the two from the front.

OPERATION

TORQUE CONVERTER

The hydraulic torque converter (Fig. 3) consists of an impeller (pump), a turbine, and a stator. All these parts are enclosed and operate in a fluid-filled housing.

When the engine is running, the fluid in the torque converter flows

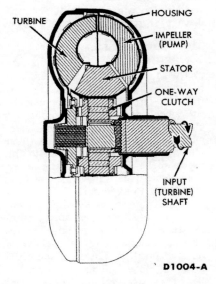

FIG. 3—Sectional View of Typical Torque Converter

from the impeller to the turbine and back to the impeller through the stator. This flow produces a maximum torque increase of about 2 to 1 when the turbine is stalled. When enough torque is developed by the impeller, the turbine begins to rotate, turning the turbine shaft (input shaft).

The converter torque multiplication gradually tapers off as turbine speed approaches impeller speed, and it becomes 1 to 1 when the turbine is being driven at $9/10$ impeller speed. This is known as the coupling point.

When the turbine is rotating at less than $9/10$ impeller speed the converter is multiplying torque. The fluid leaving the turbine blades strikes the front face of the stator blades. These blades are held stationary by the action of a one-way clutch (Fig. 3) as long as the fluid is directed against the front face of the blades.

When the turbine rotates faster than $9/10$ impeller speed the converter no longer multiplies torque. The fluid is directed against the back face of the stator blades. As the one-way clutch permits the stator to rotate only in the direction of impeller rotation, the stator begins to turn with the impeller and turbine. The converter operates as an efficient fluid coupling as long as the turbine speed remains greater than $9/10$ impeller speed.

A constant flow of fluid into and out of the converter is maintained. The fluid coming out of the converter is forced through a cooler located in the radiator tank.

PLANETARY GEAR TRAIN, CLUTCHES, BANDS, AND SERVOS

Planetary Gear Train

The gear train consists of an input shaft that is splined to the turbine of the converter and the forward clutch cylinder (Fig. 4). The forward clutch cylinder rotates the steel internal clutch plates of the forward clutch and the composition clutch plates of the reverse-high clutch. When the reverse-high clutch is applied, the external area of the clutch hub is splined to and drives the input shell to rotate the sun gear. When the forward clutch is applied, the composition clutch plates drive the forward clutch hub and ring gear. The ring gear rotates the forward planet gears.

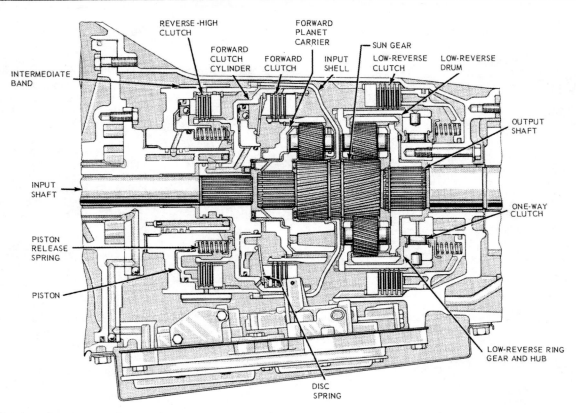

FIG. 4—Gear Train, Clutches and Band

When applied, the intermediate band holds the reverse-high clutch drum, input shell and sun gear from rotating.

The sun gear, which is driven by the input shell, is meshed with the forward and reverse planet gears. The reverse planet carrier is splined to the composition plates of the low-reverse clutch. The steel plates of the low-reverse clutch are prevented from rotating by the splines machined in the transmission case. The low-reverse clutch hub is also held from rotating by a roller type one-way clutch.

The forward planet carrier, reverse ring gear hub, park gear and governor distributor are all splined to the output shaft.

Forward Clutch

The input shaft is splined to and drives the forward clutch cylinder (Fig. 4). *Rotation of the cylinder* drives the steel clutch plates in the forward clutch and the composition clutch plates of the reverse-high clutch.

When the forward clutch piston is applied by hydraulic pressure, the movement of the piston against the disc spring locks the steel and composition clutch plates together to drive the forward clutch hub and ring gear.

When hydraulic pressure is released from the piston, the disc spring moves the piston to the released position. As the disc spring moves, the steel and composition clutch plates are released. This stops the rotation of the forward clutch hub and ring gear (Fig. 4). The forward clutch is applied in all forward drive gear ratios.

Reverse-High Clutch

When hydraulic pressure is directed to the clutch piston, the piston moves against the release springs (Fig. 4). The piston movement locks the steel and rotating composition clutch plates together. The steel clutch plates drive the reverse-high clutch drum which is splined to the input shell. Rotation of the input shell drives the sun gear which is splined to the input shell.

To release the reverse-high clutch, hydraulic pressure is exhausted from the apply side of the piston. The return springs move the piston to the released position. The steel and composition clutch plates are now released to stop rotation of the reverse-high clutch drum, input shell, and sun gear.

Intermediate Servo and Band

The intermediate servo is machined into the transmission case and the band has an **external** adjustment screw (Fig. 5). To apply the servo, hydraulic pressure is directed from the control valve body, through a hole in the case to the hole in the servo piston stem. The pressure passes through the center of the piston stem and then to the apply side of the piston. The piston moves against the return spring to tighten the intermediate band around the reverse-high clutch drum.

To release the servo piston, hydraulic pressure is directed to the release side of the piston. The release pressure is assisted by the compressed return spring to move the servo piston and intermediate band to the off position. The intermediate servo and band are applied only during the intermediate gear operation.

Power Flow

Table 2 shows the gear ratios obtained in the different selector lever positions. **All gear rotations are viewed from the front of transmission.**

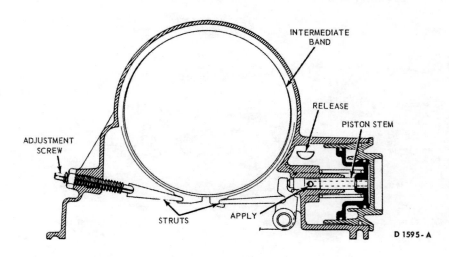

FIG. 5—Intermediate Servo and Band

TABLE 2—Gear Ratios

Gear	Gear Ratio	Intermediate Band	Direct Clutch	Forward Clutch	Reverse Clutch	One-Way Clutch
Low	2.46:1	Off	Off	On	On①	Holding①
Intermediate	1.46:1	On	Off	On	Off	Overrunning
Direct	1.00:1	Off	On	On	Off	Overrunning
Reverse	2.175:1	Off	On	Off	On	Not Affected

①Reverse clutch is applied in manual low; one-way clutch is holding in low gear of Drive Range.

Power Flow Neutral

In neutral (Fig. 6), the clutches or bands are not applied therefore no power is transmitted to the output shaft.

Power Flow First Gear

In low gear (Fig. 6), the forward clutch is applied, and the planet one-way clutch or low-reverse clutch is holding the low-reverse clutch hub and reverse planet carrier from rotating. The power flow is through the input shaft and into the forward clutch. The input shaft is splined to and drives the forward clutch cylinder. Rotation of the forward clutch drives the forward clutch hub and ring gear. The ring gear rotates the forward planet gears clockwise to cause the sun gear to rotate counterclockwise.

Counterclockwise rotation of the sun gear turns the reverse planet gears clockwise. The reverse planet carrier being splined to the low-reverse drum is held from rotating by the one-way clutch or low-reverse clutch.

With the reverse planet carrier held stationary, the clockwise rotation of the reverse planet gears ro-

tates the reverse ring gear and hub clockwise. The hub of the reverse ring gear is splined to the output shaft and rotates the output shaft clockwise.

The output shaft rotation is at a reduced speed, compared to the input shaft rotation, but at an increased torque.

The output shaft rotation at a reduced speed is caused by the fact that the forward carrier rotates at the same speed of the output shaft and in the same direction since the carrier is splined to the output shaft. The forward ring gear and planet assembly are rotating in the same direction but the planet carrier is rotating at a slower speed than the ring gear. Therefore, the low gear ratio (torque multiplication) is a combination of the ratios provided by the forward and reverse planet assemblies.

Power Flow Intermediate Gear

In intermediate gear (Fig. 6), the forward clutch is applied and the intermediate band is holding the reverse-high clutch drum, input shell and sun gear from turning.

The power flow is through the input shaft into the forward clutch and forward planet assembly ring gear. The sun gear is held from rotating by the intermediate band. This causes the forward planet pinions to rotate (walk) around the sun gear, carrying the forward planet carrier with them. The forward planet carrier, being splined to the output shaft, causes clockwise rotation of the output shaft at a reduction in speed compared to the speed of the input shaft, and at an increase in torque.

Clockwise rotation of the output shaft causes clockwise rotation of the output shaft ring gear, causing the reverse planet pinions to also rotate (walk) around the sun gear in

a clockwise direction. The reverse planet carrier will also rotate clockwise and the one-way clutch outer race being splined to the reverse planet carrier, will overrun.

Power Flow High Gear

In high gear (Fig. 6), the forward and reverse-high clutches are applied. The power flow is through the input shaft into the forward clutch cylinder. The forward clutch cylinder rotates the steel clutch plates of the forward clutch and the composition clutch plates of the reverse-high clutch. The forward clutch directs the power flow through the forward clutch hub and ring gear to the forward planet carrier.

The reverse-high clutch directs the power flow through the input shell to the sun gear. With the sun gear and the forward clutch hub ring gear driven at the same speed, the front planet assembly (that is splined to the output shaft) is forced to rotate the output shaft at the same speed and direction to provide high gear.

Power Flow Reverse

In reverse (Fig. 6), the reverse-high clutch and clutch are applied.

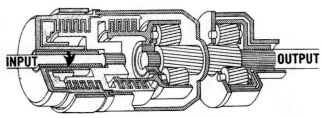

CLUTCHES AND THE BAND ARE RELEASED

NEUTRAL

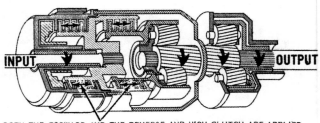

BOTH THE FORWARD AND THE REVERSE AND HIGH CLUTCH ARE APPLIED.
ALL PLANETARY GEAR MEMBERS ARE LOCKED TO EACH OTHER AND ARE
LOCKED TO THE OUTPUT SHAFT.

HIGH GEAR

THE FORWARD CLUTCH IS APPLIED. THE FRONT PLANETARY UNIT RING
GEAR IS LOCKED TO THE INPUT SHAFT.

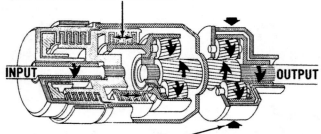

THE LOW AND REVERSE CLUTCH (LOW RANGE) OR THE ONE-WAY CLUTCH
(D1 RANGE) IS HOLDING THE REVERSE UNIT PLANET CARRIER STATIONARY.

FIRST GEAR

THE REVERSE AND HIGH CLUTCH IS APPLIED. THE INPUT SHAFT IS LOCKED
TO THE REVERSE AND HIGH CLUTCH DRUM, THE INPUT SHELL AND THE
SUN GEAR.

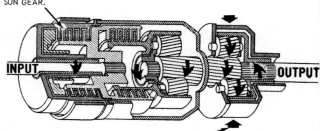

THE LOW AND REVERSE CLUTCH IS APPLIED. THE REVERSE UNIT PLANET
CARRIER IS HELD STATIONARY.

REVERSE

THE INTERMEDIATE BAND IS APPLIED. THE REVERSE AND HIGH CLUTCH
DRUM, THE INPUT SHELL AND THE SUN GEAR ARE HELD STATIONARY.

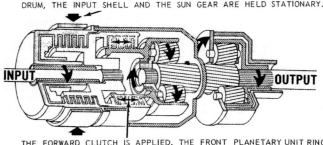

THE FORWARD CLUTCH IS APPLIED. THE FRONT PLANETARY UNIT RING
GEAR IS LOCKED TO THE INPUT SHAFT.

SECOND GEAR

GEAR RATIOS			
FIRST 2.46:1			
	SECOND 1.46:1		
		HIGH 1.00:1	
			REVERSE 2.17:1

D 1596 - A

FIG. 6—Power Flow

The power flow is through the input shaft, reverse-high clutch, input shell, and to the sun gear. Clockwise rotation of the sun gear causes counterclockwise rotation of the reverse planet gears.

HYDRAULIC CONTROL SYSTEM

Front Pump

Fluid for operation of the hydraulic control system (Fig. 7) is supplied by a gear type pump mounted on the front of the transmission case. Pump intake is through a screen which is part of the main control assembly, into the case casting and pump. Discharge is through the case into the main control assembly. Fluid from the front pump is directed to the main oil pressure regulator valve, throttle booster valve, manual valve, 1-2 accumulator valve.

In addition, fluid is also directed to the primary throttle valve, which is located in the rear of the case. Fluid delivered to these valves is at a pressure controlled by the main oil pressure regulator valve.

Main Oil Pressure Regulator Valve

The main regulator valve assembly consists of the main oil pressure regulator valve and spring, main oil pressure booster valve, spring and sleeve. This assembly is located in one bore of the main control assembly.

Fluid is delivered to two valleys of the main regulator valve from the front pump. The difference in diameter between the end land and the second land provides an area differential for regulation. Fluid pressure in this area tends to move the valve against spring force. Spring force is such that at approximately 60 psi front pump pressure, the main valve will move so that the fourth land uncovers the converter feed port, allowing additional pump volume to be used to charge the converter and provide fluid for cooling and lubrication. If volume supplied by the front pump is greater than that required to maintain 60 psi line pressure and converter and lube requirements, the valve will move further allowing the third land to uncover the port which allows excess pump volume to be discharged into the sump.

Pressures over 60 psi which are required under various operating conditions are obtained by delivering fluid under pressure to the pressure booster valve, where it will cause the pressure booster valve to assist the main regulator valve spring in increasing regulated line pressure.

Source of these pressures which cause variations in control pressure are discussed later.

Manual Valve

Two passages deliver control pressure to the manual valve. The valve is positioned by the manual linkage according to mode of operation desired, to direct fluid out of two or more of the line passages which lead from the manual valve. The five passages leading from the manual valve (from left to right) are:

1. D2
2. D1
3. D
4. L—R
5. R

The D2 passage is charged in D2 range only.

The D1 passage is charged in D2 and D1 ranges.

The D passage is charged in all forward ranges, (including manual low).

The L—R passage is charged in L and R ranges.

The R passage is charged in reverse range only.

In Park and Neutral, the valve blocks the flow of control pressure and exhausts the five passages leading from the manual valve.

The D passage supplies fluid pressure to the governor secondary valve, D2 valve and forward clutch.

The D2 passage supplies fluid to the adjoining ends of the D2 and 1-2 shift valves.

The D1 passage supplies fluid to the 2-3 shift valve, downshift valve and coasting boost valve.

The L and R passage supplies fluid to the end of the manual low valve and to the D2 valve. When the D2 valve is in the closed (up) position, fluid passes through the valve and to the following places:

1. Spring end of the D2 valve.
2. Reverse clutch.
3. Through the downshift valve to the throttle modulator valve bore, under the 2-3 shift valve and to the underside of the first land of the 1-2 shift valve.

The R passage supplies fluid to the upper valley of the pressure booster valve, through the 2-3 shift valve to

the reverse-high clutch to apply it and to the release side of the intermediate servo. Fluid is also supplied to the end of the 2-3 backout valve, and to the 3-2 coasting control valve.

Primary Throttle Valve

The primary throttle valve is actuated by changes in manifold vacuum. Primary throttle pressure starts at 20 inches (nominal) of mercury vacuum. Primary throttle pressure is delivered to the:

1. End of the pressure booster valve.
2. Lower valley of pressure booster valve (through cutback valve and coasting boost valves).
3. Throttle modulator valve (through throttle booster valve).
4. End of the throttle booster valve.
5. Spring end of the 2-3 backout valve and manual low valve.

Fig. 8 shows how primary throttle pressure varies with engine vacuum.

Altitude-Compensating Diaphragm Assembly

To compensate for change in shift feel which might result from operation at higher altitudes, an altitude-compensating throttle diaphragm assembly will be available for service.

The operating principle of the altitude-compensating device is dependent upon the collapsing force obtained from an evacuated bellows located within the diaphragm assembly. The force created by the bellows increases or decreases the force on the throttle valve actuating rod. At higher altitudes the force that the bellows transmits to the actuating rod is decreased, resulting in a decrease in primary TV pressure, which tends to make shift feel comparable with that obtained at lower altitudes. Fig. 9 shows the construction of the altitude-compensating diaphragm assembly.

Pressure specifications for a car equipped with the altitude-compensating diaphragm will not be the same at altitude, as at sea level. Refer to Section 7-1, Table 3 for differences.

Pressure Booster Valve

Forward Driving Ranges (D1, D2, L). TV pressure is delivered to the lower valley of the pressure booster valve and to the end of the pressure booster valve. When force created on the booster valve by TV pres-

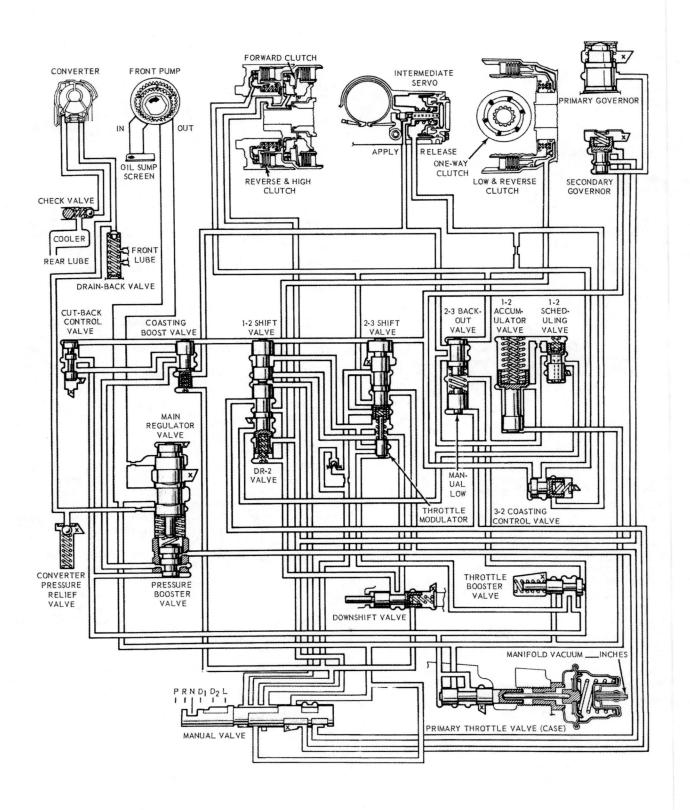

D 1624-A

FIG. 7—Hydraulic System

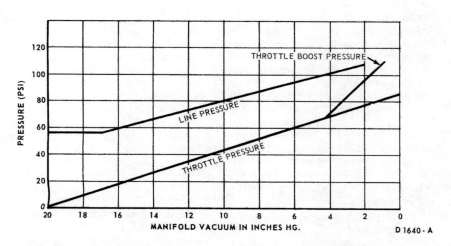

FIG. 8—Primary Throttle Pressure, Boost Pressure and Control Pressure Versus Engine Manifold Vacuum

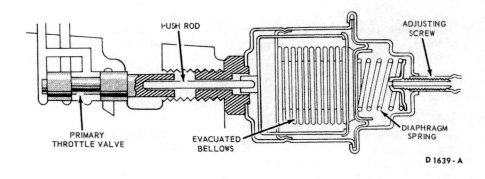

FIG. 9—Altitude—Compensating Vacuum Diaphragm

sures in these two areas exceeds pressure booster valve spring force, the force will be added to the main regulator valve spring force transmitted to the main regulator valve. This will provide increased control pressures required to compensate for increased throttle openings and engine torque output. Fig. 10 shows how control pressure varies with engine vacuum at zero output shaft rpm.

Reverse (R). Additional fluid pressure is required in reverse to prevent clutch and/or band slippage under stall or partial stall conditions. This additional pressure is provided by directing line pressure to the upper valley of the pressure booster valve when reverse range is selected. The differential in area between the lands of this valve provides a force which is added to the TV pressure forces

pressure to a higher value than is available in the forward driving ranges.

Governor

At Rest (0 mph). Control pressure (line) is fed to the secondary governor valve through the center passage in the valve body. Because of the differential in area of the inner and outer lands of the valve, the valve will be forced inward, shutting off line pressure feed to the governor passage and allowing this passage to be opened to exhaust, at the inner end of the valve. At the same time, line pressure will pass by two flats on the outer end of the valve, pressurizing the line leakage passage leading to the primary governor valve. At rest, the spring on the outer end of the primary governor valve holds the primary governor valve inward, blocking further flow of the fluid in the line leakage passage. This causes pressure in the line leakage passage to build to the same value as line pressure. As a consequence, the secondary governor valve is held in and there is no pressure in the governor circuit.

Above 10 MPH. When speed reaches approximately 10 mph, centrifugal force on the primary governor valve overcomes spring force, and the valve moves outward, opening the line leakage passage to exhaust. This action reduces the pressure on the end of the secondary governor valve to zero (0), allowing the secondary valve to also move

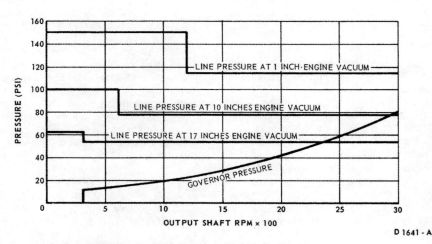

FIG. 10—Control Line Pressure and Governor Pressure Versus Output Shaft RPM

present in the lower valley and on the end of the valve, to boost line

outward, due to spring force and centrifugal force. When the secondary valve moves outward, it closes the governor exhaust passage, and allows line pressure to enter the governor passage. As pressure builds in the governor passage, it will create a force on the secondary governor valve due to the differential in areas of the inner and outer lands of the valve. This force tends to move the valve inward. When the force on the valve created by pressure in the governor passage exceeds the centrifugal force plus spring force, the valve will move inward, allowing governor pressure to exhaust, and close the passage between line pressure and governor pressure. When governor pressure is reduced, the secondary valve will again move outward, closing the governor exhaust port and opening the line pressure to governor passage. Above 10 mph, governor pressure is regulated in this manner, and will vary with the car speeds.

If the car speed drops below 10 mph, the primary valve spring will move the primary governor valve in, closing the line leakage exhaust port at the primary valve. Pressure in the line leakage passage will become equal to line pressure, forcing the secondary governor valve in. This action shuts off line pressure feed to the governor passage and exhausts the governor circuit.

When the secondary governor valve is regulating, governor pressure will be delivered to the cutback valve, end of the 2-3 shift valve, 1-2 shift valve and end of the line pressure coasting boost valve and 3-2 coasting control valve. Fig. 10 shows the relationship between governor pressure and output shaft rpm.

Throttle Booster Valve

Throttle plate openings above 50° provide very little change in engine vacuum as compared to throttle plate openings below 50°. The throttle booster valve is used to boost throttle pressure and provide the necessary shift delay for engine throttle plate openings above 50°.

Below approximately 65 psi primary TV pressure, TV pressure flows to and through the throttle boost valve unaffected, working on the end of the boost valve and on the area differential in the first valley.

When TV pressure increases above 65 psi, the force created by TV pressure acting on the end of the throttle boost valve, minus the force

of TV pressure acting on the area differential in the first valley will exceed the force of the spring. This causes the valve to move against the spring, closing off primary TV pressure to the area differential and permitting this area to be fed from line pressure, causing a boost in the pressure used for shift delay only. Because the area of the end of the throttle boost valve exceeds the area differential in the first valley by 3 to 1, throttle boost pressure above 65 psi primary TV pressure will increase 3 psi for each 1 psi increase in primary TV.

Figure 8 shows the relationship between primary TV pressure and boosted throttle pressure.

Throttle Modulator Valve

The throttle modulator valve, located in the end of the 2-3 shift valve bore reduces throttle pressure which acts on the end of the 2-3 shift valve and on the area differential of the 1-2 shift valve. Modulated throttle pressure in these areas provides shift delay in relation to throttle opening.

Cutback Valve

Increased line pressure is required to prevent clutch and band slippage under stall conditions. Dependent upon car speed, the requirements for increased line pressure are considerably reduced. When governor pressure acting on the end of the cutback valve exceeds the force of TV pressure acting on its area opposing governor, the cutback valve will move cutting off primary TV pressure being fed to the lower valley of the pressure booster valve, thru the coasting boost valve. This action reduces the assist that the pressure booster valve provides to the main regulator valve spring. The cutback valve movement will therefore vary with engine throttle opening and car speed. Figure 10 shows how line pressure varies with output shaft rpm (car speed) at constant vacuum values.

Coasting Boost Valve

When using manual low to force a 3-2 coasting (throttle closed) downshift in order to use the engine as a brake, additional pressure may be required to insure positive band applications. With the throttle closed there will be no TV pressure present at the pressure booster valve.

At speeds above approximately 55

mph, additional pressure is obtained thru the use of the coasting boost valve. When the manual valve is shifted to manual low (L), line pressure is exhausted from the end of the coasting boost valve, allowing governor pressure to move the valve downward. This action blocks the TV pressure passage from the cutback control valve and allows intermediate servo apply pressure to pass thru the coasting boost valve to the lower valley of the pressure booster valve, increasing main line pressure.

1-2 Shift Valve Train

The 1-2 shift valve train is composed of the 1-2 shift valve, the D2 valve, and the 1-2 shift valve spring.

D1 Range. In D1 range the 1-2 shift valve is held closed (up) by modulated throttle pressure acting on the differential area between the two lands of the 1-2 shift valve, by D fluid pressure acting on the differential in area between the two lands at the spring end of the D2 valve, and by the 1-2 shift valve spring. Governor pressure tends to move the 1-2 shift valve train against these forces. When force created by governor pressure exceeds the forces holding the 1-2 shift valve train closed, the 1-2 shift valve and D2 valve will be opened (move downward), closing the exhaust port and allowing D fluid to pass through the D2 valve to accomplish the 1-2 shift. When the D2 valve is moved downward, D fluid is exhausted from the differential in areas provided by the lower two lands of the D2 valve and modulated throttle pressure from area differential on 1-2 valve. This action eliminates the force created by D fluid which tends to hold the 1-2 shift valve train closed.

If governor pressure is reduced to the point where spring force exceeds governor pressure force, the 1-2 shift valve train will move up (close) cutting off the flow of D fluid through the valve and opening the exhaust port allowing a downshift to low gear.

If the throttle is opened through detent, the downshift valve moves to allow line pressure to enter the modulated throttle pressure passage at the 1-2 shift valve to provide a forced 2-1 downshift.

L Range. Once the transmission is in low gear L-R fluid, which is directed to the D2 valve, passes through the D2 valve and is delivered to the spring end of the D2 valve, preventing an upshift. L-R fluid which passes through the D2 valve also applies the reverse clutch. Coasting downshifts to first gear are not possible above approximately 10 mph in low range.

D2 Range. In D2 range, D2 fluid is introduced between the 1-2 shift and D2 valves. This action opens the D2 valve and holds it open, providing a second gear start and preventing a 2-1 downshift.

1-2 Scheduling Valve and 1-2 Accumulator Valve

The 1-2 scheduling and 1-2 accumulator valves are used to control the rate of band application during a 1-2 shift.

During operation in first gear prior to the 1-2 shift, control pressure is present on the end of the 1-2 accumulator valve and holds the valve up in its bore against spring pressure.

When the 1-2 shift valve train moves to make a 1-2 shift, line pressure passes thru the D-2 valve and goes to the 1-2 scheduling valve. This pressure passes thru the scheduling valve bore, goes to the differential in area between the two lands of the 1-2 accumulator valve and thru the 2-3 backout valve to apply the intermediate servo. This same fluid also passes thru a hole in the center of the 1-2 scheduling valve to the end of the valve, and also thru an orifice which feeds the fluid to the spring ends of the 1-2 accumulator and 1-2 scheduling valves.

The fluid which passes thru the center of the 1-2 scheduling valve tends to move the valve upward against spring force. However, the spring effort and fluid pressure created by the fluid which has passed thru the orifice to the spring end of the valve will hold the valve down.

As fluid flows thru the orifice to the spring ends of the 1-2 accumulator and scheduling valves, and pressure increases on the spring ends of the valves, the 1-2 accumulator valve starts to move downward. This movement of the 1-2 accumulator valve causes a flow of fluid thru the orifice, resulting in a lower pressure existing on the spring sides of the valves.

As a consequence, the fluid pressure on the end of the 1-2 scheduling valve opposite the spring will be higher than the pressure on the spring end of the valve, causing the valve to move upward. This action

cuts off fluid supply to the intermediate servo (and thru the orifice) and opens an exhaust port at the end of the 1-2 scheduling valve. When the exhaust port opens, the pressure on the end of the 1-2 scheduling valve opposite the spring is reduced, allowing the valve to again move downward and opening the line to the intermediate servo apply.

In this manner, the 1-2 scheduling valve regulates to control the intermediate servo apply during a 1-2 shift, until the 1-2 accumulator valve has fully bottomed in its bore and there is no more fluid flow thru the orifice.

2-3 Shift Valve

The 2-3 shift valve is held closed by throttle modulator valve spring force, modulated throttle pressure force, and by D1 fluid pressure force acting on the differential in area of the lands of the valve to which it is delivered.

Governor pressure tends to open the 2-3 shift valve. When force created by governor pressure exceeds the forces holding the valve closed, the valve will move downward (open) closing the exhaust passage (through the manual valve) and opening the D1 passage to allow D1 fluid to apply the reverse-high clutch and release the intermediate servo.

With the shift valve open (down) the throttle modulator valve is held down cutting off modulated throttle pressure to the 2-3 shift valve and 1-2 shift valve. In addition, the port which delivered D1 fluid to the differential in area of the shift valve lands, is closed.

The shift valve will be reopened (moved up) causing a downshift under one or more of the following conditions:

Governor Pressure Reduced. If governor pressure is reduced to the point where it can no longer hold the shift valve down against spring force, the valve will move up causing a downshift. Under closed throttle conditions, the 2-3 shift valve will close at approximately 10 mph, (speed at which governor pressure is cut off). Since governor pressure is cut off at this speed, the 1-2 shift valve train also closes at the same time. This will provide a 3-1 downshift when coasting in D1 range.

Throttle Pressure Increased. If throttle pressure is increased suffi-

ciently, it will move the throttle modulator valve and consequently the 2-3 shift valve up, causing a 3-2 torque demand downshift.

Line Pressure Introduced Below 2-3 Shift Valve. If the downshift valve is moved through detent, line pressure is directed to the underside of the 2-3 shift valve, forcing the valve up and causing a forced 3-2 downshift. Maximum 3-2 forced downshift speed is controlled by governor pressure.

In addition to the above, a 3-2 downshift will occur when the manual valve is moved to L range. The D1 passage which feeds fluid to the 2-3 shift valve will then be opened to exhaust, allowing reverse-high clutch apply—intermediate servo release fluid to exhaust and causing a 3-2 downshift.

2-3 Back-out Valve

The purpose of the 2-3 back-out valve is to provide smooth upshifts, when the throttle is suddenly closed while accelerating in second gear. Operation is as follows:

Normal Throttle-On 2-3 Upshifts. When the 2-3 shift valve moves to cause a 2-3 upshift, D1 fluid passes through the valve to apply the direct clutch and release the intermediate servo. This same fluid is also directed to the end of the 2-3 back-out valve. However, with throttle open, primary throttle pressure on the opposite end of the 2-3 back-out valve, assists spring force in holding the valve up, so that there will be no valve movement until after the 2-3 shift has been completed.

Back-Out 2-3 Upshifts. When the throttle is closed during a 2-3 upshift, and before the shift is completed, there may be enough pressure in the reverse-high clutch cylinder to apply the clutch at the reduced engine torque input, but not enough pressure to release the intermediate servo. This condition could cause a harsh 2-3 shift. However, if the throttle is closed during a 2-3 shift, primary throttle pressure will be reduced to zero (0), and reverse-high clutch apply pressure on the end of the 2-3 back-out valve will move the valve down against spring force. This action immediately connects the clutch apply circuit to the intermediate servo apply circuit, reducing the pressure on apply side of the servo to the same valve as in the reverse-high clutch (and also on the release side of the intermediate servo). When this happens, the intermediate band is released, to provide a smooth 2-3 shift.

3-2 Coasting Control Valve

The 3-2 coasting control valve controls the intermediate servo apply force to provide acceptable 3-2 downshifts under both coasting and throttle-on conditions.

Throttle-On 3-2 Shift. During a 3-2 throttle-on downshift, car speed will be such that governor pressure will hold the 3-2 coasting control valve bottomed in its bore against its spring. In this position, intermediate servo release fluid exhausts through the coasting control valve and 2-3 shift valve during a 3-2 downshift, allowing a rapid apply of the intermediate band.

Coasting 3-2 Shift (D2 Range). At the 3-2 coasting downshift speed, governor pressure is reduced to zero and the 3-2 coasting control valve will be moved by spring force to the bottom of its bore. This blocks the direct passage of intermediate servo release fluid to exhaust and requires that this fluid be exhausted through a controlling orifice. Therefore, the band application is cushioned during a 3-2 coasting downshift, resulting in a smooth shift.

Manual Low Valve

The manual low valve insures that the 2-3 back-out valve will be moved up the instant that pressure drops in the reverse-high clutch apply—intermediate servo release circuit, when a shift to manual low range is made. This is accomplished by directing control pressure to the end of the manual low valve, when L range is selected.

---

2   IN-CAR ADJUSTMENTS AND REPAIRS

CONTROL LINKAGE ADJUSTMENTS

The transmission control linkage adjustments should be performed in the order in which they appear in this section of the manual.

THROTTLE AND DOWNSHIFT LINKAGE ADJUSTMENTS

1. Apply the parking brake, and place the selector lever at N.

2. Run the engine at normal idle speed. If the engine is cold, run the engine at fast idle speed (about 1200 rpm) until it reaches normal operating temperature. When the engine is warm, slow it down to normal idle speed.

3. Connect a tachometer to the engine.

4. Adjust engine idle speed to the specified rpms with the transmission selector lever at D1 (large dot) or D2 (circle) the drive position.

5. The carburetor throttle lever must be against the hot idle speed adjusting screw at specified idle speed in D1 (circle) or D2 (small dot). To make sure that the carburetor throttle lever is against the adjusting screw, refer to Group 10 for the carburetor adjusting procedures.

6. With the engine stopped, disconnect the carburetor return spring (Fig. 11) from the throttle lever.

7. Loosen the accelerator cable conduit attaching clamp.

8. With the accelerator pedal to the floor and the throttle lever held to the wide open position, slide the cable conduit to the rear to remove the slack from the cable. Tighten the cable conduit attaching clamp.

9. Disconnect the downshift lever return spring (Fig. 11).

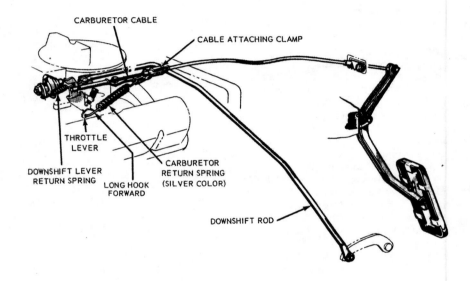

CARBURETOR CABLE

CABLE ATTACHING CLAMP

THROTTLE LEVER

DOWNSHIFT LEVER RETURN SPRING

LONG HOOK FORWARD

CARBURETOR RETURN SPRING (SILVER COLOR)

DOWNSHIFT ROD

D 1570 - B

FIG. 11—Throttle Linkage—V-8 Engine

10. Hold the throttle lever at the wide open position and depress the downshift rod to the through detent stop. Set the downshift lever (at carburetor) adjusting screw against the throttle lever.

11. Connect both return springs to their respective levers.

MANUAL LINKAGE ADJUSTMENT

Column Shift

1. Place the selector lever in the D1 (circle) position tight against the D stop.

2. Loosen the nut at point A enough to permit column shift lever to slide on the shift rod (Fig. 12).

3. Shift the manual lever at the transmission into the D1 detent position, second from the rear.

4. Make sure that the selector lever has not moved from the D1 stop; then, tighten the nut at point A.

5. Check the pointer alignment and the transmission operation for all selector lever detent positions.

Floor Shift

1. Position the transmission selector lever in D1 (circle) position.

2. Raise the car and loosen the manual lever control rod retaining nut. Move the transmission manual lever to the D1 position, second detent position from the back of the

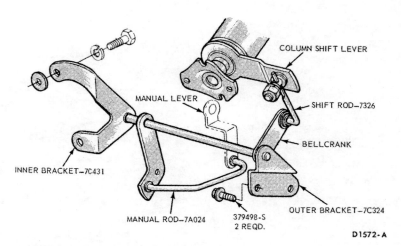

FIG. 12—Manual Linkage—Column Shift

transmission. The last detent position is manual low.

3. With the transmission selector lever and manual lever in the D1 positions, torque the retaining nut 20 to 25 ft-lbs.

4. Check the operation of the transmission in each selector lever position.

NEUTRAL START SWITCH ADJUSTMENT

1. With the manual linkage properly adjusted, loosen the two switch retaining bolts (Fig. 13). Position the transmission manual lever in neutral detent position.

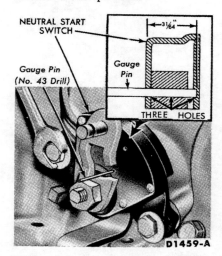

FIG. 13—Neutral Start Switch

2. Rotate the switch and insert the shank end of the gauge pin (No. 43 drill) into the gauge pin holes of the switch. **The gauge pin has to be inserted a full 31/64 inch into the 3 holes of the switch (Fig. 12).**

3. Torque the two switch attach-

ing bolts to specification. Remove the gauge pin tool from the switch.

4. Check the operation of the switch. The engine should start only with the transmission selector lever in N (neutral) and P (park).

NEUTRAL START SWITCH REPLACEMENT

1. Remove the downshift linkage rod from the transmission downshift lever.

2. Remove the transmission downshift outer lever attaching nut and lever.

3. Remove the two neutral start switch attaching bolts.

4. Disconnect the two multiple wire connectors. Remove the neutral start switch from the transmission.

5. Install the neutral start switch on the transmission. Install the two attaching bolts.

6. With the transmission manual lever in neutral, check the location of the switch with the gauge pin and adjust the switch if necessary.

7. Tighten the switch attaching bolts to specifications and remove the gauge pin.

8. Install the outer downshift lever and attaching nut, and torque the nut to specification. Install the downshift linkage rod to the downshift lever.

9. Install the switch wires, **red to red and blue to blue.** Connect the wire multiple connectors. Check the operation of the switch in each detent position. The engine should start only with the transmission selector lever in N (neutral) and P (park).

When the engine will not start in neutral or park, check the multiple connectors to make sure the red wire

is connected to the red wire and the blue wire is connected to the blue wire.

SELECTOR LEVER REMOVAL ADJUSTMENT AND INSTALLATION

REMOVAL

1. Raise the car and disconnect the link (Fig. 14) from the shift lever.

2. Lower the car. Place the selector lever in the neutral position and remove the selector lever handle attaching screw. Lift the handle off the selector lever.

3. Remove the chrome trim panel from the console.

4. Remove the three screws that attach the quadrant to the selector lever housing. Lift the quadrant from the housing. Disconnect the bulb socket.

5. Remove the four screws that attach the selector lever housing to the console.

6. Lift the selector lever and housing from the console.

DETENT PAWL ADJUSTMENT

1. Install the handle to make the detent pawl adjustment.

2. Move the selector lever to the D1-D2 range.

3. Place a 0.010-inch feeler gauge between the detent pawl and plate.

4. Loosen the cable lock nut and turn the screw clockwise to decrease the clearance or counterclockwise to increase the clearance as shown in Fig. 15. Tighten the lock nut after a clearance of 0.010 inch has been established.

5. Remove the handle from the selector lever.

INSTALLATION

1. Position the selector lever and housing assembly in the console.

2. Install the four attaching screws to secure it in place.

3. Connect the bulb socket to the quadrant. Position the quadrant and secure with the three attaching screws.

4. Raise the car and install the link on the shift lever (Fig. 14). Adjust the manual linkage and then the neutral switch as required. Lower the car.

5. Install the chrome trim cover on the console.

6. Place the selector lever handle

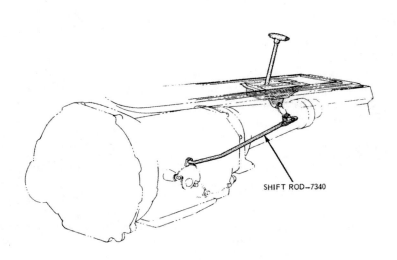

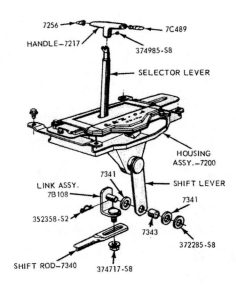

D 1577-A

FIG. 14—Manual Linkage—Floor Shift

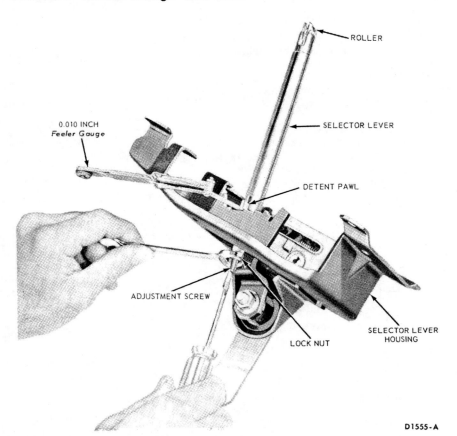

D1555-A

FIG. 15—Adjusting Selector Lever Detent Pawl

on the lever with the attaching screw tapped hole facing toward the right side of the console. Install and tighten the handle attaching screw.

BAND ADJUSTMENT

INTERMEDIATE BAND

1. Clean all the dirt from the band adjusting screw area. Loosen the lock nut several turns.

2. With the tool shown in Fig. 16,

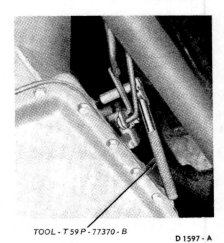

TOOL - T 59 P - 77370 - B   D 1597 - A

FIG. 16—Adjusting Band

tighten the adjusting screw until the tool handle clicks. The tool is a preset torque wrench which clicks and overruns when the torque on the adjusting screw reaches 10 ft-lbs.

3. Back off the adjusting screw exactly 1 full turn.

4. Hold the adjusting screw from turning and torque the lock nut to specification.

GOVERNOR REPLACEMENT

REMOVAL

1. Raise the car on a hoist or stands.

2. Disconnect the driveshaft from the rear axle flange and remove it from the transmission.

3. Disconnect the speedometer cable from the extension housing.

4. Remove the engine rear support-to-extension housing attaching bolts.

5. Place a jack under the transmission and raise it just enough to remove the weight from the engine rear support.

6. Remove the bolt that secures the engine rear support to the cross member and remove the support.

7. Place a drain pan under the rear of the transmission case.

8. Lower the transmission and remove the extension housing attaching bolts. Slide the extension housing off the output shaft and allow the fluid to drain.

9. Remove the governor attaching bolts (Fig. 17) and remove the governor from the flange.

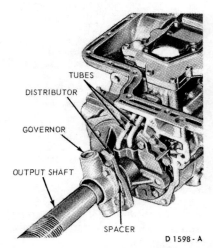

FIG. 17—Governor Installed

INSTALLATION

1. Secure the governor (Fig. 17) to the distributor flange with the attaching bolts. Torque the bolts to specification.

2. Clean the mounting surface on the transmission and on the extension housing. Position a new gasket on the transmisson.

3. Hold the extension housing in place and secure it with the attaching bolts.

4. Raise the transmission high enough to position the engine rear support on the crossmember.

5. Secure the support to the cross member with the attaching bolt and nut. Torque the bolt to specification.

6. Lower the transmission and remove the jack. Install and torque the engine rear support-to-extension housing attaching bolts to specification.

7. Secure the speedometer cable to the extension housing with the attaching bolt.

8. Connect the parking brake cable to the equalizer and adjust as required.

9. Install the drive shaft.

10. Fill the transmission to the correct level with the specified fluid.

SERVO REPLACEMENT

REMOVAL

1. Raise the car on a hoist or stands.

2. Remove the engine rear support-to-extension housing attaching bolts.

3. Raise the transmission high enough to remove the weight from the engine rear support.

4. Remove the bolt that secures the engine rear support to the crossmember. Remove the support.

5. Lower the transmission and remove the jack.

6. Place a drain pan beneath the servo. Remove the bolts that attach the servo cover to the transmission case.

7. Remove the cover, piston, spring and gasket from the case.

SEAL REPLACEMENT

1. Apply air pressure to the port in the servo cover to remove the piston and stem.

2. Remove the seals from the piston (Fig. 18).

3. Remove the seal from the cover.

4. Dip the new seals in transmission fluid.

5. Install the new seals on the piston.

6. Install the new gasket on the cover.

7. Dip the piston in transmission fluid and install it in the cover.

INSTALLATION

1. Position a new gasket on the servo cover.

2. Position the servo spring on the piston stem.

3. Insert the servo piston stem in the case. Secure the cover with the attaching bolts making sure that the vent tube retaining clip and the transmission identification tag is in place.

4. Raise the transmission high enough to install the engine rear support. Secure the support to the extension housing with the attaching bolts. Lower the transmission as required to install the support to crossmember attaching bolt. Torque the attaching bolts to specification.

5. Remove the jack.

6. Adjust the band as detailed in Section 2.

7. Lower the car and replenish the fluid as required.

VALVE BODY REPLACEMENT

REMOVAL

1. Raise car on a hoist or jack stands.

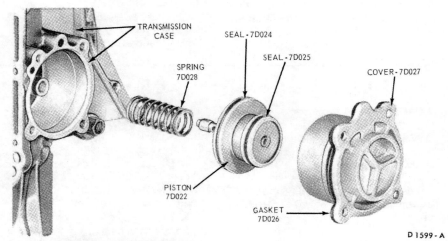

FIG. 18—Servo Disassembled

2. Place a drain pan under the transmission and loosen the bolts to drain the fluid from the transmission.

3. Loosen the transmission pan attaching bolts and allow the fluid to drain. Remove the transmission pan attaching bolts from both sides and the rear to allow the fluid to drain further. Finally, remove the remainder of the attaching bolts.

4. Remove the valve body attaching bolts and remove the valve body from the case.

5. Position the valve body to the case making sure that the selector and downshift levers are engaged, then install and torque the attaching bolts to specification.

6. Clean the oil pan and gasket surfaces thoroughly.

7. Using a new pan gasket, secure the pan to the transmission case and torque the attaching bolts to specification.

8. Lower the car and fill the transmission to the correct level with the specified fluid.

EXTENSION HOUSING BUSHING AND REAR SEAL REPLACEMENT

1. Disconnect the drive shaft from the transmission.

2. When only the rear seal needs replacing, carefully remove it with a tapered chisel or the tools shown in Fig. 19. Remove the bushing as shown in Fig. 20. **Use the bushing remover carefully so that the spline seal is not damaged.**

3. When installing a new bushing use the special tool shown in Fig. 21.

4. Before installing a new seal, inspect the sealing surface of the universal joint yoke for scores. If scores are found, replace the yoke.

5. Inspect the counterbore of the housing for burrs with crocus cloth.

6. Install the seal into the housing with the tool shown in Fig. 22. The seal should be firmly seated in the

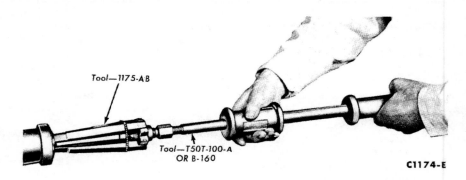

FIG. 19—Removing Extension Housing Seal

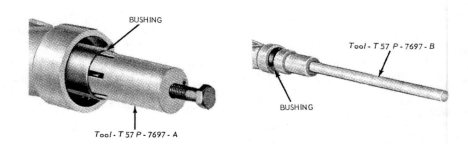

FIG. 20—Installing Extension Housing Bushing

FIG. 21—Removing Extension Housing Bushing

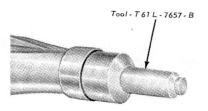

FIG. 22—Installing Extension Housing Seal

bore. Coat the inside diameter of the fiber portion of the seal with B8A-19589-A lubricant.

7. Coat the front universal joint spline with B8A-19589-A lubricant and install the drive shaft.

3 REMOVAL AND INSTALLATION

REMOVAL

1. Working from under the hood, disconnect the starter neutral switch from the wiring harness connector at the dash panel.

2. Raise the car on a hoist or stands. Drain the fluid from the transmission and from the converter.

3. Disconnect the drive shaft from the rear axle and slide the

shaft rearward from the transmission. Install a seal installation tool in the extension housing to prevent fluid leakage.

4. Disconnect the cable from the terminal on the starter motor. Remove the three attaching bolts and remove the starter motor.

5. Remove the four converter-to-flywheel attaching nuts. Place a wrench on the crankshaft pulley at-

taching bolt to turn the converter to gain access to the nuts.

6. Disconnect the parking brake front cable from the equalizer.

7. Remove the two crossmember-to-frame attaching bolts.

8. Remove the two engine rear support-to-extension housing attaching bolts.

9. Disconnect the downshift and

selector rods from the levers at the transmission.

10. Remove the two nuts that attach each muffler inlet pipe to the exhaust manifolds. Separate the pipes from the manifolds. Remove the exhaust thermostat and gaskets.

11. Raise the transmission with a transmission jack to provide clearance to remove the crossmember.

12. Disconnect the parking brake rear cables from the equalizer.

13. Remove the crossmember from the side supports.

14. Lower the transmission to *gain access to* the oil cooler lines.

15. Disconnect each oil line from the fittings on the transmission.

16. Disconnect the vacuum line from the diaphragm located at the right rear of the transmission. Remove the metal line from the retaining clip on the transmission.

17. Disconnect the speedometer cable from the extension housing.

18. Remove the bolt that secures the transmission fluid filler tube to the cylinder block. Lift the filler tube and the dipstick from the transmission.

19. Secure the transmission to the jack with the chain.

20. Remove the converter housing-to-cylinder block attaching bolts.

21. Carefully move the transmission away from the engine and, at the same time, lower it to clear the underside of the car.

22. Remove the converter and mount the transmission in a holding fixture.

INSTALLATION

1. Torque the two converter drain plugs to specification.

2. Install the converter on the stator support.

3. Secure the transmission to the jack with the chain.

4. Rotate the flywheel to place two converter mounting stud holes that are adjacent to the drain plug holes in a vertical position.

5. Rotate the converter so that the studs and drain plugs are in alignment with those in the flywheel.

6. Move the transmission toward the cylinder block until they are in contact. Install and torque the attaching bolts to specification making sure that the starter neutral switch wire and vacuum tube retaining clips are properly positioned.

7. Remove the transmission jack chain from around the transmission.

8. Install a new O-ring on the lower end of the transmission filler tube. Insert the tube in the transmission case and secure the tube to the engine with the attaching bolt.

9. Connect the speedometer cable to the extension housing.

10. Connect the oil cooler lines to the right side of transmission case.

11. Connect the vacuum line to the vacuum diaphragm making sure that the metal tube is secured in the retaining clip.

12. Position the cross member on the side supports and connect the front and the rear parking cables to the equalizer.

13. Secure the engine rear sup-

port to the extension housing and torque the bolts to specification.

14. Lower the transmission and remove the jack.

15. Secure the crossmember to the side supports with the attaching bolts and torque them to specification.

16. Position the exhaust thermostat and new gaskets on the exhaust manifolds. Secure the muffler inlet pipes to the exhaust manifolds.

17. Connect the downshift and selector rods to their respective levers on the transmission.

18. Secure the converter-to-flywheel attaching nuts and torque them to specification. Use a wrench on the crankshaft pulley attaching nut to rotate the flywheel. Do not use a wrench on the converter attaching nuts to rotate it.

19. Install the converter housing dust shield and secure it with the attaching bolts.

20. Secure the starter motor in place with the attaching bolts. Connect the cable to the terminal on the starter.

21. Install the driveshaft.

22. Adjust the starter neutral switch and shift linkage as detailed in Section 2.

23. Lower the car. Working from under the hood, connect the neutral starter switch wires to the harness.

24. Fill the transmission to the correct level with the specified lubricant. Start the engine and shift the transmission to all ranges, then recheck the fluid level.

4 MAJOR REPAIR OPERATIONS

DISASSEMBLY OF TRANSMISSION

1. Mount the transmission in holding fixture T59P-7000-A (Fig. 23).

2. Remove the 17 oil pan attaching bolts. Remove pan and gasket.

3. Remove the 8 valve body attaching bolts (Fig. 24). Lift the valve body from the transmission case. Remove the vacuum diaphram rod.

4. Attach a dial indicator to the front pump as shown in Fig. 25. Install tool T61L-7657-B in the extension housing to center the shaft.

5. Pry the gear train to the rear of the case and at the same time, press the input shaft inward until

it bottoms (Fig. 25). Set the dial indicator to read zero.

6. Pry the gear train forward (Fig. 25) and note the amount of gear train end play on the dial indicator. Record the end play to facilitate assembling the transmission. Remove the dial indicator from the pump and the tool from the extension housing.

7. Remove the vacuum diaphragm, rod and the primary throttle valve from the case. Slip the input shaft out of the front pump.

8. Remove the front pump attaching bolts. Pry the gear train forward as shown in Fig. 26 to remove the pump.

9. Loosen the band adjustment screw and remove the two struts.

10. Rotate the band 90° counterclockwise to align the ends with the slot in the case (Fig. 27). Slide the band off the reverse-high clutch drum.

11. Remove the forward part of the gear train as an assembly as shown in Fig. 28.

12. Remove the large snap ring that secures the reverse planet carrier in the low-reverse clutch hub. Lift the planet carrier from the drum.

13. Remove the snap ring (Fig. 29) that secures the reverse ring gear and hub on the output shaft. Slide the ring gear and hub off the shaft.

14. Rotate the low-reverse clutch hub in a clockwise direction and at

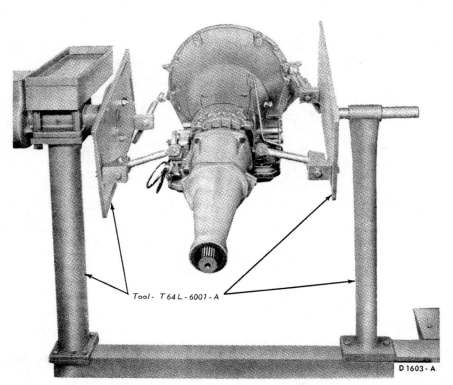

FIG. 23—Transmission Mounted in Holding Fixture

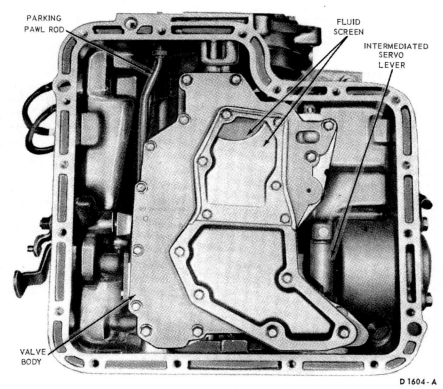

FIG. 24—Transmission with Oil Pan Removed

the same time, withdraw it from the case.

15. Remove the reverse clutch snap ring from the case, then re-move the clutch discs, plates and pressure plate from the case.

16. Remove the extension housing attaching bolts and vent tube from the case. Remove the extension housing and gasket.

17. Slide the output shaft assembly from the transmission case.

18. Remove the distributor sleeve attaching bolts and remove the sleeve, parking pawl gear and the thrust washer.

19. Compress the reverse clutch piston release spring with tool T65P-77515-A (Fig. 30). Remove the snap ring. Remove the tool and the spring retainer.

20. Remove the one-way clutch inner race attaching bolts from the rear of the case. Remove the inner race from inside of the case.

21. Remove the reverse clutch piston from the case as shown in Fig. 31.

PARTS REPAIR OR REPLACEMENT

During the repair of the sub-as-semblies, certain general instruc-tions which apply to all units of the transmission must be followed. Fol-lowing these instructions will avoid unnecessary repetition.

All transmission parts must be handled carefully to avoid nicking or burring the bearing or mating sur-faces.

Lubricate all internal parts of the transmission with clean automatic transmission fluid before assembling them.

Do not use any other lubricants except on gaskets and thrust wash-ers. These may be coated with vase-line to facilitate assembly. Always use new gaskets and seals when as-sembling a transmission.

Tighten all bolts and screws to the recommended torque as outlined in the Specification Section.

TRANSMISSION CASE AND LINKAGE

DOWNSHIFT AND MANUAL LINKAGE

1. Remove the nut and lock wash-er that secures the outer downshift lever to the transmission and re-move the lever.

2. Remove the two bolts that se-cure the neutral safety switch to the case. Insert a screwdriver between the switch and case as close as pos-

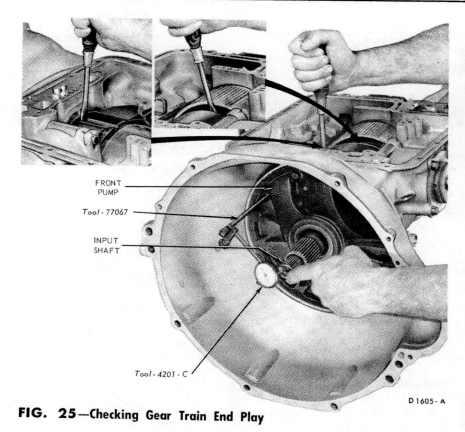

FRONT PUMP

Tool - 77067

INPUT SHAFT

Tool - 4201 - C

D 1605 - A

FIG. 25—Checking Gear Train End Play

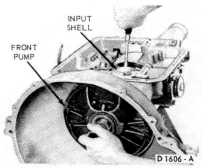

INPUT SHELL

FRONT PUMP

D 1606 - A

FIG. 26—Removing Front Pump

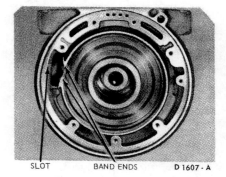

SLOT   BAND ENDS   D 1607 - A

FIG. 27—Removing or Installing Band

sible to the shaft. Gently pry the switch from the case.

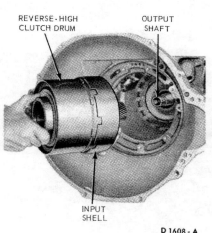

REVERSE-HIGH CLUTCH DRUM   OUTPUT SHAFT

INPUT SHELL

D 1608 - A

FIG. 28—Removing or Installing Forward Part of Gear Train

3. Slide the downshift lever out from the inside of the case (Fig. 32). Remove the seal from the recess in the manual lever shaft.

4. Remove the C-ring that secures the parking pawl actuating rod to the manual lever. Remove the rod from the case.

5. Remove the nut that secures the inner manual lever to the shaft.

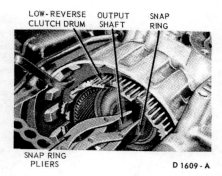

LOW-REVERSE CLUTCH DRUM   OUTPUT SHAFT   SNAP RING

SNAP RING PLIERS   D 1609 - A

FIG. 29—Removing or Installing Reverse Ring Gear Hub Retaining Ring

Remove the inner lever from the shaft. Slide the outer lever and shaft from the case.

6. Remove the seal from the case with Tools T59L-100-B and T58L-101-A or 7600-E.

7. Dip the new seal in transmission fluid and install it in the case as shown in Fig. 33.

8. Slide the outer manual lever and shaft in the transmission case.

9. Position the inner lever on the shaft and install the attaching nut. Tighten the nut to specification. Install the parking pawl actuating rod and secure it to the inner manual lever with a C-washer.

10. Install a new downshift lever seal in the recess of the outer lever shaft. Slide the downshift lever and shaft into position.

11. Position the neutral safety switch on the manual lever and secure it with the two attaching bolts. Leave the attaching bolts loose to adjust the switch after installing the control valve.

12. Place the outer downshift lever on the shaft and secure it with a lock washer and nut.

PARKING PAWL LINKAGE

1. Remove the bolts that secure the parking pawl guide plate to the case (Fig. 34). Remove the plate.

2. Remove the spring, parking pawl and shaft from the case.

3. Working from the pan mounting surface, drill a ⅛ inch diameter hole through the center of the cupped plug. Pull the plug from the case with a wire hook.

4. Lift the end of the spring off the park plate pin to relieve the tension.

5. Thread a ¼-20 inch screw (Fig. 35) into the park plate shaft.

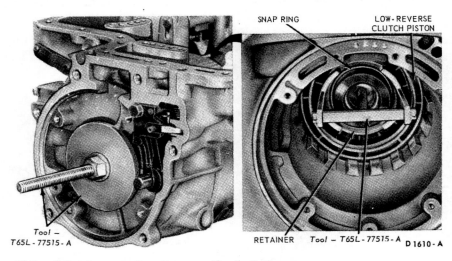

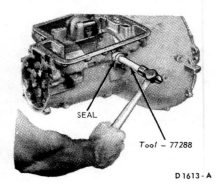

FIG. 33—Installing Manual Lever Seal

FIG. 30—Compressing Reverse Clutch Springs

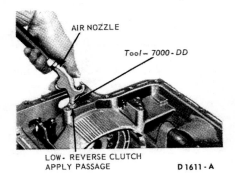

FIG. 31—Removing Reverse Clutch Piston

Secure the plate with two bolts and lock washers.

SERVO APPLY LEVER

1. Working from inside of the transmission case, carefully drive on the servo apply lever shaft to remove the ball. The shaft (Fig. 36) can be withdrawn from the case by hand.

2. Hold the servo apply lever in position and install the new shaft.

3. Press the ball into position and stake it in two places as shown in Fig. 36.

THREAD REPAIR CASE

Thread service kits may be pur-

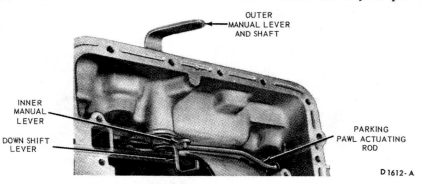

FIG. 32—Downshift and Manual Linkage

Pull the shaft from the case with the screw.

6. Position *the spring* and park plate in the case and install the shaft. Hook the end of the spring over the pin on the park plate.

7. Install a new cupped washer (Fig. 34) to retain the shaft.

8. Install the parking pawl shaft in the case. Slip the parking pawl and spring into place on the shaft.

9. Position the guide plate on the case making sure that the actuating rod is seated in the slot of the plate.

chased from local jobbers or the Heli-Coil Corporation. To repair a damaged thread, the following procedures should be carefully followed:

1. Drill out the damaged threads **using the same size threads as the thread OD.** For example, use a $5/16$-inch drill when repairing a $5/16$-18 inch thread.

2. Select the proper **special** tap and tap the drilled hole. The tap is marked for the size of the thread being repaired. Thus, the special tap supplied with the repair kit marked

$5/16$-18 will not cut the same thread as a standard $5/16$-inch tap. It will cut a thread large enough to accommodate the insert, and after the insert is installed, the original thread size ($5/16$-18 inch) is restored.

3. Select the proper coil inserting tool. These tools are marked with the thread size being repaired. Place the insert on the tool and adjust the sleeve to the length of the insert being used.

Press the insert against the face of the tapped hole. Turn the tool clockwise and wind the insert into the hole until the insert is one half turn below the face.

4. Working through the insert, bend the insert tang straight up and down until it breaks off at the notch.

5. If the inserts are not properly installed, they can be removed with the extractor tool. Place the extractor tool in the insert so that the blade rests against the top coil $1/4$-$1/2$ turn away from the end of the coil. Tap the tool sharply with a hammer so that the blade cuts into the insert. Exert downward pressure on the tool and turn it counterclockwise until the insert is removed.

CONTROL VALVE

DISASSEMBLY

1. Remove the nine screws that attach the screen to the lower valve body (Fig. 37) and remove the screen.

2. Remove the twelve screws and the 2 plates that attach the two valve bodies.

3. Separate the bodies and remove the separator plate and gasket.

4. Depress the manual valve detent spring with the tool shown in Fig. 38. Remove the retaining pin from the upper valve body. Remove the spring and detent plunger.

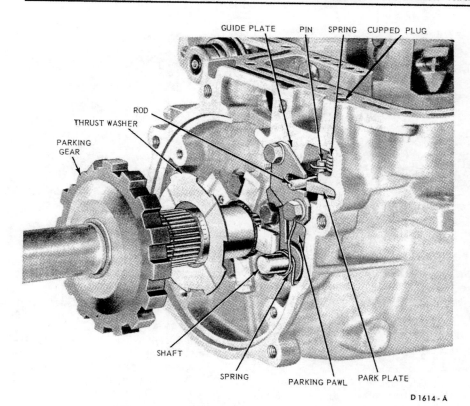

FIG. 34—Parking Pawl Mechanism

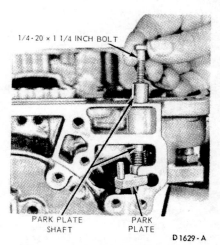

FIG. 35—Removing Park Plate Shaft

5. Slide the manual valve (Fig. 39) out of the valve body.

6. Cover the downshift valve port with a finger, then working from the underside of the body remove the downshift valve retainer. Remove the spring and downshift valve.

7. Apply pressure on the pressure booster valve retaining plate and remove the two attaching screws. Slowly release the pressure and re-

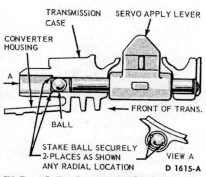

FIG. 36—Servo Apply Lever Installation

move the plate, sleeve and the pressure booster valve. Remove the two springs and the main regulator valve from the same bore.

8. Apply pressure on the throttle booster valve retaining plate and remove the two attaching screws. Slowly release the pressure and remove the plate, throttle booster valve and spring, and the 3-2 coasting control valve and spring from the body.

9. Apply pressure on the remaining valve retaining plate and remove the eight attaching screws.

10. Hold the valve body so that the plate is facing upward. Slowly release the pressure and remove the plate.

11. When removing the various valves from the control valve body, keep all ports covered with your fingers except the bore the valve is being removed from. Remove the 1-2 shift capacity scheduling and accumulator valves (Fig. 39) from the valve body.

12. Remove the 2-3 back-out valve, spring and the manual low valve.

13. Remove the 2-3 shift valve, spring and the throttle modulator valve.

14. Remove the 1-2 shift valve, D2 shift valve and the spring from the valve body.

15. Remove the coasting boost valve and the spring from the body.

16. Remove the cutback control valve to complete the disassembly of the control valve.

ASSEMBLY

1. Place the cutback control valve (Fig. 39) in the valve body.

2. Place the spring and the coasting boost valve in the body.

3. Place the spring, D2 shift valve and the 1-2 shift valve in the body.

4. Place the throttle modulator valve and spring and the 2-3 shift valve in the valve body.

5. Place the manual low valve and spring and the 2-3 backout valve in the valve body.

6. Place the 1-2 shift accumulator valve and springs and the 1-2 shift scheduling valve and spring in the valve body.

7. Carefully place the valve retaining plate on the body and secure it with the eight attaching screws. Tighten the screws to specification.

8. Place the throttle booster valve and spring in the valve body. Place the 3-2 coasting control valve and spring in the valve body and install the retaining plate. Torque the attaching screws to specification.

9. Place the main regulator, two springs, pressure booster valve and the sleeve in the valve body.

10. Install the pressure booster plate and torque the two attaching screws to specification.

11. Place the downshift valve and spring in the valve body. Compress the spring and install the retainer from the underside of the body.

12. Place the manual valve in the valve body and install the detent plug, spring and the retaining pin in the body.

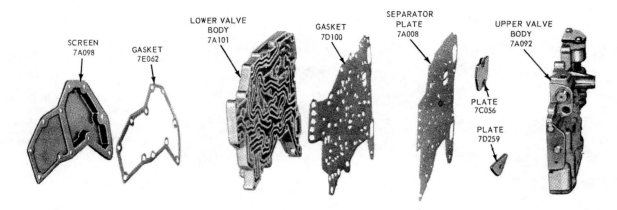

FIG. 37—Upper and Lower Valve Bodies Disassembled

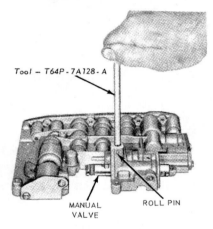

FIG. 38—Removing Manual Valve

13. Place the valve body on a clean surface with the passage side facing up. Place the converter relief valve spring in its bore (Fig. 40). Coat the converter relief valve check ball with vaseline and place it on top of the spring. Place the 2-3 shift check valve ball in its cavity.

14. Carefully position the separator plate, new gasket and the lower valve body on the upper valve body and install and torque the attaching bolts to specification.

15. Secure the screen to the lower valve body with the attaching bolts and torque them to specification.

FRONT PUMP

The front seal can be replaced after the pump has been installed on the transmission.

DISASSEMBLY

1. Remove the two seal rings and the selective thrust washer (Fig. 41).

2. Remove the O-ring seal from the pump housing.

3. Remove the 5 bolts that secure the pump support to the pump housing. Lift the support from the housing.

4. Remove the drive and the driven gear from the housing.

ASSEMBLY

1. Install the drive and driven gears in the pump housing. Each gear has an identification mark on one face. **The identification mark on each gear must be toward the front of the pump housing.**

2. Position the pump support in the pump housing and install and torque the five attaching bolts to specification.

3. Carefully install two new seal rings on the pump support. Make sure that the ends of the rings are engaged to lock them in place.

4. Install the selective thrust washer. Make sure that the correct thickness selective washer is being used to obtain the specified end play.

5. Place the pump on converter making sure that the drive gear engages the converter hub. Rotate the pump to make sure that the gears rotate freely.

REVERSE-HIGH CLUTCH

DISASSEMBLY

1. Separate the drive train as shown in Fig. 42. Remove the pressure plate retaining snap ring as shown in Fig. 43.

2. Remove the pressure plate and the drive and driven clutch plates (Fig. 44).

3. Install Tool T65L-77515-A (Fig. 45) on the reverse-high clutch drum. Make sure that the legs clear the snap ring enough to permit expanding it enough for removing it. Remove the snap ring and remove the tool.

4. Remove the spring retainer and the piston return springs.

5. Apply air pressure to the piston apply hole in the clutch hub (Fig. 46) and remove the piston.

6. Remove the piston outer seal from the piston and the inner seal from the clutch drum (Fig. 44).

ASSEMBLY

1. Dip the new seals in transmission fluid and install one on the drum and one on the piston.

2. Install the piston in the clutch drum.

3. Position the piston return springs in the piston sockets. Place the spring retainer on the springs.

4. Install Tool T65L-77515-A (Fig. 45) and compress the springs. Make certain that the spring retainer is centered while compressing the springs. Install the snap ring. Before releasing the pressure on the tool, make certain that the snap ring is positioned inside of the four snap ring guides on the spring retainer.

5. Dip the clutch plates in clean transmission fluid. Install the clutch plates alternately starting with a steel *drive plate and a bronze plate* (Fig. 44).

6. After all clutch plates have been installed, position the pressure plate in the clutch drum with the

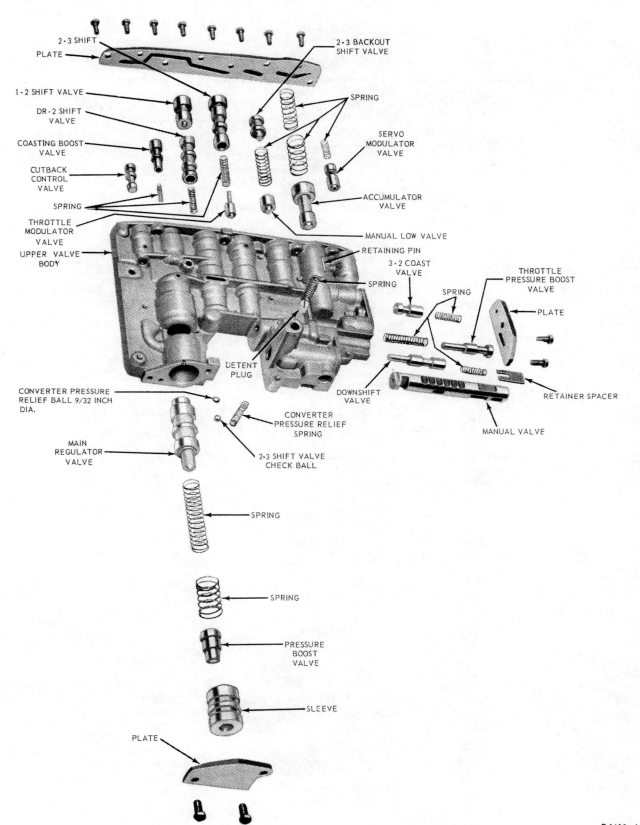

FIG. 39—Upper Valve Body Disassembled

D 1618-A

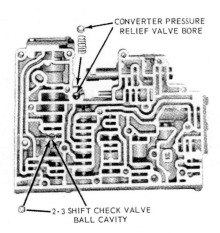

FIG. 40—Converter Pressure Relief Valve and 2-3 Shift Check Valve Location

chamfered side facing up. Install the pressure plate snap ring.

7. With a feeler gauge, check the clearance between the pressure plate and snap ring. (Fig. 47).

8. The pressure plate should be held downward as the clearance is checked. The clearance should be 0.022-0.036 inch for B, C, K, T, U, and W models, or 0.027-0.043 inch for D, L, H and N models. If the clearance is not within specifications, selective thickness snap rings are available in the following thicknesses: 0.065-0.069, 0.074-0.078, and 0.083-0.087 inch. Install the correct size snap ring and recheck the clearance.

FORWARD CLUTCH
DISASSEMBLY

1. Remove the clutch pressure plate retaining snap ring (Fig. 48).

2. Remove the rear pressure plate, the drive and driven plates and the forward pressure plate from the clutch hub (Fig. 49).

3. Remove the snap ring (Fig. 50) that secures the disc spring in the clutch cylinder. Remove the disc spring.

4. Apply air pressure to the clutch apply passage in the cylinder (Fig. 51) to remove the piston.

5. Remove the seal from the piston and the seal from the clutch hub (Fig. 49).

ASSEMBLY

1. Dip two new seals in transmission fluid. Install the smaller seal on the clutch hub and the other seal on the clutch piston.

2. Install the clutch piston in the cylinder.

3. Make sure that the steel pres-

sure ring is in the groove on the piston. Position the disc spring in the cylinder with the dished face downward. Install the spring as shown in Fig. 50. Secure the disc with the retaining snap ring.

4. Install the forward pressure plate with the flat side up and the radius side downward. Install first a bronze driven plate and a steel drive plate (Fig. 49). Install the remaining plates in this sequence. The last plate installed will be the rear pressure plate. Install the snap ring and make certain that it seats fully in the groove.

5. With a feeler gauge, check the clearance between the snap ring and the pressure plate (Fig. 52). Downward pressure on the plate should be maintained when making this

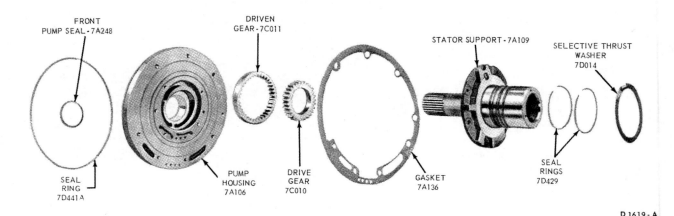

FIG. 41—Front Pump Disassembled

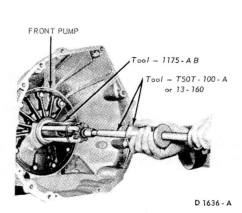

FIG. 42—Removing Front Pump Seal

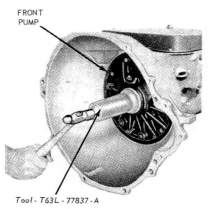

FIG. 43—Installing Front Pump Seal

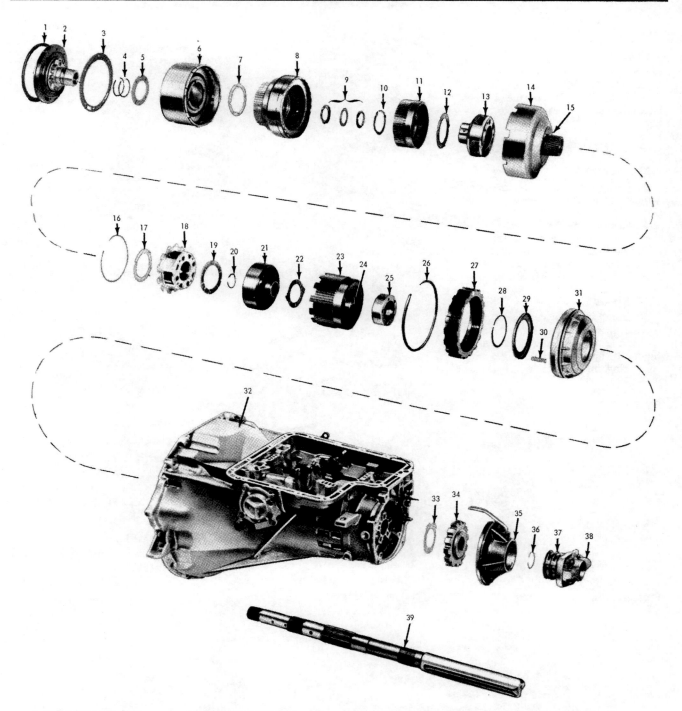

1. FRONT PUMP SEAL RING
2. FRONT PUMP
3. GASKET
4. SEAL
5. NUMBER 1 THRUST WASHER
   (SELECTIVE)
6. REVERSE — HIGH CLUTCH
   ASSEMBLY
7. NUMBER 2 THRUST WASHER
8. FORWARD CLUTCH ASSEMBLY
9. NUMBER 3 THRUST WASHER
10. NUMBER 4 THRUST WASHER

11. FORWARD CLUTCH HUB
    ASSEMBLY
12. NUMBER 5 THRUST WASHER
13. FORWARD PLANET ASSEMBLY
14. INPUT SHELL AND SUN
    GEAR ASSEMBLY
15. NUMBER 6 THRUST WASHER
16. SNAP RING
17. NUMBER 7 THRUST WASHER
18. REVERSE PLANET ASSEMBLY
19. NUMBER 8 THRUST WASHER

20. REVERSE RING GEAR AND
    HUB RETAINING RING
21. REVERSE RING GEAR AND HUB
22. NUMBER 9 THRUST WASHER
23. LOW — REVERSE CLUTCH HUB
24. ONE — WAY CLUTCH
25. ONE — WAY CLUTCH INNER RACE
26. SNAP RING
27. LOW — REVERSE CLUTCH
28. SNAP RING
29. LOW — REVERSE PISTON RETURN

    SPRING RETAINER
30. RETURN SPRING
31. LOW — REVERSE PISTON
32. CASE
33. NUMBER 10 THRUST WASHER
34. PARKING GEAR
35. GOVERNOR DISTRIBUTOR SLEEVE
36. SNAP RING
37. GOVERNOR DISTRIBUTOR
38. GOVERNOR
39. OUTPUT SHAFT

D 1620 - A

FIG. 44—Drive Train Disassembled

check. The clearance should be 0.048-0.061 inch.

6. If the clearance is not within specifications, selective snap rings are available in the following thicknesses: 0.065-0.069, 0.074-0.078, and 0.083-0.087 inch. Insert the correct size snap ring and recheck the clearance.

INPUT SHELL AND SUN GEAR

DISASSEMBLY

1. Remove the external snap ring from the sun gear as shown in Fig. 53.

2. Remove the thrust washer from the input shell and sun gear (Fig 54).

3. Working from inside the input shell remove the sun gear. Remove the internal snap ring from the gear.

ASSEMBLY

1. Install the forward snap ring on the forward end (short end) of the sun gear. Working from inside the input shell, slide the sun gear and snap ring into place making sure

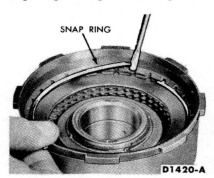

FIG. 45—Removing or Installing Reverse-High Clutch Pressure Plate Snap Ring

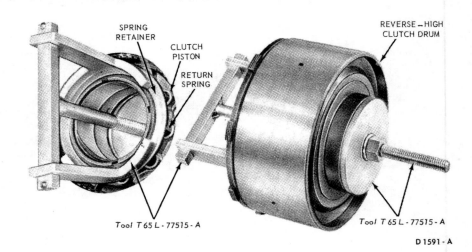

FIG. 47—Removing or Installing Reverse-High Pressure Plate Snap Ring

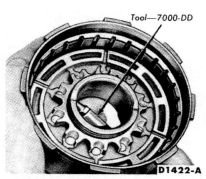

FIG. 48—Removing Reverse-High Clutch Piston

that the longer end is at the rear (Fig. 54).

2. Place the No. 6 thrust washer on the sun gear and install the external snap ring.

FIG. 49—Checking Reverse-High Clutch Snap Ring Clearance

OUTPUT SHAFT HUB AND RING GEAR

DISASSEMBLY

1. Remove the hub retaining snap ring (Fig. 55) from the ring gear.

2. Lift the hub from the ring gear.

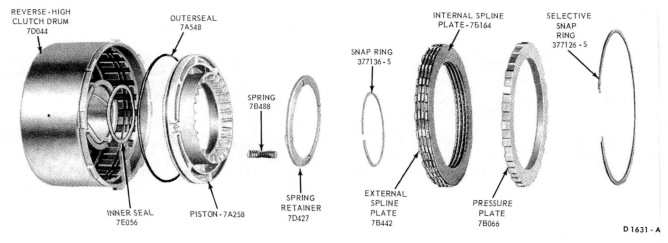

FIG. 46—Reverse-High Clutch Disassembled

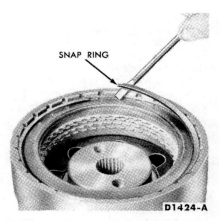

FIG. 50—Removing Forward Clutch Pressure Plate Snap Ring

ONE-WAY CLUTCH

DISASSEMBLY

1. Remove the snap ring (Fig. 56) from the rear of the low-reverse clutch hub.

2. Lift the one-way clutch from the hub.

3. Remove the remaining snap ring from the hub.

ASSEMBLY

1. Install the snap ring in the inner groove of the low-reverse clutch hub.

2. Make sure that all of the roll-

the hub so that the springs load the rollers in a counterclockwise direction when looking downward at the unit (Fig. 57).

5. Work each roller inward just enough to enter it in the ramp. Do this to each individual roller until the one-way clutch is positioned in the race. Placing a rubber band around the clutch as shown in Fig. 57 helps to contact the rollers to permit installation. After all of the rollers have started, remove the rubber band.

6. Install the snap ring at the rear of the low-reverse clutch hub to secure the one-way clutch.

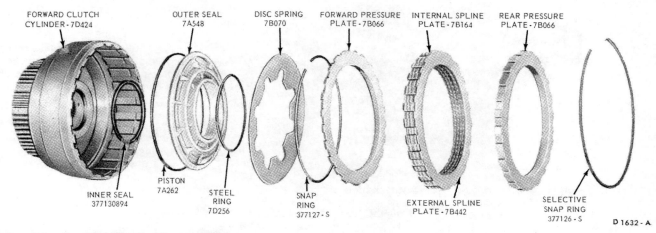

FIG. 51—Forward Clutch Disassembled

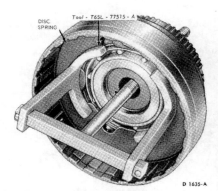

FIG. 52—Removing or Installing Disc Spring

ASSEMBLY

1. Position the hub in the ring gear.

2. Secure the hub with the retaining snap ring. Make certain that the snap ring is fully engaged with the groove.

FIG. 53—Removing Forward Clutch Piston

ers are in place and that the springs contact them properly.

3. Place the low-reverse clutch hub on the bench with the one-way clutch race facing upward.

4. Place the one-way clutch on

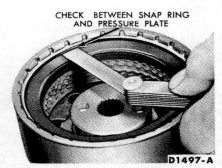

FIG. 54—Checking Forward Clutch Clearance

SERVO

DISASSEMBLY

1. Apply air pressure to the port in the servo cover to remove the piston and stem.

2. Remove the seals from the piston.

3. Remove the seal from the cover.

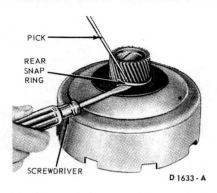

FIG. 55—Removing Sun Gear Snap Ring

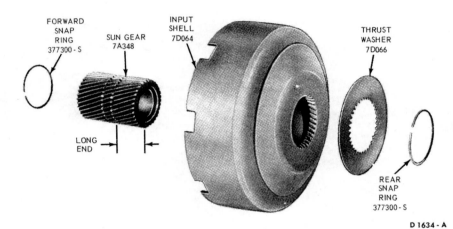

FIG. 56—Input Shell and Sun Gear Disassembled

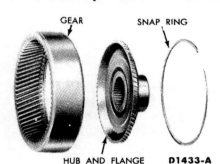

FIG. 57—Output Shaft Hub and Ring Gear

ASSEMBLY

1. Dip the new seals in transmission fluid.
2. Install the new seals on the piston.
3. Install the new seal on the cover.
4. Dip the piston in transmission fluid and install it in the cover.

LOW-REVERSE CLUTCH PISTON

DISASSEMBLY

1. Remove the inner and the outer

seal from the reverse clutch piston.

ASSEMBLY

1. Dip the two new seals in clean transmission fluid.
2. Install the seals on the piston.

OUTPUT SHAFT

DISASSEMBLY

1. Remove the governor attaching bolts and remove the governor and spacer.
2. Remove the snap ring that secures the governor distributor on the output shaft (Fig. 58) and slide

it off the front of the shaft.
3. Remove the seal rings from the distributor.

DISASSEMBLY

1. Carefully install new seal rings on the distributor.
2. Working from the front end of

the output shaft, slide the governor distributor into place on the shaft. Install the snap ring to secure it. Make sure that the snap ring is seated in the groove.

3. Position the spacer and the governor on the distributor (Fig. 58) and secure them with the attaching screws.

ASSEMBLY OF TRANSMISSION

1. Place the transmission case in a holding fixture.
2. Tap the reverse clutch piston into place in the case with a clean rubber hammer.
3. Hold the one-way clutch inner race in position and install and torque the attaching bolts to specification.
4. Install a low-reverse clutch return spring in each pocket in the clutch piston. Press the springs firmly into the piston to prevent them from falling out.
5. Position the spring retainer over the springs and position the retainer snap ring in place on the one-way clutch inner race.
6. Install the compressing tool shown in Fig. 26 and compress the springs just enough to install the low-reverse clutch piston retainer snap ring.
7. Install the snap ring, then remove the compressing tool.
8. Place the transmission case on the bench with the front end facing downward.
9. Position the parking gear thrust washer and the gear on the case (Fig. 30).
10. Position the oil distributor and tubes in place on the rear of the case. Install and torque the attaching bolts to specification.

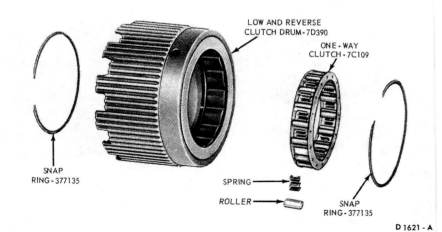

FIG. 58—One-Way Clutch Disassembled

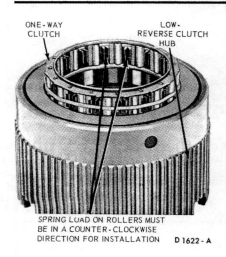

ONE-WAY CLUTCH   LOW-REVERSE CLUTCH HUB

SPRING LOAD ON ROLLERS MUST BE IN A COUNTER-CLOCKWISE DIRECTION FOR INSTALLATION

D 1622-A

FIG. 59—Installing One-Way Clutch

them in clean transmission fluid for fifteen minutes before installation. Install the pressure plate and the snap ring. Test the operation of the low-reverse clutch by applying air pressure at the clutch pressure apply hole in the case. Ford 390-2V and 4V and Mercury 410-4V (single exhaust) cases are machined to accommodate a five-plate clutch pack. Ford and Mercury 428-4V and Mercury 410-4V (dual exhaust) models are machined for a six-plate clutch pack.

16. Install the reverse planet ring gear thrust washer and the ring gear and hub assembly. Insert the snap ring in the groove in the output shaft.

17. Assemble the front and rear thrust washers onto the reverse

the front end of the forward planet assembly. Retain the washer with vaseline and insert the assembly into the ring gear. Install the input shell and sun gear assembly.

21. Install the reverse-high clutch, forward clutch, forward planet assembly and drive input shell and sun gear as an assembly into the transmission case.

22. Insert the intermediate band into the case around the direct clutch cylinder with the narrow band end facing toward the servo apply lever. Install the struts and then tighten the band adjusting screw sufficiently to retain the band.

23. Place a selective thickness bronze thrust washer on the rear shoulder of the stator support and retain it with vaseline. Lay a new

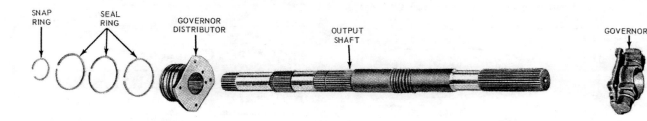

SNAP RING   SEAL RING   GOVERNOR DISTRIBUTOR   OUTPUT SHAFT   GOVERNOR

D 1623-A

FIG. 60—Output Shaft Disassembled

11. Install the output shaft, and governor as an assembly.

12. Place a new gasket on the rear of the transmission case. Position the extension housing on the case and install the attaching bolts. Torque the attaching bolts to specification.

13. Place the case in the holding fixture.

14. Align the low-reverse clutch hub and one-way clutch with the inner race at the rear of the case. Rotate the low-reverse clutch hub clockwise while applying pressure to seat it on the inner race.

15. Install the low-reverse clutch plates, starting with a steel plate and following with friction and steel plates alternately. If new composition plates are being used, soak plate assembly. Retain them with vaseline, and insert

the assembly into the ring gear. Install the snap ring in the ring gear.

18. Set the reverse-high clutch on the bench, with the front end facing down. Install the thrust washer on the rear end of the reverse-high clutch assembly. Retain the thrust washer with vaseline and insert the splined end of forward clutch into the open end of the reverse-high clutch so that the splines engage the direct clutch friction plates (Fig. 38).

19. Install the thrust washer and retain it with vaseline, on the front end of the forward planet ring gear and hub. Insert the ring gear into the forward clutch.

20. Install the thrust washer on gasket on the rear mounting face of the pump and position it on the case being careful not to damage the

O-ring. Install six of the seven mounting bolts and torque them to specification.

24. Adjust the intermediate band as detailed in Section 2 and install the input shaft.

25. Install tool 4201-C at the seventh pump mounting bolt (Fig. 21) and check the transmission end play. Remove the tool.

26. Install the control valve in the case, making sure that the levers engage the valves properly. Install the primary throttle valve, rod, and the vacuum diaphragm in the case.

27. Install a new pan gasket and the oil pan.

28. Install the converter assembly.

29. Install the transmission in the car.

PART 7-5 SPECIFICATIONS

C4 AUTOMATIC DUAL RANGE TRANSMISSION ONLY
CONTROL PRESSURE AT ZERO OUTPUT SHAFT SPEED

Engine Speed	Throttle	Manifold Vac. Ins. Hg.	Selector Lever Position	Control Pressure (P.S.I.)
Idle	Closed	①Above 18	P, N, D1, D2, L	55-62
			R	55-100
As Required	As Required	17° Approx.	D1, D2, L	Pressure Starts to Increase
As Required	As Required	10	D1, D2, L	96-105
As Required	As Required	3	D1, D2, L	138-148
			R	215-227

①Cars checked at high altitudes

At Altitudes above sea level it may not be possible to obtain 18" of vacuum at idle. For idle vacuums of less than 18" refer to following table to determine idle speed pressure specification in forward driving ranges (D1, D2, or L).

Engine Vacuum	Control Pressure (PSI)
17	55-62
16	55-68
15	55-74
14	55-80
13	55-87
12	55-93
11	55-99

STALL SPEED LIMITS

Engine Model	Engine Speed (rpm)
240 Six	1300-1500
289 V-8	1450-1650

LUBRICANT REFILL CAPACITY

Approximate Capacity—Quarts	10.25

CLUTCH PLATES

Transmission Model	Reverse-High Clutch		Forward Clutch	
	Steel Plates	Composition Plates	Steel Plates	Composition Plates
All	4	4	4	5

SHIFT SPEEDS

	Range	Shift	1	2	3	4	5	6	7	8
Minimum Throttle	D1	1—2	7—9	7—9	7—9	8—10	8—10	8—11	9—11	9—11
	D1	2—3	10—17	10—18	11—19	11—20	11—20	12—21	12—22	13—23
	D2	3—2	9	9	9	10	10	11	11	11
	D1	3—1	9	9	9	10	10	11	11	11
	L	2—1	17	18	19	20	20	21	22	23
Maximum Throttle	D1	1—2	24—34	24—35	26—37	27—38	28—40	29—41	30—43	32—44
	D1, D2	2—3	44—60	45—62	48—66	50—68	52—71	54—74	56—77	60—79
	D1, D2	3—2	58	59	62	66	68	71	74	77
	D1	2—1 or 3—1	27	28	29	31	32	33	34	36

Car	Engine Displacement	Axle Ratio	Tire Size	Use Column No.
Ford	240-1V or 289-2V	3.89:1	7.35 x 15	1
			7.75 x 15 or 8.15 x 15	2
		3.50:1	7.35 x 15	3
			7.75 x 15 or 8.15 x 15	4
		3.25:1	7.35 x 15	5
			7.75 x 15 or 8.15 x 15	6
		3.00:1	7.35 x 15	7
			7.75 x 15 or 8.15 x 15	8

CHECKS AND ADJUSTMENTS

Transmission End Play	0.008-0.042 inch Selective Thrust Washers Available
Turbine and Stator End Play Check	0.060 inch (Maximum)
Intermediate Band Adjustment	Adjust screw to 10 ft-lbs torque, then back off 1¾ turns and tighten locknut to spec.
Low-Reverse Band Adjustment	Adjust screw to 10 ft-lbs torque, then back off 3 turns and tighten locknut to spec.
Forward Clutch Pressure Plate-to-Snap Ring Clearance	No. of Composition Plates in Clutch Clearance Specification 4 0.020-0.036 inch 5 0.026-0.042 inch **Selective Snap Ring Thicknesses** 0.102-0.106 0.088-0.092 0.074-0.078 0.060-0.064
Reverse-High Clutch Pressure Plate-to-Snap Ring Clearance	0.050-0.066 inch **Selective Snap Ring Thicknesses** 0.102-0.106 0.088-0.092 0.074-0.078 0.060-0.064

SELECTIVE THRUST WASHERS (No. 1 and 2)

Thrust Washer No. 1		Thrust Washer No. 2	
Composition Thrust Washer	Color of Washer	No. Stamped on Washer	Metal Thrust Washer
0.138-0.142	Purple		
0.121-0.125	Red		
0.108-0.104	Blue	5	0.109-0.107
0.091-0.087	Yellow	4	0.092-0.090
0.074-0.070	Black	3	0.075-0.073
0.057-0.053	Tan	2	0.058-0.056
0.042-0.038	Green	1	0.043-0.041

CONTROL VALVE BODY SPRING IDENTIFICATION

Spring	Total Coils	Free Length	OD	Wire Diameter	Lbs. Load at Length	
Manual Valve Detent	9	0.74	0.295	0.045	7.5	0.601
2-3 Backout Control Valve	10	1.515	0.450	0.026	1.353	0.580
Main Oil Pressure Regulator Valve	9.75	1.86	0.615	0.047	6.200	0.608
Throttle Pressure Modulator	15	1.513	0.292	0.286	3.675	0.620
Control 1-2 Shift Valve	13	0.950	0.230	0.019	1.00	0.450
Throttle Downshift Valve	9	1.042	0.360	0.031	3.0	0.476
Throttle Pressure Booster Valve	15	1.421	0.326	0.036	5.250	0.730
Control Pressure Booster Valve	23.5	0.965	0.290	0.032	1.00	0.715
Intermediate Band Accumulator Valve	12.5	1.107	0.325	0.025	1.100	0.551

TORQUE LIMITS

Item	Ft-Lbs
Pressure Gauge Tap	9-15
Conv. Hsg. Lower Cover to Trans.	10-13
Downshift Lever to Case	12-16
Oil Pan to Case	12-16
Cooler Bracket & Oil Pan to Case	12-16
Int. Servo Cover to Case	12-20
Rev. Servo Cover to Case	12-20
Support Assy. to Frt. Pump	12-20
Distributor Sleeve to Case	12-20
Reverse Servo Piston to Rod	12-20
Outer Race to Case	13-20
Diaphragm Assy. to Case	15-23
Converter Drain Plug	20-30
Flywheel to Converter	20-30
Ext. Hsg. to Case	28-40

TORQUE LIMITS (Continued)

Item	Ft-Lbs
Front Oil Pump to Case	28-40
Converter Housing to Case	28-40
Manual Lever to Shaft	30-40
Int. Band Adj. Stop to Case	35-40
Rev. Band Adj. Stop to Case	35-40
Transmission to Engine	40-50
End Plate to Control Assy.	20-35
Lower to Upper Valve Body	40-55
Screen & Lwr. to Upper Valve Body	40-55
Neutral Switch to Case	55-75
Screen & Control Assy. to Case	80-120
Control Assy. to Case	80-120
Gov. Body to Collector Body	80-120
Cooler Line Fittings	80-120

C6 AUTOMATIC DUAL RANGE
CONTROL AND TV PRESSURE SPECIFICATIONS AT ZERO GOVERNOR RPM WITH NON-ALTITUDE COMPENSATING DIAPHRAGM

Engine Speed	Throttle	Manifold Vac (In. Hg)	Range	TV Pressure (PSI)	Control Pressure (PSI)
Idle	Closed	Above 17	P, N, D1, D2, L R	0-13 0-13	51-66 72-108
As Required	As Required	15	D1	20-22	70-78
As Required	As Required	10	D1, D2, L	40-44	98-109
As Required	Open	1.5	D1, D2, L R	77-84 77-84	157-172 230-252

At altitudes above sea level, it may not be possible to obtain 17" of engine manifold vacuum. If engine manifold vacuum at idle is less than 17" Hg., the control pressure values shown in the following list should be used:

Engine Vacuum at Idle	Control Press. (PSI)	Throttle Press. (PSI)
17"	51-66	12-14
16"	51-72	16-18
15"	51-78	20-22
14"	51-84	24-26
13"	51-90	28-31
12"	51-97	32-35
11"	51-103	36-39

These specifications are for cars equipped with the non-altitude-compensating diaphragm only.

LUBRICANT REFILL CAPACITY

Approximate Capacity .... Quarts 13.3

LOW-REVERSE CLUTCH PLATES

Transmission Model	Steel Plates	Composition Plates
PDD— B, C, K, T, U, S and W	5	5
PDD— D, L, F, H and N	6	6

REVERSE-HIGH CLUTCH PLATES

Transmission Model	Steel Plates	Composition Plates
PDD— B, C, K, T, U, S and W	3	3
PDD— D, L, F, H and N	4	4

FORWARD CLUTCH PLATES

Transmission Model	Steel Plates	Composition Plates
PDD— B, C, K, T, U, S and W	3	4
PDD— D, L, F, H and N	4	5

INTERMEDIATE BAND WIDTH (Inches)

Transmission Model	PDD— B, C, K, T, U, S and W	PDD— D, L, F, H and N
	$1^{13}/_{16}$	$2^{5}/_{16}$

CONTROL PRESSURE AT ZERO OUTPUT SHAFT SPEED—ALTITUDE COMPENSATING TYPE VACUUM DIAPHRAGM

Engine Speed			Idle			As Required		As Required		As Required		
Throttle			Closed			As Required		As Required		Open Through Detent		
Manifold Vacuum (Inches Hg)			Above 17			15		10		Below 1.0		
Range			Control Pressure (psi)		TV Pressure (psi)	Control Pressure (psi)	TV Pressure (psi)	Control Pressure (psi)	TV Pressure (psi)	Control Pressure (psi)		TV Pressure (psi)
			P, N, D1, D2, L	R		D1, D2, L		D1, D2, L		D1, D2, L	R	
	Barometric Pressure in Inches HG	Nominal Altitude (Feet)										
psi @ Barometric Pressure	29.5	Sea Level	51-66	72-108	0-13	70-78	20-22	98-109	40-44	157-172	230-252	80-84
	28.5	1000	51-59	72-104	0-11	67-75	18-20	94-105	38-41	149-163	220-242	77-81
	27.5	2000	51-59	72-99	0-8	63-71	15-17	91-101	36-38	145-159	215-236	74-78
	26.5	3000	51-59	72-99	0-5	59-67	12-14	87-97	33-36	142-157	211-231	72-76
	25.5	4000	51-59	72-92	0-3	57-64	10-12	85-94	31-33	139-154	207-227	70-74
	24.5	5000	51-59	72-83	0	51-60	7-9	81-90	28-31	136-151	202-222	67-72
	23.5	6000	51-59	72-83	0	51-60	5-7	78-87	26-28	132-147	198-217	64-68

SHIFT SPEEDS (APPROXIMATE)

	Range	Shift	1	2	3	4
Minimum Throttle	D1	1-2	7-13	7-12	7-14	7-12
	D1	2-3	12-21	11-20	12-22	11-20
	D2	3-2	7-9	7-8	7-9	7-9
	D1	3-1	7-9	7-9	7-9	7-8
	L	2-1	7-9	7-8	7-9	7-8
Maximum Throttle	D1	1-2	38-45	35-42	40-46	36-43
	D1, D2	2-3	73-83	67-76	75-84	70-77
	D1, D2	3-2	65-74	60-68	67-75	62-69
	D1	2-1 or 3-1	27-34	25-31	27-34	25-32
Vehicle		Engine Displacement		Axle Ratio	Tire Size	Use Column No.
Ford		390—2V		3.00:1	7.35 x 15	1
		390—4V			7.75 x 15	2
		428—4V		3.25:1		
Mercury		410—4V		3.00:1	8.15 x 15	3
		428—4V		3.25:1		4

CONVERTER IDENTIFICATION AND STALL SPEEDS

Converter Part Number	Size Inches Diameter	Stall Ratio	Identification No.①	Transmission Models	Engine CID	Stall Speed
C6AP-7902-A	12	2.10:1	26	PDD-B	390-2V	1750-1950
				PDD-C, S	390-4V	1800-2000
				PDD-T, U	410-4V③	1850-2050
C6SP-7902-A	12 5/16	2.10:1	27	PDD-D, L	410-4V③	1550-1750
C6SP-7902-B	12 5/16	2.10:1	29	PDD-F. H, N	428-4V	1550-1750

①Converter identification is stamped on the converter cover adjacent to the converter drive stud.
②Single Exhaust.
③Dual Exhaust.

CHECKS AND ADJUSTMENTS

Transmission End Play	0.008-0.044 inch Selective Thrust Washers Available
Turbine and Stator End Play	0.060 Inch
Intermediate Band Adjustment	Adjust screw to 10 ft-lbs torque, then back off one full turn and tighten lock nut to specification.
Forward Clutch Pressure Plate-to-Snap Ring Clearance	**0.048-0.061 Inch**
	Selective Snap Ring Thicknesses 0.065-0.069 Inch 0.083-0.087 Inch 0.074-0.078 Inch
Reverse-High Clutch Pressure Plate-to-Snap Ring Clearance	**Transmission Models**
	PDD—B, C, K, T, U, S and W PDD—D, L, F, H and N
	0.022-0.036 Inch 0.027-0.043 Inch
	Selective Snap Ring Clearances 0.065-0.069 inch 0.083-0.087 Inch 0.074-0.078 Inch

TORQUE LIMITS

Item	Ft-Lbs
Pressure Gauge Tap	9-15
Servo Cover to Case	10-14
Parking Rod Guide Plate to Case	12-16
Outer Downshift Lever to Shaft	12-16
Distributor Sleeve to Case	12-16
Support Assy. to Pump Body	12-16
Oil Pump to Case	12-16
Oil Pan to Case	12-16
Conv. Hsg. Lower Cover to Trans.	12-16
Converter Drain Plugs	14-28
Diaphragm Assy. to Case	15-23
One-Way Clutch Race to Case	18-25
Flywheel to Converter	20-30
Extension Hsg. to Case	25-30
Connector Assy. to Case	25-35
Manual Lever to Shaft	30-40
Band Adj Stop to Case	35-45
Transmission to Engine	40-50

Item	In-Lbs
Plate to Control Assy.	20-30
Lower to Upper Valve Body	40-50
Upper to Lower Valve Body	40-50
Screen & Lwr V.B. to Upper V.B.	40-50
Neutral Switch Assy. to Case	55-75
Control Assy. to Case	100-120
Governor to Collector	100-120

SPECIAL TOOLS

Tool Numbers	Description
T50T-100-A	Impact Hammer
T58L-101-A	Puller Attachment
TOOL-1175-AB	Oil Seal Remover (Head)
TOOL-4201-C	Diff. Backlash & Runout Gauge
T64L-6001-A	Portable Twin Post Stand
TOOL-7000-DD	Air Nozzle Rubber Tip
TOOL-7003	Bench Test Turning Tool
T64P-7A128-A	Manual Valve Detent Spring
T61L-7657-B	Transmission Extension Housing Oil Seal Replacer
T57P-7697-A	Transmission Extension Housing Bushing Remover
T57P-7697-B	Transmission Extension Housing Bushing Replacer
T58L-7902-A or B	Welded Converter Sprag Driver and Gauge Post
T59P-77067	Dial Indicator Support Fixture
TOOL-77288	Control Shaft Seal Replacer
T59P-77370-B	Front Band Adjustment Torque Wrench
TOOL-77530-A	Clutch Assembly Fixture
T65L-77515-A	Automatic Transmission Clutch Spring Compressor
T57L-77820-A	Automatic Transmission 400 lb Pressure Gauge
T63L-77837-A	Front Pump Seal Replacer
TOOL-FCO-24	Vacuum Unit Wrench (Snap-On)

SELECTIVE THRUST WASHERS

Identification No.	Thrust Washer Thickness—Inch
1	0.056-0.058
2	0.073-0.075
3	0.088-0.090
4	0.103-0.105
5	0.118-0.120

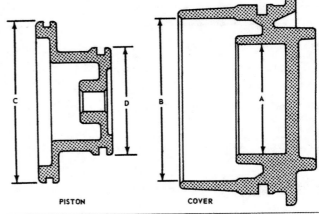

PISTON   COVER

Models	Piston	Cover	Diameter - Inches			
			A	B	C	D
PDD-B, W	C6SP-7D021-A	C6SP-7D027-A	2.040	3.025	3.016	2.031
PDD-C, K, S, T, U	C6AP-7D021-A	C6AP-7D027-A	2.075	2.980	2.971	2.066
PDD-D, F, H, L, N	C6MP-7D021-A	C6MP-7D027-A	1.980	3.072	3.063	1.967

D 1642 - A

INTERMEDIATE SERVO COVER AND PISTON DIMENSIONS

CRUISE-O-MATIC OR MERC-O-MATIC TRANSMISSIONS ONLY
CONTROL PRESSURE AT ZERO OUTPUT SHAFT SPEED

Engine Speed and Manifold Vacuum	Throttle Position	Shift Selector Lever Position	Control Line Pressure
Engine Idle-Vacuum Above 16 inches	Closed	P,N,D2,D1,L	57-77
		R	71-106
Engine RPM As Required for 16-13.7 inches of manifold vacuum	As Required	D1,D2,L	Start of Pressure Build-up
Engine RPM As Required for 10 inches of manifold vacuum	As Required	D1,D2,L	97-113
Engine RPM-Stall Vacuum Below 1.5 inches	To and Thru Detent	D1,D2,L	151-176
		R	201-213

STALL SPEEDS

Selector Lever Position	Clutch Applied	Band Applied	Engine Speed (RPM)		
			289-2V	352-4V 3	390-V8
D2	Front	Front	1450-1650	1600-1800	390-2V 1750-1950 390-4V 1800-2000
D1	Front	One-Way Clutch			
L	Front	Rear			
R	Rear	Rear			

SHIFT SPEEDS (Approximate)

Transmission Model	Automatic Shift Speeds (mph)								Manual Shift Speeds (mph)
	D1		D1 or D2		D1	D1 or D2	D1	D2	L
	1-2 Minimum Throttle	1-2 Maximum Throttle	2-3 Minimum Throttle	2-3 Maximum Throttle	3-1 Minimum Throttle	3-2 Maximum Throttle	2-1 or 3-1 Maximum Throttle	3-2 Minimum Throttle	2-1 Minimum Throttle
PCT	7—9	34—41	9—21	57—66	6—8	53—61	24—33	5—10	17—23
PCD	8—11	40—50	14—24	64—76	7—10	58—70	27—37	6—11	18—27
PCE	8—11	40—50	14—24	62—76	7—10	57—70	26—37	6—11	18—27

CHECKS AND ADJUSTMENTS

Operation	Specification
Transmission End Play Check	0.010-0.029 inch Selective Thrust Washers Available: 0.063-0.061 inch, 0.069-0.067 inch 0.076-0.074 inch, 0.083-0.081 inch
Turbine and Stator End Play Check	0.060 inch (maximum)
Front Band Adjustment (Use ¼-inch spacer between adjustment screw and servo piston stem)	Adjust screw to 10 inch-pounds torque, and back off one full turn and lock.
Rear Band Adjustment	Adjust screw to 10 ft-lbs torque, and back off 1½ turns and lock.
Primary Sun Gear Shaft Ring End Gap Check	0.002-0.009 inch

CHECKS AND ADJUSTMENTS (Continued)

Operation	Specification
Accelerator Pedal Height Adjustment	$3^{11}/_{16}$ inches above floor mat
Rear Clutch Steel Plate Coning Clearance Check—PCE model transmission	0.010 inch (maximum coned)
Rear Clutch Steel Plate all except PCE model transmissions	Flat

LUBRICANT REFILL CAPACITY

Approximate Capacity—Quarts	10

TORQUE LIMITS

Item	Foot Pounds
Converter to Flywheel Nuts	20-30
Converter Housing to Transmission Case Bolts	35-45
Front Pump to Transmission Case Bolts	17-22
Front Servo to Transmission Case Bolts	30-35
Rear Servo to Transmission Case Bolts	40-45
Planetary Support to Transmission Case Screws	20-25
Upper Valve Body to Lower Valve Body Bolts	4-6
Control Valve Body to Transmission Case Bolts	8-10
Pressure Regulator Assembly to Transmission Case Screws	17-22
Extension Assembly to Transmission Case Bolts	28-38
Oil Pan to Transmission Case Bolts	10-13
Case Assembly—Gauge Hole Plugs	7-15
Rear Band Adjusting Screw Locknut	35-40
Front Band Adjusting Screw Locknut	20-25
Manual Control Lever Nut	35-40

TORQUE LIMITS (Cont.)

Item	Foot Pounds
Downshift Lever Nut	17-20
Front Pump Cover Screws	25-35①
Rear Pump Cover Screws (¼-20)	80-90①
Rear Pump Cover Screws (10-24)	25-35①
Governor Inspection Cover Screws	50-60①
Converter Cover Drain Plug	15-28
Converter Housing to Engine Bolts	40-50
Vent Tube Nut	7-12
Governor Valve Body to Counterweight Screws	50-60①
Governor Valve Body Cover Screws	20-30①
Pressure Regulator Cover Screws	20-30①
Control Valve Body Screws (10-24)	20-30①
Front Servo Release Piston to Servo Piston Screw	20-30①
Vacuum Diaphragm Unit	20-30
Cooler Return Check Valve (Model PCE)	15-21

①Inch-Pounds

SERVICE TOOLS

Ford Tool No.	Former No.	Description
T50T-100-A	—	Impact Hammer
T59L-100-B	—	Impact Slide Hammer
T58L-101-A	—	Puller Attachment
T57L-500-A	—	Bench Mounted Holding Fixture
TOOL-1175-AB	1175-AB	Grease Seal Remover (head only)
T50T-100-A	1175-AE	Seal Remover
TOOL-1175-AB		
T53T-1175-E	—	Rear Wheel Grease Retainer Replacer
—	1202-D	Pinion Bearing Cup Remover
TOOL-4201-C	4201-C	Differential Backlash & Runout Gauge with Univ. Bracket, Dial Indicator & Bracket
TOOL-7000-CJ	7000-CC 7000-CJ	Transmission Overhaul Holding Fixture
TOOL-7000-DD	7000-DD	Air Nozzle Rubber-Tip Assembly
T52L-7000-HAE	7000-HF	Transmission Extension Housing Rear Bearing Remover
TOOL-7003	7003	Bench Test Turning Tool
T64P-7A128-A	—	Manual Valve Detent Spring
TOOL-7195-C	7195-C	Rear Band Adjustment Wrench
T58L-7195-A	—	Fordomatic Band Adjustment Wrench
TOOL-7225-B	7225-B	Front Band Adjustment Wrench
TOOL-7225-C13-B	7225-C13-B	Gauge Block and Chain Assembly
T65P-7B456-B	—	Clutch Race to Case Bolts Socket
T61L-7657-A	7657-AA	Transmission Extension Housing Oil Seal Replacer

SERVICE TOOLS (Cont.)

Ford Tool No.	Former No.	Description
T61L-7657-B	7657-AB	Transmission Extension Housing Oil Seal Replacer
T57P-7697-A	7000-AD	Transmission Extension Housing Bushing Remover
T57-7697-B	7000-J	Transmission Extension Housing Bushing Replacer
T58L-7902-A or B	7937-A 7946-A	Welded Converter Sprag Driver and Gauge Post
T59P-7902-B	7937-B	Welded Converter Sprag Driver and Gauge Post
T63P-7902-A	—	Converter Stator Check Adapter
T64L-7902-A	—	Welded Converter Sprag Driver and Gauge Post Adapter Kit for T59P-7902-B
T59P-77067	77067	Dial Indicator Support Fixture
TOOL-77288	77288	Control Shaft Seal Replacer
T59P-77370-B	7345	Front Bank Torque Wrench
T59L-77515-B	77515-A 77515	Rear Clutch Spring Compressor
TOOL-77530-A	77530-A 77530	Clutch Assembly Fixture
TOOL-77565	77565	Front Clutch Spring Compressor
T57-77820-A	77820-B	Automatic Transmission 400 Pound Pressure Gauge
T59L-77837-A	—	Front Pump Seal Replacer
T63L-77837-A	77837	Front Pump Seal Replacer
TOOL-77869-A	77869-A 77869-W	Transmission Sleeve Remover & Replacer

	GROUP 8
ENGINE	

PART 8-1   GENERAL ENGINE SERVICE

This part covers engine diagnosis, tests and adjustment and repair procedures. In addition, the cleaning and inspection procedures are covered.

On cars equipped with a Thermactor exhaust emission control system, refer to Group 12 for diagnosis, test and repair of the exhaust emission control components.

For engine removal, disassembly, assembly, installation and major repair procedures, refer to the pertinent part of this group.

An engine identification tag is attached to the engine. The symbol

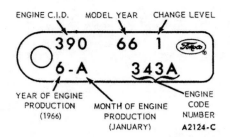

FIG. 1—Engine Identification Tag

code (Fig. 1) identifies such engine for determining parts usage; i.e., engine cubic inch displacement and model year. The change level and engine code number determine if parts are peculiar to a specific engine.

1 DIAGNOSIS AND TESTING

DIAGNOSIS

On engines equipped with a Thermactor exhaust emission control system, disconnect the Thermactor system before performing engine diagnosis procedures. Disconnect the anti-backfire valve vacuum sensing and air supply lines at the intake manifold connections. Plug the manifold connections to preclude leakage.

Engine performance complaints usually fall under one of the basic headings listed in the Diagnosis Guide. When a particular trouble can not be traced to a definite cause by a simple check, the possible items that could be at fault are listed in the order of their probable occurrence. Check the items in the order listed.

For example, under "Poor Acceleration," the ignition system is listed as a probable cause of trouble. All the conventional ignition system items that affect acceleration are listed. Check all these items before proceeding to the next probable cause.

For diagnosis procedures of ignition system malfunctions, refer to Group 9.

DIAGNOSIS GUIDE

ENGINE WILL NOT CRANK	The cause of this trouble is usually in the starting system (Group 14). If the starting system is not at fault, check for a hydrostatic lock or a seized engine as follows: Remove the spark plugs; then at-	tempt to crank the engine with the starter. If the engine cranks, it indicates that water is leaking into the cylinders. Remove the cylinder head(s) and inspect the gasket(s) and/or head(s) for cracks. Examine the cylinder block for cracks.
ENGINE CRANKS NORMALLY, BUT WILL NOT START	Check the fuel supply. If there is sufficient fuel in the tank and the proper starting procedure is used, the cause of the trouble probably lies in either the ignition or the fuel system. To determine which system is at fault, perform the following test: Disconnect a spark plug wire. Check the spark intensity at the end of the wire by installing a terminal adapter in the end of the wire. Then hold the adapter approximately $3/16$ inch from the exhaust manifold and crank the engine. **IF THERE IS NO SPARK OR A WEAK SPARK AT THE SPARK PLUGS** The cause of the trouble is in the ignition system. **Disconnect the brown lead (I terminal) and the red and blue lead (S terminal) at the starter relay.** Install an auxiliary starter switch between the battery and S terminals of the starter relay. To determine if the cause of the	trouble is in the primary or the secondary circuit, remove the coil high tension lead from the top of the distributor, **and hold it approximately $3/16$ inch from the cylinder head.** With the ignition on, crank the engine and check for a spark. If the spark at the coil high tension lead is good, the cause of the trouble is probably in the distributor cap, rotor or spark plug wires. If there is no spark or a weak spark at the coil high tension lead, the cause of the trouble is probably in the primary circuit, coil to distributor high tension lead, or the coil. **IF THERE IS A GOOD SPARK AT THE SPARK PLUGS** Check the spark plugs. If the spark plugs are not at fault, check the following items: **AUTOMATIC CHOKE** Check the position of the choke plate. If the engine is hot, the plate

CONTINUED ON NEXT PAGE

DIAGNOSIS GUIDE (Continued)

ENGINE CRANKS NORMALLY, BUT WILL NOT START (Continued)	should be open. If the plate is not open, the engine will load up due to the excessively rich mixture and will not start. If the engine is cold, the plate should be closed. If the plate is not operating properly, check the following items: The choke plate and linkage for binding. The fast idle cam linkage for binding. The thermostatic spring housing adjustment. **FUEL SUPPLY AT THE CARBURETOR** Work the throttle by hand several times. Each time the throttle is actuated, fuel should spurt from the accelerating pump discharge port (6-cylinder) or nozzles (V-8). If fuel is discharged by the accelerating pump, the engine is probably flooded, or there is water in the fuel system, or an engine mechanical item is at fault. If fuel is not discharged by the accelerating pump, disconnect the	carburetor fuel inlet line at the carburetor. Use a suitable container to catch the fuel. Crank the engine to see if fuel is reaching the carburetor. If fuel is not reaching the carburetor, check: The fuel filter. The fuel pump. The carburetor fuel inlet line for obstructions. The fuel pump flexible inlet line for a collapsed condition. The fuel tank line for obstructions. Fuel tank vent restricted. If fuel is reaching the carburetor, check: The fuel inlet system including the fuel inlet needle and seat assembly and the float assembly. **ENGINE** Mechanical failure in camshaft drive. Anti-backfire valve stuck open (if equipped with Thermactor exhaust emission control).
ENGINE STARTS, BUT FAILS TO KEEP RUNNING	**FUEL SYSTEM** Idle fuel mixture needle(s) not properly adjusted. Engine idle speed set too low. The choke not operating properly. Float setting incorrect. Fuel inlet system not operating properly. Dirt or water in the fuel lines or in the fuel filter. Carburetor icing. Fuel pump defective.	Check for dirt in the carburetor not allowing fuel to enter or be discharged from the idle system. **IGNITION SYSTEM** Defective spark plugs. Leakage in the high tension wiring. Open circuit in the primary resistance wire. Breaker points not properly adjusted.
ENGINE RUNS, BUT MISSES	Determine if the miss is steady or erratic and at what speed the miss occurs by operating the engine at various speeds under load. **MISSES STEADILY AT ALL SPEEDS** Isolate the miss by operating the engine with one cylinder not firing. This is done by operating the engine with the ignition wire removed from one spark plug at a time, until all cylinders have been checked. Ground the spark plug wire removed. If the engine speed changes when a particular cylinder is shorted out, that cylinder was delivering power before being shorted out. If no change in the engine operation is evident, the miss was caused by that cylinder not delivering power before	being shorted out. In this case, check the: **IGNITION SYSTEM** If the miss is isolated in a particular cylinder, perform a spark test on the ignition lead of that cylinder. If a good spark does not occur, the trouble is in the secondary circuit of the system. Check the spark plug wire and the distributor cap. If a good spark occurs, check the spark plug. If the spark plug is not at fault, a mechanical component of the engine is probably at fault. **ENGINE** Intake manifold gasket leak. Perform a manifold vacuum or compression test to determine which

CONTINUED ON NEXT PAGE

DIAGNOSIS GUIDE (Continued)

| ENGINE RUNS, BUT MISSES (Continued) | mechanical component of the engine is at fault.
Anti-backfire valve stuck open (if equipped with Thermactor exhaust emission control).
MISSES ERRATICALLY AT ALL SPEEDS
EXHAUST SYSTEM
Exhaust system restricted.
IGNITION SYSTEM
Breaker points not properly adjusted.
Defective breaker points, condenser, secondary wiring, coil, or spark plugs.
High tension leakage across the coil, rotor or distributor cap.
Defective ignition switch.
FUEL SYSTEM
Float setting incorrect.
Fuel inlet system not operating properly.
Dirt or water in the fuel lines or carburetor.
Restricted fuel filter.
Loose booster venturi (V-8).
COOLING SYSTEM
Check the cooling system for internal leakage and/or for a condition that prevents the engine from reaching normal operating temperature.
ENGINE
Perform a manifold vacuum or compression test to determine which mechanical component of the engine is at fault.
MISSES AT IDLE ONLY
FUEL SYSTEM
Idle fuel mixture needle(s) not properly adjusted.
Restriction in idle fuel system. | **IGNITION SYSTEM**
Excessive play in the distributor shaft.
Worn distributor cam.
Defective coil, rotor, condenser, breaker points, ignition wiring or spark plugs.
ENGINE
Valve lash (engines with mechanical valve lifters) or valve clearance (engines with hydraulic valve lifters) set too tight. Worn camshaft lobe(s).
Perform a manifold vacuum or compression test to determine which mechanical component of the engine is at fault.
MISSES AT HIGH SPEED ONLY
FUEL SYSTEM
Power valve or passages clogged or damaged.
Low or erratic fuel pump pressure.
Fuel inlet system not operating properly.
Restricted fuel filter.
Restricted main fuel system.
Positive crankcase ventilation system restricted or not operating properly.
IGNITION SYSTEM
Defective spark plugs.
COOLING SYSTEM
Engine overheating.
ENGINE
Perform a manifold vacuum or compression test to determine which mechanical component of the engine is at fault. |
| **ROUGH ENGINE IDLE** | **FUEL SYSTEM**
Engine idle speed set too low.
Idle fuel mixture needle(s) not properly adjusted.
Float setting incorrect.
Air leaks between the carburetor, spacer, and the manifold and/or fittings.
Leaking vacuum line connections, if equipped with vacuum-powered accessory equipment.
Intake manifold gasket leak (V-8).
Power valve leaking fuel.
Idle fuel system air bleeds or fuel passages restricted.
Fuel bleeding from the accelerating pump discharge nozzle(s).
Secondary throttle plate(s) not closing (4-barrel carburetor). | Improper secondary throttle plate stop adjustment (4-barrel carburetor).
Incorrect idle speed setting of the secondary carburetor (427 V-8).
Leaking fuel pump, lines or fittings.
IGNITION SYSTEM
Improperly adjusted or defective breaker points.
Fouled or improperly adjusted spark plugs.
Incorrect ignition timing.
Spark plug misfiring.
EXHAUST SYSTEM
Exhaust control valve inoperative or sticking. |

CONTINUED ON NEXT PAGE

DIAGNOSIS GUIDE (Continued)

ROUGH ENGINE IDLE (Continued)	**ENGINE** Loose engine mounting bolts or worn engine support insulator. Cylinder head bolts not properly torqued. Valve lash or valve clearance set too tight. Crankcase ventilation regulator	valve defective or a restricted vent tube. Worn camshaft lobes. Perform a manifold vacuum or compression test to determine which mechanical component is at fault. Anti-backfire valve stuck open (if equipped with Thermactor exhaust emission control).
POOR ACCELERATION	**IGNITION SYSTEM** Incorrect ignition timing. Fouled or improperly adjusted spark plugs. Improperly adjusted or defective breaker points. Distributor not advancing properly. Loose or defective spark control valve (6-cylinder). **FUEL SYSTEM** Accelerating pump malfunction. Float setting incorrect. Throttle linkage not properly adjusted. Accelerating pump stroke not properly adjusted. Leaky power valve, gasket or accelerating pump diaphragm. Power valve piston stuck in the up position (6-cylinder).	Dirt or corrosion in accelerating system. Distributor vacuum passages in the carburetor blocked. Restricted fuel filter. Defective fuel pump. **BRAKES** Improper adjustment—too tight. **TRANSMISSION** Clutch slippage (manual-shift transmissions). Improper band adjustment (automatic transmissions). Converter One-Way Clutch (automatic transmissions). **ENGINE** Perform a manifold vacuum or compression test to determine which mechanical component of the engine is at fault.
ENGINE DOES NOT DEVELOP FULL POWER, OR HAS POOR HIGH SPEED PERFORMANCE	**FUEL SYSTEM** Restricted air cleaner. Restricted fuel filter. Clogged or undersize main or secondary jets and/or low float setting. Power valve or passages clogged or damaged. Fuel pump pressure incorrect. Distributor vacuum passage in the carburetor blocked. Secondary throttle plates not opening (V-8). Automatic choke malfunctioning or improperly adjusted. **IGNITION SYSTEM** Ignition timing not properly adjusted. Defective coil, condenser or rotor. Distributor not advancing properly. Excessive play in the distributor shaft. Distributor cam worn. Fouled or improperly adjusted spark plugs or spark plugs of incorrect heat range. Improperly adjusted or defective breaker points.	**EXHAUST SYSTEM** Exhaust control valve inoperative or sticking (240 six or 427 V-8). Restriction in system. **COOLING SYSTEM** Thermostat inoperative or of incorrect heat range. Thermostat installed incorrectly. Check the cooling system for internal leakage and/or for a condition that prevents the engine from reaching normal operating temperature. **ENGINE** Positive crankcase ventilation system not operating properly. Perform a manifold vacuum or engine compression test to determine which mechanical component of the engine is at fault. One or more camshaft lobes worn beyond wear limit. Worn valves guides. Anti-backfire valve stuck open (if equipped with Thermactor exhaust emission control). **TRANSMISSION** Improper band adjustment (automatic transmissions).

CONTINUED ON NEXT PAGE

DIAGNOSIS GUIDE (Continued)

| EXCESSIVE FUEL CONSUMPTION | Determine the actual fuel consumption with test equipment installed in the car.

If the test indicates that the fuel consumption is not excessive, demonstrate to the owner how improper driving habits will affect fuel consumption.

If the test indicates that the fuel consumption is excessive, make a preliminary check of the following items before proceeding to the fuel and ignition systems.

PRELIMINARY CHECKS

CHASSIS ITEMS
Check:
Tires for proper pressure.
Front wheel alignment.
Brake adjustment.

EXHAUST SYSTEM
Check the exhaust control valve operation.
System restricted.

ODOMETER
Check calibration.

IGNITION SYSTEM
Check:
Distributor breaker points.
Ignition timing.

ENGINE
Crankcase ventilation regulator valve defective or restricted tubes (Positive Crankcase Ventilation System).
Anti-backfire valve stuck open (if equipped with Thermactor exhaust emission control).

FINAL CHECKS

FUEL SYSTEM
Check:
Fuel pump pressure.
Engine idle speed. | Idle fuel mixture needle(s) for proper adjustment.
Automatic choke for proper operation.
Fast idle speed screw for proper adjustment.
Accelerating pump stroke adjustment.
Anti-stall dashpot for proper adjustment.
Air cleaner for restrictions.
Float setting for fuel level.
Jets for wear and / or damage.
Power valve operation.
Air bleeds for obstructions.
Accelerating pump discharge port (6-cylinder) or nozzles (V-8) for siphoning.
Accelerator linkage for binds.
Choke adjustment.

IGNITION SYSTEM
Check:
Ignition timing.
Spark plug condition and adjustment.
Distributor spark advance operation.
Spark control valve for proper seating (6-cylinder).

ENGINE
Perform a manifold vacuum or engine compression test to determine which mechanical component of the engine is at fault.
Check valve clearance (hydraulic lifters) or valve lash (mechanical tappets).

COOLING SYSTEM
Check thermostat operation and heat range.

TRANSMISSION
Check band adjustment (automatic transmissions). |
| ENGINE OVERHEATS | **TEMPERATURE SENDING UNIT AND GAUGE**
Unit or gauge defective (not indicating correct temperature) or constant voltage regulator defective.

ENGINE
Cylinder head bolts not properly torqued.
Incorrect valve lash (engine with mechanical valve lifters) or valve clearance (engines with hydraulic valve lifters).
Low oil level or incorrect viscosity oil used. | **COOLING SYSTEM**
Insufficient coolant.
Cooling system leaks.
Drive belt tension incorrect.
Radiator fins obstructed.
Thermostat defective.
Thermostat improperly installed.
Cooling system passages blocked.
Water pump inoperative.
Faulty fan drive.

IGNITION SYSTEM
Incorrect ignition timing.
Incorrect distributor advance. |

CONTINUED ON NEXT PAGE

DIAGNOSIS GUIDE (Continued)

ENGINE OVERHEATS (Continued)	EXHAUST SYSTEM Restrictions in system.	BRAKES Improper adjustment—too tight.
LOSS OF COOLANT	COOLING SYSTEM Leaking radiator or water pump. Loose or damaged hose connections. Radiator cap defective. Overheating. ENGINE Cylinder head gasket defective.	Intake manifold to cylinder head gasket defective (V-8). Cylinder head or intake manifold bolts (V-8) not properly torqued. Cylinder block core plugs leaking. Temperature sending unit leaking. Cracked cylinder head or block, or warped cylinder head or block gasket surface.
ENGINE FAILS TO REACH NORMAL OPERATING TEMPERATURE	TEMPERATURE SENDING UNIT AND GAUGE Unit or gauge defective (not indicating correct temperature) or constant voltage regulator defective.	COOLING SYSTEM Thermostat inoperative or of incorrect heat range.
NOISY HYDRAULIC VALVE LIFTER	A noisy hydraulic valve lifter can be located by operating the engine at idle speed and placing a finger on the face of the valve spring retainer. If the lifter is not functioning properly, a shock will be felt when the valve seats. Another method of identifying a noisy lifter is by the use of a piece of hose. With the engine operating at idle speed, place one end of the hose near the end of the valve stem and the other end to the ear and listen for a metallic noise. Repeat the procedure on each intake and exhaust valve until the noisy lifter(s) has been located. The most common causes of hydraulic valve lifter troubles are dirt, gum, varnish, carbon deposits and air bubbles. Dirt in the lifter assembly can prevent the disc valve from seating, or it may become lodged between the plunger and body surfaces. In either case, the lifter becomes inoperative due to failure to pump-up or because the internal parts are no longer free to function properly. When dirt is found to be responsible for lifter malfunction, remove the lifter assembly and thoroughly clean it. Recommended engine oil and filter change intervals should be followed to minimize lifter problems caused by dirt (Group 19). Deposits of gum and varnish cause similar conditions to exist which may result in lifter malfunction. If these conditions are found to be present, the lifter should be disassembled and cleaned in solvent to remove all traces of deposits. Air bubbles in the lubricating oil,	caused by an excessively high or low oil level, may likewise cause lifter malfunction. A damaged oil pick-up tube may allow air to be drawn into the lubricating system. Check for engine oil aeration as follows: Check the engine oil level to be sure it is within specification and correct as required. **Be sure the correct engine oil dipstick is being used.** Operate the engine at approximately 1200 rpm until normal operating temperature is reached. Stop the engine and remove the oil pressure sending unit. Install a fitting in this opening with a petcock-type valve that will permit attachment of a ¼ to ⅜ inch diameter hose of sufficient length to direct the oil discharge into the oil filler pipe. Close the valve. Start the engine and operate it at approximately 500 rpm for a minimum of five minutes; then, open the valve slightly to permit a steady discharge of oil. Check the oil flow for air bubbles. Increase the engine speed to approximately 1000 rpm and check for air bubbles in the oil. **To facilitate checking for air bubbles, direct the oil flow over white paper or through a piece of transparent tube. The engine should not be operated at excessive speeds or for extended periods with the oil bleed attached.** If oil aeration is evident, remove the oil pan for further test and/or inspection of the oil pump intake system. Perform corrective action as required to remove air from the lubricating oil.

TESTING

CAMSHAFT LOBE LIFT

Check the lift of each lobe in consecutive order and make a note of the readings.

1. Remove the air cleaner and the valve rocker arm cover(s).

2. On a 427 V-8, **if only one camshaft lobe is to be checked,** loosen the lash adjusting screw. Slide the rocker arm assembly serving the camshaft lobe to be checked to one side. Secure it in this position with safety wire. To move the rocker arm on either end of the shaft, remove the retaining pin and washers, and slide the rocker arm off the shaft. **If all of the cam lobes are to be checked, remove the rocker arm shaft assembly(ies).**

On a 352, 390, 410 or 428 V-8, remove the valve rocker arm shaft assembly and install a solid tappet-type push rod in the push rod bore of the camshaft lobe to be checked or use the adapter for ball-end push rods shown in Fig. 2.

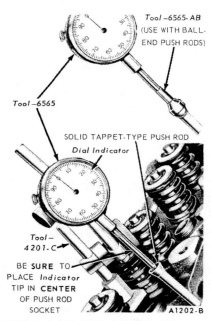

FIG. 2—Camshaft Lobe Lift —Hydraulic Valve Lifters— 352, 390, 410 and 428 V-8

On a 240 Six or a 289 V-8, remove the rocker arm stud nut, fulcrum seat and rocker arm. Use the adapter for ball-end push rods.

3. Make sure the push rod is in the valve lifter socket. Install a dial indicator in such a manner as to have the ball socket adapter of the indicator on the end of the push rod and in the same plane as the push rod movement (Fig. 2 or 3).

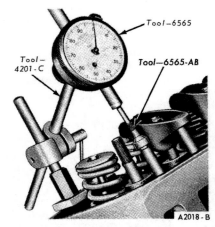

FIG. 3—Typical Camshaft Lobe Lift—240 Six and 289 V-8

On a socket-type push rod, position the actuating point of the indicator in the push rod socket and in the same plane as the push rod movement (Fig. 2 or 4).

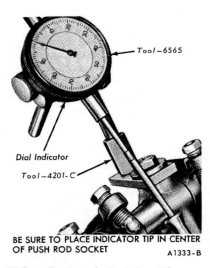

BE SURE TO PLACE INDICATOR TIP IN CENTER OF PUSH ROD SOCKET   A1333-B

FIG. 4—Camshaft Lobe Lift— Mechanical Valve Lifters—428 Special Police or 427 V-8

4. **Disconnect the brown lead (I terminal) and the red and blue lead (S terminal) at the starter relay.** Install an auxiliary starter switch between the battery and S terminals of the starter relay. **Crank the engine with the ignition switch "OFF."**

Bump the crankshaft over until the tappet or lifter is on the base circle of the camshaft lobe. **At this point, the push rod will be in its lowest position.**

5. Zero the dial indicator. Continue to rotate the crankshaft slowly until the push rod is in the fully raised position.

6. Compare the total lift recorded on the indicator with specifications.

7. To check the accuracy of the original indicator reading, continue to rotate the crankshaft until the indicator reads zero. **If the lift on any lobe is below specified wear limits, the camshaft and the valve lifters operating on the worn lobe(s) must be replaced.**

8. Remove the dial indicator and auxiliary starter switch.

On a 428 Special Police or a 427 V-8, position the valve rocker arm. If an end valve rocker arm was removed, slide it into position on the shaft and install the washers and retaining pin. Tighten the valve lash adjusting screw to hold the rocker arm and push rod in alignment. Adjust the valve lash on all rocker arms that had been moved out of position.

Install the valve rocker arm cover(s) and **partially tighten the retaining bolts.** Operate the engine until normal operating temperature has been reached. Remove the valve rocker arm cover(s). Check and adjust the valve lash (Section 2).

On a 352, 390, 410 or 428 V-8, install the rocker arm shaft assembly(ies).

On a 240 Six or a 289 V-8, install the rocker arm, fulcrum seat and stud nut. Adjust the valve clearance (Section 2).

9. Install the valve rocker arm cover(s) and the air cleaner.

COMPRESSION TEST

Dynamic Compression Check

To perform a dynamic compression check, follow the procedures in Part 9-1, Section 1 under Ignition System Tests—Rotunda Testers.

Compression Gauge Check

1. Be sure the crankcase oil is at the proper level and the battery is properly charged. Operate the engine for a minimum of 30 minutes at 1200 rpm or until the engine is at normal operating temperature. Turn the ignition switch off; then remove all the spark plugs.

2. Set the primary throttle plates and choke plate in the wide open position.

3. Install a compression gauge in No. 1 cylinder.

4. **Disconnect the brown lead (I terminal and the red and blue lead S terminal) at the starter relay.** Install an auxiliary starter switch between the battery and S terminals of the starter relay. **Crank the engine with the ignition switch OFF.** Using the auxiliary starter switch, crank the engine a minimum of five pumping strokes and record the highest reading.

Note the number of compression strokes required to obtain the highest reading.

5. Repeat the test on each cylinder, cranking the engine the same number of times for each cylinder as was required to obtain the highest reading on the No. 1 cylinder.

Test Conclusions

A variation of 20 psi from specified pressure is satisfactory. However, the compression of all cylinders should be uniform within 20 psi.

A reading of more than the allowable tolerance above normal indicates excessive deposits in the cylinder or wrong cylinder head(s) on the engine.

A reading of more than the allowable tolerance below normal indicates leakage at the cylinder head gasket, piston rings or valves or wrong cylinder head(s) on the engine.

A low, even compression in two adjacent cylinders indicates a cylinder head gasket leak. This should be checked before condemning the rings or valves.

To determine whether the rings or the valves are at fault, squirt the equivalent of a tablespoon of heavy oil into the combustion chamber. Crank the engine to distribute the oil and repeat the compression test. The oil will temporarily seal leakage past the rings. If approximately the same reading is obtained, the rings are satisfactory, but the valves are leaking. If the compression has increased substantially over the original readings, there is leakage past the rings.

During a compression test (if the pressure fails to climb steadily and remains the same during the first two successive strokes), but climbs higher on the succeeding strokes, or fails to climb during the entire test, it indicates a sticking valve.

MANIFOLD VACUUM TEST

A manifold vacuum test aids in determining the condition of an engine and in helping to locate the cause of poor engine performance. To check manifold vacuum:

1. Operate the engine for a minimum of 30 minutes at 1200 rpm or until the engine is at normal operating temperature.

2. Connect an accurate, sensitive vacuum gauge to the intake manifold vacuum fitting.

3. Operate the engine at the recommended idle rpm, with the transmission selector lever in neutral.

4. Check the vacuum reading on the gauge.

Test Conclusions

Manifold vacuum is affected by the carburetor adjustment, valve timing, ignition timing, condition of the valves, cylinder compression, condition of the positive crankcase ventilation system and leakage of the manifold carburetor, carburetor spacer or cylinder head gaskets.

Because abnormal gauge readings may indicate that more than one of the above factors is at fault, exercise caution in analyzing an abnormal reading. For example, if the vacuum is low, the correction of one item may increase the vacuum enough so as to indicate that the trouble has been corrected. It is important, therefore, that each cause

of an abnormal reading be investigated and further tests conducted, where necessary, in order to arrive at the correct diagnosis of the trouble.

Table 1 lists various types of readings and their possible causes.

Allowance should be made for the effect of altitude on the gauge reading. The engine vacuum will decrease with an increase in altitude.

HYDRAULIC VALVE LIFTER TESTS

Dirt, deposits of gum and varnish and air bubbles in the lubricating oil can cause hydraulic valve lifter failure or malfunction.

Dirt, gum and varnish can keep a check valve from seating and cause a loss of hydraulic pressure. An open valve disc will cause the plunger to force oil back into the valve lifter reservoir during the time the push rod is being lifted to force the valve from its seat.

Air bubbles in the lubricating system can be caused by too much oil in the system or too low an oil level. Air may also be drawn into the lubricating system through an opening in a damaged oil pick-up tube. **Air in the hydraulic system can cause a loss of hydraulic pressure.**

Assembled valve lifters can be tested with tool 6500-E to check the leak down rate. The leak down rate specification (Part 8-5) is the time in seconds for the plunger to move

TABLE 1—Manifold Vacuum Gauge Readings

Gauge Reading	Engine Condition
18 inches or over—All engines.	Normal.
Low and steady.	Loss of power in all cylinders possibly caused by late ignition or valve timing, or loss of compression due to leakage around the piston rings.
Very low.	Intake manifold, carburetor, spacer or cylinder head gasket leak.
Needle fluctuates steadily as speed increases.	A partial or complete loss of power in one or more cylinders caused by a leaking valve, cylinder head or intake manifold gasket, a defect in the ignition system, or a weak valve spring.
Gradual drop in reading at engine idle.	Excessive back pressure in the exhaust system.
Intermittent fluctuation.	An occasional loss of power possibly caused by a defect in the ignition system or a sticking valve.
Slow fluctuation or drifting of the needle.	Improper idle mixture adjustment or carburetor, spacer or intake manifold gasket leak, or crankcase ventilation system—restricted.

the length (Part 8-5) of its travel while under a 50 lb. load. Test the valve lifters as follows:

1. Disassemble and clean the lifter to remove all traces of engine oil. Lifters cannot be checked with engine oil in them. Only the testing fluid can be used.

2. Place the valve lifter in the tester, with the plunger facing upward. Pour hydraulic tester fluid into the cup to a level that will cover the valve lifter assembly. **The fluid can be purchased from the manufacturer of the tester. Do not use kerosene, for it will not provide an accurate test.**

3. Place a $5/16$-inch steel ball in the plunger cup (Fig. 5).

Tool—6500-E

A1894-A

FIG. 5—Placing Steel Ball in Valve Lifter Plunger

4. Adjust the length of the ram (Fig. 6) so that the pointer is $1/16$

ADJUSTING NUT

Tool—6500-E

A1895-A

FIG. 6—Adjusting the Ram Length

inch below the starting mark when the ram contacts the valve lifter plunger, to facilitate timing as the pointer passes the Start Timing mark.

Use the center mark on the pointer scale as the Stop Timing point instead of the original Stop Timing mark at the top of the scale.

5. Work the valve lifter plunger up and down until the lifter fills with fluid and all traces of air bubbles have disappeared.

6. Allow the ram and weight to force the valve lifter plunger downward. Measure the exact time it takes for the pointer to travel from the Start Timing to the Stop Timing marks of the tester.

7. A valve lifter that is satisfactory must have a leak-down rate (time in seconds) within the minimum and maximum limits specified.

8. If the valve lifter is not within specifications, replace it with a new lifter. **Always test a new lifter before installing it in the engine.** It is not necessary to disassemble and clean new valve lifters before testing, because the oil contained in new lifters is test fluid.

9. Remove the fluid from the cup and bleed the fluid from the lifter by working the plunger up and down. **This step will aid in depressing the lifter plungers when checking the valve clearance.**

POSITIVE CRANKCASE VENTILATION SYSTEM TEST

A malfunctioning positive crankcase ventilation system may be indicated by loping or rough engine idle. Do not attempt to compensate for this idle condition by disconnecting the crankcase ventilation system and making carburetor adjustments. The removal of the crankcase ventilation system from the engine will adversely affect the fuel economy and engine ventilation with resultant shortening of engine life.

To determine whether the loping or rough idle condition is caused by a malfunctioning crankcase ventilation system, perform either of the following tests.

Regulator Valve Test

Install a known good regulator valve in the crankcase ventilation system.

Start the engine and compare the engine idle condition to the prior idle condition.

If the looping or rough idle condition remains when the good regulator valve is installed, the crankcase ventilation regulator valve is not at fault. Check the crankcase ventilation system for restriction at the intake manifold or carburetor spacer. If the system is not restricted, further engine component diagnosis will have to be conducted to find the malfunction.

If the idle condition is found to be satisfactory, replace the regulator valve and clean the hoses, fittings, etc.

Air Intake Test

This test uses the AC positive crankcase ventilation tester (Fig. 7) which is operated by the engine vacuum through the oil fill opening. Follow the procedures described below to install the tester and check the crankcase ventilation system for faulty operation.

1. With the engine at normal operating temperature, remove the oil filler cap and the dipstick.

2. Connect one end of the hose to the tester body and connect the other end of the hose to the tester adapter.

3. Use the dipstick hole plug to plug the opening in the dipstick tube.

4. Insert the tester adapter in the filler cap opening and turn the selector knob (Fig. 7) to number 2.

5. On a 427 V-8 with a closed crankcase ventilation system, disconnect the air inlet hose at the oil filler tube and plug the tube and hose openings. Start the engine and let it idle.

6. With the plugs secure, and the tube free of kinks, hold the tester body upright and note the color in the tester windows. Fig. 8 lists the various colors and the probable cause or related condition of the crankcase ventilation system.

7. Clean or replace the malfunctioning or defective components, and repeat the test to ensure that the crankcase ventilation system is operating satisfactorily.

CRANKSHAFT END PLAY

1. Force the crankshaft toward the rear of the engine.

2. Install a dial indicator so that the contact point rests against the crankshaft flange and the indicator axis is parallel to the crankshaft axis (Fig. 9).

3. Zero the dial indicator. Push the crankshaft forward and note the reading on the dial.

4. If the end play exceeds the wear limit, replace the thrust bearing. If the end play is less than the minimum limit, inspect the thrust bearing faces for scratches, burrs, nicks, or dirt. If the thrust faces are not defective or dirty, they probably were not aligned properly. Install the thrust bearing and align the faces

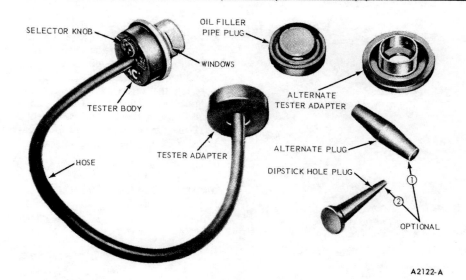

FIG. 7—AC Positive Crankcase Ventilation System Tester

FIG. 9—Typical Crankshaft End Play

FIG. 10—Flywheel Face Runout

CRANKCASE VENTILATION SYSTEM DIAGNOSIS WITH AC TESTER

COLOR	CAUSE
GREEN	SYSTEM OPERATING PROPERLY
GREEN AND YELLOW	REGULATOR VALVE OR SYSTEM PARTIALLY PLUGGED. SLIGHT KINK IN TESTER HOSE. SLIGHT ENGINE BLOW-BY. PLUGS FROM THE KIT OR THE ENGINE VACUUM LINES ARE NOT PROPERLY SEALED. TESTER KNOB IMPROPERLY SET.
YELLOW	REGULATOR VALVE OR SYSTEM PARTIALLY PLUGGED. TESTER HOSE KINKED OR BLOCKED. BLOW-BY AT MAXIMUM CAPACITY OF REGULATOR VALVE. PLUGS FROM THE KIT OR THE ENGINE VACUUM LINES ARE NOT PROPERLY SEALED. TESTER KNOB IMPROPERLY SET.
YELLOW AND RED	REGULATOR VALVE OR SYSTEM PARTIALLY OR FULLY PLUGGED. MORE ENGINE BLOW-BY THAN REGULATOR VALVE CAN HANDLE. VENT HOSE PLUGGED OR COLLAPSED.
RED	REGULATOR VALVE OR SYSTEM FULLY PLUGGED OR STUCK. VENT HOSE PLUGGED OR COLLAPSED. EXTREME BLOW-BY.

A2126-A

FIG. 8—Diagnosis of Air Intake Test

following the procedure recommended under Main Bearing Replacement in the pertinent engine section. Check the end play.

FLYWHEEL FACE RUNOUT— MANUAL-SHIFT TRANS- MISSIONS

Install a dial indicator so that the indicator point bears against the flywheel face (Fig. 10). Turn the flywheel making sure that it is full

forward or rearward so that crankshaft end play will not be indicated as flywheel runout.

If the clutch face runout exceeds specifications, remove the flywheel and check for burrs between the flywheel and the face of the crankshaft mounting flange. If no burrs exist, check the runout of the crankshaft mounting flange. Replace the flywheel or machine the crankshaft-flywheel mounting face if the mount-

ing flange runout is excessive. If the ring gear runout exceeds specifications, replace it or reinstall it on the flywheel. Refer to Ring Gear Replacement (Part 8-1, Section 2) for the proper procedure.

FLYWHEEL RUNOUT— AUTOMATIC TRANSMISSION

Remove the spark plugs.

Install a dial indicator so that the indicator point rests on the face of the ring gear adjacent to the gear teeth.

Push the flywheel and crankshaft forward or backward as far as possible to prevent crankshaft end play from being indicated as flywheel runout.

Set the indicator dial on the zero mark. Turn the flywheel one complete revolution while observing the total indicator reading (T.I.R.) If the T.I.R. exceeds specifications, the flywheel and ring gear assembly must be replaced.

FLYWHEEL RING GEAR RUNOUT

Install the dial indicator so that

the point rests on a tooth of the ring gear (Fig. 11), and check the out-

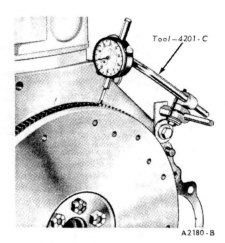

FIG. 11—Flywheel Ring Gear Runout

side diameter (O.D.) of the assembled flywheel and ring gear. **For this check, carefully adjust the indicator on the gear tooth so that the indicator point is near the extreme limit of its travel. This will prevent the indicator point from catching between the gear teeth as the flywheel is turned.** Set the indicator dial on the zero mark and slowly turn the flywheel through one revolution while observing the total indicator reading. The T.I.R. must be within specifications, or the ring gear (standard transmission) or flywheel and ring gear assembly (automatic transmission) must be replaced.

CAMSHAFT END PLAY

Push the camshaft toward the rear of the engine. Install a dial indicator so that the indicator point is on the camshaft sprocket retaining screw (Fig. 12) or gear hub (Fig. 13). Zero the dial indicator. Position a large screwdriver between the camshaft sprocket or gear and the block. Pull the camshaft forward and release it. Compare the dial indicator reading with specifications. If the end play is excessive, check the spacer for correct installation before it is removed. If the spacer is correctly installed, replace the thrust plate.

Remove the dial indicator.

TIMING CHAIN DEFLECTION

1. Rotate the crankshaft in a clockwise direction (as viewed from the front) to take up the slack on the left side of the chain.

1. PUSH CAM TO REAR OF ENGINE
2. SET DIAL ON ZERO
3. PULL CAM FORWARD AND RELEASE

FIG. 12—Typical Camshaft End Play—V-8 Engine

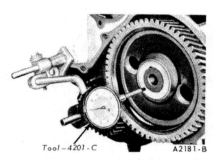

FIG. 13—Camshaft End Play—240 Six

2. Establish a reference point on the block and measure from this point to the chain (Fig. 14).

TAKE UP SLACK ON LEFT SIDE, ESTABLISH REFERENCE POINT. MEASURE DISTANCE **A**. TAKE UP SLACK ON RIGHT SIDE. FORCE LEFT SIDE OUT. MEASURE DISTANCE **B**. DEFLECTION IS **A** MINUS **B**.

FIG. 14—Typical Timing Chain Deflection—V-8 Engine

3. Rotate the crankshaft in the opposite direction to take up the slack on the right of the chain. Force the left side of the chain out with the fingers and measure the distance between the reference point and the chain. The deflection is the difference between the two measurements.

If the deflection exceeds specifications, replace the timing chain and sprockets.

TIMING GEAR BACKLASH

Install a dial indicator on the cylinder block (Fig. 15). Check the

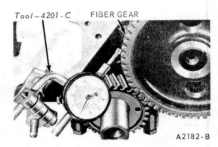

FIG. 15—Timing Gear Backlash—240 Six

backlash between the camshaft gear and the crankshaft gear with a dial indicator (Fig. 15). Hold the gear firmly against the block while making the check. Refer to the specifications for the backlash limits.

TIMING GEAR RUNOUT

Install a dial indicator on the cylinder block as shown in Fig. 16.

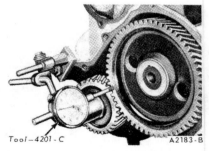

FIG. 16—Timing Gear Runout —240 Six

Hold the camshaft gear against the camshaft thrust plate and zero the indicator. Rotate the crankshaft to turn the camshaft, while holding the camshaft gear against the thrust plate. Check the gear runout through one complete revolution of the camshaft. If the gear runout exceeds specifications, remove it and check for burrs or foreign particles on or between the camshaft and gear joining flanges. Recheck the runout; if it still exceeds specifications, replace both gears.

Follow the above procedure to check crankshaft gear runout.

2 COMMON ADJUSTMENTS AND REPAIRS

ADJUSTMENTS

VALVE LASH-MECHANICAL TAPPETS

Preliminary (Cold)

If some component of the valve train has been replaced; i.e., rocker arm, push rod, camshaft, etc., it will be necessary to make a preliminary (cold) valve lash adjustment before starting the engine. If the valve lash adjustment is made for an engine tune-up, follow the final (hot) adjustment procedure.

On V-8 engines the cylinders are numbered from front to rear—right bank, 1-2-3-4; left bank, 5-6-7-8.

On the 428 Special Police and 427 V-8 engines, the valves are arranged from front to rear on both banks, E-I-E-I-I-E-I-E.

1. Check the torque required to turn the screw. If the torque required to turn a screw is less than 7 ft-lbs (84 in-lbs), try an oversize self-locking adjusting screw. If this is still unsatisfactory, replace the rocker arm and adjusting screw.

2. **Disconnect the brown lead (I terminal) and the red and blue lead (S terminal) at the starter relay.** Install an auxiliary starter switch between the battery and S terminals of the starter relay. **Crank the engine with the ignition switch OFF.**

3. On the 428 Special Police and 427 V-8 engines, make three chalk marks on the crankshaft damper (Fig. 17). Space the marks approximately 90° apart so that with the timing mark, the damper is divided into four equal parts (90° represents ¼ of the distance around the damper circumference). Set the intake and exhaust valve lash (Fig. 18) to specifications with a step-type feeler gauge ("go" and "no go").

Rotate the crankshaft until No. 1 piston is near TDC at the end of the compression stroke. Adjust the following valves:

No. 1 Exhaust   No. 1 Intake
No. 4 Exhaust   No. 7 Intake
No. 5 Exhaust   No. 8 Intake

Rotate the crankshaft 180° or ½ turn in the direction shown in Fig. 17 (this puts No. 4 piston on TDC). Adjust the following valves:

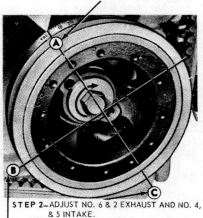

STEP 1—SET NO. 1 PISTON ON T.D.C. AT END OF COMPRESSION STROKE—ADJUST NO. 1, 4, 5, EXHAUST & NO. 1, 8, 7, INTAKE.

STEP 2—ADJUST NO. 6 & 2 EXHAUST AND NO. 4, & 5 INTAKE.

STEP 3—ADJUST NO. 8, 3, 7 EXHAUST AND NO. 3, 6, 2 INTAKE

A1203-E

FIG. 17—Preliminary Valve Lash Adjustment

Step-Type Feeler Gauge   A1466-A

FIG. 18—Valve Lash Adjustment—Mechanical Valve Lifters

No. 2 Exhaust   No. 4 Intake
No. 6 Exhaust   No. 5 Intake

Rotate the crankshaft another ¾ turn in the same direction (this puts No 3 piston on TDC). Adjust the following valves:

No. 3 Exhaust   No. 2 Intake
No. 7 Exhaust   No. 3 Intake
No. 8 Exhaust   No. 6 Intake

Final (Hot)

It is very important that the valve lash be held to the correct specifications because:

If the lash is set too close, the valve will open too early and close too late, resulting in rough engine idle. Burning and warping of the valves will occur also because the valves cannot make firm contact with the seats long enough to cool properly. If the lash is excessive, it will cause the valve to open too late and close too early causing valve bounce. In addition, damage to the camshaft lobe is likely because the tappet foot will not follow the pattern of the camshaft lobe causing a shock contact between these two parts.

1. Be sure the engine is at normal operating temperature before attempting to set the valve lash.

2. With the engine idling, set the valve lash (Fig. 18) using a step-type feeler gauge only ("go" and "no go"). The final (hot) intake and exhaust valve lash settings are listed in the Specifications (Part 8-5).

For example, to obtain the correct setting if the valve lash is 0.025 inch, use a step-type feeler gauge of 0.024 inch ("go") and 0.026 inch ("no go"). The "go" step should enter, and the "no go" step should not enter. The resultant setting will be to the required setting (0.025 inch).

VALVE CLEARANCE— HYDRAULIC VALVE LIFTERS (352, 390, 410 and 428 V-8)

The valve arrangement is E-I-E-I-I-E-I-E from front to rear on both cylinder banks.

A 0.060-inch shorter push rod or a 0.060-inch longer push rod are available for service to provide a means of compensating for dimensional changes in the valve mechanism. Refer to the Master Parts List or the specifications for the pertinent color code.

Valve stem to valve rocker arm clearance should be within specifications with the hydraulic lifter completely collapsed. Repeated valve reconditioning operations (valve and/or valve seat refacing) will decrease the clearance to the point that if not compensated for, the hydraulic valve lifter will cease to function.

To determine whether a shorter or a longer push rod is necessary, make the following check:

1. Disconnect the brown lead (I terminal) and the red and blue lead (S terminal) at the starter relay. Install an auxiliary starter switch between the battery and "S" terminals of the starter relay. **Crank the engine with the ignition switch OFF.**

2. Position the crankshaft as outlined in steps 3 and 4. Position the hydraulic lifter compressor tool on the rocker arm and slowly apply pressure to bleed down the hydraulic lifter until the plunger is completely bottomed (Fig. 19). Hold the lifter

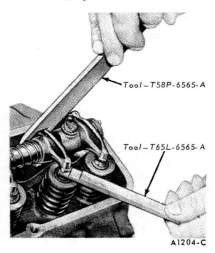

FIG. 19—352, 390, 410 and 428 V-8 Valve Clearance— Hydraulic Valve Lifters

in the fully collapsed position and insert the clearance gauge between the valve stem and the rocker arm of the valve being checked. If the first step of the gauge enters, the old push rod may be used. If the first step will not enter, replace the standard push rod with a shorter service push rod. If the second step of the gauge enters, the operating range of the lifter is excessive which indicates that the incorrect push rod has been installed or severe wear has occurred at the push rod ends, rocker arm, or valve stem. In this case, it will be necessary to determine the area of discrepancy and the incorrect or defective part(s) should be replaced. If all the valve train components except the push rod are within limits, install a 0.060-inch longer push rod.

3. Rotate the crankshaft until No. 1 piston is on TDC at the end of the compression stroke and check the following valves:

No. 1 Intake   No. 1 Exhaust
No. 3 Intake   No. 4 Exhaust
No. 7 Intake   No. 5 Exhaust

No. 8 Intake   No. 8 Exhaust

4. After these valves have been checked, rotate the crankshaft 360° (one revolution) to position No. 6 piston on TDC and check the following valves:

No. 2 Intake   No. 2 Exhaust
No. 4 Intake   No. 3 Exhaust
No. 5 Intake   No. 6 Exhaust
No. 6 Intake   No. 7 Exhaust

When compressing the valve spring to remove the push rods, be sure the piston in the individual cylinder is below TDC to avoid contact between the valve and the piston.

To replace a push rod, it will be necessary to remove the valve rocker arm shaft assembly, following the procedure in Part 8-4.

Upon replacement of a valve push rod and/or valve rocker arm shaft assembly, the engine should not be cranked or rotated until the hydraulic lifters have had an opportunity to leak down to their normal operating position. The leakdown rate can be accelerated by using the tool shown in Fig. 19 on the valve rocker arm and applying pressure in a direction to collapse the lifter.

VALVE CLEARANCE— HYDRAULIC VALVE LIFTERS (240 SIX and 289 V-8)

1. Disconnect the brown lead (I terminal) and the red and blue lead (S terminal) at the starter relay. Install an auxiliary starter switch between the battery and S terminals of the starter relay. **Crank the engine with the ignition switch "OFF."**

2. On the 240 Six engine, make two chalk marks on the crankshaft damper (Fig. 20). Space the marks approximately 120° apart so that with the timing mark, the damper is divided into three equal parts (120° represent ⅓ of the distance around the damper circumference).

On the 289 V-8 engine, make three chalk marks on the crankshaft damper (Fig. 21). Space the marks approximately 90° apart so that with the timing mark, the damper is divided into four equal parts (90° represents ¼ of the distance around the damper circumference).

3. Rotate the crankshaft until No. 1 piston is on TDC at the end of the compression stroke. **Check the breaking torque (torque required to turn nut in a counterclockwise direction)** of each stud nut. Replace the stud nut if the breaking torque does not meet specifications. If the breaking torque still is not within

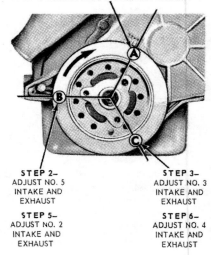

STEP 1—SET NO. 1 PISTON ON T.D.C. AT END OF COMPRESSION STROKE ADJUST NO. 1 INTAKE AND EXHAUST

STEP 4—ADJUST NO. 6 INTAKE AND EXHAUST

STEP 2— ADJUST NO. 5 INTAKE AND EXHAUST

STEP 3— ADJUST NO. 3 INTAKE AND EXHAUST

STEP 5— ADJUST NO. 2 INTAKE AND EXHAUST

STEP 6— ADJUST NO. 4 INTAKE AND EXHAUST

FIG. 20—240 Six Valve Clearance

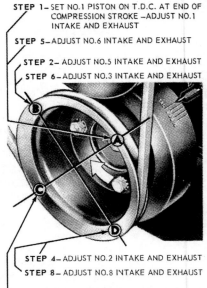

STEP 1— SET NO.1 PISTON ON T.D.C. AT END OF COMPRESSION STROKE —ADJUST NO.1 INTAKE AND EXHAUST

STEP 5—ADJUST NO.6 INTAKE AND EXHAUST

STEP 2— ADJUST NO.5 INTAKE AND EXHAUST

STEP 6—ADJUST NO.3 INTAKE AND EXHAUST

STEP 4— ADJUST NO.2 INTAKE AND EXHAUST

STEP 8— ADJUST NO.8 INTAKE AND EXHAUST

STEP 3— ADJUST NO.4 INTAKE AND EXHAUST

STEP 7— ADJUST NO.7 INTAKE AND EXHAUST

FIG. 21—289 V-8 Valve Clearance

specifications, replace the stud.

4. With No. 1 piston on TDC at the end of the compression stroke, adjust the intake and exhaust valve clearance for No. 1 cylinder. Loosen the rocker arm stud nut until *there is end clearance in the push rod*, then tighten the nut to just remove all the push rod to rocker arm clearance. This may be determined by rotating and/or moving the push rod with the fingers as the stud nut is tightened (Fig. 22). When the

FIG. 22—Typical Valve Clearance Adjustment—240 Six and 289 V-8

push rod to rocker arm clearance has been eliminated, tighten the stud nut an additional ¾ turn to place the hydraulic lifter plunger in the desired operating range.

5. Repeat this procedure for the remaining set of valves, turning the crankshaft with an auxiliary starter switch, ⅓ turn at a time (240 Six) or ¼ turn at a time (289 V-8), in the direction of rotation, while adjusting the valves in the firing order sequence. The 240 Six firing order is 1-5-3-6-2-4, and the 289 V-8 firing order is 1-5-4-2-6-3-7-8. This procedure requires two complete turns of the crankshaft.

6. Operate the engine and check for rough engine idle or a noisy lifter(s). Valve clearance set too tight will cause rough engine idle, and valve clearance set too loose will cause a noisy lifter(s). If it has been determined that these conditions are caused by improper valve clearance, adjust the affected valve(s) using the following procedure:

Position the piston(s) on TDC after the compression stroke (See Step 2 above). Apply pressure to slowly bleed down the valve lifter until the plunger is completely bottomed (Fig. 23). While holding the valve lifter in the fully collapsed position, check the available clearance between the rocker arm and valve stem tip (Fig. 23). If the clearance is not within specifications, rotate the rocker arm stud nut clockwise to decrease the clearance and "counterclockwise" to increase the clear-

Tool—6513-A.C.

FIG. 23—Typical Valve Clearance Check—240 Six and 289 V-8

ance. **Normally one turn of the rocker arm stud nut will vary the clearance by 0.066 inch.**

REPAIRS

VALVE ROCKER ARM AND/OR SHAFT ASSEMBLY

Dress up minor surface defects on the rocker arm shaft and in the rocker arm bore with a hone.

If the pad at the valve end of the rocker arm has a grooved radius, replace the rocker arm. **Do not attempt to true this surface by grinding.**

For a 240 six or a 289 V-8 engine, refer to Cylinder Head Repair for the rocker arm stud replacement procedure.

PUSH RODS

Following the procedures in Section 3 under Push Rod Inspection, check the push rods for straightness.

If the runout exceeds the maximum limit at any point, discard the rod. **Do not attempt to straighten push rods.**

CYLINDER HEADS

Thermactor Exhaust Emission Control System

On engines so equipped, replace any air nozzle that is eroded, burned or damaged to the extent that air flow is restricted or increased.

Replace the head if it is cracked. **Do not plane or grind more than 0.010 inch from the cylinder head gasket surface.** Remove all burrs or scratches with an oil stone.

Rocker Arm Stud Nut Replacement

If the rocker arm stud nut breaking torque is less than specified, install a new standard stud nut and recheck the breaking torque. Refer to "Valve Clearance Adjustment" for the torque procedure.

Rocker Arm Stud Replacement —240 Six and 289 V-8

If it is necessary to remove a rocker arm stud kit (tool T62F-6A527-B) is available which contains the following: a stud remover, a 0.006-inch reamer, and a 0.015-inch reamer. Use stud replacer T65P-6A527-A to press in replacement studs.

Rocker arm studs that are broken or have damaged threads may be replaced with standard studs. Loose studs in the head may be replaced with 0.006 or 0.015-inch oversize studs which are available for service. The standard studs have no identification markings, whereas the 0.006-inch oversize stud has two grooves around the pilot end of the stud and the 0.015 inch oversize stud has a step produced by the increased diameter of the stud approximately 1⁵/₃₂ inches from the pilot end.

When going from a standard size rocker arm stud to a 0.015-inch oversize stud, always use the 0.006-inch reamer before finish reaming with the 0.015-inch reamer.

1. Position the sleeve of the rocker arm stud remover (tool T62F-6A527-B) over the stud with the bearing end down. Thread the puller into the sleeve and over the stud until it is fully bottomed. Hold the sleeve with a wrench, then rotate the puller clockwise to remove the stud (Fig. 24).

If the rocker arm stud was broken off flush with the stud boss, use an easy-out to remove the broken stud following the instructions of the tool manufacturer.

2. If a loose rocker arm stud is being replaced, ream the stud bore using the proper reamer (or reamers in sequence) for the selected oversize stud (Fig. 25). **Make sure the metal particles do not enter the valve area.**

3. Screw the new stud into the sliding driver of the rocker arm stud installer (T65P-6A527-A) and coat the end of the stud with Lubriplate. Align the stud and installer with the stud bore, then tap the sliding driver

FIG. 24—Rocker Arm Stud Removal—240 Six and 289 V-8

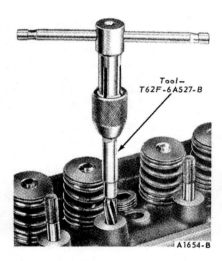

FIG. 25—Reaming Rocker Arm Stud Bore—240 Six and 289 V-8

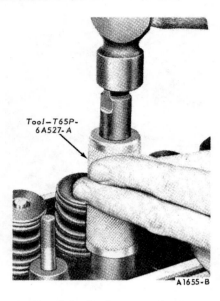

FIG. 26—Rocker Arm Stud Installation—240 Six and 289 V-8

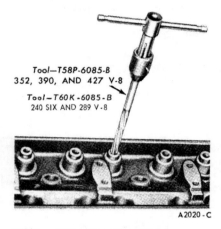

FIG. 27—Reaming Valve Guides

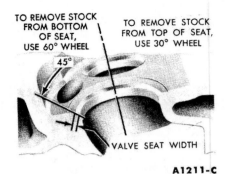

FIG. 28—Valve Seat Refacing

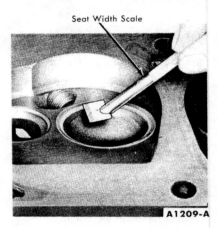

FIG. 29—Valve Seat Width

until it bottoms (Fig. 26). When the installer contacts the stud boss, the stud is installed to its correct height.

Reaming Valve Guides

If it becomes necessary to ream a valve guide (Fig. 27) to install a valve with an oversize stem, a reaming kit is available which contains the following reamer and pilot combinations: a 0.003-inch O.S. reamer with a standard diameter pilot, a 0.015-inch O.S. reamer with a 0.003-inch O.S. pilot, and a 0.030-inch reamer with a 0.015-inch O.S. pilot.

When going from a standard size valve to an oversize valve, always use the reamer in sequence. **Always reface the valve seat after the valve**

guide has been reamed.

Refacing Valve Seats

Refacing of the valve seat should be closely coordinated with the refacing of the valve face so that the finished seat and valve face will be concentric and the specified interference fit will be maintained. This is important so that the valve and seat will have a compression-tight fit. Be sure that the refacer grinding wheels are properly dressed.

Grind the valve seats of all engines to a true 45° angle (Fig. 28). Remove only enough stock to clean up pits and grooves or to correct the valve seat runout. After the seat has been refaced, use a seat width scale or a machinist scale to measure the seat width (Fig. 29). Narrow

the seat, if necessary, to bring it within specifications.

If the valve seat width exceeds the maximum limit, remove enough stock from the top edge and/or bottom edge of the seat to reduce the width to specifications.

On the valve seats of all engines use a 60° angle grinding wheel to remove stock from the bottom of the seats (raise the seats) and use a 30° angle wheel to remove stock from the top of the seats (lower the seats).

The finished valve seat should contact the approximate center of the valve face. It is good practice to determine where the valve seat contacts the face. To do this, coat the seat with Prussian blue and set the valve in place. Rotate the valve with light pressure. If the blue is transferred to the center of the valve face, the contact is satisfactory. If the blue is transferred to the top edge of the valve face, lower the valve seat. If the blue is transferred to the bottom edge of the valve face, raise the valve seat.

VALVES

For inspection procedures refer to Section 3.

Valve defects, such as minor pits, grooves, etc., may be removed. Discard valves that are severely damaged, or if the face runout or stem clearance exceeds specifications.

Discard any defective parts of the valve assembly.

Refacing Valves

The valve refacing operation should be closely coordinated with the valve seat refacing operations so that the finished angles of the valve face and of the valve seat will be to specifications and provide a compression-tight fit. Be sure that the refacer grinding wheels are properly dressed.

If the valve face runout is excessive and/or to remove pits and grooves, reface the valves to a true 44° angle. Remove only enough stock to correct the runout or to clean up the pits and grooves. If the edge of the valve head is less than $1/32$ inch thick after grinding, replace the valve as the valve will run too hot in the engine. **The interference fit of the valve and seat should not be lapped out.**

Remove all grooves or score marks from the end of the valve stem, and chamfer it as necessary. Do not remove more than 0.010 inch from the end of the valve stem.

If the valve and/or valve seat has been refaced, it will be necessary to check the clearance between the rocker arm pad and the valve stem with the valve train assembly installed in the engine.

Select Fitting Valves

If the valve stem to valve guide clearance exceeds the wear limit, ream the valve guide for the next oversize valve stem. Valves with oversize stem diameters of 0.003, 0.015 and 0.030 inch are available for service. **Always reface the valve seat after the valve guide has been reamed.** Refer to "Reaming Valve Guides."

CAMSHAFT

Remove light scuffs, scores or nicks from the camshaft machined surfaces with a smooth oil stone.

CRANKSHAFT

Dress minor imperfections with an oil stone. If the journals are severely marred or exceed the wear limit, they should be refinished to size for the next undersize bearing.

Refinishing Journals

Refinish the journals to give the proper clearance with the next undersize bearing. If the journal will not "clean up" to maximum undersize bearing available, replace the crankshaft.

Always reproduce the same journal shoulder radius that existed originally. Too small a radius will result in fatigue failure of the crankshaft. Too large a radius will result in bearing failure due to radius ride of the bearing.

After refinishing the journals, chamfer the oil holes; then polish the journal with a No. 320 grit polishing cloth and engine oil. Crocus cloth may be used also as a polishing agent.

PISTONS, PINS AND RINGS

Fitting Pistons

Pistons are available for service in standard sizes and the oversizes shown in Table 2.

TABLE 2—Oversize Service
Pistons

Engine	Piston Oversize (Inches)
352 V-8	0.003, 0.020, 0.030, 0.040, 0.060
240 Six 289 V-8 390 V-8 410 V-8 428 V-8	0.003, 0.020, 0.030, 0.040,
427 V-8	Standard Only

The standard-size pistons are color coded "red" or "blue" on the dome. Refer to the specifications for standard-size piston dimensions. Piston pins and retainers are provided with new pistons, except retainers are not used on the 240 Six and 289 V-8.

Follow the procedures in Section 3 to measure the piston O.D. and cylinder bore. The dimensions should be within specifications, and the piston to bore clearance (bore I.D. minus piston O.D.) must be within the specified limits.

If the clearance is greater than the maximum limit, recheck calculations to be sure that the proper size piston has been selected, check for a damaged piston; then try a new piston.

If the clearance is less than the minimum limit, recheck calculations before trying another piston. If none can be fitted, refinish the cylinder for the next size piston.

When a piston has been fitted, mark it for assembly in the cylinder to which it was fitted.

If the taper, out-of-round and piston to cylinder bore clearance conditions of the cylinder bore are within specified limits, new piston rings will give satisfactory service. If new rings are to be installed in a used cylinder that has not been refinished, remove the cylinder wall glaze. Be sure to clean the cylinder bore thoroughly, following the procedure in Section 3.

To Fit a Piston:

1. Calculate the size piston to be used by taking a cylinder bore check. Follow the procedures outlined in Section 3.

2. Select the proper size piston to provide the desired clearance (refer to the specifications). Measure the piston diameter in line with the centerline of the piston pin and at 90° to the piston pin axis.

3. Make sure the piston and cylinder block are at room temperature (70° F.). **After any refinishing operation allow the cylinder bore to cool, and make sure the piston and bore are clean and dry before the piston fit is checked.**

Fitting Piston Rings

1. Select the proper ring set for the size piston to be used.

2. Position the ring in the cylinder bore in which it is going to be used.

3. Push the ring down into the bore area where normal ring wear is not encountered.

4. Use the head of a piston to position the ring in the bore so that the ring is square with the cylinder wall. **Use caution to avoid damage to the ring or cylinder bore.**

5. Measure the gap between the ends of the ring with a feeler gauge (Fig. 30). If the ring gap is less or

FIG. 30—Piston Ring Gap

greater than the specified limits, try another ring set.

6. Check the ring side clearance of the compression rings with a feeler gauge inserted between the ring and its lower land (Fig. 31). The

FIG. 31—Piston Ring Side Clearance

gauge should slide freely around the entire ring circumference without binding. Any wear that occurs will form a step at the inner portion of the lower land. **If the lower lands have high steps, the piston should be replaced.**

Fitting Piston Pins

On the 352, 390, 410, 427 and 428 V-8, the piston pin should be a light thumb press fit at normal temperature (70°F.). Standard piston pins are color coded green. Pins of 0.001-inch oversize (color coded blue) and 0.002-inch oversize (color coded yellow) are available.

Install the piston pin in the piston and rod. Install a new retainer at each end of the pin to hold it in place. Make sure the retainers are properly seated in their grooves.

On the 240 six and 289 V-8, install the piston pin, following the procedure under Piston Assembly (Part 8-3).

If the pin hole in the piston must be reamed or honed on the 352, 390, 410, 427 or 428 V-8 use precision honing equipment or an expansion-type, piloted reamer. **Piston pin bores must not be reamed with hand-driven reamers. Use motor-driven reamers, but do not exceed the cutting speed (rpm) recommended by the reamer manufacturer.**

If a reamer is used, set the reamer to the size of the pin bore; then expand the reamer slightly and trial ream the pin bore. Take a light cut. Use a pilot sleeve of the nearest size to maintain alignment of the bores.

Check the hole size, using the new piston pin. If the bore is small, expand the reamer slightly and make another cut. Repeat the procedure until the proper fit is obtained. Check the piston pin for fit in the respective rod or rod bushing. On the 352, 390, 410, 427 or 428 V-8, if necessary, ream or hone the rod bushing to fit the pin to specifications.

EXHAUST CONTROL VALVE REPLACEMENT—240 SIX

1. Separate the intake and exhaust manifolds.

2. Remove the valve tension spring and the thermostatic spring from the exhaust control valve shaft (Fig. 32).

3. Remove the stop pin spring

from the manifold.

4. Using an acetylene torch inside the manifold, cut the shaft on both sides of the valve plate.

5. Remove the valve plate, shaft and flat washer.

6. Remove the expansion plug from the control valve shaft bushing bore.

7. Remove the exhaust control valve bushings from the manifold.

8. Install the new control valve bushings. **The inner end of the smaller bushing should be 0.010-0.015 inch below the inner surface of the exhaust manifold. The inner end of the larger bushing should be 0.020 inch above the inner surface of the exhaust manifold.**

9. Ream the bushings to 0.251-0.253 inch ID.

10. Slide the new shaft into the bushings, flat washer and valve plate. **The flat washer must be between the valve plate and the large bushing.**

11. Install a new stop pin spring on the stop pin.

12. Position the exhaust control valve at an 84° angle with the top surface of the manifold (Fig. 33).

13. Rotate the counterweight and shaft assembly clockwise until the counterweight contacts the stop pin spring. Place a 0.030 inch feeler gauge between the counterweight and manifold to maintain the specified clearance while welding (Fig. 33).

14. With the plate and counterweight in position, **use stainless steel welding rod** to tack-weld the valve plate to the shaft.

15. Move the assembly back and forth to check for a binding condition. If there is no binding condition,

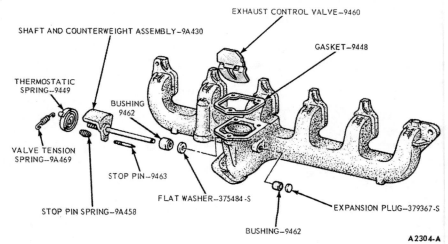

FIG. 32—Exhaust Control Valve Assembly—240 Six

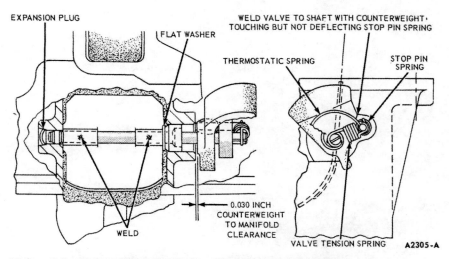

EXPANSION PLUG

FLAT WASHER

WELD VALVE TO SHAFT WITH COUNTERWEIGHT·
TOUCHING BUT NOT DEFLECTING STOP PIN SPRING

THERMOSTATIC SPRING

STOP PIN
SPRING

0.030 INCH
COUNTERWEIGHT
TO MANIFOLD
CLEARANCE

WELD

VALVE TENSION SPRING

A2305-A

FIG. 33—Valve Plate Position and Counterweight Clearance

securely weld the valve plate to the shaft.

16. Install the expansion plug in the manifold bushing bore.

17. Position the new thermostatic spring on the shaft and counterweight assembly so that it will be necessary to wind the spring approximately ½ turn in the clockwise direction in order to hook the open end over the stop pin. Use a 5/16 inch ID piece of tubing to slide the thermostatic spring on the shaft and counterweight assembly. Wind the spring clockwise and hook it over the stop pin.

18. Install a new valve tension spring on the exhaust control valve shaft and the stop pin.

CYLINDER BLOCK

Refinishing Cylinder Walls

Honing is recommended for refinishing cylinder walls only when the walls have minor imperfections, such as light scuffs and scratches, or for fitting pistons to the specified clearance. The grade of hone to be used

is determined by the amount of metal to be removed. Follow the instructions of the hone manufacturer. If coarse stones are used to start the honing operation, leave enough material so that all hone marks can be removed with the finishing hone which is used to obtain the proper piston clearance.

Cylinder walls that are severely marred and/or worn beyond the specified limits should be refinished. Before any cylinder is refinished, all main bearing caps must be in place and tightened to the proper torque so that the crankshaft bearing bores will not become distorted from the refinishing operation.

Refinish only the cylinder or cylinders that require it. **All pistons are the same weight, both standard and oversize; therefore, various sizes of pistons can be used without upsetting engine balance.**

Refinish the cylinder with the most wear first to determine the maximum oversize. If the cylinder will not clean up when refinished for the maximum oversize piston recom-

mended, replace the block.

Refinish the cylinder to within approximately 0.0015 inch of the required oversize diameter. This will allow enough stock for the final step of honing so that the correct surface finish and pattern are obtained. Use clean sharp hones of No. 180-220 grit for this operation.

For the proper use of the refinishing equipment, follow the instructions of the manufacturer. **Only experienced personnel should be allow to perform this work.**

After the final operation in either of the two refinishing methods described and prior to checking the piston fit, thoroughly clean and oil the cylinder walls, following the procedure in Section 3. Check the piston fit, following the procedure in this section and Section 3. Mark the pistons to correspond to the cylinders in which they are to be installed. When the refinishing of all cylinders that require it has been completed and all pistons are fitted, thoroughly clean the entire block and oil the cylinder walls following the procedure under Cylinder Block Cleaning in Section 3.

**FLYWHEEL RING GEAR—
MANUAL-SHIFT
TRANSMISSIONS**

To replace a defective ring gear, heat the defective ring gear with a blow torch on the engine side of the gear, and knock it off the flywheel. **Do not hit the flywheel when removing the ring gear.**

Heat the new ring gear evenly until the gear expands enough to slip onto the flywheel. Make sure the gear is seated properly against the shoulder. **Do not heat any portion of the gear to a temperature higher than 500°F. If this limit is exceeded, the temper will be removed from the ring gear teeth.**

3 CLEANING AND INSPECTION

The cleaning and inspection procedures in this section are for a complete engine overhaul; therefore, for partial engine overhaul or parts replacement, follow the pertinent cleaning or inspection procedure.

INTAKE MANIFOLD

CLEANING

Remove all gasket material from

the machined surfaces of the manifold. Clean the manifold in a suitable solvent, and dry it with compressed air.

INSPECTION

Inspect the manifold for cracks, damaged gasket surfaces, or other defects that would make it unfit for further service. Replace all studs that are stripped or otherwise dam-

aged. **Remove all filings and foreign matter that may have entered the manifold as a result of repairs.**

On the 352, 390, 410, 427 and 428 V-8 engines, check the baffle plate on the underside of the manifold; it should be securely fastened at all retaining points.

EXHAUST MANIFOLD

CLEANING

Remove all gasket material from the manifolds.

On the right exhaust manifold of the V-8 engines, make sure the automatic choke air inlet and outlet holes are completely open and the cover does not leak.

INSPECTION

Inspect the cylinder head joining flanges of the exhaust manifold(s) for evidence of exhaust gas leaks.

Inspect the manifolds for cracks, damaged gasket surfaces, or other defects that would make them unfit for further service.

VALVE ROCKER ARM AND/OR SHAFT ASSEMBLY

CLEANING

Clean all the parts thoroughly. Make sure all oil passages are open.

On ball stud rocker arms, make sure the oil passage in the push rod end of the rocker arm is open.

INSPECTION

On rocker arm shaft assemblies, check the clearance between each rocker arm and the shaft by checking the ID of the rocker arm bore and the OD of the shaft. If the clearance between any rocker arm and the shaft exceeds the wear limit, replace the shaft and/or the rocker arm. Inspect the shaft and the rocker arm bore for nicks, scratches, scores or scuffs.

Inspect the pad at the valve end of the rocker arms for a grooved radius.

On a 427 V-8 engine, check the rocker arm adjusting screws and the push rod end of the rocker arms for stripped or broken threads, and the ball end of the adjusting screw for nicks, scratches, or excessive wear. Inspect the oil tubes for cracks or sharp bends.

On a 240 Six or a 289 V-8 engine, check the rocker arm and fulcrum seat for excessive wear, cracks, nicks or burrs. Check the rocker arm stud and nut for stripped or broken threads.

PUSH RODS

CLEANING

On a 240 Six or a 289 V-8 engine, clean the push rods in a suitable solvent. Blow out the oil passage in the push rod with compressed air.

INSPECTION

Check the ends of the push rods for nicks, grooves, roughness or excessive wear.

The push rods can be visually checked for straightness while they are installed in the engine by rotating them with the valve closed. They also can be checked with a dial indicator (Fig. 34).

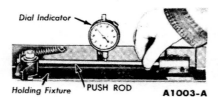

FIG. 34—Push Rod Runout

CYLINDER HEADS

CLEANING

On engines equipped with Thermactor exhaust emission control system, clean the air nozzle tips with a wire brush. Clean the nozzle air hole with a $5/16$-inch-diameter stiff wire brush.

With the valves installed to protect the valve seats, remove deposits from the combustion chambers and valve heads with a scraper and a wire brush. **Be careful not to damage the cylinder head gasket surface.** After the valves are removed, clean the valve guide bores with a valve guide cleaning tool. Use cleaning solvent to remove dirt, grease and other deposits. Clean all bolt holes; be sure the oil transfer passage is clean (352, 390, 410, 427 and 428 V-8).

Remove all deposits from the valves with a fine wire brush or buffing wheel.

INSPECTION

On engines equipped with a Thermactor exhaust emission control system, inspect the air nozzles for eroded, burned or damaged tips that would restrict the normal air flow. Inspect the connections for stripped or damaged threads and damaged tube nut seats. Inspect the cylinder heads for cracks or excessively burned areas in the exhaust outlet ports.

Check the cylinder head for cracks, and inspect the gasket surface for burrs and nicks. Replace the head if it is cracked.

The following inspection procedures are for a cylinder head that is to be completely overhauled. For individual repair operations, use only

the pertinent inspection procedure.

Cylinder Head Flatness

When a cylinder head is removed because of gasket leaks, check the flatness of the cylinder head gasket surface (Fig. 35) for conformance

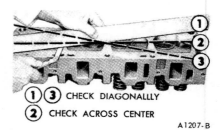

FIG. 35—Typical Cylinder Head Flatness

to specifications. If necessary to refinish the cylinder head gasket surface, **do not plane or grind off more than 0.010 inch.**

Valve Seat Runout

Check the valve seat runout with an accurate gauge (Fig. 36). Follow

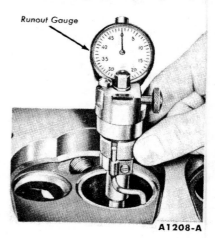

FIG. 36—Typical Valve Seat Runout

the instructions of the gauge manufacturer. If the runout exceeds the wear limit, reface the valve and valve seat.

Valve Seat Width

Measure the valve seat width (Fig. 29). Reface the valve seats if the width is not within specifications.

Valves

The critical inspection points and tolerances of the valves are illustrated in Fig. 37. Refer to the specifications for wear limits.

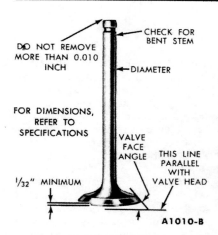

FIG. 37—Critical Valve Tolerances

Inspect the valve face and the edge of the valve head for pits, grooves, scores or other defects. Inspect the stem for a bent condition and the end of the stem for grooves or scores. Check the valve head for signs of burning, erosion, warpage and cracking. Defects, such as minor pits, grooves, etc., may be removed. Discard valves that are severely damaged.

Inspect the valve springs, valve spring retainers, locks and sleeves for defects. Discard any visually defective parts.

Valve Face Runout

Check the valve face runout as shown in Fig. 38. The valve face

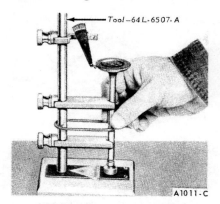

FIG. 38—Valve Face Runout

runout should not exceed the specified limits. If the runout exceeds the wear limit, the valve should be replaced or refaced as outlined under "Refacing Valves" in this section.

Valve Stem Clearance

Check the valve stem to valve guide clearance of each valve in its

respective valve guide with the tool shown in Fig. 39 or its equivalent.

FIG. 39—Typical Valve Stem Clearance

Use a flat-end indicator point.

Install the tool on the valve stem until it is fully seated, and tighten the knurled set screw firmly. Permit the valve to drop away from its seat until the tool contacts the upper surface of the valve guide.

Position the dial indicator with its flat tip against the center portion the tool's spherical section at approximately 90° to the valve stem axis. Move the tool back and forth in line with the indicator stem. Take a reading on the dial indicator without removing the tool from the valve guide upper surface. Divide the reading by two, the division factor for the tool.

Valve Spring Pressure

Check the springs for proper pressure (Fig. 40) at the specified spring

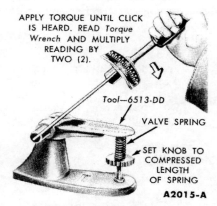

FIG. 40—Valve Spring Pressure

lengths. Do not remove the damper spring if one is installed when checking the pressure. Weak valve springs cause poor engine performance. Replace any spring not within specifications.

Valve Spring

Check each spring for squareness, using a steel square and a surface plate (Fig. 41). Stand the spring and

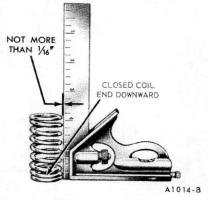

FIG. 41—Valve Spring Squareness

square on end on the surface plate. Slide the spring up to the square. Revolve the spring slowly and observe the space between the top coil of the spring and the square. The out-of-square limit is ¹⁄₁₆ inch.

Follow the same procedure to check new valve springs before installation.

Make certain the proper spring (color coded) is installed.

Visually inspect the valve spring retainer to determine if the damper spring coil has been hitting the retainer. This interference will also cause a clicking noise when the engine is operating. The damper spring is properly installed in the valve spring when positioned so that the end of the damper spring bottom coil is 135° counterclockwise from the end of the valve spring lower coil.

HYDRAULIC VALVE LIFTERS

The valve lifter assemblies should be kept in proper sequence so that they can be installed in their original position. Inspect and test each lifter separately so as not to intermix the internal parts. **If any part of the lifter assembly needs replacing, replace the entire assembly.**

CLEANING

Thoroughly clean all the parts in clean solvent and wipe them with a clean, lint-free cloth.

INSPECTION

Inspect the parts and discard the entire lifter assembly if any part shows pitting, scoring, galling or evidence of non-rotation. Replace the entire assembly if the plunger is not free in the body. The plunger should drop to the bottom of the body by its own weight when assembled dry.

Assemble the lifter assembly and check for freeness of operation by pressing down on the push rod cup. The lifters can also be checked with a hydraulic tester to test the leakdown rate. Follow the instructions of the test unit manufacturer or the procedure in Section 1.

MECHANICAL TAPPETS

CLEANING

Thoroughly clean the tappets in clean solvent and wipe them with a clean, lint-free cloth.

INSPECTION

Inspect the tappets, and discard any that show signs of pitting, scoring or galling. Replace any tappets that show evidence of non-rotation.

TIMING CHAIN AND SPROCKETS

CLEANING

Clean all parts in solvent and dry them with compressed air.

Lubricate the timing chain with engine oil before installing it on the engine.

INSPECTION

Inspect the chain for broken links. Inspect the sprockets for cracks and worn or damaged teeth. Replace all the components of the timing chain and sprocket assembly, if any one item needs replacement.

Inspect the fuel pump drive eccentric for scores, nicks and excessive wear. If the eccentric is scored, replace it.

TIMING GEARS

CLEANING

Clean the gears in solvent, and dry them with compressed air.

INSPECTION

Inspect the gear teeth for scores, nicks, etc. Note the condition of the teeth contact pattern. If the teeth are scored, replace the gears.

On a 240 Six engine, it is not necessary to replace the gears in sets. Replace the camshaft gear and check the backlash, runout, etc., to determine if the crankshaft gear should be replaced.

CAMSHAFT

CLEANING AND INSPECTION

Clean the camshaft in solvent and wipe it dry. Inspect the camshaft lobes for scoring and signs of abnormal wear. Lobe wear characteristics may result in pitting in the general area of the lobe toe. This pitting is not detrimental to the operation of the camshaft; therefore, the camshaft should not be replaced until the lobe lift loss has exceeded 0.005 inch.

The lift of the camshaft lobes can be checked with the camshaft installed in the engine or on centers. Refer to Camshaft Lobe Lift.

Check the distributor drive gear for broken or chipped teeth.

CRANKSHAFT VIBRATION DAMPER AND SLEEVE

CLEANING

Clean the oil seal contact surface on the crankshaft damper or sleeve with solvent to remove any corrosion, sludge or varnish deposits. Excess deposits that are not readily removed with solvent may be removed with crocus cloth. Use crocus cloth to remove any sharp edges, burrs or other imperfections which might damage the oil seal during installation or cause premature seal wear. **Do not use crocus cloth to the extent that the seal surface becomes polished. A finely polished surface may produce poor sealing or cause premature seal wear.**

INSPECTION

Inspect the crankshaft damper or sleeve oil seal surface for nicks, sharp edges or burrs that might damage the oil seal during installation or cause premature seal wear.

CRANKSHAFT

CLEANING

Handle the crankshaft with care to avoid possible fractures or damage to the finished surfaces. Clean the crankshaft with solvent, then blow out all oil passages with compressed air.

On a 240 Six engine, clean the oil seal contact surface at the rear of the crankshaft with solvent to remove any corrosion, sludge or varnish deposits. Excess deposits that are not readily removed with solvent may be removed with crocus cloth. Use crocus cloth to remove any sharp edges, burrs or other imperfections which might damage the oil seal during installation or cause premature seal wear. **Do not use crocus cloth to the extent that the seal surface becomes polished. A finely polished surface may produce poor sealing or cause premature seal wear.**

INSPECTION

Inspect the main and connecting rod journals for cracks, scratches, grooves or scores. Inspect the crankshaft oil seal surface for nicks, sharp edges or burrs that might damage the oil seal during installation or cause premature seal wear.

Measure the diameter of each journal in at least four places to determine an out-of-round, taper or undersize condition (Fig. 42).

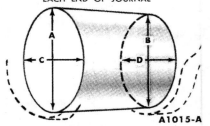

A VS B = VERTICAL TAPER
C VS D = HORIZONTAL TAPER
A VS C AND B VS D = OUT-OF-ROUND
CHECK FOR OUT-OF-ROUND AT EACH END OF JOURNAL

A1015-A

FIG. 42—Crankshaft Journal Measurement

On engines used with a manual-shift transmission, check the fit of the clutch pilot bushing in the bore of the crankshaft. The bushing is pressed into the crankshaft and should not be loose. Inspect the inner surface of the bushing for wear or a bell-mouth condition. Check the ID of the bushing (Fig. 43). Replace the bushing if it is worn or damaged or the ID is not within specifications.

Inspect the pilot bearing, when used, for roughness, evidence of overheating or loss of lubricant. Replace it if any of these conditions are found.

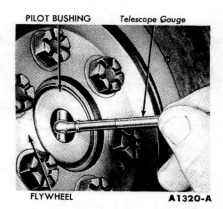

FIG. 43—Typical Clutch Pilot Bushing Wear Check

FLYWHEEL—MANUAL SHIFT TRANSMISSION

INSPECTION

Inspect the flywheel for cracks, heat check, or other defects that would make it unfit for further service. Machine the friction surface of the flywheel if it is scored or worn. If it is necessary to remove more than 0.045 inch of stock from the original thickness, replace the flywheel.

Inspect the ring gear for worn, chipped, or cracked teeth. If the teeth are damaged, replace the ring gear.

With the flywheel installed on the crankshaft, check the flywheel face runout, following the procedure in Section 1.

FLYWHEEL—AUTOMATIC TRANSMISSIONS

INSPECTION

Inspect the flywheel for cracks or other defects that would make it unfit for further service. Inspect the starter ring gear for worn, chipped or cracked teeth. If the teeth are damaged, replace the ring gear and flywheel assembly.

With the flywheel installed on the crankshaft, check the gear face runout and outside diameter runout of the flywheel (refer to Section 1 for the proper procedure).

CONNECTING RODS

CLEANING

Remove the bearings from the rod and cap. Identify the bearings if they are to be used again. Clean the connecting rod in solvent, including the rod bore and the back of the inserts. **Do not use a caustic clean-**ing solution. Blow out all passages with compressed air.

INSPECTION

The connecting rods and related parts should be carefully inspected and checked for conformance to specifications. Various forms of engine wear caused by these parts can be readily identified.

A shiny surface on the pin boss side of the piston usually indicates that a connecting rod is bent or the piston pin hole is not in proper relation to the piston skirt and ring grooves.

Abnormal connecting rod bearing wear can be caused by either a bent connecting rod, an improperly machined crankpin, or a tapered connecting rod bore.

Twisted connecting rods will not create an easily identifiable wear pattern, but badly twisted rods will disturb the action of the entire piston, rings and connecting rod assembly and may be the cause of excessive oil consumption.

Inspect the connecting rods for signs of fractures and the bearing bores for out-of-round and taper. If the bore exceeds the recommended limits and/or if the connecting rod is fractured, it should be replaced.

Check the piston pin to connecting rod bushing clearance. Replace the connecting rod if the bushing is so worn that it cannot be reamed or honed for an oversize pin.

On the 240 Six or the 289 V-8, check the I.D. of the connecting rod piston pin bore. Replace the connecting rod if the pin bore is not within specifications.

Replace defective connecting rod nuts and bolts.

Check the connecting rods for bend or twist on a suitable alignment fixture. Follow the instructions of the fixture manufacturer. If the bend and/or twist exceeds specifications, the connecting rod must be straightened or replaced.

PISTONS, PINS AND RINGS

CLEANING

Remove deposits from the piston surfaces. Clean gum or varnish from the piston skirt, piston pins and rings with solvent. **Do not use a caustic cleaning solution or a wire brush to clean pistons.** Clean the ring grooves with a ring groove cleaner (Fig. 44). Make sure the oil ring slots (or holes) are clean.

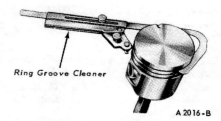

FIG. 44—Cleaning Piston Ring Grooves

INSPECTION

Carefully inspect the pistons for fractures at the ring lands, skirts and pin bosses, and for scuffed, rough or scored skirts. If the lower inner portion of the ring grooves has a high step, replace the piston. The step will interfere with ring operation and cause excessive ring side clearance.

Spongy, eroded areas near the edge of the top of the piston are usually caused by detonation or pre-ignition. A shiny surface on the thrust surface of the piston, offset from the centerline between the piston pin holes, can be caused by a bent connecting rod. Replace pistons that show signs of excessive wear, wavy ring lands or fractures or damage from detonation or pre-ignition.

Check the piston to cylinder bore clearance by measuring the piston and bore diameters. Refer to the specifications for the proper clearance. Refer to Cylinder Block Inspection for the bore measurement procedure. **Measure the O.D. of the piston with micrometers at the centerline of the piston pin bore and at 90° to the pin bore axis.** Check the ring side clearance following the procedure under Fitting Piston Rings in this section.

Replace piston pins showing signs of fracture, etching or wear. Check the piston pin fit in the piston and rod. Refer to Pistons and Connecting Rods Assembly, in the pertinent engine section.

Check the O.D. of the piston pin and the I.D. of the pin bore in the piston. Replace any piston pin or piston that is not within specifications.

Replace all rings that are scored, chipped or cracked. Check the end gap and side clearance. It is good practice to always install new rings when overhauling an engine. **Rings should not be transferred from one piston to another regardless of mileage.**

MAIN AND CONNECTING ROD BEARINGS

CLEANING

Clean the bearing inserts and caps thoroughly in solvent, and dry them with compressed air. **Do not scrape gum or varnish deposits from the bearing shells.**

INSPECTION

Inspect each bearing carefully. Bearings that have a scored, chipped, or worn surface should be replaced. Typical examples of bearing failures and their causes are shown in Fig. 45. The copper lead bearing base

clean out all the passages. Blow out all passages, bolt holes, etc., with compressed air. **On the 352, 390, 410, 427 and 428 V-8, be sure the jiggle pin in the main oil gallery front plug operates freely.**

On a 427 V-8, remove the hex-socket pipe plug and oil pressure relief valve at the rear of the main oil gallery. **Clean the relief valve and spring and install—the pipe plug must be flush to 0.020 inch below the face of the block.**

Make sure the threads in the cylinder head bolt holes are clean. Dirt in the threads may cause binding and

Replace all expansion-type plugs that show evidence of leakage.

Inspect the cylinder walls for scoring, roughness, or other signs of wear. Check the cylinder bore for out-of-round and taper. Measure the bore with an accurate bore gauge following the instructions of the manufacturer. Measure the diameter of each cylinder bore at the top, middle and bottom with the gauge placed at right angles and parallel to the centerline of the engine (Fig. 46).

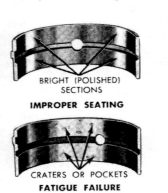

FIG. 45—Typical Bearing Failures

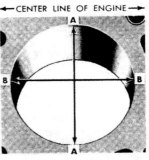

1. OUT-OF-ROUND = DIFFERENCE BETWEEN A AND B
2. TAPER = DIFFERENCE BETWEEN THE A MEASUREMENT AT TOP OF CYLINDER BORE AND THE A MEASUREMENT AT BOTTOM OF CYLINDER BORE

A1025-A

FIG. 46—Cylinder Bore Out-of-Round and Taper

may be visible through the bearing overlay. This does not mean that the bearing is worn. It is not necessary to replace the bearing if the bearing clearance is within recommended limits. Check the clearance of bearings that appear to be satisfactory with Plastigage. Fit new bearings following the recommended procedure in the pertinent part of Group 8.

CYLINDER BLOCK

CLEANING

After any cylinder bore repair operation, such as honing or deglazing, clean the bore(s) with soap or detergent and water. **Then, thoroughly rinse the bore(s) with clean water to remove the soap or detergent, and wipe the bore(s) dry with a clean, lint-free cloth. Finally wipe the bore(s) with a clean cloth dipped in engine oil. If these procedures are not followed rusting of the cylinder bore(s) may occur.**

If the engine is disassembled, thoroughly clean the block in solvent. Remove old gasket material from all machined surfaces. Remove all pipe plugs that seal oil passages; then

result in a false torque reading. Use a tap to true-up threads and to remove any deposits.

INSPECTION

After the block has been thoroughly cleaned, check it for cracks. Minute cracks not visible to the naked eye may be detected by coating the suspected area with a mixture of 25% kerosene and 75% light engine oil. Wipe the part dry and immediately apply a coating of zinc oxide dissolved in wood alcohol. If cracks are present, the coating will become discolored at the defective area. Replace the block if it is cracked.

Check all machined gasket surfaces for burrs, nicks, scratches and scores. Remove minor imperfections with an oil stone. Check the cylinder block for flatness of the cylinder head gasket surface following the procedure and specifications recommended for the cylinder head. The cylinder block can be machined to bring the cylinder head gasket surface within the flatness specifications, **but not to exceed 0.010 inch stock removal.**

Use only the measurements obtained at 90° to the engine centerline when calculating the piston to cylinder bore clearance.

Refinish cylinders that are deeply scored and/or when out-of-round and/or taper exceed the wear limits.

If the cylinder walls have minor surface imperfections, but the out-of-round and taper are within limits, it may be possible to remove the imperfections by honing the cylinder walls and installing new service piston rings providing the piston clearance is within specified limits. Use the finest grade of honing stone for this operation.

OIL PAN

CLEANING

Scrape any dirt or metal particles from the inside of the pan. Scrape all old gasket material from the gasket surface. Wash the pan in a solvent and dry it thoroughly. Be sure all foreign particles are removed from below the baffle plate.

INSPECTION

Check the pan for cracks, holes, damaged drain plug threads, and a loose baffle or a damaged gasket surface.

Repair any damage, or replace the pan if repairs cannot be made.

OIL PUMP

CLEANING

Wash all parts in a solvent and dry them thoroughly with compressed air. Use a brush to clean the inside of the pump housing and the pressure relief valve chamber. Be sure all dirt and metal particles are removed.

INSPECTION

Refer to the specifications for clearances and wear limits.

Check the inside of the pump

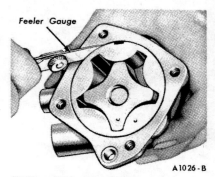

FIG. 47—Outer Race to Housing Clearance

housing and the outer race and rotor for damage or excessive wear.

Check the mating surface of the pump cover for wear. If the cover mating surface is worn, scored or grooved, replace the cover.

Measure the outer race to housing clearance (Fig. 47).

With the rotor assembly installed in the housing, place a straight edge over the rotor assembly and the housing. Measure the clearance (rotor end play) between the straight edge and the rotor and outer race (Fig. 48).

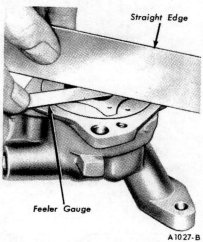

FIG. 48—Rotor End Play

The outer race, shaft and rotor are replaceable only as an assembly.

Check the drive shaft to housing

bearing clearance by measuring the OD of the shaft and the ID of the housing bearing.

Inspect the relief valve spring for a collapsed or worn condition. Check the relief valve spring tension. If the spring tension is not within specifications and/or the spring is defective, replace the spring.

Check the relief valve piston for scores and free operation in the bore.

POSITIVE CRANKCASE VENTILATION SYSTEM

Refer to Group 19 for the correct mileage interval for maintenance.

CLEANING

Do not attempt to clean the crankcase ventilation regulator valve.

The oil filler tube breather cap, located on the valve rocker arm cover should be cleaned at the proper mileage interval. Remove the cap and wash it in a low volatility, petroleum-base solvent. On open crankcase ventilation systems, probe the breather hole(s) to assure removal of any accumulated deposits. Shake the cap dry and install it. **Do not dry with compressed air as air pressure may damage the filter element.**

Clean the crankcase ventilation system connection(s) on the carburetor spacer or intake manifold by probing the inlet nipple with a flexible wire or bottle brush.

Clean the rubber hoses with a low-volatility, petroleum-base solvent and dry with compressed air.

PART 8-2   240 SIX ENGINE

1 DESCRIPTION AND OPERATION

The 240 Six engines (Figs. 1, 2, and 3), have a displacement of 240 cubic inches and a compression ratio of 9.00:1. The warranty plate identification symbols for the engines are as follows: 240 Six—Symbol V; Police Special Six—Symbol B (standard carburetor) and Taxi Special Six—Symbol E (economy carburetion).

An engine identification tag is attached to the engine; refer to Part 8-1, Section 1.

THERMACTOR EXHAUST EMISSION CONTROL SYSTEM

For engines equipped with Thermactor exhaust emission control system, refer to Group 12 for description and adjustment and repair procedures.

MANIFOLDS

A chamber (heat riser) is cast into the intake manifold center section between the carburetor and exhaust manifold. A thermostatically controlled valve, located in the exhaust manifold (Fig. 4), directs exhaust gases into this area to provide the heat necessary to assist in vaporizing the incoming fuel mixture until the engine reaches normal operating temperature.

CYLINDER HEAD

The cylinder head carries the valves, individually mounted valve rocker arms, manifold assembly, ignition coil, coolant outlet housing and thermostat. Valve guides are cast integrally in the head. The valves are arranged from the front to rear E-I-E-I-E-I-E-I-E-I.

CYLINDER BLOCK

The cylinders are numbered from 1-6 starting at the front of the engine. The firing order is 1-5-3-6-2-4.

The distributor, located on the left side of the engine, drives the oil pump through an intermediate drive shaft.

The crankshaft is supported by seven main bearings. Crankshaft end thrust is controlled by the flanges of the No. 5 main bearing.

The pistons are of the autothermic, semi-dish type design. The pistons have two compression rings and one oil control ring. The top compression ring is chrome-plated and the lower compression ring is phosphate-coated. The oil control ring assembly consists of a serrated spring and two chrome-plated steel rails.

VALVE TRAIN

The intake and exhaust valve assemblies are the rotating type.

The camshaft is supported by four bearings pressed into the block. It is driven by a fiber timing gear (pressed onto the camshaft) in mesh with a gear on the crankshaft. Camshaft thrust is controlled by a thrust plate located between the camshaft gear and the front journal of the camshaft. An eccentric, made integral with the camshaft, operates the fuel pump. A gear is cast integrally with the camshaft to drive the distributor.

Hydraulic valve lifters are used in the engine. The valve lifters are housed in bores located in the cyl-

A2173-B

FIG. 1—Typical ¾ Right Front View

A2174-B

FIG. 2—Typical ¾ Left Rear View

inder block just below the valve push rod chamber. The valve lifters operate directly on the camshaft lobes, thereby transmitting the thrust of the camshaft lobes, by the means of hydraulic pressure, to the push rods which actuate the valve train. Figure 5 shows the various components and operation of a hydraulic lifter.

When either an exhaust valve or an intake valve is closed, the actuating valve lifter is on the base circle (lowest position) of the camshaft lobe.

When the valve lifter is in this position, the lifter plunger spring expands. This action forces the lifter plunger and valve push rod upward, forcing the valve end of the rocker arm to maintain solid contact with the valve (zero valve lash).

As the lifter plunger moves upward, the volume of the compression chamber is increased, resulting in reduced oil pressure in the compression chamber. Therefore, to equalize the resulting pressure differential between the supply chamber and the compression chamber, the disc valve moves off its seat and permits oil to flow from the supply chamber to the compression chamber. When the compression chamber becomes filled with oil, the pressures in the two chambers are equalized. The oil flow ceases and the disc valve spring seats the disc valve and closes the disc valve port.

As the camshaft rotates, the lifter assembly is raised by the camshaft lobe. This increases the push rod force against the lifter plunger and hydraulic pressure immediately builds up in the compression chamber until it acts as a solid member of the valve operating mechanism. The lifter then becomes a hydraulic ram which forces the valve in the cylinder head to open. During this period, a slight leakage of oil past the plunger occurs (calibrated leak down rate).

As the high point of the camshaft lobe rotates and passes by the foot of the valve lifter, the valve in the cylinder head seats and the valve lifter assembly is forced downward. Reduced force on the lifter plunger at this time relieves the pressure on the lifter plunger and it is free to be moved upward by the plunger spring. This action allows oil to flow once again through the oil holes in the lifter body and plunger.

The operating cycle is completed for each revolution of the camshaft. Zero clearance (lash) in the valve train mechanism is maintained at all

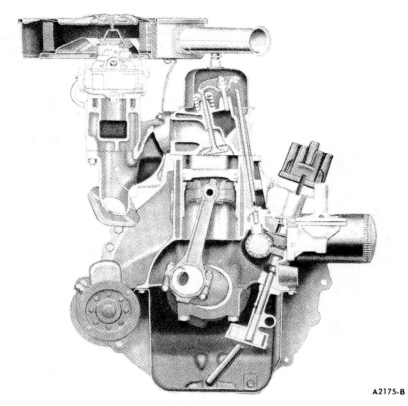

FIG. 3—Front Cross Section View

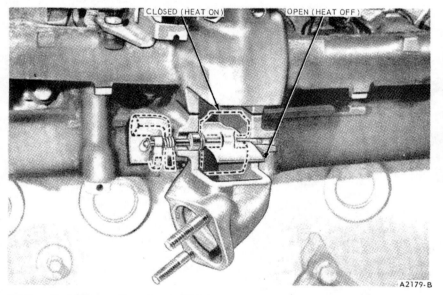

CLOSED (HEAT ON)   OPEN (HEAT OFF)

A2179-B

FIG. 4—Exhaust Gas Control Valve

times by the hydraulic force and expansion of the plunger spring between the lifter body and plunger.

LUBRICATION SYSTEM

Oil from the oil pan sump is forced through the pressure-type lubrication system (Fig. 6) by a rotor-type oil pump. A spring-loaded relief valve in the pump limits the maximum pressure of the system. Oil relieved by the valve is directed back to the intake side of the pump.

The engine has a full-flow Rotunda filter which filters the entire output of the pump before the oil enters the engine. The filter has an integral relief valve and mounting gasket. The relief valve permits oil to bypass the filter if it becomes clogged, thereby maintaining continual supply of oil to the engine at all times. An anti-drain back feature is designed into the Rotunda oil filter to prevent a reverse flow of oil when the engine is stopped.

From the filter, the oil flows into the main oil gallery. The oil gallery supplies oil to all the camshaft and main bearings through individual drilled passages in each main bearing web.

The timing gears are lubricated through a squirt hole in the front of the cylinder block. An oil slinger is installed on the front of the crankshaft to direct oil away from the front oil seal.

The crankshaft is drilled from the main bearings to the connecting rod journals to lubricate the rod bearings.

Oil, from the floor of the valve lifter chamber, is fed through a drilled passage in the cylinder block into the distributor pilot to lubricate the distributor shaft, bushings, and the distributor to oil pump intermediate shaft engagement.

The main oil gallery intersects all of the valve lifter bores supplying pressure oil to the hydraulic valve lifters. A reservoir at each valve lifter bore boss traps oil so that oil is available for valve lifter lubrication as soon as the engine starts.

When the hydraulic lifter is on the base circle of the camshaft lobe (valve closed), the oil hole in the hydraulic lifter is indexed with the oil gallery, and oil flows into the plunger.

Oil is also metered through the metering valve (disc) through the oil passages in the push rod cup and it flows up the hollow push rod. In this position, the drilled hole in the ball end of the push rod is indexed with a drilled hole in the rocker arm, and the oil lubricates the upper valve train bearing areas. Excess oil is returned to the oil pan through drain holes along the side of the cylinder head and block.

Excess oil in the push rod chamber drains back into the oil pan through openings along the cylinder block.

POSITIVE CRANKCASE VENTILATION SYSTEM

Ventilating air enters the crankcase through the oil filter (breather) cap at the front of the valve rocker arm cover (Fig. 7). On a closed crankcase ventilation system, the oil filler cap is sealed to prevent air entrance, but the top of the filler cap is connected to the engine air

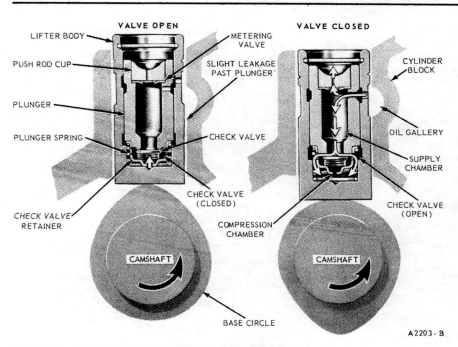

FIG. 5—Typical Hydraulic Valve Lifter Operation

cleaner by a hose to admit clean air to the crankcase. On a closed system, if the crankcase ventilation system becomes restricted, a backflow condition will occur, thereby venting the crankcase gases into the air cleaner and induction air system.

The air flow is metered by a restriction in the oil filler cap. A divider in the rocker arm cover diverts the air flow from the valve rocker arm chamber, through the push rod holes and into the push rod chamber. Air also flows between the crankcase and rocker arm chamber through the oil drain holes and push rod holes in

the cylinder head. Air flows to and from the cylinder front cover and crankcase through the front cover oil drain holes at the front of the cylinder block.

From the valve rocker arm cover, the ventilating air passes through the crankcase ventilation regulator valve at the rear of the rocker arm cover and into the intake manifold through a connecting hose and tube. The air, laden with crankcase vapors, is dispersed in the induction air and fuel mixture in the intake manifold before entering the cylinder combustion chambers.

A slight vacuum is maintained in the engine crankcase, due to a restriction (metering hole) in the oil filler cap and by the amount of air flow through the regulator valve. The amount of regulator valve opening or restriction is governed by intake manifold vacuum pressure (Fig. 8).

During idle, intake manifold vacuum is high. The high vacuum overcomes the spring pressure and moves the valve to the Low Speed Operation position (Fig. 8). With the valve in this low-flow position, the ventilating air passes between the valve (jiggle pin) and the outlet port. In this position there is minimum

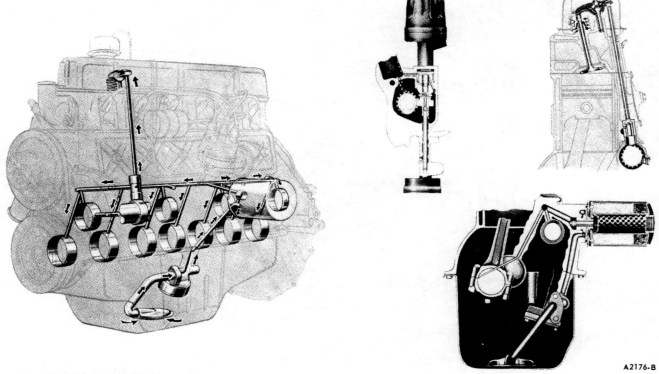

FIG. 6—Lubrication System

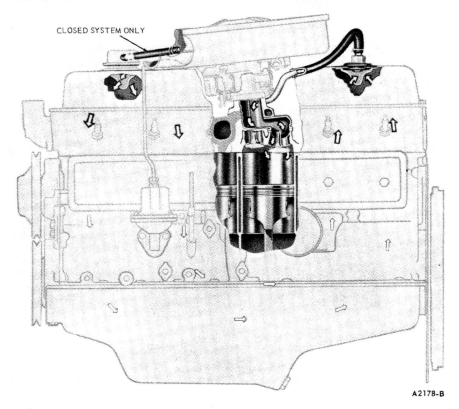

FIG. 7—Positive Crankcase Ventilation System

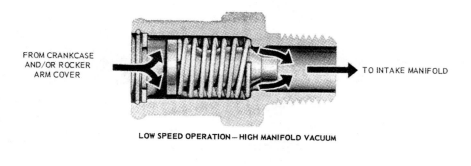

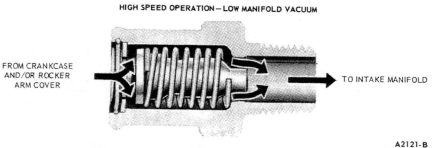

FIG. 8—Positive Crankcase Ventilation Regulator Valve Operation

ventilation, but it never completely seals off the air flow.

As engine speed increases and manifold vacuum decreases, the valve spring forces the valve to the full open position (Fig. 8). This increases the flow of ventilating air.

COOLING SYSTEM

The coolant is drawn from the bottom of the radiator by the water pump, which delivers the coolant to the cylinder block (Fig. 9).

As the coolant enters the block, it travels through cored passages to cool the entire length of each cylinder wall. Upon reaching the rear of the cylinder block, the coolant is directed upward into the cylinder head where it cools the combustion chambers, valves and valve seats on its return to the front of the engine.

The coolant from the cylinder head flows into the coolant outlet housing, past the thermostat if it is open, and into the top of the radiator. If the thermostat is closed, a small portion of the coolant is returned to the water pump for recirulation. The entire system is pressurized to 13-15 psi.

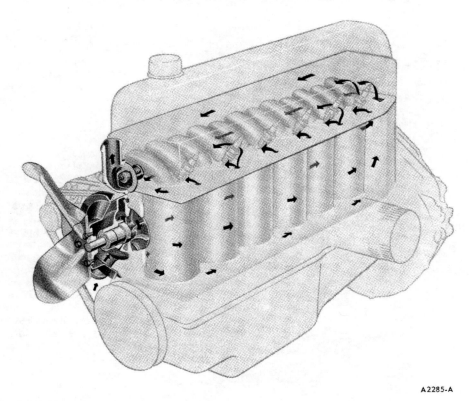

FIG. 9—Engine Coolant Flow

2 IN-CAR ADJUSTMENTS AND REPAIRS

When installing nuts or bolts that must be torqued (refer to Part 8-5 for torque specifications), oil the threads with light weight engine oil. **Do not oil threads that require oil-resistant or water-resistant sealer.**

For adjustment and repair procedures of all components of the Thermactor exhaust emission control system (if so equipped), refer to Group 12.

ENGINE SUPPORTS

The front supports are located on each side of the cylinder block (Fig. 10). The rear support is located at the transmission extension housing (Fig. 10).

FRONT SUPPORT INSULATOR

Removal

1. Raise the hood. Then raise the car with a hoist.
2. Loosen the nuts retaining the insulator assemblies to the intermediate support brackets.
3. Position a transmission jack under the oil pan and raise the engine sufficiently to remove its weight from the supports.

4. Remove the insulator assembly(ies) to engine bolts and lock washers. Remove the insulator to intermediate support bracket nut(s). Remove the insulator(s).

Installation

1. Install the insulator assembly(ies) on the intermediate support bracket(s). Install the nut, but do not tighten it.
2. Position the insulator(s) and install the bolts and lock washers securing the insulator assembly(ies) to the engine. Torque the bolts to specifications.
3. Lower the engine and remove the jack. Torque the insulator to intermediate support bracket nut(s) to specifications.

ENGINE REAR SUPPORT

Removal

1. Remove the insulator assembly to cross member retaining bolt and nut.
2. Raise the transmission with a jack to obtain clearance at the trans-

mission extension housing. Then remove the retainer and insulator assembly mounting bolts and washers. Remove the insulator assembly and the retainer.

Installation

1. Position the insulator assembly and retainer; then install the mounting bolts and lock washers. Torque the bolts to specifications.
2. Lower the transmission. Install the insulator assembly to cross member retaining bolt and nut. Torque the nut to specifications.

MANIFOLDS

REMOVAL

1. Remove the air cleaner and support bracket. Remove the accelerator retracting spring and disconnect the accelerator cable from the carburetor. Remove the accelerator cable bracket from the cylinder head and position the cable assembly out of the way.

On a car with an automatic transmission, remove the kickdown rod retracting spring. Remove the bell-

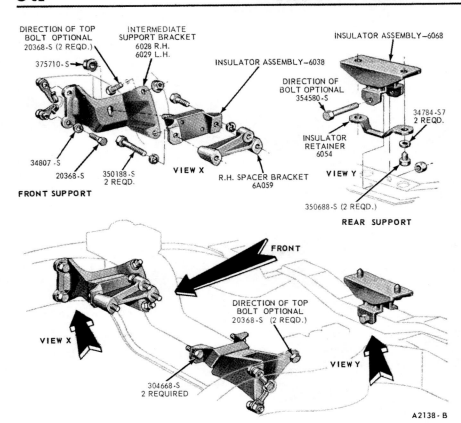

DIRECTION OF TOP BOLT OPTIONAL 20368-S (2 REQD.)
375710-S
34807-S
20368-S
350188-S 2 REQD.
INTERMEDIATE SUPPORT BRACKET 6028 R.H. 6029 L.H.
INSULATOR ASSEMBLY—6038
VIEW X
R.H. SPACER BRACKET 6A059
FRONT SUPPORT

INSULATOR ASSEMBLY—6068
DIRECTION OF BOLT OPTIONAL 354580-S
INSULATOR RETAINER 6054
34784-S7 2 REQD.
VIEW Y
350688-S (2 REQD.)
REAR SUPPORT

FRONT
DIRECTION OF TOP BOLT OPTIONAL 20368-S (2 REQD.)
VIEW X
304668-S 2 REQUIRED
VIEW Y
A2138-B

FIG. 10—Engine Supports

crank assembly from the engine.

2. If equipped with Thermactor exhaust emission control system, remove the air tube and vacuum hose from the anti-backfire valve and intake manifold. Disconnect the air pump outlet hoses at the air manifold and at the anti-backfire valve.

3. Loosen the hose clamp and remove the crankcase vent hose from the inlet tube in the intake manifold.

4. Disconnect the fuel inlet line and the distributor vacuum line from the carburetor.

Disconnect the power brake vacuum line, if so equipped.

5. Disconnect the muffler inlet pipe from the exhaust manifold.

6. Remove the bolts and nuts fastening the manifolds to the cylinder head. Lift the manifold assemblies from the head. Remove the gaskets.

7. To separate the manifolds, remove the carburetor. Remove the nuts joining the intake and exhaust manifolds. Discard the gaskets between the manifolds.

CLEANING AND INSPECTION

Refer to Part 8-1, Section 3 for the cleaning and inspection procedures.

REPAIR

If the exhaust gas control valve requires replacement, install a new valve, following the procedures in Part 8-1, Section 2.

INSTALLATION

1. Clean the joining surfaces of the cylinder head and manifolds.

2. If one of the manifolds is to be replaced, remove the tube fittings from the discarded manifold, and install in the new manifold as required. Install new studs as necessary. If the intake and exhaust manifolds have been separated, position a new gasket on the intake manifold and place the exhaust manifold over the studs on the intake manifold. Install the lock washers and nuts; then tighten them finger-tight. Install the carburetor.

3. Install a new intake manifold gasket.

4. Place a new exhaust manifold to muffler inlet pipe gasket on the muffler inlet pipe.

5. Coat the mating surfaces lightly with graphite grease. Place the manifold assemblies in position against the cylinder head. **Make sure that the gaskets have not become dislodged.** Install the attaching wash-

ers, bolts and nuts. Torque the bolts and nuts to specifications in the sequence shown in Fig. 11.

If the intake and exhaust manifolds were separated, tighten the nuts joining them.

6. Install the exhaust manifold to muffler inlet pipe lock washers and nuts. Torque the nuts to specifications.

7. Connect the crankcase vent hose to the intake manifold inlet tube, and position the hose clamp.

8. Connect the fuel inlet line and the distributor vacuum line to the carburetor. Connect the power brake vacuum line, if so equipped.

9. If equipped with Thermactor exhaust emission control system, connect the air pump to air cleaner hose at the pump. Connect the air pump outlet hoses at the anti-backfire valve and air manifold. Position the anti-backfire valve air tube and vacuum hose, and connect them to the valve and intake manifold.

10. Install the accelerator cable bracket on the cylinder head. Connect the accelerator cable to the carburetor and install the retracting spring.

On a car with an automatic transmission, install the bellcrank assembly and kickdown rod retracting spring. Adjust the transmission control linkage.

11. Install the air cleaner and support bracket. Adjust the engine idle speed and idle fuel mixture.

POSITIVE CRANKCASE VENTILATION SYSTEM

The positive crankcase ventilation system components are shown in Fig. 12.

REMOVAL

1. Remove the air cleaner.

2. Grasp the crankcase ventilation regulator valve and pull upwards to remove it from the rocker arm cover.

3. Using hose clamp pliers, slide both hose clamps toward the center of the vent hose. Remove the regulator valve from the vent hose and remove the vent hose from the inlet tube in the intake manifold.

4. Remove the inlet tube from the intake manifold, and disconnect it from the anti-backfire valve (if so equipped).

CLEANING AND INSPECTION

Refer to Part 8-1, Section 3 for the cleaning and inspection procedures.

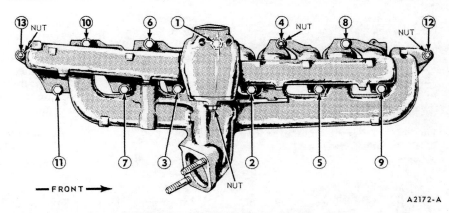

FIG. 11—Intake and Exhaust Manifold Torque Sequence

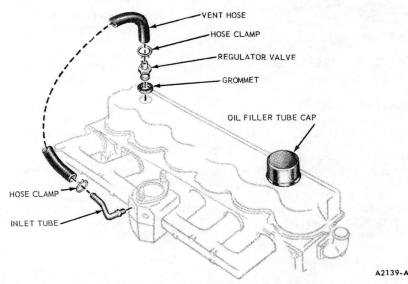

FIG. 12—Positive Crankcase Ventilation System Components

INSTALLATION

1. Install the inlet tube in the intake manifold, and connect it to the anti-backfire valve (if so equipped).

2. Position the hose clamps on the vent hose. Install the hose on the inlet tube in the intake manifold. Install the regulator valve in the hose. Using hose clamp pliers, slide the clamps into position.

3. Insert the regulator valve into the rocker arm cover mounting grommet.

4. Install the air cleaner. Operate the engine and check for leaks.

VALVE ROCKER ARM ASSEMBLY

The valve rocker arm assembly is shown in Fig. 13.

REMOVAL

1. Disconnect the clean air tube at the oil fill cap, if equipped with closed crankcase ventilation system.

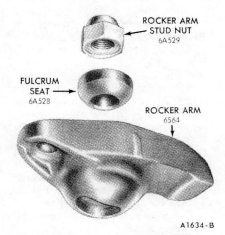

FIG. 13—Valve Rocker Arm Assembly

Remove the air cleaner. Remove the distributor vacuum line and carburetor fuel line.

2. Disconnect the accelerator ca-ble at the carburetor. Remove the cable retracting spring. Remove the accelerator cable bracket from the cylinder head and position the cable and bracket assembly out of the way.

3. If equipped with a Thermactor exhaust emission control system, disconnect the air hoses as necessary for accessibility and position them out of the way.

4. Remove the crankcase ventilation regulator valve from the valve rocker arm cover. Remove the valve rocker arm cover.

5. Remove the valve rocker arm stud nut, fulcrum seat and rocker arm.

CLEANING AND INSPECTION

Refer to Part 8-1, Section 3 for the cleaning and inspection procedures. Inspect the rocker arm cover bolts for defective seals under the bolt heads and replace as required.

REPAIRS

If removal of the rocker arm stud is necessary, refer to the procedure under Cylinder Head Repairs in Part 8-1, Section 2.

INSTALLATION

1. Apply Lubriplate to the top of the valve stem and at the push rod guide in the cylinder head.

2. Install the valve rocker arm, fulcrum seat and stud nut. Adjust the valve clearance following the procedure in Part 8-1, Section 2.

3. Clean the valve rocker arm cover and the cylinder head gasket surface. Apply oil-resistant sealer to one side of a new cover gasket. Lay the cemented side of the gasket in place in the cover. **Be sure the gasket is seated properly around the extruded bolt holes.**

4. Install the cover on the cylinder head. Make sure the gasket seats evenly all around the head. Partially tighten the cover bolts in sequence, starting at the middle bolts. Then torque the bolts to specifications in the same sequence.

5. Install the accelerator cable bracket on the cylinder head. Connect the accelerator cable to the carburetor. Install the cable retracting spring. Install the distributor vacuum line and carburetor fuel line.

6. Install the crankcase ventilation regulator valve in the valve rocker arm cover. If equipped with a Thermactor exhaust emission control system, connect the air hoses.

7. Install the air cleaner. Connect

the clean air tube at the oil fill cap, if so equipped.

CYLINDER HEAD

REMOVAL

If the cylinder head is to be replaced, follow the procedures under Cylinder Head Disassembly and Assembly, and transfer all valves, springs, seals, spark plugs, etc., to the new cylinder head. Clean and inspect all parts, reface the valves and check valve guide clearances (refer to Part 8-1) before assembling the used parts to the new cylinder head.

1. Drain the cooling system. Remove the air cleaner.

2. Disconnect the radiator upper hose and the heater hose from the coolant outlet housing.

3. Disconnect the coolant temperature sending unit wire from the sending unit.

4. Disconnect and remove the carburetor fuel inlet line and the distributor vacuum line.

5. Remove the accelerator cable retracting spring. Disconnect the accelerator cable from the carburetor. Remove the accelerator cable housing bracket from the cylinder head and position the cable and bracket assembly out of the way.

On a car with an automatic transmission, disconnect the kickdown rod at the bellcrank assembly.

6. Grasp the crankcase ventilation regulator valve and pull it from the rocker arm cover. Disconnect the crankcase vent hose from the inlet tube in the intake manifold, and remove the vent hose and regulator valve.

On a car equipped with Thermactor exhaust emission control system, disconnect the air pump outlet hose at the air manifold assembly. Unscrew the tube nuts and remove the air manifold assembly. Disconnect the anti-backfire valve air and vacuum lines at the intake manifold.

7. On a car with power brakes, disconnect the power brake vacuum line at the intake manifold.

8. Remove the valve rocker arm cover. Loosen the rocker arm stud nuts so that the rocker arms can be rotated to one side.

9. Remove the valve push rods in sequence and identify them so that they can be installed in their original position.

10. Disconnect the spark plug wires at the spark plugs.

11. Disconnect the muffler inlet

pipe from the exhaust manifold. Discard the inlet pipe gasket.

12. Remove the cylinder head bolts. Install the cylinder head lifting eyes in the locations shown in Fig. 14. Attach a hoist and lifting sling to the lifting eyes, and lift the cylinder head and intake and exhaust manifolds assembly off the engine. **Do not pry between the head and block as the gasket surfaces may become damaged.**

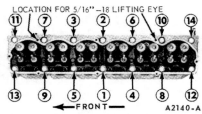

FIG. 14—Cylinder Head Torque Sequence

INSTALLATION

1. Clean the cylinder head and cylinder block gasket surfaces. Clean the exhaust manifold and muffler inlet pipe gasket surfaces.

2. If the cylinder head was removed for a cylinder head gasket replacement, check the flatness of the head and block gasket surfaces (Part 8-1, Section 3).

3. Position the gasket over the dowel pins on the cylinder block.

4. Install lifting eyes on the cylinder head in the locations shown in Fig. 14, and use a hoist and lifting sling to lift the cylinder head over the cylinder block. Lower it carefully until it is properly positioned on the block and dowel pins. Remove the hoist and lifting eyes.

5. Coat the threads of the cylinder head bolts with engine oil. Install the bolts.

6. The cylinder head bolts are tightened in three progressive steps. Follow the sequence shown in Fig. 14. Torque the bolts to 50-55 ft-lbs, then to 60-65 ft-lbs. Finally, torque the bolts to specifications.

7. Position a new gasket on the muffler inlet pipe and connect the inlet pipe to the exhaust manifold. Torque the nuts to specifications.

8. Apply Lubriplate to both ends of the push rods. Install the push rods in their original bores, positioning the lower end of the rods in the valve lifter sockets.

9. Position the rocker arms and tighten the stud nuts just enough to hold the push rods in position. Adjust the valve lash, following the

procedure in Part 8-1, Section 2.

10. Clean the valve rocker arm cover. Coat one side of a new valve rocker arm cover gasket with oil-resistant sealer. Lay the cemented side of the gasket in place in the cover. Install the cover, making sure that the gasket seats evenly around the cylinder head.

Torque the cover bolts to specifications.

11. On a car with power brakes, connect the brake vacuum line to the intake manifold.

12. Connect the spark plug wires to the spark plugs.

13. Connect the crankcase vent hose to the inlet tube in the intake manifold. Install the crankcase ventilation regulator valve in the valve rocker arm cover.

On a car with Thermactor exhaust emission control system, install the air manifold assembly on the cylinder head. Connect the air pump outlet hose to the air manifold. Connect the anti-backfire valve air and vacuum lines to the intake manifold.

14. Position the fuel inlet line and the distributor vacuum line on the engine. Connect the distributor vacuum line to the distributor and carburetor. Connect the carburetor fuel inlet line to the carburetor and the fuel pump.

15. Install the accelerator cable bracket on the cylinder head. Connect the accelerator cable and install the accelerator cable retracting spring.

On a car with an automatic transmission, connect the kickdown rod to the bellcrank assembly.

16. Connect the coolant temperature sending unit wire.

17. Connect the radiator upper hose to the coolant outlet housing. Connect the heater hose to the coolant outlet housing, but do not tighten the clamp.

18. Fill and bleed the cooling system; then tighten the heater hose clamp.

19. Operate the engine until engine temperatures have stabilized. Adjust the engine idle speed and idle fuel mixture. Check for fuel, oil and coolant leaks.

On a car with an automatic transmission, adjust the transmission control linkage.

20. Install the air cleaner.

DISASSEMBLY

1. Remove the coolant outlet

housing and thermostat. Discard the gasket.

2. Remove the coolant temperature sending unit from the cylinder head.

3. Remove the intake manifold, exhaust manifold and carburetor assembly from the cylinder head. Discard the gasket.

4. Remove the spark plugs.

5. Remove the deposits from the combustion chambers and valve heads with a scraper and a wire brush before removing the valves. *Be careful not to scratch the cylinder head gasket surface.*

6. Compress the valve springs (Fig. 15); then remove the valve spring retainer locks and release the spring.

FIG. 15—Compressing Valve Spring On Bench—Typical

7. Remove the spring retainer, spring, stem seal and valve (Fig. 16). Discard the valve stem seals. Identify all valve parts.

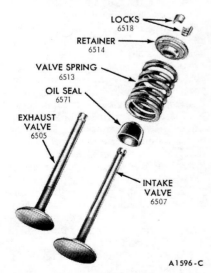

FIG. 16—Valve Assembly—Typical

CLEANING AND INSPECTION

Refer to Part 8-1, Section 3 for the cleaning and inspection procedures.

REPAIRS

Cylinder head repair operations and checks, such as valve and valve seat refacing, cylinder head flatness checks, etc., are covered in Part 8-1, Section 2.

ASSEMBLY

1. Lubricate the valve guides and valve stems with engine oil. Apply Lubriplate to the tip of the valve stems.

2. Install each valve (Fig. 16) in the valve guide from which it was removed or to which it was fitted. Install a new stem seal on the valve.

3. Install the valve spring over the valve. **Be sure the closed coil end is placed against the cylinder head.** Install the spring retainer.

4. Compress the spring and install the retainer locks (Fig. 15).

5. Measure the assembled height of the valve spring from the surface of the cylinder head spring pad to the underside of the spring retainer with dividers (Fig. 17).

FIG. 17—Valve Spring Assembled Height—Typical

Check the dividers against a scale. If the assembled height is greater than the specified limit, install the necessary 0.030-inch thick spacer(s) between the cylinder head spring pad and the valve spring to bring the assembled height to the recommended dimension. **Do not install spacers unless necessary.** Use of spacers in excess of recommendations will result in overstressing the valve springs and overloading the camshaft lobes which could lead to

spring breakage and worn camshaft lobes.

6. Position a new intake manifold gasket on the cylinder head. Install the intake manifold, exhaust manifold and carburetor assembly. Torque the manifold bolts and nuts in sequence (Fig. 11) to specifications.

7. Install the temperature sending unit. Install the spark plugs.

8. Using a new outlet elbow gasket coated with water-resistant sealer, install the thermostat and coolant outlet elbow. Torque the retaining bolts to specifications.

VALVE SPRING, RETAINER AND STEM SEAL REPLACEMENT

Broken valve springs, or defective valve stem seals and retainers may be replaced without removing the cylinder head, provided damage to the valve or valve seat has not occurred.

1. Remove the air cleaner. Remove the distributor vacuum line and carburetor fuel line.

2. Remove the accelerator cable retracting spring. Disconnect the accelerator cable at the carburetor. Remove the accelerator cable housing bracket from the cylinder head and position the accelerator cable assembly out of the way.

3. If equipped with a Thermactor exhaust emission control system, disconnect the air hoses as necessary for accessibility and position them out of the way.

4. Remove the crankcase ventilation regulator valve from the valve rocker arm cover and remove the valve rocker arm cover. Remove the applicable spark plug.

5. Remove the valve rocker arm stud nut, fulcrum seat, valve rocker arm and push rod for both valves of the cylinder being serviced.

6. Install an air line adapter in the spark plug hole (Fig. 18) and connect the air line.

7. Install the stud nut and position the compressor tool as shown in Fig. 18. Compress the valve spring and remove tre retainer locks, spring retainer and valve spring. Remove and discard the valve stem seal (Fig. 19).

If air pressure fails to hold the valve in the closed position during this operation, it can be presumed that the valve is not seating or is damaged. If this condition occurs, remove the cylinder head for further inspection.

Tool—T62F-6565-A
(6513-HH)

Air Line Adapter
Tool—6513-ABA
or 6513-AB

ROCKER ARM STUD NUT

FULCRUM SEAT

A2141-A

FIG. 18—Compressing Valve Spring—In-Chassis

Tool—6513-ABA
or 6513-AB

OIL SEAL

A2142-A

FIG. 19—Valve Stem Seal Removal or Installation

8. If air pressure has forced the piston to the bottom of the cylinder any removal of air pressure will allow the valve(s) to fall into the cylinder. A rubber band, tape or string wrapped around the end of the valve stem will prevent this condition and will still allow enough travel to check the valve for binds.

9. Inspect the valve stem for damage. Rotate the valve and check the valve stem tip for eccentric movement during rotation. Move the valve up and down through normal travel in the valve guide and check the stem for binds. **If the valve has been damaged, it will be necessary to remove the cylinder head for repairs as outlined in Part 8-1, Section 2.**

10. If the condition of the valve proved satisfactory, hold the valve in the closed position and apply the air pressure within the cylinder.

11. Install a new valve stem seal (Fig. 19). Place the spring in position over the valve; **be sure the closed coil end is next to the cyl-**

inder head. Install the valve spring retainer. Compress the valve spring and install the valve spring retainer locks. Remove the compressor tool and stud nut. Turn off the air and remove the air line and adapter.

12. Apply Lubriplate to both ends of the push rod. Install the push rod. Apply Lubriplate to the tip of the valve stem and at the push rod guide in the cylinder head.

13. Install the valve rocker arm, fulcrum seat and stud nut. Adjust the valve clearance following the procedure in Part 8-1, Section 2.

14. Install the spark plug and connect the spark plug wire.

15. Clean the valve rocker arm cover. Coat one side of a new gasket with oil-resistant sealer. Position the gasket on the rocker arm cover; **be sure the cemented side is towards the cover.** Install the cover, making sure that the gasket seats evenly around the cylinder head. Torque the cover bolts in sequence to specifications.

16. Install the accelerator cable housing bracket on the cylinder head. Connect the accelerator cable to the carburetor. Install the accelerator cable retracting spring. Install the distributor vacuum line and carburetor fuel line.

17. If equipped with a Thermactor exhaust emission control system, connect the air hoses.

18. Install the crankcase ventilation regulator valve in the valve rocker arm cover. Install the air cleaner.

CYLINDER FRONT COVER

REMOVAL

1. Drain the cooling system.

On a car with an automatic transmission, disconnect the transmission oil cooler lines from the radiator.

2. Disconnect the radiator upper hose from the coolant outlet housing and the radiator lower hose at the water pump. Remove the radiator.

On a car with air conditioning, remove the condenser retaining bolts, and position the condenser to one side for accessibility. **Do not disconnect the condenser refrigerant lines.** Remove the compressor drive belt.

On a car with Thermactor exhaust emission control system, remove the air supply pump drive belt.

3. On a car with power steering, loosen the nut retaining the power steering pump to the pump rear mounting bracket. Remove two bolts

retaining the pump front mounting bracket to the cylinder front cover. Remove the power steering pump drive belt. Position the power steering pump and mounting bracket out of the way.

4. Remove the cooling fan and alternator drive belts. Remove the alternator adjusting arm bolt, and swing the adjusting arm out of the way. Remove the fan, spacer and pulley.

5. Remove the accessory drive pulley (if so equipped) from the crankshaft damper. Remove the cap screw and washer from the end of the crankshaft; then remove the damper (Fig. 20).

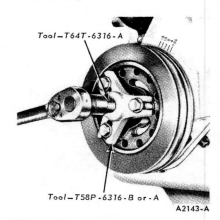

Tool—T64T-6316-A

Tool—T58P-6316-B or -A

A2143-A

FIG. 20—Crankshaft Damper Removal—Typical

6. Remove the oil level dipstick.

7. Remove the cylinder front cover and accessory drive belt idler pulley assembly (if so equipped), and discard the gasket.

8. Raise the car on a hoist. Drain the engine crankcase.

9. Disconnect the starter cable at the starter. Remove the retaining bolts and remove the starter.

10. Remove the engine front support insulator to intermediate support bracket nuts on both supports. Remove the engine rear support insulator to crossmember bolt and insulator to transmission extension housing bolts. Raise the transmission, remove the support insulator, and lower the transmission to the crossmember.

11. Raise the engine with a transmission jack and place 2-inch thick wood blocks between both front support insulators and intermediate support brackets.

12. Remove the oil pan retaining bolts. Remove the oil pump retaining bolts. Remove the oil pump from the cylinder block and leave it lay in

the bottom of the oil pan. Rotate the crankshaft as required to remove the oil pan; then remove the oil pan and gaskets. Remove the inlet tube and screen from the oil pump.

CRANKSHAFT FRONT OIL SEAL REPLACEMENT

It is good practice to replace the oil seal each time the cylinder front cover is removed.

1. Drive out the old seal with a pin punch. Clean out the recess in the cover.

2. Coat a new seal with grease, and install the seal (Fig. 21). Drive the seal in until it is fully seated in the recess. After installation, check to be sure the seal is properly positioned in the cover and the spring is properly positioned in the seal.

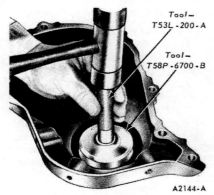

FIG. 21—Crankshaft Front Oil Seal Installation

CLEANING AND INSPECTION

Refer to Part 8-1, Section 3 for the cleaning and inspection procedures. Clean the crankshaft damper following the referenced procedure.

INSTALLATION

1. Coat the gasket surface of the block and cover with oil-resistant sealer. Position a new gasket on the block.

2. Insert the small diameter end of the cover alignment tool in the bore of the cover. Position the cover and pilot assembly over the end of the crankshaft and against the block (Fig. 22), being careful to align the cover flush with the cylinder block oil pan gasket surface.

3. Install the accessory drive belt idler pulley assembly (if so equipped) and retaining bolts. Install the alternator adjusting arm and cylinder front cover bolts. Torque all the bolts except the power steering

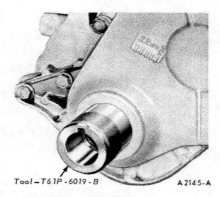

FIG. 22—Cylinder Front Cover Alignment

pump bracket bolts (if so equipped) to specifications.

4. Lubricate the crankshaft with a white lead and oil mixture to facilitate installation and removal of the damper. Lubricate the front oil seal rubbing surface on the damper inner hub and the inner surface (sealing area) of the oil seal with Lubriplate.

5. Align the damper keyway with the key on the crankshaft. Install the damper on the crankshaft (Fig. 23).

FIG. 23—Damper Installation—Typical

6. Install the washer and cap screw. Torque the cap screw to specifications.

Install the accessory drive pulley (if so equipped) on the crankshaft damper. Torque the bolts to specifications.

7. Clean and install the oil pump screen and inlet tube assembly.

8. Clean the gasket surfaces of the oil pump, oil pan and cylinder block. Remove the rear main bearing cap to oil pan seal and cylinder front cover to oil pan seal. Clean the seal grooves.

9. Apply oil-resistant sealer in the cavities between the bearing cap and

cylinder block (Fig. 46). Install a new seal in the rear main bearing cap (Fig. 46), and apply a bead of oil-resistant sealer to the tapered ends of the seal (Fig. 46).

10. Install new side gaskets on the oil pan with oil-resistant sealer (Fig. 47). Position a new cylinder front cover seal on the oil pan.

11. Prime the oil pump and place the oil pump and inlet tube assembly in the oil pan. Position the oil pan under the engine. Install the oil pump with a new gasket on the cylinder block. The correct installation of the oil pump is shown in Fig. 48. Torque the screws to specifications. Position the oil pan against the cylinder block and install the retaining screws. Torque the screws in sequence to specifications.

12. Raise the engine and remove the wood blocks from the engine front supports. Lower the engine until the front support insulators are positioned on the intermediate support brackets.

13. Raise the transmission and install the rear support insulator on the transmission extension housing. Torque the bolts to specifications. Lower the transmission and install the rear support insulator to crossmember bolt and nut. Torque the nut to specifications. Install and torque the front support insulator nuts to specification.

14. Install the starter and connect the starter cable.

15. Install the water pump pulley(s), spacer and fan. Install the cooling fan and alternator drive belts.

On a car with power steering, install the power steering pump and front mounting bracket assembly. Torque the mounting bracket to cylinder front cover and cylinder block bolts to specification. Install the power steering drive belt. Torque the adjusting nut and bolts to specifications.

16. On a car with air conditioning, position the condenser, and install the retaining bolts. Install the compressor drive belt.

On a car with Thermactor exhaust emission control system, install the air supply pump drive belt.

17. Adjust the tension of all the drive belts to specification.

18. Install the radiator. Connect the radiator lower hose at the water pump and the radiator upper hose at the coolant outlet housing.

On a car with an automatic transmission, connect the transmission oil cooler lines.

19. Fill and bleed the cooling system. Install the oil level dipstick. Fill the crankcase.

20. Operate the engine at fast idle and check all hose connections and gaskets for leaks.

TIMING GEARS

The engine has a gear driven camshaft. **When the crankshaft and camshaft lose their timing relationship through the removal of the timing gears, interference may occur between the crankshaft and cam lobes. Therefore, to prevent possible damage to the camshaft lobes, do not rotate the camshaft or crankshaft in the engine without the timing gears installed.**

REMOVAL

1. Drain the cooling system and crankcase.

2. Remove the cylinder front cover, camshaft and oil pan following the procedures in this section.

3. Remove the oil slinger from the crankshaft. Use the gear puller as shown in Fig. 24 and remove the crankshaft gear. Remove the key from the crankshaft.

FIG. 24—Crankshaft Gear Removal

4. Press the camshaft gear off the camshaft in an arbor press (Fig. 25). Remove the thrust plate, spacer and key.

CLEANING AND INSPECTION

Refer to Part 8-1, Section 3 for the *cleaning and inspection* procedures.

INSTALLATION

1. Install the camshaft in the engine and install the spacer and thrust plate on the camshaft. Insert the key in the keyway. Position the camshaft gear on the camshaft with the timing marks aligned (Fig. 26) and install it as shown in Fig. 27. **Be sure the gear and spacer are tight against the shoulder on the camshaft and**

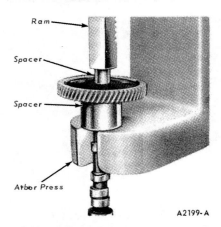

FIG. 25—Camshaft Gear Removal

FIG. 26—Aligning Timing Marks

FIG. 27—Camshaft Gear Installation

that the thrust plate can be moved freely. Install the thrust plate screws and torque to specifications.

2. Install the key in the crankshaft keyway. Install the crankshaft gear, using the tool shown in Fig. 28. Install the oil slinger.

3. Be sure to check the timing gear runout and backlash and camshaft gear end play, following the procedures in Part 8-1, Section 1.

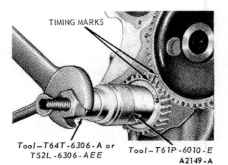

FIG. 28—Crankshaft Gear Installation

4. Install the cylinder front cover and oil pan following the procedures in this section.

5. Fill the crankcase and cooling system. Start the engine and adjust the ignition timing. Operate the engine at fast idle and check all hose connections and gaskets for leaks.

CAMSHAFT

The camshaft and related parts are shown in Fig. 29.

REMOVAL

1. Drain the cooling system and the crankcase.

2. Disconnect the clean air tube at the oil fill cap, if equipped with closed crankcase ventilation system. Remove the air cleaner. Remove the crankcase ventilation regulator valve from the valve rocker arm cover.

If equipped with a Thermactor exhaust emission control system, disconnect the air hoses as necessary for accessibility, and position them out of the way.

3. Disconnect the accelerator cable at the carburetor. Remove the accelerator cable retracting spring. Remove the accelerator cable housing bracket from the cylinder head and position the cable and bracket assembly out of the way. Remove the valve rocker arm cover.

On a car with air conditioning, remove the condenser retaining bolts, and position the condenser to one side for accessibility. **Do not disconnect condenser refrigerant lines.**

4. Remove the cylinder front cover, oil pan and related parts, following the procedure under Cylinder Front Cover Removal.

5. Disconnect the spark plug wires at the spark plugs and disconnect the high tension wire at the ignition coil. Remove the distributor cap and spark plug wires assembly.

6. Disconnect the fuel outlet line at the fuel pump. Remove the fuel pump mounting bolts and position

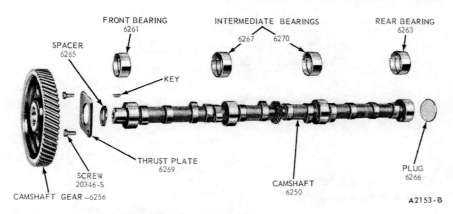

FIG. 29—Camshaft and Related Parts

the fuel pump out of the way.

7. Disconnect the vacuum line at the distributor and the primary wire at the coil. Remove the distributor.

8. Loosen the rocker arm stud nuts; move the rocker arms to one side, and remove the push rods in sequence. Place the push rods in a rack so they can be installed in their original location.

9. Remove the valve push rod cover; then remove the valve lifters in sequence, using the tool shown in Fig. 30. Place the valve lifters in a tray or rack to facilitate installation in the same sequence from which they were removed.

FIG. 30—Valve Lifter Removal or Installation

10. Turn the crankshaft to align the timing marks as shown in Fig. 26. Remove the camshaft thrust plate screws (Fig. 31).

11. Carefully remove the camshaft with the gear attached. **Avoid damaging the camshaft lobes during removal.**

12. Press the camshaft out of the camshaft gear in an arbor press (Fig. 25). Remove the key, thrust plate and spacer.

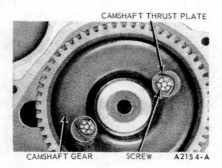

FIG. 31—Camshaft Removal or Installation—Typical

CLEANING AND INSPECTION

Refer to Part 8-1, Section 3 for the cleaning and inspection procedures.

REPAIR

Refer to Part 8-1, Section 2 for the repair procedures.

INSTALLATION

1. Oil the camshaft journals and apply Lubriplate to all the lobes. Carefully slide the camshaft through the bearings.

2. Install the thrust plate, spacer and key. Torque the thrust plate retaining screws to specifications.

3. Position the camshaft gear on the camshaft. Align the timing marks on the timing gears as shown in Fig. 26. Install the camshaft gear with the tool shown in Fig. 27. Be sure the gear and spacer are tight against the shoulder on the camshaft.

4. Check the backlash between the camshaft gear and crankshaft gear with a dial indicator (Part 8-1, Section 1). Hold the gear firmly against the block while making the check. Refer to the specifications for the backlash limits.

5. Check the camshaft gear runout and end play with a dial indi-

cator (Part 8-1, Section 1). If the gear runout is excessive, remove the gear and remove any burrs from the shaft, or replace the gear. If the camshaft end play exceeds the specified limits, replace the thrust plate.

6. Crank the engine until the timing marks are aligned as shown in Fig. 26.

7. Set the distributor rotor so the points are about to open for No. 1 cylinder firing position. Install the distributor. Check the points. If the camshaft timing marks are still aligned (step 6 above), the points should be fully open in No. 1 cylinder firing position. If the points are not open, remove the distributor and rotate the shaft in the proper direction. Install the distributor and hold-down clamp.

8. Clean the cylinder front cover and cylinder block gasket surfaces. Clean the oil pump screen, oil pan and gasket surfaces of the cylinder block.

9. Install a new oil seal in the cylinder front cover. Install the cylinder front cover, oil pan, crankshaft damper and accessory drive belts, following the procedures under Cylinder Front Cover Installation. Adjust the drive belt tension to specifications.

10. Lubricate the valve lifters with engine oil and install the lifters (Fig. 30) in the same bores from which they were removed. Apply Lubriplate to both ends of the push rods and install the push rods in the same sequence that they were removed. Be sure the push rods are seated in the valve lifter sockets.

11. Clean the valve push rod cover and cylinder block gasket surfaces. Apply oil-resistant sealer to one side of a new gasket and place the gasket on the push rod cover with the cemented side next to the cover. Install the cover and torque the bolts in sequence to specifications.

12. Apply Lubriplate to the valve pad on the rocker arms. Align the valve rocker arms with the valves and push rods; then tighten the rocker arm stud nuts sufficiently to hold the push rods in place. Adjust the valve clearance (Part 8-1, Section 2).

13. Clean the valve rocker arm cover and cylinder head gasket surface. Apply oil-resistant sealer to one side of a new gasket and install the gasket on the cover (sealer side next to cover). Install the cover and torque the screws in sequence to specifications.

14. Connect the distributor primary wire at the ignition coil. Connect the vacuum line to the distributor.

15. Clean the fuel pump and cylinder block gasket surfaces. Install the fuel pump with a new gasket. Torque the mounting bolts to specifications. Connect the fuel outlet line to the fuel pump.

16. Install the distributor cap and spark plug wires assembly. Connect the spark plug wires.

17. Install the crankcase ventilation regulator valve in the valve rocker arm cover. Install the accelerator cable housing bracket on the cylinder head. Connect the accelerator cable to the carburetor. Install the cable retracting spring.

18. If equipped with a Thermactor exhaust emission control system, connect the air hoses.

19. On a car with air conditioning, position the condenser and install the retaining bolts.

20. Install the radiator. Connect the radiator upper hose to the coolant outlet housing, and connect the lower hose to the water pump. Install the hood latch support bracket. Install the radiator grille assembly.

21. Install the air cleaner.

22. Fill the crankcase and cooling system.

23. Start the engine and check for oil, coolant and fuel leaks. Adjust the ignition timing. Adjust the carburetor idle speed and fuel mixture.

CAMSHAFT REAR BEARING BORE PLUG REPLACEMENT

1. On an automatic transmission, remove the transmission oil level dipstick and tube. Dispose of the oil drained at the dipstick tube opening. Disconnect the transmission shift linkage and drive shaft. Support the transmission on a transmission jack. Disconnect the transmission at the engine and at the support insulator. Move the transmission and converter (automatic transmission) to one side, leaving it on the transmission jack. **Do not drain the converter.**

On a manual-shift transmission, remove the clutch pressure plate and disc following the procedure in Group 5.

2. Remove the flywheel retaining bolts. Remove the flywheel and the engine rear cover.

3. Drill a ⅝-inch hole in the camshaft rear bearing bore plug. Remove the plug as shown in Fig. 32.

4. Clean out the plug bore recess.

5. Coat the flange of a new plug

FIG. 32—Camshaft Rear Bearing Bore Plug Removal

with oil-resistant sealer and install it with the flange facing out (Fig. 33).

FIG. 33—Camshaft Rear Bearing Bore Plug Installation

6. Install the engine rear cover plate and flywheel. **Coat the threads of the flywheel retaining bolts with oil-resistant sealer,** and install the bolts. Torque the bolts in sequence across from each other to specifications.

On a car with a manual-shift transmission, install the clutch pressure plate and disc, following the procedure in Group 5.

7. Install the transmission. Torque all attaching bolts to specifications. Connect the driveshaft and transmission shift linkage. Remove the transmission jack. Install the oil level dipstick and tube (if so equipped). Add transmission oil as necessary. **Do not adjust the transmission linkage.**

VALVE LIFTER REPLACEMENT

REMOVAL

1. Remove the air cleaner. Remove the crankcase ventilation regulator valve from the valve rocker arm cover.

On a car with Thermactor exhaust emission system, disconnect the air hoses as necessary for accessibility.

2. Disconnect the accelerator cable at the carburetor. Remove the

retracting spring. Remove the accelerator cable housing bracket from the cylinder head. Position the cable and bracket assembly out of the way.

3. Remove the valve rocker arm cover.

4. Disconnect the spark plug wires at the spark plugs. Remove the valve push rod cover.

5. Loosen the rocker arm stud nut(s) until the rocker arm(s) can be disengaged from the push rod(s). Remove the push rod(s). Remove the valve lifter(s) with the tool shown in Fig. 30. If more than one push rod and valve lifter is removed, do it in sequence and place the parts in a rack so they can be installed in their original location.

CLEANING AND INSPECTION

For the cleaning and inspection procedures, refer to Part 8-1, Section 3. The hydraulic valve lifter leak-down test is covered in Part 8-1, Section 1.

INSTALLATION

1. Clean the rocker arm cover, push rod cover, and cylinder head and block gasket surfaces.

2. Apply Lubriplate to the cam lobe contact surface of the valve lifter(s). Coat the rest of the valve lifter(s) with engine oil. Install the valve lifters with the tool shown in Fig. 30.

3. Apply Lubriplate to both ends of the push rod(s). Install the push rod(s) in sequence. Engage the rocker arm(s) with the push rod(s) and tighten the rocker arm stud nut(s) sufficiently to hold the push rod(s) in place. **Be sure the push rod(s) is properly seated in the valve lifter socket(s).**

4. Adjust the valve clearance, following the procedure in Part 8-1, Section 2.

5. Coat one side of new gaskets with oil-resistant sealer and position the gaskets, cemented side toward covers, on the rocker arm and push rod covers. Install the push rod cover and the rocker arm cover. Torque the cover screws in sequence to specifications.

6. Connect the spark plug wires.

7. Install the accelerator cable housing bracket on the cylinder head. Connect the accelerator cable to the carburetor. Install the cable retracting spring.

If equipped with Thermactor exhaust emission control system, connect the air supply hoses.

8. Start the engine and adjust the

carburetor idle speed and mixture. Install the air cleaner.

MAIN AND CONNECTING ROD BEARING REPLACEMENT

The main and connecting rod bearing inserts are selective fit. **Do not file or lap bearing caps or use shims to obtain the proper bearing clearance.**

Selective fit bearings are available for service in standard sizes and 0.002 inch undersize. Standard bearings are divided into two sizes and are identified by a daub of red or blue paint. Refer to the Parts Catalog for the available sizes. **Red marked bearings increase the clearance; blue marked bearings decrease the clearance.** Undersize bearings, which are not selective fit, are available for use on journals that have been refinished.

MAIN BEARINGS

Since the one-piece crankshaft rear oil seal must be replaced when the crankshaft bearings are replaced, it is necessary to remove the engine from the car for main bearing replacement.

Refer to Section 4 for the proper procedures.

CONNECTING ROD BEARING

1. Drain the crankcase. Remove the oil pan and oil pump, following the procedure under Oil Pan Removal.

2. Turn the crankshaft until the connecting rod to which new bearings are to be fitted is down. Remove the connecting rod cap. Remove the bearing inserts from the rod and cap.

3. Be sure the bearing inserts and the bearing bore in the connecting rod and cap are clean. Foreign material under the inserts will distort the bearing and cause a failure.

4. Clean the crankshaft journal. **When replacing standard bearings with new bearings, it is good practice to first try to obtain the proper clearance with two blue bearing halves.**

5. Install the bearing inserts in the connecting rod and cap with the tangs fitted in the slots.

6. Pull the connecting rod assembly down firmly on the crankshaft journal.

7. Place a piece of Plastigage on the lower bearing surface, the full width of the cap and about ¼ inch off center (Fig. 34).

8. Install the cap and torque the

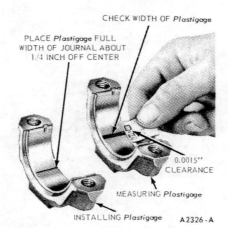

CHECK WIDTH OF *Plastigage*

PLACE *Plastigage* FULL WIDTH OF JOURNAL ABOUT 1/4 INCH OFF CENTER

0.0015" CLEARANCE

MEASURING *Plastigage*

INSTALLING *Plastigage*   A2326-A

FIG. 34—Installing and Measuring Plastigage— Connecting Rod

connecting rod nuts to specifications. **Do not turn the crankshaft while the Plastigage is in place.**

9. Remove the cap; then using the Plastigage scale, check the width of the Plastigage. **When checking the width of the Plastigage, check at the widest point in order to get the minimum clearance. Check at the narrowest point in order to get the maximum clearance. The difference between the two readings is the taper.**

10. If the clearance is less than the specified limits, try two red bearing halves or a combination of red and blue depending upon the condition. If the clearance exceeds specified limits, try 0.002 inch undersize bearings in combination with blue or red bearings. The bearing clearance must be within specified limits. If the standard and 0.002 inch undersize bearings do not bring the clearance within the desired limits, refinish the crankshaft journal; then install undersize bearings.

11. After the bearing has been fitted, clean and apply a light coat of engine oil to the journal and bearings. Install the connecting rod cap and torque the nuts to specifications.

12. Repeat the procedure for the remaining connecting rods that require new bearings.

13. Install the oil pan and oil pump, following the procedures under Oil Pan Installation.

14. Fill the crankcase and cooling system. Start the engine and check for oil pressure. Operate the engine at fast idle and check for oil and coolant leaks.

CLEANING AND INSPECTION

Refer to Part 8-1, Section 3 for the cleaning and inspection procedures.

PISTONS AND CONNECTING RODS

REMOVAL

1. Drain the cooling system and the crankcase.

2. Refer to Cylinder Head Removal and remove the cylinder head and related parts.

3. Remove the oil pan following the procedure under Oil Pan Removal. Remove the oil pump inlet tube and the oil pump.

4. Turn the crankshaft until the piston to be removed is at the bottom of its travel and place a cloth on the piston head to collect the cuttings. Remove any ridge and/or deposits from the upper end of the cylinder bore with a ridge cutter. Follow the instructions furnished by the tool manufacturer. **Never cut into the ring travel area in excess of 1/32 inch when removing ridges.**

5. Make sure all the connecting rod caps are marked so that they can be installed in their original locations. Remove the connecting rod cap.

6. Push the connecting rod and piston assembly out the top of the cylinder with the handle end of a hammer. Avoid damage to the crankshaft journal or the cylinder wall when removing the piston and rod.

INSTALLATION

1. Clean the oil pump inlet tube screen and the oil pan and block gasket surfaces.

2. Oil the piston rings, pistons and cylinder walls with light engine oil.

3. **Be sure to install the pistons in the same cylinders from which they were removed, or to which they were fitted. The connecting rods and bearing caps are numbered from 1 to 6 beginning at the front of the engine. The numbers on the connecting rods and bearing caps must be on the same side when installed in the cylinder bore. If a connecting rod is ever transposed from one block or cylinder to another, new bearings should be fitted and the connecting rod should be numbered to correspond with the new cylinder number.**

4. Make sure the ring gaps are properly spaced around the circumference of the piston (Fig. 35). Install a piston ring compressor on the piston and push the piston in with a

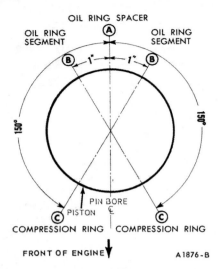

OIL RING SPACER

OIL RING SEGMENT   OIL RING SEGMENT

PIN BORE

PISTON

COMPRESSION RING   COMPRESSION RING

FRONT OF ENGINE ↓   A 1876-B

FIG. 35—Piston Ring Spacing

hammer handle until it is slightly below the top of the cylinder (Fig. 36).

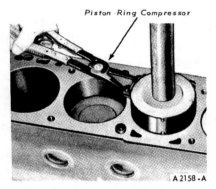

Piston Ring Compressor

A 2158-A

FIG. 36—Piston Installation

Be sure to guide the connecting rods to avoid damaging the crankshaft journals. **Install the piston with the indentation in the piston head toward the front of the engine.**

5. Check the clearance of each bearing following the procedure under Connecting Rod Bearing Replacement.

6. After the bearings have been fitted, apply a light coat of engine oil to the journals and bearings.

7. Turn the crankshaft throw to the bottom of its stroke, then push the piston all the way down until the connecting rod bearing seats on the crankshaft journal. Install the connecting rod cap. Torque the nuts to specifications.

8. After the piston and connecting rod assemblies have been installed, check the connecting rod side clearance on each crankshaft journal (Fig. 37).

9. Prime and install the oil pump. Install the oil pan and oil pump inlet

Feeler Gauge

A2159-A

FIG. 37—Checking Connecting Rod Side Clearance

tube following the procedure under, Oil Pan Installation.

10. Refer to Cylinder Head Installation and install the cylinder head and related parts. Adjust the valve clearance, refer to Part 8-1, Section 2.

11. Fill and bleed the cooling system. Fill the crankcase.

12. Start the engine and check for oil pressure. Operate the engine at fast idle and check for oil and coolant leaks.

13. Operate the engine until engine temperatures have stabilized. Check and adjust the ignition timing. Adjust the engine idle speed and fuel mixture.

DISASSEMBLY

1. Remove the bearing inserts from the connecting rod and cap.

2. Mark the pistons and pins to assure assembly with the same rod and installation in the same cylinders from which they were removed.

3. Remove the piston pin from the piston and connecting rod using the tool shown in Fig. 38. Remove the piston rings.

CLEANING AND INSPECTION

Refer to Part 8-1, Section 3 for the cleaning and inspection procedures.

REPAIRS

Refer to Part 8-1, Section 2 for the repair procedures.

ASSEMBLY

The piston, connecting rod and related parts are shown in Fig. 39.

Check the fit of a new piston in the cylinder bore before assembling the piston and piston pin to the connecting rod, following the procedures in Part 8-1, Sections 2 and 3.

The piston pin bore of a connect-

ing rod and the diameter of the piston pin must be within specifications.

1. Apply a light coat of engine oil to all parts. **Assemble the piston to the connecting rod with the bearing tang notches in the connecting rod (at the parting line of the cap) and the indentation notch in the piston positioned as shown in Fig. 40.**

2. Start the piston pin in the piston and connecting rod. Draw the piston pin through the piston and connecting rod until the end of the pin seats in Detail 2 (Fig. 41).

3. Check the end gap of all piston rings (Part 8-1). They must be within specifications (Part 8-5).

4. Follow the instructions contained on the piston ring package and install the piston rings.

5. Check the ring side clearance of the compression rings with a feeler gauge inserted between the ring and its lower land (Part 8-1, Section 2). The gauge should slide freely around the entire ring circumference without binding. Any wear that occurs will form a step at the inner portion of the lower land. **If the lower lands have high steps, the piston should be replaced.**

6. Be sure the bearing inserts and the bearing bore in the connecting rod and cap are clean. Foreign material under the inserts will distort the bearing and cause a failure. Install the bearing inserts in the connecting rod and cap with the tangs fitting in the slots provided.

FLYWHEEL

REMOVAL

1. On an automatic transmission remove the transmission, remove the transmission oil level dipstick and tube. Dispose of the oil drained at dipstick tube opening.

Disconnect the transmission shift linkage and drive shaft. Support the transmission on a transmission jack. Disconnect the transmission at the engine and at the support insulator. Move the transmission and converter (automatic transmission) to one side, leaving it on the transmission jack. **Do not drain the converter.**

2. On a manual shift transmission, remove the clutch pressure plate and cover assembly following the procedure in Group 5.

3. Remove the flywheel retaining bolts and remove the flywheel.

CLEANING AND INSPECTION

Refer to Part 8-1, Section 3 for the cleaning and inspection procedures

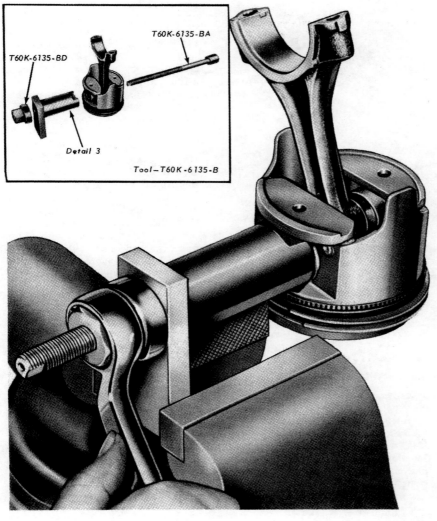

FIG. 38—Piston Pin Removal—Typical

for manual-shift transmissions.

REPAIRS

To check flywheel face runout or replace flywheel ring gear for manual shift transmissions, refer to Part 8-1, Section 2.

INSTALLATION

1. Position the flywheel on the crankshaft flange. **Coat the threads of the flywheel retaining bolts with oil-resistant sealer,** and install the bolts. Torque the bolts in sequence across from each other to specifications.

2. On a manual-shift transmission, install the clutch disc and the pressure plate and cover assembly following the procedure in Group 5.

3. Install the transmission. Torque all attaching bolts to specifications. Connect the driveshaft and transmission shift linkage. Remove the trans-

mission jack. Install the oil level dipstick and tube (if so equipped). Add transmission oil as necessary. **Adjust the transmission linkage only if necessary.**

CLUTCH PILOT BUSHING REPLACEMENT

Inspection procedures are outlined under Crankshaft Cleaning and Inspection in Part 8-1, Section 3.

1. Disconnect the transmission from the engine and slide it to the rear following the procedure in Group 5.

2. Remove the pressure plate and cover assembly following the procedure in Group 5.

3. Remove the clutch pilot bushing (Fig. 42).

4. Coat the clutch pilot bushing bore in the crankshaft with a small quantity of wheel bearing lubricant.

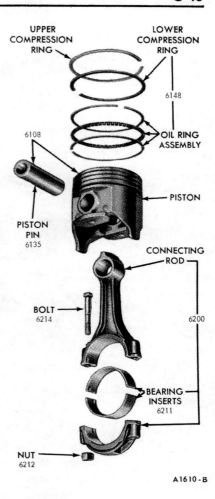

FIG. 39—Typical Piston, Connecting Rod and Related Parts

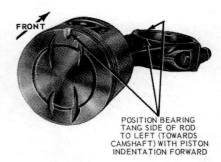

FIG. 40—Piston and Connecting Rod Assembly

Avoid using too much lubricant because it may be thrown onto the disc when the clutch revolves.

5. Install the clutch pilot service bearing (Fig. 43).

6. Install the clutch disc and the pressure plate and cover assembly following the procedure in Group 5.

7. Connect the transmission to the

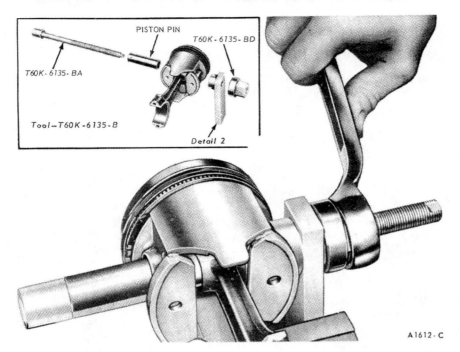

FIG. 41—Piston Pin Installation

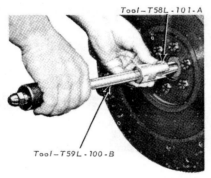

FIG. 42—Clutch Pilot Bushing Removal

FIG. 43—Clutch Pilot Bushing Installation

engine following the procedure in Group 5, except it is not necessary to adjust the transmission linkage.

CRANKSHAFT REAR OIL SEAL REPLACEMENT

If the crankshaft rear oil seal replacement is the only operation being performed, it can be done in the car, according to the following procedure. **If the oil seal is being replaced in conjunction with a rear main bearing replacement, the engine must be removed from the car and installed on a work stand.**

1. Remove the starter.

2. On an automatic transmission remove the transmission oil level dipstick and tube. Dispose of the oil drained at the dipstick tube opening. Disconnect the transmission shift linkage and drive shaft. Support the transmission on a transmission jack. Disconnect the transmission at the engine and at the support insulator. Move the transmission and converter (automatic transmission) to one side, leaving it on the transmission jack. **Do not drain the converter.**

3. On a manual-shift transmission, remove the pressure plate and cover assembly following the procedure in Group 5.

4. Remove the flywheel retaining bolts and remove the flywheel and engine rear cover plate.

5. Use an awl to punch two holes in the crankshaft rear oil seal. Punch the holes on opposite sides of the crankshaft and just above the bearing cap to cylinder block split line. Install a sheet metal screw in each hole. Use

two large screwdrivers or small pry bars and pry against both screws at the same time to remove the crankshaft rear oil seal. It may be necessary to place small blocks of wood against the cylinder block to provide a fulcrum point for the pry bars. **Use caution throughout this procedure to avoid scratching or otherwise damaging the crankshaft oil seal surface.**

6. Clean the oil seal recess in the cylinder block and main bearing cap. **Inspect and clean the oil seal contact surface on the crankshaft, following the procedures in Part 8-1.**

7. Coat the oil seal to cylinder block surface of the oil seal with oil. Coat the seal contact surface of the oil seal and crankshaft with Lubriplate. Start the seal in the recess and install it with the tool as shown in Fig. 44. Keep the tool straight with

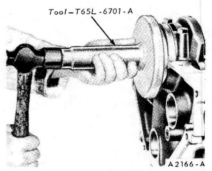

FIG. 44—Crankshaft Rear Oil Seal Installation

the centerline of the crankshaft, and install the seal until it is flush to 0.005 inch below the face of the cylinder block. **Remove the tool and inspect the seal to be sure it was not damaged during installation.**

8. Install the engine rear cover plate. Position the flywheel on the crankshaft flange. **Coat the threads of the flywheel retaining bolts with oil-resistant sealer,** and install the retaining bolts. Torque the bolts in sequence across from each other to specifications.

9. On a manual-shift transmission, install the clutch disc and the pressure plate and cover assembly following the procedure in Group 5.

10. Install the transmission. Torque all attaching bolts to specifications. Connect the driveshaft and transmission shift linkage. Remove the transmission jack. Install the oil level dipstick and tube (if so equipped). Add transmission oil as necessary. **Do not adjust the transmission linkage.**

11. Install the starter.

OIL FILTER REPLACEMENT

1. Place a drip pan under the oil filter. Unscrew the filter from the cylinder block with a filter wrench.

2. Coat the gasket on the filter with oil. Place the filter in position on the cylinder block (Fig. 45). Hand

FIG. 45—Oil Filter Installed

tighten the filter until the gasket contacts the adapter face; then advance it ½ turn.

3. Operate the engine at fast idle, and check for oil leaks. If oil leaks are evident, perform the necessary repairs to correct the leakage. Check the oil level and fill the crankcase if necessary.

OIL PAN AND OIL PUMP

REMOVAL

1. Drain the crankcase and the cooling system.

2. Disconnect the radiator upper hose at the coolant outlet elbow and the lower hose at the radiator. Disconnect the automatic transmission oil cooler lines at the radiator (if so equipped). Remove the radiator.

On a car with air conditioning, remove the condenser retaining bolts, and position the condenser to one side for accessibility. **Do not disconnect the condenser refrigerant lines.**

3. Raise the car on a hoist.

4. Disconnect the starter cable at the starter. Remove the retaining bolts and remove the starter.

5. Remove the engine front support insulator to intermediate support bracket nuts on both supports. Remove the engine rear support insulator to crossmember bolt and insulator to transmission extension housing bolts. Raise the transmission, remove the support insulator, and lower the transmission to the crossmember.

6. Raise the engine with a trans-

mission jack and place 3-inch thick wood blocks between both front support insulators and intermediate support brackets.

7. Remove the oil pan retaining bolts. Remove the oil pump retaining bolts. Remove the oil pump from the cylinder block and leave it lay in the bottom of the oil pan. Rotate the crankshaft as required to remove the oil pan; then remove the oil pan and gaskets. Remove the inlet tube and screen from the oil pump.

CLEANING AND INSPECTION

Refer to Part 8-1, Section 3 for the cleaning and inspection procedures.

REPAIR

Refer to Part 8-1, Section 2 for the repair procedures.

INSTALLATION

1. Clean the inlet tube and screen assembly and install it on the oil pump using a new gasket.

2. Clean the gasket surfaces of the oil pump, oil pan and cylinder block. Remove the rear main bearing cap to oil pan seal and cylinder front cover to oil pan seal. Clean the seal grooves.

3. Apply oil-resistant sealer in the cavities between the bearing cap and cylinder block (Fig. 46). Install a

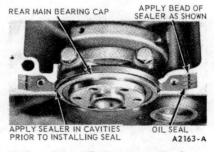

FIG. 46—Oil Pan Rear Seal Installation

new seal in the rear main bearing cap (Fig. 46), and apply a bead of oil-resistant sealer to the tapered ends of the seal (Fig. 46).

4. Install new side gaskets on the oil pan with oil-resistant sealer (Fig. 47). Position a new cylinder front cover seal on the oil pan.

5. Prime the oil pump. Place the oil pump and inlet tube assembly in the oil pan. Position the oil pan under the engine. Install the oil pump with a new gasket on the cylinder block. The correct installation of the oil pump is shown in Fig. 48. Torque

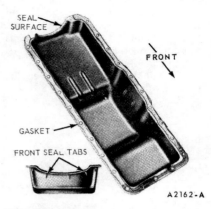

FIG. 47—Oil Pan Gaskets and Front Seal Installed

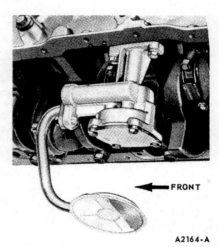

FIG. 48—Oil Pump Installed

the screws to specifications. Position the oil pan against the cylinder block and install the retaining screws. Torque the screws in sequence to specifications.

6. Raise the engine and remove the wood blocks from the engine front supports. Lower the engine until the front support insulators are positioned on the intermediate support brackets.

7. Raise the transmission and install the rear support insulator on the transmission extension housing. Torque the bolts to specifications. Lower the transmission and install the rear support insulator to crossmember bolt and nut. Torque the nut to specifications. Install and torque the front support insulator nuts to specification.

8. Install the starter and connect the starter cable.

9. On a car with air conditioning, position the condenser and install the retaining bolts.

10. Install the radiator and connect the radiator upper and lower hoses. Connect the automatic transmission oil cooler lines (if so equipped).

11. Fill the crankcase and cooling system.

12. Start the engine and check for coolant and oil leaks.

OIL PUMP DISASSEMBLY

1. Remove the oil inlet tube from the oil pump. Remove and discard the gasket.

2. Remove the cover retaining screws and remove the cover. Remove the inner rotor and shaft assembly; then remove the outer race.

3. Scrape away the staking marks in the body around the oil pressure relief valve cap. Drill a ⅛-inch hole in the relief valve cap, and insert a self-threading sheet metal screw of proper diameter into the cap. Pull the

cap out of the chamber. Remove the spring and plunger.

CLEANING AND INSPECTION

Refer to Part 8-1, Section 3 for the cleaning and inspection procedures.

OIL PUMP ASSEMBLY

The oil pump assembly is shown in Fig. 49.

1. Clean all parts thoroughly. Install the oil pressure relief valve plunger, spring and a new cap. Stake the cap into position.

2. Install the outer race (recessed dot facing out—on same side as dot on rotor) and the inner rotor and shaft assembly. **The inner rotor and shaft and the outer race are serviced as an assembly. One part should not be replaced without replacing the other.** Install the cover and torque the retaining screws to specifications.

3. Position a new oil inlet tube

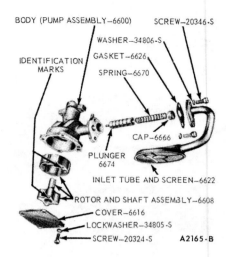

FIG. 49—Oil Pump Assembly

gasket on the oil pump and install the inlet tube. Prime the oil pump with engine oil before installing it on the engine.

---

3   ENGINE REMOVAL AND INSTALLATION

The engine removal and installation procedures are for the engine only without the transmission attached.

REMOVAL

1. Drain the cooling system and the crankcase. Remove the hood. Remove the air cleaner.

2. Disconnect the battery positive cable. Disconnect the heater hoses from the water pump and coolant outlet housing. Disconnect the flexible fuel line from the fuel tank line.

3. Disconnect the radiator upper hose at the coolant outlet housing, and disconnect the radiator lower hose from the water pump.

On a car with an automatic transmission, disconnect the transmission oil cooler lines from the radiator.

4. Remove the radiator. Remove the cooling fan, spacer, water pump pulley and fan drive belt.

5. Disconnect the accelerator cable at the carburetor. Remove the cable retracting spring. Remove the cable housing bracket from the cylinder head, and position the cable and bracket assembly out of the way.

On a car with power brakes, disconnect the vacuum line at the intake manifold.

On a car with an automatic transmission, disconnect the transmission kickdown rod at the bellcrank assembly.

On a car with air conditioning, remove the compressor from the mounting bracket, and position it out of the way, **leaving the refrigerant lines connected.**

If equipped with Thermactor exhaust emission control system, disconnect the air cleaner hose at the air pump.

6. Disconnect the exhaust manifold from the muffler inlet pipe. Disconnect the body ground strap and the battery ground cable at the engine.

7. Disconnect the engine wiring harness at the ignition coil, coolant temperature sending unit and oil pressure sending unit. Position the harness out of the way.

8. Remove the alternator mounting bolts and position the alternator out of the way, leaving the wires attached.

On a car with power steering, remove the power steering pump from the mounting brackets and position it to the side, leaving the lines attached.

9. Raise the car. Remove the starter (and the automatic transmission fluid filler tube bracket). Remove the engine rear plate upper right bolt.

On a car with a manual-shift transmission, remove all the flywheel housing lower retaining bolts.

On a car with an automatic transmission, remove the converter housing access cover assembly. Remove

the flywheel to converter nuts; then secure the converter assembly in the housing. Remove the transmission oil cooler lines from the retaining clip at the engine. Remove the converter housing to engine lower retaining bolts.

10. Remove the insulator to intermediate support bracket nut from each engine front support.

11. Lower the car and position a transmission jack under the transmission to support it. Remove the remaining flywheel or converter housing to engine bolts.

12. Attach the engine lifting hook (Fig. 50). Remove two bolts attaching the right side engine support insulator to the engine. Remove the insulator. Raise the engine slightly; then carefully pull it from the transmission. Lift the engine out of the chasis.

INSTALLATION

1. Place a new gasket on the muffler inlet pipe.

2. Lower the engine carefully into the chassis. Make sure the studs on the exhaust manifold are aligned with the holes in the muffler inlet pipe and the dowels in the block engage the holes in the flywheel or converter housing.

On a car with an automatic transmission, start the converter pilot into the crankshaft. Remove the re-

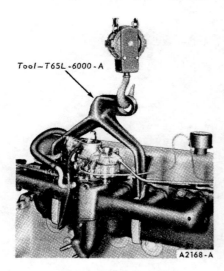

Tool—T65L-6000-A

A2168-A

FIG. 50—Engine Removal or Installation

tainer securing the converter in the housing.

On a car with a manual-shift transmission, start the transmission main drive gear into the clutch disc. It may be necessary to adjust the position of the transmission with relation to the engine if the transmission input shaft will not enter the clutch disc. **If the engine hangs up after the shaft enters, turn the crankshaft slowly (with the transmission in gear) until the shaft splines mesh with the clutch disc splines.**

3. Install the converter or flywheel housing upper retaining bolts. Remove the jack supporting the transmission.

4. Install the engine front support insulator on the right side of the en-

gine. Install the insulator to engine bolts and torque to specifications. Lower the engine until it rests on the engine supports and remove the lifting hook.

5. Raise the car and install the engine left and right support insulator to intermediate support bracket retaining nuts. Torque the nuts to specifications. Install the automatic transmission oil cooler lines bracket.

6. Install the remaining converter or flywheel housing retaining bolts.

7. Install the starter and connect the starter cable, and attach the automatic transmission fluid filler tube bracket (if so equipped).

On a car with an automatic transmission, install the transmission oil cooler lines in the bracket at the engine block.

8. Install the exhaust manifold to muffler inlet pipe lock washers and nuts. Torque the nuts to specifications.

9. Lower the car. Connect the engine ground strap and the battery ground cable.

10. On a car with an automatic transmission, connect the kickdown rod to the bellcrank assembly on the intake manifold.

Install the accelerator cable housing bracket on the cylinder head. Connect the cable to the carburetor and install the retracting spring.

On a car with power brakes, connect the brake vacuum line to the intake manifold.

11. Connect the coil primary wire, oil pressure and coolant temperature sending unit wires, flexible fuel line,

heater hoses, and the battery positive cable.

12. Install the alternator on the mounting bracket.

On a car with power steering, install the power steering pump on the mounting brackets.

On a car with air conditioning, install the compressor on the mounting bracket, and adjust the belt tension to specifications.

If equipped with Thermactor exhaust emission control system, connect the air cleaner hose at the air pump.

13. Install the water pump pulley, spacer, cooling fan and drive belt. Torque the fan bolts to specifications.

Adjust the fan drive belt and power steering pump drive belt (if so equipped) tension to specifications. Tighten the alternator and power steering pump mounting bolts.

14. Install the radiator. Connect the radiator lower hose to the water pump and the radiator upper hose to the coolant outlet housing.

On a car with an automatic transmission, connect the oil cooler lines.

15. Install and adjust the hood.

16. Fill and bleed the cooling system. Fill the crankcase. Operate the engine at fast idle and check all hose connections and gaskets for leaks.

17. Adjust the carburetor idle speed and mixture.

On a car with standard transmission, adjust the clutch pedal free-travel. On a car with an automatic transmission, adjust the transmission control linkage.

18. Install the air cleaner.

4 MAJOR REPAIRS AND OPERATIONS

To perform the operations in this section, it will be necessary to remove the engine from the car and install it on a work stand as shown in Fig. 51. For engine removal and installation procedures, refer to Section 3.

When installing nuts or bolts that must be torqued (refer to Part 8-5 for torque specifications), oil the threads with light weight engine oil. **Do not oil threads that require oil-resistant or water-resistant sealer.**

MAIN BEARING REPLACEMENT

1. Remove the engine from the car, following the procedure in Section 3, and install it on a work stand.

2. On cars equipped with standard

transmission, remove the clutch disc and pressure plate.

Remove the flywheel and engine rear cover plate.

3. Turn the engine on the work stand so that the bottom of the engine is up. Remove the oil pan, gaskets and seals. Remove the oil pump and inlet tube assembly. Discard the oil pump gasket.

4. Remove the main bearing caps, and remove the bearings from the caps.

5. Remove the crankshaft rear oil seal and discard it.

6. Insert the upper bearing removal tool (tool 6331) in the oil hole in one of the crankshaft journals.

7. Rotate the crankshaft in the direction of engine rotation to force the bearing out of the block.

8. Clean the crankshaft journals. Inspect the journals and thrust faces (thrust bearing) for nicks, burrs or bearing pick-up that would cause premature bearing wear. **When replacing standard bearings with new bearings, it is good practice to first try to obtain the proper clearance with two blue bearing halves.**

9. **The upper and lower bearing halves are not interchangeable. The upper half is identifiable by the oil hole and groove. To install the upper main bearing, place the plain end of the bearing over the shaft on the locking tang side of the block and**

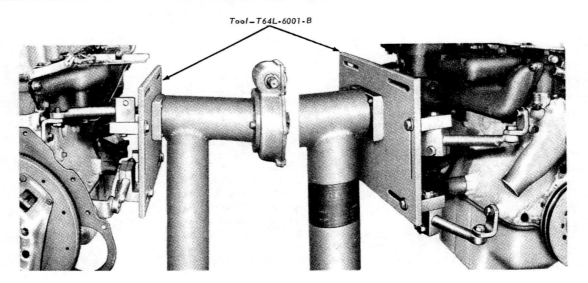

Tool—T64L-6001-B

A2169-A

FIG. 51—Engine Mounted on Work Stand—Typical

partially install the bearing so that tool 6331 can be inserted in the oil hole in the crankshaft. With tool 6331 positioned in the oil hole in the crankshaft, rotate the crankshaft in the opposite direction of engine rotation until the bearing is seated. Remove the tool.

10. Install the remaining main bearing upper halves.

11. Clean the bearing caps and install the main bearing lower halves in the caps.

12. Place a piece of Plastigage on the bearing surface the full width of the bearing cap and about ¼ inch off center (Fig. 52).

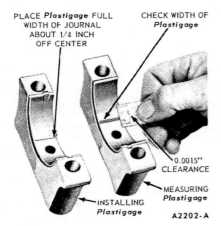

PLACE *Plastigage* FULL WIDTH OF JOURNAL ABOUT 1/4 INCH OFF CENTER

CHECK WIDTH OF *Plastigage*

0.0015" CLEARANCE

MEASURING *Plastigage*

INSTALLING *Plastigage*

A2202-A

FIG. 52—Installing and Measuring Plastigage on Bearing and Cap

13. Install the cap and torque the bolts to specifications. **Do not turn**

the crankshaft while the Plastigage is in place.

14. Remove the cap, then using the Plastigage scale, check the width of the Plastigage. **When checking the width of the Plastigage, check at the widest point in order to get the minimum clearance. Check at the narrowest point in order to get the maximum clearance. The difference between the two readings is the taper.**

15. If the clearance is less than the specified limits, try two red bearing halves or a combination of red and blue depending upon the condition. If the clearance exceeds specified limits, try 0.002 inch undersize bearings in combination with blue or red bearings. **The bearing clearance must be within specified limits. If 0.002 inch undersize main bearings are used on more than one journal, be sure they are all installed on the same side (cap or cylinder block) of the crankshaft.** If the standard and 0.002 inch undersize bearings do not bring the clearance within the desired limits, refinish the crankshaft journal, then install undersize bearings.

16. After the bearing has been fitted, apply a light coat of engine oil to the journal and bearings, then install the bearing cap. Torque the cap bolts to specifications.

17. Repeat the procedure for the remaining bearings.

18. If the thrust bearing cap (No. 5 main bearing) has been removed, install it as follows:

Install the thrust bearing cap with the bolts finger-tight. Pry the crankshaft forward against the thrust sur-

face of the upper half of the bearing (Fig. 53). Hold the crankshaft forward and pry the thrust bearing cap to the rear (Fig. 53). This will align the thrust surfaces of both halves of the bearing. Retain the forward pressure on the crankshaft. Torque the cap bolts to specifications (Fig. 53).

19. If the rear main bearing is replaced (on a work stand), be sure the main bearing is fitted and the cap bolts torqued to specifications; then install the new crankshaft rear oil seal.

20. Clean the oil pan, oil pump and oil pump screen.

21. Install the inlet tube and screen on the oil pump. Prime the oil pump with engine oil and install it with a new gasket. Torque the retaining bolts to specifications.

22. Apply oil-resistant sealer in the cavities between the bearing cap and cylinder block (Fig. 46). Install a new oil pan rear seal in the rear main bearing cap (Fig. 46), and apply a bead of oil-resistant sealer to the tapered ends of the seal (Fig. 46). Install new side gaskets on the oil pan with oil-resistant sealer (Fig. 47). Position a new cylinder front cover seal on the oil pan.

23. Turn the engine on the work stand so that the rear of the engine is up. Position the engine rear cover plate on the cylinder block. Position the flywheel on the crankshaft. **Coat the threads of the retaining bolts with oil-resistant sealer and install the retaining bolts.** Torque the bolts to specifications.

On a flywheel for a manual-shift

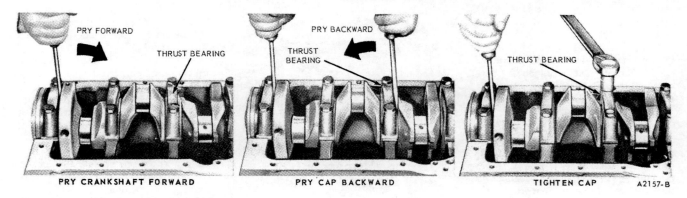

PRY CRANKSHAFT FORWARD   PRY CAP BACKWARD   TIGHTEN CAP   A2157-B

FIG. 53—Thrust Bearing Alignment

transmission, locate the clutch disc following the procedure in Part 5-3. Install the pressure plate. Torque the retaining bolts to specifications.

24. Remove the engine from the work stand and install it in the car following the procedure in Section 3.

25. Fill the crankcase and cooling system. Start the engine and check for oil pressure. Operate the engine at fast idle and check for oil and coolant leaks.

CRANKSHAFT

The crankshaft and related parts are shown in Fig. 54.

2. Remove the oil level dipstick.

3. Remove the accessory drive pulley (if so equipped). Remove the crankshaft damper retaining capscrew and lock washer; then remove the crankshaft damper (Fig. 20).

4. Remove the cylinder front cover and air conditioning drive idler pulley assembly (if so equipped). Remove the cover gasket. Remove the oil slinger.

5. Remove the flywheel and engine rear cover plate.

6. Turn the engine on the work stand so that the bottom of the engine is up. Remove the oil pan, gaskets and seals. Remove the oil pump and inlet tube assembly. Discard the oil pump gasket.

7. Make sure all bearing caps

(main and connecting rod) are marked so that they can be installed in their original locations. Turn the crankshaft until the connecting rod from which the cap is being removed is at the bottom of the stroke. Remove the connecting rod cap and bearings. Push the connecting rod and piston assembly up in the cylinder. **Do not turn the crankshaft completely around as the rod bolts may damage the crankpin journals.** Repeat this procedure and remove all connecting rod caps.

8. Remove the clutch pilot bushing, if necessary (Fig. 42).

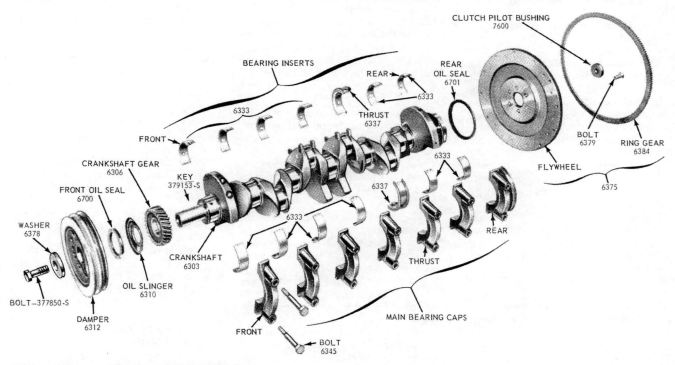

FIG. 54—Crankshaft and Related Parts

REMOVAL

1. Install the engine on a work stand. Remove the spark plugs to allow easy rotation of the crankshaft.

9. Align the timing marks (Fig. 26). Remove the crankshaft gear (Fig. 24).

10. Remove the main bearing caps

and bearings. Remove the crankshaft rear oil seal.

11. Carefully lift the crankshaft out of the cylinder block so that the thrust bearing surfaces are not damaged. **Handle the crankshaft with care to avoid possible fracture or damage to the finished surfaces.**

CLEANING AND INSPECTION

Refer to Part 8-1, Section 3 for the cleaning and inspection procedures. **Be sure the oil seal surfaces on the crankshaft and crankshaft damper are properly cleaned.**

REPAIRS

To refinish journals, dress minor imperfections, etc., refer to Part 8-1, Section 2.

INSTALLATION

1. Remove the main bearing inserts from the block and bearing caps.
2. Remove the bearing inserts from the connecting rod caps.
3. Clean the crankshaft rear oil seal recess in the cylinder block and rear main bearing cap.
4. If the crankshaft main bearing journals have been refinished to a definite undersize, install the correct undersize bearings. Be sure the bearing inserts and bearing bores are clean. Foreign material under the inserts will distort the bearing and cause a failure.
5. Place the upper main bearing inserts in position in the bore with the tang fitting in the slot provided. Be sure the oil holes in the bearing inserts are aligned with the oil holes in the cylinder block transverse webs.
6. Install the lower main bearing inserts in the bearing caps with the tang fitted in the slot.
7. Carefully lower the crankshaft into place. **Be careful not to damage the bearing surfaces.**
8. Check the clearance of each main bearing. Place a piece of Plastigage on the crankshaft journal the full width of the journal and about ¼ inch off center (Fig. 55). Follow steps 13 thru 16 under *Main Bearing Replacement.*
9. After the bearings have been installed, apply a light coat of engine oil to the journals and bearings. Install all the bearing caps, except the thrust bearing cap (No. 5 bearing). **Be sure that the main bearing caps are installed in their original locations.** Torque the bearing cap bolts to specifications.
10. Install the thrust bearing cap

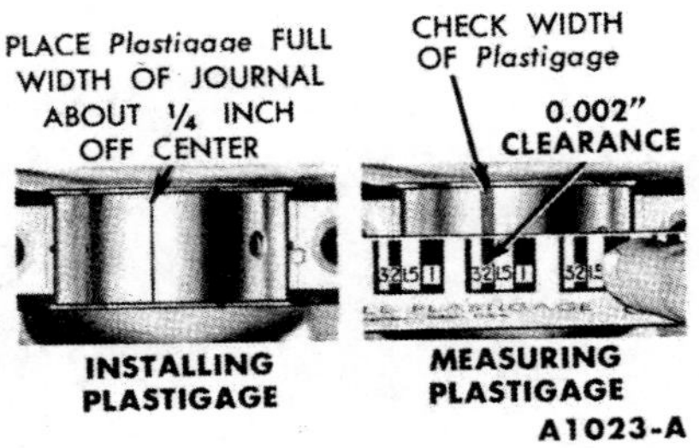

PLACE *Plastigage* FULL WIDTH OF JOURNAL ABOUT ¼ INCH OFF CENTER

CHECK WIDTH OF *Plastigage*

0.002" CLEARANCE

INSTALLING PLASTIGAGE

MEASURING PLASTIGAGE

A1023-A

FIG. 55—Installing and Measuring Plastigage on Crankshaft Journal

with the bolts finger-tight.

11. Pry the crankshaft forward against the thrust surface of the upper half of the bearing (Fig. 53).
12. Hold the crankshaft forward and pry the thrust bearing cap to the rear (Fig. 53). This will align the thrust surfaces of both halves of the bearing.
13. Retain the forward pressure on the crankshaft. Torque the cap bolts to specifications (Fig. 53).
14. Check the crankshaft end play, following the procedures in Part 8-1, Section 1.
15. If the end play exceeds the wear limit, replace the thrust bearing. If the end play is less than the minimum limit, inspect the thrust bearing faces for scratches, burrs, nicks or foreign matter. If the thrust faces are not defective, they probably were not aligned properly. Install the thrust bearing and align the faces following the recommended procedure (Steps 10 thru 13); then check the end play.
16. Coat the oil seal to cylinder block surface of the oil seal with oil. Coat the seal contact surface of the oil seal and crankshaft with Lubriplate. Install the seal with the tool shown in Fig. 44. Inspect the seal to be sure it was not damaged during installation.
17. Install the bearing inserts in the connecting rods and caps. Check the clearance of each bearing following the procedure under Connecting Rod Bearing Replacement.
18. If the bearing clearances are to specifications, apply a light coat of engine oil to the journals and bearings.
19. Turn the crankshaft throw to the bottom of its stroke, and pull the piston all the way down until the connecting rod bearing seats on the crankshaft journal.
20. Install the connecting rod cap and torque the nuts to specifications.
21. After the piston and connect-

ing rod assemblies have been installed, check the connecting rod side clearance on each crankshaft journal (Fig. 37).

22. Clean the oil pan, oil pump and oil pump screen.
23. Install the inlet tube and screen on the oil pump. Prime the oil pump with engine oil and install it with a new gasket. Torque the retaining bolts to specifications.
24. On a crankshaft for a standard transmission, install the clutch pilot bushing (refer to Clutch Pilot Bushing Replacement).
25. Turn the engine on the work stand so that the rear of the engine is up. Position the engine rear cover plate on the cylinder block. Position the flywheel on the crankshaft. **Coat the threads of the retaining bolts with oil-resistant sealer and install the retaining bolts.** Torque the bolts to specifications.

On a flywheel for a manual-shift transmission, locate the clutch disc following the procedure in Part 5-3. Install the pressure plate. Torque the retaining bolts to specifications.

26. Turn the engine on the work stand so that the front end is up.
27. Install the crankshaft gear following the procedure under Timing Gears Installation. Install the oil slinger.
28. Install a new crankshaft front oil seal in the cylinder front cover, (Fig. 21). Install the cylinder front cover and crankshaft damper by following the procedure outlined under Cylinder Front Cover Installation in Part 8-2.
29. Apply oil-resistant sealer in the cavities between the bearing cap and cylinder block (Fig. 46). Install a new oil pan rear seal in the rear main bearing cap (Fig. 46), and apply a bead of oil-resistant sealer to the tapered ends of the seal (Fig. 46). Install new side gaskets on the oil pan with oil-resistant sealer (Fig. 47). Position a new cylinder front cover seal on the oil pan.
30. Install the oil level dipstick.
31. Remove the engine from the work stand and install it in the car.
32. Check the ignition timing and adjust if necessary.

CAMSHAFT BEARING REPLACEMENT

Camshaft bearings are available pre-finished to size for standard and 0.015-inch undersize journal diameters.

1. Remove the camshaft, flywheel and crankshaft, following the appro-

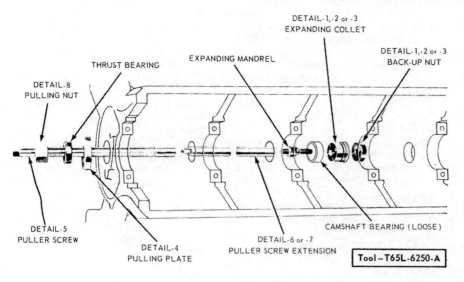

DETAIL-1, -2 or -3
EXPANDING COLLET

EXPANDING MANDREL

DETAIL-1, -2 or -3
BACK-UP NUT

THRUST BEARING

DETAIL-8
PULLING NUT

DETAIL-5
PULLER SCREW

DETAIL-4
PULLING PLATE

DETAIL-6 or -7
PULLER SCREW EXTENSION

CAMSHAFT BEARING (LOOSE)

Tool — T65L-6250-A

A2133-A

FIG. 56—Typical Camshaft Bearing Replacement

priate procedures in Part 8-2, Section 2 or Section 4. Push the pistons to the top of the cylinders.

2. Remove the camshaft rear bearing bore plug (Fig. 32). Remove the camshaft bearings with the tool shown in Fig. 56.

3. Select the proper size expanding collet and back-up nut and assemble on the expanding mandrel. With the expanding collet collapsed, install the collet assembly in the camshaft bearing, and tighten the back-up nut on the expanding mandrel until the collet fits the camshaft bearing.

4. Assemble the puller screw and extension (if necessary) as shown and install on the expanding mandrel. Wrap a cloth around the threads of the puller screw to protect the front bearing or journal. Tighten the pulling nut against the thrust bearing and pulling plate to remove the camshaft bearing. Be sure to hold a wrench on the end of the puller screw to prevent it from turning.

5. Repeat the procedure for each bearing. To remove the front bearing, install the puller screw from the rear of the cylinder block.

6. Position the new bearings at the bearing bores, and press them in place with the tool shown in Fig. 56. Be sure to center the pulling plate and puller screw to avoid damage to the bearing. **Failure to use the correct expanding collet can cause severe bearing damage.** Align the oil holes in the bearings with the oil holes in the cylinder block when the bearings are installed. **Be sure the front bearing is installed 0.020-0.035 inch**

below the front face of the cylinder block.

7. Clean out the camshaft rear bearing bore plug recess thoroughly. Coat the flange of a new plug with oil resistant sealer and install the plug (Fig. 33) with the flange edge of the plug facing outward.

8. Install the camshaft, crankshaft, flywheel and related parts, following the appropriate procedures in Part 8-2, Section 2 or Section 4, except do not check connecting rod and main bearing clearances as a part of Camshaft Bearing Replacement. Install the engine in the car.

CYLINDER ASSEMBLY REPLACEMENT

DISASSEMBLY

Follow steps 1 thru 19 under Engine Disassembly. Remove the cylinder head dowels from the cylinder block. Remove the cylinder block drain plugs and remove the cylinder assembly from the work stand.

CLEANING

Clean the gasket and seal surfaces of all parts and assemblies (refer to Part 8-1, Section 3).

ASSEMBLY

Install the replacement cylinder assembly on a work stand. Install the cylinder block drain plugs and cylinder head dowels. Transfer all parts removed from the old cylinder assembly to the new cylinder assembly, following the procedures in steps 19 thru 21, 23 thru 27, 29 thru 33 and 36 thru 47 under Engine Assembly.

Check all assembly clearances and correct as required.

CYLINDER BLOCK REPLACEMENT

DISASSEMBLY

Follow steps 1 thru 29 under Engine Disassembly. Remove the cylinder head dowels and cylinder block drain plugs. Remove the intake and exhaust manifolds and cylinder head as an assembly. Remove the cylinder block from the work stand.

CLEANING

Clean the gasket and seal surfaces of all parts and assemblies (Part 8-1, Section 3).

ASSEMBLY

Install the replacement cylinder block on a work stand. Install the cylinder block drain plugs and cylinder head dowels. Transfer all parts removed from the old cylinder block to the new cylinder block, following steps 5 thru 27, 29 thru 33, and 36 thru 47 under Engine Assembly. Install the manifolds and cylinder head as an assembly. Check all assembly clearances and correct as required.

ENGINE DISASSEMBLY

1. Remove the engine support insulators from the engine.

2. Install the engine on a work stand (Fig. 51).

3. Disconnect the spark plug wires at the spark plugs. Disconnect the distributor high tension lead at the coil. Remove the distributor cap and spark plug wires assembly.

4. On a car with Thermactor exhaust emission control system (Group 12), disconnect the air and vacuum lines. Remove the air supply pump and bracket, air manifold assembly, air cleaner assembly, anti-backfire valve and bracket, and air and vacuum lines.

5. Disconnect the fuel line at the carburetor and fuel pump. Disconnect the vacuum line at the distributor and carburetor. Remove the fuel and vacuum lines.

6. Remove the fuel pump and discard the gasket.

7. Remove the oil pressure sending unit and the oil level dipstick.

8. Disconnect the distributor primary wire at the coil; then remove the distributor. Remove the ignition coil and bracket assembly.

9. Remove the oil filter and oil filter mounting adapter.

10. Remove the crankcase venti-

lation regulator valve from the valve rocker arm cover. Remove the rocker arm cover.

11. Loosen the rocker arm stud nuts, rotate the rocker arms to one side, and remove the push rods in sequence. Place the push rods in a rack so they can be installed in the same location from which they were removed.

12. Remove the valve push rod cover. Remove the valve lifters in sequence (Fig. 30) to facilitate installation in the same sequence.

13. Remove the cooling fan, spacer, water pump pulley and fan and alternator drive belts.

14. Remove the alternator mounting bracket and adjusting arm bracket.

If equipped with air conditioning, remove the compressor mounting bracket.

15. Remove the water pump.

16. Remove the carburetor, intake and exhaust manifold and cylinder head as an assembly.

17. Remove the accessory drive pulley (if so equipped). Remove the crankshaft damper (Fig. 20). Remove the cylinder front cover and air conditioning drive idler pulley assembly (if so equipped). Remove the crankshaft oil slinger. Remove the crankshaft front oil seal from the cylinder front cover.

18. Remove the flywheel and engine rear cover plate.

19. Remove the oil pan and oil pump and pickup tube assembly. Discard the gaskets and seals.

20. Check the camshaft end play with a dial indicator following the procedure in Part 8-1, Section 1. Position the camshaft gear as shown in Fig. 31 and remove the camshaft thrust plate screws. Remove the camshaft, thrust plate and gear as an assembly.

21. Remove the crankshaft gear as shown in Fig. 24.

22. Remove any ridge and/or deposits from the upper end of the cylinder bores. Remove the cylinder ridge with a ridge cutter. Follow the instructions furnished *by the tool manufacturer.* **Never cut into the ring travel area in excess of 1/32 inch when removing ridges.**

23. **Make sure all bearing caps (main and connecting rod) are marked so that they can be installed in their original locations.** Turn the crankshaft until the connecting rod being removed is down. Remove the connecting rod cap.

24. **Push each connecting rod and**

piston assembly out the top of the cylinder with the handle end of a hammer. **Avoid damage to the crankshaft journal or the cylinder wall when removing the piston and rod.**

25. Remove the bearing inserts from the connecting rods and caps. Install the rod caps on the connecting rods from which they were removed.

26. Remove the main bearing caps. Carefully lift the crankshaft out of the cylinder block so that the thrust bearing surfaces are not damaged. Remove the crankshaft rear oil seal. **Handle the crankshaft with care to avoid possible fracture or damage to the finished surfaces.**

27. Remove the main bearing inserts from the cylinder block and main bearing caps.

28. Remove the oil dipstick tube from the cylinder block. Remove the cylinder head dowel pins and cylinder block drain plugs.

29. Disassemble the pistons, piston rings and connecting rods, following the procedures under Pistons and Connecting Rods Disassembly (Part 8-2, Section 2).

30. If the camshaft gear is removed from the camshaft, press the camshaft out of the gear in an arbor press. Remove the thrust plate and spacer.

31. Drill a hole in the camshaft rear bearing bore plug and remove the plug as shown in Fig. 32. Remove the camshaft bearings; refer to Camshaft Bearing Replacement.

32. Remove the carburetor from the intake manifold and discard the gasket. Remove the intake and exhaust manifolds from the cylinder head and separate the manifolds. Disassemble the cylinder head, removing the rocker arms, valves, valve springs, coolant outlet elbow, etc. Place all parts in a rack or identify them so they can be installed in the same location from which they were removed.

ENGINE ASSEMBLY

1. Clean and inspect all parts per the appropriate procedures in Part 8-1, except do not disassemble the oil pump and hydraulic valve lifters for cleaning.

2. Remove the glaze from the cylinder bores by following the instructions of the tool manufacturer.

3. Invert the engine on the work stand. Position new camshaft bearings in the bearing bores and press them in place (Fig. 56). Align the oil holes in the bearing with the oil holes

in the cylinder block when the bearings are installed. **Be sure the camshaft front bearing is installed 0.020-0.035 inch below the front face of the cylinder block.**

4. Coat the flange of a new camshaft rear bearing bore plug with oil-resistant sealer and install it with the flange facing out (Fig. 33). Drive the plug in until the edge of the flange is flush with the inner corner of the chamfered bore.

5. Oil the camshaft journals and apply Lubriplate to all *the* lobes. Carefully slide the camshaft through the bearings. Install the thrust plate screws and torque to specifications.

6. If the camshaft gear was removed, install the spacer, thrust plate and gear, using the tool shown in Fig. 27.

7. If the crankshaft main bearing journals have been refinished to a definite undersize, install the correct undersize bearings. Be sure the bearing inserts and bearing bores are clean.

8. Place the upper main bearing inserts in position in the bore with the tang fitting in the slot provided.

9. Install the lower main bearing inserts in the bearing caps.

10. Carefully lower the crankshaft into place. **Be careful not to damage the bearing surfaces.**

11. Check the clearance of each main bearing following the procedure under Main Bearing Replacement.

12. After the bearings have been fitted, apply a light coat of engine oil to the journals and bearings. Install all the bearing caps, except the thrust bearing cap (No. 5 bearing). **Be sure that the main bearing caps are installed in their original locations.** Torque the bearing cap bolts to specifications.

13. Install the thrust bearing cap and check the crankshaft end play by following steps 10 thru 15 under Crankshaft Installation.

14. Check the camshaft end play and camshaft gear backlash following the procedures in Part 8-1, Section 1. If the end play exceeds specifications, replace the thrust plate. If the gear backlash exceeds specifications, replace the camshaft gear (and crankshaft gear as necessary).

15. Check the camshaft gear runout with a dial indicator (Part 8-1, Section 1). If the gear runout is excessive, remove the gear and clean any burrs from the shaft, or replace the gear.

16. Check the piston to cylinder bore fit of each piston, following the

procedure in Part 8-1, Section 3.

17. Check the end gap of all piston rings (Part 8-1, Section 3). Assemble the pistons, piston rings and connecting rods, following the procedure under Pistons and Connecting Rods Assembly (Part 8-2, Section 2). Check the piston ring side clearance (Part 8-1, Section 3).

18. Install the piston and connecting rod assemblies, and check the clearance of the connecting rod bearings. Refer to Piston and Connecting Rod Installation and Connecting Rod *Bearing Replacement* (Part 8-2, Section 2).

19. Coat a new crankshaft front oil seal with grease and install it in the cylinder front cover (Fig. 21).

20. Install the crankshaft oil slinger. Coat the gasket surfaces of the cylinder front cover and cylinder block with oil-resistant sealer. Position the gasket on the block and install the cylinder front cover (Fig. 22). Install the air conditioning drive belt idler pulley assembly, if so equipped. Torque the bolts to specifications.

21. Lubricate the damper end of the crankshaft with a white lead and oil mixture. Apply Lubriplate to the seal surfaces of the front oil seal and crankshaft damper. Install the crankshaft damper (Fig. 23). Install the accessory drive pulley if so equipped.

22. Apply a light film of engine oil on a new crankshaft rear oil seal and apply Lubriplate on the seal contact surface of the crankshaft. Install the seal (Fig. 44) flush to 0.005 inch below the face of the cylinder block.

23. Position the engine rear cover plate on the rear of the cylinder block and install the flywheel on the crankshaft. **Apply oil-resistant sealer to the threads of the flywheel retaining bolts.** Install the bolts and torque them to specifications.

24. Use a new gasket and install the inlet tube and screen on the oil pump. Prime the oil pump with engine oil. Position a new gasket on the oil pump body and install the oil pump and inlet tube assembly. Torque the retaining bolts to specifications.

25. Apply oil-resistant sealer in the cavities between the bearing cap and

cylinder block (Fig. 46). Install a new oil pan rear seal in the rear main bearing cap (Fig. 46), and apply a bead of oil-resistant sealer to the tapered ends of the seal (Fig. 46).

26. Install new side gaskets on the oil pan with oil-resistant sealer (Fig. 47). Position a new cylinder front cover seal on the oil pan.

27. Coat both sides of a new water pump gasket with water-resistant sealer and position the gasket on the cylinder block. Coat the threads of the water pump bolts with sealer. Install the water pump. Torque the bolts to specifications.

28. Assemble the valves, springs, rocker arms, coolant outlet elbow, etc., following the procedures under Cylinder Head Assembly (Part 8-2, Section 2).

29. Place a new cylinder head gasket on the block. Carefully position the cylinder head on the block and install the bolts. Torque the bolts in sequence (Fig. 14) to specifications.

30. Clean the exterior surface of the valve lifters with a clean, lintfree cloth and oil the surface with engine oil. Install the valve lifters (Fig. 30) in the same sequence that they were removed.

31. Apply Lubriplate to both ends of the push rods and to the push rod bores in the cylinder head. Install the push rods in the same sequence that they were removed. Be sure the push rods are properly seated in the valve lifters. Engage the rocker arms with the push rods and tighten the stud nuts sufficiently to hold the push rods in place.

32. Adjust the valve clearance (Part 8-1, Section 2).

33. Coat the gasket surface of the push rod cover with oil-resistant sealer and position a new gasket on the cover. Install the cover and gasket on the cylinder block. Torque the cover bolts in sequence to specifications.

34. Install the intake and exhaust manifold, following the procedure under Intake and Exhaust Manifolds Installation (Part 8-2, Section 2).

35. Install the carburetor with a new gasket.

36. Install a new gasket with oil-

resistant sealer on the valve rocker arm cover. Install the cover on the cylinder head and torque the coverscrews in sequence to specifications. Install the crankcase ventilation regulator valve in the rocker arm cover. Attach the vent hose to the intake manifold inlet tube.

37. Install the cylinder block drain plugs and oil pressure sending unit. Install the oil level dipstick tube and dipstick.

38. If equipped with air conditioning, install the compressor mounting bracket.

39. Install the alternator mounting bracket and adjusting arm bracket.

40. Install the water pump pulley, accessory drive pulley (if so equipped), spacer and cooling fan.

41. On a car with Thermactor exhaust emission control system, install the anti-backfire valve and bracket, air cleaner assembly, air manifold assembly and air supply pump and bracket. Install the air and vacuum lines.

42. Install the oil filter mounting adapter. Coat the seal surface of a new oil filter with grease (or engine oil). Install the oil filter until the seal surface contacts the cylinder block; then tighten the filter an additional ½ turn.

43. Install the ignition coil and bracket.

44. Position No. 1 cylinder on TDC after the compression stroke. Set the distributor points to No. 1 cylinder firing position and install the distributor. With the distributor in points open position (No. 1 cyl.) install the hold down clamp and screw. Tighten the screw snug, but not tight.

45. Use a new gasket and install the fuel pump. Torque the bolts alternately and evenly to specifications. Install the carburetor fuel inlet line and distributor vacuum line.

46. Install the distributor cap and spark plug wires assembly. Connect the spark plug wires. Connect the distributor primary and high tension wires to the ignition coil.

47. Remove the engine from the work stand. Install the engine front support insulators on the engine.

PART 8-3   CHALLENGER 289 V-8

1   DESCRIPTION AND OPERATION

The Challenger 289 V-8 engine (Figs. 1, 2, 3 and 4) has a piston displacement of 289 cubic inches and a compression ratio of 9.0:1. The warranty plate symbol for the engine is C.

An engine identification tag is attached to the ignition coil bracket; refer to Part 8-1, Section 1.

THERMACTOR EXHAUST EMISSION CONTROL SYSTEM

For engines equipped with Thermactor exhaust emission control system, refer to Group 12 for description and operation and repair procedures.

MANIFOLDS

Coolant flows from the front of the engine through the intake manifold into the heater inlet hose and circulates through the heater. On cars, that do not have a heater, the coolant is returned to the water pump through a bypass hose.

Exhaust gases flowing through the crossover passage (Fig. 5) provide the initial heat necessary to assist in vaporizing the incoming fuel mixture.

A2286-A

FIG. 1 — ¾ Left Front View

A2287-A

FIG. 2 —¾ Right Front View

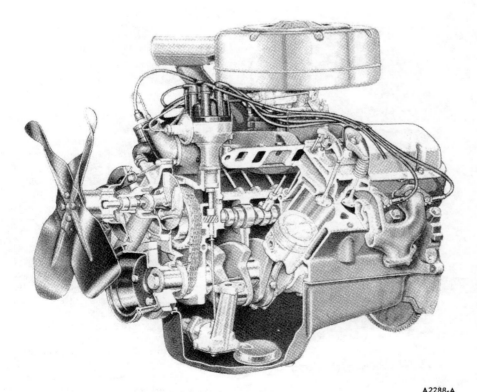

A2288-A

FIG. 3—Front ¾ Sectional View

The intake manifold has two sets of fuel passages, each with its own separate inlet connection to the carburetor (Fig. 6). The right barrel of the carburetor feeds Nos. 1, 4, 6 and 7 cylinders and the left barrel feeds Nos. 2, 3, 5 and 8 cylinders.

Filtered air is drawn from the air cleaner, through an air inlet tube, into the heat chamber in the right exhaust manifold. Here the air is heated and then directed to the automatic choke through the air outlet choke tube (Fig. 7).

CYLINDER HEADS

The cylinder head assemblies contain the valves and the valve rocker arm assemblies. The valve guides and push rods guides are machined in the head with a cast combustion chamber. The valve arrangement from front to rear on the left bank is E-I-E-I-E-I-E-I and on the right bank I-E-I-E-I-E-I-E (Fig. 8).

CYLINDER BLOCK

The cylinders are numbered from front to rear, on the right bank, 1, 2, 3 and 4 and on the left bank 5, 6, 7 and 8. The firing order is 1-5-4-2-6-3-7-8.

The oil pump, mounted inside the oil pan at the left front, is driven by the distributor through an intermediate drive shaft.

The oil filter is mounted on the left lower front of the block.

The crankshaft is supported by five main bearings. Crankshaft end thrust is controlled by the flanges of the No. 3 main bearing.

The pistons have two compression rings and one control ring. The top compression ring is chrome-plated and the lower compression ring is phosphate-coated. The oil control ring assembly consists of a serrated spring and two chrome-plated steel rails.

VALVE TRAIN

The push rods are tubular steel with ball ends. The push rods supply oil from a metering valve (disc) in the hydraulic valve lifters through drilled holes in the ball ends for independent lubrication of each rocker arm.

The rocker arms have a drilled hole in the push rod end for lubrication. They are individually mounted on a stud that is pressed into the cylinder head. A fulcrum seat permits the rocker motion and a nut secures the rocker arm on the stud.

The camshaft is supported by five stepped bearings pressed into the block. A dowel is used for positioning the camshaft sprocket. The camshaft

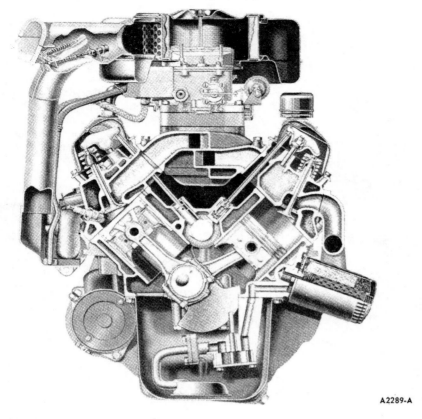

A2289-A

FIG. 4—Front Cross Sectional View

A1578-B

FIG. 5—Intake Manifold Exhaust Gas Crossover Passage

is driven by a sprocket and timing chain in mesh with a sprocket on the crankshaft. Camshaft end play is controlled by a thrust plate attached to the cylinder block. An eccentric, bolted to the front end of the camshaft, operates the fuel pump.

Hydraulic valve lifters are used which provide zero valve lash. The operation and parts identification of the hydraulic valve lifters are shown in Fig. 9.

When the valve is closed, the lifter assembly is on the base circle of the camshaft lobe and the valve push rod is in its lowest position. With the lifter assembly in this position, the plunger

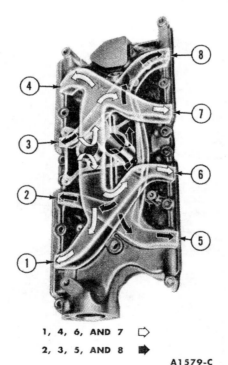

1, 4, 6, AND 7 ⇨

2, 3, 5, AND 8 ➡

A1579-C

FIG. 6—Intake Manifold Fuel Passages

spring expands, forcing the plunger upward. This action is transmitted to the valve rocker arm via the valve

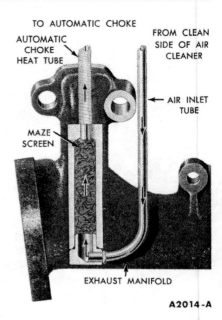

A2014-A

FIG. 7—Automatic Choke Heat Chamber

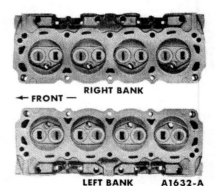

A1632-A

FIG. 8—Valve Port Arrangement

push rod until there is solid contact between the valve and the valve end of the valve rocker arm (zero valve lash).

As the lifter plunger moves upward, the volume of the compression chamber is increased, resulting in reduced oil pressure in the compression chamber. Therefore, to equalize the resulting pressure differential between the supply chamber and the compression chamber, the check valve moves off its seat and permits oil to flow from the supply chamber to the compression chamber. When the compression chamber becomes filled with oil, the pressure in the two chambers is equalized. The oil flow *ceases and the check valve spring* seats the check valve and closes the check valve port.

As the camshaft rotates, the lifter assembly is raised by the camshaft

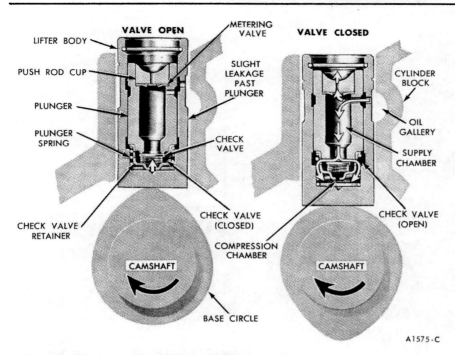

FIG. 9—Typical Hydraulic Valve Lifter Operation

lobe. This increases the push rod force against the lifter plunger and hydraulic pressure immediately builds up in the compression chamber until it acts as a solid member of the valve operating mechanism. The lifter then becomes a hydraulic ram which forces the valve in the cylinder head to open. During this period, a slight leakage of oil past the plunger occurs (calibrated leak down rate).

As the high point of the camshaft lobe rotates and passes by the foot of the valve lifter, the valve in the cylinder head seats and the valve lifter assembly is forced downward. Reduced force on the lifter plunger at this time relieves the pressure on the lifter plunger and it is free to be moved upward by the plunger spring. This action allows oil to flow once again through the oil holes in the lifter body and plunger.

The operating cycle is completed for each revolution of the camshaft. Zero clearance (lash) in the valve train mechanism is maintained at all times by the hydraulic force and expansion of the plunger spring between the lifter body and plunger.

LUBRICATION SYSTEM

Oil from the oil pan sump, located in the front of the oil pan, is forced through the pressure type lubrication system (Fig. 10) by a rotor oil pump. A spring-loaded relief valve in the pump limits the maximum pressure of the system. Oil relieved by the

valve is directed back to the intake side of the pump.

All the oil discharged by the pump passes through an exclusive design full flow-type Rotunda filter before it enters the engine. The filter is mounted at the lower left front of the engine.

On a cartridge-type oil filter, a relief valve in the filter permits oil to bypass the filter if the element becomes clogged.

On an element-type oil filter, a bypass provides oil to the engine in case the filter element becomes clogged. The bypass is located in the hollow center bolt of the filter and consists of a spring-loaded valve. When the element is clean and oil will flow through it, the pressure difference between the inner and outer faces of the valve is not great enough to overcome the spring pressure behind the valve. Therefore, no oil flows through the bypass. When the element is dirty and will not permit a sufficient flow of oil, the pressure acting on the inner face of the valve drops. If the pressure difference between the valve faces is great enough to overcome spring pressure, the valve will open. Oil then bypasses the element, maintaining an emergency supply of oil to the engine.

From the filter, the oil flows into the main oil gallery which is located to the right side of the camshaft. The oil gallery supplies oil to each individual main bearing, through drilled pas-

sages in the block. Passages are drilled from each main bearing to each camshaft bearing. Number 1 main bearing feeds No. 1 camshaft bearing, and No. 2 main bearing feeds No. 2 camshaft bearing, etc. The oil then flows through notches or grooves in the main bearings to lubricate the crankshaft journals. The timing chain and sprockets are lubricated by oil deflected from the front camshaft bearing by an oil drip trough on the cylinder front cover.

The crankshaft is drilled from the main bearings to the connecting rod bearings.

A small groove is located in the connecting rod at the mating face where the cap contacts the connecting rod. This groove is used as an oil squirt hole for cylinder wall lubrication. Oil from the connecting rod squirt hole lubricates the opposite cylinder wall. For example, the No. 1 connecting rod oils No. 5 cylinder, etc. As the crankshaft turns, the hole in the connecting rod bearing aligns with the hole in the journal causing a direct squirt of oil onto the cylinder wall (Fig. 10).

Oil passages are drilled from the main oil gallery to each valve lifter oil gallery. Oil from here feeds the valve lifter assemblies. A reservoir at each valve lifter bore boss traps oil so that oil is available for valve lifter lubrication as soon as the engine starts.

The oil hole in the hydraulic lifter is indexed with the lifter oil gallery and oil flows into the lifter. Oil in the lifter is then metered through the metering valve (disc), through the oil passages in the push rod cup and then flows up the hollow push rod. In this position, the drilled hole in the ball end of the push rod is indexed with a drilled hole in the rocker arm and the oil lubricates the upper valve train bearing areas (Fig. 10). Excess oil is returned to the oil pan through drain back holes located at each end of the cylinder heads and block (Fig. 10).

AIR INTAKE SYSTEM

The temperature of the air entering the air cleaner is thermostatically controlled by an air intake duct and thermostat assembly (Fig. 4). This system supplies warm air to the engine during the warm-up period, resulting in better fuel vaporization and reducing the possibility of carburetor icing. The air duct shroud and tube assembly together with the air duct

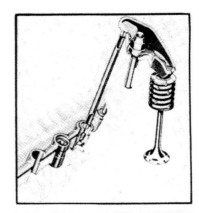

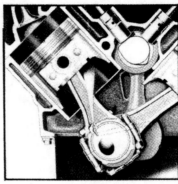

A2290-A

FIG. 10—Lubrication System

and thermostat assembly direct warm air into the air cleaner and carburetor.

If the temperature of the air passing over the thermostat is less than 75°F., the valve plate in the air duct is held in an up or heat on position by a valve plate tension spring. When the valve plate is in the heat on position, the air entering the air cleaner is drawn through the shroud and tube assembly. The air passing through the shroud and tube is first directed over the exhaust manifold and heated.

A wax-filled thermostat is connected to the valve plate by a thermostat rod. The incoming air passes over the thermostat before entering the air cleaner. As the temperature of the air passing over the thermostat approaches 85°F., the wax begins to expand and pushes the thermostat rod against the valve plate. The tension of the valve plate spring is overcome and the valve plate is moved downward to partially close off the warm air duct to allow the cooler air from the engine compartment to mix with the warm air directed from the exhaust manifold.

If the temperature of the incoming air is approximately 105°F., the valve plate moves downward to a heat off position to close off the

warm air duct. Cooler air from the engine compartment is then directed to the air cleaner without passing over the exhaust manifold.

CRANKCASE VENTILATION

The engine is equipped with a positive crankcase ventilation system. In the positive system, the crankcase vapors are directed to the intake manifold.

OPEN VENTILATION SYSTEM

The air flow in the positive crankcase ventilation system is shown in Fig. 11.

Ventilating air enters the engine through the oil filler cap located on the front of the left valve rocker arm cover. The filler cap contains a filtering element which filters the incoming air.

From the oil filler cap, the air flows into the front section of the valve rocker arm chamber. The ventilating air moves down past the push rods into the front of the lower crankcase and into the timing chain chamber.

The rotating action of the crankshaft causes the air to flow towards the rear of the crankcase and up into

the rear section of the right valve rocker arm cover. The air then enters a spring-loaded regulator valve that regulates the amount of air to meet changing operating conditions. The air is then directed to the intake manifold through the crankcase vent hose.

At idle speed, intake manifold is high. The high vacuum overcomes the tension of the spring pressure and moves the valve to the Low Speed Operation position (Fig. 12). With the valve in this position, the ventilating air passes between the valve (jiggle pin) and the outlet port. With the valve in this position, there is minimum ventilation.

As engine speed increases and manifold vacuum decreases, the spring forces the valve to the full open position (Fig. 12). This increases the flow of ventilating air.

CLOSED VENTILATION SYSTEM

The closed ventilation system is the same as the open ventilation system except for the following:

The ventilating air is picked up at the air cleaner and transferred through a tube to the oil filler cap.

The oil filler cap is otherwise closed to the atmosphere.

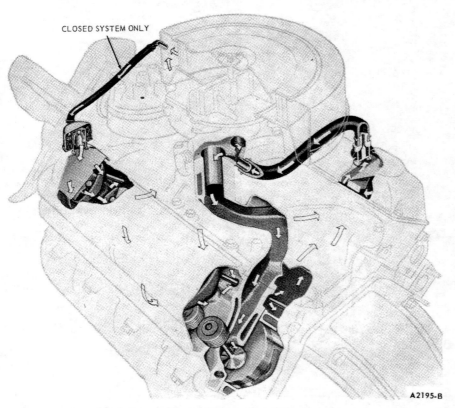

CLOSED SYSTEM ONLY

A2195-B

FIG. 11—Positive Crankcase Ventilation System

COOLING SYSTEM

The coolant is drawn from the bottom of the radiator by the water pump which delivers the coolant to the cylinder block (Fig. 13).

The coolant travels through cored passages to cool the entire length of each cylinder wall. Upon reaching the rear of the cylinder block, the coolant is directed upward into the cylinder heads, where it cools the combustion chambers, valves and valve seats on its return to the front of the engine.

The coolant from each cylinder head flows through the water passages in the intake manifold past the water thermostat, if it is open, into the top of the radiator. If the thermostat is closed, a small portion of the coolant is returned to the water pump for recirculation. The entire system is pressurized to 13-15 psi.

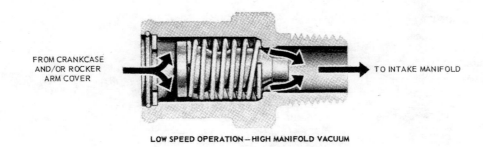

FROM CRANKCASE
AND/OR ROCKER
ARM COVER

TO INTAKE MANIFOLD

LOW SPEED OPERATION—HIGH MANIFOLD VACUUM

HIGH SPEED OPERATION—LOW MANIFOLD VACUUM

FROM CRANKCASE
AND/OR ROCKER
ARM COVER

TO INTAKE MANIFOLD

A2121-B

FIG. 12—Positive Crankcase Ventilation Regulator Valve Operation

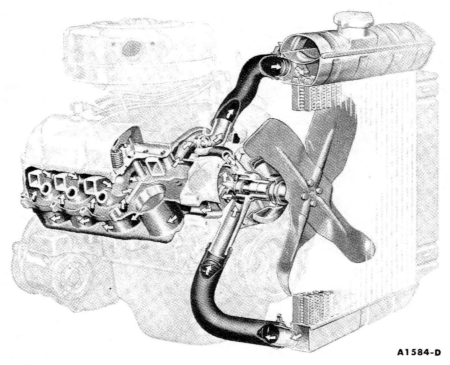

A1584-D

FIG. 13—Cooling System

2 IN-CAR ADJUSTMENTS AND REPAIRS

When installing nuts or bolts that must be torqued (refer to Part 8-5 for torque specifications), oil the threads with light weight engine oil. **Do not oil threads that require oil-resistant or water-resistant sealer.**

ENGINE FRONT SUPPORTS

The front supports are located on each side of the cylinder block (Fig. 14). The procedures given apply to either a right or left installation.

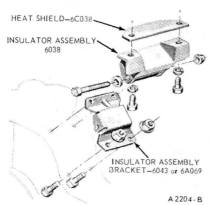

HEAT SHIELD—6C038
INSULATOR ASSEMBLY 6038
INSULATOR ASSEMBLY BRACKET—6043 or 6A069
A2204-B

FIG. 14—Engine Front Supports

REMOVAL

1. Remove the engine insulator as-sembly to insulator assembly brack-et nut, bolt and washer from both en-gine supports.

2. Raise the engine slightly with a jack and a wood block placed under the oil pan.

3. Remove the engine insulator as-sembly to cylinder block retaining bolts and lock washers. Remove the engine insulator assembly and the heat shield.

INSTALLATION

1. Position the engine insulator as-sembly and the heat shield to the cyl-inder block and install the retaining bolts and lock washers. Torque the bolts to specifications.

2. Lower the engine into position, install the engine insulator assembly bolts and flat washers and remove the jack and wood block.

3. Install the engine insulator as-sembly to insulator assembly bracket nuts. Torque the nuts to specifica-tions.

ENGINE REAR SUPPORT

The rear support is located at the transmission extension housing (Fig. 15).

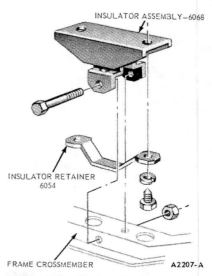

INSULATOR ASSEMBLY—6068
INSULATOR RETAINER 6054
FRAME CROSSMEMBER
A2207-A

FIG. 15—Engine Rear Support

REMOVAL

1. Remove the support insulator to cross member retaining bolt and lock nut.

2. Remove the support insulator to transmission extension housing bolts and lock washers.

3. Raise the transmission with a floor jack. Remove the support insu-

lator and retainer.

INSTALLATION

1. Position the support insulator and retainer on the transmission extension housing.

2. Install the support insulator to transmission extension housing bolts and lock washers. Torque the bolts to specifications. Lower the transmission.

3. Install the support insulator to cross member retaining bolt and lock nut. Torque the nut to specifications.

VALVE ROCKER ARM ASSEMBLY

The valve rocker arm assembly is shown in Fig. 16.

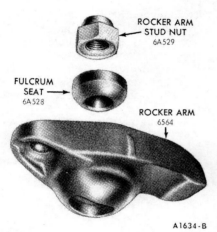

FIG. 16—Valve Rocker Arm Assembly

REMOVAL

1. To remove a valve rocker arm assembly from the right cylinder head, disconnect the automatic choke heat chamber air inlet hose from the inlet tube near the right valve rocker arm cover.

Remove the air cleaner and intake duct assembly.

Remove the automatic choke heat tube. Remove the crankcase ventilation regulator valve from the valve rocker arm cover.

If the engine is equipped with a Thermactor exhaust emission control system, disconnect the air hose and remove the check valve from the right air manifold.

2. Disconnect the spark plug wires from the spark plugs by grasping, twisting and pulling the moulded cap only. Remove the wires from the bracket on the valve rocker arm cover(s) and position the wires out of the way.

3. If the engine is equipped with

a Thermactor exhaust emission control system, disconnect the air hose at the left air manifold.

4. Remove the valve rocker arm cover(s).

5. Remove the valve rocker arm stud nut, fulcrum seat and rocker arm.

CLEANING AND INSPECTION

Refer to Part 8-1, Section 3 for the cleaning and inspection procedures.

REPAIRS

If removal of the rocker arm stud is necessary, refer to the procedure under Cylinder Head Repairs in Part 8-1, Section 2.

INSTALLATION

1. Apply Lubriplate to the top of the valve stem and at the push rod guide in the cylinder head.

2. Install the valve rocker arm, fulcrum seat and stud nut. Adjust the valve clearance following the procedure in Part 8-1, Section 2.

3. Clean the valve rocker arm cover(s) and the cylinder head gasket surface(s). Apply oil-resistant sealer to one side of new cover gasket(s). Lay the cemented side of the gasket(s) in place in the cover(s).

4. Position the cover(s) on the cylinder head(s). Make sure the gasket seats evenly all around the head. Install the bolts. The cover is tightened in two steps. Torque the bolts to specifications. Two minutes later, torque the bolts to the same specifications.

If the engine is equipped with a Thermactor exhaust emission control system, connect the air hose to the left air manifold.

If the right cover was removed, install the automatic choke heat tube and the crankcase ventilation regulator valve.

If the engine is equipped with a Thermactor exhaust emission control system, install the check valve on the right air manifold, and connect the air hose.

Connect the automatic choke heat chamber air inlet hose.

Install the air cleaner and intake duct assembly.

5. Install the spark plug wires in the bracket on the valve rocker arm cover(s). Connect the spark plug wires.

INTAKE MANIFOLD

The intake manifold assembly is

shown in Fig. 17.

REMOVAL

1. Drain the cooling system. Disconnect the automatic choke heat chamber air inlet hose at the inlet tube near the right valve rocker arm cover. Remove the air cleaner and intake duct assembly.

2. Disconnect the accelerator rod from the carburetor. Remove the accelerator retracting spring.

On a car with an automatic transmission, disconnect the transmission vacuum line at the intake manifold.

On a car with vacuum-operated accessories disconnect the vacuum line at the intake manifold.

3. Disconnect the high tension lead and wires from the coil.

4. Disconnect the spark plug wires from the spark plugs by grasping, twisting and pulling the moulded cap only. Remove the wires from the harness brackets on the valve rocker arm covers. Remove the distributor cap and spark plug wire assembly.

5. Remove the carburetor fuel inlet line and the automatic choke heat tube.

6. Disconnect the distributor vacuum line from the carburetor. Remove the distributor hold down bolt and remove the distributor and vacuum line.

7. Disconnect the radiator upper hose from the coolant outlet housing, and the water temperature sending unit wire at the sending unit. Remove the heater hose from the automatic choke housing and disconnect the hose from the intake manifold.

8. Loosen the clamp on the water pump bypass hose at the coolant outlet housing and slide the hose off the outlet housing.

9. Disconnect the crankcase vent hose at the valve rocker arm cover.

10. If equipped with Thermactor exhaust emission system, remove the air pump to left air manifold hose at the air pump and position it out of the way.

Remove the air hose at the antibackfire valve. Remove the air hose bracket from the right valve rocker arm cover and position the air hose out of the way.

11. If the car is equipped with air conditioning, remove the compressor to intake manifold brackets.

12. Remove the intake manifold and carburetor as an assembly. **It may be necessary to pry the intake manifold away from the cylinder head(s). Remove the intake mani-**

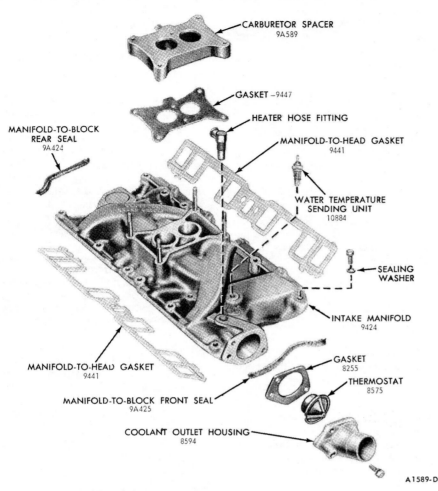

FIG. 17—Intake Manifold Assembly

fold gaskets and seals. Discard the intake manifold retaining bolt sealing washers.

13. If the manifold assembly is to be disassembled, remove the coolant outlet housing, gasket and thermostat. Remove the ignition coil, temperature sending unit, carburetor, spacer and gaskets.

CLEANING AND INSPECTION

Refer to Part 8-1, Section 3 for the cleaning and inspection procedures.

INSTALLATION

Intake manifold alignment tools are required when installing the intake manifold on the cylinder block and cylinder heads. Fabricate two alignment tools according to the specifications shown in Fig. 18.

1. If the intake manifold assembly was disassembled, install the temperature sending unit (threads coated with electrical conductive sealer), ignition coil, carburetor, spacer and gaskets. Position the thermostat in

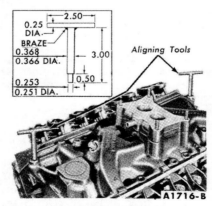

FIG. 18—Intake Manifold Alignment

the coolant outlet housing. Coat the thermostat gasket with water-resistant sealer and position it on the coolant outlet housing. Install the coolant outlet housing.

If equipped with Thermactor exhaust emission control system, install the anti-backfire valve and bracket.

2. Clean the mating surfaces of the intake manifold, cylinder heads

and cylinder block. Use a suitable solvent to remove all traces of oil. Coat the cylinder block seal surfaces with oil-resistant sealer.

3. Position new seals on the cylinder block and new gaskets on the cylinder heads with the gaskets interlocked with the seal tabs. Be sure the holes in the gaskets are aligned with the holes in the cylinder heads.

Apply non-hardening sealer at the four junction points of the seals and gaskets.

4. Carefully lower the intake manifold into position on the cylinder block and cylinder heads. **After the intake manifold is in place, run a finger around the seal area to make sure the seals are in place. If the seals are not in place, remove the intake manifold and position the seals.**

5. Be sure the holes in the manifold gaskets and manifold are in alignment. Position the intake manifold alignment tools (Fig. 18) in the front and rear bolt holes (Nos. 10 and 12) on the left bank of the manifold.

6. Using new sealing washers, install the intake manifold retaining bolts. Torque the bolts in sequence (Fig. 19) to 15-17 ft-lbs.

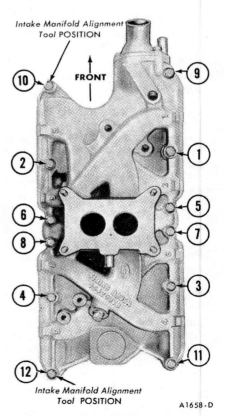

FIG. 19—Intake Manifold Torque Sequence

7. Remove the manifold alignment tools from the front and rear bolt holes (Nos. 10 and 12). Using new sealing washers, install the two remaining bolts and torque to 15-17 ft-lbs.

8. Torque all the manifold retaining bolts in sequence to 20-22 ft-lbs.

9. Install the water pump bypass hose on the coolant outlet housing. Slide the clamp into position and tighten the clamp.

10. Connect the radiator upper hose. Install the heater hose against the automatic choke housing and connect the hose at the intake manifold.

11. Install the carburetor fuel inlet line and the automatic choke heat tube.

12. Rotate the crankshaft damper until the No. 1 piston is on TDC at the end of the compression stroke. Position the distributor in the block with the rotor at the No. 1 firing position and the points open. Install the hold down clamp.

13. Install the distributor cap. Position the spark plug wires in the harness brackets on the valve rocker arm covers and connect the wires to the plugs.

14. Connect the crankcase vent hose. Connect the high tension lead and coil wires.

15. Connect the accelerator rod and retracting spring.

On a car with an automatic transmission, connect the transmission vacuum line.

On a car equipped with vacuum-operated accessories, connect any vacuum lines that were disconnected from the intake manifold during removal.

On a car with air conditioning, install the compressor to intake manifold brackets.

16. If equipped with Thermactor exhaust emission control system, connect the hose from the left air manifold to the air pump, connect the air hose bracket to the right valve rocker arm cover.

17. Fill and bleed the cooling system.

18. Start the engine and check and adjust the ignition timing. Connect the distributor vacuum line at the carburetor.

19. Operate the engine at fast idle and check all hose connections and gaskets for leaks. Operate the engine until engine temperatures have stabilized and adjust the engine idle speed and idle fuel mixture.

20. Connect the automatic choke heat chamber air inlet hose.

21. Adjust the transmission throttle linkage. Install the air cleaner and intake duct assembly.

EXHAUST MANIFOLDS

REMOVAL

1. On a right exhaust manifold, disconnect the automatic choke heat chamber air inlet hose from the inlet tube near the right valve rocker arm cover.

Remove the automatic choke heat tube.

2. Remove the air cleaner and intake duct assembly.

3. Disconnect the exhaust manifold from the muffler inlet pipe.

4. Remove the retaining bolts and tab washers and remove the exhaust manifold.

CLEANING AND INSPECTION

Refer to Part 8-1, Section 3 for the cleaning and inspection procedures.

INSTALLATION

1. Clean the mating surfaces of the exhaust manifold and cylinder head. Clean the mounting flange of the exhaust manifold and muffler inlet pipe.

2. Apply graphite grease to the mating surface of the exhaust manifold.

3. Position the exhaust manifold on the cylinder head and install the retaining bolts and tab washers. Working from the center to the ends, torque the bolts to specifications. Lock the bolts by bending one tab of the washer over a flat on the bolt.

4. Place new gaskets on the muffler inlet pipe. Position the muffler inlet pipe to the manifold. Install and torque the retaining nuts to specifications.

5. Install the automatic choke heat tube on the right exhaust manifold. Install the air cleaner and intake duct assembly.

6. Connect the automatic choke heat chamber air inlet hose.

7. Start the engine and check for exhaust leaks.

POSITIVE CRANKCASE VENTILATION SYSTEM

The positive crankcase ventilation system components are shown in Fig. 20.

REMOVAL

1. On a closed ventilation system,
remove the ventilation system air intake hose from the air cleaner and the oil filler cap.

2. Remove the air cleaner and intake duct assembly.

3. Using hose clamp pliers, slide both crankcase vent hose clamps towards the center of the vent hose.

If the car is air conditioned, slide the vent hose clamps away from the hot idle compensator.

Disconnect the crankcase vent hose from the carburetor spacer, regulator valve and hot idle compensator (if so equipped).

4. Pull the regulator valve and fitting (elbow) out of the valve rocker arm cover mounting grommet.

INSTALLATION

1. Insert the regulator valve and fitting (elbow) into the valve rocker arm cover mounting grommet.

2. Position the hose clamps on the vent hose. Connect the vent hose to the carburetor spacer, regulator valve and hot idle compensator (if so equipped). Using hose clamp pliers, slide the clamps into position.

3. Install the air cleaner and intake duct assembly.

4. On a closed ventilation system, install the ventilation system air intake hose to the air cleaner and the oil filler cap.

5. Start the engine and check for leaks.

CLEANING AND INSPECTION

Refer to Part 8-1, Section 3 for the cleaning and inspection procedures.

TESTING

Refer to Part 8-1, Section 1 for the test procedures.

CYLINDER HEADS

If a cylinder head is to be replaced, follow the procedures under Cylinder Head Disassembly and Assembly, and transfer all valves, springs, spark plugs, etc., to the new cylinder head. Clean and inspect all parts, reface the valves (refer to Part 8-1) and check all assembly clearances before assembling the new or used parts to the new cylinder head.

REMOVAL

1. Remove the intake manifold and carburetor as an assembly following the procedure under Intake Manifold Removal.

2. Remove the rocker arm cover(s).

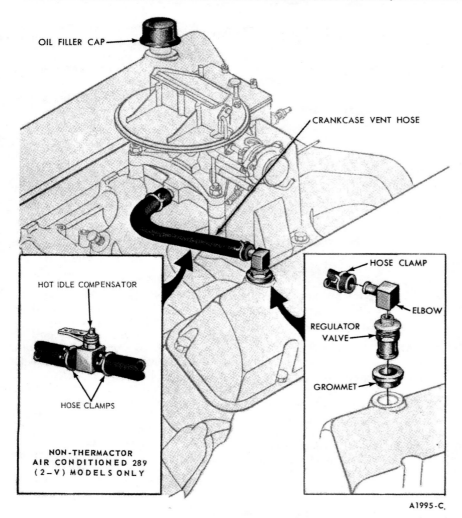

OIL FILLER CAP

CRANKCASE VENT HOSE

HOT IDLE COMPENSATOR

HOSE CLAMPS

NON-THERMACTOR
AIR CONDITIONED 289
(2-V) MODELS ONLY

HOSE CLAMP

ELBOW

REGULATOR
VALVE

GROMMET

A1995-C.

FIG. 20—Positive Crankcase Ventilation System Components

If the left cylinder head is to be removed on a car with an air conditioner, isolate and remove the compressor as outlined in Group 16.

If the left cylinder head is to be removed on a car with power steering, disconnect the power steering pump bracket from the left cylinder head and remove the drive belt from the pump pulley. Wire the power steering pump out of the way and in a position that will prevent the oil from draining out.

If the left cylinder head is being removed on an engine with Thermactor exhaust emission control system, disconnect the hose from the air manifold on the left cylinder head.

3. If the right cylinder head is to be removed, remove the alternator mounting bracket bolt and spacer, ignition coil and air cleaner inlet duct from the right cylinder head assembly.

If the right cylinder head is being removed on an engine with Thermac-

tor exhaust emission control system, remove the air pump and bracket. Disconnect the hose from the hose on the right cylinder head.

4. Disconnect the exhaust manifold(s) from the muffler inlet pipe(s).

5. Loosen the rocker arm stud nuts so that the rocker arms can be rotated to the side. Remove the push rods in sequence (Fig. 21) so that they may be installed in their original positions.

A1593-A

FIG. 21—Valve Push Rod Removal

6. Install the cylinder head holding fixtures (Fig. 22). Remove the

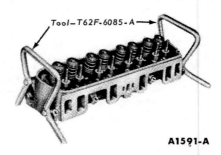

Tool—T62F-6085-A

A1591-A

FIG. 22—Cylinder Head Holding Fixtures

cylinder head retaining bolts and lift the cylinder head off the block. Remove and discard the cylinder head gasket.

INSTALLATION

1. Clean the cylinder head, intake manifold, valve rocker arm cover and cylinder head gasket surfaces. If the cylinder head was removed for a cylinder head gasket replacement, check the flatness of the cylinder head and block gasket.

2. Position the new cylinder head gasket over the cylinder dowels on the block. Coat the head bolts with water-resistant sealer. Position the cylinder head on the block and install the retaining bolts. Remove the holding fixtures.

3. The cylinder head bolts are tightened in three progressive steps. Torque all the bolts in sequence (Fig. 23) to 50 ft-lbs., then to 60 ft-lbs.

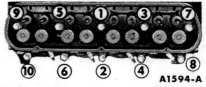

A1594-A

FIG. 23—Cylinder Head Bolt Torque Sequence

and finally to specifications. **After the cylinder head bolts have been torqued to specifications, the bolts should not be disturbed.**

4. Clean the push rods in a suitable solvent. Blow out the oil passage in the push rod with compressed air. Check the ends of the push rods for nicks, grooves, roughness or excessive wear. Visually check the push rods for straightness or check push rod runout with a dial indicator. If runout exceeds the maximum limit at any point, discard the rod. **Do not attempt to straighten push rods.**

5. Install the push rods in their original positions. Apply Lubriplate

to the valve stem tips and the push rod guides in the cylinder head.

6. Install the rocker arms. Perform a valve clearance adjustment as outlined in Part 8-1, Section 2.

7. Position a new gasket(s) on the muffler inlet pipe(s). Connect the exhaust manifold(s) at the muffler inlet pipe(s). Torque the nuts to specifications.

8. If the right cylinder head was removed, install the alternator retaining bolt and spacer, ignition coil and air cleaner inlet duct on the right cylinder head assembly. Adjust the drive belt tension to specifications.

If the right cylinder head was removed on an engine equipped with Thermactor exhaust emission control system, connect the hose to the air manifold on the right cylinder head. Install the air pump and alternator.

9. Apply oil-resistant sealer to one side of new cover gaskets. Lay the cemented side of the gaskets in place in the cover(s). Install the valve rocker arm cover(s).

If the left cylinder head was removed on a car with an air conditioner, install the compressor as outlined in Group 16.

If the left cylinder head was removed on a car with power steering, install the drive belt and power steering pump bracket. Install the bracket retaining bolts. Adjust the drive belt to specifications.

10. Install the intake manifold and related parts following the procedure under Intake Manifold Installation.

11. If the left cylinder head was removed on an engine equipped with Thermactor exhaust emission control system, connect the hose to the air manifold on the left cylinder head.

DISASSEMBLY

1. Remove the exhaust manifolds and the spark plugs.

2. Clean the carbon out of the cylinder head combustion chambers before removing the valves.

3. Compress the valve springs (Fig. 24). Remove the spring retainer locks and release the spring.

4. Remove the spring retainer, spring, stem seal and valve. Discard the valve stem seals. Identify all valve parts.

CLEANING AND INSPECTION

Refer to Part 8-1, Section 3 for the cleaning and inspection procedures.

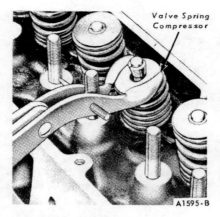

FIG. 24—Compressing Valve Spring—On Bench

REPAIRS

Cylinder head repair and rocker arm stud replacement procedures, and checks such as valve and valve seat refacing, cylinder head flatness checks, etc., are covered in Part 8-1, Section 2.

ASSEMBLY

1. Install each valve (Fig. 25) in

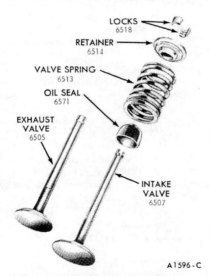

FIG. 25—Valve Assembly

the port from which it was removed or to which it was fitted. Install a new stem seal on the valve.

2. Install the valve spring over the valve, and then install the spring retainer. Compress the spring and install the retainer locks (Fig. 24).

3. Measure the assembled height of the valve spring from the surface of the cylinder head spring pad to the underside of the spring retainer with dividers (Fig. 26). Check the dividers against a scale. If the assembled height is greater than specifications,

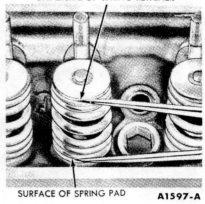

FIG. 26—Valve Spring Assembled Height

install the necessary 0.030-inch thick spacer(s) between the cylinder head spring pad and the valve spring to bring the assembled height to the recommended height.

Do not install the spacers unless necessary. Use of spacers in excess of recommendations will result in overstressing the valve springs and overloading the camshaft lobes which could lead to spring breakage and worn camshaft lobes.

4. Install the exhaust manifolds and the spark plugs.

VALVE SPRING, RETAINER AND STEM SEAL REPLACEMENT

Broken valve springs or defective valve stem seals and retainers may be replaced without removing the cylinder head, provided damage to the valve or valve seat has not occurred.

1. Disconnect the automatic choke heat chamber air inlet hose from the inlet tube near the right valve rocker arm cover.

2. Remove the air cleaner and intake duct assembly.

To remove the right valve rocker arm cover, remove the automatic choke heat tube. Remove the crankcase ventilation regulator valve from the valve rocker arm cover. If the engine is equipped with Thermactor exhaust emission control system, disconnect the anti-backfire valve air line and position it out of the way and remove the check valve from the right air manifold.

To remove the left valve rocker arm cover on an engine with Thermactor exhaust emission control system, disconnect the air tube from the left air manifold.

3. Remove the valve rocker arm cover and the applicable spark plug.

4. Remove the valve rocker arm stud nuts, fulcrum seats, valve rocker arms and push rods from the applicable cylinder.

5. Install an air line with an adapter in the spark plug hole and turn on the air supply.

6. Install the stud nut and position the compressor tool as shown in Fig. 27. Compress the valve spring and

Air Line　Tool—T62F-6565-A
　　　　　or 6513-HH　　　A1598-C

FIG. 27—Compressing Valve Spring—In Chassis

remove the retainer locks, spring retainer and valve spring.

7. Remove and discard the valve stem seal (Fig. 28.).

Air Line　　SEAL　　A1599-B

FIG. 28—Valve Stem Seal Removal or Installation

If air pressure fails to hold the valve in the closed position during this operation, it can be presumed that the valve is not seating or is damaged. If this condition occurs, remove the cylinder head for further inspection.

8. **If air pressure has forced the piston to the bottom of the cylinder, any removal of air pressure will allow the valve(s) to fall into the cylinder. A rubber band, tape or**

string wrapped around the end of the valve stem will prevent this condition and will still allow enough travel to check the valve for binds.

9. Inspect the valve stem for damage. Rotate the valve and check the valve stem tip for eccentric movement during rotation. Move the valve up and down through normal travel in the valve guide and check the stem for binds. **If the valve has been damaged, it will be necessary to remove the cylinder head for repairs as outlined in Part 8-1, Section 2.**

10. If the condition of the valve proved satisfactory, hold the valve in the closed position and apply the air pressure within the cylinder.

11. Install a new valve stem seal (Fig. 28). Place the spring in position over the valve and install the valve spring retainer. Compress the valve spring and install the valve spring retainer locks. Remove the compressor tool and stud nut.

12. Install the push rod. Apply Lubriplate to the tip of the valve stem and at the push rod guide in the cylinder head.

13. Install the valve rocker arms, fulcrum seats and stud nuts. Adjust the valve clearance following the procedure in Part 8-1, Section 2.

14. Turn off the air and remove the air line and adapter. Install the spark plug and connect the spark plug wire.

15. Clean and install the rocker arm cover.

If the right cover was removed, install the automatic choke heat tube and the crankcase ventilation regulator valve. If the engine is equipped with Thermactor exhaust emission control system, install the check valve on the right air manifold and connect the anti-backfire valve air line.

If the left cover was removed on an engine with Thermactor exhaust emission control system, connect the air tube to the left air manifold.

16. Install the air cleaner and intake duct assembly.

17. Connect the automatic choke heat chamber air inlet hose.

CYLINDER FRONT COVER AND TIMING CHAIN

REMOVAL

1. Drain the cooling system and the crankcase.

2. Disconnect the radiator lower hose from the water pump.

3. Disconnect the heater hose

from the water pump. Slide the water pump bypass hose clamp toward the water pump.

4. Loosen the alternator to cylinder head mounting bolt. Remove the alternator bracket bolts at the water pump and position the alternator and brackets out of the way.

If the engine is equipped with a Thermactor exhaust emission control system, remove the air pump and brackets.

5. On a car with power steering and/or air conditioning, loosen the drive belt tension and remove the belt(s).

6. Remove the fan, spacer, pulley and drive belt.

7. Remove the crankshaft pulley from the crankshaft vibration damper. Remove the damper retaining screw and washer. Install the puller on the crankshaft vibration damper (Fig. 29) and remove the vibration damper.

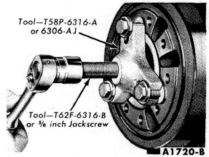

Tool—T58P-6316-A
or 6306-AJ

Tool—T62F-6316-B
or ⅝ inch Jackscrew

A1720-B

FIG. 29—Crankshaft Vibration Damper Removal

8. Disconnect the fuel pump outlet line from the fuel pump. Remove the fuel pump retaining bolts and lay the pump to one side with the flexible fuel line still attached.

9. Remove the oil level dipstick.

10. Remove the oil pan to cylinder front cover retaining bolts. Remove the cylinder front cover and water pump as an assembly.

If a new cylinder front cover is to be installed, remove the water pump and dipstick tube from the old cylinder front cover and install them on the new cover.

11. Discard the cylinder front cover gasket. Remove the crankshaft front oil slinger.

12. Check the timing chain deflection (refer to Part 8-1, Section 1).

13. *Crank the engine until the timing marks on the sprockets are positioned as shown in Fig. 30.*

14. Remove the camshaft sprock-

FIG. 30—Aligning Timing Marks

et cap screw, washers and fuel pump eccentric. Slide both sprockets and the timing chain forward, and remove them as an assembly (Fig. 31).

FIG. 31—Timing Chain Removal or Installation

17. Remove the oil pan and oil pump pickup tube by following the procedure under Oil Pan Removal.

CLEANING AND INSPECTION

Refer to Part 8-1, Section 3 for the cleaning and inspection procedures. Clean the crankshaft damp-

er following the referenced procedure.

FRONT OIL SEAL REPLACEMENT

It is good practice to replace the oil seal each time the cylinder front cover is removed.

REMOVAL

1. Drive out the old seal with a pin-punch. Clean out the recess in the cover.
2. Coat a new seal with grease, then install the seal in the cover (Fig. 32). Drive the seal in until it is fully

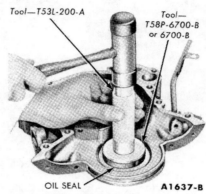

FIG. 32—Crankshaft Front Oil Seal Replacement

seated in the recess. Check the seal after installation to be sure the spring is properly positioned in the seal.

INSTALLATION

1. Position the sprockets and timing chain on the camshaft (Fig. 31). Be sure the timing marks on the sprockets are positioned as shown in Fig. 30.
2. Install the fuel pump eccentric, washers and camshaft sprocket cap screw. Torque the sprocket cap screw to specifications. Install the crankshaft front oil slinger (Fig. 33).
3. Clean the cylinder front cover, oil pan and the block gasket surfaces.
4. Lubricate the timing chain with engine oil.
5. Coat the gasket surfaces of the block and cover with sealer. Position a new gasket on the block.
6. Install the alignment pilot tool on the cylinder front cover so that the keyway in the pilot aligns with the key in the crankshaft. Position the cover and pilot over the end of the crankshaft and against the block (Fig. 34). Coat the threads of the retaining screws with oil-resistant sealer and in-

FIG. 33—Fuel Pump Eccentric and Front Oil Slinger Installed

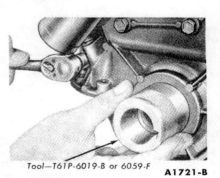

FIG. 34—Cylinder Front Cover Alignment

stall the screws. While pushing in on the pilot, torque the screws to specifications. Remove the pilot.

7. Apply Lubriplate to the oil seal rubbing surface of the vibration damper inner hub to prevent damage to the seal. Apply a white lead and oil mixture to the front of the crankshaft for damper installation.

8. Line up the crankshaft vibration damper keyway with the key on the crankshaft. Install the vibration damper on the crankshaft (Fig. 35). Install the cap screw and washer. Torque the screw to specifications. Install the crankshaft pulley.

9. Install the oil pump pickup tube

FIG. 35—Crankshaft Vibration Damper Installation

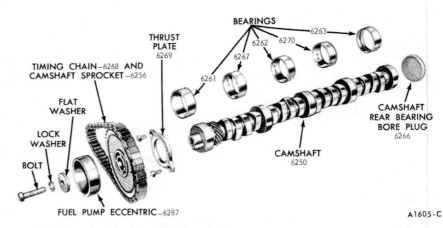

FIG. 36—Camshaft and Related Parts

and oil pan following the procedure under Oil Pan Installation.

10. Install the fuel pump using a new gasket. Connect the fuel pump outlet pipe.

11. Install the oil level dipstick.

12. Install the water pump pulley, drive belt, spacer and fan.

13. On an engine equipped with Thermactor exhaust emission control system, install the air pump and brackets.

14. Install the alternator bracket. Adjust the drive belt tension to specifications and tighten the alternator mounting bolts.

15. Connect the heater hose and the water pump bypass hose. Slide the bypass hose clamp into position.

16. Connect the radiator hose.

17. On a car with power steering and/or air conditioning, install and adjust the drive belt(s).

18. Fill and bleed the cooling system. Fill the crankcase with the proper grade and quality of engine oil.

19. Operate the engine at fast idle and check the coolant and oil leaks. Check and adjust the ignition timing.

CAMSHAFT

The camshaft and related parts are shown in Fig. 36.

REMOVAL

1. Remove the cylinder front cover and the timing chain following the procedure under Cylinder Front Cover and Timing Chain Removal.

2. Disconnect the spark plug wires from the spark plugs and remove the wires from the ignition harness brackets on the valve rocker arm covers. Disconnect the coil high tension lead from the coil. Remove

the distributor cap and spark plug wire assembly.

3. Disconnect the ignition coil wires from the coil.

4. Disconnect the distributor vacuum line from the carburetor. Remove the distributor hold down bolt and clamp and remove the distributor.

5. Disconnect the automatic choke heat tube from the carburetor. Remove the heater hose from the automatic choke and disconnect the heater hose from the intake manifold.

On a car with an automatic transmission, disconnect the throttle valve vacuum line from the intake manifold. Disconnect the transmission oil cooler lines from the radiator.

6. Disconnect the radiator upper hose and remove the radiator.

7. Disconnect the accelerator rod from the carburetor. Remove the accelerator retracting spring.

8. Disconnect the water temperature sending unit wire from the sending unit and the engine ground strap at the engine.

9. Remove the crankcase ventilation regulator valve from the valve rocker arm cover. Remove the valve rocker arm covers. Loosen the valve rocker arm stud nuts and rotate the rocker arms to the side.

10. Remove the intake manifold and carburetor as an assembly. Remove the intake manifold gaskets and seals.

11. Remove the valve push rods in sequence so that they can be installed in their original positions.

12. Using a magnet, remove the valve lifters and place them in a rack so that they can be installed in their original bores (Fig. 37).

If the valve lifters are stuck in

FIG. 37—Valve Lifter Removal

their bores by excessive varnish, etc., it may be necessary to use a plier-type tool (T52T-6500-DJD or 6500-D) to remove the lifters. Rotate the lifter back and forth to loosen it from the gum or varnish that may have formed at the lifter.

13. Remove the camshaft thrust plate. Carefully remove the camshaft by pulling toward the front of the engine. **Use caution to avoid damaging the camshaft bearings.**

CLEANING AND INSPECTION

Refer to Part 8-1, Section 3 for the cleaning and inspection procedures.

REPAIRS

Refer to Part 8-1, Section 2 for the repair procedures.

INSTALLATION

1. Oil the camshaft journals and apply Lubriplate to the lobes. Carefully slide the camshaft through the bearings. Install the camshaft thrust plate.

2. Install the valve lifters in the bores from which they were removed.

3. Install the push rods in their original positions. Apply Lubriplate to the valve stem tips and the push rod guides in the cylinder head. Position the rocker arms over the push rods.

4. Install the intake manifold and related parts by following steps 1 thru 6 under Intake Manifold Installation.

5. Connect the water temperature sending unit and the engine ground strap.

6. Connect the accelerator rod and retracting spring.

7. Install the radiator.

On a car with an automatic transmission, connect the transmission oil cooler lines and throttle valve vacuum line.

8. Connect the heater hose at the intake manifold. Position and connect the fuel line.

9. Replace the crankshaft front oil seal. Install the timing chain, cylinder front cover and related parts following steps 1 thru 17 under Cylinder Front Cover and Timing Chain Installation.

10. With No. 1 piston on TDC at the end of the compression stroke, position the distributor in the block with the rotor at the No. 1 firing position and the points open. Install the hold down clamp.

11. Perform a valve clearance adjustment as outlined in Part 8-1, Section 2.

12. Clean the valve rocker arm covers and the cylinder head gasket surface. Apply oil-resistance sealer to one side of new cover gaskets. Lay the cemented side of the gaskets in place in the covers.

13. Position the covers on the cylinder heads. Make sure the gasket seats evenly all around the head. Install the bolts. The cover is tightened in two steps. Torque the bolts to specifications. Two minutes later, torque the bolts to the same specifications.

14. Clean and install the crankcase ventilation system.

15. Install the automatic choke heat tube. Connect the ignition coil wires.

16. Install the distributor cap. Position the spark plug wires in the harness brackets on the valve rocker

arm covers and connect the wires to the plugs. Connect the high tension lead at the coil.

17. Fill and bleed the cooling system. Fill the crankcase with the proper grade and quantity of engine oil.

18. Start the engine and check and adjust the ignition timing. Connect the distributor vacuum line at the carburetor.

19. Operate the engine at fast idle and check all hose connections and gaskets for leaks. Operate the engine until engine temperatures have stabilized and adjust the engine idle speed and idle fuel mixture.

20. Adjust the transmission throttle linkage. Install the air cleaner and intake duct assembly.

21. Connect the automatic choke heat chamber air inlet hose.

CAMSHAFT REAR BEARING BORE PLUG REPLACEMENT

1. On a car with a manual-shift transmission, remove the transmission, clutch pressure plate and disc following the procedures in Group 5.

On a car with an automatic transmission, remove the transmission and converter housing following the procedure in Group 7.

2. Remove the flywheel retaining bolts and remove the flywheel. Remove the engine rear cover plate.

3. Drill a ½-inch hole in the camshaft rear bearing bore plug and remove the plug, using the tools shown in Fig. 58.

4. Clean out the plug bore recess thoroughly and coat the flange of a new plug with oil-resistant sealer. Install the new plug with the flange facing outward. Drive the plug in until it is slightly below the chamfer in the bore (Fig. 61).

5. Coat the flywheel retaining bolts with oil-resistant sealer. Position the engine rear cover plate on the cylinder block dowels. Position the flywheel on the crankshaft flange. Install and torque the retaining bolts in sequence across from each other to specifications.

On a car with a manual-shift transmission, install the clutch pressure plate, disc and the transmission following the procedures in Group 5.

On a car with an automatic transmission, install the transmission and converter housing following the procedure in Group 7.

VALVE LIFTERS

REPLACEMENT

1. Remove the intake manifold

and related parts by following steps 1 thru 10 under Intake Manifold Removal.

2. Remove the crankcase ventilation regulator valve from the valve rocker arm cover. Remove the valve rocker arm covers. Loosen the valve rocker arm stud nuts and rotate the rocker arms to the side.

3. Remove the valve push rods in sequence so that they can be installed in their original positions.

4. Using a magnet, remove the valve lifters and place them in a rack so that they can be installed in their original bores (Fig. 37).

If the valve lifters cannot be removed from their bores due to excessive varnish, etc., it may be necessary to use a plier-type tool (T52T-6500-DJD or 6500-D) to remove the lifters. Rotate the lifter back and forth to loosen it from the gum or varnish that may have formed at the lifter.

The internal parts of each hydraulic valve lifter assembly are matched sets. Do not intermix the parts. Keep the assemblies intact until they are to be cleaned.

5. Clean and install the valve lifters in the bores from which they were removed. If a new lifter(s) is being installed, test the new lifter(s) for a free fit in the bore in which it is to be installed.

6. Install the push rods in their original position. Apply Lubriplate to the valve stem tips and the push rod guides in the cylinder head.

7. Position the rocker arms over the push rods. Perform a valve clearance adjustment as outlined in Part 8-1, Section 2.

8. Install the valve rocker arm covers. Install the crankcase ventilation regulator valve in the valve rocker arm cover.

9. Install the intake manifold and related parts by following steps 2 thru 20 under Intake Manifold Installation.

DISASSEMBLY

Each valve lifter is a matched assembly. If the parts of one lifter are intermixed with those of another, improper valve operation may result. Disassemble and assemble each lifter separately. Keep the lifter assemblies dle nose pliers to release it from the in proper sequence so that they can be installed in their original bores.

1. Grasp the lock ring with needle groove. It may be necessary to de-

press the plunger to fully release the lock ring.

2. Remove the push rod cup, metering valve (disc), plunger and spring.

3. Invert the plunger assembly and remove the check valve retainer by carefully prying up on it with a screw driver. Remove the check valve (disc or ball check) and spring.

CLEANING AND INSPECTION

Refer to Part 8-1, Section 3 for the cleaning and inspection procedures.

ASSEMBLY

A typical hydraulic valve lifter assembly is shown in Fig. 38.

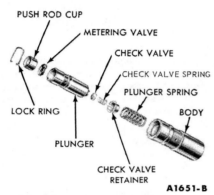

PUSH ROD CUP
METERING VALVE
CHECK VALVE
CHECK VALVE SPRING
PLUNGER SPRING
LOCK RING
BODY
PLUNGER
CHECK VALVE RETAINER
A1651-B

FIG. 38—Typical Hydraulic Valve Lifter Assembly

1. Place the plunger upside down on a clean work bench.

2. Place the check valve (disc or ball check) in position over the oil hole on the bottom of the plunger. Set the check valve spring on top of the check valve (disc or ball check).

3. Position the check valve retainer over the check valve and spring and push the retainer down into place on the plunger.

4. Place the plunger spring, and then the plunger (open end up) into the lifter body.

5. Position the metering valve (disc) in the plunger, and then place the push rod seat in the plunger.

6. Depress the plunger, and position the closed end of the lock ring in the groove of the lifter body. With the plunger still depressed, position the open ends of the lock ring in the groove. Release the plunger, and then depress it again to fully seat the lock ring.

TESTING

Refer to Part 8-1, Section 1 for the testing procedures.

CRANKSHAFT REAR OIL SEAL REPLACEMENT

Replacement of a crankshaft rear oil seal because of oil leakage requires replacement of both the upper and lower seals. Remove the engine; then remove the crankshaft and replace the seals following the procedure under Crankshaft Removal and Installation (Section 4).

MAIN AND CONNECTING ROD BEARING REPLACEMENT

The main and connecting rod bearing insets are selective fit. Do not file or lap bearing caps or use bearing shims to obtain the proper bearing clearance.

Selective fit bearings are available for service in standard sizes and 0.002 inch undersize. Standard bearings are divided into two sizes and are identified by a daub of red or blue paint. Refer to the Parts Catalog for the available sizes. Red marked bearings increase the clearance; blue marked bearings decrease the clearance. Undersize bearings, which are not selective fit, are available for use on journals that have been refinished.

MAIN BEARING

1. Drain the crankcase. Remove the oil level dipstick. Remove the oil pan and related parts.

2. Remove the oil pump inlet tube assembly and the oil pump.

3. **Replace one bearing at a time, leaving the other bearings securely fastened.** Remove the main bearing cap to which new bearings are to be installed.

4. Insert the upper bearing removal tool (tool 6331) in the oil hole in the crankshaft.

5. Rotate the crankshaft in the direction of the engine rotation to force the bearing out of the block.

6. Clean the crankshaft journals. Inspect the journals and thrust faces (thrust bearing) for nicks, burrs or bearing pick-up that would cause premature bearing wear. **When replacing standard bearings with new bearings, it is good practice to fit the bearing to the minimum specified clearance and to first try to obtain the proper clearance with two blue bearing halves.**

7. To install the upper main bearing, place the plain end of the bearing over the shaft on the locking tang side of the block and partially install the bearing so that tool 6331 can be inserted in the oil hole in the crankshaft. With tool 6331 positioned in the oil hole in the crankshaft, rotate the crankshaft in the opposite direction of engine rotation until the bearing seats itself. Remove the tool.

8. Replace the cap bearing.

9. Support the crankshaft so that its weight will not compress the Plastigage and provide an erroneous reading. Position a jack so that it will bear against the counterweight adjoining the bearing which is being checked.

10. Place a piece of Plastigage on the bearing surface the full width of the bearing cap and about ¼ inch off center (Fig. 39).

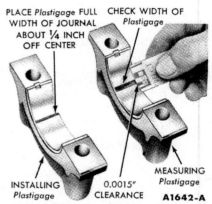

PLACE *Plastigage* FULL WIDTH OF JOURNAL ABOUT ¼ INCH OFF CENTER
CHECK WIDTH OF *Plastigage*
INSTALLING *Plastigage*
0.0015" CLEARANCE
MEASURING *Plastigage*
A1642-A

FIG. 39—Installing and Measuring Plastigage—Engine Installed

11. Install the cap and torque the bolts to specifications. **Do not turn the crankshaft while the Plastigage is in place.**

12. Remove the cap. Using the Plastigage scale, check the width of the Plastigage. When checking the width of the Plastigage, check at the widest point in order to get the minimum clearance. Check at the narrowest point in order to get the maximum clearance. The difference between the two readings is the taper.

13. If the clearance is less than the specified limits, try two red bearing halves or a combination of red and blue depending upon the condition.

If the clearance exceeds specified desired limits, try 0.002 inch undersize bearings in combination with red or blue bearings. **The bearing clearance must be within specified desired limits.** If 0.002 undersize main bearings are used on more than one journal, be sure they are all installed on the same side (cap or cylinder block) of the crankshaft. If the standard and 0.002 inch undersize bearings do not bring the clearance within the desired limits, refinish the crankshaft journal and install undersize bearings.

14. After the bearing has been fitted, apply a light coat of engine oil to the journal and bearings and install the bearing cap. Torque the cap bolts to specifications.

15. Repeat the procedure for the remaining bearings that require replacement.

16. If the rear main bearing is to be replaced, remove the rear main bearing cap. Remove and discard the rear oil seal.

17. Clean the rear journal oil seal groove and the mating surfaces of the block and rear main bearing cap. Preform the new seal by hand to the approximate radius of the cap.

18. Insert the seal in the oil seal groove, seating the center of the seal first and allowing the seal to extend equally on both ends. Press the seal down firmly with the thumb at the center of the seal, and then press both ends of the seal into the groove, working from the ends to the center.

19. Position the seal forming tool as shown in Fig. 40 and complete

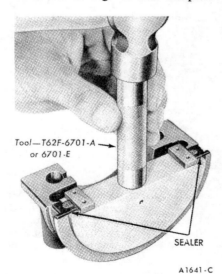

Tool—T62F-6701-A
or 6701-E

SEALER

A1641-C

FIG. 40—Seal to Rear Bearing Cap Installation

the seal installation. After installation, cut the ends of the seal flush.

20. Apply a thin coating of oil-re-

sistant sealer to the rear main bearing cap at the rear of the top mating surface (Fig. 40). **Do not apply sealer to the area forward of the oil slinger groove.** Install the rear main bearing cap and torque the cap bolts to specifications.

21. If the thrust bearing cap (No. 3 main bearing) has been removed, install it as follows:

Install the thrust bearing cap with the bolts finger-tight. Pry the crankshaft forward against the thrust surface of the upper half of the bearing (Fig. 57). Hold the crankshaft cap to the rear (Fig. 57). This will align the thrust surfaces of both halves of the bearing. Retain the forward pressure on the crankshaft. Torque the cap bolts to specifications (Fig. 57).

22. Clean the oil pump inlet tube screen. Prime and install the oil pump and the inlet tube assembly.

23. Position the oil pan gaskets on the oil pan. Position the oil pan front seal on the cylinder front cover. Position the oil pan rear seal on the rear main bearing cap. Install the oil pan and related parts. Install the oil level dipstick.

24. Fill the crankcase. Start the engine and check for oil pressure. Operate the engine at fast idle and check for oil leaks.

CONNECTING ROD BEARING

1. Follow steps 1 & 2 under Main Bearing Replacement.

2. Turn the crankshaft until the connecting rod to which new bearings are to be fitted is down. Remove the connecting rod cap. Remove the bearing inserts from the rod and cap.

3. Be sure the bearing inserts and the bearing bore in the connecting rod and cap are clean. Foreign material under the inserts may distort the bearing and cause a failure.

4. Clean the crankshaft journal. **When replacing standard bearings with new bearings, it is good practice to fit the bearing to the minimum specified clearance and to first try to obtain the proper clearance with two blue bearing halves.**

5. Install the bearing inserts in the connecting rod and cap with the tangs fitting in the slots provided.

6. Pull the connecting rod assembly down firmly on the crankshaft journal.

7. Place a piece of Plastigage on the lower bearing surface, the full

width of the cap and about ¼ inch off-center.

8. Install the cap and torque the connecting rod nuts to specifications. **Do not turn the crankshaft while the Plastigage is in place.**

9. Refer to Steps 12 and 13 under Main Bearing Replacement.

10. After the bearing has been fitted, clean and apply a light coat of engine oil to the journal and bearings. Install the connecting rod cap. Torque the nuts to specifications.

11. Repeat the procedure for the remaining connecting rods that require new bearings.

12. Follow steps 22 thru 24 under Main Bearing Replacement.

CLEANING AND INSPECTION

Refer to Part 8-1, Section 3 for the cleaning and inspection procedures.

PISTONS AND CONNECTING RODS

REMOVAL

1. Drain the cooling system and the crankcase. Remove the intake manifold, cylinder heads, oil pan and oil pump, following the procedures in this section.

2. Remove any ridges and/or deposits from the upper end of the cylinder bores as follows:

Turn the crankshaft until the piston to be removed is at the bottom of its travel and place a cloth on the piston head to collect the cuttings. Remove any ridge and/or deposits from the upper end of the cylinder bores. Remove the cylinder ridge with a ridge cutter. Follow the instructions furnished by the tool manufacturers. **Never cut into the ring travel area in excess of 1/32 inch when removing ridges.**

3. Make sure all connecting rod caps are marked so that they can be installed in their original positions.

4. Turn the crankshaft until the connecting rod being removed is down.

5. Remove the connecting rod nuts and cap.

6. Push the connecting rod and piston assembly out the top of the cylinder with the handle end of a hammer. **Avoid damage to the crankshaft journal or the cylinder wall when removing the piston and rod.**

7. Remove the bearing inserts from the connecting rod and cap.

8. Install the cap on the connecting rod from which it was removed.

INSTALLATION

1. If new piston rings are to be installed, remove the cylinder wall glaze. Follow the instructions of the tool manufacturer.

2. Oil the piston rings, pistons and cylinder walls with light engine oil. **Be sure to install the pistons in the same cylinders from which they were removed or to which they were fitted. The connecting rod and bearing caps are numbered from 1 to 4 in the right bank and from 5 to 8 in the left bank, beginning at the front of the engine. The numbers on the connecting rod and bearing cap must be on the same side when installed in the cylinder bore. If a connecting rod is ever transposed from one block or cylinder to another, new bearings should be fitted and the connecting rod should be numbered to correspond with the new cylinder number.**

3. Make sure the ring gaps are properly spaced around the circumference of the piston (Fig. 41).

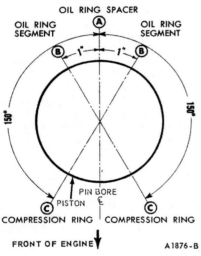

FIG. 41—Piston Ring Spacing

4. Install a piston ring compressor on the piston and push the piston in with a hammer handle until it is slightly below the top of the cylinder (Fig. 42). Be sure to guide the connecting rods to avoid damaging the crankshaft journals. **Install the piston with the indentation notch in the piston head toward the front of the engine.**

5. Check the clearance of each bearing following the procedure under Connecting Rod Bearing Replacement.

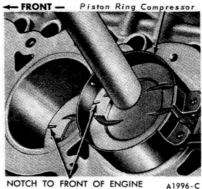

FIG. 42—Piston Installation

6. After the bearings have been fitted, apply a light coat of engine oil to the journals and bearings.

7. Turn the crankshaft throw to the bottom of its stroke. Push the piston all the way down until the connecting rod bearing seats on the crankshaft journal.

8. Install the connecting rod cap. Torque the nuts to specifications.

9. After the piston and connecting rod assemblies have been installed, check the side clearance between the connecting rods on each crankshaft journal (Fig. 43).

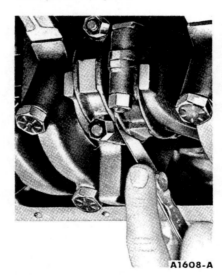

FIG. 43—Connecting Rod Side Clearance

10. Disassemble, clean, and assemble the oil pump. Clean the oil pump inlet tube screen and the oil pan and block gasket surfaces.

11. Prime the oil pump by filling either the inlet port or outlet port with engine oil and rotating the pump shaft to distribute the oil within the housing. Install the oil pump and the oil pan.

12. Install the cylinder heads following steps 1 thru 9 under Cylinder Head Installation.

13. Install the intake manifold following steps 2 thru 15 under Intake Manifold Installation.

14. Fill and bleed the cooling system. Fill the crankcase with the proper grade and quantity of engine oil.

15. Start the engine and check and adjust the ignition timing. Connect the distributor vacuum line at the carburetor.

16. Operate the engine at fast idle and check for oil and coolant leaks. Operate the engine until engine temperatures have stabilized and adjust the engine idle speed and idle fuel mixture.

On a car with power steering and air conditioning, adjust the speed-up control assembly as outlined in Group 3.

17. Adjust the transmission throttle linkage. Install the air cleaner and intake duct assembly.

18. Connect the automatic choke heat chamber air inlet hose.

DISASSEMBLY

1. Remove the bearing inserts from the connecting rod and cap.

2. Mark the pistons and pins to assure assembly with the same rod and installation in the same cylinders from which they were removed.

3. Remove the piston pin from the piston and connecting rod (Fig. 44). Remove the piston rings.

CLEANING AND INSPECTION

Refer to Part 8-1, Section 3 for the cleaning and inspection procedures.

REPAIRS

Refer to Part 8-1, Section 2 for the repair procedures.

ASSEMBLY

The piston, connecting rod and related parts are shown in Fig. 45. **Check the fit of a new piston in the cylinder bore before assembling the piston and piston pin to the connecting rod.**

The piston pin bore of a connecting rod and the diameter of the piston pin must be within specifications. *Refer to Part 8-5.*

1. Apply a light coat of engine oil to all parts. **Assemble the piston to the connecting rod with the oil squirt**

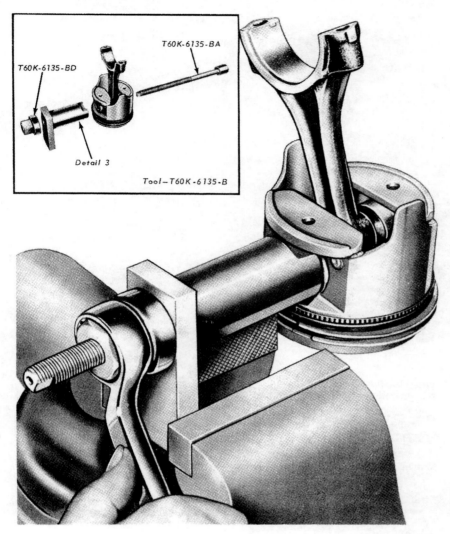

FIG. 44—Piston Pin Removal

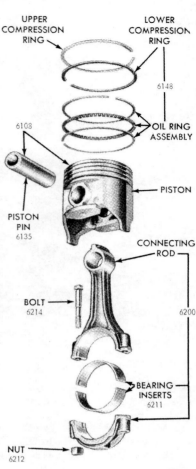

FIG. 45—Piston, Connecting Rod and Related Parts

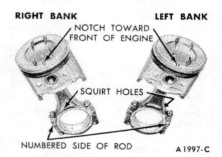

FIG. 46—Correct Piston and Rod Positions

FIG. 44—Piston Pin Removal

hole in the connecting rod and the **indentation notch in the piston positioned as shown in Fig. 46.**

2. Start the piston pin in the piston and connecting rod. Draw the piston pin through the piston and connecting rod until the end of the pin seats in Detail 2 (Fig. 47).

3. Follow the instructions contained on the piston ring package and install the piston rings.

4. Check the ring side clearance of the compression rings with a feeler gauge inserted between the ring and its lower land (Part 8-1, Section 2). The gauge should slide freely around the entire ring circumference without binding. Any wear that occurs will form a step at the inner portion of the lower land. **If the lower lands have high steps, the piston should be replaced.**

5. Be sure the bearing inserts and the bearing bore in the connecting rod and cap are clean. Foreign material under the inserts will distort the bearing and cause a failure. Install the bearing inserts in the connecting rod and cap with the tangs fitting in the slots provided.

FLYWHEEL

REMOVAL

1. On a car with a manual-shift transmission, remove the transmission, clutch pressure plate and disc following the procedures in Group 5.

On a car with automatic transmission, remove the transmission and converter housing following the procedure in Group 7.

2. Remove the flywheel retaining bolts and remove the flywheel.

CLEANING AND INSPECTION

Refer to Part 8-1, Section 3 for the cleaning and inspection procedures for manual-shift transmissions.

REPAIRS

To check flywheel face runout or replace flywheel ring gear for manual-shift transmissions, refer to Part 8-1, Section 2.

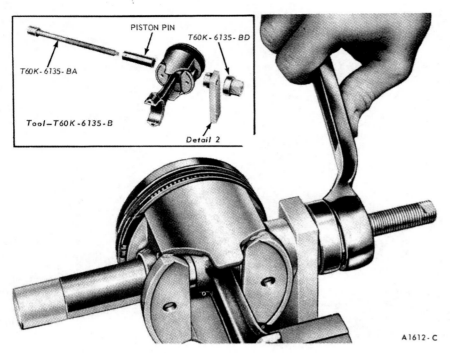

FIG. 47—Piston Pin Installation

INSTALLATION

1. Coat the threads of the flywheel retaining bolts with oil-resistant sealer. Position the flywheel on the crankshaft flange. Install and torque the bolts in sequence across from each other to specifications.

2. On a car with a manual-shift transmission, check the flywheel runout, following the procedure in Part 8-1, Section 1 and install the clutch pressure plate, disc and the transmission following the procedures in Group 5.

On a car with an automatic transmission, check the flywheel runout, following the procedure in Part 8-1, Section 1 and install the transmission and converter housing following the procedure in Group 7.

CLUTCH PILOT BUSHING REPLACEMENT

1. Remove the transmission, clutch pressure plate and disc, following the procedures in Group 5.

2. Remove the pilot bushing as shown in Fig. 62.

3. Coat the pilot bushing bore in the crankshaft with a small quantity of wheel bearing lubricant. **Avoid using too much lubricant as it may be thrown onto the clutch disc when the clutch revolves.**

4. Install the pilot service bearing as shown in Fig. 63.

5. Install the clutch pressure plate,

disc and the transmission, following the procedures in Group 5.

OIL FILTER REPLACEMENT

CARTRIDGE-TYPE OIL FILTER

The Rotunda oil filter assembly is shown in Fig. 48.

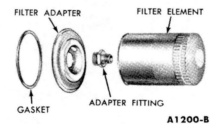

FIG. 48—Cartridge-Type Oil Filter Assembly

1. Place a drip pan under the filter. Unscrew the filter from the adapter fitting and clean the adapter recess.

2. Coat the gasket on a new Rotunda filter with oil. Place the new Rotunda filter in position on the adapter fitting. Hand tighten the filter until the gasket contacts the adapter face, and then advance it ½ turn.

3. Operate the engine at fast idle, and check for oil leaks. If oil leaks are evident, perform the necessary repairs to correct leakage. Check the oil level and fill the crankcase if necessary.

ELEMENT-TYPE OIL FILTER

The oil filter assembly is shown in Fig. 49.

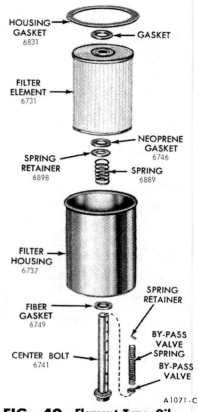

FIG. 49—Element-Type Oil Filter Assembly

1. Place a drip pan under the filter. Loosen the filter center bolt, and then remove the filter assembly and gasket.

2. Remove the filter element, neoprene gasket, spring and seat. Remove the center bolt from the filter cover and the fiber gasket from the bolt. Discard the filter element and all gaskets.

3. Wash all parts in solvent. Make sure all the openings in the center bolt are clean.

4. Install a new Rotunda filter element in the filter cover following the instructions furnished with the new element.

5. Clean the oil filter cover mounting surface on the adapter. Position a new gasket in the adapter recess.

6. Place the filter assembly in position, and thread the center bolt into the adapter finger-tight. Rotate *the filter slightly, in each direction,* to make sure the gasket is seated evenly.

7. Torque the center bolts to

specifications. Do not over-tighten the center bolt.

8. Add oil to the crankcase if necessary. Operate the engine at fast idle, and check for leaks.

9. If oil leaks are evident, perform the necessary repairs to correct the leakage.

OIL PAN

REMOVAL

1. Drain the crankcase. Remove the oil level dipstick.

2. Remove the oil pan retaining *bolts and* position the pan on the number 2 crossmember.

3. Remove one of the oil inlet tube retaining bolts and loosen the other oil inlet tube retaining bolts. This allows the inlet tube to be positioned out of the way when removing the oil pan.

4. Crank the engine as required to obtain clearance and remove the oil pan.

5. Remove the oil pump inlet tube and screen assembly.

CLEANING AND INSPECTION

Refer to Part 8-1, Section 3 for the cleaning and inspection procedures.

INSTALLATION

1. Clean the oil pickup tube and screen assembly.

2. Position the oil inlet tube and a new gasket and loosely install one of the retaining bolts.

3. Clean the gasket surfaces of the block and oil pan. The oil pan has a two-piece gasket. Coat the block surface and the oil pan gasket with sealer. Position the oil pan gaskets on the cylinder block (Fig. 50).

4. Position the oil pan front seal on the cylinder front cover (Fig. 50). Be sure the tabs on the seal are over the oil pan gasket.

5. Position the oil pan rear seal on the rear main bearing cap (Fig. 50). Be sure the tabs on the seal are over the oil pan gasket.

6. Position the oil pan on the number 2 crossmember and install the other oil pump inlet tube retaining bolt. Torque the inlet tube retaining bolts to specifications.

7. Hold the oil pan in place against the block and install a bolt, finger-tight, on each side of the oil pan. Install the remaining bolts. Torque the bolts from the center outward in each direction to specifications.

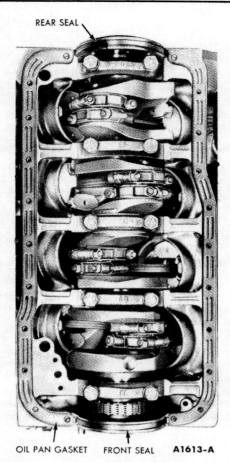

REAR SEAL

OIL PAN GASKET   FRONT SEAL   A1613-A

FIG. 50—Oil Pan Gaskets and Seals Installed

8. Install the oil level dipstick. Fill the crankcase with the proper grade and quantity of engine oil. Start the engine and check for oil leaks.

OIL PUMP

REMOVAL

1. Remove the oil pan and related parts as outlined under Oil Pan Removal.

2. Remove the oil pump inlet tube and screen assembly.

3. Remove the oil pump retaining bolts and remove the oil pump, gasket and intermediate drive shaft.

INSTALLATION

1. Prime the oil pump by filling either the inlet or outlet port with engine oil. Rotate the pump shaft to distribute the oil within the pump body.

2. Position the intermediate drive shaft into the distributor socket. With the shaft firmly seated in the distributor socket, the stop on the shaft should touch the roof of the crankcase. Remove the shaft and

position the stop as necessary.

3. Position a new gasket on the pump housing. With the stop properly positioned, insert the intermediate drive shaft into the oil pump. Install the pump and shaft as an assembly. **Do not attempt to force the pump into position if it will not seat readily. The drive shaft hex may be misaligned with the distributor shaft. To align, rotate the intermediate drive shaft into a new position.** Torque the oil pump retaining screws to specifications.

4. Clean and install the oil pump inlet tube and screen assembly (Fig. 51).

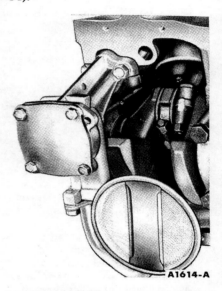

A1614-A

FIG. 51—Oil Pump and Inlet Tube Installed

5. Install the oil pan and related parts as outlined under Oil Pan Installation.

DISASSEMBLY

1. Remove the oil inlet tube from the oil pump and remove the gasket.

2. Remove the cover retaining screws, then remove the cover. Remove the inner rotor and shaft assembly, then remove the outer race.

3. Insert a self-threading sheet metal screw of the proper diameter into the oil pressure relief valve chamber cap and pull the cap out of the chamber. Remove the spring and plunger.

CLEANING AND INSPECTION

Refer to Part 8-1, Section 3 for the cleaning and inspection procedures.

ASSEMBLY

The oil pump assembly is shown in Fig. 52.

1. Oil all parts thoroughly.

2. Install the oil pressure relief valve plunger, spring and a new cap.

3. Install the outer race and the inner rotor and shaft assembly. **Be sure the dimple (identification mark) on the outer race is facing**

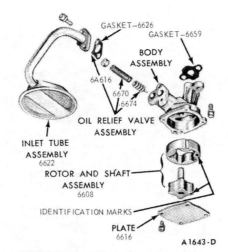

FIG. 52 — Oil Pump Assembly

outward and on same side as identification mark on rotor. The race rotor and shaft and the outer race are serviced as an assembly. One part should not be replaced without replacing the other. Install the cover and torque the cover retaining screws to specifications.

4. Position a new gasket and the oil inlet tube on the oil pump and install the retaining bolts.

3   REMOVAL AND INSTALLATION

The engine removal and installation procedures are for the engine only without the transmission attached.

REMOVAL

1. Drain the cooling system and the crankcase.

2. Remove the hood. Disconnect the battery and alternator ground cables from the cylinder block.

3. Disconnect the automatic choke heat chamber air inlet hose from the inlet tube near the right valve rocker arm cover. Remove the air cleaner and intake duct assembly.

4. Disconnect the radiator upper hose from the coolant outlet housing and the radiator lower hose at the water pump.

On a car with an automatic transmission, disconnect the transmission oil cooler lines from the radiator.

5. Remove the radiator. Remove the fan, spacer, belt and pulley.

6. Remove the alternator bolts and position the alternator out of the way.

7. Disconnect the oil pressure sending unit wire from the sending unit, and *the flexible fuel line* at the fuel tank line. Plug the fuel tank line.

8. Disconnect the accelerator rod from the carburetor.

On a car with an automatic transmission disconnect the throttle valve vacuum line from the intake manifold. Disconnect the manual shift rod and remove the retracting spring. Disconnect the transmission filler tube bracket from the cylinder block.

On a car with an air conditioner, isolate and remove the compressor as outlined in Group 16.

On a car with power steering, disconnect the power steering pump bracket from the cylinder head. Remove the drive belt. Wire the power steering pump out of the way and in a position that will prevent the oil from draining out.

On a car with power brakes, disconnect the brake vacuum line from the intake manifold.

On an engine equipped with Thermactor exhaust emission control system, remove the air pump air filter if it is not connected to the engine.

9. Remove the heater hose from the automatic choke housing. Disconnect the heater hoses from the water pump and intake manifold. Disconnect the water temperature sending unit wire from the sending unit.

10. Remove the flywheel or converter housing to engine upper bolts.

11. Disconnect the primary wire from the ignition coil. Remove the wire harness from the left rocker arm cover and position the wires out of the way. Disconnect the ground strap from the block.

12. Raise the front of the car. Disconnect the starter cable from the starter. Remove the starter and dust seal.

13. Disconnect the muffler inlet pipes from the exhaust manifolds. Disconnect the engine support in-

sulators from the brackets on the frame underbody.

On a car with a manual-shift transmission, remove the remaining flywheel housing to engine bolts.

On a car with an automatic transmission, remove the converter housing inspection cover. Disconnect the flywheel from the converter. Secure the converter assembly in the housing. Remove the remaining converter housing to engine bolts.

14. Lower the car, and then support the transmission. Install the engine left lifting bracket on the front of the left cylinder head, and install the engine right lifting bracket at the rear of the right cylinder head. Then attach the engine lifting sling (Fig. 53).

15. Raise the engine slightly and carefully pull it from the transmission. Carefully lift the engine out of the engine compartment so that the rear cover plate is not bent or other components damaged. Install the engine on a work stand.

INSTALLATION

1. Position new gaskets on the muffler inlet pipes.

2. Attach the engine lifting brackets and sling (Fig. 53). Remove the engine from the work stand.

3. Lower the engine carefully into the engine compartment. Make sure the exhaust manifolds are properly aligned with the muffler inlet pipes *and the dowels in the block* are through the rear cover plate and engage the holes in the flywheel housing.

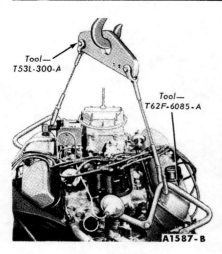

Tool—
T53L-300-A

Tool—
T62F-6085-A

A1587-B

FIG. 53—Typical Engine Lifting Brackets and Sling

On a car with an automatic transmission, start the converter pilot into the crankshaft.

On a car with a manual-shift transmission, start the transmission main drive gear into the clutch disc. It may be necessary to adjust the position of the transmission in relation to the engine if the input shaft will not enter the clutch disc. **If the engine hangs up after the shaft enters, turn the crankshaft slowly (transmission in gear) until the shaft splines mesh with the clutch disc splines.**

4. Install the flywheel or converter housing upper bolts.

5. Install the engine support insulator to bracket retaining nuts.

Disconnect the engine lifting sling and remove the lifting brackets.

6. Raise the front of the car. Connect both exhaust manifolds to the muffler inlet pipes. Torque the nuts to specifications.

7. Position the dust seal and install the starter and the starter cable.

On a car with a manual-shift transmission, install the remaining flywheel housing to engine bolts.

On a car with an automatic transmission, remove the retainer securing the converter in the housing. Attach the converter to the flywheel. Install the converter housing inspection cover. Install the remaining converter housing retaining bolts.

8. Remove the support from the transmission and lower the car.

9. Connect the wiring harness to the left valve rocker arm cover and connect the coil wire.

10. Connect the water temperature sending unit wire. Install the heater hose on the automatic choke housing and connect the hose to the intake manifold.

11. Connect the bellcrank to the intake manifold.

On a car with an automatic transmission, connect the transmission filler tube bracket. Connect the manual shift rod and install the retracting spring. Connect the throttle valve vacuum line.

Connect the accelerator rod.

12. Remove the plug from the fuel tank line and connect the fuel line and the oil pressure sending unit wire.

13. Install the pulley, belt, spacer and fan.

14. Position the alternator and install the alternator bolts. Connect the alternator and the battery ground cables. Adjust the belt tension to specifications.

On a car with an air conditioner, install the compressor as outlined in Group 16.

On a car with power steering, install the drive belt and power steering pump bracket. Install the bracket retaining bolts. Adjust the drive belt tension to specifications.

On a car with power brakes, connect the brake vacuum line.

15. Install the radiator. Connect the radiator upper and lower hoses. On a car with an automatic transmission, connect the transmission oil cooler lines.

16. Connect the heater hose at the water pump. Fill and bleed the cooling system. Fill the crankcase with the proper grade and quantity of oil.

17. Adjust the transmission throttle linkage.

18. Operate the engine at fast idle and check all gaskets and hose connections for leaks.

19. Install the air cleaner and intake duct assembly. Connect the automatic choke heat chamber air inlet hose.

On an engine equipped with Thermactor exhaust emission control system, install the air pump air filter if it was removed.

20. Install and adjust the hood.

4 MAJOR REPAIR OPERATIONS

When installing nuts or bolts that must be torqued (refer to Part 8-5 for torque specifications), oil the threads with light weight engine oil. **Do not oil threads that require oil-resistant or water-resistant sealer.**

To perform the operations in this section, it will be necessary to remove the engine from the car and install it on a work stand.

CRANKSHAFT

The crankshaft and related parts are shown in Fig. 54.

REMOVAL

1. Disconnect the spark plug wires at the spark plugs and remove the wires from the ignition harness brackets on the valve rocker arm covers. Disconnect the coil to distributor high tension lead at the coil. Remove the distributor cap and spark plug wire assembly. Remove the spark plugs to allow easy rotation of the crankshaft.

2. Remove the fuel pump and oil filter. Slide the water pump bypass hose clamp toward the water pump. Remove the alternator and mounting brackets.

If the engine is equipped with Thermactor exhaust emission control system, remove the air pump and brackets from the right cylinder head.

3. Remove the crankshaft pulley from the crankshaft vibration damper. Remove the cap screw and washer from the end of the crankshaft. Install the puller on the crankshaft vibration damper (Fig. 35) and remove the damper.

4. Remove the cylinder front cover and water pump as an assembly.

5. Remove the crankshaft front oil slinger. Check the timing chain deflection, then remove the timing chain and sprockets by following steps 12 thru 16 under Cylinder Front Cover and Timing Chain Removal.

6. Invert the engine on the work stand. Remove the clutch pressure plate and disc (manual-shift transmission). Remove the flywheel and engine rear cover plate. Remove the oil pan and gasket. Remove the oil pump.

7. Make sure all bearing caps

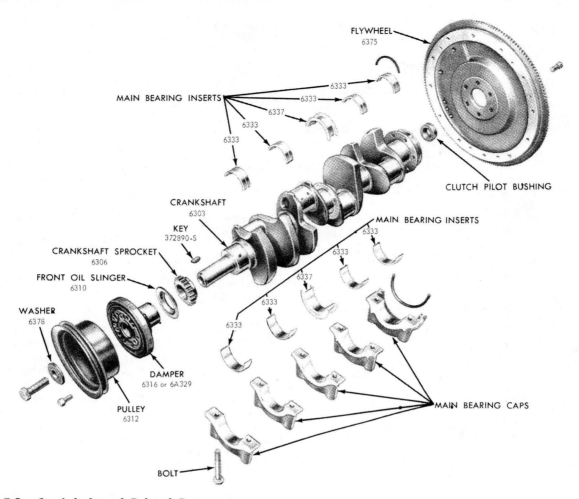

FIG. 54 —Crankshaft and Related Parts

(main and connecting rod) are marked so that they can be installed in their original locations. Turn the crankshaft until the connecting rod from which the cap is being removed is down, and remove the bearing cap. Push the connecting rod and piston assembly up into the cylinder. Repeat this procedure until all the connecting rod bearing caps are removed.

8. Remove the main bearing caps.

9. Carefully lift the crankshaft out of the block so that the thrust bearing surfaces are not damaged. **Handle the crankshaft with care to avoid possible fracture or damage to the finished surfaces.**

CLEANING AND INSPECTION

Refer to Part 8-1, Section 3 for the cleaning and inspection procedures. Clean the crankshaft damper, following the referenced procedure.

REPAIRS

To refinish journals, dress minor imperfections, etc., refer to Part 8-1, Section 2.

INSTALLATION

1. Remove the rear journal oil seal from the block and rear main bearing cap.

2. Remove the main bearing inserts from the block and bearing caps.

3. Remove the connecting rod bearing inserts from the connecting rods and caps.

4. If the crankshaft main bearing journals have been refinished to a definite undersize, install the correct undersize bearings. Be sure the bearing inserts and bearing bores are clean. Foreign material under the inserts will distort the bearing and cause a failure.

5. Place the upper main bearing inserts in position in the bores with the tang fitting in the slot provided.

6. Install the lower main bearing inserts in the bearing caps.

7. Clean the rear journal oil seal groove and the mating surfaces of the block and rear main bearing cap. Preform the new seal by hand to the approximate radius of the cap.

8. Insert the seal in the oil seal groove, seating the center of the seal first and allowing the seal to extend equally on both ends. Press the seal down firmly with the thumb at the center of the seal, and then press both ends of the seal into the groove, working from the ends to the center.

9. Position the seal forming tool as shown in Fig. 55 and complete the seal installation. After installation, cut the ends of the seal flush.

10. Carefully lower the crankshaft into place. **Be careful not to damage the bearing surfaces.**

11. Check the clearance of each main bearing as follows:

Place a piece of Plastigage on the crankshaft journal the full width of the journal and about ¼ inch off-center (Fig. 56). Follow steps 11 thru 15 under Main Bearing Replacement.

12. After the bearings have been

Tool—T62F-6701-A or 6701-E

A1644-B

FIG. 55—Rear Oil Seal to Block Installation

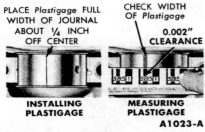

PLACE *Plastigage* FULL WIDTH OF JOURNAL ABOUT ¼ INCH OFF CENTER

CHECK WIDTH OF *Plastigage*

0.002" CLEARANCE

INSTALLING PLASTIGAGE

MEASURING PLASTIGAGE

A1023-A

FIG. 56—Installing and Measuring Plastigage—Engine on Work Stand

fitted, apply a light coat of engine oil to the journals and bearings. Install a new seal in the rear main bearing cap and install the rear main bearing cap by following steps 17 thru 20 under Main Bearing Replacement. Install all the bearing caps, except the thrust bearing cap (No. 3 bearing). **Be sure that the main bearing caps are installed in their original locations.** Torque the bearing cap bolts to specifications.

13. Install the thrust bearing cap with the bolts finger-tight.

14. Pry the crankshaft forward against the thrust surface of the upper half of the bearing (Fig. 57).

15. Hold the crankshaft forward and pry the thrust bearing cap to the rear (Fig. 57). This will align the thrust surfaces of both halves of the bearing.

16. Retain the forward pressure on the crankshaft. Tighten the cap bolts to specifications (Fig. 57).

17. Force the crankshaft toward the rear of the engine.

18. Check the crankshaft end play (refer to Part 9-1, Section 2).

19. Install new bearing inserts in the connecting rods and caps. Check the clearance of each bearing following the recommended procedure.

20. After the connecting rod bearings have been fitted, apply a light coat of engine oil to the journals and bearings.

21. Turn the crankshaft throw to the bottom of its stroke. Push the piston all the way down until the rod bearing seats on the crankshaft journal.

22. Install the connecting rod cap. Torque the nuts to specifications.

23. After the piston and connecting rod assemblies have been installed, check the side clearance between the connecting rods on each connecting rod crankshaft journal (Fig. 43).

24. Install the timing chain and sprockets, cylinder front cover and crankshaft pulley and adapter, fol-lowing steps 1 thru 8 under Cylinder Front Cover and Timing Chain Installation.

25. Coat the threads of the flywheel retaining bolts with oil-resistant sealer. Position the flywheel on the crankshaft flange. Install and torque the bolts to specifications.

On a flywheel for a manual-shift transmission, use tool 6392-N to locate the clutch disc. Install the pressure plate. Tighten the retaining bolts.

26. Clean the oil pan, oil pump and oil pump screen. Prime the oil pump by filling either the inlet or outlet port with engine oil and rotating the pump shaft to distribute oil within the housing. Install the oil pump and oil pan by following the procedures under Oil Pan and Oil Pump Installation.

27. Install the Rotunda oil filter, fuel pump and connect the fuel lines. Install the alternator, shield and mounting bracket.

If the engine is equipped with Thermactor exhaust emission control system, install the air pump mounting bracket.

28. Install the spark plugs, distributor cap and spark plug wires. Connect the spark plug wires and high tension lead.

29. Install the engine in the car.

CAMSHAFT BEARING REPLACEMENT

Camshaft bearings are available pre-finished to size for standard and 0.015-inch undersize journal diameters. The bearings are not interchangeable from one bore to another.

1. Remove the camshaft, flywheel

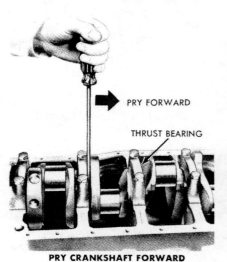

PRY FORWARD

THRUST BEARING

PRY CRANKSHAFT FORWARD

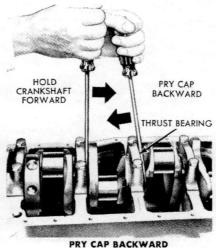

HOLD CRANKSHAFT FORWARD

PRY CAP BACKWARD

THRUST BEARING

PRY CAP BACKWARD

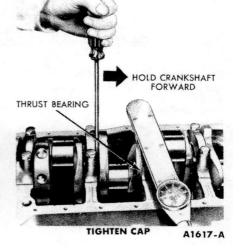

HOLD CRANKSHAFT FORWARD

THRUST BEARING

TIGHTEN CAP

A1617-A

FIG. 57—Thrust Bearing Alignment

and crankshaft, following the appropriate procedures in Section 2 or Section 4. Push the pistons to the top of the cylinders.

2. Remove the camshaft rear bearing bore plug (Fig. 58). Remove the camshaft bearings (Fig. 59).

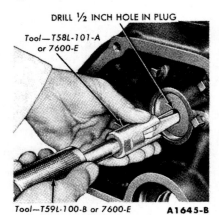

DRILL ½ INCH HOLE IN PLUG
Tool—T58L-101-A or 7600-E

Tool—T59L-100-B or 7600-E   A1645-B

FIG. 58—Camshaft Rear Bearing Bore Plug Removal

3. Select the proper size expanding collet and back-up nut and assemble on the expanding mandrel. With the expanding collet collapsed, install the collet assembly in the camshaft bearing, and tighten the back-up nut on the expanding mandrel until the collet fits the camshaft bearing.

4. Assemble the puller screw and extension (if necessary) as shown and install on the expanding mandrel. Wrap a cloth around the threads of the puller screw to protect the front bearing or journal. Tighten the

pulling nut against the thrust bearing and pulling plate to remove the camshaft bearing. Be sure to hold a wrench on the end of the puller screw to prevent it from turning.

5. Repeat the procedure for each bearing. To remove the front bearing, install the puller screw from the rear of the cylinder block.

6. Position the new bearings at the bearing bores, and press them in place with the tool shown in Fig. 60. Be sure to center the pulling plate and puller screw to avoid damage to the bearing. **Failure to use the correct expanding collett can cause severe bearing damage.** Align the oil holes in the bearings with the oil holes in the cylinder block when the bearings are installed. **Be sure the front bearing is installed 0.005-0.020 inch below the front face of the cylinder block (Fig. 60).**

7. Clean out the camshaft rear

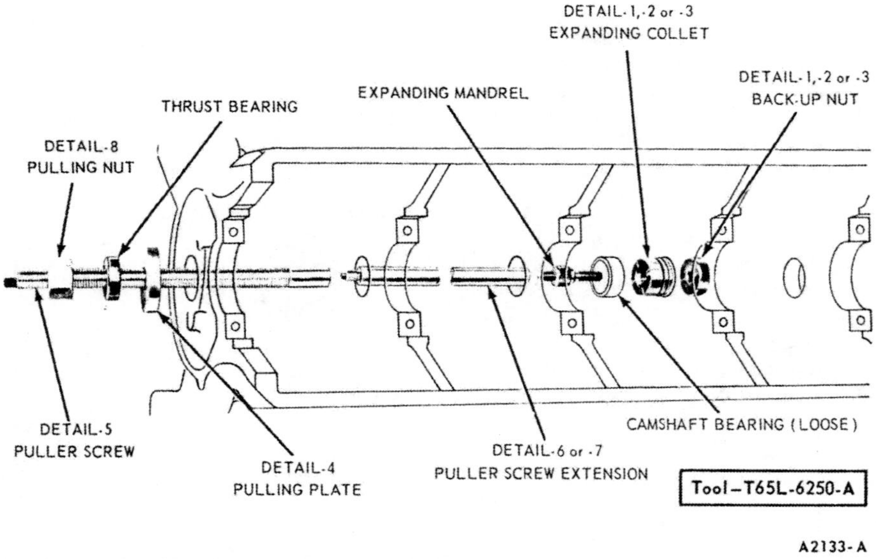

bearing bore plug recess thoroughly. Coat the flange of a new plug with oil-resistant sealer and install the plug (Fig. 61) with the flange edge of the plug facing outward.

8. Install the camshaft, crankshaft, flywheel and related parts, following the appropriate procedures in Section 2 or Section 4, except do not check connecting rod and main bearing clearances as a part of Camshaft Bearing Replacement. Install the engine in the car.

INSTALL FRONT BEARING 0.005-0.020 INCH BELOW FRONT FACE OF BLOCK
A1647-A

FIG. 60—Camshaft Front Bearing Measurement

Tool—T62F-6266-A or 6266-B
Tool—T53L-200-A
A1648-B

FIG. 61—Camshaft Rear Bearing Bore Plug Installation

CYLINDER ASSEMBLY REPLACEMENT

DISASSEMBLY

Follow steps 1 thru 9, 11 thru 13, and 16 thru 18 under Engine Disassembly. Remove 4 cylinder head dowels from the cylinder block. Remove the cylinder block drain plugs, and remove the cylinder assembly from the work stand.

CLEANING

Clean the gasket and seal surfaces of all parts and assemblies (refer to Part 8-1, Section 3).

ASSEMBLY

Install the replacement cylinder assembly on a work stand. Install the cylinder block drain plugs and cylinder head dowels. Transfer all parts removed from the old cylinder assembly, following the procedures in steps 21 thru 31 and 35 thru 59 under Engine Assembly. Check all assembly clearances and correct as necessary.

DETAIL-1,-2 or -3 EXPANDING COLLET
DETAIL-1,-2 or -3 BACK-UP NUT
THRUST BEARING
EXPANDING MANDREL
DETAIL-8 PULLING NUT
DETAIL-5 PULLER SCREW
DETAIL-4 PULLING PLATE
DETAIL-6 or -7 PULLER SCREW EXTENSION
CAMSHAFT BEARING (LOOSE)
Tool—T65L-6250-A
A2133-A

FIG. 59—Camshaft Bearing Replacement

CYLINDER BLOCK REPLACEMENT

DISASSEMBLY

Follow steps 1 thru 9, 11 thru 14, 17 thru 24, 27 and 28 under Engine Disassembly. Remove the 4 cylinder head dowels and the cylinder block drain plugs from the cylinder block. Remove the cylinder block from the work stand.

CLEANING AND INSPECTION

Clean the crankshaft damper and the gasket and seal surfaces of all the parts and assemblies (refer to Part 8-1, Section 3).

ASSEMBLY

Install the replacement cylinder block on the work stand. Install the cylinder block drain plugs and cylinder head dowels. Transfer the parts removed from the old cylinder block to the new cylinder block by following steps 5, 6, 9 thru 12, 14 thru 31 and 34 thru 59 under Engine Assembly. Check all assembly clearances and correct as necessary.

ENGINE DISASSEMBLY

1. Install the engine on the work stand.

2. Remove the distributor cap, coil high tension wire and spark plug wires as an assembly.

3. Disconnect the distributor vacuum line from the distributor. Remove the carburetor fuel inlet line and fuel pump outlet line. Remove the fuel pump and discard the gasket. Remove the oil filter and adapter.

4. Slide the clamp on the water pump bypass hose toward the water pump. Remove the automatic choke heat tube.

5. Remove the valve rocker arm covers and the crankcase ventilating system.

If the engine is equipped with a Thermactor exhaust emission control system, remove the anti-backfire valve and bracket, the air pump and brackets and all the hoses.

6. Remove the alternator mounting brackets. Remove the ignition coil. Remove the distributor hold-down bolt and remove the distributor.

7. Remove the intake manifold retaining bolts. Raise the manifold and carefully remove it from the engine. Discard the intake manifold gaskets, seals and sealing washers.

8. Loosen the valve rocker arm stud nuts so that the valve rocker arms can be rotated to the side. Remove the valve push rods in sequence and put them in a rack or holder so that they can be installed in their original position.

9. Using a magnet, remove the valve lifters and place them in a rack so that they can be installed in their original bores (Fig. 37).

If the valve lifters are stuck in their bores by excessive varnish, etc., it may be necessary to use a plier-type tool (T52T-6500-DJD or 6500-D) to remove the lifters. Rotate the lifter back and forth to loosen it from the gum or varnish that may have formed at the lifter. **The internal parts of each hydraulic valve lifter assembly are matched sets. Do not intermix the parts. Keep the assemblies intact until they are to be cleaned.**

10. Remove the exhaust manifolds and the spark plugs.

11. Install the cylinder head holding fixtures (Fig. 22). Remove the cylinder head bolts and lift the cylinder heads off the block. Discard the cylinder head gaskets.

12. Remove the crankshaft pulley from the crankshaft vibration damper. Remove the cap screw and washer from the end of the crankshaft. Install the puller on the crankshaft vibration damper (Fig. 29) and remove the vibration damper.

13. Remove the oil pan to cylinder front cover retaining bolts. Remove the cylinder front cover retaining screws. Remove the cylinder front cover and water pump as an assembly. Discard the gasket and remove the crankshaft front oil slinger.

14. Check the timing chain deflection and remove the timing chain and sprockets by following steps 12 thru 16 under Cylinder Front Cover and Timing Chain Removal. Remove the crankshaft sprocket key.

15. Remove any ridge and/or carbon deposits from the upper end of the cylinder bores. Move the piston to the bottom of its travel and place a cloth on the piston head to collect the cuttings. Remove the cylinder ridge with a ridge cutter. Follow the instructions furnished by the tool manufacturer. **Never cut into the ring travel area in excess of 1/32 inch when removing ridges.** After the ridge has been removed, remove the cutter from the cylinder bore.

16. On a flywheel for a manual-shift transmission, remove the clutch pressure plate and disc.

17. Remove the flywheel and rear cover plate. Remove the clutch pilot bushing (Fig. 62).

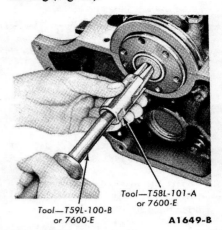

Tool—T59L-100-B or 7600-E
Tool—T58L-101-A or 7600-E
A1649-B

FIG. 62—Clutch Pilot Bushing Removal

18. Invert the engine. Remove the oil pan and discard the gaskets and seals.

19. Remove the oil pump and inlet tube as an assembly. Remove the intermediate drive shaft. Discard the oil pump gasket.

20. Make sure all connecting rods and caps are marked so that they can be installed in their original locations. Turn the crankshaft until the connecting rod being removed is down. Remove the rod cap.

21. Push the connecting rod and piston assembly out the top of the cylinder with the handle end of a hammer. **Avoid damage to the connecting rod journal or the cylinder wall when removing the piston and rod.**

22. Remove the bearing inserts from the connecting rods and caps. Install the rod caps on the connecting rods from which they were removed.

23. Remove the main bearing caps.

24. Carefully lift the crankshaft out of the cylinder block so that the thrust bearing surfaces are not damaged. **Handle the crankshaft with care to avoid possible fracture or damage to the finished surfaces.**

25. Remove the rear journal oil seal from the block and rear bearing cap.

26. Remove the main bearing inserts from the block and bearing caps. Install the main bearing caps in their original positions.

27. Remove the camshaft thrust

plate. Carefully remove the camshaft by pulling it toward the front of the engine. Use caution to avoid damaging the journals and lobes.

28. Remove the oil filter adapter.

29. Remove the camshaft rear bearing bore plug (Fig. 58). Remove the camshaft bearings (Fig. 59).

ENGINE ASSEMBLY

If the cylinder block is to be replaced, transfer the cylinder head dowels and cylinder block drain plugs to the new cylinder block and start the assembly procedures with step number 5.

1. If the original cylinder block is used, remove the glaze from the cylinder bores by following the instructions of the tool manufacturer.

2. Invert the engine on the work stand.

3. Position the new camshaft bearings at the bearing bores, and press them in place with the tool shown in Fig. 59. Align the oil holes in the cylinder block when the bearings are installed. **Be sure the camshaft front bearing is installed 0.005-0.020 inch below the front face of the cylinder block (Fig. 60).**

4. Clean out the camshaft rear bearing bore plug recess thoroughly. Coat the flange of a new plug with oil-resistant sealer and install it with the flange facing out (Fig. 61). Drive the plug in until it is slightly below the chamfer in the bore.

5. Oil the camshaft and apply Lubriplate to all lobes, and then carefully slide it through the bearings.

6. Clean the rear journal oil seal groove and the mating surfaces of the block and rear main bearing cap. Preform the new seal by hand to the approximate radius of the cap.

7. Insert the seal in the oil seal groove, seating the center of the seal first and allowing the seal to extend equally on both ends. Press the seal down firmly with the thumb at the center of the seal, and then press both ends of the seal into the groove, working from the ends to the center.

8. Position the seal forming tool as shown in Fig. 55 and complete the seal installation. After installation, cut the ends of the seal flush.

9. If the crankshaft main bearing journals have been refinished to a definite undersize, install the correct undersize bearings. Be sure the bearing inserts and bearing bores are clean. Foreign material under the inserts will distort the bearing and cause a failure.

Place the upper main bearing inserts in position in the bore with the tang fitting in the slot provided.

10. Install the lower main bearing inserts in the bearing caps.

11. Carefully lower the crankshaft into place. **Be careful not to damage the bearing surfaces.**

12. Check the clearance of each main bearing following the procedure under Main Bearing Replacement.

13. After the bearings have been fitted, apply a light coat of engine oil to the journals and bearings.

14. Install a new journal oil seal in the cap (Fig. 40) by following steps 6, 7 and 8. Apply a thin coating of oil-resistant sealer to the rear main bearing cap at the rear of the top mating surface (Fig. 40). **Do not apply sealer to the area forward of the oil slinger groove.** Install the rear main bearing cap and the remainder of the caps, except the thrust bearing cap (No. 3 bearing). **Be sure that the main bearing caps are installed in their original positions.** Torque the bearing cap bolts to specifications.

15. Install the thrust bearing cap and check crankshaft end play by following steps 13 thru 20 under Crankshaft Installation.

16. Turn the engine on the work stand so that the front end is up.

17. Install the pistons and connecting rods by following steps 1 thru 9 under Piston and Connecting Rod Installation.

18. Position the sprockets and timing chain on the camshaft and crankshaft (Fig. 31). Be sure the timing marks on the sprockets are positioned as shown in Fig. 30.

19. Lubricate the timing chain and sprockets with engine oil.

20. Install the fuel pump eccentric, washer and camshaft sprocket cap screw. Torque the sprocket cap screw to specifications. Install the crankshaft front oil slinger (Fig. 33).

21. Clean the cylinder front cover and the cylinder block gasket surfaces. Install a new crankshaft front oil seal (Fig. 32).

22. Coat the gasket surface of the block and cover and the cover bolt threads with oil-resistant sealer. Position a new gasket on the block.

23. Install the alignment pilot tool on the cylinder front cover so that the keyway in the pilot aligns with the key in the crankshaft. Position the cover (and water pump and pilot over the end of the crankshaft and against the block) (Fig. 34).

24. Install the cylinder front cover screws finger-tight. While pushing in on the pilot, torque the cover bolts to specifications. Remove the pilot.

25. Lubricate the crankshaft with a white lead and oil mixture and apply lubriplate to the oil seal rubbing surface of the vibration damper inner hub to prevent damage to the oil seal.

26. Line up the crankshaft vibration damper keyway with the key on the crankshaft, and then install the vibration damper on the crankshaft (Fig. 35). Install the damper cap screw and washer, and torque the screw to specifications. Install the crankshaft pulley.

27. Using a new gasket install the fuel pump.

28. Turn the engine on the work stand so that the top of the engine is up.

29. Clean the cylinder head and block gasket surfaces. Install the head gasket over the cylinder head dowels.

30. Place the cylinder head on the engine, then remove the holding fixtures. Coat the head bolt threads with water-resistant sealer, and then install the bolts.

31. The cylinder head bolt tightening procedure is performed in three progressive steps. Torque the bolts in sequence (Fig. 23) to 50 ft-lbs, then to 60 ft-lbs and finally to specifications. **After the cylinder head bolts have been torqued to specifications, the bolts should not be disturbed.**

32. Coat the mating surfaces of the exhaust manifold with a light film of graphite grease. Position new gaskets on the muffler inlet pipe.

33. Position the exhaust manifolds on the cylinder heads and install the retaining bolts and tab washers. Torque the retaining bolts to specifications, working from the center to the ends. Lock the bolts by bending one tab of the washer over a flat on the bolt.

34. Install the spark plugs.

35. Coat the outside of each valve lifter with engine oil to provide initial lubrication. **Do not fill the lifters with oil. The lifters will fill much faster after the engine is started if they are free of any oil film which may cause an oil seal between the plunger and the lifter body.** Place each lifter in the bore from which it was removed.

36. Install the push rods in their

original positions. Apply Lubriplate over the valve stem tips and the push rod guides in the cylinder head. Install the rocker arms over the push rods. Perform a valve clearance adjustment as outlined in Part 8-1, Section 2.

37. Clean the mating surfaces of the intake manifold, cylinder heads and cylinder block.

38. Coat the intake manifold and cylinder block seal surfaces with quick setting adhesive.

39. Position new seals on the cylinder block and new gaskets on the *cylinder* heads with the gaskets interlocked with the seal tabs. Apply non-hardening sealer at the four junction points of the seals and gaskets. Be sure the holes in the gaskets are aligned with the holes in the cylinder heads.

40. Carefully lower the intake manifold on the cylinder block and cylinder heads. **After the intake manifold is in place, run a finger around the seal area to make sure the seals are in place. If the seals are not in place, remove the intake manifold and position the seals.**

41. Be sure the holes in the manifold gaskets and manifold are in alignment. Position the intake manifold alignment tools (Fig. 18) in the front and rear (Nos. 10 and 12) bolt holes on the left bank of the manifold.

42. Using new sealing washers, install the intake manifold retaining bolts. Working from the center to the ends, torque the bolts in sequence (Fig. 19) to 15-17 ft-lbs.

43. Remove the manifold alignment tools from the front and rear bolt holes (Nos. 10 and 12). Using new sealing washers, install the two remaining bolts and torque to 15-17 ft.-lbs.

44. Torque all the manifold retaining bolts in sequence to 20-22 ft.-lbs.

45. Install the water pump bypass hose on the coolant outlet housing. Slide the clamp into position and tighten the clamp.

46. Rotate the crankshaft until the No. 1 piston is on TDC, then position the distributor in the block with the rotor at the No. 1 firing position and the points open. Install the hold down clamp.

47. Install the ignition coil. Posi-

tion and install the alternator mounting bracket.

If the engine is equipped with Thermactor exhaust emission control system, install the anti-backfire valve and bracket, the air pump and bracket and the hoses.

48. Clean the valve rocker arm covers and the cylinder head gasket surface. Apply oil-resistant sealer to one side of new cover gaskets. Lay the cemented side of the gaskets in place in the covers.

49. Position the covers on the cylinder heads. Make sure the gasket seats evenly all around the head. Install the bolts. The cover is tightened in two steps. Torque the bolts to specifications. Two minutes later, torque the bolts to the same specifications.

50. Install the crankcase ventilation system.

51. Install the automatic choke heat tube. Install the distributor cap. Position the spark plug wires in the brackets on the valve rocker arm covers. Connect the spark plug wires and the coil wire.

52. Connect the carburetor fuel inlet line and pump outlet line.

53. Prime the oil pump by filling either the inlet or outlet port with engine oil. Rotate the pump shaft to distribute the oil within the pump body.

54. Invert the engine on the work stand. Position the intermediate drive shaft into the distributor socket. With the shaft firmly seated in the distributor socket, the stop on the shaft should touch the roof of the crankcase. Remove the shaft and position the stop as necessary.

55. With the stop properly positioned, insert the intermediate drive shaft into the oil pump.

56. Position a new gasket on the pump housing and install the pump and shaft as an assembly. **Do not attempt to force the pump into position if it will not seat readily. The drive shaft hex may be misaligned with the distributor shaft. To align, rotate the intermediate shaft into a new position.** Torque the oil pump retaining screw to specifications.

57. Clean the gasket surfaces of the block and oil pan. Coat the block surface and the oil pan gasket surface with sealer. Position new gaskets on the block and position a new seal

on the cylinder front cover and rear main bearing cap. Make sure the tabs on the seal are over the oil pan gasket. Install the retaining screws and torque them from the center outward to specifications (one screw retains the fuel line bracket).

58. Install the oil filter adapter. Clean the oil filter gasket surface. Coat the gasket on the filter with oil. Place the Rotunda filter in position on the adapter fitting. Hand tighten the filter until the gasket contacts the adapter face, then advance it ½ turn.

59. Install the clutch pilot service

Tool—7600-H

A1650-C

FIG. 63—Clutch Pilot Bearing Installation

bearing (Fig. 63). Coat the threads of the flywheel retaining bolts with oil-resistant sealer. Position the rear cover plate on the block and the flywheel on the crankshaft flange. Install and torque the bolts to specifications.

On a flywheel for a manual-shift transmission, use tool T58P-7563-A to locate the clutch disc. Install the pressure plate.

60. Install the engine in the car. Fill and bleed the cooling system. Fill the crankcase with the proper grade and quantity of engine oil.

61. Operate the engine and check for oil and coolant leaks. Check and adjust the ignition timing. Connect the distributor vacuum line to the distributor.

62. Adjust the engine idle speed, fuel mixture and anti-stall dashpot (if applicable). Adjust the transmission throttle linkage.

PART 8-4

352, 390, 410, 427, AND 428 V-8

1 DESCRIPTION AND OPERATION

The 352, 390, 410, 427, and the 428 V-8 engines (Figs. 1 and 2) have the same basic design. Typical engine sections are shown in Figs. 3 and 4. Differences in the engines are called out when they exist. Refer to Table 1 for the engine identification and application.

An engine identification tag is attached to the ignition coil bracket; refer to Part 8-1, Section 1.

THERMACTOR EXHAUST EMISSION CONTROL SYSTEM

For engines equipped with Thermactor exhaust emission control system, refer to Group 12 for description and adjustment and repair procedures.

MANIFOLDS

On the 352 V-8 engines, an engine coolant-heated spacer is located between the carburetor and the intake manifold (Fig. 5). The coolant flows from the front of the engine through the spacer inlet hose and into the carburetor coolant spacer. The coolant circulates through the spacer and flows into the heater inlet hose and into the heater. Exhaust gases provide the initial heat necessary to as-

A2026-C

FIG. 1—Typical 352, 390, 410 or 428 V-8

A1785-D

FIG. 2—¾ Left Front View 427 V-8 (8V) High Performance

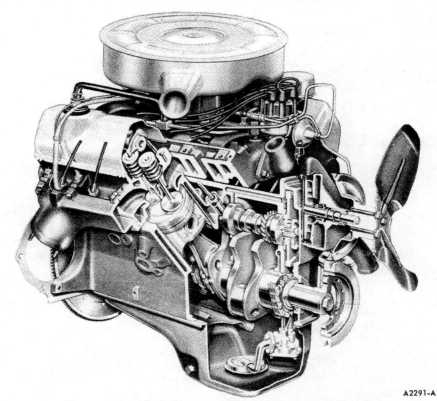

A2291-A

FIG. 3—Typical 352, 390, 410, or 428 V-8 Engine ¾ Section

sist in vaporizing the incoming fuel mixture.

On all engines, except the 352 V-8 when not Thermactor equipped, an exhaust control valve, located between the right exhaust manifold and muffler inlet pipe, remains closed during engine warmup. This directs exhaust gases through a heat crossover passage in the intake manifold, to provide the heat necessary to assist in vaporizing the incoming fuel mixture (Fig. 6).

The intake manifold has two sets of fuel passages, each with its own separate inlet connection to the carburetor (Fig. 7). The right barrel(s) of the carburetor feed Nos. 1, 4, 6 and 7 cylinders, and the left barrel(s) feed Nos. 2, 3, 5 and 8 cylinders.

Exhaust manifolds are mounted to the cylinder heads. Compression pressure in the cylinder heads forces engine exhaust gases through the exhaust manifolds into the exhaust system.

The distributor is mounted at the left front of the intake manifold.

Warm air for the automatic choke is drawn from the heat chamber of the right exhaust manifold (Fig. 8) for all engines but the 427 V-8. The warm air for the automatic choke for the 427 V-8 is drawn from the left exhaust manifold.

CYLINDER HEADS

The cylinder head assemblies contain the valves and the valve rocker arm shaft assembly. The combustion chambers are machined in the head. Valve guides are an integral part of the head. The valves are arranged from front to rear on both banks E-I-E-I-I-E-I-E (Fig. 9).

CYLINDER BLOCK

The cylinders are numbered from front to rear, on the right bank 1, 2, 3 and 4 and on the left bank 5, 6, 7 and 8. The firing order is 1-5-4-2-6-3-7-8.

The oil pump, mounted inside the oil pan at the front, is driven by the distributor through an intermediate drive shaft.

The crankshaft is supported by five main bearings. Crankshaft end thrust is controlled by the flanges of the No. 3 main bearing.

On the 427 V-8 engine, cross-bolted main bearing caps are used to reinforce the cylinder block for high-speed, high-stress operation.

The pistons have two compression rings and one oil control ring. The top compression ring is molybdenum-coated, and the lower compression ring is phosphate-coated.

A1561-B

FIG. 5—Typical Engine Coolant—Heated Spacer Passages 352 V-8

by a thrust plate bolted to the front of the cylinder block. An eccentric, bolted to the front end of the camshaft, operates the fuel pump.

On the 428 Police Interceptor V-8 and 427 V-8 engines, mechanical valve lifters are used. Valve lash is maintained by self-locking adjusting screws.

On all other engines, hydraulic valve lifters are used which provide zero valve lash. The valve lifters are housed in bores located in the cylinder block valve lifter chamber. The

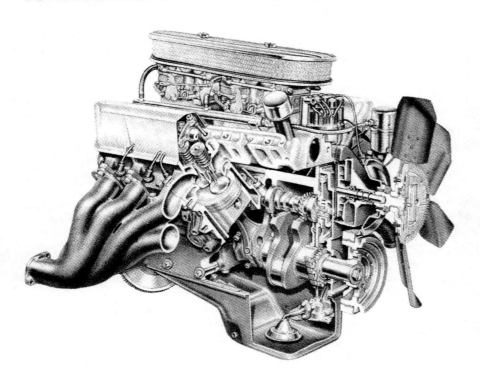

A2292-A

FIG. 4—¾ Section View—427 V-8 Engine

TABLE 1—Engine Identification and Application

Engine	Warranty Plate Engine Code	Engine Prefix	Piston Displacement	Bore and Stroke	Compression Ratio	Valve Lifters	Carburetor Type and Make	Distributor	Fuel Required
352 V-8	X	EDT	352	4.00 x 3.50	9.3:1	Hydraulic	4-V Ford	Dual Advance	Regular
390 Special V-8	H	EES	390	4.05 x 3.78	9.5:1	Hydraulic	2-V Ford	Dual Advance	Regular
390 V-8	Y	EES	390	4.05 x 3.78	9.5:1	Hydraulic	2-V Ford	Dual Advance	Regular
390 V-8	Z	EES	390	4.05 x 3.78	10.0:1	Hydraulic	4-V Ford	Dual Advance	Premium
410 V-8	M	EHK	410	4.05 x 3.98	10.5:1	Hydraulic	4-V Ford	Dual Advance	Premium
427 High Performance V-8	R	EHJ	428	4.23 x 3.78	11.2:1	Mechanical	Two 4-V Holley	Centrifugal Advance	Super-Premium
428 V-8	Q	EHJ	428	4.13 x 3.98	10.0:1	Hydraulic	4-V Ford	Dual Advance	Premium
428 Police Interceptor	P	EHJ	428	4.13 x 3.98	10.0:1	Mechanical	4-V Ford	Dual Advance	Premium

The oil control ring assembly consists of a serrated spring and two chrome-plated steel rails. The pistons are the slipper type, except those on the 352 engine which are the full skirted type. Eyebrows are provided for valve clearance.

VALVE TRAIN

The intake and exhaust valve as-

semblies are the rotating-type which rotate slightly each time the valve opens and closes.

The push rods are solid steel with oil cushioned sockets.

The camshaft is supported by five bearings pressed into the block. It is driven by a sprocket and timing chain in mesh with a sprocket on the crankshaft. Camshaft thrust is controlled

valve lifters operate directly on the camshaft lobes, thereby transmitting the thrust of the camshaft lobes, by the means of hydraulic pressure, to the push rods which actuate the valve train. Figure 10 shows the various components and operation of a typical hydraulic valve lifter.

When either an exhaust valve or an intake valve is closed, the actu-

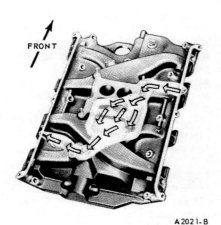

FIG. 6—Typical Intake Manifold Exhaust Gas Passages

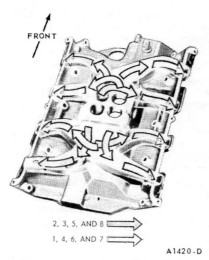

2, 3, 5, AND 8 ⇨
1, 4, 6, AND 7 ⇨

A1420-D

FIG. 7—Typical Intake Manifold Fuel Passages

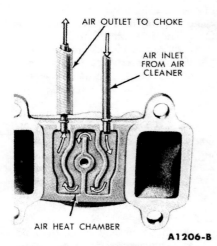

AIR OUTLET TO CHOKE

AIR INLET FROM AIR CLEANER

AIR HEAT CHAMBER

A1206-B

FIG. 8—Automatic Choke Heat Chamber—352, 390, 410 and 428 V-8

A1244-A

FIG. 9—Valve Port Arrangement

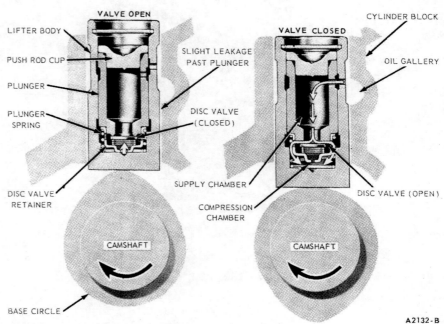

FIG. 10—Typical Hydraulic Valve Lifter Operation

force against the lifter plunger and hydraulic pressure immediately builds up in the compression chamber until it acts as a solid member of the valve operating mechanism. The lifter then becomes a hydraulic ram which forces the valve in the cylinder head to open. During this period,

ating valve lifter is on the base circle (lowest position) of the camshaft lobe.

When the valve lifter is in this position, the lifter plunger spring expands. This action forces the lifter plunger and valve push rod upward, forcing the valve end of the rocker arm to maintain solid contact with the valve (zero valve lash).

As the lifter plunger moves upward, the volume of the compression chamber is increased, resulting in reduced oil pressure in the compression chamber. Therefore, to equalize the resulting pressure differential between the supply chamber and the compression chamber, the disc valve moves off its seat and permits oil to flow from the supply chamber to the compression chamber. When the compression chamber becomes filled with oil, the pressures in the two chambers are equalized. The oil flow ceases and the disc valve spring seats the disc valve and closes the disc valve port.

As the camshaft rotates, the lifter assembly is raised by the camshaft lobe. This increases the push rod

a slight leakage of oil past the plunger occurs (calibrated leak down rate).

As the high point of the camshaft lobe rotates and passes by the foot of the valve lifter, the valve in the cylinder head seats and the valve lifter assembly is forced downward. Reduced force on the lifter plunger at this time relieves the pressure on the lifter plunger and it is free to be moved upward by the plunger spring. This action allows oil to flow once again through the oil holes in the lifter body and plunger.

The operating cycle is completed for each revolution of the camshaft. Zero clearance (lash) in the valve train mechanism is maintained at all times by the hydraulic force and expansion of the plunger spring between the lifter body and plunger.

LUBRICATION SYSTEM

Oil from the oil pan sump, located in the front of the oil pan, is forced through the pressure-type lubrication system (Figs. 11 and 12) by a roto-type oil pump. A spring-loaded

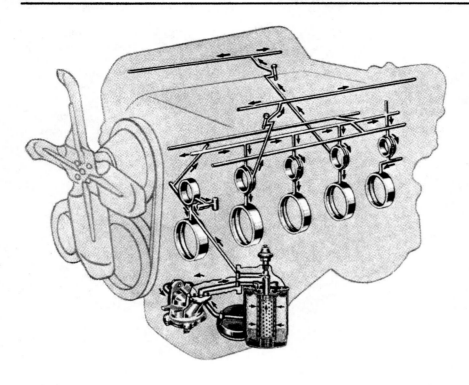

FIG. 11—Lubrication System—352, 390, 410 and 428 V-8

A2023-C

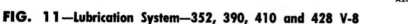

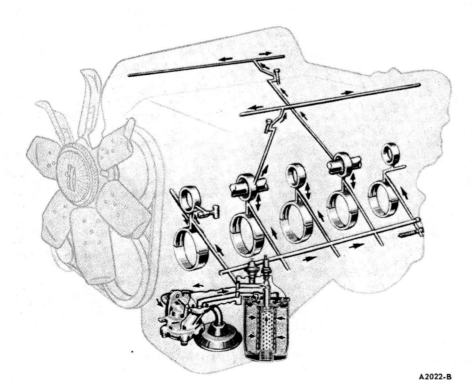

FIG. 12—Lubrication System—427 V-8

A2022-B

relief valve in the pump limits the maximum pressure of the system. Oil

relieved by the valve is directed back to the intake side of the pump.

All the oil discharged by the pump passes through a full-flow filter before it enters the engine. The filter is mounted in a vertical position at the lower left front of the engine. A relief valve in the filter permits oil to bypass the filter element if it becomes clogged.

On the 427 V-8 engine, an auxiliary oil pressure safety relief valve is located at the rear of the main oil gallery to prevent excessively high oil pressures in system during cold starts.

From the filter, the oil flows into the main oil gallery which is located in the center of the valve push rod chamber floor (except on the 427 engine). The oil gallery supplies oil to each individual camshaft bearing, through drilled passages in the block. Passages are drilled from each camshaft bearing to each main bearing. Number 1 camshaft bearing feeds No. 1 main bearing, and No. 2 camshaft bearing feeds No. 2 main bearing, etc.

On the 427 V-8, the oil gallery is located along the left side of the engine. From the gallery oil is delivered to the passages connecting the camshaft bearings and the main bearings. In this manner each bearing receives oil under direct pressure from the oil pump.

The oil then flows through notches or grooves in the main bearings to lubricate the crankshaft journals.

On the 352, 390, 410, and 428 V-8 engines, a jiggle pin in the main oil gallery front plug allows any air that may be trapped in the oil to escape.

Oil drains from the front cam bearing and a bore in the front of the cylinder block to the thrust face of the camshaft sprocket that rides against the cylinder block front surface. The rotation of the camshaft sprocket sprays the oil onto the timing chain and crankshaft sprockets.

The crankshaft is drilled from the main bearings to the connecting rod bearings.

A small groove is located in the connecting rod at the mating face where the cap contacts the connecting rod. This groove is used as an oil squirt hole for cylinder wall lubrication. Oil from the connecting rod squirt hole lubricates the opposite cylinder wall. For example, the No. 1 connecting rod oils No. 5 cylinder, etc. As the crankshaft turns, the hole in the *connecting rod bearing* aligns with the hole in the journal causing a direct squirt of oil onto the cylinder wall (Fig. 13).

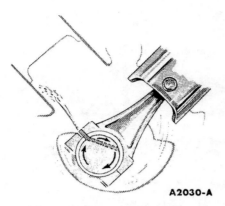

FIG. 13—Connecting Rod Bearing and Cylinder Bore Lubrication

On engines with hydraulic valve lifters, oil passages are drilled from the main oil gallery to each valve lifter oil gallery. Oil from here feeds the valve lifter assemblies. A reservoir at each valve lifter bore boss traps oil so that oil is available for valve lifter lubrication as soon as the engine starts.

An oil passage is drilled from the camshaft No. 2 bearing web to the left cylinder head between Nos. 5 and 6 cylinders to lubricate the valve rocker arm shaft assembly (Fig. 14).

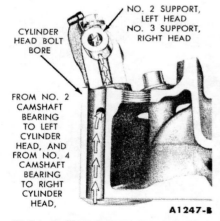

FIG. 14—Valve Rocker Arm Shaft Lubrication

The oil passage in the cylinder head is drilled from the cylinder head bolt bore to the No. 2 valve rocker and shaft support.

The oil flows through the valve rocker arm shaft through drilled holes in each valve rocker arm to lubricate the bushing and both ends of the valve rocker arm. The excess oil spirals down the rotating push rods and lubricates the push rod seats. The right valve rocker arm shaft assembly is similarly lubricated from No. 4 camshaft bearing via the No. 3 valve rocker arm shaft support.

A baffle located under the valve rocker arm shaft assembly shields the valve stems from oil splash. Excess oil is returned to the oil pan through drain holes located at each end of the cylinder head and in the push rod chamber floor.

CRANKCASE VENTILATION

The engines are equipped with a positive crankcase ventilation system of either the open or closed type.

OPEN VENTILATION SYSTEM

The positive crankcase ventilation system is shown in Fig. 15.

The system as used on the 352 engine is shown in Fig. 16.

Ventilating air enters the engine through the oil filler cap located on the front of the left valve rocker arm cover. The filler cap contains a filtering element which filters the incoming air.

From the oil filler cap, the air flows into the front section of the valve rocker arm chamber. The ventilating air moves down past the push rods into the front of the lower crankcase and into the timing chain chamber.

The rotating action of the crankshaft causes the air to flow towards the rear of the crankcase and up into the rear section of the right valve rocker arm cover. The air then enters a spring-loaded regulator valve that regulates the amount of air to meet changing operating conditions (Fig. 17). The air is then directed to the intake manifold through the crankcase vent hose, tube and fittings.

During idle, intake manifold vacuum is high. The high vacuum over-comes the tension of the spring pressure and moves the valve to the Low Speed Operation position (Fig. 17). With the valve in this position, the ventilating air passes between the valve (jiggle pin) and the outlet port. With the valve in this position, there is minimum ventilation.

As engine speed increases and manifold vacuum decreases, the spring forces the valve to the full open position (Fig. 17). This increases the flow of ventilating air.

CLOSED VENTILATION SYSTEM

The closed ventilation system is the same as the open ventilation system except for the following:

The crankcase ventilating air source is the carburetor air cleaner. The air passes through a hose connecting the air cleaner to the oil filler cap (Fig. 15 or 16). The oil filler cap is sealed at the filler opening to prevent the entrance of atmospheric air. A restriction in the air cleaner at the hose connection, assists the crankcase ventilation regulator valve in maintaining a slight vacuum in the crankcase.

COOLING SYSTEM

The coolant is drawn from the bottom of the radiator by the water pump which delivers the coolant to the cylinder block (Fig. 18).

The coolant travels through cored passages to cool the entire length of each cylinder wall. Upon reaching the rear of the cylinder block, the coolant is directed upward into the cylinder heads where it cools the combustion chambers, valves, and valve seats on its return to the front of the engine.

The coolant from each cylinder head flows through the water passages in the intake manifold past the water thermostat, if it is open, into the radiator header tank or supply tank. If the thermostat is closed, a small portion of the coolant is returned to the water pump for recirculation. The entire system is pressurized to 12-15 psi.

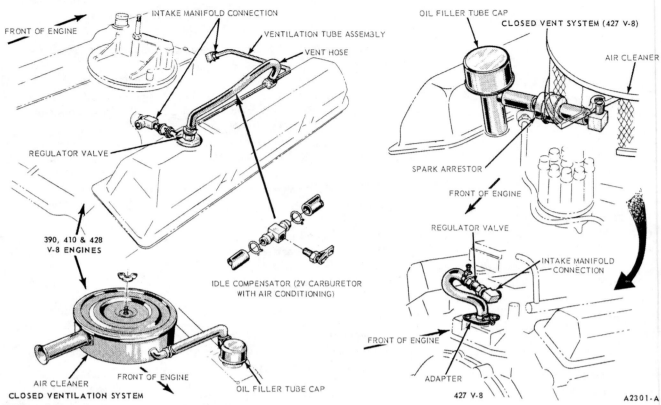

FIG. 15—Positive Crankcase Ventilation System

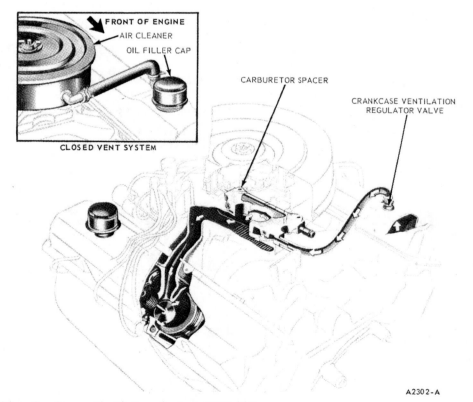

FIG. 16—Positive Crankcase Ventilation System—352 V-8

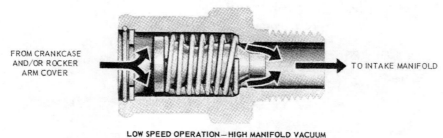

LOW SPEED OPERATION—HIGH MANIFOLD VACUUM

HIGH SPEED OPERATION—LOW MANIFOLD VACUUM

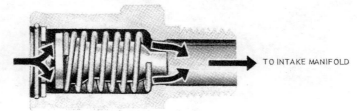

A2121-B

FIG. 17—Positive Crankcase Ventilation Regulator Valve Operation

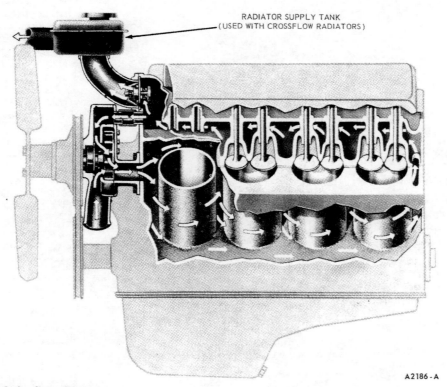

A2186-A

FIG. 18—Typical Cooling System

2   IN CAR ADJUSTMENTS AND REPAIRS

When installing nuts or bolts that must be torqued (refer to Part 8-5 for torque specifications), oil the threads with light weight engine oil. **Do not oil threads that require oil-resistant or water-resistant sealer.**

For adjustment and repair procedures of all components of the Thermactor exhaust emission control system (if so equipped), refer to group 12.

ENGINE SUPPORTS

The front supports are located on each side of the cylinder block and the rear support is located at the transmission extension housing (Fig. 19).

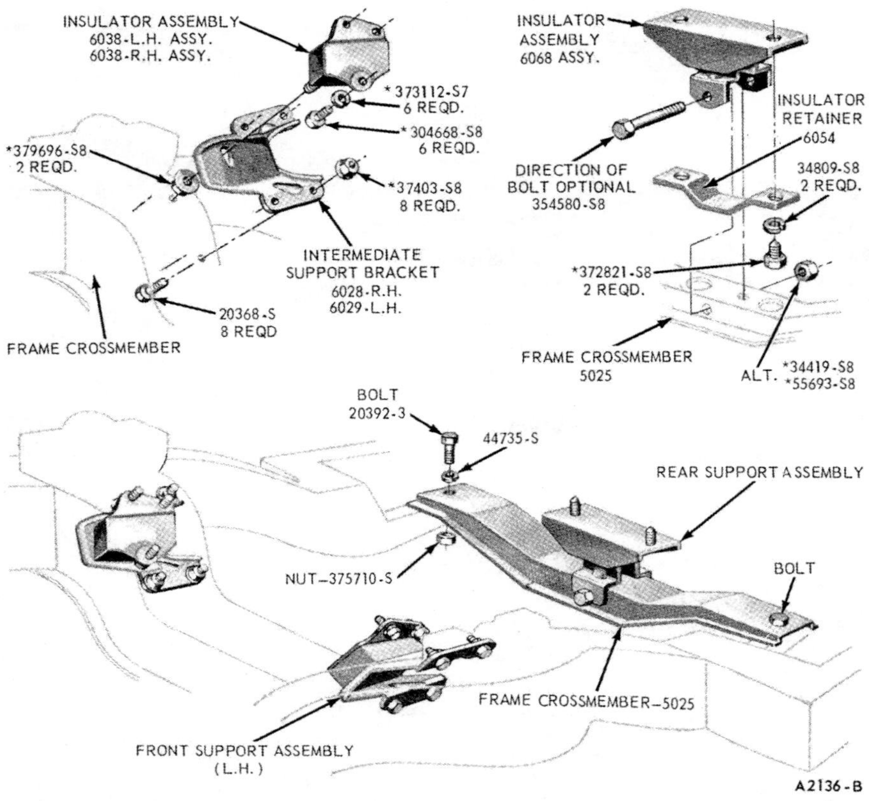

FIG. 19—Engine Front and Rear Supports

FRONT SUPPORT INSULATOR

The procedures given apply to either a right or left installation.

Removal

1. On a car with an automatic transmission, remove the transmission oil cooler inlet and outlet tubes from the retaining bracket on the cylinder block.
2. Remove the insulator to intermediate support bracket nut and lock washer. **If only one support is being removed, loosen the other support.**
3. Using a jack and a wood block placed under the oil pan, raise the engine to allow just enough clearance for removal of the insulator(s).
4. Remove the insulator to engine bolts and lock washers. Remove the insulator.

Installation

1. Position the insulator assembly on the engine. Install the insulator to engine bolts and lock washers finger-tight.
2. Lower the engine carefully to make sure the insulator stud engages the intermediate support bracket mounting hole.
3. Install the nut and lock washer on the insulator stud. Torque the insulator nut and bolts to specifications.
4. If only one support was removed, tighten the other support.
5. On a car with an automatic transmission, install the transmission oil cooler inlet and outlet tubes in the retaining bracket on the cylinder block.

REAR SUPPORT INSULATOR

Removal

1. Remove the retaining bolts, nut, washers and insulator retainer.
2. Raise the engine slightly to gain clearance and remove the insulator assembly.

Installation

1. Position the insulator assembly and retainer. Install the insulator to

extension housing flat washers, lock washers and bolts.
2. Lower the engine and install the insulator to frame crossmember bolt. Torque the nut and bolts to specifications.

VALVE ROCKER ARM SHAFT ASSEMBLY

REMOVAL

1. Remove the air cleaner.
2. If equipped with a Thermactor exhaust emission control system, disconnect the air hoses as necessary for accessibility and position them out of the way.
3. Disconnect the spark plug wires at the spark plugs. Remove the wires from the bracket on the valve rocker arm cover(s) and position the wires out of the way.

To remove the right valve rocker arm cover, remove the carburetor choke air heat tube, and the heat chamber air inlet tube (except 427 V-8). Remove the crankcase ventilation regulator valve or vent tube from the rocker cover.

To remove the left valve rocker arm cover on cars with power brakes, disconnect the brake booster vacuum line at the manifold and position the line out of the way.
3. Remove the valve rocker arm cover(s).

If the left cover is removed, position the wire loom out of the way.
4. Starting at the No. 4 cylinder, loosen the right valve rocker arm shaft support bolts in sequence, two turns at a time. After the bolts are all loosened, remove the valve rocker arm shaft assembly and the oil baffle plate. Starting at the No. 5 cylinder, follow the same procedure on the left valve rocker arm shaft support bolts. **This procedure must be followed to avoid damage to the valve mechanism.**

INSTALLATION

1. Apply Lubriplate to the pad end of the rocker arms, to the tip of the valve stems, and to both ends of the push rods.
2. Crank the engine until the No. 1 piston is on TDC at the end of the compression stroke.
3. Rotate the crankshaft damper an additional 45° (identified by XX on the damper).
4. Position the baffle plate and the valve rocker arm shaft assembly(ies) on the cylinder heads with the valve push rods in place and the rocker

shaft support bolts finger-tight. **Be sure the shaft is positioned so that the oil holes are to the bottom. Also, the identification notch (Fig. 20)**

NOTCH　　　　A1832-A

FIG. 20—Typical Installation Identification Mark—Rocker Arm Shaft Assembly

must be downward and toward the front on the right bank, or toward the rear on the left bank.

5. Starting at the No. 4 cylinder, tighten the bolts in sequence, two turns at a time, until the supports fully contact the cylinder head. Torque the bolts in sequence to specifications.

6. Starting at the No. 5 cylinder, follow the same procedure for the left valve rocker arm shaft support bolts. The additional time consumed in this procedure will permit the hydraulic lifters (if so equipped) to leak down. This will minimize the possibility of bending the push rods, valves or rocker arms. **Be sure that the hydraulic lifters have leaked down to their normal operating position before cranking the engine. This is necessary in order to avoid possible damage to the valves, push rods or valve rocker arms.**

7. On engines with hydraulic valve lifters, check the valve clearance and correct if necessary (Part 8-1, Section 2).

On engines with mechanical tappets, perform a preliminary (cold) valve lash adjustment (Part 8-1, Section 2) if any part of the valve train components has been replaced; i.e., push rod valve, rocker, arm, etc. Temporarily lay the valve rocker arm covers in place and temporarily connect the spark plug wires. Install the air cleaner and operate the engine for 30 minutes at 1200 rpm to stabilize engine temperatures. Remove the air cleaner and the valve rocker arm covers and perform a hot valve

lash adjustment with the engine idling (Part 8-1, Section 2).

8. Clean the valve rocker arm cover(s). Apply oil-resistant sealer to one side of new cover gasket(s). Lay the cemented side of the gasket(s) in place in the cover(s).

9. Position the cover(s) on the cylinder head(s). Make sure the gasket seats evenly all around the head. Install the bolts (and the wire loom clamps on the left cover). The cover is tightened in two steps. Torque the bolts to specifications. Two minutes later, torque the bolts to the same specifications.

On a car with power brakes, if the left cover was removed, connect the brake booster vacuum line to the intake manifold. If equipped with a Thermactor exhaust emission control system, connect the air hoses.

If the right cover was removed, install the carburetor choke air heat tube, and connect the automatic choke heat chamber air inlet tube (except 427 V-8). Install the crankcase ventilation regulator valve in the rocker cover.

10. Connect the spark plug wires. Install the air cleaner.

DISASSEMBLY

1. Remove the cotter pins from each end of the valve rocker arm shaft. Remove the flat washer and spring washer from each end of the shaft.

2. Slide the rocker arms, springs and supports off the shaft. Be sure to identify all the parts.

3. If it is necessary to remove the plugs from each end of the shaft, drill or pierce one plug. Then insert a steel rod through the drilled plug and knock out the plug on the opposite end. Working from the open end, knock out the remaining plug.

CLEANING AND INSPECTION

Refer to Part 8-1, Section 3 for the cleaning and inspection procedures.

REPAIRS

Refer to Part 8-1, Section 2 for the repair procedures.

ASSEMBLY

1. Oil all the moving parts with engine oil. Apply Lubriplate to the pad of the valve rocker arms.

2. If the plugs were removed from the ends of the shaft, use a blunt tool or large diameter pin punch, and install a plug, cup side out, in

each end of the rocker arm shaft.

3. Install the rocker arms, supports and springs in the order shown in Figs. 21 or 22. **Be sure the oil holes in the shaft are facing downward. When properly assembled, the identification notch (Fig. 20) on the right rocker shaft assembly must be facing downward and toward the front of the engine. On the left rocker shaft assembly, the notch is downward and toward the rear.** Complete the assembly by installing the remaining flat washer, spring washer and cotter pin.

INTAKE MANIFOLD

REMOVAL

1. Drain the cooling system. Remove the engine hood. Remove the air cleaner.

Disconnect the accelerator cable at the carburetor. Remove the accelerator retracting spring. Remove the accelerator cable bracket from the intake manifold, and position the cable and bracket assembly out of the way.

On a car with an automatic transmission, remove the kickdown rod retracting spring. Disconnect the kickdown rod at the carburetor, and the spacer vacuum line.

2. Disconnect the coil high tension lead and the primary wire at the distributor. Disconnect the oil pressure sending unit wire at the sending unit (and oil temperature sending unit wire on the 427 V-8 engine if so equipped).

3. Disconnect the spark plug wires at the spark plugs and remove the wires from the ignition harness brackets on the valve rocker arm covers. Remove the distributor cap and spark plug wire assembly. Disconnect the distributor vacuum line at the distributor (except 427 V-8).

4. Remove the carburetor fuel inlet line at the fuel filter, and the automatic choke air heat tube and the heat chamber air inlet tube (except 427 V-8). Disconnect the brake booster vacuum line at the intake manifold and at the flexible hose. Remove the vacuum line.

5. Remove the distributor hold down bolt and clamp and remove the distributor.

6. Disconnect the radiator upper hose at the radiator supply tank (or at the thermostat housing). Disconnect the heater hose at the rear of the carburetor spacer (352) and from the intake manifold on other engines. Disconnect the water tem-

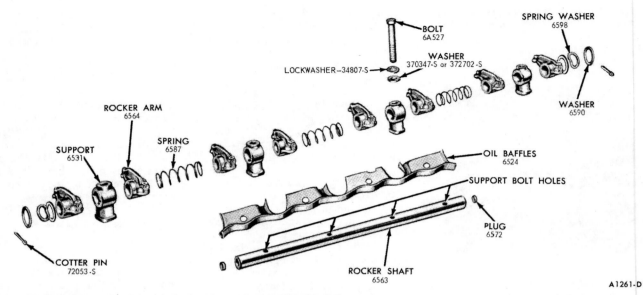

FIG. 21—Valve Rocker Arm Shaft Assembly—Hydraulic Valve Lifters

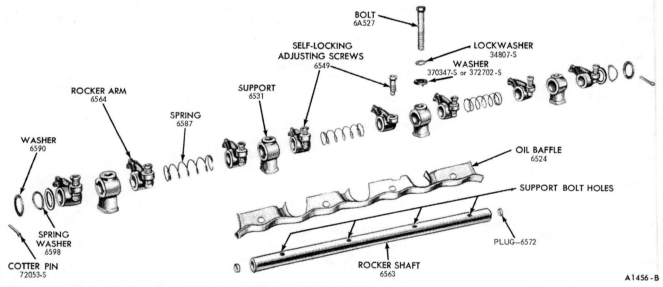

FIG. 22—Valve Rocker Arm Shaft Assembly—Mechanical Valve Tappets

perature sending unit wire at the sending unit. Disconnect the heater hose at the water pump and remove it from the automatic choke housing bracket.

7. Slide the clamp on the water pump bypass hose toward the water pump.

8. Remove the crankcase ventilation regulator valve from the right valve rocker arm cover. If equipped with Thermactor exhaust emission control system, disconnect the air lines and hoses as necessary for accessibility. Remove the valve rocker arm covers. Position the wire loom attached to the left valve rocker arm cover out of the way.

9. Refer to Valve Rocker Arm Shaft Assembly—Removal and remove the valve rocker arm shaft assemblies by following step 4.

10. Remove the valve push rods in sequence and place them in a rack so they can be installed in the same location.

11. Remove the intake manifold retaining bolts.

12. Install standard eye bolts with 5/16-18 threads in the left front and right rear rocker arm cover screw holes and attach the engine lifting sling (Fig. 23).

13. Use a hoist to raise the manifold. Remove the intake manifold and radiator supply tank (if so equipped) as an assembly. Remove the intake manifold gaskets and seals.

14. If the intake manifold assembly is to be disassembled, remove the radiator supply tank (or thermostat housing), thermostat and gasket. Remove the carburetor, spacer and gaskets. Remove the coolant temperature sending unit.

On 390, 410, and 428 V-8 engines remove the crankcase ventilation inlet tube and fittings.

CLEANING AND INSPECTION

Refer to Part 8-1, Section 3 for the cleaning and inspection procedures.

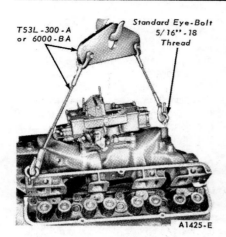

FIG. 23—Intake Manifold Removal or Installation

INSTALLATION

The intake manifold assembly is shown in Fig. 24.

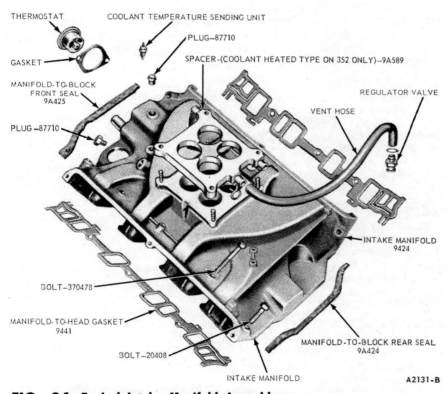

FIG. 24—Typical Intake Manifold Assembly

Engines With Hydraulic Valve Lifters

1. If the intake manifold assembly was disassembled, install the carburetor, spacer and gaskets. Coat the thermostat gasket with water-resistant sealer and place it in position on the intake manifold. Install the thermostat and thermostat housing (or radiator supply tank). Coat the coolant temperature sending unit threads

with electrical-conductive sealer, and install the sending unit in the intake manifold.

2. Clean the mating surfaces of the intake manifold, cylinder heads and cylinder block. Use a suitable solvent to remove all traces of oil.

3. Coat the intake manifold and cylinder block seal surfaces with a quick-setting seal adhesive. Apply a non-hardening sealer to the mating lines of the cylinder heads and cylinder block.

4. Position new seals on the cylinder block and new gaskets on the cylinder heads. **Be sure the seals are properly positioned during installation as the adhesive sticks to the seals immediately on contact.** Position the manifold gasket slots over the end tabs on the seals. Coat these four connections with a non-hardening sealer. Be sure the holes in the gaskets are aligned with the holes in the cylinder heads.

5. Install the eye bolts in the intake manifold and attach the engine lifting sling.

6. Use a hoist to lower the intake manifold on the engine (Fig. 23), and at the same time engage the coolant outlet nipple with the water pump bypass hose.

7. **After the intake manifold is in** place, run a finger around the seal area to make sure the seals are in place. If the seals are not in place, remove the intake manifold and reposition the seals.

8. Be sure the holes in the manifold gaskets and manifold are in alignment. Coat the underside of the heads of the retaining bolts with oil resistant, non-hardening sealer. Install the manifold retaining bolts and torque the bolts to specifications in sequence as shown in Fig. 25.

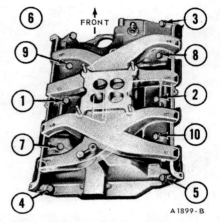

FIG. 25—Intake Manifold Torque Sequence

9. Remove the engine lifting sling and eye bolts, and install the distributor.

10. Slide the water pump bypass hose clamp into position. Connect the coolant temperature sending unit wire. Connect the heater hoses and the radiator upper hose. Install the water pump heater hose in the automatic choke housing bracket.

11. Refer to Valve Rocker Arm Shaft Assembly Installation, and install the valve rocker arm shaft assembly by following steps 1 thru 7.

12. Rotate the crankshaft damper until the No. 1 piston is on TDC at the end of the compression stroke. Position the distributor in the block with the rotor at the No. 1 firing position and the points open. Install the hold down clamp.

13. Clean the valve rocker arm covers. Apply oil-resistant sealer to one side of new cover gaskets. Lay the cemented side of the gaskets in place in the covers. Install the valve rocker arm covers, bolts and wire loom clamps. Tighten the covers in two steps. First, torque the bolts to specifications. Two minutes later, torque the bolts to the same specifications.

14. Install the positive crankcase ventilation system components. If equipped with Thermactor exhaust emission control system, connect the hoses.

15. Connect the brake booster vacuum line and connect the flexible hose.

16. Using a new clamp, install the carburetor fuel inlet line at the fuel filter; then (except for 427 V-8) connect the distributor vacuum line. Install the automatic choke air heat tube and air inlet tube.

17. Install the distributor cap. Connect the spark plug wires.

18. Connect the oil pressure sending unit wire, coolant temperature sending unit wire, coil high tension lead and coil primary wire.

Install the accelerator cable bracket on the intake manifold. Connect the accelerator cable to the carburetor. Install the accelerator retracting spring.

On a car with an automatic transmission, connect the kickdown rod. Install the kickdown rod retracting spring, and the spacer vacuum line.

19. Fill and bleed the cooling system.

20. Install the air cleaner, start the engine, and check and adjust the ignition timing. Operate the engine until engine temperatures have stabilized and adjust the engine idle speed and idle fuel mixture.

On a car with automatic transmission, adjust the transmission control linkage (Part 7-2 or 7-3).

21. Install the engine hood.

Engines with Mechanical Valve Tappets

1. Follow steps 1 thru 10 under Engines With Hydraulic Valve Lifters.

2. Refer to Valve Rocker Arm Shaft Assembly Installation and install the valve rocker arm shaft assemblies by following steps 1 thru 6.

3. Install the carburetor fuel inlet line. Install the automatic choke air heat tube.

4. Install the distributor, following step 12 under Engines With Hydraulic Valve Lifters.

5. Temporarily lay the valve rocker arm covers in place. Install the positive crankcase ventilation system components. If equipped with Thermactor exhaust emission control system, connect the hoses.

6. Install the brake booster vacuum line.

7. Install the distributor cap. Temporarily connect the spark plug wires.

8. Connect the oil pressure sending unit, coil high tension lead, coolant temperature sending unit, and coil primary wire.

Install the accelerator cable bracket on the intake manifold. Connect the accelerator cable to the carburetor. Install the accelerator retracting spring.

On a car with automatic transmission, connect the kickdown rod. Install the kickdown rod retracting spring, and the carburetor spacer vacuum line.

9. Fill and bleed the cooling system.

10. Install the air cleaner, start the engine, and check and adjust the ignition timing. Operate the engine until engine temperatures have stabilized. Adjust the engine idle speed and idle fuel mixture. Remove the valve rocker arm covers, and perform a hot valve lash adjustment with the engine idling (Part 8-1, Section 2).

On a car with an automatic transmission, adjust the transmission control linkage (Part 7-2 or 7-3).

11. Turn the engine off. Clean the valve rocker arm covers. Apply oil-resistant sealer to one side of new cover gaskets. Lay the cemented side of the gaskets in place in the covers. Install the valve rocker arm covers, bolts, and wire loom clamps. Tighten the covers in two steps. First, torque the bolts to specifications. Two minutes later, torque the bolts to the same specifications. Install the crankcase ventilation regulator valve in the right valve rocker cover. Install the spark plug wires.

12. Install the engine hood.

EXHAUST MANIFOLDS

REMOVAL—EXCEPT 427 V-8

1. Disconnect the exhaust manifold from the muffler inlet pipe.

2. Remove the automatic choke air heat tube and air inlet tube from the right exhaust manifold, and exhaust control valve assembly.

3. Remove the retaining bolts and tab washers and remove the exhaust manifolds.

REMOVAL—427 V-8

1. Remove the exhaust manifold retaining bolts that are accessible from the top of the engine.

To remove the left exhaust manifold, remove the clutch pedal to equalizer rod lower adjusting nut. Remove the automatic choke air heat tube.

2. Raise the car. Remove the remaining manifold retaining bolts.

To remove the left exhaust manifold, remove the equalizer inner bracket from the engine and the equalizer bar. Disconnect the retracting spring and release rod. Position the equalizer bar out of the way.

To remove the right exhaust manifold, remove the idler arm to chassis bolts and lower the idler arm assembly. Disconnect the engine front support insulators at the frame. Raise the engine approximately 1 or 2 inches to provide necessary clearance to remove the right manifold.

3. Disconnect the muffler inlet pipe at the exhaust manifold and remove the exhaust manifolds.

On the right exhaust manifold, remove the exhaust control valve assembly.

CLEANING AND INSPECTION

Refer to Part 8-1, Section 3 for the cleaning and inspection procedures.

INSTALLATION— EXCEPT 427 V-8

1. Clean the mating surfaces of the exhaust manifold and cylinder head. Scrape the gasket material from the mounting flange of the exhaust manifold and muffler inlet pipe, and exhaust control valve assembly.

2. Apply graphite grease to the cylinder head mating surface of the exhaust manifold.

3. Position the exhaust manifold on the cylinder head and install the retaining bolts and tab washers. Working from the center to the ends, torque the retaining bolts to specifications. Lock the bolts by bending one tab of the washer over a flat on the bolt.

4. Install the automatic choke air heat tube and air inlet tube on the right exhaust manifold.

5. Position new gaskets on both sides of the exhaust control valve assembly, and install between the muffler inlet pipe and the exhaust manifold. Install and torque the retaining nuts to specifications.

6. Start the engine and check for exhaust leaks.

INSTALLATION—427 V-8

1. Clean the muffler inlet pipe gasket surfaces.

On a right manifold, clean both

sides of the exhaust control valve assembly.

2. Position the manifold to the cylinder and install the bolts accessible from beneath the engine. Working from the center to the ends, torque the retaining bolts to specifications. Lock the bolts by bending one tab of the washer over a flat on the bolt.

If the right manifold was removed, lower the engine and install the front insulator lock washers and nuts. Torque the nuts to specifications. Position and install the idler arm assembly. Torque the retaining bolts to specifications.

If the left manifold was removed, position the equalizer bar to the outer bracket. Position the release rod and connect the retracting spring. Install the equalizer inner bracket.

3. On the left manifold, position a new gasket to the manifold and connect the muffler inlet pipe to the manifold. Torque the nuts to specifications.

On the right manifold, place new gaskets on both sides of the exhaust control valve and position it over the inlet pipe studs on the manifold. Connect the muffler inlet pipe to the manifold and torque the nuts to specifications.

4. Lower the car and install the remaining manifold retaining bolts. Working from the center to the ends, torque the retaining bolts to specifications. Lock the bolts by bending one tab of the washer over a flat on the bolt.

If the left manifold was removed, install the clutch pedal to equalizer rod lower adjusting nut. Install the automatic choke air heat tube.

5. Start the engine and check for exhaust leaks.

POSITIVE CRANKCASE VENTILATION SYSTEM

REMOVAL

1. Loosen or remove the hose clamps, and remove the vent hose (closed system only) from the air cleaner and/or oil filler tube breather (Fig. 15 or 16). Remove the carburetor air cleaner.

2. Disconnect the inlet vent tube assembly at the two elbow fittings on the intake manifold (390, 410, and 428). Grasp the crankcase ventilation regulator valve and pull it straight upwards and out of the grommet in the right valve rocker arm cover.

3. Use a hose clamp tool to slide both hose clamps off the ends of the regulator valve inlet hose. Remove the inlet hose and hose clamp assembly, and separate the hose from the regulator valve.

CLEANING AND INSPECTION

Refer to Part 8-1, Section 3 for cleaning and inspection procedures on the inlet and vent hoses, carburetor spacer (352 only), and breather cap connection. **Do not clean the regulator valve. It should be replaced at the specified interval.**

INSTALLATION

1. Install the inlet hose and hose clamp on the regulator valve. Install the inlet hose and hose clamp assembly. Position the hose clamps.

2. Install the crankcase ventilation regulator valve in the right valve rocker arm cover, and connect the inlet vent tube assembly at the two elbow fittings on the intake manifold (390, 410, 428). Be sure the grommet is properly seated around the regulator valve and valve rocker arm cover.

3. Install the air cleaner. Install the breather cap vent hose, if equipped with a closed emission system, and tighten or position the hose clamps.

CYLINDER HEADS

REMOVAL

If a cylinder head is to be replaced, follow the procedures under Cylinder Head Disassembly and Assembly, and transfer all valves, springs, spark plugs, etc., to the new cylinder head. On a 427 V-8, if the left cylinder head is to be replaced, remove the fuel filter mounting bracket from the old cylinder head and install it on the new cylinder head. Clean and inspect all parts and reface the valves (refer to Part 8-1) before assembling the used parts to the new cylinder head. Check all assembly clearances.

1. If equipped with Thermactor exhaust emission control system, disconnect the air lines and hoses as necessary for accessibility. Remove the intake manifold, positive crankcase vent system components (if applicable), carburetor and thermostat housing (or radiator supply tank) as an assembly following the procedure under Intake Manifold Removal.

2. On all engines except the 427 V-8, disconnect the exhaust manifolds at the muffler inlet pipes. Re-

move the exhaust control valve. Leave the manifolds attached to the cylinder heads.

On the 427 V-8, remove the exhaust manifold to cylinder head retaining bolts. Refer to Exhaust Manifold Removal. Leave the manifolds attached to the muffler inlet pipes, and secure them to the car frame with wire.

3. If the left cylinder head is to be removed, remove the ignition coil, engine identification tag, and the fuel filter (428 Police Interceptor V-8 and 427 V-8).

Remove the power steering pump mounting bracket bolts, and position the power steering pump and bracket assembly out of the way. **Leave the fluid lines attached to the power steering pump.**

On a car with air conditioning, remove the compressor mounting bracket bolts and position the compressor out of the way.

4. Remove the cylinder head bolts.

5. Do not pry the cylinder heads loose from the cylinder block. Lift the cylinder heads off the block. Remove and discard the cylinder head gasket. Remove the baffle plate.

INSTALLATION

1. Clean the cylinder head and cylinder block gasket surfaces.

On the 427 V-8, clean the exhaust manifold gasket surfaces.

2. Inspect the cylinder head, following the procedures in Part 8-1, Section 3. **If the cylinder head was removed for a cylinder head gasket replacement, check the flatness of the cylinder head and block gasket surfaces (Part 8-1, Section 3).**

3. On a 427 engine apply cylinder head gasket sealer to both sides of a new gasket. All other engines use a specially treated composition gasket. **Do not apply sealer to a composition gasket.** Guided by the word FRONT on the gasket, install the gasket over the cylinder head dowels.

4. Place the cylinder head on the engine.

5. Install the cylinder head bolts. The cylinder head bolts are tightened in three progressive steps.

On all engines except the 427 V-8, torque all the bolts in sequence (Fig. 26) to 70 ft-lbs. Then torque them to 80 ft-lbs, and finally to specifications.

On the 427 V-8 engine, torque all the bolts in sequence (Fig. 26) to 90 ft-lbs. Then torque them to 100 ft-lbs, and finally to specifications.

FIG. 26—Cylinder Head Bolt Torque Sequence

After the cylinder head bolts have been torqued to specifications, the bolts should not be disturbed.

6. On the left cylinder head, install the ignition coil, engine identification tag and power steering pump. Adjust the power steering pump belt tension to specifications.

On a car with an air conditioner, install the compressor mounting bracket with the power steering pump. Adjust the compressor drive belt tension to specifications.

7. On all engines except the 427 V-8, position new gaskets on the muffler inlet pipes. Position the exhaust control valve plus the gasket required above it; then connect the exhaust manifolds to the muffler inlet pipes. On a 352 engine not Thermactor equipped, a spacer is used in place of the exhaust control valve. Torque the nuts to specifications.

On the 427 V-8, use new gaskets and position the exhaust manifolds to the cylinder heads. Install and torque the retaining bolts to specifications.

If the left cylinder head was removed, install the ignition coil and the fuel filter (428 Police Interceptor V-8 and 427 V-8).

8. Install the baffle plate. Install the intake manifold and related parts following the procedure under Intake Manifold Installation. If equipped with Thermactor exhaust emission control system, connect the hoses.

DISASSEMBLY

1. Remove the Thermactor exhaust emission control system components. On all engines except the 427 V-8, remove the exhaust manifolds.

2. Taking special care not to damage the exposed machined surfaces, remove the spark plugs. Clean the carbon out of the cylinder head combustion chambers before removing the valves.

3. Compress the valve springs (Fig. 27). Remove the spring retainer locks and release the spring.

On the 427 V-8, and the Police

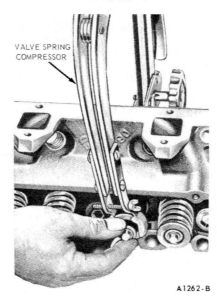

FIG. 27—Compressing Valve Spring—On Bench

Interceptor 428 V-8 engines only, inspect the valve springs before removal to determine if the damper spring(s) is intertwined with the valve spring(s). If this condition exists, replace all defective or worn components (refer to inspection procedures in Part 8-1, Section 3).

4. Remove the sleeve, spring retainer, spring (and damper spring if applicable), stem seal and valve. Discard the valve stem seals. Identify all valve parts.

CLEANING AND INSPECTION

Refer to Part 8-1, Section 3 for the cleaning and inspection procedures.

REPAIRS

Cylinder head repair procedures and checks such as valve and valve seat refacing, cylinder head flatness checks, etc., are covered in Part 8-1, Sections 2 and 3.

ASSEMBLY

1. Install each valve (Fig. 28) in the port from which it was removed or to which it was fitted. Install a new stem seal on the valve. **The exhaust valve stem seal is approximately 0.025 inch shorter in over-all height than the intake valve stem seal (identified with yellow paint); therefore, be sure the seals are installed on the proper valves.**

2. Install the valve spring (closed coils downward) over the valve, and install the spring retainer and sleeve.

On the 427 V-8, and the Police In-

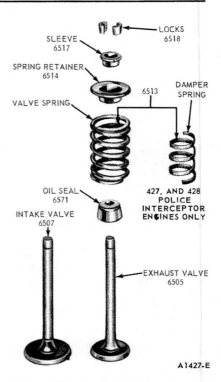

FIG. 28—Typical Valve Assembly

terceptor 428 V-8 engines only, make sure the damper spring is installed in the valve spring so that the coil end of the damper spring is 135° counterclockwise from the coil end of the valve spring.

3. Compress the spring and install the retainer locks (Fig. 27).

4. Measure the assembled height of the valve spring from the surface of the cylinder head spring pad to the underside of the spring retainer with dividers (Fig. 29). Check the

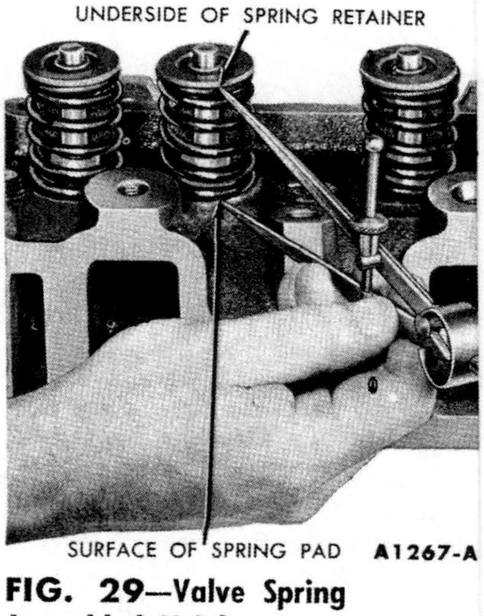

UNDERSIDE OF SPRING RETAINER

SURFACE OF SPRING PAD   A1267-A

FIG. 29—Valve Spring Assembled Height

dividers against a scale. If the assembled height is greater than specified, install the necessary 0.030-inch thick spacer(s) between the cylinder head spring pad and the valve spring (Fig. 30) to bring the assembled

FIG. 30—Valve Spring Spacer Installation

height to the recommended specifications.

Do not install spacers unless necessary. Use of spacers in excess of recommendations will result in overstressing the valve springs and overloading the camshaft lobes which could lead to spring breakage and worn camshaft lobes.

5. On all engines except the 427 V-8, install the exhaust manifolds.

6. Install the spark plugs.

Install the Thermactor exhaust emission control components.

VALVE SPRING, RETAINER AND STEM SEAL REPLACEMENT

Broken valve springs, or defective valve stem seals and retainers may be replaced without removing the cylinder head provided damage to the valve or valve seat has not occurred.

1. Remove the valve rocker arm cover(s), following step 1, 2, and 3 under Valve Rocker Arm Shaft Assembly Removal.

2. Loosen the valve rocker arm support bolts evenly and alternately, two turns at a time, until the valve spring tension has been released. Remove both of the push rods of the cylinder to be serviced.

3. Tighten the valve rocker arm support bolts evenly and alternately, two turns at a time, until they are snug. Push the rocker arm to one side and secure it in this position (Fig. 31). If an end valve is to be worked on, it will be necessary to remove the rocker arm from the shaft.

FIG. 31—Compressing Valve Spring—In Chassis

4. Remove the applicable spark plug. Install an air adapter in the spark plug hole and connect the air supply hose to the adapter (Fig. 32).

FIG. 32—Installation of Air Adapter Tool in Spark Plug Hole

Turn on the air supply. **Air pressure may turn the crankshaft until the piston reaches the bottom of its stroke.**

5. Compress the valve spring and remove the valve retainer locks from the valve (Fig. 31). **If air pressure fails to hold the valve in the closed position during this operation, it can be presumed that the valve is not seating or is damaged. If this condition occurs, remove the cylinder head for further inspection.**

6. Remove the valve spring and related parts. Remove the valve stem

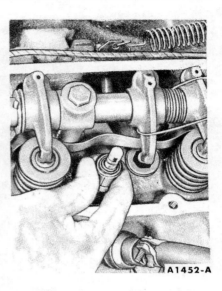

FIG. 33—Valve Stem Seal Removal

seal (Fig. 33). **If air pressure has forced the piston to the bottom of the cylinder, any removal of air pressure will allow the valve(s) to fall into the cylinder. A rubber band, tape or string wrapped around the end of the valve stem will prevent this condition and will still allow enough travel to check the valve for binds.**

7. Inspect the valve stem for damage. Rotate the valve and check the valve stem tip for eccentric movement during rotation. Move the valve up and down through normal travel in the valve guide and check the stem for binds. **If the valve has been damaged, it will be necessary to remove the cylinder head for repairs as outlined in Part 8-1, Section 2.**

8. If the condition of the valve proved satisfactory, hold the valve in the closed position and apply the air pressure within the cylinder.

9. Inspect the valve stem seal for a cracked, torn or brittle condition, and replace it if necessary. Install the seal on the valve stem. **The exhaust valve stem seal (identified by yellow paint) is approximately 0.025 inch shorter in overall height than the intake valve stem seal; therefore, be sure the proper seal is installed.**

10. Install the valve springs, retainer and sleeve over the valve stem. **On 427 V-8, and the Police Interceptor 428 V-8 engines only, make sure the valve damper spring is installed in the valve spring so that the coil end of the damper spring is 135° counterclockwise from the coil end**

of the valve spring.

11. Compress the valve spring (Fig. 31) and install the valve retainer locks. Tap the valve stem tip with a soft mallet to make certain that the retainer locks are properly seated.

12. Remove the air line and adapter. Install the spark plug. Remove the wire securing the valve rocker arm and slide the rocker arm in position. Install the end rocker arm(s), if they were removed.

13. Loosen the valve rocker arm support bolts evenly and alternately, two turns at a time, until spring tension is removed. Apply Lubriplate to both ends of the push rod. Position the push rod within the rocker arm socket and the valve lifter seat.

14. Tighten the rocker arm shaft support bolts evenly and alternately, two turns at a time, until they are snug. Torque the bolts to specifications.

15. Install the spark plug wires. On engines with hydraulic valve lifters, check the valve clearances and correct if necessary (Part 8-1, Section 2).

16. On engines with mechanical valve tappets, temporarily lay the valve rocker arm covers in place and temporarily connect the spark plug wires. Operate the engine until engine temperatures have stabilized. Remove the valve rocker arm covers and perform a hot valve lash adjustment with the engine idling (Part 8-1, Section 2).

17. Clean the valve rocker arm cover(s). Apply oil-resistant sealer to one side of new cover gasket(s). Lay the cemented side of the gasket(s) in place on the cover(s).

Position the cover(s) on the cylinder head(s). Make sure the gasket seats evenly all around the head. Install the bolts (and the wire loom clamps on the left cover). The cover is tightened in two steps. Torque the bolts to specifications. Two minutes later, torque the bolts to the same specifications. If equipped with a Thermactor exhaust emission control system, connect the air hoses.

18. Connect the automatic choke heat chamber air inlet tube (except 427 V-8). Install the air cleaner.

CYLINDER FRONT COVER AND TIMING CHAIN

If the cylinder front cover is being removed to replace the gasket or to replace the fuel pump drive eccentric, it is not necessary to check the timing chain deflection. For cylinder front cover gasket replacement, it is not necessary to remove the timing chain and sprockets.

REMOVAL

1. Drain the cooling system and the crankcase. Disconnect the battery ground cable.

2. Disconnect the radiator upper hose at the thermostat housing (or radiator supply tank). Disconnect the radiator lower hose at the water pump. On a car with automatic transmission, disconnect the transmission oil cooler lines from the radiator.

3. Remove the radiator.

4. Disconnect the heater hose at the water pump and remove the hose from the choke housing clamp. Slide the water pump bypass hose clamp toward the engine.

On a car with power steering, remove the power steering pump bracket mounting bolts. Wire the pump assembly to the left side of the car in a position that will prevent the oil from draining out.

On a car with an air conditioner, remove the compressor mounting bracket bolts, and position the compressor out of the way. **Do not disconnect the compressor refrigerant lines.**

5. Loosen the alternator mounting bolts at the alternator. Remove the drive belt. Remove the alternator support bracket bolts at the water pump and remove the brackets out of the way. Remove the water pump and fan assembly.

On a car with air conditioning remove the condenser retaining bolts and position the condenser forward. **Do not disconnect the refrigerant lines.** Remove the compressor drive belt. On a car equipped with Thermactor exhaust emission control system remove the air supply pump drive belt. If so equipped, remove the accessory drive pulley.

6. Remove the cap screw and washer from the end of the crankshaft. On a car with power steering, remove the power steering pulley from the crankshaft damper. Install the puller on the crankshaft damper (Fig. 34) and remove the damper.

7. Disconnect the carburetor fuel inlet line at the fuel pump.

8. Remove the fuel pump retain-

Tool—T58P-6316-A or-B or 6306-AJ   A1257-D

FIG. 34—Crankshaft Damper Removal

ing bolts and lay the pump to one side with the flexible fuel line still attached.

9. Remove the crankshaft sleeve as shown in Fig. 35.

10. Remove the screws fastening the cylinder front cover to the block and to the oil pan. Remove the cylinder front cover.

11. Discard the cylinder front cover gasket. Remove the crankshaft front oil slinger.

12. Check the timing chain deflection by following the procedure in Part 8-1, Section 1.

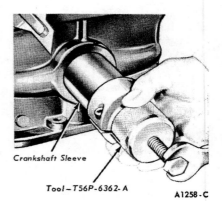

Crankshaft Sleeve

Tool—T56P-6362-A   A1258-C

FIG. 35—Crankshaft Sleeve Removal

13. Crank the engine until the timing marks on the sprockets are positioned as shown in Fig. 36.

14. Remove the camshaft sprocket cap screw and the fuel pump eccentric.

15. Slide both sprockets and the timing chain forward, and remove them as an assembly (Fig. 37).

16. Remove the oil pan and oil pump screen, following the procedure under Oil Pan Removal.

FIG. 36—Aligning Timing Marks

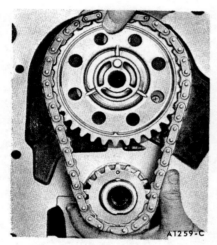

FIG. 37—Timing Chain and Sprocket Removal or Installation

FRONT OIL SEAL REPLACEMENT

It is good practice to replace the oil seal each time the cylinder front cover is removed.

1. Drive out the old seal with a pin punch. Clean out the recess in the cover.

2. Coat a new seal with grease, and install the seal (Fig. 38). Drive the seal in until it is fully seated in the recess. Check the seal after installation to be sure the spring is properly positioned in the seal.

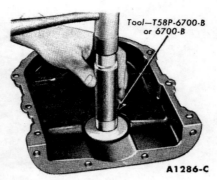

FIG. 38—Oil Seal Installation

CLEANING AND INSPECTION

Refer to Part 8-1, Section 3 for the cleaning and inspection procedures. Clean the crankshaft damper, following the referenced procedures.

INSTALLATION

1. Position the sprockets and timing chain on the camshaft and crankshaft (Fig. 37). Be sure the timing marks on the sprockets are positioned as shown in Fig. 36.

2. Install the fuel pump eccentric and the camshaft sprocket cap screw (Fig. 39). Torque the sprocket cap

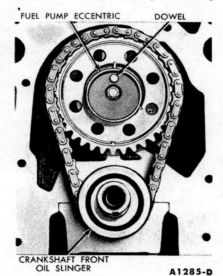

FIG. 39—Fuel Pump Eccentric and Front Oil Slinger Installed

screw to specifications. Install the crankshaft front oil slinger.

3. Clean the cylinder front cover, oil pan, and the cylinder block gasket surfaces.

4. Coat the gasket surface of the block and cover and the cover bolt

threads with sealer. Position a new gasket on the block.

5. Lubricate and install the alignment pilot tool on the cylinder front cover so that the keyway in the pilot aligns with the key in the crankshaft. Position the cover and pilot over the end of the crankshaft and against the block (Fig. 40). Install the retaining screws.

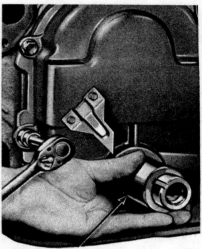

FIG. 40—Cylinder Front Cover Alignment

While pushing in on the pilot, torque the screws to specifications. Remove the pilot.

6. Install the crankshaft sleeve.

7. Lubricate the inside diameter of the hub and line up the damper keyway with the key on the crankshaft. Install the camper on the crankshaft (Fig. 41).

FIG. 41—Crankshaft Damper Installation

8. On a car with power steering, install the power steering pump pulley on the damper. Torque the

screws to specifications. Install the damper cap screw and washer. Torque the screw to specifications.

9. Clean the oil pan and the oil pump screen. Install the oil pump screen and oil pan, following the procedure under Oil Pan and Oil Pump Installation.

10. Clean the water pump gasket surfaces. Coat new gaskets with sealer and position the gaskets on the block. Install the water pump and fan, and torque the water pump mounting bolts to specifications. Attach the alternator adjusting arm and mounting bracket to the water pump.

11. Install and adjust the alternator drive belt(s) to the specified tension.

12. Install the fuel pump, using a new gasket. Connect the carburetor fuel inlet line, at the fuel pump and at the carburetor filter. Use a new clamp.

13. On a car with an air conditioner, install the compressor and adjust the drive belt.

On a car with power steering, install the power steering pump and drive belt. Adjust the drive belt tension to specifications.

14. Connect the heater hoses. Slide the water pump bypass tube clamp forward on the tube.

15. Install the radiator. Connect the radiator lower hose at the water pump and the radiator upper hose at the thermostat housing (or radiator supply tank). Connect the battery ground cable.

On a car with an automatic transmission, connect the transmission oil cooler lines.

16. Fill and bleed the cooling system. Fill the crankcase with the proper grade and quantity of engine oil. Connect the heater hose to the intake manifold.

17. Operate the engine at fast idle and check for coolant and oil leaks. Adjust the ignition timing.

CAMSHAFT

The camshaft and related parts are shown in Fig. 42.

REMOVAL

1. Remove the cylinder front cover and the timing chain and sprockets following steps 1 thru 11 under Cylinder Front Cover and Timing Chain Removal. If equipped with a Thermactor exhaust emission control system, disconnect the air hoses as necessary for accessibility, and position them out of the way.

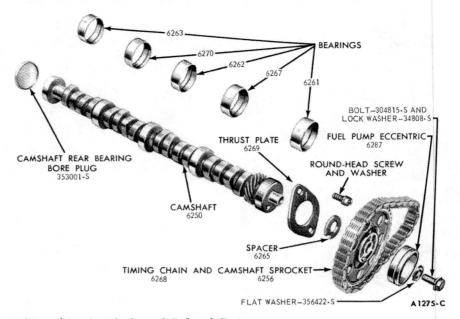

FIG. 42—Camshaft and Related Parts

2. Remove the grille. On a car with air conditioning, remove the condenser retaining bolts, and position the condenser to one side. **Do not disconnect the condenser refrigerant lines.**

3. Refer to Valve Rocker Arm Shaft Assembly Removal and remove the valve rocker arm covers and the valve rocker arm shaft assemblies.

4. Remove the intake manifold and baffle plate, following the procedures under Intake Manifold Removal.

5. Remove the valve lifters in sequence and place them in a rack so they can be installed in their original locations.

6. Remove the oil pan and oil pump screen by following the procedure under Oil Pan and Oil Pump Removal.

7. Remove the timing chain and sprockets following steps 12 thru 17 under Cylinder Front Cover and Timing Chain Removal.

8. Remove the camshaft thrust plate and spacer. Carefully remove the camshaft by pulling it toward the front of the engine. **Use caution to avoid damaging the camshaft bearings.**

CLEANING AND INSPECTION

Refer to Part 8-1, Section 3 for the cleaning and inspection procedures.

REPAIRS

Refer to Part 8-1, Section 2 for the repair procedures.

INSTALLATION—ENGINES WITH HYDRAULIC VALVE LIFTERS

1. Oil the camshaft journals and apply Lubriplate to the lobes. Carefully slide the camshaft through the bearings. Install the thrust plate and spacer. **The chamfered ID of the spacer must be toward the camshaft front journal. Be sure the thrust plate oil groove is up and towards the front (next to camshaft sprocket).**

2. Check the camshaft end play. Install a dial indicator so the indicator point is on the camshaft sprocket retaining screw. Push the camshaft toward the rear of the engine and set the dial indicator on zero. Pull the camshaft forward and release it. Compare the indicator reading with the specifications. If the end play is excessive, check the spacer for correct installation. If the spacer is installed correctly, replace the thrust plate.

3. Position the sprockets and timing chain on the camshaft and crankshaft (Fig. 37) with the timing marks on the sprockets aligned as shown in Fig. 36.

4. Install the fuel pump eccentric and the camshaft sprocket cap screw (Fig. 39). Torque the sprocket cap screw to specifications. Install the front oil slinger.

5. Replace the crankshaft front oil seal. Install the cylinder front cover, crankshaft damper, and related parts following steps 3 thru 15 under Cylinder Front Cover and Timing Chain Installation.

6. Install the grille.

7. Install the valve lifters in the bores from which they were removed. Install the intake manifold, following the procedures under Engines With Hydraulic Valve Lifters.

8. Install the push rods in their original positions. Refer to Valve Rocker Arm Shaft Assembly Installation and install the valve rocker arm shaft assembly following steps 1 thru 9.

If equipped with a Thermactor exhaust emission control system, connect *the air hoses.*

On a car with air conditioning, position the condenser and install the retaining bolts. Install the radiator.

9. Fill and bleed the cooling system. Fill the crankcase with the proper grade and quantity of engine oil.

10. Start the engine and check and adjust the ignition timing. Connect the distributor vacuum line (except 427 V-8, and 428 V-8, Police Interceptor). Operate the engine at fast idle and check all hose connections and gaskets for leaks.

INSTALLATION—ENGINES WITH MECHANICAL VALVE TAPPETS

1. Follow steps 1 thru 4 under Installation—Engines With Hydraulic Valve Lifters.

2. Replace the crankshaft front oil seal. Install the cylinder front cover, crankshaft damper and related parts following steps 3 thru 15 under Cylinder Front Cover and Timing Chain Installation.

3. Install the grille.

4. Install the tappets in the bores from which they were removed. Install the intake manifold, following steps 1 thru 10 under Engines With Hydraulic Valve Lifters.

5. Install the push rods in their original positions. Refer to Valve Rocker Arm Shaft Assembly Installation and install the valve rocker arm shaft assembly following steps 1 thru 6.

6. Temporarily install the valve rocker arm covers and connect the spark plug wires.

7. Fill and bleed the cooling system. Fill the crankcase with the proper grade and quantity of engine oil.

8. Start the engine and check and adjust the ignition timing. Connect the distributor vacuum line, except on 427 V-8. Operate the engine at fast idle and check all hose connec-

tions and gaskets for leaks. Operate the engine for 30 minutes at 1200 rpm to stabilize engine temperatures. Remove the valve rocker arm covers and perform a hot valve lash adjustment with the engine idling (Part 8-1, Section 2).

9. Clean the valve rocker arm cover(s). Apply oil-resistant sealer to one side of new cover gasket(s). Lay the cemented side of the gasket(s) in place in the cover(s).

10. Position the cover(s) on the cylinder head(s). Make sure the gasket seats evenly all around the head. Install the bolts (and the wire loom clamps on the left cover). The cover is tightened in two steps. Torque the bolts to specifications. Two minutes later, torque the bolts to the same specifications.

11. Connect the brake booster vacuum line. Install the carburetor choke heat tube.

12. Connect the spark plug wires.

CAMSHAFT REAR BEARING BORE PLUG REPLACEMENT

1. On a car with a manual-shift transmission, slide the transmission to the rear and remove the clutch pressure plate, disc and flywheel housing following the procedure in Group 5.

On a car with an automatic transmission, remove the transmission and converter housing following the procedure in Group 7.

2. Remove the flywheel retaining bolts and remove the flywheel. Remove the rear cover plate.

3. Drill a ½-inch hole in the camshaft rear bearing bore plug and use tool T-7600-E to remove the plug.

4. Clean out the plug bore recess thoroughly.

5. Coat the flange of a new plug with oil-resistant sealer and install it with the flange facing inward (Fig. 68).

6. Install the rear cover plate. Install the flywheel.

On a car with a manual-shift transmission, install the clutch pressure plate, disc and flywheel housing and install the transmission following the procedure in Group 5.

On a car with an automatic transmission, install the transmission and converter housing following the procedure in Group 7.

VALVE LIFTER OR TAPPET REPLACEMENT

The following procedure is appli-

cable for removing one or all of the valve lifters and it applies to either hydraulic valve lifters or solid valve tappets.

1. Remove the intake manifold, following the procedures under Intake Manifold Removal.

2. Remove the valve lifters or tappets with a magnet through the push rod openings. Place the lifters in a rack so that they can be installed in their original positions.

On an engine with hydraulic valve lifters, the internal parts of each hydraulic valve lifter assembly are matched sets. Do not inter-mix the parts. Keep the assemblies intact until they are to be cleaned.

3. Install the new (or cleaned) hydraulic valve lifters or tappets through the push rod openings with a magnet.

4. Install the intake manifold, following the procedures under Intake Manifold Installations for hydraulic valve lifters or mechanical valve tappets.

HYDRAULIC VALVE LIFTER DISASSEMBLY

Each valve lifter is a matched assembly. If the parts of one lifter are intermixed with those of another, improper valve operation may result. Disassemble and assemble each lifter separately. Keep the lifter assemblies in proper sequence so that they can be installed in their original bores.

1. Grasp the lock ring with the needle nose pliers to release it from the groove. It may be necessary to depress the plunger to fully release the lock ring.

2. Remove the push rod cup. Remove the plunger (Fig. 43) and plunger spring.

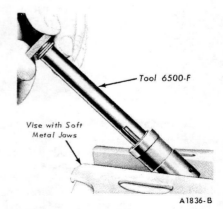

Tool 6500-F

Vise with Soft Metal Jaws

A1836-B

FIG. 43—Lifter Plunger Removal

3. Invert the plunger assembly and remove the disc valve retainer by carefully prying up on it with a screw driver. Remove the disc valve and spring.

CLEANING AND INSPECTION

Refer to Part 8-1, Section 3 for the cleaning and inspection procedures.

HYDRAULIC VALVE LIFTER ASSEMBLY

A typical hydraulic valve lifter assembly is shown in Fig. 44.

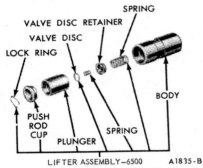

FIG. 44—Typical Hydraulic Valve Lifter Assembly

1. Place the plunger upside down on a clean work bench.

2. Place the disc valve in position over the oil hole on the bottom of the plunger. Set the disc valve spring on top of the disc.

3. Position the disc valve retainer over the disc and spring and push the retainer down into place on the plunger.

4. Place the plunger spring and then the plunger (open end up) into the lifter body.

5. Place the push rod cup in the plunger.

6. Push the plunger and push rod cup into the body and install the lock ring (Fig. 45). Release the plunger; then depress it again to fully seat the lock ring.

TESTING

Refer to Part 8-1, Section 1 for the test procedure.

CRANKSHAFT REAR OIL SEAL REPLACEMENT

Replacement of a crankshaft rear oil seal requires replacement of both the upper and lower seals. Remove the engine; then, remove the crankshaft and replace the seals, following the procedure under Crankshaft

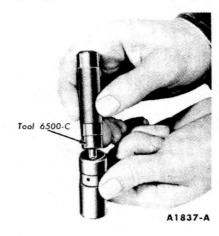

FIG. 45—Valve Lifter Lock Ring Installation

Removal and Installation (Section 4). Refer to Part 8-1, Section 3 (Crankshaft Cleaning) and clean the oil seal surface.

MAIN AND CONNECTING ROD BEARING REPLACEMENT

The main and connecting rod bearing inserts are selective fit. **Do not file or lap bearing caps or use shims to obtain the proper bearing clearance.**

Selective fit bearings are available for service in standard sizes and 0.002 inch undersize. Standard bearings are divided into two sizes and are identified by a daub of red or blue paint. Refer to the Parts Catalog for the available sizes. **Red marked bearings increase the clearance; blue marked bearings decrease the clearance.** Undersize bearings, which are not selective fit, are available for use on journals that have been refinished.

MAIN BEARING REPLACEMENT

1. Drain the crankcase. Remove the oil level dipstick. Remove the oil pan and oil pump. Remove the spark plugs to allow easy rotation of the crankshaft.

2. Replace one bearing at a time leaving the other bearing securely fastened. Remove the main bearing cap to which new bearings are to be installed.

On a 427 V-8, remove the main bearing cap cross-bolts, washers and spacers (Fig. 71) before removing the cap retaining bolts.

3. Insert the upper bearing removal tool (tool 6331-E) in the oil hole in the crankshaft (Fig. 46).

4. Rotate the crankshaft in the direction of engine rotation to force

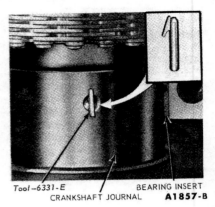

FIG. 46—Upper Main Bearing Insert Removal or Installation

the bearing out of the block.

5. Clean the crankshaft journal and bearing inserts. **When replacing standard bearings with new bearings, it is good practice to first try to obtain the proper clearances with two blue bearing halves.**

6. To install the upper main bearing, place the plain end of the bearing over the shaft on the locking tang side of the block and partially install the bearing so that tool 6331-E can be inserted in the oil hole in the crankshaft (Fig. 46). With tool 6331-E positioned in the oil hole in the crankshaft, rotate the crankshaft in the opposite direction of engine rotation until the bearing seats itself. Remove the tool.

7. Install the cap bearing.

8. Support the crankshaft so that its weight will not compress the Plastigage and provide an erroneous reading. Position a small jack so that it will bear against the counterweight adjoining the bearing which is being checked.

9. Place a piece of Plastigage on the bearing surface the full width of the bearing cap and about ¼ inch off-center (Fig. 47).

10. Install the cap and torque the bolts to specifications. **Do not turn the crankshaft while the Plastigage is in place. When checking the width of the Plastigage, check at the widest point in order to get the minimum clearance. Check at the narrowest point in order to get the maximum clearance. The difference between the two readings is the taper.**

11. If the clearance is less than the specified limits, try to red bearing halves or a combination of red and blue depending upon the condition. If the clearance exceeds specified limits, try 0.002 inch undersize

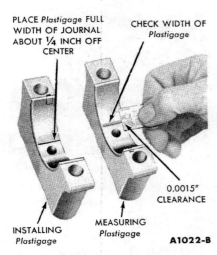

PLACE *Plastigage* FULL WIDTH OF JOURNAL ABOUT ¼ INCH OFF CENTER

CHECK WIDTH OF *Plastigage*

0.0015" CLEARANCE

INSTALLING *Plastigage*

MEASURING *Plastigage*

A1022-B

FIG. 47—Installing and Measuring Plastigage—Engine in Chassis

bearings in combination with blue or red bearings. **The bearing clearance must be within specified limits. If 0.002 inch undersize main bearings are used on more than one journal, be sure they are all installed on the same side (cap or cylinder block) of the crankshaft.** If the standard and 0.002 inch undersize bearings do not bring the clearance within the desired limits, refinish the crankshaft journal. Then install undersize bearings.

12. After the bearing has been checked and found to be satisfactory, apply a light coat of engine oil to the journal and bearings; then install the bearing cap. Torque the cap bolts to specifications.

13. If the thrust bearing cap (No. 3 main bearing) has been removed, install it as follows:

Install the thrust bearing cap with the bolts finger-tight. Pry the crankshaft forward against the thrust surface of the upper half of the bearing (Fig. 65). Hold the crankshaft forward and pry the thrust bearing cap to the rear (Fig. 65). This will align the thrust surfaces of both halves of the bearing. Retain the forward pressure on the crankshaft. Torque the cap bolts to specifications.

14. On a 427 V-8, after all the main bearings have been fitted, torque all the main bearing cap bolts to specifications.

Make sure the cross-bolt spacers are installed in their proper locations (Fig. 71). Production spacers are marked L-2, R-2, L-3, R-3, L-4 and R-4.

Install and torque the cross-bolts

in two steps, following the sequence shown in Fig. 71. First, torque all the cross-bolts to 20 ft-lbs. Finally, torque all the cross-bolts to specifications.

15. Repeat the procedure for the remaining bearings that require replacement.

16. If the rear main bearing is to be replaced, remove the rear main bearing cap. Remove and discard the rear seal and side seals.

17. Clean the rear journal oil seal groove.

18. Install a new rear journal oil seal in the rear main bearing cap (Fig. 48). After installation, cut the ends of the seals flush.

19. Apply a thin coating of oil resistant sealer to the rear main bearing cap at the rear of the top mating surface (Fig. 48). **Do not**

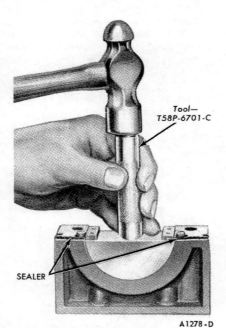

Tool— T58P-6701-C

SEALER

A1278-D

FIG. 48—Seal to Rear Bearing Cap Installation

apply sealer to the area forward of the side seal groove. Install the rear main bearing cap. Torque the cap bolts to specifications.

20. Dip the side seals in light engine oil; then immediately install them in the grooves. **Do not use sealer on the side seals. The seals are designed to expand when dipped in oil. Using sealer may retard this expansion.** It may be necessary to tap the seals into place for the last ½ inch of travel. Do not cut the seal projecting ends.

21. Check the retainer side seals for leaks by squirting a few drops

of oil into the parting lines between the rear main bearing cap and the cylinder block from the outside. Blow compressed air against the seals from the inside of the block. If air bubbles appear in the oil, it indicates possible oil leakage. **This test should not be performed on newly installed seals until sufficient time has been allowed for the seals to expand into the seal grooves.**

22. Disassemble, clean and assemble the oil pump if necessary. Prime the oil pump. Install the oil pump and oil pan.

23. Install the oil level dipstick. Fill the crankcase with the proper amount and viscosity oil. Install the spark plugs.

24. Operate the engine and check for oil leaks.

CONNECTING ROD BEARING REPLACEMENT

1. Follow step 1 under Main Bearing Replacement.

2. Turn the crankshaft until the connecting rod to which new bearings are to be fitted is down.

3. Remove the connecting rod cap. Push the connecting rod up into the cylinder and remove the bearing insert from the rod and cap.

4. Follow step 5 under Main Bearing Replacement.

5. Install the new bearings in the connecting rod and cap. Pull the connecting rod assembly down firmly on the crankshaft journal.

6. Place a piece of Plastigage on the lower bearing surface, the full width of the cap and about ¼ inch off-center.

7. Install the cap and torque the connecting rods nuts to specifications. **Do not turn the crankshaft while the Plastigage is in place.**

8. Remove the cap; then, using the Plastigage scale, check the width of the Plastigage. **When checking the width of the Plastigage, check at the widest point in order to get the minimum clearance. Check at the narrowest point in order to get the maximum clearance. The difference between the two readings is the taper.**

9. If the clearance is less than the specified limits, try two red bearing halves or a combination of red and blue depending upon the condition.

If the clearance exceeds the specified limits, try 0.002 inch undersize bearings in combination with blue or red bearings. **The bearing clearance must be within specified limits.**

If the proper clearance cannot be achieved with standard or 0.002 undersize bearings, the crankshaft will have to be ground undersize and fitted with undersize bearings.

10. After the bearing clearance has been checked and found to be satisfactory, apply a light coat of engine oil to the journal and bearings. Install the connecting rod cap.

11. Repeat the procedure for the remaining connecting rods that require new bearings.

12. Follow step 22, 23 and 24 under Main Bearing Replacement.

CLEANING AND INSPECTION

Refer to Part 8-1, Section 3 for the cleaning and inspection procedures.

PISTON AND CONNECTING ROD ASSEMBLY

REMOVAL

1. Drain the cooling system and the crankcase. Remove the intake manifold, cylinder heads, oil pan and oil pump following the procedures in this section.

2. Remove any ridge and/or deposits from the upper end of the cylinder bores as follows:

Turn the crankshaft until the piston to be removed is at the bottom of its travel and place a cloth on the piston head to collect the cuttings. Remove any ridge and/or deposits from the upper end of the cylinder bores. Remove the cylinder ridge with a ridge cutter (tool 6011-E). Follow the instructions furnished by the tool manufacturer. **Never cut into the ring travel area in excess of 1/32 inch when removing ridges.**

3. Make sure all connecting rod caps are marked so that they can be installed in their original locations.

4. Turn the crankshaft until the connecting rod being removed is down.

5. Remove the connecting rod cap.

6. Push the connecting rod and piston assembly out of the top of the cylinder with the handle end of a hammer. **Avoid damage to the crankshaft journal or the cylinder wall when removing the piston and rod.**

7. Remove the bearing inserts from the connecting rod and cap.

8. Install the cap on the connecting rod from which it was removed.

INSTALLATION

1. If new piston rings are to be installed, remove the cylinder wall glaze (Part 8-1, Section 2, Repairs —Cylinder Block). Follow the instructions of the tool manufacturer. After performing cylinder bore repairs, clean the bore(s), following the procedure in Part 8-1, Section 3.

2. Oil the piston rings, pistons and cylinder walls with light engine oil. **Be sure to install the pistons in the same cylinders from which they were removed or to which they were fitted. The connecting rod and bearing cap are numbered from 1 to 4 in the right bank and from 5 to 8 in the left bank, beginning at the front of the engine. The numbers on the connecting rod and bearing cap must be on the same side when installed in the cylinder bore. If a connecting rod is ever transposed from one block or cylinder to another, new bearings should be fitted, and the connecting rod should be numbered to correspond with the new cylinder number.**

3. Make sure the ring gaps are properly spaced around the circumference of the piston (Fig. 49).

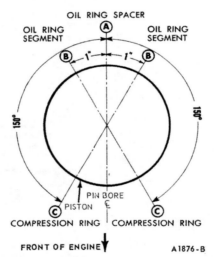

FIG. 49—Piston Ring Gap Spacing

4. Install a piston ring compressor on the piston and push the piston in with a hammer handle until it is slightly below the top of the cylinder (Fig. 50). Be sure to guide the connecting rods to avoid damaging the crankshaft journals. **Install the piston with the indentation in the piston head toward the front of the engine.**

5. Check the clearance of each bearing following the procedure un-

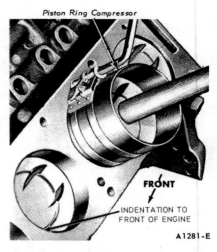

FIG. 50—Typical Piston Installation

der Connecting Rod Bearing Replacement.

6. After the bearings have been fitted, apply a light coat of engine oil to the journals and bearings.

7. Turn the crankshaft throw to the bottom of its stroke. Push the piston all the way down until the connecting rod bearing seats on the crankshaft journal.

8. Install the connecting rod cap. Torque the nuts to specifications.

9. After the piston and connecting rod assemblies have been installed, check the side clearance between the connecting rods on each crankshaft journal (Fig. 51).

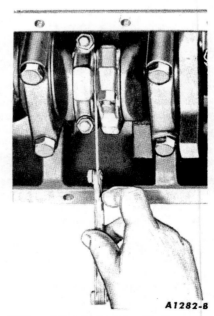

FIG. 51—Connecting Rod Side Clearance

10. Disassemble, clean and assemble the oil pump. Clean the oil pump inlet tube screen and the oil pan and block gasket surfaces.

11. Prime and install the oil pump. Install the oil pan.

12. Install the cylinder heads by following steps 1 thru 6 under Cylinder Head Installation.

13. Refer to Intake Manifold Installation and install the intake manifold by following steps 2 thru 18 under Engines with Hydraulic Valve Lifters or steps 1 thru 8 under Engines with Mechanical Tappets.

14. *Fill* and bleed the cooling system. Fill the crankcase with the proper grade and quantity of engine oil.

15. Install the automatic choke heat chamber air inlet tube (except 427 V-8). Install the air cleaner. Operate the engine and check for oil and coolant leaks. Check and adjust the ignition timing.

On an engine with mechanical lifters, perform a final (hot) valve lash adjustment (Part 8-1, Section 2), and install the valve rocker arm covers.

16. Adjust the engine idle speed and fuel mixture.

DISASSEMBLY

1. Mark the pistons and pins to assure assembly with the same rod and installation in the same cylinder from which they were removed.

2. Remove the piston rings. Remove the piston pin retainers. Drive the pin out of the piston and connecting rod (Fig. 52). Discard the retainers.

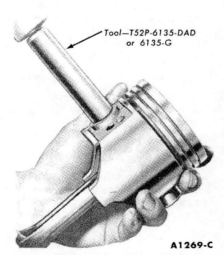

FIG. 52—Piston Pin Removal

CLEANING AND INSPECTION

Refer to Part 8-1, Section 3 for

the cleaning and inspection procedures.

REPAIRS

Refer to Part 8-1, Section 2 for the repair procedures.

ASSEMBLY

The piston, connecting rod and related parts are shown in Fig. 53.

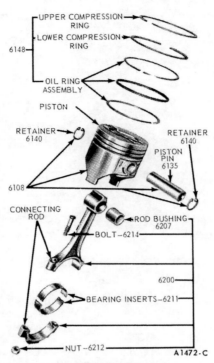

FIG. 53—Typical Piston Connecting Rod and Related Parts

1. Lubricate all parts with light engine oil. Position the connecting rod in the piston and push the pin into place. Assemble the piston and connecting rod as shown in Fig. 54.

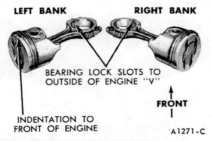

FIG. 54—Correct Piston and Connecting Rod Position

2. Insert new piston pin retainers into the piston. Check the end gap of all piston rings (Part 8-1). It must be within specifications (Part 8-4).

Follow the instructions contained on the piston ring package and install the piston rings. Be sure the piston ring gaps are properly spaced (Fig. 49).

3. Check the ring side clearance of the compression rings with a feeler gauge (step 6 under Fitting Piston Rings in Part 8-1 Section 2).

4. Be sure the bearing inserts and the bearing bore in the connecting rod and cap are clean. Foreign material under the inserts will distort the bearing and cause a failure. Install the bearing inserts in the connecting rod and cap with the tangs fitting in the slots provided.

FLYWHEEL

REMOVAL

1. Disconnect the transmission from the engine and slide it to the rear as outlined in Group 5 (manual-shift transmission) or on an automatic transmission remove the transmission (Group 7).

On a manual-shift transmission, remove the pressure plate and cover assembly as outlined in Group 5.

2. Remove the flywheel retaining bolts and remove the flywheel.

CLEANING AND INSPECTION

Refer to Part 8-1, Section 3 for the cleaning and inspection procedures.

REPAIRS

To check flywheel face runout or replace flywheel ring gear, refer to Part 8-1, Section 2.

INSTALLATION

1. Install the flywheel on the crankshaft flange and install the retaining bolts. Torque the bolts in sequence across from each other to specifications.

2. Check the flywheel runout, following the procedure in Part 8-1, Section 1.

3. On a manual-shift transmission, install the pressure plate and cover assembly (Group 5).

4. Connect the transmission to the engine as outlined in Group 5 (manual-shift transmissions) or on an automatic transmission, install the transmission (Group 7). It is not necessary to adjust the transmission, when it has been removed only for flywheel removal.

CLUTCH PILOT BUSHING REPLACEMENT

Inspection procedures are outlined under Crankshaft Cleaning and Inspection in Part 8-1, Section 3.

1. Disconnect the transmission from the engine and slide it to the rear as outlined in Group 5.

2. Remove the pressure plate and cover assembly and the clutch disc as outlined in Group 5.

3. Remove the pilot bushing (Fig. 55).

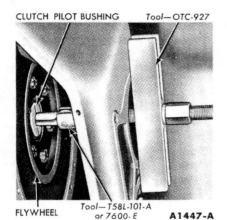

FLYWHEEL Tool—T58L-101-A or 7600-E A1447-A

FIG. 55—Typical Clutch Pilot Bushing Removal

4. Coat the pilot bushing bore in the crankshaft with a small quantity of wheel bearing lubricant. **Avoid using too much lubricant as it may be thrown onto the clutch disc when the clutch revolves.**

5. Install the pilot service bearing (Fig. 56).

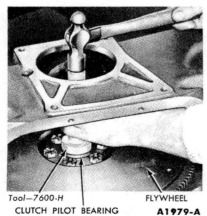

Tool—7600-H FLYWHEEL
CLUTCH PILOT BEARING A1979-A

FIG. 56—Typical Clutch Pilot Service Bearing Installation

6. Install the clutch disc and the pressure plate and cover assembly as outlined in Group 5.

7. Connect the transmission to the engine as outlined in Group 5.

OIL FILTER REPLACEMENT

The Rotunda oil filter assembly is shown in Fig. 57.

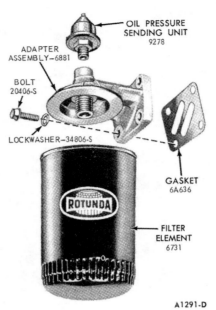

FIG. 57—Typical Rotunda Oil Filter Assembly

1. Place a drip pan under the filter. Unscrew the filter from the adapter fitting. Clean the adapter filter recess.

2. Coat the gasket on the new filter with oil. Place the filter in position on the adapter (Fig. 58). Hand tighten the filter until the gasket contacts the adapter face. Then advance it ½-turn.

3. Operate the engine at fast idle and check for leaks. If oil leaks are evident, perform the necessary repairs to correct the leakage. Check the oil level and fill the crankcase if necessary.

OIL PAN

REMOVAL

1. Raise the car and place safety stands into position. Drain the oil from the crankcase. On a car equipped with air conditioning, remove the fan shroud from the radiator and position it over the fan.

2. Disconnect the stabilizer bar at the connecting links and pull the ends down.

3. To allow clearance for removal of the oil pan, remove the engine front support insulator to intermediate support bracket nuts and

FIG. 58—Rotunda Oil Filter Replacement

lock washers. Install a block of wood on a floor jack and position the jack under the front leading edge of the oil pan. Raise the engine approximately 1¼ inches and insert a 1 inch block of wood between the insulators and the frame cross member. Remove the floor jack.

4. Remove the oil pan retaining screws and lower the oil pan to the frame cross member.

5. Crank the engine to obtain the necessary clearance between the crankshaft counterweight and the rear of the oil pan. Remove the upper bolt and loosen the lower bolt on the inlet tube (Fig. 59). Position the inlet tube and screen out of the way, and remove the oil pan.

CLEANING AND INSPECTION

Refer to Part 8-1, Section 3 for the cleaning and inspection procedures.

INSTALLATION

1. Clean the oil pan and cylinder block gasket surfaces. Clean the oil pump inlet tube screen. Position a new oil pump inlet tube gasket on the oil pump and install the inlet tube (Fig. 59) with the lower bolt only. Do not tighten the bolt.

2. Apply oil-resistant sealer to the oil pan gasket surfaces and position the gasket on the oil pan.

3. Position the oil pan on the

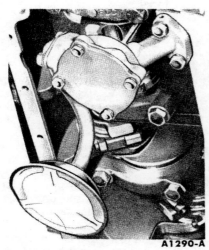

FIG. 59—Typical Oil Pump and Inlet Tube Installation

crossmember and install the inlet tube to oil pump upper mounting bolt. Tighten both bolts.

4. Hold the oil pan in place against the cylinder block and install a retaining screw on each side of the pan. Using the special spring washers, install the oil pan to rear main bearing cap bolts. Install the remaining screws and tighten them from the center outward. Torque the screws to specifications.

5. Position the floor jack and block of wood under the leading edge of the oil pan. Raise the engine slightly and remove the wood blocks from beneath the insulators. Lower the engine and remove the jack. Install the insulator to frame lock washers and nuts. Torque the nuts to specifications.

6. Connect the stabilizer bar. **Replace the oil filter.** Remove the safety stands and lower the car. If the fan shroud was removed, install it on the radiator.

7. Fill the crankcase with the proper grade and quantity of engine oil. Operate the engine and check for oil leaks.

OIL PUMP

REMOVAL

1. Remove the oil pan, refer to Oil Pan Removal.

2. Remove the oil pump retaining screws; then remove the oil pump and intermediate drive shaft.

3. Remove the inlet tube and screen assembly from the oil pump. Discard the gasket.

INSTALLATION

1. Prime the oil pump by filling either the inlet or outlet port with engine oil. Rotate the pump shaft to distribute the oil within the pump body.

2. Position a new gasket on the pump housing. Insert the intermediate drive shaft into the oil pump. Install the pump and shaft as an assembly (Fig. 59). **Do not attempt to force the pump into position if it will not seat readily. The drive shaft hex may be misaligned with the distributor shaft. To align, rotate the intermediate shaft into a new position.** Torque the oil pump retaining screws to specifications.

3. Install the inlet tube and screen assembly and oil pan, following the procedure under Oil Pan Installation.

DISASSEMBLY

1. Remove the oil inlet tube from the oil pump and remove the gasket.

2. Remove the cover retaining screws, then remove the cover. Remove the inner rotor and shaft assembly and the outer race.

3. Remove the staking marks at the relief valve chamber cap. Insert a self-threading sheet metal screw of the proper diameter into the oil pressure relief valve chamber cap and pull the cap out of the chamber. Remove the spring and plunger.

CLEANING AND INSPECTION

Refer to Part 8-1, Section 3 for the cleaning and inspection procedures.

ASSEMBLY

The oil pump assembly is shown in Fig. 60.

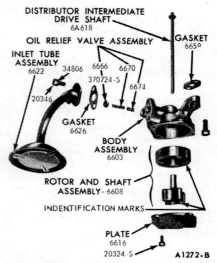

FIG. 60—Typical Oil Pump Assembly

1. Oil all parts thoroughly.

2. Install the oil pressure relief valve plunger, spring and a new cap. Stake the cap.

3. Install the outer race and the inner rotor and shaft assembly. **Be sure the dimple (identification mark) on the outer race is facing outward and on same side as identification mark on rotor. The inner rotor and shaft and the outer race are serviced as an assembly. One part should not be replaced without replacing the other.** Install the cover. Torque the cover retaining screws to specifications.

4. Position a new gasket and the oil inlet tube on the oil pump and install the retaining bolts.

---

3 ENGINE REMOVAL AND INSTALLATION

The engine removal and installation procedures are for the engine only without the transmission attached.

352, 390, 410, AND 428 V-8

REMOVAL

1. Drain the cooling system and the crankcase. Remove the hood. Remove the air cleaner and disconnect the battery positive cable.

2. Disconnect the radiator upper hose at the engine and the radiator lower hose at the water pump. On a car with automatic transmission disconnect the transmission oil cooler lines from the radiator.

3. Remove the cooling fan and spacer (or fan drive clutch) and power steering pump drive belt (if so equipped). Remove the radiator.

Remove the oil level dipstick.

4. Disconnect the oil pressure sending unit wire at the sending unit and the flexible fuel line at the fuel tank line.

Disconnect the accelerator cable at the carburetor. Remove the accelerator retracting spring. Remove the accelerator cable bracket from the intake manifold. Position the accelerator cable and body ground strap out of the way.

On a car with automatic transmission, disconnect the kickdown rod at the carburetor. Remove the kickdown rod retracting spring. Disconnect the transmission vacuum line at the engine.

On a car with power steering, remove the power steering pump from the mounting bracket. Remove the power steering hose bracket bolt. Wire the power steering pump in a position that will prevent the oil from draining out. Remove the power steering pump bracket, coil bracket, and compressor bracket and compressor assembly (if equipped with air conditioning). Remove the coil. Position the compressor (with lines attached) out of the way. On a car with power brakes, disconnect the brake vacuum hose at the pipe and position the hose out of the way.

5. Disconnect the heater hoses at the water pump and intake manifold and remove the heater hose from the automatic choke bracket. On a 352 engine, disconnect the hose at the rear of the coolant heated spacer. Disconnect the coolant temperature sending unit at the sending unit. Remove the wire loom from the clips on the left valve rocker arm cover and position it out of the way.

On a car with air conditioning, remove the compressor from the mounting bracket, and position it out of the way, **leaving the refrigerant lines attached.**

6. Remove the battery ground cable and alternator ground cable bolt at the engine. Remove the alternator mounting bolts and spacer, and position the alternator out of the way.

7. Disconnect the fuel inlet line at the pump.

8. Raise the front of the car. Remove the starter.

9. Disconnect the muffler inlet pipes from the exhaust manifolds.

10. Remove the engine support insulator to intermediate support bracket nuts, and loosen the right side support insulator to engine bolts.

On a car with an automatic transmission, remove the flywheel housing cover. Remove the oil cooler lines retaining clip from the engine block. Disconnect the converter from the flywheel. Secure the converter assembly in the housing. Remove the remaining flywheel housing to engine bolts, and remove the transmission fluid filler tube bracket.

On a car with a manual-shift transmission, remove the flywheel housing inspection cover and the clutch pedal retracting spring. Disconnect the clutch release bracket at the equalizer rod and remove the bracket from the engine. Remove the remaining flywheel housing to engine bolts.

11. Lower the car; then support the transmission. Install the engine left lifting bracket on the front of the left cylinder head, and install the engine right lifting bracket at the rear of the right cylinder head, then attach the engine lifting sling (Fig. 61).

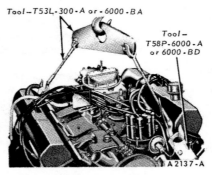

Tool—T53L-300-A or 6000-BA

Tool— T58P-6000-A or 6000-BD

A 2137-A

FIG. 61—Typical Engine Lifting Bracket and Sling

12. Remove the flywheel or converter housing to engine upper bolts.

13. Raise the engine slightly and carefully pull it from the transmission. Lift the engine out of the engine compartment.

INSTALLATION

1. Attach the engine lifting brackets and sling (Fig. 61).

2. Lower the engine carefully into the engine compartment. Make sure the exhaust manifolds are properly aligned with the muffler inlet pipes and the dowels in the block engage the holes in the flywheel housing.

On a car with an automatic transmission, start the converter pilot into the crankshaft.

On a car with a manual-shift transmission, start the transmission main drive gear into the clutch disc. It may be necessary to adjust the position of the transmission in relation to the engine if the input shaft will not enter the clutch disc. **If the engine hangs up after the shaft enters, turn the crankshaft slowly (transmission in gear) until the shaft splines mesh with the clutch disc splines.**

3. Install the flywheel or converter housing upper bolts.

4. Remove the transmission jack. Lower the engine until the front support insulators are properly positioned in the intermediate support brackets. Torque the right side insulator bolts to specifications. Disconnect the engine lifting sling and remove the lifting brackets.

5. Raise the car and install the remaining flywheel housing to engine block retaining bolts. Torque the bolts to specifications.

6. Install the lock washers and nuts on the engine support insulators. Torque both insulator nuts to specifications.

7. Install new muffler inlet pipe gaskets, and connect the muffler inlet pipes to the exhaust manifolds. Torque the nuts to specifications.

8. On a car with an automatic transmission, remove the retainer securing the converter in the housing. Attach the converter to the flywheel. Install the transmission fluid filler tube bracket. Install the flywheel housing cover assembly. Install the oil cooler lines bracket. Connect the kickdown rod to the transmission.

On a car with a manual-shift transmission, install the clutch bracket. Connect the clutch release rod and install the clutch retracting spring. Install the flywheel housing lower cover.

9. Install the starter and transmission oil filler tube bracket. Attach the starter cable.

10. Lower the car. Install the power steering pump bracket, coil bracket, and compressor and bracket assembly (if equipped with air conditioning).

11. Connect the flexible fuel line and the oil pressure sending unit wire.

12. Place the alternator drive belt on the crankshaft pulley. Install the power steering pump and adjust the belt tension to specifications. On a car with air conditioning, install the compressor on the mounting bracket, and adjust the belt tension to specifications.

13. Install the alternator and attach the battery ground cable. Connect the alternator wires and coolant temperature sending unit wire. Connect the heater hoses at the water pump and intake manifold (on 352 engines at the rear of the coolant heated spacer).

14. Install the ignition coil and

connect the coil primary and high tension wires. Position the wire loom in the retaining clips on the left valve rocker arm cover. Install the oil level dipstick.

15. On a car with an automatic transmission, connect the kickdown rod to the carburetor. Install the kickdown rod retracting spring. Connect the transmission vacuum line.

Install the accelerator cable bracket and body ground strap. Connect the accelerator cable to the carburetor and install the retracting spring.

16. Install the radiator. Connect the radiator upper and lower hoses. Install the hood.

On a car with an automatic transmission, connect the transmission oil cooler lines.

17. Install the fan and spacer (or fan drive clutch). Torque the bolts to specifications. Position the alternator drive belt and adjust the tension to specifications. Tighten the alternator mounting bolts to specifications. Connect the battery positive cable.

On a car with air conditioning, adjust the compressor belt tension to specifications.

18. Fill and bleed the cooling system. Connect the heater hose at the water pump. Fill the crankcase with the proper grade and quantity of oil. Install the hood.

19. Install the air cleaner and operate the engine at fast idle and check all gaskets and hose connections for leaks.

20. Adjust the accelerator cable and the idle speed and fuel mixture.

On a car with an automatic transmission, adjust the transmission control linkage.

427 V-8

REMOVAL

1. Drain the cooling system and the crankcase. Remove the hood and the air cleaner. Disconnect the battery ground cable.

2. Disconnect the radiator upper hose at the engine and the radiator lower hose at the water pump.

3. Remove the radiator. Remove the oil level dipstick.

4. Disconnect the oil pressure sending unit wire at the sending unit, and the flexible fuel line at the fuel tank line. Plug the fuel tank line.

5. Disconnect the accelerator rod at the carburetor. Remove the accelerator retracting spring.

6. Disconnect the heater hoses at the water pump and intake manifold, the generator or alternator wires at the alternator, and the water temperature sending unit at the sending unit.

7. Disconnect the wire loom at the distributor and ignition coil. Remove the wire loom from the clips on the left valve rocker arm cover and position it out of the way.

8. Remove the flywheel housing to engine upper bolts.

9. Raise the front of the car. Disconnect the muffler inlet pipe at the right exhaust manifold. Remove the heat control valve.

10. Disconnect the engine front support insulators at the frame. Raise the engine approximately 1 or 2 inches to provide necessary clearance to remove the right exhaust manifold.

11. Remove the right exhaust manifold. Disconnect the muffler inlet pipe at the left exhaust manifold.

12. Disconnect the starter cable. Remove the starter.

13. Remove the flywheel housing inspection cover and the clutch pedal retracting spring. Disconnect the clutch release bracket at the equalizer rod and remove the bracket from the engine. Remove the remaining flywheel housing to engine bolts.

14. Lower the car and support the transmission. Install the engine left lifting bracket on the front of the left cylinder head, and install the engine right lifting bracket at the rear of the right cylinder head, then attach the engine lifting sling (Fig. 61).

15. Raise the engine slightly and carefully pull it from the transmission. Lift the engine out of the engine compartment.

INSTALLATION

1. Clean the muffler inlet pipe gasket surfaces and both sides of the exhaust control valve assembly.

2. Attach the engine lifting brackets and sling (Fig. 61).

3. Lower the engine carefully into the engine compartment. Make sure the exhaust manifolds are properly aligned with the muffler inlet pipes and the dowels in the block engage the holes in the flywheel housing.

4. Start the transmission main drive gear into the clutch disc. It may be necessary to adjust the position of the transmission in relation to the engine if the input shaft will

not enter the clutch disc. If the engine hangs up after the shaft enters, turn the crankshaft slowly (transmission in gear) until the shaft splines mesh with the clutch disc splines.

5. Install the flywheel housing upper bolts. Install the remaining flywheel housing to engine block retaining bolts.

6. Raise the front of the car. Install the starter. Connect the starter cable.

7. Raise the engine approximately 1 or 2 inches and position the right exhaust manifold. Install and torque the retaining bolts to specifications.

8. Make sure the engine support insulator bolts are properly aligned with the support brackets on the frame. Completely lower the engine and install the engine support insulator lock washers and nuts. Torque the nuts to specifications.

9. Disconnect the engine lifting sling and remove the lifting brackets.

10. Place new gaskets on both sides of the exhaust control valve and position it over the inlet pipe studs on the right exhaust manifold. Connect the muffler inlet pipe to the exhaust manifold and torque the nuts to specifications.

11. Position a new gasket to the left exhaust manifold and connect the muffler inlet pipe to the manifold. Install and torque the nuts to specifications.

12. Install the clutch bracket. Connect the clutch release rod and install the clutch retracting spring. Install the flywheel housing lower cover.

13. Remove the support from the transmission and lower the car.

14. Connect the alternator wires, the water temperature sending unit wire, and connect the heater hose at the intake manifold. Connect the battery ground cable.

15. Connect the flexible fuel line and the oil pressure sending unit wire.

16. Connect the coil primary and high tension wires. Connect the wire loom at the distributor. Position the wire loom in the retaining clips on the left valve rocker arm cover.

17. Install the oil level dipstick. Install the accelerator retracting spring. Connect the accelerator rod and adjust the accelerator linkage.

18. Install the radiator. Connect the radiator upper and lower hoses.

Install the hood.

19. Fill and bleed the cooling system. Connect the heater hose at the water pump. Fill the crankcase with the proper grade and quantity of oil.

20. Install the air cleaner, and operate the engine at fast idle and check all gaskets and hose connections for leaks.

4 MAJOR REPAIR OPERATIONS

To perform the operations in this section, it will be necessary to remove the engine from the car and install it on a work stand. For engine removal and installation procedures, refer to Section 3.

When installing nuts or bolts that must be torqued (refer to Part 8-5 for torque specifications), oil the threads with light weight engine oil. **Do not oil threads that require oil-resistant or water-resistant sealer.**

CRANKSHAFT

The crankshaft and related parts are shown in Fig. 62.

pulley (if so equipped). Remove the crankshaft damper cap screw and washer. Remove the power steering drive pulley. Install the puller on the damper (Fig. 34) and remove the damper.

4. Remove the crankshaft sleeve as shown in Fig. 35.

5. Remove the carburetor fuel inlet line. Remove the fuel pump. Remove the cylinder front cover and air conditioning idler pulley assembly (if so equipped). Remove the cover gasket.

6. Remove the crankshaft front oil slinger. Check the timing chain

pump and inlet tube and screen assembly.

8. Make sure all bearing caps (main and connecting rods) are marked so that they can be installed in their original locations. Remove the connecting rod bearing caps. Turn the crankshaft until the connecting rod from which the cap is being removed is down and remove the cap. Push the connecting rod and piston assembly up into the cylinder.

8. Remove the main bearing caps.

On a 427 V-8, remove the main bearing cap cross bolts, washers and spacers (Fig. 71) before removing

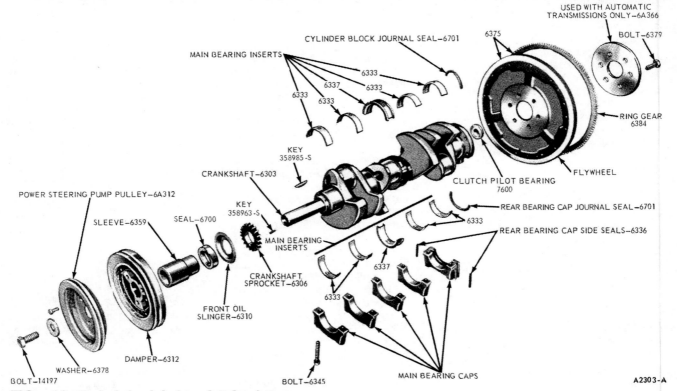

FIG. 62—Typical Crankshaft and Related Parts

REMOVAL

1. Install the engine on a work stand. Remove the spark plugs to allow easy rotation of the crankshaft.

2. Remove the fuel pump. Slide the water pump bypass hose clamp toward the intake manifold. Remove the water pump.

3. Remove the accessory drive

deflection, then remove the timing chain and sprockets by following the applicable steps under Cylinder Front Cover Removal.

7. Invert the engine on the work stand. Remove the flywheel, and engine rear cover plate. Remove the oil pan and gasket. Remove the oil

the cap retaining bolts.

9. Carefully lift the crankshaft out of the block so that the thrust bearing surfaces are not damaged. **Handle the crankshaft with care to avoid possible fracture or damage to the finished surfaces.**

CLEANING AND INSPECTION

Refer to Part 8-1, Section 3 for the cleaning and inspection procedures. **Be sure the oil seal surfaces on the crankshaft and crankshaft damper are properly cleaned.**

REPAIRS

To refinish journals, dress minor imperfections, etc., refer to Part 8-1, Section 2.

INSTALLATION

1. Remove the rear journal oil seal from the block and rear main bearing cap. Remove the rear main bearing cap to block side seals.
2. Remove the main bearing inserts from the block and bearing caps.
3. Remove the connecting rod bearing inserts from the connecting rods and caps.
4. If the crankshaft main bearing journals have been refinished to a definite undersize, install the correct undersize bearings. Be sure the bearing inserts and bearing bores are clean. Foreign material under the inserts will distort the bearing and cause a failure.
5. Place the upper main bearing inserts in position in the bores with the tang fitting in the slot provided.
   If the oil hole does not line up with the cylinder block oil passage, check the holes with a rod corresponding to the following diameters:
   No. 1 Bearing—7/64 inch
   No. 2 Bearing—9/64 inch
   No. 3 Bearing—9/32 inch
   No. 4 Bearing—5/32 inch
   No. 5 Bearing—9/32 inch
   If the rod passes through both the bearing and the block, sufficient lubrication is assured.
6. Install the lower main bearing inserts in the bearing caps.
7. Install a new rear journal oil seal in the block, using the specified tool (Fig. 63). After installation, cut the ends of the seals flush. **It is very important that the seal be cut flush with the surface of the cylinder block. This prevents rough edges which may project from the groove and lodge between the bearing cap and cylinder block.**
8. Carefully lower the crankshaft into place. **Be careful not to damage the bearing surfaces.**
9. Check the clearance of each main bearing as follows:
   Place a piece of Plastigage on the crankshaft journal the full width of the journal and about 1/4 inch off-

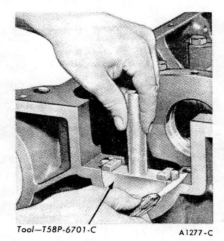

Tool—T58P-6701-C A1277-C

FIG. 63—Seal to Cylinder Block Installation

center (Fig. 64). Follow steps 10 and 11 under Main Bearing Replacement in Part 8-2, Section 2.

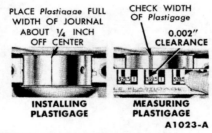

PLACE *Plastigage* FULL WIDTH OF JOURNAL ABOUT 1/4 INCH OFF CENTER — INSTALLING PLASTIGAGE

CHECK WIDTH OF *Plastigage* — 0.002″ CLEARANCE — MEASURING PLASTIGAGE A1023-A

FIG. 64—Installing and Measuring Plastigage—Engine on Work Stand

10. After the bearings have been fitted, apply a light coat of engine oil to the journals and bearings. Install a new seal in the rear main bearing cap and install the rear main bearing cap by following steps 17 thru 21 under Main Bearing Replacement. Install all the bearing caps, except the thrust bearing cap (No. 3 bearing). **Be sure that the main bearing caps are installed in their original locations.** Torque the bearing cap bolts to specifications.
   On a 427 V-8 install the main bearing caps, following the procedure in step 15 of Engine Assembly.
11. Install the thrust bearing cap with the bolts finger-tight.
12. Pry the crankshaft forward against the thrust surface of the upper half of the bearing (Fig. 65).
13. Hold the crankshaft forward and pry the thrust bearing cap to the rear (Fig. 65). This will align the thrust surfaces of both halves of the bearing.

14. Retain the forward pressure on the crankshaft. Torque the cap bolts to specifications (Fig. 65).
15. Check the crankshaft end play by following the procedure in Part 8-1, Section 1.
16. Install new bearing inserts in the connecting rods and caps. Check the clearance of each bearing following the procedure under Main Bearing Replacement.
17. After the connecting rod bearings have been fitted, apply a light coat of engine oil to the journals and bearings.
18. Turn the crankshaft throw to the bottom of its stroke. Push the piston all the way down until the rod bearing seats on the crankshaft journal.
19. Install the connecting rod cap. Torque the nuts to specifications.
20. After the piston and connecting rod assemblies have been installed, check the side clearance between the connecting rods on each connecting rod crankshaft journal (Fig. 52).
21. Install the engine rear cover plate; then position the flywheel on the crankshaft. Install the retaining bolts. Torque the bolts to specifications.
   On a flywheel for a manual-shift transmission, use tool 7563 to locate the clutch disc. Install the pressure plate. Tighten the retaining bolts.
22. Install the timing chain and sprockets, cylinder front cover and crankshaft damper, following steps 1 thru 9 under Cylinder Front Cover Installation.
23. Clean the oil pan, oil pump and oil pump screen. Prime the oil pump. Install the oil pump and oil pan.
24. Install the oil filter, fuel pump and carburetor fuel inlet line. Install the spark plugs.
25. Remove the engine from the work stand.

CAMSHAFT BEARING REPLACEMENT

Camshaft bearings are available pre-finished to size or standard and 0.015-inch undersize journal diameters. The bearings are not interchangeable from one bore to another.

1. Install the engine on a work stand. Remove the camshaft, flywheel and crankshaft. Push the pistons to the top of the cylinders.

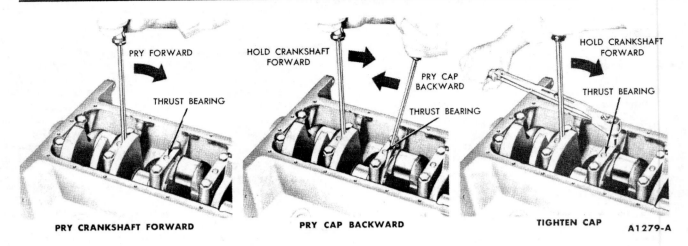

FIG. 65—Thrust Bearing Alignment

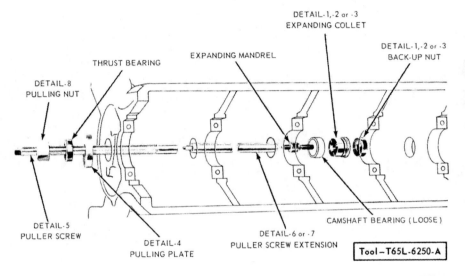

FIG. 66—Typical Camshaft Bearing Replacement

FIG. 67—Camshaft Front Bearing Measurement

2. Remove the camshaft rear bearing bore plug. Remove the camshaft bearings (Fig. 66).

If the camshaft bearings are being removed with the tool shown in Fig. 66, the following procedure will apply. Select the proper size expanding collet and back-up nut and assemble on the expanding mandrel. With the expanding collet collapsed, install the collet assembly in the camshaft bearing, and tighten the back-up nut on the expanding mandrel until the collet fits the camshaft bearing. Assemble the puller screw and extension (if necessary) as shown and install on the expanding mandrel. Tighten the pulling nut against the thrust bearing and pulling plate to remove the camshaft bearing. Be sure to hold a wrench on the end of the puller screw to prevent it from

turning. Repeat the procedure for each bearing. To remove the front bearing, install the puller screw from the rear of the cylinder block.

3. Position the new bearing at the bearing bores, and press them in place with the tool shown in Fig. 66. Be sure to center the pulling plate and the puller screw to avoid damage to the bearing. Wrap a cloth around the threads of the puller screw to protect the front bearing or journal. **Failure to use the correct expanding collet can cause severe bearing damage.** Align the oil holes in the bearings with the oil holes in the cylinder block when the bearings are installed. **Be sure the front bearing is installed 0.005-0.020 inch below the front face of the cylinder block (Fig. 67).**

4. Clean out the camshaft rear bearing bore plug recess thoroughly. Coat the flange of a new plug with oil-resistant sealer and install the plug, with the flange edge of the plug facing inward (Fig. 68).

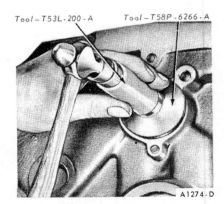

FIG. 68—Camshaft Rear Bearing Bore Plug Installation

5. Install the camshaft, crankshaft, flywheel and related parts, following the appropriate procedures in Section 2 or Section 4, except do not check the connecting rod and main bearing clearances as a part of Camshaft Bearing Replacement. Remove the engine from the work stand.

CYLINDER ASSEMBLY REPLACEMENT

DISASSEMBLY

Follow steps 1 thru 11, 13 thru 20, and 24 thru 26 under Engine Disassembly. Remove the cylinder head dowels from the cylinder block. Remove the cylinder block drain plugs and remove the cylinder assembly from the work stand.

CLEANING

Clean the gasket and seal surfaces of all parts and assemblies (refer to Part 8-1, Section 3).

ASSEMBLY

Install the replacement cylinder block assembly on a work stand. Install the cylinder block drain plugs and cylinder head dowels. Transfer all parts removed from the old cylinder assembly to the new cylinder assembly, following the procedures in steps 22 thru 34 and 41 thru 62, under Engine Assembly. Check all assembly clearances.

CYLINDER BLOCK REPLACEMENT

DISASSEMBLY

Follow steps 1 thru 34 under Engine Disassembly. Remove the cylinder head dowels and cylinder block drain plugs. Remove the intake and exhaust manifolds and cylinder head as an assembly. Remove the cylinder block from the work stand.

CLEANING

Clean the gasket and seal surfaces of all parts and assemblies (Part 8-1, Section 3).

ASSEMBLY

Install the replacement cylinder block on a work stand. Install the cylinder block drain plugs and cylinder head dowels. Transfer all parts removed from the old cylinder block to the new cylinder block, following steps 7 thru 62. Check all assembly clearances. Install the manifolds and cylinder head as an assembly.

ENGINE DISASSEMBLY

1. Install the engine on the work stand.

2. Remove the distributor cap and spark plug wire assembly.

3. Disconnect the distributor vacuum line at the distributor except on 427 V-8. Remove the carburetor fuel inlet line. Remove the fuel pump and discard the gasket.

4. Slide the clamp on the water pump by-pass hose toward the water pump. Remove the automatic choke air heat tube and air inlet tube. On a car with Thermactor exhaust emission control system (Group 12), disconnect the air and vacuum lines. Remove the air supply pump, air manifold assembly, air cleaner assembly, anti-backfire valve, and air and vacuum lines and brackets. Remove the valve rocker arm covers and positive crankcase ventilation system components.

On an engine with mechanical lifters, loosen the valve rocker arm shaft support bolts in sequence, two turns at a time. After all the bolts are loosened, remove the valve rocker arm shaft assembly.

On an engine with hydraulic valve lifters, starting at the No. 4 cylinder, loosen the right rocker arm shaft support bolts in sequence, two turns at a time. After the bolts are all loosened, remove the valve rocker arm shaft assembly and the oil baffle plate. Starting at the No. 5 cylinder, follow the same procedure on the left valve rocker arm shaft support bolts.

5. Remove the valve push rods in sequence and put them in a rack so that they can be installed in their original bore.

6. Remove the distributor hold down bolt and clamp and remove the distributor.

7. Remove the intake manifold retaining bolts.

8. Install standard eye bolts with $5/16$-18 threads in the left front and right rear rocker arm cover screw holes and attach the engine lifting sling (Fig. 23).

9. Raise the intake manifold and carefully remove it from the engine. Discard the intake manifold gaskets and seals.

10. Remove the baffle plate from the valve push rod chamber floor by prying up on the baffle with a screwdriver (Fig. 69).

11. Lift the valve lifters or tappets from the cylinder block and place them in a rack so that they

FIG. 69—Baffle Plate Removal

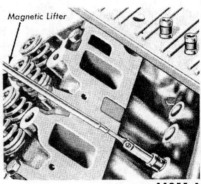

FIG. 70—Valve Lifter or Tappet Removal—Intake Manifold Removed

can be installed in their original bore (Fig. 70).

The internal parts of each hydraulic valve lifter assembly are matched sets. Do not intermix the parts. Keep the assemblies intact until they are to be cleaned.

12. Remove the exhaust manifolds and the spark plugs. Remove the automatic choke air chamber cover from the right exhaust manifold.

13. Remove the cylinder head bolts.

14. Lift the cylinder heads off the block. **Do not pry between the head and the block.** Discard the cylinder head gaskets.

15. Remove the oil filter. Remove the oil filter adapter assembly and oil pressure sending unit as an assembly. Discard the gasket.

16. Remove the alternator, bracket and drive belt.

17. Remove the water pump, pul-

ley and fan as an assembly. Remove the accessory drive pulley (if so equipped).

18. On a car with power steering, remove the power steering pulley. Remove the damper (Fig. 34).

19. Remove the crankshaft sleeve as shown in Fig. 35.

20. Remove the cylinder front cover. Discard the gasket. Remove the crankshaft front oil slinger.

21. Check the timing chain deflection by following the procedure in Part 8-1, Section 1.

22. Remove the camshaft sprocket cap screw and the fuel pump eccentric. Remove the sprockets and timing chain as an assembly (Fig. 37). Remove the crankshaft sprocket key.

23. Remove any ridge and/or carbon deposits from the upper end of the cylinder bores. Move the piston to the bottom of its travel and place a cloth on the piston head to collect the cuttings. Remove the cylinder ridge with a ridge cutter. Follow the instructions furnished by the tool manufacturer. **Never cut into the ring travel area in excess of 1/32 inch when removing ridges.** After the ridge has been removed, remove the cutter from the cylinder bore.

24. On a flywheel for a manual-shift transmission, mark the pressure plate cover so that it can be replaced in the same position, and remove the clutch pressure plate and cover assembly. Remove the flywheel. Remove the rear cover plate.

25. Invert the engine. Remove the oil pan. Discard the gasket.

26. Remove the oil pump and inlet tube as an assembly. Remove the oil pump intermediate shaft. Discard the oil pump gasket.

27. Make sure all connecting rods and caps are marked so that they can be installed in their original locations. Turn the crankshaft until the connecting rod being removed is down. Remove the rod cap.

28. Push the connecting rod and piston assembly out the top of the cylinder with the handle end of a hammer. **Avoid damage to the connecting rod journal or the cylinder wall when removing the piston and rod.**

29. Remove the bearing inserts from the connecting rods and caps. Install the rod caps on the connecting rods from which they were removed.

30. Remove the main bearing caps.

On a 427 V-8, remove the main bearing cap cross-bolts, washers and spacers (Fig. 71) before removing the cap retaining bolts.

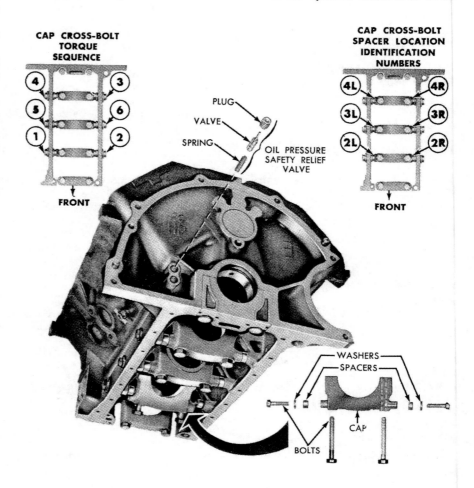

FIG. 71—427 V-8 Cylinder Block Details

A1789-C

31. Carefully lift the crankshaft out of the cylinder block so that the thrust bearing surfaces are not damaged. **Handle the crankshaft with care to avoid possible fracture or damage to the finished surfaces.**

32. Remove the rear journal oil seal from the block and rear bearing cap, and remove the cap to block side seals.

33. Remove the main bearing inserts from the block and bearing caps. Install the main bearing caps in their original positions.

34. Carefully remove the camshaft. Avoid damaging the journals and lobes.

35. Remove the camshaft rear bearing bore plug. Remove the camshaft bearings (Fig. 66).

CLEANING AND INSPECTION

For cleaning and inspection proce-

dures, refer to Part 8-1, Section 3.

ENGINE ASSEMBLY

If the cylinder block is to be re-placed, transfer the cylinder head dowels and cylinder block drain plugs to the new cylinder block. Also, omit steps 1 thru 6 below, if a new cylinder block is used.

1. If the original cylinder block is used, remove the glaze from the cylinder bores by following the instructions of the tool manufacturer.

2. Invert the engine on the work stand.

3. Position the new camshaft bearings at the bearing bores and press them in place with the tool shown in Fig. 66. Align the oil holes in the cylinder block when the bearings are installed. **Be sure the camshaft front bearing is installed 0.005-0.020 inch below the front face of the cylinder block (Fig. 67).**

4. Check the oil passage that feeds the rocker arm shafts for obstructions by squirting oil into the opening on each cylinder bank and observing the flow through the oil holes at Nos. 2 and 4 bearings.

5. Clean out the camshaft rear bearing bore plug recess thoroughly.

6. Coat the flange of a new plug with oil-resistant sealer and install it with the flange facing inward (Fig. 68). Drive the plug in until it is flush or slightly below the casting surface.

7. Oil the camshaft and apply Lubriplate to all lobes; then carefully slide it through the bearings.

8. Be sure that the rear oil seal grooves are clean. Install a new rear *journal oil seal* in the block using the specified tool (Fig. 63). After installation, cut the ends of the seals flush.

9. If the crankshaft main bearing journals have been refinished to a definite undersize, install the correct undersize bearings. Be sure the bearing inserts and bearing bores are clean. Foreign material under the inserts will distort the bearing and cause a failure.

Place the upper main bearing inserts in position in the bore with the tang fitting in the slot provided.

10. Install the lower main bearing inserts in the bearing caps.

11. Carefully lower the crankshaft into place. **Be careful not to damage the bearing surfaces.**

12. Check the clearance of each main bearing following the procedure under Main Bearing Replacement.

13. After the bearings have been fitted, apply a light coat of engine oil to the journals and bearings.

14. Be sure that the oil seal grooves in the rear main bearing cap are clean. Install a new journal seal in the cap using the specified tool (Fig. 48). After installation, cut the ends of the seal flush. Apply a thin coating of oil-resistant sealer to the rear main bearing cap at the rear of the top mating surface (Fig. 48). **Do not apply sealer to the area forward of the side seal groove.** Install the rear main bearing cap and the remainder of the caps, except the thrust bearing cap (No. 3 bearing). **Be sure that the main bearing caps are installed in their original locations.** Torque the bearing cap bolts to specifications.

15. Install the thrust bearing cap following steps 11 thru 14 under Crankshaft Installation. Check the crankshaft end play by following the procedure in Part 8-1, Section 1.

16. On a 427 V-8, torque the main bearing cap bolts to specifications.

Make sure the cross-bolt spacers are installed in their proper locations (Fig. 71). Production spacers are marked L-2, R-2, L-3, R-3, L-4 and R-4.

Install and torque the cross-bolts in two steps, following the sequence shown in Fig. 71. First, torque all the cross-bolts to 20 ft-lbs. Finally, torque all the cross-bolts to 40 ft-lbs.

17. Turn the engine on the work stand so that the front end is up.

18. Install the pistons and connecting rods by following steps 1 thru 9 under Piston and Connecting Rod Assembly Installation.

19. Position the sprockets and timing chain on the camshaft and crankshaft (Fig. 37). Be sure the timing marks on the sprockets are positioned as shown in Fig. 36.

20. Lubricate the timing chain and sprockets with engine oil.

21. Install the fuel pump eccentric (Fig. 39) and the camshaft sprocket cap screw. Torque the sprocket cap screw to specifications. Install the crankshaft front oil slinger.

22. Clean the cylinder front cover and the cylinder block gasket surfaces. Grease and install a new crankshaft front oil seal (Fig. 38).

23. Coat the gasket surface of the block and cover and the cover bolt threads with sealer. Position a new gasket on the block.

24. Install the alignment pilot tool on the cylinder front cover so that the keyway in the pilot aligns with the key in the crankshaft. Position the cover and pilot over the end of the crankshaft and against the block (Fig. 40).

25. Install the cylinder front cover bolts finger-tight. While pushing in on the pilot, torque the cover bolts to specifications. Remove the pilot.

26. Apply Lubriplate to the outer surface of the crankshaft sleeve, and install the sleeve.

27. Apply a white lead and oil mixture to the inside diameter of the crankshaft damper.

28. Line up the damper keyway with the key on the crankshaft, and install the damper on the crankshaft (Fig. 41). Install the power steering pulley on the crankshaft damper. Install the damper cap screw and washer, and torque the screw to specifications.

29. Clean the water pump gasket

surfaces and apply sealer. Position new gaskets on the pump and install the water pump, pulley, and fan as an assembly.

30. Using a new gasket, install the fuel pump.

31. Turn the engine on the work stand so that the top of the engine is up.

32. Clean the cylinder head and block gasket surfaces. On a 427 engine apply sealer to both sides of a new gasket. All other engines use a specially treated composition gasket. **Do not apply sealer to a composition gasket.** Guided by the word FRONT on the gasket, install the head gasket over the cylinder head dowels.

33. Place the cylinder head on the engine. Coat the head bolt threads with water-resistant sealer and install the bolts.

34. The cylinder head bolt tightening procedure is performed in three progressive steps. Torque the bolts in sequence (Fig. 26) to 70 ft-lbs, then to 80 ft-lbs, and finally to specifications. **After the cylinder head bolts have been torqued to specifications, the bolts should not be disturbed.**

35. Coat the mating surfaces of the exhaust manifold with a light film of graphite grease.

36. Using a new gasket, install the automatic choke air chamber cover on the right exhaust manifold. **Be sure the cover is securely fastened.**

37. Position a new gasket over the muffler inlet pipe studs of the exhaust manifolds.

38. Position the exhaust manifolds on the cylinder heads and install the retaining bolts and tab washers.

On a 427 V-8, do not install the right exhaust manifold until the engine has been installed in the car. Refer to Engine Installation.

Torque the retaining bolts to specifications, working from the center to the ends. Lock the bolts by bending one tab of the washer over a flat on the bolt.

39. Install the spark plugs.

40. Install the baffle plate in the valve push rod chamber. Position one side of the baffle plate and press the other side into place.

On an engine with hydraulic valve lifters, coat the outside of each valve lifter with engine oil to provide initial lubrication. **Do not fill the lifters with oil. The lifters will fill much faster after the engine is started, if** they are free of any oil film which may cause an oil seal between the plunger and the lifter body. Place each lifter in the bore from which it was removed.

On an engine with mechanical lifters, coat each tappet with engine oil and install them in the bores from which they were removed.

41. Clean the mating surfaces of the intake manifold, cylinder heads and cylinder block. Use a suitable solvent to remove all traces of oil.

42. Coat the intake manifold and cylinder block seal surfaces with a quick-setting seal adhesive. Apply a non-hardening sealer to the mating lines of the cylinder heads and cylinder block.

43. Position new seals on the cylinder block and new gaskets on the cylinder heads. **Be sure the seals are properly positioned during installation as the adhesive sticks to the seals immediately on contact.** Position the manifold gasket slots over the end tabs on the seals. Coat these four connections with a non-hardening sealer. Be sure the holes in the gaskets are aligned with the holes in the cylinder heads.

44. Install the eye bolts in the intake manifold and attach the engine lifting sling and carefully lower the intake manifold on the engine (Fig. 23).

45. Position the intake manifold. **After the intake manifold is in place, run a finger around the seal area to make sure the seals are in place. If seals are not in place, remove the intake manifold and position the seals.**

46. Start the water pump bypass hose on the intake manifold.

47. Be sure the holes in the manifold gaskets and manifold are in alignment. Apply a non-hardening, oil-resistant sealer to the under side of each manifold retaining bolt head. Install the manifold retaining bolts

and torque them to specifications, in sequence as shown in Fig. 25.

48. Remove the engine lifting sling and eye bolts.

49. Refer to Valve Rocker Arm Shaft Assembly Installation and install the valve rocker arm shaft assemblies by following steps 1 thru 9.

On an engine with mechanical lifters, it is necessary to perform a final (hot) valve lash adjustment after the engine is installed in the car.

50. Install the automatic choke air heat tube and air inlet tube.

51. Rotate the crankshaft damper until the No. 1 piston is on TDC of the compression stroke; then position the distributor in the block with the rotor at the No. 1 firing position and the points open. Install the hold down clamp.

52. Install the distributor cap and spark plug wire assembly. Connect the spark plug wires.

53. Install the carburetor fuel inlet line at the fuel pump, and using a new clamp, connect the line at the fuel filter.

54. Invert the engine on the work stand. Position the oil pump drive shaft into the distributor socket. With the shaft firmly seated in the distributor socket, the stop on the shaft should touch the roof of the crankcase. Remove the shaft and position the stop as necessary.

55. With the stop properly positioned, insert the oil pump drive shaft into the oil pump.

56. Prime the oil pump by filling either the inlet or outlet port with engine oil. Rotate the pump shaft to distribute the oil within the pump body.

57. Position a new gasket on the pump housing and install the pump and shaft as an assembly. **Do not attempt to force the pump into position if it will not seat readily. The drive shaft hex may be misaligned**

with the distributor shaft. To align, rotate the intermediate shaft into a new position.

58. Position a new gasket on the oil pan and place the oil pan assembly on the block. Install the retaining screws and torque them from the center outward to specifications.

59. Install the engine rear cover plate. Position the flywheel on the crankshaft and install the retaining bolts. Torque the bolts alternately to specifications.

On a flywheel for a manual-shift transmission, use tool 7563-E to locate the clutch disc. Install the pressure plate.

60. Clean the oil filter adapter gasket surfaces. Apply oil-resistant sealer to a new adapter gasket, and install the adapter assembly and gasket.

61. Clean the adapter filter recess. Coat the gasket on a new filter with oil. Place the filter in position on the adapter. Hand tighten the filter until the gasket contacts the adapter face, and advance it ½-turn.

On a car with Thermactor exhaust emission control system, install the anti-backfire valve, air manifold assembly and air supply pump. Install the air and vacuum lines and brackets.

62. Remove the engine from the work stand, and install it in the car. Install the air cleaner; then operate the engine and check for oil and coolant leaks. Check the ignition timing; adjust the engine idle speed, idle fuel mixture, accelerator cable, and anti-stall dashpot (if applicable). Connect the distributor vacuum line, except on 427 V-8.

On a car with an automatic transmission, adjust the transmission control linkage.

On an engine with mechanical valve lifters, perform a final (hot) valve lash adjustment. Install the valve rocker arm covers.

PART 8-5 SPECIFICATIONS

NOTE: All specifications are given in inches unless otherwise noted.

GENERAL ENGINE

MODEL PREFIX
240 Six	EHA
289 V-8	EGA
352 V-8	EDT
390 V-8	EES
410 V-8	EHK
427 V-8	EGB
428 V-8	EHJ

ENGINE MODELS AND PISTON DISPLACEMENT—Cubic Inches
240 Six	240
289 V-8 (2-V)	289
352 V-8 (4-V)	352
390 V-8 (2-V and 4-V)	390
410 V-8 (4-V)	410
427 High Performance V-8 (8-V)	427
428 V-8 (4-V)	428

COMPRESSION RATIO
240 Six	9.2:1
289 V-8 (2-V)	9.3:1
352 V-8 (4-V)	9.3:1
390 V-8 (2-V) Ford	9.5:1
390 V-8 (2-V) Mercury	9.5:1
390 V-8 (4-V) Ford	10.5:1
410 V-8 (4-V) Mercury	10.5:1
427 High Performance V-8 (8-V)	11.1:1
428 V-8 (4-V)	10.5:1
428 Police Interceptor V-8 (4-V)	

BRAKE HORSEPOWER @ Specified rpm
240 Six	155 @ 4200
289 V-8 (2-V)	200 @ 4400
352 V-8 (4-V)	250 @ 4400
390 V-8 (2-V) Ford	265 @ 4400
390 V-8 (2-V) Mercury (Std. Transmission)	265 @ 4400
390 V-8 (2-V) Mercury (Auto. Transmission	275 @ 4400
390 V-8 (4-V) Ford	315 @ 4600
410 V-8 (4-V) Mercury	330 @ 4600
427 High Performance V-8 (8-V)	425 @ 6000
428 V-8 (4-V)	345 @ 4600
428 Police Interceptor V-8 (4-V)	

TORQUE—Ft-lbs @ Specified rpm
240 Six	239 @ 2200
289 V-8 (2-V)	282 @ 2400
352 V-8 (4-V)	352 @ 2800
390 V-8 (2-V) Ford	401 @ 2600
390 V-8 (2-V) Mercury (Std. transmission)	397 @ 2600
390 V-8 (2-V) Mercury (Auto. transmission	405 @ 2600
390 V-8 (4-V) Ford	427 @ 2800
410 V-8 (4-V) Mercury	444 @ 2800
427 High Performance V-8 (8-V)	480 @ 3700
428 V-8 (4-V)	462 @ 2800
428 Police Interceptor V-8 (4-V)	

BORE AND STROKE
240 Six	4.00 x 3.18
289 V-8	4.00 x 2.87
352 V-8	4.00 x 3.50
390 V-8 (All)	4.05 x 3.78
410 V-8	4.05 x 3.98
427 V-8	4.23 x 3.78
428 V-8	4.13 x 3.98

COMPRESSION PRESSURE—PSI (Sea Level @ Cranking Speed)
240 Six	150-200
289 V-8	130-170
352, 390 (2-V) and 427 V-8	160-200
390 (4-V), 410 and 428 V-8	170-210
Allowable tolerance between cylinders	20 psi

GENERAL ENGINE (Continued)

TAXABLE HORSEPOWER
240	38.40
289 and 352	51.20
390 and 410	52.49
427	57.33
428	54.48

FIRING ORDER
240	1-5-3-6-2-4
All V-8's	1-5-4-2-6-3-7-8

VALVE ARRANGEMENT—Front to Rear
240	E-I-E-I-E-I-E-I-E-I-E-I
289	Right I-E-I-E-I-E-I-E
	Left E-I-E-I-E-I-E-I
352, 390, 410, 427, and 428	E-I-E-I-I-E-I-E

ENGINE IDLE RPM①
Manual-Shift Transmissions
240	500-525
With Thermactor	625-650
289, 390, 410 and 428	575-600
289, 352, 390, 410 and 428 With Thermactor	610-635
352	550-575
427	700-800

Automatic Transmissions
240	500-525
With Thermactor	525-550
289, 352, 390, 410 and 428	475-500
428 Police	550-575

①Refer to Group 10, Part 10-1, Section 2, for proper procedures in setting idle speed.

ENGINE IDLE MANIFOLD VACUUM—Minimum Inches of Mercury @ Specified Engine Neutral Idle rpm (Sea Level)
240	15
289 and 352	18
390, 410 and 428	17
428 Police	16

INITIAL IGNITION TIMING—BTDC②
Manual-Shift Transmission
240	*6°
240 and 289 With Thermactor	TDC
289	6°
390	①10°
390, 410 and 428 With Thermactor	6°
410 and 428	10°
427	8°
428 Police	12°

Automatic Transmission
240	①12°
240 and 289 With Thermactor	TDC
289	6°
352, 410 and 428	10°
390	①10°
390, 410 and 428 With Thermactor	6°
427	8°
428 Police	12°

①For altitude operation, and/or to obtain optimum engine performance and fuel economy, the initial ignition timing may be advanced 5° over the "normal" setting. No further improvement in engine performance or fuel economy will be achieved by advancing beyond this point. Advance the timing progressively until engine detonation (spark knock) is evident under actual road test acceleration. Retard the timing until the detonation (spark knock) is eliminated.

②If the individual requirements of the car and/or the use of sub-standard fuels dictate, the initial timing may have to be retarded from the recommended setting to eliminate detonation (spark knock). If retarding is necessary, it should be done progressively and not to exceed 2°BTDC.

GENERAL ENGINE (Continued)

OIL CAPACITY①	U.S. MEASURE	IMPERIAL MEASURE
240, 289, 390, 410 and 428	5 quarts	4 quarts
352 and 427	6 quarts	4¾ quarts

①Includes one U.S. quart required with oil filter replacement.

OIL PRESSURE—Hot @ 2000 rpm
240 ....35-60 psi
427 ....40-55 psi
428 Police Interceptor V-8 ....45-70 psi
Other Engines ....35-55 psi

CYLINDER HEAD

GASKET SURFACE FLATNESS
240
    0.003 inch in any 6 inches or 0.007 inch overall
All V-8 Engines
    0.003 inch in any 6 inches or 0.006 inch overall

VALVE GUIDE BORE DIAMETER—Standard
Intake and Exhaust
  240 and 289 ....0.3433-0.3443
  352, 390, 410, 427 and 428 ....0.3728-0.3735

VALVE SEAT WIDTH
Intake
  240, 289, 352 and 427 ....0.060-0.080
  390, 410 and 428 ....0.040-0.060
Exhaust
  289 ....0.060-0.080
  All Other Engines 0.070-0.090

VALVE SEAT ANGLE
Intake
  427 ....30°
  Other Engines ....45°
Exhaust
  All Engines ....45°

VALVE SEAT RUNOUT
  Maximum 240 and 289 ....0.0015
  Maximum Other Engines 0.002

ROCKER ARM STUD BORE DIAMETER
  240 ....0.3685-0.3695
  289 ....0.3680-0.3695

COMBUSTION CHAMBER VOLUME—CC
  240 ....66.00-69.00
  289 ....52.00-55.00
  352, 390, 410 and 428 ....73.10-76.10
  427 ....73.00-76.00

VALVE MECHANISM

VALVE LASH
Cold
   INTAKE AND EXHAUST
     428 Police and 427 with Mechanical Lifters 0.028
Hot
   INTAKE AND EXHAUST
     428 Police and 427 with Mechanical Lifters 0.025

VALVE CLEARANCE①
  240 and 289 ....0.082-0.152
  Other Engines 0.050-0.150
①Hydraulic valve lifters—Clearance specified is obtained at the valve step tip with the tappet collapsed.

VALVE MECHANISM (Continued)

VALVE STEM DIAMETER
Standard
  INTAKE
   240 and 289 ....0.3416-0.3423
   Other Engines 0.3711-0.3718
  EXHAUST
   240 ....0.3416-0.3423
   289 ....0.3406-0.3413
   352, 390, 410 and 428 ....0.3711-0.3718
   427 ....0.3701-0.3708
0.003 Oversize
  INTAKE
   240 and 289 ....0.3446-0.3453
   All Other Engines 0.3741-0.3748
  EXHAUST
   240 ....0.3446-0.3453
   289 ....0.3436-0.3443
   352, 390, 410 and 428 ....0.3741-0.3748
   427 ....0.3731-0.3738
0.015 Oversize
  INTAKE
   240 and 289 ....0.3566-0.3573
   All Other Engines 0.3861-0.3868
  EXHAUST
   240 ....0.3566-0.3573
   289 ....0.3556-0.3563
   352, 390, 410 and 428 ....0.3861-0.3868
   427 ....0.3851-0.3858
0.030 Oversize
  INTAKE
   240 and 289 ....0.3716-0.3723
   All Other Engines 0.4011-0.4018
  EXHAUST
   240 ....0.3716-0.3723
   289 ....0.3706-0.3713
   352, 390, 410 and 428 ....0.4011-0.4018
   427 ....0.4001-0.4008

VALVE FACE ANGLE
  427 (Intake Valve) ....29°
  All Other Intake and Exhaust ....44°

VALVE STEM TO VALVE GUIDE CLEARANCE
Intake
  240 ....0.0010-0.0027—Wear Limit 0.0047
  289 ....0.0010-0.0027—Wear Limit 0.0045
  Other Engines ....0.0010-0.0024—Wear Limit 0.0045
Exhaust
  240 ....0.0010-0.0027—Wear Limit 0.0047
  352, 390, 410 and 428 ..0.0010-0.0024—Wear Limit 0.0055
  289 ....0.002-0.0037—Wear Limit 0.0055
  427 ....0.002-0.0034—Wear Limit 0.0055

VALVE HEAD DIAMETER
Intake
  240 ....1.772-1.787
  289 ....1.662-1.677
  All Other Engines 2.022-2.037
Exhaust
  240 ....1.552-1.567
  289 ....1.442-1.457
  352, 390, 410 and 428 ....1.551-1.566
  427 ....1.645-1.660

VALVE FACE RUNOUT
Intake and Exhaust
  All Engines 0.002

VALVE MECHANISM (Continued)

VALVE SPRING FREE LENGTH—Approximate
240	1.99
289	2.09
352	2.26
390, 410 and 428	2.15
427 and 428 Police	2.06

VALVE SPRING OUT OF SQUARE—Maximum
All Engines	0.072

VALVE SPRING PRESSURE—Lbs. @ Specified Length
240	76-84 @ 1.700
	Wear Limit 68 @ 1.700
INTAKE	180.5-199.5 @ 1.325
	Wear Limit 168 @ 1.325
EXHAUST	187-207 @ 1.300
	Wear limit 162 @ 1.300
289	71-79 @ 1.780
	Wear Limit 64 @ 1.780
	161-177 @ 1.390
	Wear Limit 145 @ 1.390
352	94-104 @ 1.820
	Wear Limit 85 @ 1.820
	180-198 @ 1.420
	Wear Limit 162 @ 1.420
390, 410 and 428	80-90 @ 1.820
	Wear Limit 72 @ 1.820
	233-257 @ 1.380
	Wear Limit 210 @ 1.380
427 and 428 Police	80-90 @ 1.820
	Wear Limit 72 @ 1.820
	255-280 @ 1.320
	Wear Limit 230 @ 1.320

VALVE SPRING ASSEMBLED HEIGHT
240	1 43/64-1 47/64
289	1 3/4-1 25/32
352, 390, 410 and 428	1 13/16-1 27/32
427 and 428 Police	1 51/64-1 53/64

VALVE PUSH ROD MAXIMUM RUNOUT
289	0.015
Other Engines	0.025

VALVE TAPPET DIAMETER—Standard
All Engines	0.8740-0.8745

VALVE TAPPET TO TAPPET BORE CLEARANCE
All Engines	0.0005-0.0020—Wear Limit 0.005

HYDRAULIC VALVE LIFTER LEAK DOWN RATE
All Engines (measured at $1/16$ inch plunger travel)	5-50 Sec.

ROCKER ARM TO ROCKER ARM SHAFT CLEARANCE
352, 390, 410, 427 and 428	0.003-0.005—Wear Limit 0.006

ROCKER ARM SHAFT O.D.
352, 390, 410, 427 and 428	0.838-0.839

ROCKER ARM BORE DIAMETER
352, 390, 410, 427 and 428	0.843-0.844

ROCKER ARM LIFT RATIO
240	1.61:1
289	1.60:1
352, 390, 410 and 428	1.73:1
427	1.76:1

CAMSHAFT AND TIMING CHAIN

CAMSHAFT JOURNAL DIAMETER—Standard
240	2.0170-2.0180
352, 390, 410, 427 and 428	2.1238-2.1248
289—No. 1	2.0805-2.0815
No. 2	2.0655-2.0665
No. 3	2.0505-2.0515
No. 4	2.0355-2.0365
No. 5	2.0205-2.0215

CAMSHAFT AND TIMING CHAIN (Continued)

CAMSHAFT JOURNAL TO BEARING CLEARANCE
All Engines	0.001-0.003—Wear Limit 0.006

CAMSHAFT JOURNAL MAXIMUM OUT-OF-ROUND
289	0.0005
Other Engines	0.001

CAMSHAFT JOURNAL RUNOUT—Maximum
All Engines	0.005

TIMING CHAIN MAXIMUM DEFLECTION
All Engines (Except 240)	0.5

CAMSHAFT LOBE LIFT
Intake
240	0.233—Wear Limit 0.228
289	0.2303—Wear Limit 0.2253
352	0.232—Wear Limit 0.227
390, 410 and 428	0.2530—Wear Limit 0.2480
427 and 428 Police	0.298—Wear Limit 0.293

Exhaust
240	0.249—Wear Limit 0.244
289	0.2375—Wear Limit 0.2325
352	0.232—Wear Limit 0.227
390, 410 and 428	0.2530—Wear Limit 0.2480
427 and 428 Police	0.298—Wear Limit 0.293

CAMSHAFT END PLAY
240	0.003-0.007—Wear Limit 0.012
Other Engines	0.001-0.007—Wear Limit 0.012

CAMSHAFT BEARINGS

INSIDE DIAMETER
249	2.019-2.020
352, 390, 410, 427 and 428	2.1258-2.1268
289—No. 1	2.0825-2.0835
No. 2	2.0675-2.0685
No. 3	2.505-2.0515
No. 4	2.0375-2.0385
No. 5	2.0225-2.0235

240
No. 1 bearing is installed with the front edge 0.020-0.035 inch toward the rear from the front face of the cylinder block.

Other Engines
No. 1 bearing is installed with the front edge 0.005 to 0.020 inch toward the rear from the front face of the cylinder block.

CRANKSHAFT

MAIN BEARING JOURNAL DIAMETER
Standard
240	2.3982-2.3990
289	2.2482-2.2490
352, 390, 410, 427 and 428	2.7484-2.7492

MAIN BEARING JOURNAL RUNOUT—Maximum
All Engines	0.002—Wear Limit 0.003

CONNECTING ROD AND MAIN BEARING JOURNALS MAXIMUM OUT-OF-ROUND
All Engines	0.0004

MAIN BEARING JOURNALS MAXIMUM TAPER
All Engines	0.0003 per inch

CONNECTING ROD JOURNALS MAXIMUM TAPER
289 and 352	0.0004 per inch
All Other Engines	0.0003 per inch

CRANKSHAFT (Continued)

THRUST BEARING JOURNAL LENGTH
240 ....1.199-1.201
289 ....1.137-1.139
352, 390, 410, 427 and 428 ....1.124-1.126

MAIN BEARING JOURNAL THRUST FACE RUNOUT
All Engines 0.001

CONNECTING ROD JOURNAL DIAMETER
240 and 289 ....2.1228-2.1236
352, 390, 410, 427 and 428 ....2.4380-2.4388

CRANKSHAFT FREE END PLAY
240 and 289 ....0.004-0.008—Wear Limit 0.012
Other Engines ....0.004-0.010—Wear Limit 0.014

ASSEMBLED FLYWHEEL CLUTCH FACE MAXIMUM RUNOUT
All Engines 0.010

ASSEMBLED FLYWHEEL O.D. MAXIMUM RUNOUT
Manual Shift Transmission
240, 289 and 352 ....0.018
390, 410, 427 and 428 ....0.020

Automatic Transmission
All Engines 0.020

ASSEMBLED SPROCKET FACE RUNOUT
All Engines 0.006

MAIN BEARINGS

BEARING TO CRANKSHAFT CLEARANCE

	Desired	Allowable
240 ....0.0005-0.0015		0.0005-0.0022
289 ....0.0005-0.0015		0.0005-0.0024
352, 390, 410 and 428 ....0.0005-0.0015		0.0005-0.0025
427 ....0.0007-0.0031		0.0007-0.0031
428 Police No. 1 ....0.0008-0.0012		0.0008-0.0012
428 Police No. 2, 3, 4 and 5 ..0.0005-0.0015		0.0005-0.0025

WALL THICKNESS

	Standard	0.002 U.S.
240 ....0.0954-0.957		0.0964-0.0967
289 ....0.0957-0.0962		0.0967-0.0972
352, 390, 410 and 428 ....0.0956-0.0961		0.0966-0.0971
427 ....Coded Red		0.0953-0.0958
	Coded Blue	0.0957-0.0962
	0.002 U.S.	0.0967-0.0972

CONNECTING ROD

PISTON PIN BUSHING I.D.
Standard
240 and 289 ....0.9104-0.9112
352, 390, 410 and 428 ....0.9752-0.9755
427 ....0.9754-0.9757

PISTON PIN BUSHING OUT-OF-ROUND—Maximum
All Engines except 240 and 289 ....0.0004

CONNECTING ROD (Continued)

BEARING BORE DIAMETER
240 ....2.2750-2.2758
289 ....2.2390-2.2398
352, 390, 410 and 427 ....2.5907-2.5915
428 ....2.5907-2.5915

BEARING BORE MAXIMUM OUT-OF-ROUND AND TAPER
All Engines 0.0004

CONNECTING ROD LENGTH—Center to Center
240 ....6.7932-6.7962
289 ....5.1535-5.1565
352 ....6.538-6.542
390, 410, 427 and 428 ....6.486-6.490

CONNECTING ROD
Twist Maximum Total Difference①
All Engines 0.012
Bend Maximum Total Difference①
All Engines 0.004
①Pin Bushing and Crankshaft Bearing Bore must be parallel and in the same vertical plane within the specified total difference at ends of 8-inch long bar measured 4-inches on each side of rod.

CONNECTING ROD ASSEMBLY—Assembled to Crankshaft
Side Clearance
240 ....0.006-0.013—Wear Limit 0.018
289, 352, 390, 410 and 428 ..0.010-0.020—Wear Limit 0.023
427 ....0.014-0.024—Wear Limit 0.027

CONNECTING ROD BEARINGS

BEARING TO CRANKSHAFT CLEARANCE

	Allowable	Desired
240 ....0.0008-0.0024		0.0008-0.0015
289, 352, 390, 410 and 428 ...0.0008-0.0026		0.0008-0.0015
427 ....0.0013-0.0032		0.0013-0.0032

WALL THICKNESS

	Standard	0.002 U.S.
240 ....0.0754-0.0757		0.0762-0.0767
289 ....0.0572-0.0577		0.0582-0.0587
352, 390, 410 and 428 ....0.0755-0.0760		0.0765-0.0770
427 ....Coded Red		0.0751-0.0756
	Coded Blue	0.0755-0.0760
	0.002 U.S.	0.0765-0.0770

PISTON

PISTON DIAMETER①
Color Coded Red
240 and 289 ....3.9984-3.9990
352 ....3.9982-3.9988
390 and 410 ....4.0484-4.0490
427 ....4.2284-4.2290
428 ....4.1284-4.1290
Color Coded Blue
240 and 289 ....3.9996-4.0002
352 ....3.9994-4.0000
390 and 410 ....4.0496-4.0502
427 ....4.2296-4.2302
428 ....4.1296-4.1302
0.003 Oversize
240 and 289 ....4.0008-4.0014
352 ....4.0006-4.0012
390 and 410 ....4.0508-4.0514
427 ....4.2308-4.2314
428 ....4.1308-4.1314
①Measured at the piston pin bore centerline at 90° to the pin bore.

PISTON TO CYLINDER BORE CLEARANCE
240 and 289 ....0.0014-0.0022
352, 390, 410 and 428 ....0.0015-0.0023
427 ....0.0042-0.0066

PISTON PIN BORE DIAMETER
240 ....0.9123-0.9126
289 ....0.9124-0.9127
Other Engines 0.9752-0.9755

PISTON PIN

```
PISTON PIN DIAMETER
   Standard
      240 and 289 ........................0.9119-0.9124
      Other Engines ......................0.9750-0.9753
   0.001 Oversize
      352, 390, 410, 427 and 428 ...........0.9760-0.9763
   0.002 Oversize
      352, 390, 410, 427 and 428 ...........0.9770-0.9773

PISTON PIN LENGTH
   240 and 289 ...............................3.010-3.040
   352, 390 and 410 ..........................3.156-3.170
   427 .......................................3.202-3.212
   428 .......................................3.480-3.500

PISTON PIN TO PISTON CLEARANCE—Loose
   240 ..................0.0002-0.0004—Wear Limit 0.0007
   289 ..................0.0003-0.0005—Wear Limit 0.0008
   Other Engines ........0.0001-0.0003—Wear Limit 0.0008

PISTON PIN TO CONNECTING ROD BUSHING CLEARANCE—Loose
   352, 390, 410 and 428 ......0.0001-0.0005—Wear Limit 0.001
   427 .......................0.0003-0.0005—Wear Limit 0.001
```

PISTON RINGS

```
RING WIDTH
Compression Ring
   UPPER
      Other Engines ......................0.0770-0.0781
      427 ................................0.0774-0.0781
   LOWER
      Other Engines ......................0.0770-0.0780
      427 ................................0.0930-0.0940

SIDE CLEARANCE
Compression Ring
   UPPER
      240 and 289 .........0.0019-0.0036—Wear Limit 0.006
      427 ................0.0024-0.0041—Wear Limit 0.006
      325, 390, 410 and 428 ....0.02-0.004—Wear Limit 0.006
   LOWER
      All Engines ..............0.002-0.004—Wear Limit 0.006
Oil Ring
   All Engines ...................................Snug

RING GAP WIDTH
Compression Ring—Standard Bore—Upper and Lower
   UPPER
      240, 289 and 352 ....................0.010-0.020
      390, 410 and 427 ....................0.010-0.031
      428 ................................0.010-0.033
   BOTTOM
      All Engines .........................0.010-0.020
Oil Ring①—Standard Bore
   240 ....................................0.015-0.055
   289 ....................................0.015-0.069
   352, 390, 410 and 427 ..................0.015-0.066
   428 ....................................0.015-0.060
①Steel Rail
```

CYLINDER BLOCK

```
CYLINDER BORE DIAMETER—Standard Spreads for 8 Grades
   240, 289 and 352 ......................4.0000-4.0024
   390 and 410 ...........................4.0500-4.0524
   427 ...................................4.2328-4.2352
   428 ...................................4.1300-4.1324

CYLINDER BORE MAXIMUM OUT-OF-ROUND
   All Engines ................0.001—Wear Limit 0.005

CYLINDER BORE TAPER
   All Engines ................0.001—Wear Limit 0.010

HEAD GASKET SURFACE FLATNESS
   240 .......0.003 inch in only 6 inches or 0.007 inch overall
   Other Engines ..0.003 inch in any 6 inches or 0.006 inch overall
```

OIL PUMP—Rotor Type

```
RELIEF VALVE SPRING TENSION—Lbs. @ Specified Length
   240 ..............................20.6-22.6 @ 2.49
   289 ............................11.15-11.75 @ 1.704
   352, 390, 410 and 428 ..............9.0-9.6 @ 1.53
   427 ..............................8.0-13.0 @ 1.56

RELIEF VALVE CLEARANCE
   All Engines .........................0.0015-0.0029

DRIVE SHAFT TO HOUSING BEARING CLEARANCE
   All Engines .........................0.0015-0.0029

ROTOR ASSEMBLY END CLEARANCE
   All Engines .........................0.0011-0.0041

OUTER RACE TO HOUSING—Radial Clearance
   All Engines ..........................0.006-0.012
```

TORQUE LIMITS—Ft-Lbs

Oil the threads with light weight engine oil, except do not oil threads that require oil-resistant or water-resistant sealer.

```
MAIN BEARING CAP BOLTS
   240 and 289 ................................60-70
   352, 390, 410, 427 and 428 ................95-105

MAIN BEARING CROSS BOLTS
   427
      Step 1 ....................................20
      Step 2 ....................................40

CYLINDER HEAD BOLTS
   240
      Step 1 .................................50-55
      Step 2 .................................60-65
      Step 3 .................................70-75
   289
      Step 1 ....................................50
      Step 2 ....................................60
      Step 3 .................................65-70
   352, 390, 410 and 428
      Step 1 ....................................70
      Step 2 ....................................80
      Step 3 .................................80-90
   427
      Step 1 ....................................90
      Step 2 ...................................100
      Step 3 .................................100-110

OIL PAN TO CYLINDER BLOCK
   240 and 352 ...............................10-12
   289 ................................7-9—¼-20
                                     9-11—⁵⁄₁₆-18
   Other Engines .............................9-11
```

TORQUE LIMITS—Ft-Lbs (Continued)

OIL PAN DRAIN PLUG
All Engines 15-20

MANIFOLDS TO CYLINDER HEAD
Intake
240 20-25
289 20-22
352, 390, 410, 427 and 428 32-35
Exhaust
240 20-25
289 13-18
352, 390, 410, 427 and 428 12-18

FLYWHEEL TO CRANKSHAFT
All Engines 75-85

OIL PUMP TO CYLINDER BLOCK
240 12-15
289 23-28
Other Engines 20-25

OIL PUMP COVER PLATE
All Engines 6-9

OIL FILTER ADAPTER TO CYLINDER BLOCK
240 15-20
289 60-100
352, 390, 410, 427 and 428 12-15

OIL FILTER TO ADAPTER OR CYLINDER BLOCK
All Engines........With grease on the gasket surface, hand
tighten until gasket contacts adapter face.
Then tighten ½ turn more.

CYLINDER FRONT COVER
All Engines 12-15

WATER OUTLET HOUSING
All Engines 12-15

WATER PUMP TO CYLINDER BLOCK OR FRONT COVER
240 and 289 12-15
Other Engines 20-25

CAMSHAFT SPROCKET TO CAMSHAFT
289 40-45
352, 390, 410, 427 and 428 35-45

CAMSHAFT THRUST PLATE TO BLOCK
240 19-21
289 6-9
Other Engines 12-15

TORQUE LIMITS—Ft-Lb (Continued)

DAMPER OR PULLEY TO CRANKSHAFT
240 130-145
289, 352, 390, 410, 427 and 428 70-90

CONNECTING ROD NUTS
289 19-24
427 and 428 Police 53-58
240, 352, 390, 410 and 428 40-45

VALVE ROCKER ARM COVER
240 7-9
289 3-5
352 10-12
390, 410, 427 and 428 4-7

VALVE ROCKER SHAFT SUPPORT TO CYLINDER HEAD
352, 390, 410 and 427 40-45
428 45-50

VALVE ROCKER ARM ADJUSTING SCREW
Self-Locking—Minimum Torque to Rotate
427 and 428 Police 3

VALVE PUSH ROD CHAMBER COVER
240 ....1.0-1.5

OIL INLET TUBE TO OIL PUMP
All Engines 12-15

FUEL PUMP TO CYLINDER BLOCK OR CYLINDER FRONT COVER
240 12-15
All V-8 Engines 20-25

VALVE ROCKER ARM ADJUSTING NUT
240 and 289 ....4.5-15
With tappet on camshaft base circle turn adjusting nut
counterclockwise.

ENGINE FRONT SUPPORT
Bracket to Insulator
240 20-30
Bracket to Crossmember
All Engines 20-30
Insulator to Frame
289 35-50
240, 352, 390 and 427 45-60
Insulator to Engine
All Engines 35-50

ENGINE REAR SUPPORT
Support Retainer to Extension Housing
All Engines 40-50
Support to Frame
All Engines 20-30

TORQUE LIMITS FOR VARIOUS SIZE BOLTS

CAUTION: If any of the torque limits listed in this table disagree with any of those listed in the preceding tables, the limits listed in the preceding tables prevail.

Size (Inches)	¼-20	¼-28	⁵/₁₆-18	⁵/₁₆-24	⅜-16	⅜-24
Torque (Ft-lbs)	6-9	6-9	12-15	15-18	23-28	30-35
Size (Inches)	⁷/₁₆-14	⁷/₁₆-20	½-13	½-20	⁹/₁₆-18	⅝-18
Torque (Ft-lbs)	45-50	50-60	60-70	70-80	85-95	130-145

SPECIAL TOOLS

Description	Ford Tool No.	Former No.	Application in Engine Size			
			240 Six	289 V-8	427 V-8	Other V-8 Engines
Impact Hammer	T50T-100-A	—	X	X	X	X
Impact Slide Hammer	T59L-100-B	—	X	X	X	X
Puller Attachment Use with T50T-100-A or T59L-100-B	T58L-101-A	—	X	X	X	X
Handle Adapter	T53L-200-A	—	X	X	X	X
Engine Lifting Sling	T53L-300-A	6000-BA	X	X	X	X

SPECIAL TOOLS (Continued)

Description	Ford Tool No.	Former No.	240 Six	289 V-8	427 V-8	Other V-8 Engines
Gauge—Valve Stem to Rocker Arm Clearance	T65L-6565-A	—				X
Valve Face Runout Gauge	T64L-6507-A	—	X	X	X	X
Differential Backlash and Runout Gauge, with Universal Bracket and Dial Indicator (¼ inch range) Includes indicator TOOL-6565	TOOL-4201-C	4201-C	X	X	X	X
Engine Lifting Bracket Use with T53L-300-A	T58P-6000-A	6000-BD			X	X
Engine Lifting Hook	T65L-6000-A	—	X			
Adapter Mount To fit K. R. Wilson 1009 or Manzel 6001-TES	T64L-6001-B	—	X	X	X	X
Cylinder Front Cover Pilot	T61P-6019-B	6059-F	X	X	X	X
Valve Guide Reamer Kit	T58P-6085-B	—				X
Valve Guide Reamer Kit	T60K-6085-B	—	X	X		
Engine Lifting and Head Holding Brackets	T62F-6085-A	6005-BDA		X		
Piston Pin Remover	T52P-6135-DAD	—			X	X
Piston Pin Remover and Replacer Press	T60K-6135-B	6135-J	X	X		
Camshaft Bearings Remover and Replacer Adapters	T65L-6250-A	T52L-6261-CEE	X	X	X	X
Cylinder Head Core Plug, Cylinder Block Core Plug and Camshaft Bearing Bore Plug Replacer	T52L-6266-BGD	6266-B	X			
Camshaft Rear Bearing Bore Plug Replacer—Adapter—Use with T53L-200-A	T62F-6266-A	—		X		
Camshaft Bearing Bore Plug Replacer—Adapter—Use with T53L-208-A	T58P-6266-A	—			X	X
Crankshaft Sprocket and Crankshaft Damper Replacer	T52L-6306-AEE	3355-D		X		
Crankshaft Damper Replacer	T64T-6306-A	—	X	X	X	X
Crankshaft Damper Replacer Use with T64T-6306-A	T65L-6306-A	—	X			
Crankshaft Damper Remover	T58P-6316-B	—				X
Crankshaft Damper Remover Adapter Screw Use with T58P-6316-B	T62F-6316-B	—		X		
Crankshaft Damper Remover Adapter Screw Use with T58P-6316-B	T64T-6316-A	—	X			
Upper Main Bearing Insert Remover and Replacer	TOOL-6331	6331	X	X		
Upper Main Bearing Remover and Replacer	TOOL-6331-E	6331-E			X	X
Crankshaft Pulley Spacer Remover	T56P-6362-A	—			X	X
Solid Tappet Remover (High Performance Only 428 Police Interceptor Only)	T52T-6500-DJD	6500-D		X	X	X
Hydraulic Tappet Clip Replacer	TOOL-6500-C	6500-C	X	X		X
Hydraulic Tappet Leakdown Tester	TOOL-6500-E	6500-E	X	X		X
Hydraulic Tappet Plunger Remover and Replacer	TOOL-6500-F	6500-F	X	X		X
Valve Stem Clearance Checking Tool	TOOL-6505-E	6505-E	X			
Valve Stem Clearance Checking Tool	TOOL-6505-F	6505-F			X	X
Valve Stem Clearance Checking Tool	TOOL-6505-G	6505-G		X		
Air Adapter and Hose-Valve Holdup	TOOL-6513-ABA	6513-AB	X	X	X	X
Compressor—Tappet Bleed-Down	TOOL-6513-AC	6513-AC		X		
Valve and Clutch Spring Tester	TOOL-6513-DD	6513-DD	X	X	X	X
Valve Spring and Rocker Arm Compressor	TOOL-6513-J	6513-J			X	X
Rocker Arm Stud Kit	T62F-6A527-B	—	X	X		
Rocker Arm Stud Installer (Supplements T65F-6A527-B)	T65P-6A527-A	—	X	X		
Cam Lift and Push Rod Stroke Dial Indicator (1 inch range) use with Bracket from TOOL-4201-C	TOOL-6565	6565	X	X	X	X
Cup Shaped Adapter to TOOL-6565	TOOL-6565-AB	6565-AB	X	X	X	X
Valve Spring Compressor	T62F-6565-A	6513-HH	X	X		
Valve Stem to Rocker Arm Clearance Compressor and Gauge (Except 428 Police)	T58P-6565-A	—				X
Crankcase Ventilation System Tester (kit)		AC Spark Plug	X	X	X	X
Cylinder Block Front Cover Oil Seal Replacer Adapter Use with T53L-200-A	T58P-6700-B	6700-B	X	X	X	X
Crankshaft Rear Oil Seal Forming Tool	T58P-6701-C	6701-C			X	X
Crankshaft Rear Seal Replacer	T62F-6701-A	6701-E		X		
Crankshaft Rear Oil Seal Forming Tool	T65L-6701-A	—	X			
Clutch Disc Pilot	T58P-7563-A	—		X		
Clutch Pilot Bearing Replacer	TOOL-7600-H	7600-H		X	X	X
Clutch Pilot Bearing Replacer	T65L-7600-A	—	X			

IGNITION SYSTEM

GROUP 9

PART 9-1   GENERAL IGNITION SYSTEM SERVICE

This part covers ignition system description and operation, general ignition system diagnosis, tests, adjustments and repair operations. In addition, the cleaning and inspection procedures are covered.

For distributor removal, disassembly, assembly, installation, major repair procedures and specifications, refer to the pertinent part of this group.

The distributor identification number is stamped on the distributor housing. The basic part number for ungoverned distributors is 12127. To procure replacement parts, it is necessary to know the part No. prefix and suffix and, in some cases, the design code change (Fig. 1).

Always refer to the Master Parts Catalog for parts usage and interchangeability before replacing a distributor or a component part for a distributor.

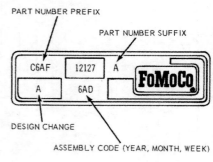

FIG. 1—Distributor Identification

B2574-A

1   DIAGNOSIS AND TESTING

GENERAL INFORMATION

CONVENTIONAL IGNITION SYSTEM

The ignition system consists of a primary (low voltage) and a second-ary (high voltage) circuit (Fig. 2).

The primary circuit consists of the:
1. Battery.
2. Ignition switch.
3. Primary circuit resistance wire.

4. Primary windings of the ignition coil.
5. Breaker points.
6. Condenser.

The secondary circuit consists of the:

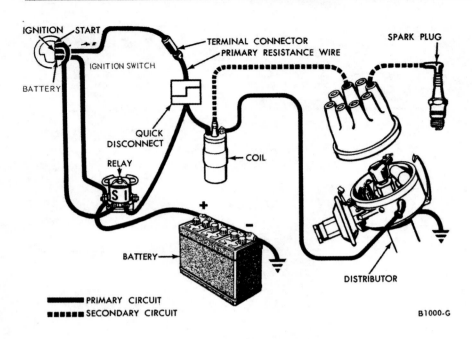

ings of the coil producing high voltage current. **High voltage current is produced each time the breaker points open.** The high voltage flows through the coil high tension lead to the distributor cap where the rotor distributes it to one of the spark plug terminals in the distributor cap. This process is repeated for every power stroke of the engine.

TRANSISTOR IGNITION SYSTEM

The permatuned transistor ignition system is available on the 1966 Fords and Mercurys. Fig. 3 shows a schematic of the transistor ignition system.

The ignition coil primary in the transistor system is designed to draw 12 amperes peak current, or approximately 5.5 amperes average current as indicated on a conventional ammeter, in order to provide high spark plug voltage at the higher engine speeds.

The transistor in the system acts as a heavy duty switch or relay. It is similar in action to a horn relay, except that it has no moving parts, and thus acts with very little time lag. The transistor is connected between the battery and the coil, and is used to make and break the coil primary circuit.

FIG. 2—Typical Conventional Ignition System Circuit

1. Secondary windings of the ignition coil.
2. Distributor rotor.
3. Distributor cap.
4. High tension wires.
5. Spark plugs.

When the breaker points are closed, the primary or low voltage current flows from the battery through the ignition switch to the primary windings in the coil, then to ground through the closed breaker points. When the breaker points open, the magnetic field built up in the primary windings of the coil moves through the secondary wind-

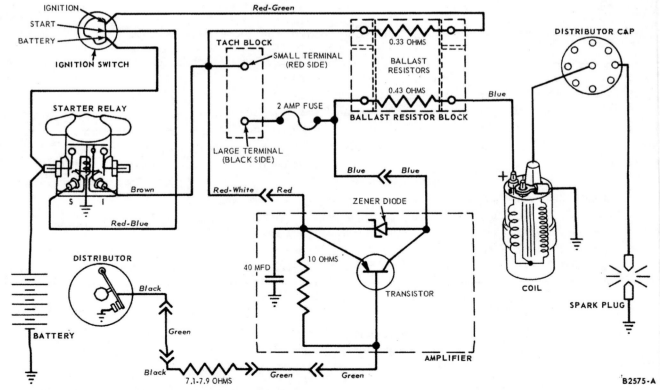

FIG. 3—Typical Transistor Ignition System Circuit

The distributor controls the transistor. The 7.1-7.9-ohm resistor, connected between the distributor and the transistor (in the wiring harness), limits the transistor control current (and distributor point current) to 0.5 ampere. The low distributor point current eliminates pitting and gives long distributor point life.

The amplifier assembly (Fig. 4) is mounted under the instrument panel to protect the parts from engine heat.

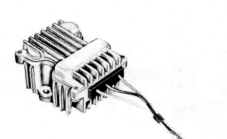

B1844-B

FIG. 4—Amplifier Assembly

A ceramic ballast resistor block and a tachometer connector block are mounted in the engine compartment.

A 2-ampere fuse between the black (large) terminal of the tach block and the coil primary circuit prevents the transistor from being damaged by the application of external devices other than normal testing equipment.

The tachometer block is used to connect a tachometer or dwell meter into the circuit. **Do not connect a tachometer or dwell meter into the circuit in any other manner, or readings will be inaccurate and damage may occur to the transistor, or change its operating characteristics.**

Connect the tachometer red lead to the tachometer block red (small) terminal and black lead to the black (large) terminal.

IGNITION SYSTEM TESTS— CONVENTIONAL TEST EQUIPMENT

CONVENTIONAL IGNITION SYSTEM

Trouble Isolation

Ignition system troubles are caused by a failure in the primary and/or the secondary circuit or incorrect ignition timing. If an engine trouble has been traced to the ignition system from the "Engine Trouble Diagnosis Guide," the trouble can be found by performing an ignition system test on a scope or by further isolating the trouble to the primary or secondary circuit as follows:

1. Disconnect the brown wire from the starter relay "I" terminal and the red and blue wire from the starter relay "S" terminal.

2. Remove the coil high tension lead from the distributor cap.

3. Turn on the ignition switch.

4. While holding the high tension lead approximately $3/16$ inch from the cylinder head or any other good ground, crank the engine by using an auxiliary starter switch between the starter relay battery and "S" terminals.

If the spark is good, the trouble lies in the secondary circuit.

If there is no spark or a weak spark, the trouble is in the primary circuit, coil to distributor high tension lead, or the coil.

Primary Circuit. A breakdown or energy loss in the primary circuit can be caused by:

1. Defective primary wiring, or loose or corroded terminals.

2. Burned, shorted, sticking or improperly adjusted breaker points.

3. A defective coil.

4. A defective condenser.

To isolate a trouble in the primary circuit, proceed as follows:

Turn the ignition switch off and remove the auxiliary starter switch from the starter relay.

Install the coil high tension lead in the distributor cap, the red and blue wire on the starter relay "S" terminal and the brown wire on the starter relay "I" terminal.

Now perform a primary circuit test.

Secondary Circuit. A breakdown or energy loss in the secondary circuit can be caused by:

1. Fouled or improperly adjusted spark plugs.

2. Defective high tension wiring.

3. High tension leakage across the coil, distributor cap or rotor resulting from an accumulation of dirt.

To isolate a trouble in the secondary circuit, proceed as follows:

Turn the ignition switch off and remove the auxiliary starter switch from the starter relay.

Install the coil high tension lead in the distributor cap, the red and blue wire on the starter relay "S" terminal and the brown wire on the starter relay "I" terminal.

Now perform a secondary circuit test.

Primary Circuit Tests

A complete test of the primary circuit consists of checking the circuit from the battery to the coil, the circuit from the coil to ground, and the starting ignition circuit.

Excessive voltage drop in the primary circuit will reduce the secondary output of the ignition coil, resulting in hard starting and poor performance.

Battery to Coil Test

1. Connect the voltmeter leads as shown in Fig. 5.

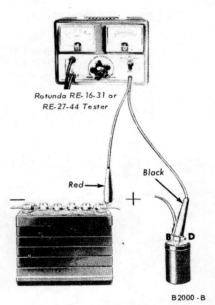

Rotunda RE-16-31 or RE-27-44 Tester

Red→   Black

B←→D

B2000-B

FIG. 5—Battery to Coil and Starting Ignition Circuit Test

2. Install a jumper wire from the distributor terminal of the coil to a good ground on the distributor housing.

3. Turn the lights and accessories off.

4. Turn the ignition switch on.

5. If the voltmeter readings is 6.9 volts or less, the primary circuit from the battery to the coil is satisfactory.

6. If the voltmeter reading is greater than 6.9 volts, check the following:

The battery and cables for loose connections or corrosion.

The primary wiring for worn insulation, broken strands, and loose or corroded terminals.

The resistance wire for defects.

The starter relay to ignition switch for defects.

Starting Ignition Circuit Test

1. Connect the voltmeter leads as shown in Fig. 5.

2. Disconnect and ground the coil to distributor high tension lead at the distributor.

3. With the ignition switch off, crank the engine by installing a jumper wire between the battery and the "S" terminal of the starter relay while observing the voltage drop.

4. If the voltage drop is 0.1 volt or less, the starting ignition circuit is satisfactory.

5. If the voltage drop is greater than 0.1 volt, clean and tighten the terminals in the circuit or replace the wiring as necessary.

Ignition Switch Test

1. Connect the voltmeter leads as shown in Fig. 6.

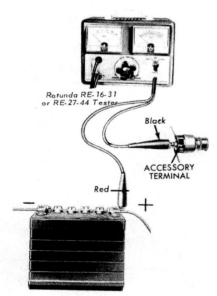

B 2002-B

FIG. 6—Ignition Switch Test

2. Install a jumper wire from the distributor terminal of the coil to a good ground on the distributor body.

3. Turn all of the accessories and lights off.

4. Turn the ignition switch on.

5. If the voltmeter reading is 0.3 volt or less, the ignition switch and the relay to switch wire are satisfactory.

6. If the voltmeter reading is greater than 0.3 volt, either the ignition switch and/or the wire are defective.

Resistance Wire Test

1. Connect the voltmeter leads as shown in Fig. 7.

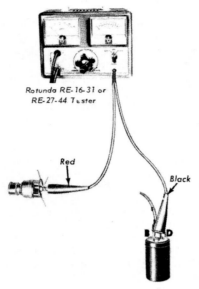

Rotunda RE-16-31 or RE-27-44 Tester

Red

Black

B 2004-B

FIG. 7—Resistance Wire Test

2. Install a jumper wire from the distributor terminal of the coil to a good ground on the distributor housing.

3. Turn all of the accessories and lights off.

4. Turn the ignition switch on.

5. If the voltmeter reading is 6.6 volts or less, the resistance wire is satisfactory.

6. If the voltmeter reading is greater than 6.6 volts, replace the resistance wire.

COIL TO GROUND TEST

1. Connect the voltmeter leads as shown in Fig. 8.

2. Close the breaker points.

3. Turn all lights and accessories off.

4. Turn the ignition switch on.

5. If the voltmeter reading is 0.1 volt or less, the primary circuit from coil to ground is satisfactory.

6. If the voltmeter reading is greater than 0.1 volt, test the voltage drop between each of the following:

The coil and the breaker point terminals of the coil to distributor primary wire.

The movable breaker point and the breaker plate.

The breaker plate and the distributor housing.

The distributor housing and engine ground.

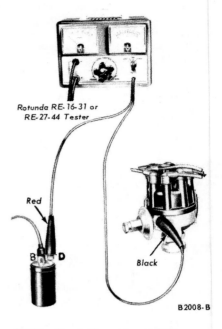

Rotunda RE-16-31 or RE-27-44 Tester

Red

Black

B 2008-B

FIG. 8—Coil to Ground Test

Breaker Points. Clean and inspect the breaker points by following the procedure under "Cleaning and Inspection" (Section 3 of this part).

The breaker point dwell can be checked with a distributor tester or a dwell meter by following the procedure under "Distributor Tests" in this section of the manual.

The breaker point resistance can be checked with a Rotunda RE-1416 distributor tester by following the procedure under "Distributor Tests" in this section of the manual.

Coil. Clean and inspect the coil by following the procedure under "Cleaning and Inspection" (Section 3 of this part).

Check the coil on a coil tester by following the manufacturers instructions.

Secondary Circuit Tests

Distributor Cap. Clean and inspect the distributor cap by following the procedure under "Cleaning and Inspection" (Section 3 of this part).

Rotor. Clean and inspect the rotor by following the procedure under "Cleaning and Inspection" (Section 3 of this part).

Secondary (High Tension) Wires. The secondary wires include the wires connecting the distributor cap to the spark plugs and the wire connecting the center terminal of the distributor cap to the center terminal of the ignition coil.

Clean and inspect the secondary wiring by following the procedure under "Cleaning and Inspection" (Section 3 of this part).

These wires are the radio resistance-type which filter out the high frequency electrical impulses that are the source of ignition noise interference. The resistance of each wire should not exceed 7,000 ohms per foot. **When checking the resistance of the wires or setting ignition timing, do not puncture the wires with a probe. The probe may cause a separation in the conductor.**

When removing the wires from the spark plugs grasp and twist the *moulded* cap, then pull the cap off the spark plug. Do not pull on the wire because the wire connection inside the cap may become separated or the insulator may be damaged.

To check the spark intensity at the spark plugs, proceed as follows:

1. Disconnect a spark plug wire. **Check the spark intensity of one wire at a time.**

2. Install a terminal adapter in the terminal of the wire to be checked. Hold the adapter approximately 3/16-inch from the exhaust manifold and crank the engine, using a remote starter switch. The spark should jump the gap regularly.

3. If the spark intensity of all the wires is satisfactory, the coil, condenser, rotor, distributor cap and the secondary wires are probably satisfactory.

If the spark is good at only some wires, check the resistance of the faulty leads.

If the spark is equal at all wires, but weak or intermittent, check the coil, distributor cap and the coil to distributor high tension wire.

Spark Plugs. Inspect, clean and gap the plugs following the instructions in Sections 2 and 3. After the proper gap is obtained, check the plugs on a testing machine. Compare the sparking efficiency of the cleaned and gapped plug with a new plug. Replace the plug if it fails to meet 70% of the new plug performance.

Test the plugs for compression leakage at the insulator seal. Apply a coating of oil to the shoulder of the plug where the insulator projects through the shell, and to the top of the plug, where the center electrode and terminal project from the insulator. Place the spark plug under pressure with the tester's high tension wire removed from the spark plug. Leakage is indicated by air bubbling through the oil. If the test indicates compression leakage, replace the

plug. If the plug is satisfactory, wipe it clean.

Ignition Timing. Incorrect ignition timing can be caused by:

1. Timing incorrectly adjusted.

2. Distributor bushing and/or shaft worn, or a bent distributor shaft.

3. Defective vacuum advance system.

4. Defective centrifugal advance system.

TRANSISTOR IGNITION SYSTEM

Do not use any other testing procedures or conventional short-cuts than those listed below, or extensive damage can result to the system.

Trouble Isolation

Ignition troubles are caused by a failure in the primary or secondary circuit, or incorrect ignition timing. Isolate the trouble as follows:

1. Remove the coil high tension lead from the distributor cap.

2. Disconnect the brown wire from the starter relay "I" terminal and the red and blue wire from the starter relay "S" terminal.

3. Turn the ignition switch on.

4. While holding the high tension lead approximately ¼ inch from a good engine ground, crank the engine by using an auxiliary starter switch between the starter relay battery and "S" terminals.

If the spark is good, the trouble lies in the secondary (high voltage) circuit. If there is no spark or a weak spark, the trouble is in the primary (low voltage) circuit.

Primary Circuit. A breakdown or energy loss in the primary circuit can be caused by:

1. Defective primary wiring.

2. Improperly adjusted, contaminated or defective distributor points.

3. Defective amplifier assembly.

The trouble can be isolated by performing a primary circuit test.

Secondary Circuit. A breakdown or energy loss in the secondary circuit can be caused by:

1. Fouled or improperly adjusted spark plugs.

2. Defective high voltage wiring.

3. High voltage leakage across the coil distributor cap or rotor.

To isolate a trouble in the secondary circuit, turn the ignition switch off, remove the auxiliary starter switch from the starter relay, install the coil high tension lead in the distributor cap, the red and blue wire to the starter relay (this goes on the

"S" terminal) and the brown wire to the starter relay (this goes on the "I" terminal) and perform a secondary circuit test.

Primary Circuit Tests

When diagnosis procedures isolate trouble to the primary circuit, make the following tests to locate the defective item. **Do not use any other procedure, conventional short-cut, or connect test equipment in any other manner than that described, or extensive damage can be caused to the transistor ignition system.** Fig. 9 shows the transistor ignition system tests in outline form.

Connect a dwell meter to the tachometer block. Connect the black lead to the black (large) terminal and the red lead to the red (small) terminal.

With the auxiliary starter switch installed and the ignition switch on as in the trouble isolation procedures, ground the coil high tension wire and crank the engine with the auxiliary starter and observe the dwell reading.

0° Dwell. A dwell reading of 0° indicates:

1. The distributor points are contaminated or are not closing.

2. An open circuit in the distributor lead to the amplifier.

To determine which item listed is causing the trouble, proceed as follows:

Disconnect the distributor lead at the bullet connector and connect a voltmeter red lead to the red (small) tach block terminal and the voltmeter black lead to the distributor lead from the distributor. **Do not connect the voltmeter to the lead from the amplifier.** Crank the engine and note the voltmeter reading.

If a steady indication of voltage is obtained, the trouble is in the distributor lead to the amplifier. Absence of any voltage indication on the voltmeter shows that there is an open circuit between the distributor lead and the breaker point ground.

0° to 45° Dwell. A dwell reading between 0° and 45° indicates:

1. The transistor and the primary circuit are functioning properly.

2. The trouble could be in the secondary circuit.

45° Dwell. A dwell reading of 45° indicates:

1. No power from the ignition switch.

2. The distributor points are closed and not opening.

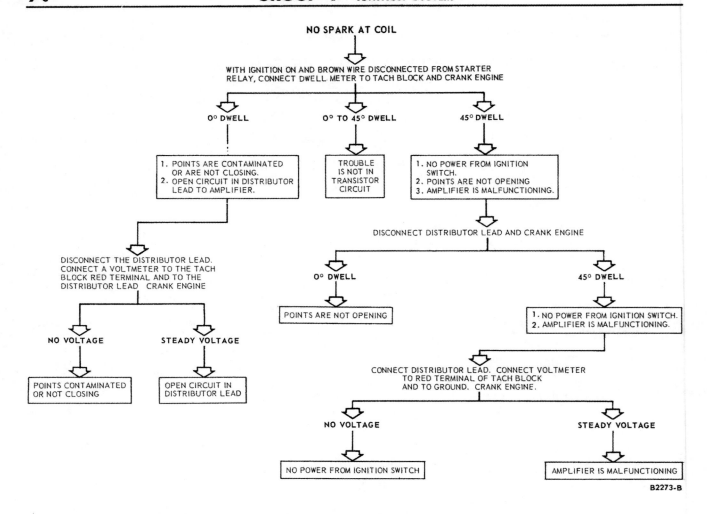

NO SPARK AT COIL

WITH IGNITION ON AND BROWN WIRE DISCONNECTED FROM STARTER RELAY, CONNECT DWELL METER TO TACH BLOCK AND CRANK ENGINE

0° DWELL | 0° TO 45° DWELL | 45° DWELL

1. POINTS ARE CONTAMINATED OR ARE NOT CLOSING.
2. OPEN CIRCUIT IN DISTRIBUTOR LEAD TO AMPLIFIER.

TROUBLE IS NOT IN TRANSISTOR CIRCUIT

1. NO POWER FROM IGNITION SWITCH.
2. POINTS ARE NOT OPENING
3. AMPLIFIER IS MALFUNCTIONING.

DISCONNECT DISTRIBUTOR LEAD AND CRANK ENGINE

DISCONNECT THE DISTRIBUTOR LEAD. CONNECT A VOLTMETER TO THE TACH BLOCK RED TERMINAL AND TO THE DISTRIBUTOR LEAD CRANK ENGINE

0° DWELL | 45° DWELL

POINTS ARE NOT OPENING

1. NO POWER FROM IGNITION SWITCH.
2. AMPLIFIER IS MALFUNCTIONING.

NO VOLTAGE | STEADY VOLTAGE

POINTS CONTAMINATED OR NOT CLOSING

OPEN CIRCUIT IN DISTRIBUTOR LEAD

CONNECT DISTRIBUTOR LEAD. CONNECT VOLTMETER TO RED TERMINAL OF TACH BLOCK AND TO GROUND. CRANK ENGINE.

NO VOLTAGE | STEADY VOLTAGE

NO POWER FROM IGNITION SWITCH

AMPLIFIER IS MALFUNCTIONING

B2273-B

FIG. 9—Transistor Ignition System Test Procedures

3. Defective amplifier assembly.

To determine which of the three items listed is causing the trouble, proceed as follows:

Disconnect the distributor lead at the bullet connector, and crank the engine. If the dwell meter indicates 0° dwell, the distributor points are not opening. If 45° dwell is indicated, the amplifier is malfunctioning or there is no power from the ignition switch.

Use a voltmeter or test light to determine if the transistor (amplifier assembly) is at fault. Connect the voltmeter to the red-green lead terminal of the ballast resistor and to ground. Crank the engine.

Absence of any voltage indication on the voltmeter shows there is an open circuit, or no power between the ignition switch and the amplifier. The ballast resistor could be defective. Replace it with a known good ballast resistor, and repeat the test.

A steady indication of voltage on the voltmeter indicates either a defective amplifier or the coil to am-

plifier lead is defective or improperly connected to the ballast resistor. Proceed as follows:

1. Disconnect the amplifier at the quick disconnect.

2. Connect an ohmmeter across the outside terminals of the amplifier side of the quick disconnect.

3. Reverse the ohmmeter leads.

If a very high resistance is obtained one way and a very low or zero resistance is obtained the other way, the amplifier is not defective. Check the coil to amplifier wiring for a loose connection or defective wiring.

After a repair has been made, run through the test again to check for any other malfunctions.

Secondary Circuit Tests

Refer to the conventional ignition system secondary circuit tests for the proper procedure.

IGNITION SYSTEM TESTS— ROTUNDA OSCILLOSCOPE TESTERS

The following is a complete step-

by-step procedure for connecting the scope, checking the ignition system primary and secondary circuits and checking the engine dynamic compression (RE-881 only).

The primary and secondary superimposed pattern checks can be performed with the engine cranking. This allows the dwell, coil and condenser to be checked if the engine will not start.

TEST CONNECTIONS—RE-27-55, AND RE-881

The test connections for the RE-27-55 tester are shown in Fig. 10 and the test connections for the RE-881 tester are shown in Fig. 11.

1. With the tester turned off, plug the power plug into a proper AC outlet.

2. Connect the green lead to the distributor terminal of the coil. **On an engine equipped with a transistor ignition, connect this green lead to the terminal on the red side (small terminal) of the tachometer block.**

3. Remove the No. 1 plug wire

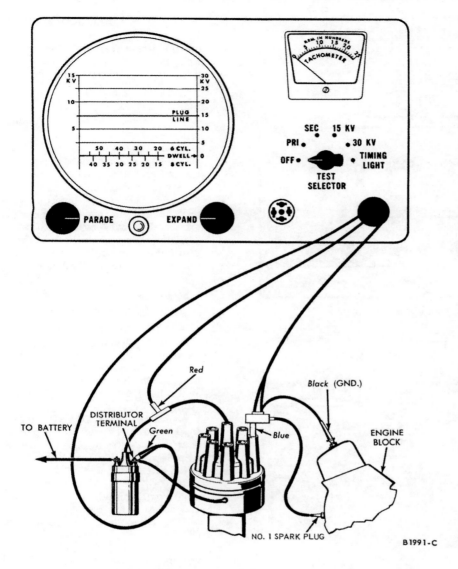

FIG. 10—Rotunda RE-27-55 Test Connections

from the distributor cap; place the blue pickup in the cap, and place the plug wire in the pickup.

4. On the RE-27-55 tester, connect the black lead to a good ground.

5. Clip the red pickup over the coil-to-distributor high tension wire.

6. If the engine timing is to be checked, plug the timing light into its socket.

The following steps pertain to the RE-881 tester only.

7. Disconnect the battery positive and negative cables at the battery.

8. Install the battery adapter on the positive battery post.

9. Connect the battery positive cable to the battery adapter.

10. Connect the shunt spade terminal and the yellow lead to the battery cable post on the battery adapter.

11. Connect the shunt to the adapter.

12. Connect the battery negative cable to the battery negative terminal and connect the black lead to the battery negative terminal.

13. Turn the ground polarity switch to the minus position. Turn the VOLTS switch to the 20-volt position.

POINT RESISTANCE TEST— RE-881 TESTER

Conventional Ignition System. This test checks the voltage drop from the distributor terminal of the coil, through the primary wire and the breaker points and to ground.

1. Remove and ground the high tension wire from the center of the distributor.

2. Depress the VOLT AMP push-

button and turn the VOLTS switch to the PT. RES. position.

3. Disconnect the brown wire ("I" terminal) and the red and blue wire ("S" terminal) at the starter relay. Install an auxiliary starter switch between the battery and "S" terminals of the starter relay. With the ignition switch ON, tap the auxiliary starter switch until the lowest voltmeter reading is obtained.

4. Depress the PT. RES. pushbutton.

5. The voltmeter pointer should read in the 12V black, PT. RES. area. If it doesn't, check for improper breaker point spring tension, a loose or defective primary or ground wire or for burned or pitted points.

6. Connect the high tension wire to the distributor.

7. Turn the ignition switch OFF and turn the VOLTS switch to the 20V position.

8. Remove the auxiliary starter switch from the starter relay and connect the brown wire and the red and blue wire to the starter relay.

IGNITION TIMING

The following procedure checks the initial ignition timing and the ignition advance mechanism.

Section 2 of this part gives the ignition timing mark locations.

Disconnect the distributor vacuum line (if so equipped). Clean and mark the desired timing mark if using the RE-27-55 tester or the TDC timing mark if using the RE-881 tester.

RE-27-55 Tester

1. Start the engine and allow it to warm up.

2. Turn the TEST SELECTOR to the TIMING LIGHT position.

3. Operate the engine at the specified idle rpm and point the timing light toward the pointer. The desired timing mark should line up with the pointer. If it doesn't, loosen the distributor hold-down bolt and rotate the distributor until the mark lines up with the pointer. Now tighten the hold-down bolt and check the timing again in case the timing changed while the distributor hold-down bolt was being tightened.

4. Connect the distributor vacuum line (if so equipped).

5. With the timing light pointed towards the timing marks, accelerate the engine to see if the timing advances.

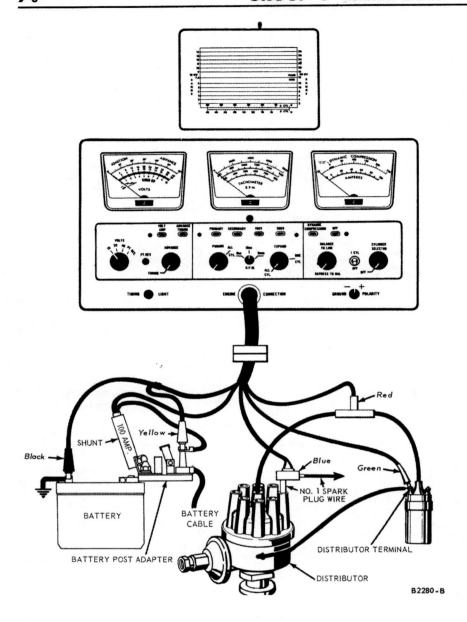

FIG. 11—Rotunda RE-881 Test Connections

RE-881 Tester

1. Turn the RPM selector to the 800 position.

2. Depress the ADVANCE TIMING pushbutton.

3. Start the engine and allow it to warm up.

4. Operate the engine at the specified idle rpm.

5. Point the timing light toward the timing pointer and turn the ADVANCE control until the TDC mark lines up with the pointer. The IGNITION ADVANCE scale of the VOLTS meter will indicate the initial timing. If the initial timing is incorrect, loosen the distributor hold-down bolt and rotate the distributor until the desired timing is obtained.

Tighten the distributor hold-down bolt and check the timing again in case the timing changed while the distributor hold-down bolt was being tightened.

6. Connect the distributor vacuum line (if so equipped).

7. Turn the RPM switch to the 8000 position and adjust the engine speed to 2000 rpm.

8. Point the timing light toward the timing pointer and turn the ADVANCE control until the TDC mark lines up with the pointer. The IGNITION ADVANCE scale of the VOLTS meter will indicate the total ignition advance for 2000 rpm. The total ignition advance should be the sum of the initial ignition timing,

twice the centrifugal advance at 1000 distributor rpm and twice the maximum vacuum advance. If it isn't, the distributor advance should be checked on a distributor tester.

PRIMARY CIRCUIT SUPERIMPOSED PATTERN

This pattern shows the individual firing patterns as seen by the primary circuit. The individual firing patterns are superimposed to give the appearance of one firing pattern.

The primary circuit superimposed pattern will indicate incorrect battery polarity, incorrect dwell angle, excessive primary circuit resistance, partially shorted condenser, uneven distributor cam lobes, bent distributor shaft or worn distributor bushings.

Procedure
RE-27-55 Tester

1. With the engine running at 1000 rpm, turn the TEST SELECTOR switch to the PRI. position.

2. Adjust the PARADE control to position the left end of the pattern at the 6-cyl 60° dwell mark on the scope screen.

3. Adjust the EXPAND control so that the right end of the pattern is at the 6-cyl 0° dwell mark on the scope screen.

RE-881 Tester

1. Turn the RPM selector to the 1600 rpm position. Start the engine and adjust it to 1000 rpm.

2. Depress the PRI. pushbutton on the console panel.

3. Adjust the PARADE control to position the left end of the pattern at the 6-cyl 60° dwell mark on the scope screen.

4. Adjust the EXPAND control so that the right end of the pattern is at the 6-cyl 0° dwell mark on the scope screen.

Results. A normal test pattern is shown in Fig. 12.

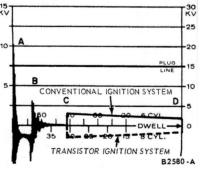

FIG. 12—Normal Primary Circuit Superimposed Pattern

Point A indicates the spark plug line which is the time when the points open. At B, the coil energy is used up sufficiently so that the plug no longer fires and only the energy stored in the breaker point condenser remains. The coil/condenser oscillation which is indicated in the pattern between B and C is completely used up at C which is the points close mark. The portion of the pattern between C and D is the points close time, which is cam angle or dwell time. At D, the points again open and the firing cycle repeats.

If points A and C are below the 0 line, the battery polarity is incorrect. This could be caused by a battery that is either installed incorrectly or improperly charged, causing a polarity reversal.

If the firing line is not below the 0 horizontal line and there are no oscillations at point C, there is an open circuit at the coil high tension tower. This could be caused by a broken wire inside the coil tower, or a broken center contact on the distributor rotor.

If the dwell time is too long or short, the breaker points are incorrectly set (the larger the gap, the smaller the dwell).

If point A is at a reduced height, and the distance to B is short or non-existent, there is a high resistance in the coil primary circuit. This could be caused by a fouled plug, defective ignition switch, or a bad wire or connection. If the scope pattern is still the same after the above ignition parts have been checked and proven satisfactory, run the 15 KV test to check for a gasket leak or a lean fuel mixture.

If point A is at a greatly reduced height and there are no oscillations at point B, the condenser is partially shorted.

If there is a variation of more than 3° at point C, the cam lobes are uneven, the distributor shaft is bent, or the distributor bushings are worn.

SECONDARY CIRCUIT SUPERIMPOSED PATTERN

This pattern shows the individual firing patterns as seen by the secondary circuit. The individual firing patterns are superimposed to give the appearance of one firing pattern.

The secondary circuit superimposed pattern will indicate arching breaker points, defective coil or coil high tension wire, excessive resistance in the distributor cap, rotor, secondary wiring or spark plugs or a

loose connection in the primary circuit.

The ignition system, as seen by the secondary circuit, can be further checkd by checking the 15 KV and 30 KV patterns.

Procedure

RE-27-55 Tester

1. With the engine running at 1000 rpm, turn the TEST SELECTOR switch to the SEC. position.

2. Adjust the PARADE control so that the left end of the pattern is at the 6-cyl 60° dwell mark on the scope screen.

3. Adjust the EXPAND control so that the right end of the pattern is at the 6-cyl 0° dwell mark on the scope screen.

RE-881 Tester. The procedure is the same as the procedure for the primary (superimposed) except, the SEC. pushbutton is depressed instead of the PRI. pushbutton.

Results. A normal test pattern is shown in Fig. 13.

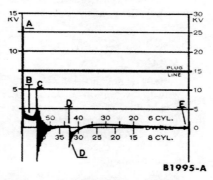

FIG. 13—Normal Secondary Circuit Superimposed Pattern

Point A is the points open time. The height of the pattern at point A indicates the high tension voltage required to overcome the spark plug gap resistance.

Point B is the plug firing line. Notice that this portion of the pattern is quite thick. Remember that this pattern is actually 6 or 8 firing patterns superimposed one on top of the other. This increase in thickness of the pattern at B is caused by slight variations in the plug gap, distributor rotor gap and slight differences in the resistance of the individual spark plug circuits.

The pattern area between points C and D shows the coil/condenser oscillations to be correct. No point bounce at D indicates correct

breaker point spring tension.

The few so-called damped oscillations appearing at D are normal and are caused by the surge of current through the coil primary winding when the breaker points first close.

This current levels off and decreases slightly toward the points open position at E as indicated by the slight downward slope of the curve at about the 8-cyl 15° mark on the cam angle scale.

To observe the coil/condenser oscillations and the damped oscillations at D in the greater detail, adjust the expand control so that the pattern area between points C and D nearly fills the screen.

If there is erratic action at points C and D, and there is a blotch above point E, the breaker points are burned or badly pitted.

If there are no condenser oscillations between C and D and no damped oscillations at point D, there are shorted primary windings in the coil.

If the line at B is sloping downward greatly from A to C (resistor plugs will cause a slight slope), there is a high resistance in the spark plug wires, distributor cap or rotor. If the line at B is sloping upward, there is a high resistance in the spark plugs. If some of the firing patterns are correct and others are sloping incorrectly, perform a 15 KV pattern check to find out which cylinder has the defective part.

If the dwell line between points D and E is not the smooth line shown, there is a loose connection in the primary circuit. Check the primary circuit for loose connections, damaged wires or a defective starter switch.

SECONDARY CIRCUIT 15 KV PATTERN

This pattern shows the individual firing patterns as seen by the secondary circuit. The individual firing patterns are paraded from left to right in order of firing order.

The secondary circuit 15 KV pattern will indicate weak breaker point spring tension, improper breaker point contact, incorrect condenser capacitance, excessive resistance in the distributor cap terminal or a spark plug wire, shorted or improperly adjusted spark plugs, partially shorted coil primary windings or an incorrect idle fuel mixture.

Procedure

RE-27-55 Tester

1. With the engine operating at 1000 rpm, turn the test selector switch to the 15 KV position.

2. Adjust the PARADE control so that the left end of the pattern is at the 6-cyl 60° dwell mark on the scope screen.

3. Adjust the EXPAND control so that the right end of the pattern is at the 6-cyl 0° dwell mark on the scope screen (Fig. 14).

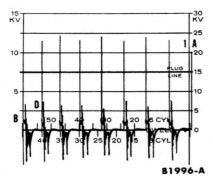

FIG. 14—Normal Secondary Circuit 15KV Pattern

RE-881 Tester

1. With the RPM selector at the 1600 position and the engine operating at 1000 rpm, depress the 15 KV pushbutton.

2. Adjust the PARADE control so that the left end of the pattern is at the 6-cyl 60° dwell mark on the scope screen.

3. Adjust the EXPAND control so that the right end of the pattern is at the 6-cyl 0° dwell mark on the scope screen (Fig. 14).

Results. A normal eight cylinder engine 15 KV pattern is shown in Fig. 14. The six cylinder pattern would have six similar images. The spark plug line (A) for the No. 1 spark plug is on the extreme right hand side of the screen. The remainder of the No. 1 firing pattern is on the left side of the screen. The remainder of the patterns are shown from left to right in their firing order.

With the exception of the No. 1 spark plug line (which should be shorter than the others), the patterns should be similar. If one of the patterns differs from the others, adjust the expand and parade controls until that pattern fills the screen in the same manner as in the secondary test (Fig. 13).

The following list of symptoms

will refer to Fig. 13.

If there is a fluctuation at point C, the points may have incorrect spring tension.

The condenser oscillation signal from C to D should diminish to a straight line at D. If it doesn't, the condenser capacitance is incorrect.

If the points open line (A) is higher than the rest and the plug firing line (B) is sloped downward at an unusually large slope, there is excessive resistance in the high tension wire to that cylinder or in the distributor cap.

If the points open line (A) is low and the firing line (B) is long and nearly straight, the spark plug is shorted out.

If the points open line (A) is low and the firing line (B) is long and wide, the spark plug gap is out of adjustment.

If there are no oscillations at points C or D, the coil primary windings are partially shorted.

If all of the points open lines (A) are at varied heights, check the idle adjustment of the carburetor (always adjust the idle mixture on the rich side).

SECONDARY CIRCUIT 30 KV PATTERN

This pattern is like the 15 KV pattern with the exception of the height. The height has been reduced to allow for checking the coil reserve.

The secondary circuit 30 KV pattern will indicate excessive resistance in the plugs, insufficient coil reserve voltage or leakage at the rotor, distributor cap or spark plug wire.

Procedure

RE-27-55 Tester

1. With the engine running at 600 rpm, turn the test selector switch to the 30 KV position.

2. Adjust the PARADE control so that the left end of the pattern is at the 6-cyl 60° dwell mark on the scope screen.

3. Adjust the EXPAND control so that the right end of the pattern is at the 6-cyl 0° dwell mark on the scope screen (Fig. 15).

RE-881 Tester

1. With the RPM selector at the 1600 position and the engine operating at 600 rpm, depress the 30 KV pushbutton.

2. Adjust the PARADE control so that the 6-cyl 60° dwell mark on the scope screen.

3. Adjust the EXPAND control so that the right end of the pattern is at the 6-cyl 0° dwell mark on the scope screen (Fig. 15).

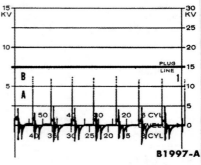

FIG. 15—Normal Secondary Circuit 30KV Pattern

Results. A normal eight cylinder engine 30 KV pattern is shown in Fig. 15. The six cylinder pattern would have six similar images. The spark plug line (A) for the No. 1 spark plug is on the extreme right hand side of the screen. The remainder of the No. 1 firing pattern is on the left side of the screen. The remainder of the patterns are shown from left to right in their firing order.

Notice the average height of the solid part of the points open line. Increase the speed of the engine and notice the height of the dotted lines. The difference is the required ignition output under load. The maximum should be between 13.5 and 15 KV.

If the maximum for one or more of the plugs is above 15 KV, check the complete circuit(s) of the plug(s) for any trouble that would cause resistance. If the maximum does not increase during the increase in engine speed, check for a fouled or improperly gaped spark plug or for very low compression.

Remove the high tension wire at the distributor cap for any plug except No. 1. Notice the change between the average points open line and the points open line of the cylinder with the high tension wire removed. This height difference is the coil reserve. The coil reserve should be at least 20 KV. If it is less than 20 KV, replace the coil.

Remove and do not ground one spark plug wire at the spark plug. If a plug firing line shows up on the scope for that cylinder, check the plug wire, rotor and distributor cap for bad insulation.

DYNAMIC COMPRESSION TEST—RE-881 TESTER

Procedure

1. Turn the RPM selector to the 1600 position and depress the DYNAMIC COMPRESSION pushbutton.

2. On a car equipped with a transistor ignition system, insert the RE-500 adapter into the test circuit. To do this, proceed as follows:

Remove the RE-881 green lead and connect it to the RE-500 green lead.

Connect the RE-500 red lead to the coil positive (+) terminal.

Connect the RE-500 black lead to the coil negative (—) terminal.

Turn the RE-500 control switch to the DYNAMIC COMPRESSION position.

3. Adjust the engine to 1500 rpm.

4. Adjust the EXPAND and PARADE controls so that the six patterns (6-cyl) or eight patterns (8-cyl) fill the scope screen dwell range.

5. Press and turn the BALANCE TO LINE control to position the needle on the DYNAMIC COMPRESSION scale at the 0 mark.

6. The pattern indication as shown at 5 in Fig. 16 will appear at point A.

7. Turn the CYLINDER SELECTOR control clockwise from its OFF position. As the switch is turned clockwise, the pattern indication will move to the right across the scope.

8. When the pattern indication passes through the firing pattern for cylinder number 5, the plug firing line will disappear (Fig. 16) and the engine will miss on the number 5 cylinder.

9. Observe the dynamic compression meter reading for the number 5 cylinder.

10. Continue to rotate the CYLINDER SELECTOR control to duplicate the above condition for each cylinder in the system except number one (last plug firing line).

11. Turn the CYLINDER SELECTOR control to its maximum clockwise rotation.

12. Turn the NO. 1 CYL. switch on.

13. Slowly turn the CYLINDER SELECTOR control counterclockwise until the pattern shown in Fig. 17 is obtained.

14. Observe the dynamic compression meter reading for the number 1 cylinder.

NOTE: If the engine rpm should change from 1500 rpm, set the speed

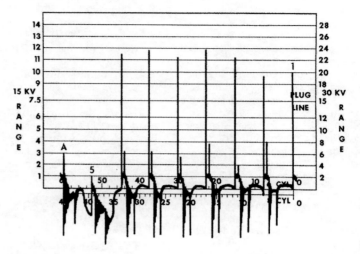

FIG. 16—Typical Dynamic Compression Test Pattern—All Except No. 1 Cylinder

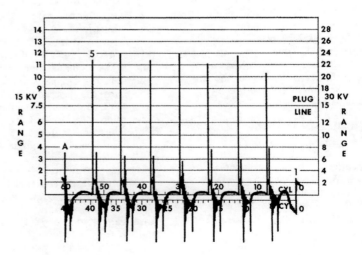

FIG. 17—Typical Dynamic Compression Test Pattern—No. 1 Cylinder

back to 1500 rpm and repeat step 5.

Results. The readings obtained are relative readings. However, if the engine compression and firing conditions are normal, the readings for all cylinders will be approximately the same.

If the readings are not within 3 divisions of each other, the cylinder(s) with the low reading(s) are not operating as efficiently as the other cylinders.

A cylinder (or cylinders) that is not operating efficiently indicates one or more of the following causes:

Low Compression caused by worn piston rings, leaking valves, leaking cylinder head gasket and/or damaged piston or rings.

Intake Vacuum Leak caused by leaking manifold, carburetor or carburetor spacer gaskets.

Malfunctioning Crankcase Ventilation Regulator Valve.

Carburetor Air Cleaner Restricted.

DISTRIBUTOR CHECKS
DISTRIBUTOR GEAR BACKLASH—LOADOMATIC DISTRIBUTOR

The distributor gear backlash can not be accurately checked on the dual advance or centrifugal advance distributor.

1. Mount a dial indicator on the distributor so that the indicator point rests on the rotor, ⅝-inch from the center.

2. Turn the rotor as far as it will go and set the indicator on zero.

3. Turn the rotor in the opposite direction and note the reading on the dial indicator. This is the backlash.

4. The backlash should be 0.003 to 0.005 inch. If the backlash is not to specifications, it indicates an incorrect number of teeth on the distributor or camshaft gear, or excessively worn gears.

DISTRIBUTOR SHAFT END PLAY

If the shaft end play is not to specifications, check the location of the gear on the shaft (6-cyl. engine distributor) or the distributor shaft collar (8-cyl. engine distributor).

6-cyl. Engine Distributor. The shaft end play can be checked with the distributor installed on the engine.

1. Mount a dial indicator on the distributor so that the indicator tip rests on the top of the distributor shaft.

2. Push the shaft down as far as it will go and set the dial indicator on zero.

3. Pull the distributor shaft upward as far as it will go and read the end play. The end play should be within specifications with the distributor removed or installed.

8-cyl. Engine Distributor

1. Remove the distributor from the engine.

2. Place the distributor in the holding tool and clamp it in a vise with the gear end up.

3. Push the distributor shaft upward as far as it will go, and check the end play with a feeler gauge placed between the collar and the distributor base. The end play should be within the specified limits.

DISTRIBUTOR TESTS—ROTUNDA RE-27-44 WELL TESTER

TEST CONNECTIONS

Conventional Ignition System Distributor

1. Connect the red lead to the distributor terminal of the coil.

2. Connect the black lead to a good ground on the engine.

Transistor Ignition System Distributor

1. Connect the red lead to the red (small) tach block terminal.

2. Connect the black lead to the black (large) tach block terminal.

DWELL ANGLE CHECK

1. Connect the tester.

2. Turn the test control knob to the set position.

3. Adjust the set control knob until the needle on the dwell meter lines up with the set line.

4. Start the engine and let it idle.

5. Turn the test control knob to the 8 CYL position for eight cylinder engines or to the 6 CYL position for 6 cylinder engines.

6. Read the dwell angle on the dwell meter and compare the reading to specifications.

7. Turn off the engine.

8. If the dwell angle was below the specified amount, the breaker point gap is too large. If the dwell angle was above the specified amount, the breaker point gap is too small.

On dual point distributors, the gaps of both breaker point assemblies should be the same.

If the dwell is to specifications,

turn the test selector knob to the OFF position and disconnect the tester leads.

DWELL ANGLE ADJUSTMENT

If the dwell angle is not within specifications, proceed as follows:

1. Remove the coil high tension lead from the distributor and ground it.

2. Remove the distributor cap and place it out of the way.

3. Disconnect the brown wire ("I" terminal) and the red and blue wire ("S" terminal) from the starter relay.

4. Loosen the breaker point assembly retaining screw near the breaker point contacts.

5. With the ignition on, crank the engine with an auxiliary starter switch connected between the battery and "S" terminals of the starter relay and adjust the gap to specifications.

6. Release the auxiliary starter switch and tighten the breaker point assembly retaining screw.

7. Since the adjustment may have changed when the retaining screw was tightened, crank the engine again with the auxiliary starter switch and check the dwell.

On dual-point distributors, when the combined dwell has been set to specifications, the individual dwell settings should be checked. To check the individual dwell settings, block one set of points open with a piece of insulating material and check the dwell of the other set. The individual dwell settings should be the same.

DISTRIBUTOR TESTS—ROTUNDA RE-236 DISTRIBUTOR TESTER

MOUNTING DISTRIBUTOR

1. Adjust the distributor support arm in relation to the distributor shaft length.

2. Set the distributor in the support arm and enter the lower end of the distributor shaft in the Syncrograph chuck.

3. Tighten the chuck on the distributor shaft, using the wrench located near the support arm column.

4. Align the distributor shaft by shifting the support arm and distributor, and tighten the clamp screw.

5. Clamp the distributor securely in the distributor support arm clamp so that it will not turn in its mounting.

6. Connect the Synchrograph test lead to the primary or distributor-

transistor lead wire of the distributor. **Since the transistor ignition distributor does not have a condenser, it will be necessary to install one in the circuit of the tester (Fig. 18).**

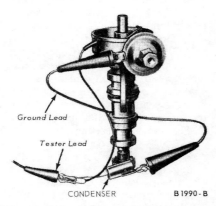

FIG. 18—Testing Transistor Ignition System Distributors

MECHANICAL OPERATIONS

1. Turn the OFF, SET, CAM, SYNC. switch to the SET position.

2. Adjust the SET TACH control so that tachometer pointer is on the SET line.

3. Turn the OFF, SET, CAM, SYNC. switch to the SYNC. position.

4. Turn the MOTOR switch to the LEFT for 8 cylinder cars or to the RIGHT for 6 cylinder cars.

5. Adjust the speed control to vary the distributor speed between 400 and 4000 engine rpm, or at the maximum speed of the engine on which the distributor is used. Erratic or thin faint flashes of light preceding the regular flashes as the speed of rotation is increased can be due to weak breaker arm spring tension or binding of the breaker arm on the pivot pin.

6. Operate the distributor at approximately 2500 engine rpm and move the protractor scale so that the zero degree mark on the scale is opposite one of the neon flashes. The balance of all the flashes should come within 1°, plus or minus, evenly around the protractor scale. A variation larger than 1° or erratic or wandering flashes may be caused by a worn cam or distributor shaft or a bent distributor shaft.

DWELL ANGLE

Single Point Distributors

1. Turn the OFF, SET, CAM, SYNC. switch to the CAM position. Operate the distributor at about 1000 rpm.

2. Adjust the breaker point gap until the cam angle is to specifications.

Dual Point Distributors

1. Turn the OFF, SET, CAM, SYNC. switch to the CAM position. Operate the distributor at about 1000 rpm.

2. Adjust the breaker points until the combined dwell is to specifications and the individual dwell settings are the same.

The individual dwell settings are checked by isolating one set of points from the circuit. This is done by placing a piece of insulating material between the contacts.

BREAKER PLATE WEAR

A worn breaker plate on the loadomatic or dual advance distributors will cause the breaker point gap and contact dwell to change as engine speed and load conditions are varied.

On the loadomatic distributor, there should not be over a 3° variation in dwell between engine idle speed and 2500 rpm. If the contact dwell changes more than 3°, the plate and bushing should be replaced.

On the dual advance distributor, adjust the test set to 0° advance, 0 inches vacuum, and 1000 rpm. Adjust the dwell angle to 26°. Apply vacuum to the distributor diaphragm and increase it very slowly while observing the indicated dwell angle. The maximum dwell angle variation should not exceed 6° when going from zero to maximum vacuum at constant rpm. If the dwell angle variation exceeds this limit, there is excessive wear at the stationary subplate pin or the diaphragm rod is bent or distorted.

DISTRIBUTOR SPARK ADVANCE

The spark advance is checked to determine if the ignition timing advances in proper relation to engine speed and load.

Loadomatic Distributor

1. Check the breaker point contact dwell. If the contact dwell is not within specifications, adjust the breaker points.

2. Check the breaker arm spring tension. Adjust it if necessary.

3. Adjust the test set to 0° advance, 0 inch vacuum and the initial rpm setting listed in the specifications.

4. Check the operation of the vacuum advance at the lowest and highest vacuum and rpm settings given in the specifications.

If the spark advance is not within the limits under low vacuum, the primary spring adjustment is at fault. If the spark advance is not within the limits under high vacuum, the secondary spring adjustment is at fault.

To adjust the spark advance, release the tension on the retard springs by turning the adjusting posts as required (Fig. 19). Adjust the primary spring (spring closest to the vacuum chamber) first, for the low vacuum settings. Adjust the secondary spring last, for the high vacuum settings. As a final check, check the advance throughout the entire range.

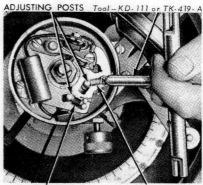

FIG. 19—Spark Advance Adjustment

If it is impossible to adjust both springs to give the correct spark advance throughout the range, one or both springs should be replaced and the spark advance readjusted. If the advance characteristics still cannot be brought within specifications, check the diaphragm assembly as follows:

Adjust the vacuum pressure of a distributor tester to its maximum position. Hold your hand over the end of the tester's vacuum hose and note the maximum reading obtained. **Do not exceed 25 inches Hg.**

If the maximum reading is 25 inches Hg or less, connect the tester's vacuum line to the vacuum fitting on the diaphragm **without changing any of the adjustments.** The maximum gauge reading should not be less than it was above. If it is less, the diaphragm is leaking and should be replaced.

Dual Advance Distributor

1. Check the contact dwell. If the contact dwell is not within specifications, adjust the breaker points.

2. Check the breaker arm spring tension and adjust it, if necessary.

The dual advance distributor has two independently operated spark advance systems. Each system is adjusted separately. **Adjust the centrifugal advance before adjusting the vacuum advance.**

Centrifugal Advance

1. Operate the distributor in the direction of rotation and adjust the speed to the initial rpm setting listed in the specifications. Move the protractor scale so that one of the flashes lines up with the zero degree mark.

2. Slowly increase the rpm to the setting specified for the first advance reading listed in the specifications. If the correct advance is not indicated at this rpm, stop the distributor and bend one spring adjustment bracket to change its tension (Fig. 20). Bend the adjustment bracket away from the distributor shaft to decrease advance (increase spring tension) and toward the shaft to increase advance (decrease spring tension). After the adjustment is made, identify the bracket.

3. After an adjustment has been made to one spring, check the minimum advance point again.

4. Operate the distributor at the specified rpm to give an advance just below the maximum. If this advance is not to specifications, stop the distributor and bend the other spring bracket to give the correct advance.

5. Check the advance at all rpm settings listed in the specifications. Operate the distributor both up and down the rpm range.

Vacuum Advance

1. Connect the test set vacuum line to the fitting on the diaphragm.

2. Set the test set at 0° advance, 0 vacuum, and at 1000 rpm.

3. Check the advance at the first vacuum setting given in the specifications.

4. If the advance is incorrect, change the calibration washers between the vacuum chamber spring and nut (Fig. 21). After installing or removing the washers, position the gasket in place and tighten the nut. **The addition of a washer will decrease advance and the removal of a washer will increase advance.**

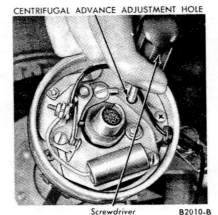

CENTRIFUGAL ADVANCE ADJUSTMENT HOLE

Screwdriver   B2010-B

FIG. 20—Centrifugal Advance Adjustment

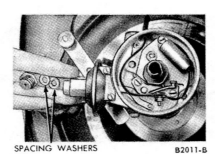

SPACING WASHERS   B2011-B

FIG. 21—Vacuum Advance Adjustment

5. After one vacuum setting has been adjusted, the others should be checked. **Do not change the original rpm setting when going to a different vacuum setting.** If the other settings are not within limits, there is incorrect spring tension, leakage in the vacuum chamber and/or line, or the wrong fibre stop has been installed in the vacuum chamber of the diaphragm housing.

To check the diaphragm for leakage:

Remove the vacuum line from the distributor. Adjust the vacuum pressure of a distributor tester to its maximum position. Hold your hand over the end of the tester's vacuum hose and note the maximum reading obtained. **Do not exceed 25 inches Hg.**

If the maximum reading is 25 inches Hg or less, connect the tester's vacuum line to the vacuum fitting on the diaphragm **without changing any of the adjustments.** The maximum gauge reading should not be less than it was above. If it is less, the diaphragm is leaking and should be replaced.

Centrifugal Advance Distributor

1. On a high performance centrifugal advance distributor, check the gap of the breaker point assembly(ies) or the dwell (combined dwell on dual points).

2. Check the breaker arm spring tension and adjust it if necessary.

3. Turn the OFF, SET, CAM, SYNC, switch to SYNC. position.

4. Operate the distributor in the direction of rotation and adjust the speed to the initial rpm setting listed in the specifications. Move the protractor scale so that one of the flashes lines up with the zero degree mark.

5. Slowly increase the rpm to the setting specified for the first advance reading listed in the specifications.

If the correct advance is not indicated at this rpm, stop the distributor and bend one spring adjustment bracket to change its tension (Fig. 22). **Bend the adjustment bracket away from the distributor shaft to decrease advance (increase spring tension) and toward the shaft to increase advance (decrease spring tension).** After the adjustment is made, identify the bracket.

6. After an adjustment has been made to one spring, check the mini-

CENTRIFUGAL ADVANCE ADJUSTMENT HOLE

Screwdriver   B2326-B

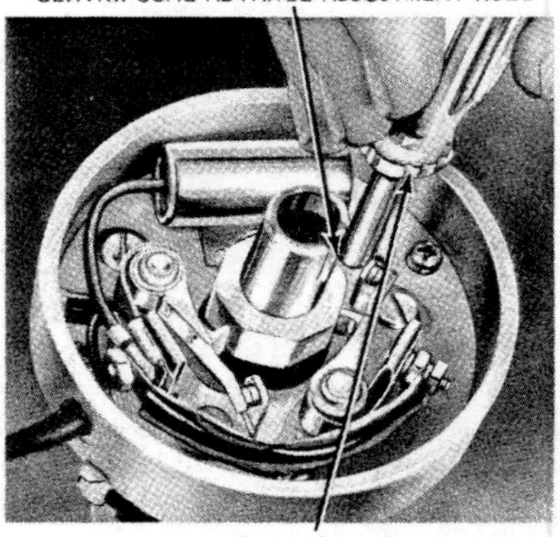

FIG. 22—Centrifugal Advance Distributor Advance Adjustment

mum advance point again.

7. Operate the distributor at the specified rpm to give an advance just below the maximum. If this advance is not to specifications, stop the distributor and bend the other spring bracket to give the correct advance.

8. *Check the advance at all rpm settings listed in the specifications.* Operate the distributor both up and down the rpm range.

Lack of synchronization, excessive

cam wear, worn bearings, or weak breaker arm spring tension causing contact point chatter are all disclosed by uneven or intermittent flashes around the protractor scale.

DISTRIBUTOR TESTS— ROTUNDA RE-1416 DISTRIBUTOR TESTER

MOUNTING DISTRIBUTOR

1. Clamp the distributor securely in the distributor support arm clamp so that it will not turn in its mounting.

2. Loosen the hand-operated locking screw on the side of the distributor support arm, and adjust the support arm column up or down by turning the crank on the knob at the top of the column until the distributor shaft or adapter shaft can be securely fastened in the driving chuck.

3. Securely tighten the drive chuck to the distributor drive shaft by means of the chuck key, attached by a chain to the Syncrograph.

4. Rotate the drive chuck by hand to make sure the distributor shaft turns freely and then tighten the locking screw on the distributor support arm.

5. Connect the Syncrograph test lead to the primary or distributor-transistor lead wire of the distributor. Since the transistor ignition distributor does not have a condenser, it will be necessary to install one in the circuit of the tester (Fig. 18).

BREAKER POINT RESISTANCE

1. Turn the test selector to POINT RES. position.

2. Revolve the chuck by hand until the distributor breaker points are closed.

3. The meter pointer on the cam angle meter should read in the OK zone at the left side of the meter scale. If the meter pointer does not fall in the OK zone, there is excessive resistance caused by a faulty contact across the distributor points, a faulty primary lead, or a poorly grounded base plate. A faulty contact across the distributor points indicates improper spring tension or burned or pitted points.

INSULATION AND LEAKAGE

1. Turn the test selector to the cam angle position and revolve the chuck by hand until the distributor breaker contacts are open.

2. The cam angle meter should show a zero reading. If a zero read-ing is not obtained, a short circuit to ground exists.

A short could be caused by poor primary or distributor-transistor lead wire insulation, a shorted condenser, or a short between the breaker arm and breaker plate.

MECHANICAL OPERATION

1. Turn the test selector to the SYNCHRO. position and check to make sure the drive chuck is securely tightened on the distributor shaft.

2. Turn the motor control switch to the left for an eight cylinder car or to the right for a six cylinder car.

If it is necessary to reverse the rotation of the drive motor, turn the motor control switch to the OFF position and allow the chuck to come to a complete stop before reversing the switch.

3. Adjust the rpm control to vary the distributor speed between 400 and 4000 engine rpm or at the maximum speed of the engine on which the distributor is used. Erratic or thin faint flashes of light preceding the regular flashes as the speed of rotation is increased can be due to weak breaker arm spring tension or binding of the breaker arm on the pivot pin.

4. Operate the distributor at approximately 2500 engine rpm.

5. Move the protractor scale with the adjustment control so that the zero degree mark on the scale is opposite one of the neon flashes. The balance of all the flashes should come within 1°, plus or minus, evenly around the protractor scale. A variation larger than 1° or erratic or wandering flashes may be caused by a worn cam or distributor shaft or a bent distributor shaft.

DWELL ANGLE

Single Point Distributor

1. Turn the cylinder selector to the figure corresponding to the number of lobes on the cam of the distributor being tested.

2. Turn the test selector switch to the cam angle position and operate the distributor at approximately 1000 engine rpm.

3. Adjust the distributor breaker point gap to the dwell angle shown in the specifications.

Dual Point Distributor

1. Follow steps 1 and 2 under "Single Point Distributor."

2. Adjust the breaker points until the combined dwell is to specifica-tions and the individual dwell settings are the same.

The individual dwell settings are checked by isolating one set of points from the circuit. This is done by placing a piece of insulating material between the contacts.

BREAKER PLATE WEAR

A worn breaker plate on the loadomatic or dual advance distributors will cause the breaker point dwell to change as engine speed and load conditions are varied.

On the loadomatic distributor there should not be over a 3° variation in dwell between engine idle speed and 2500 rpm. If the contact dwell changes more than 3°, the plate bushing should be replaced.

On the dual advance distributor adjust the test set to 0° advance, 0 inches vacuum, and 1000 rpm. Adjust the dwell angle to 26°. Apply vacuum to the distributor diaphragm and increase it very slowly while observing the indicated dwell angle. The maximum dwell angle variation should not exceed 6° when going from zero to maximum vacuum at constant rpm. If the dwell angle variation exceeds this limit, there is excessive wear at the stationary sub-plate pin or the diaphragm rod is bent or distorted.

DISTRIBUTOR SPARK ADVANCE

The spark advance is checked to determine if the ignition timing advances in proper relation to engine speed and load.

Loadomatic Distributor

1. Check the breaker point contact dwell. If the contact dwell is not within specifications, adjust the breaker points.

2. Check the breaker arm spring tension. Adjust if necessary.

Attach the vacuum adapter fitting to the vacuum unit and attach the vacuum hose between the distributor vacuum control and the vacuum outlet located at the upper right of the front panel. Check the zero setting of the vacuum gauge and, if necessary, adjust the small knob at the lower edge of the dial rim so that the vacuum gauge hand rests on zero.

Turn the vacuum supply switch to the ON position.

3. Adjust the test set to 0° advance, 0 inch vacuum and the initial

rpm setting listed in the specifications.

4. Check the operation of the vacuum advance at the lowest and highest vacuum and rpm settings given in the specifications.

If the spark advance is not within the limits under low vacuum, the primary spring adjustment is at fault. If the spark advance is not within the limits under high vacuum, the secondary spring adjustment is at fault.

To adjust the spark advance, release the tension on the retard springs by turning the adjusting posts as required (Fig. 19). Adjust the primary spring (spring closest to the vacuum chamber) first, for the low vacuum settings. Adjust the secondary spring last, for the high vacuum settings. As a final check, check the advance throughout the entire range.

If it is impossible to adjust both springs to give the correct spark advance throughout the range, one or both springs should be replaced and the spark advance readjusted. If the advance characteristics still cannot be brought within specifications, check the diaphragm assembly as follows:

Adjust the vacuum pressure of a distributor tester to its maximum position. Hold your hand over the end of the tester's vacuum hose and note the maximum reading obtained. **Do not exceed 25 inches Hg.**

If the maximum reading is 25 inches Hg or less, connect the tester's vacuum line to the vacuum fitting on the diaphragm **without changing any of the adjustments.** The maximum gauge reading should not be less than it was above. If it is less, the diaphragm is leaking and should be replaced.

Dual Advance Distributor

1. Check the contact dwell. If the contact dwell is not within specifications, adjust the breaker points.

2. Check the breaker arm spring tension and adjust it if necessary.

The dual advance distributor has two independently operated spark advance systems. Each system is adjusted separately. **Adjust the centrifugal advance before adjusting the vacuum advance.**

Centrifugal Advance

1. Operate the distributor in the direction of rotation and adjust the speed to the initial rpm setting listed in the specifications. Move the protractor scale so that one of the flashes lines up with the zero degree mark.

2. Slowly increase the rpm to the setting specified for the first advance reading listed in the specifications.

If the correct advance is not indicated at this rpm, stop the distributor and bend one spring adjustment bracket to change its tension (Fig. 20). **Bend the adjustment bracket away from the distributor shaft to decrease advance (increase spring tension) and toward the shaft to increase advance (decrease spring tension).** After the adjustment is made, identify the bracket.

3. After an adjustment has been made to one spring, check the minimum advance point again.

4. Operate the distributor at the specified rpm to give an advance just below the maximum. If this advance is not to specifications, stop the distributor and bend the other spring bracket to give the correct advance.

5. Check the advance at all rpm settings listed in the specifications. Operate the distributor both up and down the rpm range.

Vacuum Advance

1. Connect the test set vacuum line to the fitting on the diaphragm and turn the vacuum supply switch on.

2. Set the test set to 0° advance, 0 vacuum, and at 1000 rpm.

3. Check the advance at the first vacuum setting given in the specifications.

4. If the advance is incorrect, change the calibration washers between the vacuum chamber spring and nut (Fig. 21). After installing or removing the washers, position the gasket in place and tighten the nut. **The addition of a washer will decrease advance and the removal of a washer will increase advance.**

5. After one vacuum setting has been adjusted, the others should be checked. **Do not change the original rpm setting when going to a different vacuum setting.** If the other settings are not within limits, it indicates incorrect spring tension, leakage in the vacuum diaphragm and/or line, or the wrong fiber stop has been installed in the vacuum chamber of the diaphragm housing.

To check the diaphragm for leakage:

Remove the vacuum line from the distributor. Adjust the vacuum pressure of a distributor tester to its maximum position. Hold your hand

over the end of the tester's vacuum hose and note the maximum reading obtained. **Do not exceed 25 inches Hg.**

If the maximum reading is 25 inches Hg or less, connect the tester's vacuum line to the vacuum fitting on the diaphragm **without changing any of the adjustments.** The maximum gauge reading should not be less than it was above. If it is less, the diaphragm is leaking and should be replaced.

Centrifugal Advance Distributor

1. On a high performance centrifugal advance distributor, check the dwell (combined dwell on dual points). If it is not within specifications, adjust the gap.

2. Check the breaker arm spring tension and adjust it if necessary.

3. Turn the test selector to the SYNCRO. position.

4. Operate the distributor in the direction of rotation (counterclockwise) and adjust the speed to the initial rpm setting listed in the specifications. Move the protractor scale so that one of the flashes lines up with the zero degree mark.

5. Slowly increase the rpm to the setting specified for the first advance reading listed in the specifications.

If the correct advance is not indicated at this rpm, stop the distributor and bend one spring adjustment bracket to change its tension (Fig. 22). **Bend the adjustment bracket away from the distributor shaft to decrease advance (increase spring tension) and toward the shaft to increase advance (decrease spring tension).** After the adjustment is made, identify the bracket.

6. After an adjustment has been made to one spring, check the minimum advance point again.

7. Operate the distributor at the specified rpm to give an advance just below the maximum. If the advance is not to specifications, stop the distributor and bend the other spring bracket to give the correct advance.

8. Check the advance at all rpm settings listed in the specifications. Operate the distributor both up and down the rpm range.

Lack of synchronization, excessive cam wear, worn bearings, or weak breaker arm spring tension causing contact point chatter are all disclosed by uneven or intermittent flashes around the protractor scale.

2 COMMON ADJUSTMENTS AND REPAIRS

BREAKER POINTS AND CONDENSER

REPLACEMENT

Loadomatic Distributors

Removal

1. Remove the distributor cap and rotor.

2. Disconnect the condenser and primary lead wires from the breaker point assembly.

3. Remove the breaker point assembly and condenser retaining screws and lift the breaker point assembly and condenser out of the distributor.

Installation

1. Place the breaker point assembly and condenser in position on the breaker plate and install the screws. Be sure that the ground wire is under the breaker point assembly screw nearest the breaker point contacts. Align and adjust the breaker points.

2. Connect the primary and condenser wires to the breaker point assembly.

3. Install the rotor and distributor cap.

Dual Advance Distributors— Conventional Ignition System

Removal

1. Remove the distributor cap and the rotor.

2. Disconnect the primary and the condenser wires from the breaker point assembly.

3. Remove the breaker point assembly and condenser retaining screws. Lift the breaker point assembly and condenser out of the distributor.

Installation

1. Place the breaker point assembly and the condenser in position and install the retaining screws. Be sure to place the ground wire under the breaker point assembly screw farthest from the breaker point contacts on an eight cylinder engine distributor or under the condenser retaining screw on a six cylinder engine distributor.

2. Align and adjust the breaker point assembly.

3. Connect the primary and condenser wires to the breaker point assembly.

4. Install the rotor and the distributor cap.

Dual Advance Distributor— Transistor Ignition System

Removal

1. Remove the distributor cap, the rotor, and the dust cover.

2. Disconnect the distributor-transistor wire from the breaker point assembly.

3. Remove the retaining screws from the breaker point assembly and lift the breaker point assembly out of the distributor.

Installation

1. Place the breaker point assembly in position and install the retaining screws. Be sure to place the ground wire under the breaker point assembly screw farthest from the breaker point contacts.

2. Align and adjust the breaker point assembly.

3. Connect the distributor-transistor wire to the breaker point assembly.

4. Install the dust cover, the rotor, and the distributor cap.

Centrifugal Advance Distributor—Conventional Ignition System

Removal

1. Remove the distributor cap and the rotor.

2. Disconnect the primary lead, the jumper strap, and the condenser lead from the breaker point assemblies.

3. Remove the retaining screws from the breaker point assemblies and the condenser. Lift the breaker point assemblies and the condenser out of the distributor.

Installation

1. Place the breaker point assemblies and the condenser in position and install the retaining screws.

2. Align and adjust the breaker point assemblies.

3. Connect the primary lead, the jumper strap, and the condenser lead to the breaker point assemblies.

4. Install the rotor and the distributor cap.

Centrifugal Advance Distributor—Transistor Ignition System

The replacement procedure is the same as the dual advance distributor with a transistor ignition system.

BREAKER POINT ALIGNMENT

The vented-type breaker points must be accurately aligned and strike squarely in order to realize the full advantages provided by this design and assure normal breaker point life. Any misalignment of the breaker point surfaces will cause premature wear, overheating and pitting.

1. Turn the cam so that the breaker points are closed and check the alignment of the points (Fig. 23).

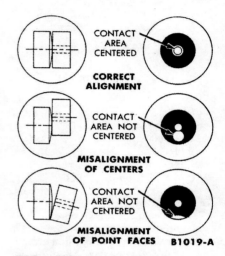

FIG. 23—Breaker Point Alignment

If the distributor is in the engine, close the points by proceeding as follows:

Disconnect the brown wire and the red and blue wire from the starter relay and, with the ignition switch off, crank the engine by using an auxiliary starter switch between the "S" and the battery terminals of the starter relay.

2. Align the breaker points to make full face contact by bending the stationary breaker point bracket (Fig. 24.) **Do not bend the breaker arm.**

3. After the breaker points have been properly aligned, adjust the breaker point gap or dwell.

BREAKER POINT GAP ADJUSTMENT

A scope, a dwell meter, or a feeler gauge can be used to check the gap of new breaker points.

A scope or a dwell meter can be used to check the gap of used breaker points. Due to the roughness of used points, it is not advisable to use a feeler gauge to check the gap.

To check and adjust the breaker points with a feeler gauge:

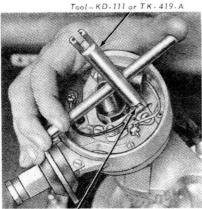

Tool—KD-111 or TK-419-A

BEND STATIONARY BRACKET   B2012-C

FIG. 24—Aligning Breaker Points

1. Check and adjust the breaker point alignment.

2. Rotate the distributor until the rubbing block rests on the peak of a cam lobe.

If the distributor is in the engine, place the rubbing block on the peak of the cam by proceeding as follows:

Disconnect the brown wire and the red and blue wire from the starter relay and, with the ignition switch off, crank the engine by using an auxiliary starter switch between the "S" and battery terminals of the starter relay.

Insert the correct blade of a clean feeler gauge between the breaker points (Fig. 25).

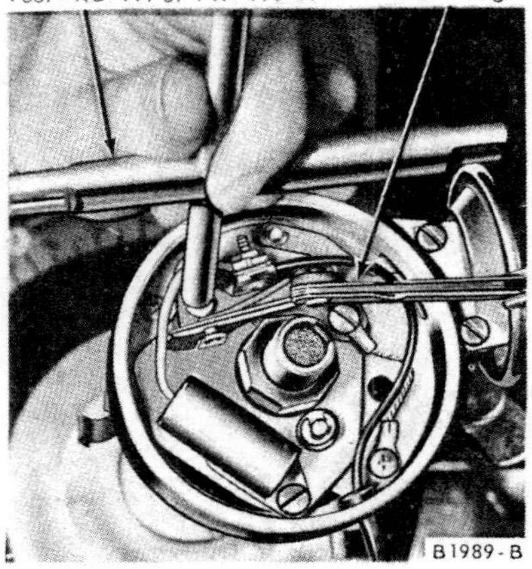

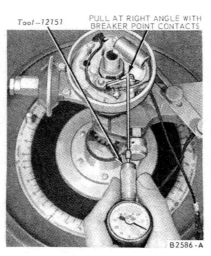

Tool—KD-111 or TK-419-A   Feeler Gauge

B1989-B

FIG. 25—Adjusting New Breaker Point Gap

Apply a light film of distributor cam lubricant (C4AZ-19D530-A) to the cam when new points are installed. **Do not use engine oil to lubricate the distributor cam.**

Set the igniton timing.

If a scope or a dwell meter is used to adjust new points, be sure the points are in proper alignment. Also, set the contact dwell to the low setting.

To check and adjust the breaker points with a scope, refer to "Ignition System Test—Rotunda Oscilloscope Testers."

To check and adjust the breaker points with a dwell meter, refer to "Distributor Tests—Rotunda RE-27-55 Dwell Tester."

BREAKER POINT SPRING TENSION ADJUSTMENT

Correct breaker point spring tension is essential to proper engine operation and normal breaker point life. If the spring tension is too great, rapid wear of the breaker arm rubbing block will result, causing the breaker point gap to close up and retard the spark timing. If the spring tension is too weak, the breaker arm will flutter at high engine rpm resulting in an engine miss.

To check the spring tension on either the pivot-type or the pivotless breaker points, place the hooked end of the spring tension gauge over the movable breaker point. Pull the gauge at a right angle (90°) to the movable arm until the breaker points just start to open (Fig 26). If the tension is not within specifications, adjust the spring tension on the pivot-type points or replace the breaker point assembly on the pivotless points.

Tool—12151   PULL AT RIGHT ANGLE WITH BREAKER POINT CONTACTS

B2586-A

FIG. 26—Checking Breaker Point Spring Tension

To adjust the spring tension (Fig. 27):

1. Disconnect the primary or distributor-transistor lead wire and the

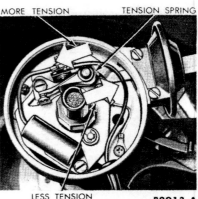

MORE TENSION   TENSION SPRING

LESS TENSION   B2013-A

FIG. 27—Adjusting Breaker Point Spring Tension

condenser lead if so equipped, and the jumper strap on the centrifugal advance distributor at the breaker point assembly primary terminal.

2. Loosen the nut holding the spring in position. **Move the spring toward the breaker arm pivot to decrease tension and in the opposite direction to increase tension.**

3. Tighten the lock nut; then check spring tension. Repeat the adjustment until the specified spring tension is obtained.

4. Install the primary or distributor-transistor lead wire, the condenser lead (if so equipped) and the jumper strap on the centrifugal advance distributor with the lockwasher and tighten the nut securely.

On the centrifugal advance distributor with dual breaker points, loosen the lock nut holding the jumper strap to the other breaker point assembly and follow steps 2 and 3. After the adjustment has been completed, connect the jumper strap.

IGNITION TIMING
TIMING MARK LOCATIONS

Six Cylinder Engines. The timing pointer (Fig. 28), has five timing marks ranging from top dead center (TDC) to 14° before top dead center (BTDC). The crankshaft pulley or damper has a timing notch.

V-8 Engines. The crankshaft damper for the 289 V-8 engine (Fig. 29) has five timing marks ranging from top dead center (TDC to 12° before top dead center (BTDC).

The 352, 390, 410, 427 and 428 V-8 engines (Fig. 30) have 4 timing marks ranging from top dead center (TDC) to 10° before top dead center (BTDC).

ADJUSTMENT

The procedure for checking and

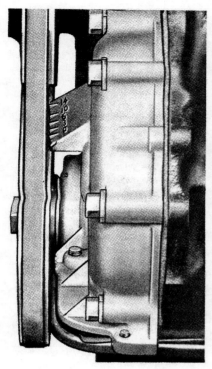

FIG. 28—Typical Six-Cylinder Engine Timing Marks

FIG. 29—289 V-8 Engine Timing Marks

adjusting the ignition timing with a scope is given in Section 1 of this part.

To check and adjust the timing with a Rotunda 13-07 power timing light, proceed as follows:

1. Remove the plug wire from the number 1 spark plug.

2. Install the spark plug adaptor on the spark plug.

FIG. 30—Typical 352, 390, 410, 427 and 428 V-8 Engine Timing Marks

3. Connect the plug wire to the spark plug adaptor.

4. Clamp the timing light spark plug lead to the spark plug adaptor.

5. Connect the timing light battery leads to the battery terminals.

6. Disconnect the distributor vacuum line (if so equipped).

7. If necessary, clean and mark the timing marks.

8. Operate the engine at the specified idle rpm and point the timing light at the timing pointer.

9. If the timing is incorrect, loosen the distributor hold down bolt and rotate the distributor until the desired initial advance is obtained.

10. Tighten the distributor hold down bolt and check the timing again.

11. Turn off the engine.

12. Remove the timing light and connect the vacuum line.

SPARK PLUG WIRE REPLACEMENT

When removing the wires from the spark plugs, grasp, twist and pull the moulded cap only. Do not pull on the wire because the wire connection inside the cap may become separated or the weather seal may be damaged.

240 SIX

The ignition wiring installation for this engine is shown in Fig. 31.

Removal

1. Disconnect the wires at the spark plugs and at the distributor cap.

2. Remove the coil high tension lead.

Cleaning and Inspection. Refer to Part 9-1, Section 3 for the proper cleaning and inspection procedures.

Installation

1. Connect the wires to the proper spark plugs.

2. Install the weather seals on the distributor end of the wires and install the wires in the correct sockets in the distributor cap. Be sure the wires are forced all the way down into their sockets and that they are held firmly in position. The No. 1 socket is identified on the cap. Install the wires in a clockwise direction in the firing order (1-5-3-6-2-4) starting at the No. 1 socket.

3. Install the coil high tension lead. Push all weather seals into position.

ALL V8 ENGINES

The ignition wiring installation is shown in Fig. 32.

Removal

1. Disconnect the wires from the spark plugs and distributor cap.

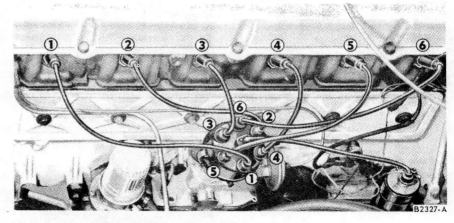

FIG. 31—240 Six Ignition Wiring

FIRING ORDER-1-5-4-2-6-3-7-8   B2584-A

FIG. 32—Typical V-8 Ignition Wiring

2. Pull the wires from the brackets on the valve rocker arm covers and remove the wires.

3. Remove the coil high tension lead.

Cleaning and Inspection. Refer to Part 9-1, Section 3 for the cleaning and inspection procedures.

Installation

1. Insert each wire in the proper socket of the distributor cap. Be sure the wires are forced all the way down into their sockets. The No. 1 socket is identified on the cap. Install the wires in a counterclockwise direction in the firing order (1-5-4-2-6-3-7-8) starting at the No. 1 socket. Cylinders are numbered from front to rear; right bank 1-2-3-4, left bank 5-6-7-8.

2. Remove the brackets from the old spark plug wire set and install them on the new set in the same relative position. Install the wires in the brackets on the valve rocker arm covers (Fig. 32). Connect the wires to the proper spark plugs. Install the coil high tension lead. **Be sure the No. 7 spark plug wire is positioned in the bracket as shown in Fig. 32.**

SPARK PLUGS
REMOVAL

1. Remove the wire from each

spark plug by grasping, twisting and then pulling the moulded cap of the wire only. **Do not pull on the wire because the wire connection inside the cap may become separated or the weather seal may be damaged.**

2. Clean the area around each spark plug port with compressed air, then remove the spark plugs.

CLEANING AND INSPECTION

Refer to Part 9-1, Section 3 for the cleaning and inspection procedures.

ADJUSTMENT

Set the spark plug gap to specifications by bending the ground electrode (Fig. 33).

B1391-C

FIG. 33—Check Spark Plug Gap

INSTALLATION

1. Install the spark plugs and torque each plug to 15-20 ft-lbs.

When a new spark plug is installed in a new replacement cylinder head, torque the plug to 20-30 ft-lbs.

2. Connect the spark plug wires.

RESISTANCE WIRE REPLACEMENT

CONVENTIONAL IGNITION SYSTEM

1. Cut the brown wire and the red wire (with a green band) from the upper quick disconnect at the dash panel. Cut the wires as close to the quick disconnect as possible.

2. Solder a male bullet-type terminal to the brown wire and to the red wire (with green band). Make a single terminal of the two wires. Using a female bullet terminal connector, connect the wires to one end of the service replacement resistance wire.

Do not splice the resistance wire.

3. Drill a ¾-inch hole through one of the accessory dimples in the dash panel.

4. Install a grommet into the hole drilled in the dash panel.

5. Thread one end of the service replacement resistance wire through the grommet in the dash panel and connect it to the jumper wire at the ignition switch. Make sure the wire is routed through the retaining clips.

6. Cut off and discard (at the point where it enters the taped area of the wiring harness) the length of defective resistance wire which is not enclosed in the taped portion of the wiring assembly.

TRANSISTOR IGNITION SYSTEM

The resistance wire used on the transistor ignition system is black. The resistance wire has a quick disconnect at both ends for easy replacement. The resistance wire is connected to the green wire from the amplifier and to the green wire from the main quick disconnect.

1. Disconnect the defective resistance wire.

2. Route the replacement resistance wire along the old resistance wire and connect it to the quick disconnects.

3. Cut off and discard (at the point where it enters the taped area of the wiring harness) the length of defective resistance wire which is not enclosed in the taped portion of the wiring harness.

3 CLEANING AND INSPECTION

SPARK PLUGS

Examine the firing ends of the spark plugs, noting the type of deposits and the degree of electrode erosion. Refer to Fig. 34 for the various types of spark plug fouling and their causes.

Clean the plugs on a sand blast cleaner, following the manufacturer's instructions. **Do not prolong the use of the abrasive blast as it will erode the insulator and electrodes.**

Clean the electrode surfaces with a small file (Fig. 35). Dress the electrodes to obtain flat parallel surfaces on both the center and side electrodes.

After cleaning, examine the plug carefully for cracked or broken insulators, badly pitted electrodes, and other signs of failure. Replace as required.

DISTRIBUTORS

Soak all parts of the distributor assembly (except the condenser, breaker point assembly, lubricating wick, vacuum diaphragm, distributor base oil seal and electrical wiring) in a mild cleaning solvent or mineral spirits. Do not use a harsh cleaning solution. Wipe all parts that can not be immersed in a solvent with a clean dry cloth.

After foreign deposits have been loosened by soaking, scrub the parts with a soft bristle brush. **Do not use a wire brush, file, or other abrasive object.** Dry the parts with compressed air.

Examine the bushing surface(s) of the distributor shaft and the bushing(s) for wear.

Inspect the distributor cam lobes for scoring and signs of wear. If any lobe is scored or worn, replace the cam assembly (dual advance and centrifugal advance distributor) or the shaft on a loadomatic distributor.

Inspect the breaker plate assembly for signs of distortion. In addition, on the dual advance distributor, inspect the stationary sub-plate for worn nylon contact buttons. Replace the breaker plate assembly if it is defective.

The breaker point assembly(ies) and condenser (if so equipped) should be replaced whenever the distributor is overhauled.

Inspect all electrical wiring for fraying, breaks, etc., and replace any

---

CARBON FOULED

IDENTIFIED BY BLACK, DRY FLUFFY CARBON DEPOSITS ON INSULATOR TIPS, EXPOSED SHELL SURFACES AND ELECTRODES.
CAUSED BY TOO COLD A PLUG, WEAK IGNITION, DIRTY AIR CLEANER, DEFECTIVE FUEL PUMP, TOO RICH A FUEL MIXTURE, IMPROPERLY OPERATING HEAT RISER OR EXCESSIVE IDLING. CAN BE CLEANED.

OIL FOULED

IDENTIFIED BY WET, BLACK DEPOSITS ON THE INSULATOR, SHELL BORE AND ELECTRODES.
CAUSED BY EXCESSIVE OIL ENTERING COMBUSTION CHAMBER THROUGH WORN RINGS AND PISTONS, EXCESSIVE CLEARANCE BETWEEN VALVE GUIDES AND STEMS, OR WORN OR LOOSE BEARINGS. CAN BE CLEANED.

GAP BRIDGED

IDENTIFIED BY DEPOSIT BUILD-UP CLOSING GAP BETWEEN ELECTRODES.
CAUSED BY OIL OR CARBON FOULING. IF DEPOSITS ARE NOT EXCESSIVE, THE PLUG CAN BE CLEANED.

LEAD FOULED

IDENTIFIED BY DARK GRAY, BLACK, YELLOW OR TAN DEPOSITS OR A FUSED GLAZED COATING ON THE INSULATOR TIP.
CAUSED BY HIGHLY LEADED GASOLINE. CAN BE CLEANED.

NORMAL

IDENTIFIED BY LIGHT TAN OR GRAY DEPOSITS ON THE FIRING TIP.
CAN BE CLEANED.

WORN

IDENTIFIED BY SEVERELY ERODED OR WORN ELECTRODES.
CAUSED BY NORMAL WEAR. SHOULD BE REPLACED.

FUSED SPOT DEPOSIT

IDENTIFIED BY MELTED OR SPOTTY DEPOSITS RESEMBLING BUBBLES OR BLISTERS.
CAUSED BY SUDDEN ACCELERATION. CAN BE CLEANED.

OVERHEATING

IDENTIFIED BY A WHITE OR OR LIGHT GRAY INSULATOR WITH SMALL BLACK OR GRAY BROWN SPOTS AND WITH BLUISH-BURNT APPEARANCE OF ELECTRODES.
CAUSED BY ENGINE OVERHEATING, WRONG TYPE OF FUEL, LOOSE SPARK PLUGS, TOO HOT A PLUG, LOW FUEL PUMP PRESSURE OR INCORRECT IGNITION TIMING.

PRE-IGNITION

IDENTIFIED BY MELTED ELECTRODES AND POSSIBLY BLISTERED INSULATOR. METALLIC DEPOSITS ON INSULATOR INDICATE ENGINE DAMAGE.
CAUSED BY WRONG TYPE OF FUEL, INCORRECT IGNITION TIMING OR ADVANCE, TOO HOT A PLUG, BURNT VALVES OR ENGINE OVERHEATING. REPLACE THE PLUG.

B2581-A

FIG. 34—Spark Plug Inspection

FIG. 35—Cleaning Spark Plug Electrode

that are not in good condition.

Check the distributor base for cracks or other damage.

On a loadomatic or dual advance distributor, check the diaphragm housing, bracket, and rod for damage. Check the vacuum line fitting for stripped threads or other damage. Test the vacuum fittings, case, and diaphragm for leakage as explained under "Distributor Tests." Replace all defective parts.

The breaker point assembly consists of the stationary point bracket assembly, breaker arm and the mirmary wire terminal.

Breaker points should be inspected, cleaned and adjusted as neces-

sary. Breaker points can be cleaned with chloroform and a stiff bristle brush. Replace the breaker point assembly if the contacts are badly burned or excessive metal transfer between the points is evident (Fig. 36). Metal transfer is considered excessive when it equals or exceeds the gap setting.

SECONDARY WIRING

Wipe the wires with a damp cloth and check for fraying, breaks or cracked insulation. Inspect the terminals and weather seals for looseness or corrosion. Replace any wires that are not in good condition.

COIL

Wipe the coil with a damp cloth

and check for any cracks or other defects.

DISTRIBUTOR CAP

Clean the distributor cap with a soft bristle brush and mild cleaning solvent or mineral spirits. Dry the cap with compressed air. Inspect the cap for cracks, burned contacts, permanent carbon tracks or dirt or corrosion in the sockets. Replace the cap if it is defective.

ROTOR

Clean the rotor with a soft bristle brush and mild cleaning solvent or mineral spirits. Dry the rotor with compressed air. Inspect the rotor for cracks or burning. Replace the rotor if it is defective.

CONDITION	CAUSED BY
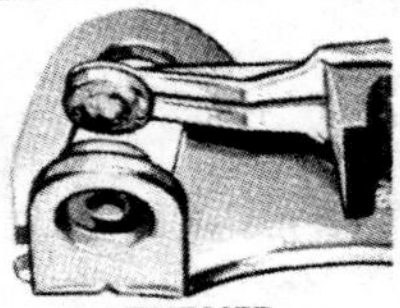 BURNED	Any discoloration other than a frosted slate grey shall be considered as burned points.
 EXCESSIVE METAL TRANSFER OR PITTING	Incorrect alignment. Incorrect voltage regulator setting. Radio condenser installed to the distributor side of the coil. Ignition condenser of improper capacity. Extended operation of the engine at speeds other than normal.

B1443-B

FIG. 36—Breaker Point Inspection

PART 9-2

LOADOMATIC DISTRIBUTORS

DESCRIPTION AND OPERATION

The direction of distributor rotation is clockwise as viewed from the top of the distributor.

Engine speed and load requirements are satisfied by the action of the breaker plate which is controlled by a vacuum-actuated diaphragm working against the tension of two calibrated breaker plate springs (Figs. 1 and 2).

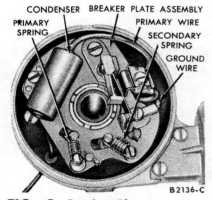

FIG. 1—Breaker Plate Installation

The breaker plate is free to rotate on the shaft bushing. The diaphragm moves the breaker plate in a counterclockwise direction to advance the spark, and the springs

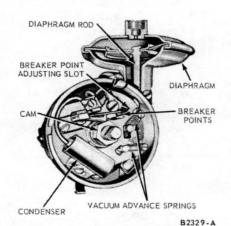

FIG. 2—Spark Advance Mechanism

move the plate in a clockwise direction to retard the spark. The degree of spark advance is determined by the strength of the vacuum acting on the diaphragm.

Vacuum is transmitted to the distributor diaphragm from two interconnected passages in the carburetor, The opening of one passage is in the throat of the venturi and the opening(s) of the other passage is in the throttle bore just above the closed throttle plae.

All manifold vacuum to the distributor passes through a spark control valve located in the carburetor throttle body or main body. Under steady part throttle operation, the spark valve is held open against the pressure of a calibrated spring. A combination of atmospheric pressure ouside the spark valve diaphragm and manifold vacuum from within holds the spark valve open. When accelerating, manifold vacuum momentarily drops below a predetermined point and the calibrated spring closes the spark valve shutting off the manifold vacuum port. Vacuum from the venturi prevents full spark retard.

As engine speed approaches the throttle setting, manifold vacuum increases sufficiently to open the spark valve and allow a higher vacuum to operate the distributor.

At high engine speed, manifold vacuum falls and the valve closes. This prevents loss of venturi vacuum due to bleed back caused by the lower manifold vacuum. This assures full spark advance at high engine speed.

The spark valve functions in a similar manner to provide an intermediate spark retard whenever the load on the engine is increased to a degree where normal road load spark advance would be too great and the wide-open throttle spark retard would reduce the efficiency of the engine.

2 IN-CAR ADJUSTMENTS AND REPAIRS

BREAKER POINT AND CONDENSER REPLACEMENT

The breaker point and condenser replacement procedure is in Part 9-1, Section 2.

VACUUM DIAPHRAGM REPLACEMENT
REMOVAL

1. Remove the distributor cap and rotor.

2. Remove the vacuum line from the diaphragm.

3. Remove the spring clip that secures the diaphragm link to the breaker plate.

4. Remove the diaphragm retaining screws and remove the diaphragm.

INSTALLATION

1. Install the vacuum unit on the distributor body. Insert the tip of the vacuum rod through the breaker plate and attach the rod with the spring clip.

2. Install the vacuum line in the diaphragm assembly and tighten the fitting.

3. Install the rotor and distributor cap.

ADJUSTMENTS

Refer to Part 9-1 for the proper procedures for adjusting the breaker points and spark advance.

3 REMOVAL AND INSTALLATION

REMOVAL

1. Disconnect the primary wire at the coil and remove the distributor cap.
2. Disconnect the vacuum line at the distributor.
3. Scribe a mark on the distributor body, indicating the position of the rotor, and scribe another mark on the body and engine block, indicating the position of the body in the block. These lines will be used as guides when installing the distributor in the correctly timed engine.
4. Remove the retaining bolt and lock washer and lift the distributor out of the block. **Do not rotate the crankshaft while the distributor is removed, or it will be necessary to time the engine.**

INSTALLATION

1. If the crankshaft has not been rotated while the distributor was removed, position the distributor in the block with the rotor aligned with the mark previously scribed on the distributor body and install the distributor retaining screw.
2. If the crankshaft has been rotated while the distributor was removed, rotate the crankshaft until the No. 1 piston is on TDC after the compression stroke. Position the distributor in the block with the rotor at the No. 1 firing position. Install, but do not tighten, the distributor retaining bolt. Rotate the distributor body clockwise until the breaker points are just starting to open. Tighten the retaining bolt.

3. Connect the distributor primary wire and install the distributor cap.

4. Start the engine and adjust the ignition timing to specifications with a timing light. Connect the distributor vacuum line, and check the advance with the timing light when the engine is accelerated.

4 MAJOR REPAIR OPERATIONS

To perform the operations in this section, it will be necessary to remove the distributor from the car.

BENCH DISASSEMBLY

The distributor assembly is shown in Fig. 3.
1. Install the distributor in a vise.
2. Remove the rotor and retaining clip.
3. Remove the vacuum diaphragm rod spring clip. Push the diaphragm rod out of the plate. Remove the vacuum diaphragm unit from the distributor.
4. Disconnect the primary and condenser wires from the breaker point terminal. Working from the inside of the distributor, pull the primary wire through the opening in the distributor.
5. Remove the condenser.
6. Remove the breaker point assembly.
7. Mark the primary spring (spring nearest the condenser).
8. Release the tension on the return springs and disconnect the springs. **Do not stretch the springs as distortion may result, making it impossible to obtain an adjustment.**

If the springs are distorted, discard them.
9. Remove the distributor from the vise. Remove the distributor cap clamps.
10. Drive out the drive gear pin with a punch (Fig. 4).
11. If the gear and shaft are to be used again, mark the gear and shaft so that the pin holes can be easily aligned for assembly.
12. Press the gear off the shaft (Fig. 5) Slide the distributor shaft out of the body.
13. Position the distributor in a vise.
14. Remove the lock ring attaching the breaker plate to the upper bushing. Lift the breaker plate from the body.
15. Remove the ground wire.
16 Remove the oil filler cap and the oil wick.
17. Compress and insert the slotted end of the bushing removal tool in the distributor body. Allow it to expand and butt against the bushing. Drive out the bushing (Fig. 6).

BENCH ASSEMBLY

1. Oil the bushing and position it in the body with the lock ring end up. Install the bushing (Fig. 7). Press the adapter until the bushing bottoms firmly against the distributor body.
2. Burnish the bushing to the proper size (Fig. 8).
3. Install the ground wire. Position the breaker plate in the body. Install the lock ring to secure the plate.
4. Position a new breaker point assembly on the breaker plate. Be sure the pivot pin enters the hole in the breaker plate.
5. Connect the ground wire to the breaker point screw nearest the contacts. Install the other screw at the opposite end of the assembly.
6. Install a new condenser. Pass the primary wire assembly through the opening in the distributor, working from the inside to the outside of the distributor housing. Pull the wire through the opening until the locating stop is flush with the inside of the distributor. Place the condenser lead, primary lead, lock washer, and nut on the primary terminal.
7. Install the return springs on the adjustment and breaker plate posts.

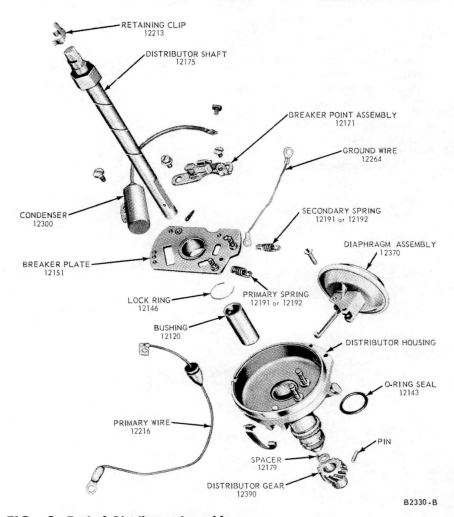

FIG. 3—Typical Distributor Assembly

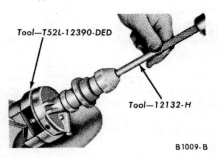

FIG. 6—Bushing Removal

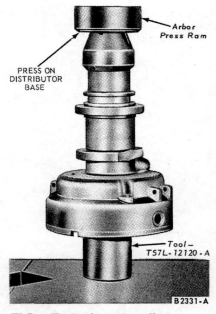

FIG. 7—Bushing Installation

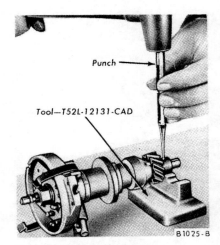

FIG. 4—Gear Pin Removal or Installation

Make certain that the primary spring is installed near the condenser.

8. Install the vacuum diaphragm on the distributor body.

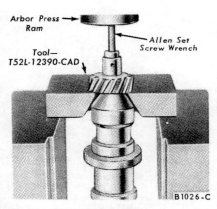

FIG. 5—Gear Removal

9. Insert the tip of the vacuum diaphragm rod through the breaker plate. Attach the rod with the spring clip.

10. Slide the shaft into the body using care not to damage the rubbing block on the breaker points. **The shaft and gear are replaced as an**

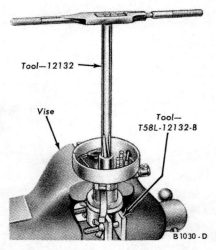

FIG. 8—Burnishing Bushing

assembly. One part should not be replaced without replacing the other.

11. Attach the distributor shaft supporting tool to the distributor. Tighten the backing screw in the tool

enough to remove all shaft end play.

12. Place the spacer on the gear end of the shaft. Press the gear on the shaft (Fig. 9) until the specified end clearance is obtained. **When installing a new gear and shaft, press the gear on so that the holes in the gear are parallel with the notch on the shaft.** If a new shaft is being installed, drill the shaft with a 1/8-inch drill using the hole in the gear shoulder as a guide.

13. Install the pin through the gear and shaft. Install the distributor cap clamps. Lubricate the cam with distributor cam lubricant (C4AZ-19D530-A).

14. Fill the oil reservoir with engine oil (approximately 40 drops).

Install the felt oil wick and the oiler.

15. Refer to Part 9-1 and adjust the breaker point spring tension, align the breaker points, and adjust the gap. Check the vacuum advance, and the breaker point dwell and resistance.

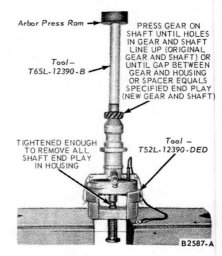

FIG. 9—Gear Installation

PART 9-3 DUAL ADVANCE DISTRIBUTORS

1 DESCRIPTION AND OPERATION

The dual advance distributor has two independently operated spark advance systems. A centrifugal advance mechanism (Fig. 1) is located below the stationary sub-plate assembly, and a vacuum operated spark control diaphragm is located on the side of the distributor base (Fig. 2). As speed increases, the centrifugal weights cause the cam to advance or move ahead with respect to the distributor drive shaft. The rate of advance is controlled by calibrated springs.

The vacuum advance mechanism has a spring-loaded diaphragm which is connected to the breaker plate. The spring-loaded side of the diaphragm is airtight and is connected through a vacuum line to the carburetor throttle bore. When the throttle plates open, the distributor vacuum passage is exposed to manifold vacuum, which causes the diaphragm to move against the tension of the spring. This action causes the movable breaker plate to pivot on the stationary sub-plate. The breaker point rubbing block, which is positioned on the opposite side of the cam from the pivot pin, then moves against distributor rotation and advances the spark timing. As the movable breaker plate is rotated from retard position to full advance position, the dwell decreases slightly. This is because the breaker point rubbing block and the cam rotate on different axes.

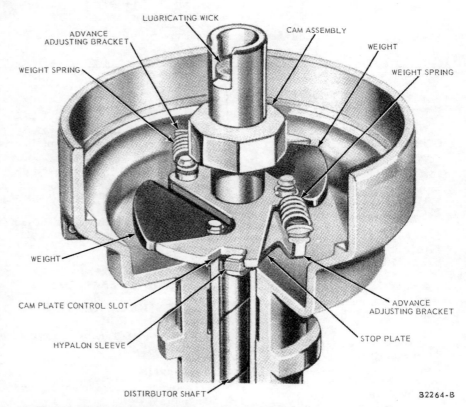

FIG. 1—Typical Centrifugal Advance Mechanism

LUBRICATING WICK
ADVANCE ADJUSTING BRACKET
CAM ASSEMBLY
WEIGHT
WEIGHT SPRING
WEIGHT SPRING
WEIGHT
CAM PLATE CONTROL SLOT
HYPALON SLEEVE
DISTIRBUTOR SHAFT
ADVANCE ADJUSTING BRACKET
STOP PLATE

B2264-B

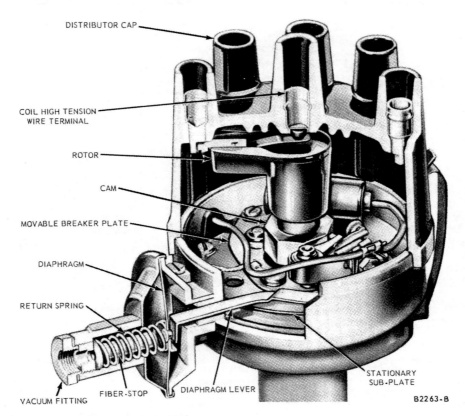

DISTRIBUTOR CAP

COIL HIGH TENSION WIRE TERMINAL

ROTOR

CAM

MOVABLE BREAKER PLATE

DIAPHRAGM

RETURN SPRING

VACUUM FITTING   FIBER-STOP   DIAPHRAGM LEVER

STATIONARY SUB-PLATE

B2263-B

FIG. 2—Typical Vacuum Advance Mechanism

2 IN-CAR ADJUSTMENTS AND REPAIRS

BREAKER POINT AND CONDENSER REPLACEMENT

The replacement procedures are covered in Part 9-1, Section 2.

VACUUM DIAPHRAGM REPLACEMENT

CONVENTIONAL AND TRANSISTOR IGNITION SYSTEM DISTRIBUTORS

Removal

1. Remove the distributor cap, the rotor, and the dust cover (if so equipped).
2. Remove the vacuum line from the diaphragm fitting.
3. Remove the spring clip that secures the diaphragm link to the movable breaker plate.
4. Remove the diaphragm retaining screws and slide the diaphragm out of the distributor.

Installation

1. Slide the diaphragm into the opening in the distributor and place

the link in its position.
2. Install the spring clip that secures the diaphragm link to the movable breaker plate and the diaphragm retaining screws.
3. Install the vacuum line on the diaphragm fitting.
4. Install the dust cover (if so equipped), the rotor and the distributor cap.

BREAKER PLATE AND SUB-PLATE REPLACEMENT

CONVENTIONAL IGNITION SYSTEM DISTRIBUTOR

Refer to Figs. 3 and 4 for the correct location of parts.

Removal

1. Remove the distributor cap and the rotor.
2. Remove the breaker point assembly, the condenser, and the vacuum diaphragm.
3. Working from the inside of the distributor, pull the primary wire through the opening in the distributor.
4. Remove the spring clip, the

flat washer and the spring washer securing the breaker plate to the sub-plate.
5. Remove the sub-plate retaining screws and lift both plates out of the distributor.

Installation

1. Place the breaker plate in position on the sub-plate.
2. Install the spring washer, the flat washer and the spring clip that secures the breaker plate to the sub-plate.
3. Install the sub-plate hold down screws (the ground wire should be under the sub-plate hold down screw near the primary wire opening in the distributor).
4. Working from the inside of the distributor, push the primary wire through the opening in the distributor.
5. Install the breaker point assembly, the condenser and the vacuum diaphragm.
6. Install the rotor and the distributor cap.

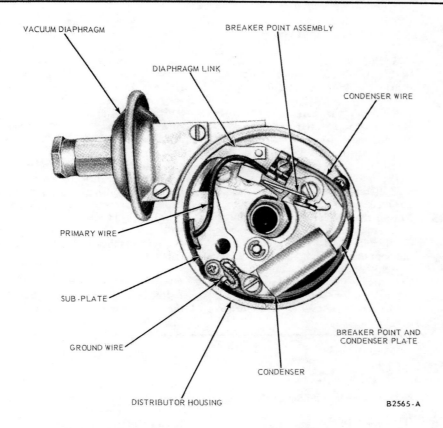

FIG. 3—Breaker Plate Installed—6-Cylinder Engine

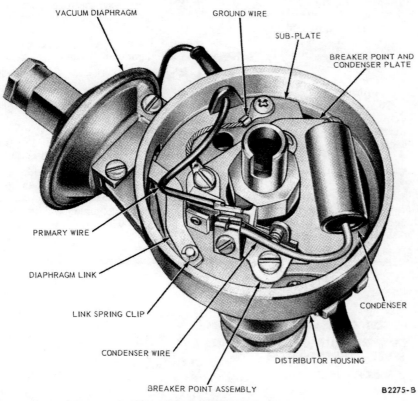

FIG. 4—Breaker Plate Installed—8-Cylinder Engine

TRANSISTOR IGNITION SYSTEM DISTRIBUTOR

The transistor ignition system distributor does not have a condenser. It does not have a lubricating wick on the breaker point assembly rubbing block. With the exception of these two items, Fig. 3 shows the correct location of parts.

Removal

1. Remove the distributor cap, the rotor and the dust cover.
2. Remove the breaker point assembly and the vacuum diaphragm.
3. Working from the inside of the distributor, pull the distributor-transistor wire through the opening in the distributor.
4. Remove the spring clip, the flat washer and the spring washer securing the breaker plate to the sub-plate.
5. Remove the sub-plate retaining screws and lift both plates out of the distributor.

Installation

1. Place the breaker plate in position on the sub-plate.
2. Install the spring washer, the flat washer and the spring clip that secures the breaker plate to the sub-plate.
3. Install the sub-plate hold down screws (the ground wire should be under the sub-plate hold down screw near the distributor-transistor wire opening in the distributor).
4. Working from the inside of the distributor, push the distributor-transistor wire through the opening in the distributor.
5. Install the breaker point assembly and the vacuum diaphragm.
6. Install the dust cover, the rotor and the distributor cap.

CAM AND CENTRIFUGAL ADVANCE MECHANISM REPLACEMENT

CONVENTIONAL AND TRANSISTOR IGNITION SYSTEM DISTRIBUTORS

Removal

1. Remove the distributor cap, the rotor and the dust cover (if so equipped).
2. Working from the inside of the distributor, pull the primary or distributor-transistor wire through the opening in the distributor.
3. Remove the sub-plate retaining screws and lift the plate assembly out of the distributor.

4. Mark one of the distributor weight springs and its brackets. Also mark one of the weights and its pivot pin.

5. Carefully unhook and remove the weight springs.

6. Lift the lubricating wick from the cam assembly. Remove the cam assembly retainer and lift the cam assembly off the distributor shaft. Remove the thrust washer.

7. Remove the weight retainers and lift the weights out of the distributor.

Installation

1. Fill the grooves in the weight pivot pins with distributor lubricant (C4AZ-19D530-A).

2. Position the weights in the distributor (the marked weight is placed on the marked pivot pin) and install

the weight retainers.

3. Place the thrust washer on the shaft.

4. Fill the grooves in the upper portion of the distributor shaft with distributor cam lubricant (C4AZ-19D530-A).

5. Install the cam assembly. Be sure that the marked spring bracket on the cam assembly is near the marked spring bracket on the stop plate. If a new cam assembly is being installed, make sure that the cam is installed with the hypalon covered stop in the correct cam plate control slot. This can be done by measuring the length of the slot used on the old cam and by using the corresponding slot on the new cam. Some of the cams will have the size of the slot in degrees stamped near the slot. If the wrong slot is used, an incor-

rect maximum advance will be obtained.

Place a light film of distributor cam lubricant (C4AZ-19D530-A) on the distributor cam lobes. Install the retainer and the wick. Saturate the wick with SAE 10W engine oil.

6. Install the weight springs. Be sure that the marked spring is attached to the marked spring brackets.

7. Install the plate assembly.

8. Working from the inside of the distributor, push the primary or distributor-transistor wire through the opening in the distributor.

9. Install the dust cover (if so equipped), the rotor and the distributor cap.

ADJUSTMENTS

Refer to Part 9-1, Section 2 for the adjustment procedures.

3 REMOVAL AND INSTALLATION

REMOVAL

1. On a conventional ignition system, disconnect the primary wire at the coil.

On a transistor ignition system, disconnect the distributor-transistor lead from the quick disconnect.

Disconnect the vacuum advance line at the distributor. Remove the distributor cap.

2. Scribe a mark on the distributor body and the engine block indicating the position of the body in the block, and scribe another mark on the distributor body indicating the position of the rotor. These marks can be used as guides when installing the distributor in a correctly timed engine.

3. Remove the distributor hold down bolt and clamp. Lift the distributor out of the block.

Do not rotate the crankshaft while the distributor is removed, or it will

be necessary to time the engine.

INSTALLATION

1. If the crankshaft was rotated while the distributor was removed, it will be necessary to time the engine. Rotate the crankshaft until No. 1 piston is on TDC after the compression stroke. Align the TDC mark on the timing pointer with the timing pin on the crankshaft damper. Position the distributor in the block with the rotor at the No. 1 firing position.

Make sure the oil pump intermediate shaft properly engages the distributor shaft. It may be necessary to crank the engine with the starter, after the distributor drive gear is partially engaged, in order to engage the oil pump intermediate shaft.

Install, but do not tighten, the retaining clamp and bolt. Rotate the distributor body counterclockwise on

eight cylinder engines or clockwise on six cylinder engines until the breaker points are just starting to open. Tighten the clamp.

2. If the crankshaft has not been rotated, position the distributor in the block with the rotor aligned with the mark previously scribed on the distributor body and the marks on the distributor body and engine block in alignment. Install the retaining clamp.

3. Install the distributor cap.

4. On a conventional ignition system, connect the primary wire to the coil. On a transistor ignition system, connect the distributor-transistor lead to the quick disconnect.

5. Check the ignition timing with a timing light and adjust to specifications. Connect the vacuum line, and check the advance with the timing light when the engine is accelerated.

4 MAJOR REPAIR OPERATIONS

To perform the operations in this section, it will be necessary to remove the distributor from the engine and place it in a vise.

BENCH DISASSEMBLY
CONVENTIONAL IGNITION SYSTEM DISTRIBUTOR

Six Cylinder Engine
The distributor assembly is shown in Fig. 5.

1. Remove the rotor.

2. Disconnect the primary and the condenser wires from the breaker point assembly.

3. Remove the breaker point assembly and condenser retaining screws. Lift the breaker point assem-

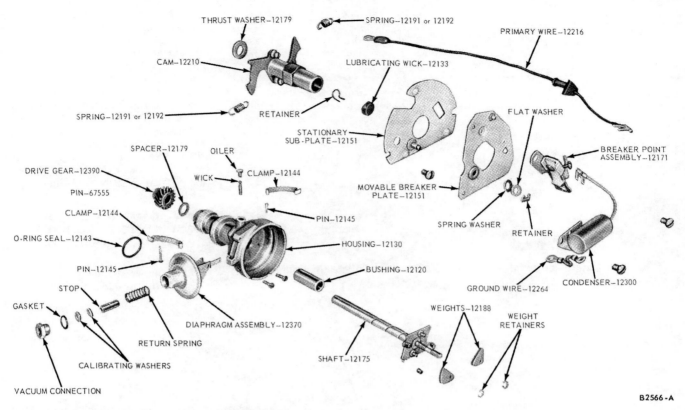

FIG. 5—Distributor Assembly—6-Cylinder Engine

bly and condenser out of the distributor.

4. Remove the spring clip that secures the diaphragm link to the moveable breaker plate.

5. Remove the diaphragm retaining screws and slide the diaphragm out of the distributor.

6. Working from the inside of the distributor, pull the primary wire through the opening in the distributor.

7. Remove the spring clip, the flat washer, and the spring washer securing the breaker plate to the sub-plate.

8. Remove the sub-plate retaining screws and lift both plates out of the distributor.

9. Mark one of the distributor weight springs and its brackets. Also mark one of the weights and its pivot pin.

10. Carefully unhook and remove the weight springs.

11. Lift the lubricating wick from the cam assembly. Remove the cam assembly retainer and lift the cam assembly off the distributor shaft. Remove the thrust washer.

12. Remove the weight retainers and lift the weights out of the distributor.

13. Remove the distributor cap clamps.

14. If the gear and shaft are to be used again, mark the gear and the shaft so that the pin holes can be easily aligned for assembly. Remove the gear roll pin (Fig. 6).

15. Invert the distributor and place it on a support plate in a position that will allow the distributor shaft to clear the support plate and press the shaft out of the gear and the distributor housing (Fig. 7).

16. Refer to Fig. 8 and remove the distributor shaft bushing.

17. Remove the oil filler cap and wick.

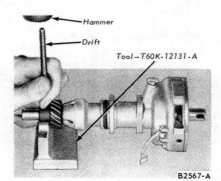

FIG. 6—Typical Gear Pin Removal or Installation

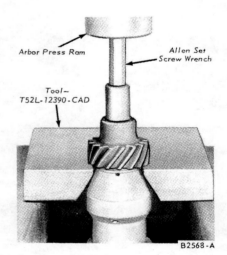

FIG. 7—Shaft and Gear Removal—6-Cylinder Engine

Eight Cylinder Engine

The distributor assembly is shown in Fig. 9.

1. Follow steps 1-13 under "Six Cylinder Engine."

2. If the gear and shaft are to be used again, mark the gear and the shaft so that the pin holes can be easily aligned for assembly. Remove the gear roll pin (Fig. 6), and then remove the gear (Fig. 10).

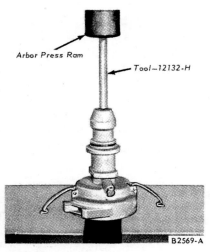

**FIG. 8—Bushing Removal—
6-Cylinder Engine**

3. Remove the shaft collar roll pin (Fig. 11).

4. Invert the distributor and place it on a support plate in a position that will allow the distributor shaft to clear the support plate and press the shaft out of the collar and the distributor housing (Fig. 12).

5. Refer to Figs. 13 and 14 and

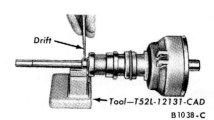

**FIG. 11—Collar Pin Removal
or Installation**

cures the diaphragm link to the moveable breaker plate.

5. Remove the diaphragm retaining screws and slide the diaphragm out of the distributor.

6. Working from the inside of the distributor, pull the distributor-transistor wire through the opening in the distributor.

7. Follow steps 7-13 under "Conventional Ignition System Distributor-Six Cylinder Engine" and steps 2-5 under "Conventional Ignition System Distributor—Eight Cylinder Engine."

**BENCH ASSEMBLY
ORIGINAL SHAFT AND GEAR**

Conventional Ignition System Distributors

Six Cylinder Engine

1. Oil the new bushing and posi-

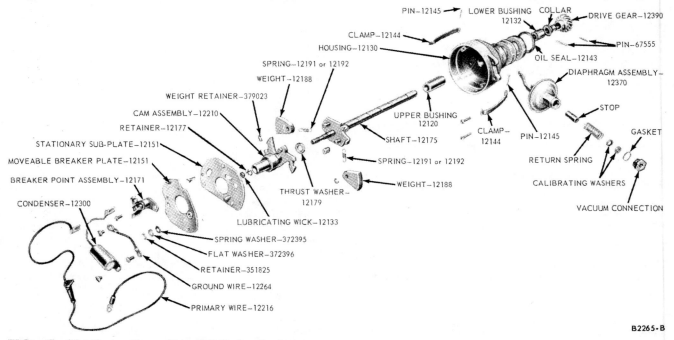

FIG. 9—Distributor Assembly—8-Cylinder Engine

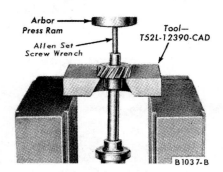

**FIG. 10—Gear Removal—
8-Cylinder Engine**

remove the distributor shaft upper and lower bushings.

**TRANSISTOR IGNITION
SYSTEM DISTRIBUTOR**

1. Remove the rotor and the dust cover.

2. Disconnect the distributor-transistor lead from the breaker point assembly.

3. Remove the retaining screws from the breaker point assembly and lift the breaker point assembly out of the distributor.

4. Remove the spring clip that se-

tion it on the bushing replacer tool. Install the bushing (Fig. 15). When the tool bottoms against the distributor base, the bushing will be installed to the correct depth.

2. Burnish the bushing to the proper size (Fig. 16).

3. Oil the shaft and slide it into the distributor body.

4. Attach the distributor shaft supporting tool to the distributor. *Tighten the backing screw in the tool enough to remove all shaft end play.*

5. Install the assembly in a press. Press the gear on the shaft (Fig. 17).

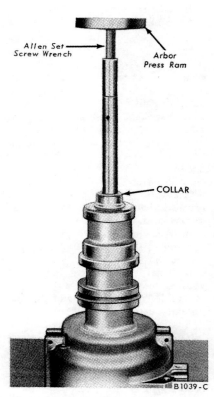

FIG. 12—Shaft Removal—8-Cylinder Engine

FIG. 13—Lower Bushing Removal—8-Cylinder Engine

6. Check the shaft end play with a feeler gauge placed between the collar and the base of the distributor. If the end play is not within specifi-

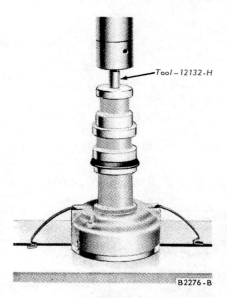

FIG. 14—Upper Bushing Removal—8-Cylinder Engine

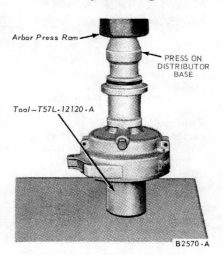

FIG. 15—Bushing Installation—6-Cylinder Engine

cations, replace the shaft and gear.

7. Remove the distributor from the press. Install the gear retaining pin (Fig. 6).

8. Position the distributor in a vise. Fill the grooves in the weight pivot pins with a distributor cam lubricant (C4AZ-19D530-A).

9. Position the weights in the distributor **(the marked weight is placed on the marked pivot pin)** and install the weight retainers.

10. Place the thrust washer on the shaft.

11. Fill the grooves in the upper portion of the distributor shaft with distributor cam lubricant (C4AZ-19D530-A).

12. Install the cam assembly. **Be**

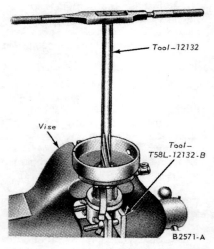

FIG. 16—Burnishing Bushing—Typical

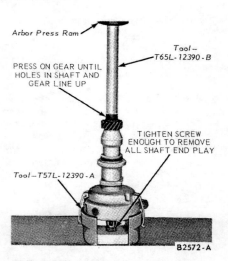

FIG. 17—Original Shaft and Gear Installation—6-Cylinder Engine

sure that the marked spring bracket on the cam assembly is near the marked spring bracket on the stop plate.

If a new cam assembly is being installed, make sure that the cam is installed with the hypalon covered stop in the correct cam plate control slot. This can be done by measuring the length of the slot on the old cam and by using the corresponding slot on the new cam. Some of the cams will have the size of the slot in degrees stamped near the slot. **If the wrong slot is used, an incorrect maximum advance will be obtained.**

Place a light film of distributor cam lubricant on the distributor cam lobes. Install the retainer and the wick. Saturate the wick with SAE 10W engine oil.

13. Install the weight springs. **Be sure that the marked spring is attached to the marked spring brackets.**

14. Place the breaker plate in position on the sub-plate.

15. Install the spring washer, the flat washer, and the spring clip that secures the breaker plate to the sub-plate.

16. Install the sub-plate hold down screws (the ground wire should be under the sub-plate hold down screw near the primary wire opening in the distributor).

17. Working from the inside of the distributor, push the primary wire through the opening in the distributor.

18. Slide the diaphragm into the opening in the distributor and place the link in its position.

19. Install the spring clip that secures the diaphragm link to the moveable breaker plate and install the retaining screws.

20. Place the breaker point assembly and the condenser in position and install the retaining screws. Be sure to place the ground wire under the breaker point assembly screw farthest from the breaker point contacts on an eight cylinder engine distributor or under the condenser retaining screw on a six cylinder engine distributor. Align and adjust the breaker point assembly by following the procedure in Part 9-1.

21. Connect the primary and condenser leads to the breaker point assembly.

22. Install the rotor and the distributor cap.

23. Check and adjust (if necessary) the centrifugal and vacuum advance (Refer to Part 9-1, Section 1).

Eight Cylinder Engine

1. Oil the new upper bushing, and position it on the bushing replacer tool. Install the bushing (Fig. 18). When the tool bottoms against the distributor base, the bushing will be installed to the correct depth.

2. Burnish the bushing to the proper size (Fig. 16).

3. Invert *the* distributor and install and burnish the lower bushing in a similar manner.

4. Oil the shaft and slide it into the distributor body.

5. Place the collar in position on the shaft and align the holes in the collar and the shaft, then install a new pin. Install the distributor cap clamps.

6. Check the shaft end play with

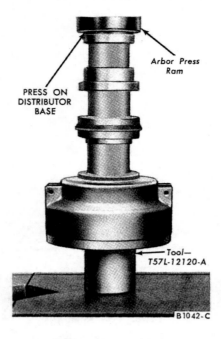

FIG. 18—Upper Bushing Installation—8-Cylinder Engine

a feeler gauge placed between the collar and the base of the distributor. If the end play is not within specifications, replace the shaft and gear.

7. Attach the distributor shaft supporting tool to the distributor. Tighten the backing screw in the tool enough to remove all shaft end play.

8. Install the assembly in a press. Press the gear on the shaft (Fig. 19), using the marks on the gear and shaft as guides to align the pin holes.

9. Follow steps 7-23 under "Six Cylinder Engine."

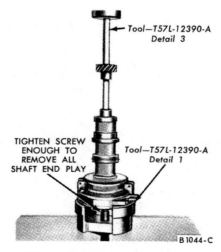

FIG. 19—Original Shaft and Gear Installation—8-Cylinder Engine

Transistor Ignition System Distributor

1. Follow steps 1-8 under "Conventional Ignition System Distributor—Eight Cylinder Engine" and steps 7-15 under "Conventional Ignition System Distributor—Six Cylinder Engine."

2. Install the sub-plate hold down screws (the ground wire should be under the sub-plate hold down screw near the distributor-transistor wire opening in the distributor).

3. Working from the inside of the distributor, push the distributor-transistor wire through the opening in the distributor.

4. Slide the diaphragm into the opening in the distributor and place the link in its position.

5. Install the spring clip that secures the diaphragm link to the moveable breaker plate and the diaphragm retaining screws.

6. Place the breaker point assembly in position and install the retaining screws.

7. Align and adjust the breaker point assembly by following the procedure in Part 9-1, Section 2.

8. Connect the distributor-transistor wire to the breaker point assembly.

9. Check and adjust (if necessary) the centrifugal and vacuum advance (Refer to Part 9-1, Section 1).

10. Install the dust cover and the rotor.

NEW SHAFT AND GEAR

Conventional and Transistor Ignition Distributor

Six Cylinder Engine

The shaft and gear are replaced as an assembly. One part should not be replaced without replacing the other. Refer to Fig. 5 for the correct location of parts.

1. Follow steps 1,2 and 3 under "Installing Original Shaft end Gear—Conventional Ignition System—Six Cylinder Engine."

2. Attach the distributor shaft supporting tool to the distributor and install the assembly in a vise. Insert a 0.003 inch feeler gauge between the backing screw and the shaft. Tighten the backing screw on the tool enough to remove all shaft end play. Remove the feeler gauge and allow the shaft to rest on the backing screw. Place the gear thrust washer in position. Press the gear on the shaft until it bottoms on the gear thrust washer (Fig. 20). Drill a ⅛-

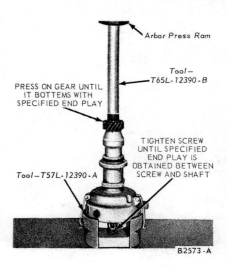

FIG. 20—New Shaft and Gear Installation—6-Cylinder Engine

inch hole through the shaft using the access opening in the gear as a pilot.

3. Remove the distributor from the press and remove the support tool. Install the gear retaining pin (Fig. 6).

4. Complete the assembly by following steps 8-23 under "Installing Original Shaft and Gear—Conventional Ignition System—Six Cylinder Engine."

Eight Cylinder Engine

The shaft and gear are replaced as an assembly. One part should not be replaced without replacing the other. Refer to Fig. 9 for the correct location of the parts.

1. Follow steps 1,2,3 and 4 under "Installing Original Shaft and Gear—Conventional Ignition System—Eight Cylinder Engine."

2. Attach the distributor shaft supporting tool to the distributor and install the assembly in a vise. Insert a 0.024 inch feeler gauge between the backing screw and the shaft. Tighten the backing screw on the tool enough to remove all shaft end play. Remove the feeler gauge and allow the shaft to rest on the backing screw. Slide the collar on the shaft. While holding the collar in place against the distributor base, drill a ⅛-inch hole through the shaft using the access opening in the collar as a pilot.

3. Position the gear on the end of the shaft. Install the assembly in a press.

4. With the backing screw on the support tool tightened enough to remove all end play, press the gear on the shaft to the specified distance from the bottom face of the gear to the bottom face of the distributor mounting flange (Fig. 21). Drill a ⅛-inch hole through the shaft using the hole in the gear as a pilot.

5. Remove the distributor from the press and remove the support tool. Install the collar retaining pin (Fig. 11) and the gear retaining pin (Fig. 6).

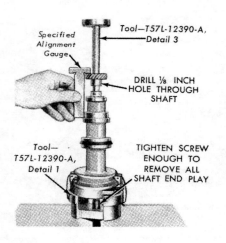

FIG. 21—New Shaft and Gear Installation—8-Cylinder Engine

6. On a conventional ignition system distributor, complete the assembly by following steps 7-thru 23 under "Installing Original Shaft and Gear-Conventional Ignition System—Six Cylinder Engine."

On a transistor ignition system distributor, complete the assembly by following steps 7-15 under "Installing Original Shaft and Gear-Conventional Ignition System—Six Cylinder Engine." and steps 2-10 under "Installing Original Shaft and Gear-Transistor Ignition System Distributor."

PART 9-4 CENTRIFUGAL ADVANCE DISTRIBUTORS

1 DESCRIPTION AND OPERATION

The centrifugal advance distributor is a straight mechanical-type unit. A governor-type centrifugal advance is located below the stationary breaker plate (Fig. 1). Two centrifugal weights cause the cam to advance or move ahead with respect to the distributor drive shaft the rate of advance is controlled by two calibrated springs.

The conventional ignition system distributor has dual breaker points. The breaker points are located on the stationary breaker plate and are connected in parallel with an insulated jumper strap. One breaker point assembly closes the primary circuit and the other opens the primary circuit. This type of construction results in a greater amount of dwell with approximately the same amount of gap spacing as the single breaker point distributor. The breaker arm spring tension is greater than on the loadomatic or dual advance distributors. This increased dwell and breaker arm spring tension assures reserve spark plug voltage for high speed performance.

On a transistorized ignition system distributor, there is only one set of breaker points. The transistorized ignition system distributor also has a dust cover.

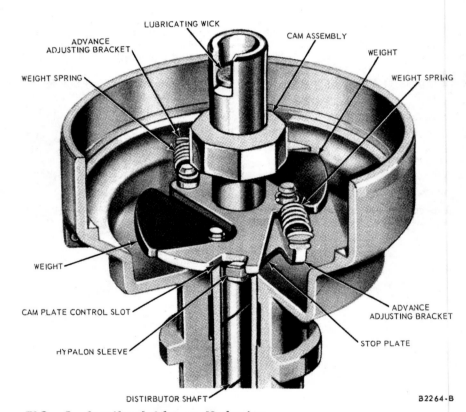

FIG. 1—Centrifugal Advance Mechanism

2 IN-CAR ADJUSTMENTS AND REPAIRS

BREAKER POINT AND CONDENSER REPLACEMENT

The replacement procedures are covered in Part 9-1, Section 2.

CONVENTIONAL IGNITION SYSTEM DISTRIBUTOR

Removal

1. Remove the distributor cap and the rotor.

2. Remove the breaker point assemblies and the condenser.

3. Working from the inside of the distributor, pull the primary wire through the opening in the distributor.

4. Remove the breaker point and condenser plate retaining screws and lift the plate out of the distributor.

Installation

The breaker point and condenser plate assembly installation is shown in Fig. 2.

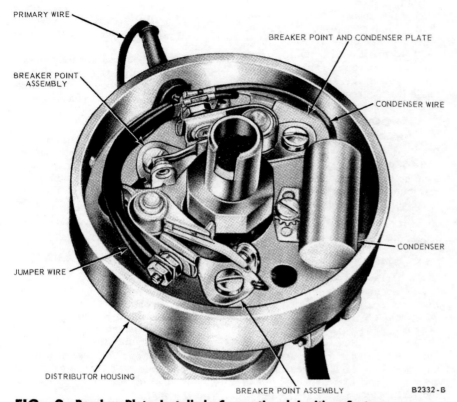

PRIMARY WIRE

BREAKER POINT ASSEMBLY

JUMPER WIRE

DISTRIBUTOR HOUSING

BREAKER POINT AND CONDENSER PLATE

CONDENSER WIRE

CONDENSER

BREAKER POINT ASSEMBLY

B2332-B

FIG. 2—Breaker Plate Installed—Conventional Ignition System

1. Place the breaker point and condenser plate in position and install the retaining screws.

2. Working from the inside of the distributor, push the primary wire through the opening in the distributor housing.

3. Install the breaker point assemblies and the condenser.

4. Install the rotor and the distributor cap.

TRANSISTOR IGNITION SYSTEM DISTRIBUTOR

Removal

1. Remove the distributor cap, the rotor, the dust cover, and the breaker point assembly.

2. Working from the inside of the distributor, pull the distributor-transistor lead through the opening in the distributor.

3. Remove the breaker point and condenser plate retaining screws and lift the plate out of the distributor.

Installation

1. Place the breaker point and condenser plate in position and install the retaining screws.

2. Working from the inside of the distributor, push the distributor-transistor wire through the opening in the distributor housing.

3. Install the breaker point assembly, the dust cover, the rotor, and the distributor cap.

CAM AND CENTRIFUGAL ADVANCE MECHANISM REPLACEMENT

CONVENTIONAL AND TRANSISTOR IGNITION SYSTEM DISTRIBUTORS

Removal

1. Remove the distributor cap, the rotor, and the dust cover (if so equipped).

2. Working from the inside of the distributor, pull the primary wire through the opening in the distributor.

3. Remove the breaker point and condenser plate retaining screws and lift the plate assembly out of the distributor.

4. **Mark one of the distributor weight springs and its brackets. Also mark one of the weights and its pivot pin.**

5. Carefully unhook and remove the weight springs.

6. Lift the lubricating wick from the cam assembly. Remove the cam assembly retainer and lift the cam assembly off the distributor shaft. Remove the thrust washer.

7. Remove the weight retainers and lift the weights out of the distributor.

Installation

1. Fill the grooves in the weight pivot pins with distributor cam lubricant (C4AZ-19D530-A).

2. Position the weights in the distributor **(the marked weight is placed on the marked pivot pin)** and install the weight retainers.

3. Place the thrust washer on the shaft.

4. Fill the grooves in the upper portion of the distributor shaft with distributor cam lubricant (C4AZ-19D530-A).

5. Install the cam assembly. **Be sure that the marked spring bracket on the cam assembly is near the marked spring bracket on the stop plate.**

If a new cam assembly is being installed, make sure that the cam is installed with the hypalon covered stop in tthe correct cam plate control slot. This can be done by measuring the length of the slot used on the old cam and by using the corresponding slot on the new cam. Some of the cams will have the size of the slot in degrees stamped near the slot. **If the wrong slot is used, an incorrect maximum advance will be obtained.**

Place a light film of distributor cam lubricant (C4AZ-19D530-A) on the distributor cam lobes. Install the retainer and the wick. Saturate the wick with SAE 10W engine oil.

6. Install the weight springs. **Be sure that the marked spring is attached to the marked spring brackets.**

7. Install the breaker point and condenser plate assembly.

8. Working from the inside of the distributor, push the primary wire through the opening in the distributor.

9. Install the dust cover (if so equipped), the rotor, and the distributor cap.

ADJUSTMENTS

Refer to Part 9-1, Section 3 for the adjustment procedures.

3 REMOVAL AND INSTALLATION

REMOVAL

1. Disconnect the primary wire at the coil or the distributor-transistor wire at the quick disconncet. Remove the distributor cap.

2. Scribe a mark on the distributor body and engine block indicating the position of the body in the block, and scribe another mark in the distributor body indicating the position of the rotor. The marks can be used as guides when installing the distributor in a correctly timed engine.

3. Remove the distributor hold down cap bolt and clamp, and then lift the distributor out of the block.

Do not rotate the crankshaft while the distributor is removed, or it will be necessary to time the engine.

INSTALLATION

1. If the crankshaft was rotated while the distributor was removed from the engine, it will be necessary to time the engine. Rotate the crankshaft until No. 1 piston is on TDC (after the compression stroke). Align the TDC mark on the timing pointer with the timing pin on the crankshaft damper. Position the distributor in the block with the rotor at the No. 1 firing position.

If the crankshaft has not been rotated, position the distributor in the block with rotor aligned with the mark previously scribed on the distributor body, and the marks on the distributor body and engine block in alignment. Install the retaining clamp.

Make sure the oil pump intermediate shaft properly engages the distributor shaft. It may be necessary to crank the engine with the starter, after the distributor drive gear is partially engaged, in order to engage the oil pump intermediate shaft.

2. Install, but do not tighten, the retaining clamp and bolt. Rotate the distributor body counterclockwise until one set of breaker points are just starting to open. Tighten the clamp.

3. Install the distributor cap.

4. Connect the primary wire to the coil or the distributor-transistor lead wire to the quick disconnect.

5. Check the ignition timing with a timing light and adjust it if necessary.

4 MAJOR REPAIR OPERATIONS

To perform the operations in this section, it will be necessary to remove the distributor from the car and place it in a vise.

BENCH DISASSEMBLY

Refer to Fig. 3 for the location of parts.

CONVENTIONAL IGNITION SYSTEM DISTRIBUTOR

1. Remove the rotor.

2. Disconnect the primary wire, the jumper strap, and the condenser wire from the breaker point assemblies.

3. Remove the retaining screws from the breaker point assemblies and condenser. Lift the breaker point assemblies and the condensor out of the distributor.

4. Working from the inside of the distributor, pull the primary wire

through the opening in the distributor.

5. Remove the breaker point and condenser plate retaining screws and lift the plate out of the distributor.

6. **Mark one of the distributor weight springs and its brackets. Also mark one of the wieghts and its pivot pin.**

7. Carefully unhook and remove the weight springs.

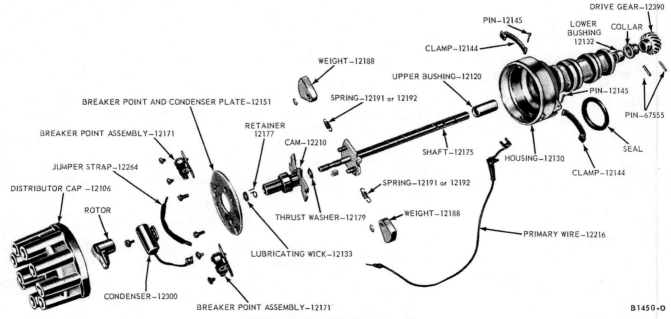

FIG. 3—Distributor Assembly

8. Lift the lubricating wick from the cam assembly. Remove the cam assembly retainer and lift the cam assembly off the distributor shaft. Remove the thrust washer.

9. Remove the weight retainers and lift the weights out of the distributor.

10. Remove the distributor cap clamps.

11. If the gear and shaft are to be used again, mark the gear and the shaft so that the pin holes can be easily aligned for assembly. Remove the gear roll pin (Fig. 4), and then remove the gear. (Fig. 5).

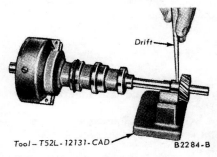

FIG. 4—Gear Pin Removal or Installation

FIG. 5—Gear Removal

FIG. 6—Collar Pin Removal or Installation

12. Remove the shaft collar roll pin (Fig. 6).

13. Invert the distributor and place it on a support in a position that will allow the distributor shaft to clear the support plate and press the shaft out of the collar and the

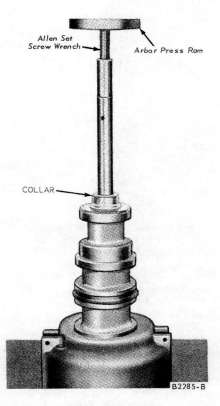

FIG. 7—Shaft Removal

distributor housing (Fig. 7).

14. Remove the distributor shaft upper bushing (Fig. 8).

15. Remove the distributor shaft lower bushing (Fig. 9).

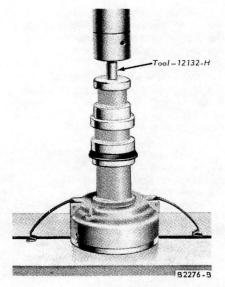

FIG. 8—Upper Bushing Removal

TRANSISTOR IGNITION SYSTEM DISTRIBUTOR

1. Remove the rotor and the dust cover.

FIG. 9—Lower Bushing Removal

2. Disconnect the distributor-transistor wire from the breaker point assembly.

3. Remove the retaining screws from the breaker point assembly and lift the breaker point assembly out of the distributor.

4. Working from the inside of the distributor, pull distributor-transistor wire through the opening in the distributor.

5. Follow steps 5-15 under "Conventional Ignition System Distributor."

BENCH ASSEMBLY

ORIGINAL SHAFT AND GEAR

Conventional Ignition System Distributor

1. Oil the new upper bushing, and install it on the bushing replacer tool. Then install the upper bushing (Fig. 10). When the tool bottoms against the distributor base, the bushing will be installed to the correct depth.

2. Burnish the bushing to the proper size (Fig. 11).

3. Invert the distributor and install the lower bushing in a similar manner.

4. Oil the shaft and slide it into the distributor body.

5. Place the collar in position on the shaft and align the holes in the collar and shaft, then install a new

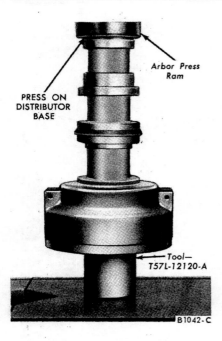

FIG. 10—Upper Bushing Installation

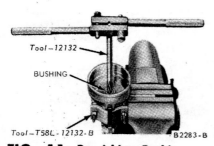

FIG. 11—Burnishing Bushing

pin (Fig. 6). Install the distributor cap clamps.

6. Check the shaft end play with a feeler gauge placed between the collar and the base of the distributor. If the end play is not within limits, replace the shaft and gear.

7. Attach the distributor shaft supporting tool to the distributor. Tighten the backing screw in the tool enough to remove all shaft end play.

8. Install the assembly in a press. Press the gear on the shaft (Fig. 12), using the marks made on the gear and shaft as guides to align the pin holes.

9. Remove the distributor from the press. Install the gear retaining pin (Fig. 4).

10. Position the distributor in a vise. Fill the grooves in the weight pivot pins with distributor cam lubricant (C4AZ-19D530-A).

11. Position the weights in the distributor (the marked weight is

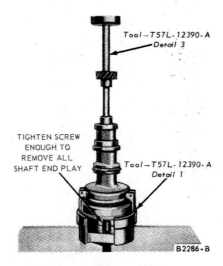

FIG. 12—Original Shaft and Gear Installation

placed on the marked pivot pin) and install the weight retainers.

12. Place the thrust washer on the shaft.

13. Fill the grooves in the upper portion of the distributor shaft with distributor cam lubricant (C4AZ-19D530-A).

14. Install the cam assembly. **Be sure that the marked spring bracket on the cam assembly is near the marked spring bracket on the stop plate.**

If a new cam assembly is being installed, make sure that the cam is installed with the hypalon covered stop in the correct cam plate control slot. This can be done by measuring the length of the slot used on the old cam and by using the corresponding slot on the new cam. Some of the cams will have the size of the slot in degrees stamped near the slot. **If the wrong slot is used, an incorrect maximum advance will be obtained.**

Place a light film of distributor cam lubricant (C4AZ-19D530-A) on the distributor cam lobes. Install the retainer and the wick. Saturate the wick with SAE 10W engine oil.

15. Install the weight springs. **Be sure that the marked spring is attached to the marked spring brackets.**

16. Place the breaker point and condenser plate in position and install the retaining screws.

17. Working from the inside of the distributor, push the primary wire through the opening in the distributor housing.

18. Place the breaker point assemblies and the condenser in posi-

tion and install the retaining screws.

19. Align and adjust the breaker point assemblies by following the procedure in Part 9-1.

20. Connect the primary wire, the jumper strap, and the condenser wire to the breaker point assemblies.

21. Install the rotor and the distributor cap.

22. Check and adjust (if necessary) the centrifugal advance mechanism (Refer to Part 9-1).

Transistor Ignition System Distributor

1. Follow steps 1-16 under "Original Shaft and Gear—Conventional Ignition System Distributor."

2. Working from the inside of the distributor, push the distributor-transistor wire through the opening in the distributor housing.

3. Place the breaker point assembly in position and install the retaining screws.

4. Align and adjust the breaker point assembly by following the procedure in Part 9-1.

5. Connect the distributor-transistor wire to the breaker point assembly.

6. Check and adjust (if necessary) the centrifugal advance.

7. Install the dust cover and the rotor.

NEW SHAFT AND GEAR

Conventional and Transistor Ignition System Distributor

The shaft and gear are replaced as an assembly. One part should not be replaced without replacing the other.

1. Follow steps 1,2,3 and 4 under

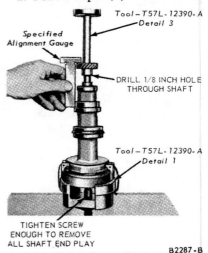

FIG. 13—New Shaft and Gear Installation

"Installing Original Shaft and Gear Conventional Ignition System Distributor."

2. Attach the distributor shaft supporting tool to the distributor and install he assembly in a vise. Insert a 0.024-inch feeler gauge between the backing screw and the shaft. Tighten the backing screw on the tool enough to remove all shaft end play, then remove the feeler gauge and allow the shaft to rest on the backing screw. Slide the collar on the shaft. While holding the collar in place *against the* distributor base, drill a ⅛-inch hole through the shaft using the hole in the collar as a pilot.

3. Position the gear on the end of the shaft. Install the assembly in a press.

4. With the backing screw on the support tool tightened enough to remove all end play, press the gear on the shaft to the specified distance from the bottom face of the gear to the bottom face of the distributor mounting flange (Fig. 13). Drill a ⅛-inch hole through the shaft using the hole in the gear as a pilot.

5. Remove the distributor from the press and remove the support tool. Install the collar retaining pin (Fig. 6) and the gear retaining pin (Fig. 4).

6. On a conventional ignition system distributor, complete the assembly by following steps 10 thru 22 under "Installing Original Shaft and Gear—Conventional Ignition System Distributor."

On a transistor ignition distributor, complete the assembly by following steps 10-16 under "Installing Original Shaft and Gear—Conventional Ignition System Distributor" and steps 2-7 under "Installing Original Shaft and Gear—Transistor Ignition System Distributor."

PART 9-5

SPECIFICATIONS

DISTRIBUTOR

GENERAL

240 Six	
Breaker Arm Spring Tension (Ounces)	17-21
Contact Spacing (Inches)	0.025
Dwell Angle at Idle Speed	37°-42°
289, 352, 390, 410 and 428 V-8	
Breaker Arm Spring Tension (Ounces)	17-21
Contact Spacing (Inches)	0.017
Dwell Angle at Idle Speed	26°-31°
427 V-8	
Breaker Arm Spring Tension (Ounces)	22-24
Contact Spacing (Inches)	0.019-0.021
Dwell Angle at Idle Speed	22°-24°

DIMENSIONS

Shaft End Play — Distributor Removed (Inches)	
240 Six	0.003-0.010
289 V-8	0.024-0.035
352, 390, 410, 427 and 428 V-8	0.022-0.032
Distance From Bottom of Mounting Flange to Bottom of Gear (Inches)	
289 V-8	4.031-4.038
352, 390, 410, 427 and 428 V-8	3.071-3.077

IGNITION TIMING

Manual-Shift Transmission — BTDC②	
240 Six Non-Thermactor①	6°
289 V-8 Non-Thermactor	6°
240 Six and 289 V-8 with Thermactor	TDC
390 V-8 Non-Thermactor①	10°
410 and 428 V-8 Non-Thermactor	10°
390, 410 and 428 V-8 with Thermactor	6°
427 V-8	8°
428 Police Interceptor V-8	12°
Automatic Transmission — BTDC②	
240 Six Non-Thermactor①	12°
289 V-8 Non-Thermactor	6°
240 Six and 289 V-8 with Thermactor	TDC
352, 410 and 428 V-8 Non-Thermactor	10°
390 V-8 Non-Thermactor①	10°
390, 410 and 428 V-8 with Thermactor	6°
427 V-8	8°
428 Police Interceptor V-8	12°

① For altitude operation, and/or to obtain optimum engine performance and fuel economy, the initial ignition timing may be advanced 5° over the "normal" setting. No further improvement in engine performance or fuel economy will be achieved by advancing beyond this point. Advance the timing progressively until engine detonation (spark knock) is evident under actual road test acceleration. Retard the timing until the detonation (spark knock) is eliminated.

② If the individual requirements of the car and/or the use of sub-standard fuels dictate, the initial timing may have to be retarded from the recommended setting to eliminate detonation (spark knock). If retiming is necessary, it should be done progressively and not to exceed 2°BTDC.

CONDENSER

Capacity (Microfarads)	0.21-0.25
Minimum Leakage (Megohms)	5
Maximum Series Resistance (Ohms)	1

APPLICATION TABLE

Engine	Transmission		Thermactor Emission System		Distributor	
	Std.	Auto.	With	Without	Type	No. (12127)
240	X			X	①	C6TF-AC
240	X		X		②	C6AF-AC
240 Economy	X			X	②	C6AF-AA
240		X		X	①	C6AF-Y
240		X	X		②	C6AF-AD
240 Economy		X		X	②	C6AF-AB
289	X			X	②	C5AF-M
289	X		X		②	C6AF-J
289		X		X	②	C5AF-N
289		X	X		②	C6AF-S
352		X		X	②	C5AF-BG
390 2-V	X			X	②	C6AF-A
390 2-V	X		X		②	C6AF-K
390 2-V		X		X	②	C6AF-B
390 2-V		X	X		②	C6AF-T
390 4-V	X			X	②	C6AF-C
390 4-V	X		X		②	C6AF-L
390 4-V		X		X	②	C6AF-D
390 4-V		X	X		②	C6AF-L
410 4-V	X			X	②	C6MF-A
410 4-V	X	X	X		②	C6AF-L
410 4-V		X		X	②	C6AF-D
427 ④	X			X	③	C5AF-F
428 4-V	X	X	X		②	C6AF-L
428 4-V	X	X		X	②	C6AF-E
428 4-V Police	X	X	X	X	②	C6AF-E

① Loadomatic ② Dual Advance ③ Centrifugal ④ Transistorized

ADVANCE CHARACTERISTICS

Note: The advance characteristics given apply to the distributor with the indicated number only. The distributor number is stamped on the distributor housing or on a plate attached to the distributor housing.

C5AF-12127-F

CENTRIFUGAL ADVANCE: Set the test stand to 0° at 250 rpm and 0 inches of mercury.		
Distributor rpm	Advance (Degrees)	Vacuum (Inches of Mercury)
650	2¼-4	0
750	4-5½	0
1000	7¼-8½	0
1600	9¾-11	0
2000	11½-13	0
Maximum Advance Limit . . . . .16°		

C5AF-12127-M

CENTRIFUGAL ADVANCE: Set the test stand to 0° at 250 rpm and 0 inches of mercury.		
Distributor rpm	Advance (Degrees)	Vacuum (Inches of Mercury)
650	1½-2½	0
800	4¾-5¾	0
1200	8½-9½	0
1600	10¼-11¾	0
2000	12-13¾	0
Maximum Advance Limit . . . . .14°		

VACUUM ADVANCE: Set the test stand at 0° at 1000 rpm and 0 inches of mercury.		
Distributor rpm	Advance (Degrees)	Vacuum (Inches of Mercury)
1000	1½-4½	8
1000	3½-6½	10
1000	6¾-9¾	14
Maximum Advance Limit . . . . .11°		

C5AF-12127-N

CENTRIFUGAL ADVANCE: Set the test stand to 0° at 250 rpm and 0 inches of mercury.		
Distributor rpm	Advance (Degrees)	Vacuum (Inches of Mercury)
450	1½-2½	0
600	5¼-6¼	0
800	7¼-8¼	0
1400	8¾-10	0
2000	10½-12	0
Maximum Advance Limit . . . . .14°		

VACUUM ADVANCE: Set the test stand to 0° at 1000 rpm and 0 inches of mercury.		
Distributor rpm	Advance (Degrees)	Vacuu m(Inchs of Mercury)
1000	1½-4¾	8
1000	5-8	10
1000	8¼-11	14
Maximum Advance Limit . . . . .12½°		

C5AF-12127-BG

CENTRIFUGAL ADVANCE: Set the test stand to 0° at 250 rpm and 0 inches of mercury.		
Distributor rpm	Advance (Degrees)	Vacuum (Inches of Mercury)
3	0-1	0
6	3¼-4¼	0
12	5½-6¾	0
18	7½-9	0
20	8¼-9¾	0
Maximum Advance Limit . . . . .11°		

VACUUM ADVANCE: Set the test stand to 0° at 1000 rpm and 0 inches of mercury.		
Distributor rpm	Advance (Degrees)	Vacuum (Inches of Mercury)
1000	3¾-7	10
1000	7-10	15
1000	7½-10½	20
Maximum Advance Limit . . . . .10½°		

C6AF-12127-A

CENTRIFUGAL ADVANCE: Set the test stand to 0° at 250 rpm and 0 inches of mercury.		
Distributor rpm	Advance (Degrees)	Vacuum (Inches of Mercury)
400	0-½	0
800	2½-3½	0
1200	4½-5½	0
1800	7¼-8¾	0
Maximum Advance Limit . . . . .14°		

VACUUM ADVANCE: Set the test stand to 0° at 1000 rpm and 0 inches of mercury.		
Distributor rpm	Advance (Degrees)	Vacuum (Inches of Mercury)
1000	0-1	5
1000	3½-6½	10
1000	7-10	15
Maximum Advance Limit . . . . .12°		

C6AF-12127-B

CENTRIFUGAL ADVANCE: Set the test stand to 0° at 250 rpm and 0 inches of mercury.		
Distributor rpm	Advance (Degrees)	Vacuum (Inches of Mercury)
625	1¾-2¾	0
1200	5¾-7	0
1500	7-8¼	0
2000	9-10½	0
Maximum Advance Limit . . . . .14°		

VACUUM ADVANCE: Set the test stand to 0° at 1000 rpm and 0 inches of mercury.		
Distributor rpm	Advance (Degrees)	Vacuum (Inches of Mercury
1000	0-1	5
1000	2-5½	9
1000	6-9	13
Maximum Advance Limit . . . . .12°		

C6AF-12127-C

CENTRIFUGAL ADVANCE: Set the test stand to 0° at 250 rpm and 0 inches of mercury.

Distributor rpm	Advance (Degrees)	Vacuum (Inches of Mercury)
600	2¼-3¼	0
1200	5¾-7	0
1600	7¼-8½	0
2000	8¾-10¼	0

Maximum Advance Limit . . . . .14°

VACUUM ADVANCE: Set the test stand to 0° at 1000 rpm and 0 inches of mercury.

Distributor rpm	Advance (Degrees)	Vacuum (Inches of Mercury)
1000	0-1	5
1000	6-9	13
1000	8¼-10¼	17

Maximum Advance Limit . . . . .12°

C6AF-12127-J

CENTRIFUGAL ADVANCE: Set the test stand to 0° at 250 rpm and 0 inches of mercury.

Distributor rpm	Advance (Degrees)	Vacuum (Inches of Mercury)
600	6-7	0
1000	11-12	0
1800	13½-15	0

Maximum Advance Limit . . . . .16°

VACUUM ADVANCE: Set the test stand to 0° at 1000 rpm and 0 inches of mercury.

Distributor rpm	Advance (Degrees)	Vacuum (Inches of Mercury)
1000	0-1	7
1000	2-5	13
1000	5-8	16

Maximum Advance Limit . . . . 8°

C6AF-12127-D

CENTRIFUGAL ADVANCE: Set the test stand to 0° at 250 rpm and 0 inches of mercury.

Distributor rpm	Advance (Degrees)	Vacuum (Inches of Mercury)
500	2¼-3	0
1200	5¾-7	0
1850	8-9½	0
2000	8½-10	0

Maximum Advance Limit . . . . .14°

VACUUM ADVANCE: Set the test stand to 0° at 1000 rpm and 0 inches of mercury.

Distributor rpm	Advance (Degrees)	Vacuum (Inches of Mercury)
1000	0-1	6
1000	1-4½	10
1000	9-12	18

Maximum Advance Limit . . . . .12½°

C6AF-12127-K

CENTRIFUGAL ADVANCE: Set the test stand to 0° at 250 rpm and 0 inches of mercury.

Distributor rpm	Advance (Degrees)	Vacuum (Inches of Mercury)
500	2-3	0
1000	6½-7¼	0
1300	7¾-9	0
2000	11½-13	0

Maximum Advance Limit . . . . .16°

VACUUM ADVANCE: Set the test stand to 0° at 1000 rpm and 0 inches of mercury.

Distributor rpm	Advance (Degrees)	Vacuum (Inches of Mercury)
1000	0-1	5
1000	6-9	13
1000	8¼-11¼	17

Maximum Advance Limit . . . . .12°

C6AF-12127-E

CENTRIFUGAL ADVANCE: Set the test stand to 0° at 250 rpm and 0 inches of mercury.

Distributor rpm	Advance (Degrees)	Vacuum (Inches of Mercury)
500	1½-2½	0
1100	5-6¼	0
1500	6¾-8	0
2000	8¾-10¼	0

Maximum Advance Limit . . . . .11°

VACUUM ADVANCE: Set the test stand to 0° at 1000 rpm and 0 inches of mercury.

Distributor rpm	Advance (Degrees)	Vacuum (Inches of Mercury)
1000	0-1	6
1000	3-6	11
1000	7-10	15

Maximum Advance Limit . . . . .12½°

C6AF-12127-L

CENTRIFUGAL ADVANCE: Set the test stand to 0° at 250 rpm and 0 inches of mercury.

Distributor rpm	Advance (Degrees)	Vacuum (Inches of Mercury)
500	2-3	0
900	6¼-7	0
1400	8¾-10	0
2000	10¾-12¼	0

Maximum Advance Limit . . . . .16°

VACUUM ADVANCE: Set the test stand to 0° at 1000 rpm and 0 inches of mercury.

Distributor rpm	Advance (Degrees)	Vacuum (Inches of Mercury)
1000	0-1	6
1000	3-6	11
1000	7-10	15

Maximum Advance Limit . . . . .12½°

C6AF-12127-S

CENTRIFUGAL ADVANCE: Set the test stand to 0° at 250 rpm and 0 inches of mercury.

Distributor rpm	Advance (Degrees)	Vacuum (Inches of Mercury)
600	2-3	0
800	6¼-7¼	0
1200	11¼-12¼	0
1800	13-14½	0

Maximum Advance Limit . . . . .16°

VACUUM ADVANCE: Set the test stand to 0° at 1000 rpm and 0 inches of mercury.

Distributor rpm	Advance (Degrees)	Vacuum Inches of Mercury
1000	0-1	5
1000	2-5	7
1000	7-10	12

Maximum Advance Limit . . . . .10°

C6AF-12127-T

CENTRIFUGAL ADVANCE: Set the test stand to 0° at 250 rpm and 0 inches of mercury.

Distributor rpm	Advance (Degrees)	Vacuum (Inches of Mercury)
475	1¼-2¼	0
700	3¾-4¾	0
1300	7-8¼	0
1800	9¾-11	0

Maximum Advance Limit . . . . .16°

VACUUM ADVANCE: Set the test stand to 0° at 1000 rpm and 0 inches of mercury.

Distributor rpm	Advance (Degrees)	Vacuum (Inches of Mercury)
1000	0-1	5
1000	6-9	13
1000	8½-11½	18

Maximum Advance Limit . . . . .12°

C6AF-12127-Y

VACUUM ADVANCE: Set the test stand to 0° at 250 rpm and 0 inches of mercury.

Distributor rpm	Advance (Degrees)	Vacuum (Inches of Mercury)
800	1-2	0.90
1200	4½-5½	2.10
1600	7-8¼	3.60
2000	8¾-10	4.80

Maximum Advance Limit . . . . .12¾°

C6AF-12127-AA

CENTRIFUGAL ADVANCE: Set the test stand to 0° at 250 rpm and 0 inches of mercury.

Distributor rpm	Advance (Degrees)	Vacuum (Inches of Mercury)
600	1¼-2¼	0
700	3¼-4¼	0
1200	7¼-8½	0
1600	9¼-10¾	0
2000	11½-13	0

Maximum Advance Limit . . . . .14°

VACUUM ADVANCE: Set the test stand to 0° at 1000 rpm and 0 inches of mercury.

Distributor rpm	Advance (Degrees)	Vacuum (Inches of Mercury)
1000	3-6	7
1000	6-9	9
1000	9½-12½	14
1000	9½-12½	20

Maximum Advance Limit . . . . .12½°

C6AF-12127-AB

CENTRIFUGAL ADVANCE: Set the test stand to 0° at 250 rpm and 0 inches of mercury.

Distributor rpm	Advance (Degrees)	Vacuum (Inches of Mercury)
500	¼-1¼	0
1000	4½-5¾	0
1200	5½-6¾	0
1600	7¼-8½	0
2000	9-10½	0

Maximum Advance Limit . . . . .11°

VACUUM ADVANCE: Set the test stand to 0° at 1000 rpm and 0 inches of mercury.

Distributor rpm	Advance (Degrees)	Vacuum (Inches of Mercury)
1000	3-5¼	8
1000	6½-9½	10
1000	8-11	15
1000	8-11	20

Maximum Advance Limit . . . . .11°

C6AF-12127-AC

CENTRIFUGAL ADVANCE: Set the test stand to 0° at 250 rpm and 0 inches of mercury.

Distributor rpm	Advance (Degrees)	Vacuum (Inches of Mercury)
400	0-½	0
600	2-3	0
1000	6-7¼	0
1550	9-10½	0

Maximum Advance Limit . . . . .16°

VACUUM ADVANCE: Set the test stand to 0° at 1000 rpm and 0 inches of mercury.

Distributor rpm	Advance (Degrees)	Vacuum (Inches of Mercury)
1000	0-1	5
1000	6-9	10
1000	8-11	15

Maximum Advance Limit . . . . .12°

C6AF-12127-AD

CENTRIFUGAL ADVANCE: Set the test stand to 0° at 250 rpm and 0 inches of mercury.

Distributor rpm	Advance (Degrees)	Vacuum (Inches of Mercury
300	0-½	0
500	2¼-3¼	0
1000	5¾-6¾	0
1500	7½-9	0
2000	9½-11	0

Maximum Advance Limit . . . . .14°

VACUUM ADVANCE: Set the test stand to 0° at 1000 rpm and 0 inches of mercury.

Distributor rpm	Advance (Degrees)	Vacuum (Inches of Mercury)
1000	0-1	4
1000	4¾-7¾	10
1000	8½-11½	15
1000	9-12	18

Maximum Advance Limit . . . . .12°

C6MF-12127-A

CENTRIFUGAL ADVANCE: Set the test stand to 0° at 250 rpm and 0 inches of mercury.

Distributor rpm	Advance (Degrees)	Vacuum (Inches of Mercury)
500	2¼-3¼	0
1000	5-6¼	0
1500	6¾-8¼	0
2000	8½-10	0

Maximum Advance Limit . . . . .14°

VACUUM ADVANCE: Set the test stand to 0° at 1000 rpm and 0 inches of mercury.

Distributor rpm	Advance (Degrees)	Vacuum (Inches of Mercury)
1000	0-1	5
1000	2¾-5¾	10
1000	7-10	15
1000	8-11	18

Maximum Advance Limit . . . . .11°

C6TF-12127-AC

VACUUM ADVANCE: Set the test stand to 0° at 250 rpm and 0 inches of mercury.

Distributor rpm	Advance (Degrees)	Vacuum (Inches of Mercury)
800	4½-5½	1.2
1200	7½-8¾	2.1
1600	9¼-10½	3.7
2000	10¼-11¾	4.9

Maximum Advance Limit . . . . .14°

SPARK PLUGS

Engines	Type	Size	Gap (Inches)	Torque (Ft-lbs)①
240	BTF42	18MM	0.032-0.036	15-20
289, 352, 390, 410 and 428	BF-42	18MM	0.032-0.036	15-20
427	BF-32	18MM	0.028-0.032	15-20

① When a new spark plug is installed in a new replacement cylinder head, torque the spark plugs to 20-30 ft-lbs.

COIL

Conventional Ignition System
Primary Resistance (Ohms) . . . . .1.40-1.54(75°F)
Secondary Resistance (Ohms) . . . . .8000-8800(75°F)

Amperage Draw
   Engine Stopped 4.5
   Engine Idling 2.5
Primary Circuit Resistor . . . . .1.30-1.40(75°F)

Transistor Ignition System
Primary Resistance (Ohms) . . . . .0.226-0.252(75°F)
Secondary Resistance (Ohms) . . . . . . .4900-5680(75°F)

Amperage Draw
   Engine Cranking 4.0
   Engine Idling 5.00

Primary Circuit Resistors
   Emittor . . . . .0.31-0.35(75°F)
   Collector . . . . .0.41-0.45(75°F)
   Base . . . . .7.1-7.9(75°F)

SPECIAL TOOLS

Description	Tool No.
Breaker point aligning tool	KD-111 or TK-419-A
Breaker point spring tension scale	12151
Bushing burnisher	12132
Bushing installer	T57L-12120-A or 12132-A
Bushing remover	12132-H
Distributor holding clamp	T58L-12132-B
Distributor testors	RE-236 RE-1416
Drive gear installing fixture	T57L-12390-A
Drive gear locating gauge	T57L-12390-A5
Drive gear remover kit	T52L-12390-CAD
Ignition scopes	RE-27-55 RE-881
Pin removing fixture	T52L-12131-CAD
Tach-dwell tester	RE-27-44
Timing light	13-07

FUEL SYSTEM

GROUP 10

PART 10-1 GENERAL FUEL SYSTEM SERVICE

This part covers general fuel system diagnosis, tests, adjustment and repair procedures. In addition, the cleaning and inspection procedures are covered.

For fuel system component removal, disassembly, assembly, installation, major repair procedures and specifications, refer to the pertinent part of this group.

The carburetor identification tag is attached to the carburetor. The basic part number for all carburetors is 9510. To procure replacement parts, it is necessary to know the part number prefix and suffix and, in some instances, the design change code (Fig. 1).

Always refer to the Master Parts Catalog for parts usage and interchangeability before replacing a carburetor or a component part for a carburetor.

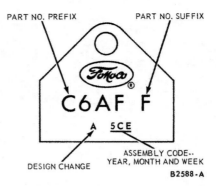

FIG. 1—Typical Carburetor Identification Tag

1 DIAGNOSIS AND TESTING

DIAGNOSIS

FUEL TANK, LINES AND FILTER

Water and dirt that accumulate in the fuel tank can cause a restricted fuel line or filter and malfunction of the fuel pump, or carburetor. Condensation, which is the greatest source of water entering the fuel tank, is formed by moisture in the air when it strikes the cold interior walls of the fuel tank.

If the accumulation of sediment in the filter is excessive, the fuel tank should be removed and flushed, and the line from the fuel pump to the tank should be blown out.

Leakage in the fuel inlet line can cause low vacuum and volume conditions, and loss of fuel.

A restricted fuel tank vent can cause low fuel pump pressure and volume may, in some instances, result in collapsed inlet line hoses or a collapsed fuel tank.

FUEL PUMP

Incorrect fuel pump pressure and low volume (flow rate) are the two most likely fuel pump troubles that will affect engine performance. Low pressure will cause a lean mixture and fuel starvation at high speeds and excessive pressure will cause high fuel consumption and carburetor flooding. Low volume will cause fuel starvation at high speeds.

FUEL PUMP, TANK AND LINES DIAGNOSIS GUIDE

LOW FUEL PUMP PRESSURE OR VOLUME	Diaphragm stretched or leaking. Fuel pump diaphragm spring is weak. Rocker arm or eccentric worn or undersize. Excessive clearance between rocker arm and fuel pump link. Fittings loose or cracked.	Fuel filter clogged (low volume). Fuel line cracked or broken. Fuel pump valves improperly seating. Dirt in fuel tank and/or lines. Fuel tank vent restricted. Diaphragm ruptured. Main body retaining screws loose.
HIGH FUEL PUMP PRESSURE OR VOLUME	Diaphragm spring too strong or improper spring. Diaphragm surface too tight (over-tensioned).	Pump link has no free play (frozen). Diaphragm vent hole is plugged or omitted.
LOW FUEL PUMP VACUUM	Diaphragm stretched or leaking. Fuel pump springs weak. Fuel pump valves improperly seating. Diaphragm ruptured.	Rocker arm or eccentric worn. Excessive clearance between rocker arm and fuel pump link. Main body retaining screws loose.
LOW FUEL PUMP VOLUME WITH NORMAL PRESSURE	Fuel filter clogged. Fuel pump to carburetor inlet line obstructed, crimped or leaks.	Restriction in fuel supply line to fuel pump.
FUEL PUMP LEAKS FUEL	Diaphragm defective. Fittings loose. Threads on fittings stripped.	Body cracked. Diaphragm pull rod oil seal defective.

FUEL PUMP, TANK AND LINES DIAGNOSIS GUIDE (Continued)

FUEL PUMP LEAKS OIL	Fuel pump retaining bolts loose.	Mounting gasket defective.
FUEL PUMP NOISE	Rocker arm or eccentric worn. Mounting bolts loose. Rocker arm springs weak or	broken. Diaphragm pull rod bumper pad defective.
FUEL TANK AND/OR INLET LINE HOSES COLLAPSED	Fuel tank vent restricted.	

CARBURETORS

Prior to performing an extensive diagnosis of carburetor malfunction on a Thermactor exhaust emission control equipped car, disconnect the anti-backfire valve vacuum sensing and air supply lines at the intake manifold. Plug the manifold connections to prevent leakage. Normal fuel system diagnosis procedures can then be performed.

Dirt accumulation in the fuel and air passages, improper idle adjustments, and improper fuel level are the major sources of carburetor troubles.

CARBURETOR DIAGNOSIS GUIDE

FLOODING OR LEAKING CARBURETOR	Cracked carburetor body, or fuel bowl (Holley 4-V). Defective main body and/or fuel bowl gasket(s) Holley 4-V). High fuel level or float setting. Fuel inlet needle not seating prop-	erly or worn needle and/or seat. Ruptured accelerating pump diaphragm. Excessive fuel pump pressure. Defective power valve gasket. Ruptured power valve diaphragm.
HARD STARTING	Anti-backfire valve stuck open (if equipped with Thermactor exhaust emission control). Improper starting procedure causing a flooded engine. Improper carburetor fuel level. Improper idle adjustments. Sticking or incorrectly seating fuel inlet needle. Incorrect fuel pump pressure.	Improper carburetor gasket and/or spacer combination. Incorrect setting of choke thermostatic spring housing. Choke linkage or plate binding. Binding or broken manual choke linkage. Restrictions or air leaks in the choke vacuum or hot air passages. Dirty air cleaner element.
STALLING	**ENGINE HOT OR COLD** Incorrect idle fuel mixture. Engine idle speed too slow (fast or cold idle adjustments). Dirt, water or ice in fuel filter. Positive crankcase ventilation system malfunctioning or restricted. Fuel lines restricted or leaking air. Fuel tank vent restricted. Leaking intake manifold or carburetor gaskets. Carburetor icing (cold, wet or humid weather).	Incorrect throttle linkage adjustment to carburetor. Clogged air bleeds or idle passages. Defective fuel pump. **ENGINE HOT ONLY** Improperly adjusted or defective carburetor dashpot (Ford carburetors). Idle compensator malfunctioning (Ford 4-V). Coolant control thermostat defective. Excessive looseness of throttle shaft in bore(s) of throttle body.
ROUGH IDLE	Anti-backfire valve stuck open (if equipped with Thermactor exhaust emission control). Positive crankcase ventilation system malfunctioning or restricted. Incorrect idle mixture adjustment. Idle compensator malfunction (Ford 4-V). Idle adjusting needle(s) grooved,	worn, or otherwise damaged. Idle air bleeds restricted. Idle air or fuel passages restricted. Idle discharge holes restricted. Idle discharge holes not in proper relation to throttle plate(s). Excessive dirt in air cleaner. High or low fuel level or float setting.

CARBURETOR DIAGNOSIS GUIDE (Continued)

ROUGH IDLE (Continued)	Fuel inlet needle not seating properly, or worn needle or seat. Power valve leaking. Restricted air bleeds. Plugged idle fuel channel restrictor. Worn or damaged main metering jet.	Accelerating pump discharge ball check or needle (Holley 4-V) and/or weight not seating properly. Fuel pump pressure too low, or excessive. Fuel siphoning from secondary main fuel system (Holley 4-V or Ford 4-V). Restriction in main fuel passage.
POOR ACCELERATION	Poor acceleration complaints fall under one of three headings: the engine is sluggish on acceleration, the engine stalls when accelerated, or the engine hesitates or develops a flat spot when accelerated. Poor acceleration is caused by either an excessively lean or rich mixture on acceleration and/or defects or improper adjustments in the ignition system. **A LEAN MIXTURE ON ACCELERATION CAN BE CAUSED BY:** Low fuel pump pressure. Sticking fuel inlet needle. Low fuel level or float setting. Restriction in main fuel passage. Air leak between the carburetor and the manifold caused by loose mounting bolts or defective gasket. Air leak at the throttle shaft caused by a worn throttle shaft. Accelerating pump diaphragm defective. Incorrect accelerating pump stroke adjustment. Accelerating pump fuel inlet valve (Elastomer valve or ball check) not seating on acceleration. Restriction in the accelerating pump discharge passage. Accelerating pump discharge Elastomer valve (Ford 2-V or 4-V), ball check or weight not coming fully off its seat, or failing to seat properly on the reverse stroke of the pump diaphragm. Air leak at the accelerating pump cover caused by a defective gasket or	warped pump cover. **4-V CARBURETORS** Defective power valve spring. Defective secondary diaphragm. Air leak where secondary vacuum pick-up tube fits into air horn, between air horn and the main body, or between the secondary diaphragm housing cover and housing. Secondary throttle plates wedged in barrels. Bent secondary throttle shaft. Secondary throttle plates operating rod binding, or disconnected from secondary diaphragm or secondary throttle lever. Secondary vacuum passage ball check stuck on its seat. Secondary vacuum probe restricted or not properly positioned. **A RICH MIXTURE ON ACCELERATION CAN BE CAUSED BY:** Excessive fuel pump pressure. High fuel level or float setting. Fuel inlet needle not seating properly or worn needle and/or seat. Malfunctioning automatic choke. Excessively dirty air cleaner. Incorrect accelerating pump stroke adjustment. Power valve leakage. Restricted air bleeds. Worn or damaged mail metering jet. Accelerating pump Elastomer valve (Ford 2-V or 4-V) ball check and/or weight not seating properly.
INCONSISTENT ENGINE IDLE SPEED	Anti-backfire valve stuck open (if equipped with Thermactor exhaust emission control). Fast idle screw contacting low step of cam at curb idle. Incorrect throttle linkage adjustment to carburetor. Binding or sticking throttle linkage or accelerator pedal. Sticking carburetor throttle shaft. Excessive looseness of throttle shaft in bores of throttle body.	Improperly adjusted or defective carburetor dashpot (automatic transmission). Incorrectly installed throttle plates. Idle compensator malfunctioning (Ford 4-V). Positive crankcase ventilation system restricted. Sticking fuel inlet needle. Defective spark valve or gasket (Ford 1-V). Defective power valve or gasket.

CARBURETOR DIAGNOSIS GUIDE (Continued)

AUTOMATIC CHOKE SLOW WARM-UP, ON TOO OFTEN	Thermostatic choke setting too rich. Choke linkage sticking or binding. Incorrect choke linkage adjustment. Choke plate misaligned or binding in air horn.	Defective coolant thermostat. Restricted coolant line at carburetor. Restriction or air leak in the choke vacuum or hot air passage. Choke heat inlet tube restricted. Choke clean air tube restricted.
SEVERE TRANSMISSION ENGAGEMENT AFTER COLD ENGINE START	Carburetor fast idle speed setting too high. Throttle operating on starting step	(highest step) of fast idle cam. Binding or sticking throttle linkage.
SURGING (CRUISING SPEEDS TO TOP SPEEDS)	Clogged main jets. Improper size main jets. Low fuel level or float setting. Low fuel pump pressure or volume. Clogged filter or filter screen.	Distributor vacuum passage clogged. Defective spark valve or gasket (Ford 1-V). Defective power valve or gasket.
REDUCED TOP SPEED	Anti-backfire valve stuck open (if equipped with Thermactor exhaust emission control). Float setting too high or too low. Fuel pump pressure or volume too high or too low. Improper size or obstructed main jets. Power valve spring weak, or power valve restricted. Restricted air bleeds. Restriction in main fuel passages. Excessive dirt in air cleaner. Throttle plates not fully open. Faulty choke operation. Improper throttle linkage adjustment.	**4-V CARBURETORS** Air leak where secondary vacuum pick-up tube fits into air horn and main body, or air leakage between the secondary diaphragm housing cover and housing or the air horn mounting gasket. Secondary diaphragm return spring too stiff. Secondary throttle plates wedged in barrels. Bent secondary throttle shaft. Secondary throttle plate operating rod binding. Secondary vacuum passage ball check sticking on its seat.

TESTS

FUEL PUMP TESTS

Two tests: fuel pump static pressure and fuel volume are necessary to determine that the fuel pump is in satisfactory condition.

If both the fuel pump volume and pressure are within specifications (Part 10-9) and the pump and lines are in satisfactory condition, a vacuum test is not required.

If the pump volume is low, but the pressure is within specifications, a fuel pump capacity test must be made with the in-line filter or filter element (427-V-8) removed. If the pump volume meets specifications with the filter or filter element removed, replace the filter or element. If the pump volume is still below specifications, repeat the capacity test, using an auxiliary fuel supply. If the pump volume still does not meet specifications, replace the pump. If the pump does meet specifications, there is a

restriction in the fuel supply from the tank or the tank is not venting properly.

The tests are performed with the engine temperature stabilized at the normal operating temperature and the fuel pump installed on the engine. **Make certain the replaceable fuel filter or fuel filter element is not restricted or clogged or has been changed within the recommended maintenance mileage interval.** When in doubt, install a new fuel filter or filter element prior to performing the tests. A clogged or restricted filter is often the cause of fuel system malfunction.

Pressure Test

1. Remove the carburetor air cleaner assembly (Part 10-6) Disconnect the fuel inlet line or fuel filter at the carburetor.

On cars equipped with an in-line fuel filter attached to the carburetor, loosen the hose clamp at the fuel

filter. Unscrew the filter from the carburetor. Connect the hose to the filter and tighten the clamp.

Use care to prevent combustion due to fuel spillage.

2. Connect a pressure gauge, restrictor and flexible hose (Fig. 2) between the carburetor inlet connector and the fuel inlet line or in-line fuel filter (if so equipped).

3. Position the flexible hose and the restrictor so that the fuel can be expelled into a suitable container (Fig. 2) for the capacity (volume) test.

4. Operate the engine. Vent the system into the container by opening the hose restrictor momentarily before taking a pressure reading.

5. Operate the engine at 500 rpm. After the fuel pump pressure has stabilized, it should be to specification (Part 10-9).

Capacity (Volume) Test

Perform this test only when the

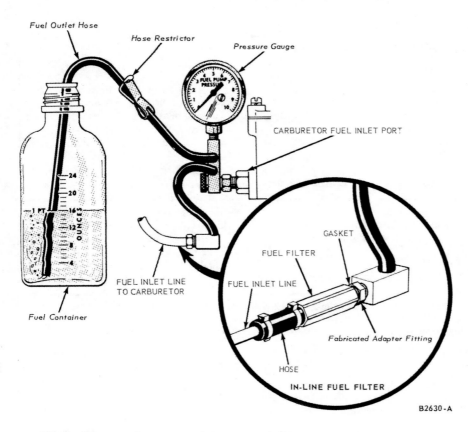

FIG. 2—Typical Fuel Pump Pressure and Capacity Tests

fuel pump pressure is within specifications (Part 10-9).

1. Operate the engine at 500 rpm.

2. Open the hose restrictor and expel the fuel into the container (Fig. 2), while observing the time required to expel one pint; then, close the restrictor. At least one pint of fuel should be expelled within the specified (Part 10-9) time limit.

3. Remove the test equipment, and connect the fuel inlet line or inline fuel filter (if so equipped) to the carburetor.

AIR INTAKE DUCT VALVE TEST—289, 352 and 390 V-8

Proper operation of the air intake duct thermostatic valve can be determined by the following test:

1. Remove the air duct (Part 10-6). Place the air duct assembly in a container of cool water (below 75°F.). Be sure that the thermostat is covered by the water.

2. Place a thermometer in the water and observe the temperature.

3. With water temperature at 75°F. or below, the valve should be in the heat-on position.

4. Using a hot plate or other suitable device, heat the water slowly.

5. When the water temperature reaches 85°F., the valve should start

to open. **If the valve does not start to open at this time, stabilize the water temperature at 85°F. for eight minutes before condemning the unit.**

6. When the water temperature reaches 100°F. or higher, the valve should be in the full heat-off position.

7. If the operation of the valve is unsatisfactory, remove the thermostat and spring assembly and check the valve plate shaft for binding.

8. If the valve plate moves freely, replace the thermostat and spring assembly. Retest the heat-on and the heat-off temperatures.

9. If the valve does not operate correctly, adjust the thermostat rod. By increasing the rod length, the valve plate will be moved toward the heat-off position. By decreasing the rod length the valve plate will be moved toward the heat-on position.

CARBURETOR TESTS

Accelerating Pump Discharge Test

1. Remove the air cleaner (Part 10-6).

2. Open the primary throttle plates and observe the fuel flow from the accelerating pump discharge nozzles. If the system is oper-

ating correctly, a quick steady stream of fuel will flow from the discharge nozzles.

Power Valve Tests

A power valve must not be replaced unless it is leaking sufficiently to cause an unadjustable rough engine idle condition. Fuel accumulation in the power valve cover does not necessarily indicate a defective power valve. Fuel vapors will be drawn into the vacuum side of the power valve and condense during periods of deceleration. Leakage in the power valve area can be caused by an improperly tightened cover or defective gaskets. Any defect in the gasket sealing qualities must be corrected before the power valve is replaced.

Power valve leakage that causes an unadjustable rough engine idle condition can be diagnosed, in most instances, by the fact that the idle mixture needle(s) must be nearly, or completely seated in order to obtain a relatively smooth engine idle condition. If power valve leakage is suspected, the following test procedure must be performed.

Ford 2-V and 4-V Carburetors

1. Remove the carburetor from the intake manifold. Invert the carburetor.

2. Remove the glass bowl from the fixture (Fig. 3). Fill the bowl half-full of water. Install the bowl on the fixture.

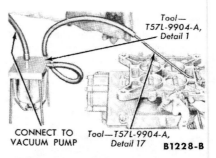

FIG. 3—Ford Carburetor Power Valve Test

3. Connect a line from the vacuum pump to the fitting on top of the fixture. Insert the large OD end of the wand into the tube and attach the other end of the tube to the fitting on the side of the fixture. Slip the rubber gasket (furnished with the tool) over the small OD end of the wand. Hold this end against the power valve vacuum pick-up port (Fig. 3).

4. Look for bubble formations in the water in the bowl. A continuous stream of bubbles indicates leakage through the power valve diaphragm or gasket, or the cover or gasket.

If leakage is encountered, the power valve, power valve gasket, cover, and cover gasket should be replaced one at a time with a new part and the test repeated until the source of leakage has been found. If the source of leakage can not be found, the gasket seats are damaged and the defective parts should be replaced.

A few bubbles may be noticed immediately upon attaching the vacuum line. The bubbling should stop within approximately 15 seconds or after the air has been removed from the system. If no bubbles are seen,

the power valve, gaskets and cover are sealing properly.

Holley 4-V Carburetor(s)

1. Remove the secondary fuel bowl(s) and secondary metering block(s) from the carburetor(s).

2. Install the fuel bowl, metering block, and gaskets on the adapter plate (Fig. 4). **Be sure the fuel bowl screws are properly tightened.**

3. Remove the glass bowl from the fixture and fill it half-full of water.

4. Install a bowl on the fixture.

5. Connect a line from a vacuum pump to the fitting on top of the fixture.

6. Connect a line from the adapter plate to the fitting on the side of the fixture.

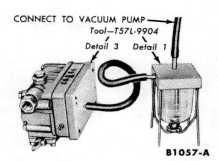

FIG. 4—Typical Holley Carburetor Power Valve Test

7. Follow step 4 under Power Valve, Ford 2-V and 4-V Carburetors.

---

2 COMMON ADJUSTMENTS AND REPAIRS

CARBURETOR ADJUSTMENTS

FLOAT ADJUSTMENT—DRY

Ford 1-V. The dry float fuel level adjustment for the Ford 1-V carburetor is a final float or fuel level adjustment.

1. Remove the carburetor air horn and gasket from the carburetor. Refer to Air Horn to Main Body Gasket Replacement in this section for the proper procedure.

2. Measure the distance from the gasket surface of the upper body (air horn) to the top of the float (Fig. 5). If the float adjustment is not within the specified dimension, bend the float arm tab, as necessary, to obtain the specified dimension. **Do not apply pressure on the fuel inlet needle. The viton tip of the fuel inlet needle may be damaged through undue pressure exerted on it and cause an improper fuel level within the bowl.**

3. Install the carburetor air horn and a new gasket on the carburetor. Refer to Carburetor Air Horn to Main Body Gasket Replacement (in this section) for the proper procedure.

Ford 2-V and 4-V. The dry float adjustment is a preliminary fuel level adjustment only. The final adjustment (Fuel Level Float Adjustment —Wet) must be made after the carburetor is mounted on the engine.

With the air horn removed, the float raised and the fuel inlet needle seated, check the distance between the top surface of the main body and

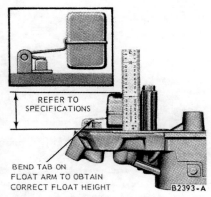

REFER TO SPECIFICATIONS

BEND TAB ON FLOAT ARM TO OBTAIN CORRECT FLOAT HEIGHT

FIG. 5—Carburetor Float Adjustment—Ford 1-V

the top surface of the float for conformance to specifications (Part 10-9). Take the measurement near the center of the float at a point 1/8 inch from the free end of the float.

If the cardboard float gauge is used, place the gauge in the corner of the enlarged end section of the fuel bowl (Fig. 6). The gauge should touch the float near the end, but not on the end radius.

Depress the float tab to seat the fuel inlet needle. **The float height is measured from the gasket surface of the main body with the gasket removed.** If necessary, bend the tab on the float to bring the setting within the specified limits. This should provide the proper preliminary fuel level setting.

Holley 4-V. The dry float adjustment is a preliminary fuel level adjustment only. The final adjustment

(Fuel Level Float Adjustment— Wet) must be performed after the carburetor is installed on the engine.

With the fuel bowl and float assembly removed, adjust the float so that it is parallel to the fuel bowl, with the fuel bowl inverted (Fig. 7).

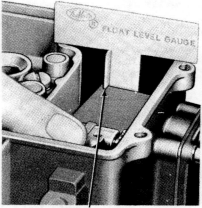

FLOAT SHOULD JUST TOUCH AT THIS POINT

FIG. 6—Fuel Level Float Adjustment (Dry)—Ford 2-V and 4-V

SECONDARY THROTTLE PLATE ADJUSTMENT—FORD AND HOLLEY 4-V

1. Hold the secondary throttle plates closed.

2. Turn the secondary throttle shaft lever adjusting screw (stop screw) out (counterclockwise) until the secondary throttle plates stick in

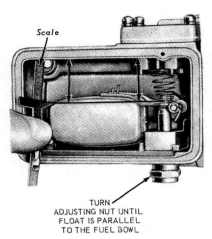

FIG. 7—Float Adjustment (Dry) Holley 4-V

the throttle bores (Figs. 8 and 9).

3. Turn the screw in (clockwise) until the screw JUST contacts the secondary lever.

4. **Turn the screw in (clockwise) the specified distance (Part 10-9).**

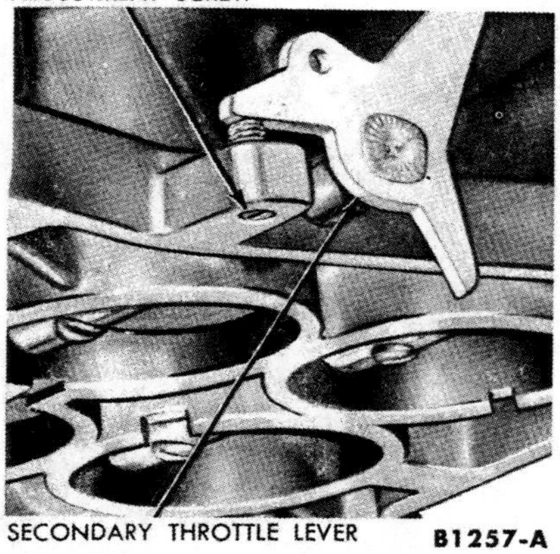

FIG. 9—Secondary Throttle Plate Adjustment—Holley 4-V

FIG. 8—Secondary Throttle Plate Adjustment—Ford 4-V

AUTOMATIC CHOKE PLATE CLEARANCE (PULL-DOWN) AND FAST IDLE CAM LINKAGE ADJUSTMENT—FORD CARBURETORS

1. Remove the air cleaner (Part 10-6) and the choke thermostatic spring housing from the carburetor, if they have not been previously removed. To remove the thermostatic spring housing with the carburetor installed on the car, refer to Thermostatic Choke Spring Housing and Gasket Replacement, in this section.

2. Bend a specified size (Part 10-9) wire gauge at a 90° angle, approximately ⅛ inch from its end (Figs. 10 and 11).

make an "S" or "Z" bend in the rod (link) between the choke piston and piston lever until the choke plate opens just wide enough to allow a gauge or drill of the specified clearance size between the front of the choke plate and the air horn (Fig. 10). **The bend in the link must be in the form of an S or Z to prevent interference or restricted movement of the piston assembly.**

6. On a Ford 2-V or 4-V carburetor, pull the choke countershaft lever counterclockwise until the gauge is snug in the piston slot. Hold the wire gauge in place by exerting light pressure on the countershaft lever, and adjust the choke plate clevis (pull-

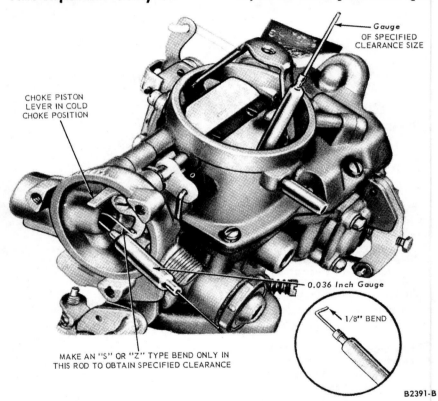

FIG. 10—Choke Plate Clearance (Pull-Down) Adjustment—Ford 1-V

3. Block the throttle about half-open so that the fast idle cam does not contact the fast idle adjustment screw.

4. Insert the bent end of the gauge between the lower edge of the piston slot and the upper edge of the right hand slot in the choke housing (Figs. 10 and 11).

5. On a Ford 1-V carburetor, pull the choke piston lever counterclockwise until the gauge is snug in the piston slot. Hold the wire gauge in place by exerting light pressure on the choke piston lever. Gradually

down) adjusting nut to obtain the specified clearance (Part 10-9) between the front of the choke plate and the air horn (Fig. 11).

7. Install the choke thermostatic spring housing and gasket on the choke housing. Install the spring housing retainer and screws.

8. Rotate the spring housing counterclockwise (rich direction) to align the center index mark on the choke *housing* with the index mark on the spring housing. Rotate the spring housing an additional 90° counterclockwise (Figs. 12 and 13) and

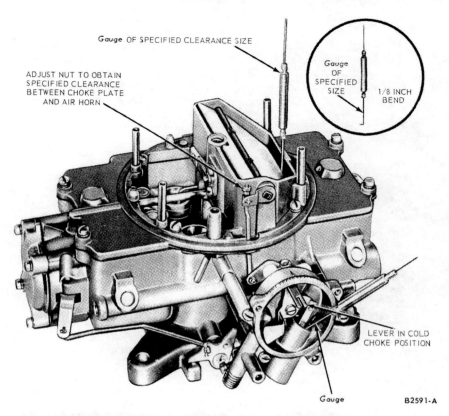

GAUGE OF SPECIFIED CLEARANCE SIZE

ADJUST NUT TO OBTAIN SPECIFIED CLEARANCE BETWEEN CHOKE PLATE AND AIR HORN

GAUGE OF SPECIFIED SIZE   1/8 INCH BEND

LEVER IN COLD CHOKE POSITION

Gauge

B2591-A

FIG. 11—Choke Plate Clearance (Pull-Down) Adjustment—(Typical) Ford 2-V and 4-V

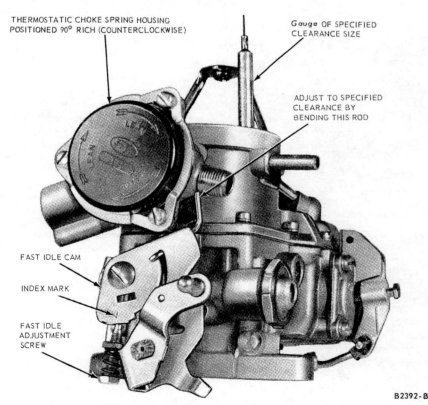

THERMOSTATIC CHOKE SPRING HOUSING POSITIONED 90° RICH (COUNTERCLOCKWISE)

GAUGE OF SPECIFIED CLEARANCE SIZE

ADJUST TO SPECIFIED CLEARANCE BY BENDING THIS ROD

FAST IDLE CAM

INDEX MARK

FAST IDLE ADJUSTMENT SCREW

B2392-B

FIG. 12—Fast Idle Cam Linkage Adjustment—Ford 1-V

tighten the spring housing retaining screws.

9. Position the fast idle adjustment screw on the index mark of the fast idle cam (Figs. 12 and 13).

10. On a Ford 1-V carburetor, adjust the fast idle cam linkage to specification by bending the choke control rod (Fig. 12) to provide the specified clearance between the front of choke plate and the air horn. **Bend the choke control rod inward to decrease the clearance or outward to increase the clearance. Make certain the fast idle screw remains on the index mark (kickdown step) of the fast idle cam during the adjustment procedure.**

11. On Ford 2-V or 4-V carburetors. Check the clearance between the front of the choke plate and the air horn (Fig. 13). Adjust the clearance to specification (Part 10-9), if required. **Turn the fast idle cam lever adjusting screw clockwise (inward) to increase the clearance and counterclockwise (outward) to decrease the clearance. Make certain the fast idle screw remains on the index mark (kickdown step) of the fast idle cam during the adjustment procedure.**

12. Set the thermostatic choke housing to the specified (Part 10-9) index mark (Fig. 14) and tighten the retaining screws.

13. If the automatic choke plate clearance (pull-down) and fast idle cam linkage adjustment was performed with the carburetor on the car, install the heater hose and mounting bracket (if so equipped) on the carburetor. Adjust the engine idle (hot engine) speed and fuel mixture, fast (cold engine) idle speed and the dashpot (if so equipped) by following the procedures in this section.

AUTOMATIC CHOKE THERMOSTATIC SPRING HOUSING ADJUSTMENT

The automatic choke has an adjustment to control its reaction to engine temperature. By loosening the clamp screws that retain the thermostatic spring housing to the choke housing, the spring housing can be turned to alter the adjustment. Turning the housing in a counterclockwise direction will require a higher thermostatic spring temperature (cold weather operation) to fully open the choke plate. Turning the spring housing in the opposite direction (clockwise) will cause the choke plate to be fully open at a

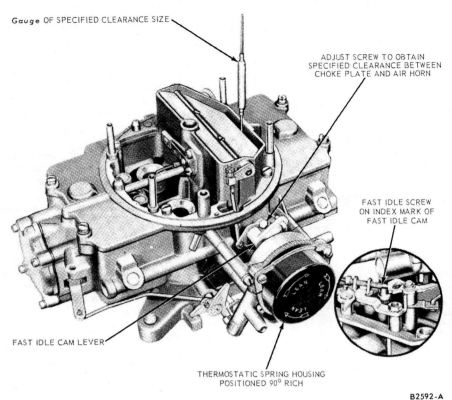

FIG. 13—Fast Idle Cam Linkage Adjustment—(Typical) Ford 2-V and 4-V

lower thermostatic spring temperature (hot weather operation). This is the lean direction, as indicated by the arrow on the choke thermostatic spring housing. Refer to the specifications (Part 10-9) for the proper setting for normal ambient temperatures.

1. Remove the air cleaner assembly (Part 10-6), heater hose and mounting bracket (if so equipped) from the carburetor, if they have not been previously removed.

2. Loosen the thermostatic spring housing clamp retaining screws. Set the spring housing to the specified (Part 10-9) index mark (Fig. 14) and tighten the clamp retaining screws.

3. If other carburetor adjustments are not required, install the heater hose and mounting bracket (if so equipped) and the air cleaner assembly (Part 10-6, Section 2) on the carburetor.

CARBURETOR INTER-CONNECTING LINKAGE ADJUSTMENT—HOLLEY CARBURETORS

The following procedure is required for adjusting the inter-carburetor linkage to achieve proper pro-

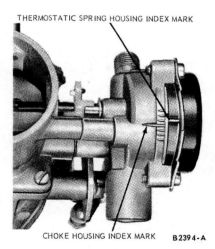

FIG. 14—Automatic Choke Thermostatic Spring Housing Adjustment—Typical

gressive opening of the primary throttle plates.

The secondary throttles are vacuum operated and are inter-connected by a rubber hose, located between the two secondary diaphragm vacuum operating chambers (Fig. 15), to assure synchronous action of the secondary throttle plates (no adjustment is required).

1. With the air cleaner removed (Part 10-6, Section 2), disconnect the inter-carburetor linkage at the front and rear carburetor primary throttle levers and at the bellcrank lever (Fig. 16). Disconnect the throttle control cable from the cross-shaft bellcrank lever.

2. Adjust the primary carburetor rod to a 4-3/16 inch length (Fig. 16) from the center line of the hole to the center line of the bent end (operating centers).

3. Install the primary carburetor rod on the bellcrank lever and on the upper stud of the front carburetor lever (Fig. 16). Tighten the locknut and install the washers and retainer pins.

4. Move the bellcrank lever so that the front carburetor throttle is in the wide open position. Hold in this position.

5. Install the slotted end of the secondary carburetor rod on the throttle lever of the rear carburetor (Fig. 16).

6. Move the throttle lever of the rear carburetor to the wide open position; then, adjust the length of the secondary carburetor rod so that the hole in the rod at the bellcrank lever just engages the stud on the bellcrank lever (Fig. 16). Install the washers and retainer pins and tighten the locknut on the rod.

7. Open the throttle wide by operating the left side of the bellcrank assembly (on the intake manifold). Be sure the accelerator lever is engaged between the pin and the pad of the accelerator pedal (inside the car). Have someone depress the accelerator to the floor and while holding the carburetor linkage open, see if the accelerator rod pin will engage the bellcrank lever. Adjust as necessary.

8. Check the idle fuel mixture and idle speed adjustments. Adjust the carburetors as required. Refer to Idle Fuel Mixture and Idle (Hot Engine) Speed Adjustments (in this section) for the proper procedure.

FUEL LEVEL FLOAT ADJUSTMENT—WET

The fuel pump pressure and volume must be to specification (Part 10-9) prior to performing the following adjustments.

Ford 2-V and 4-V

1. Operate the engine to normalize engine temperatures, and place the car on a flat surface as near level

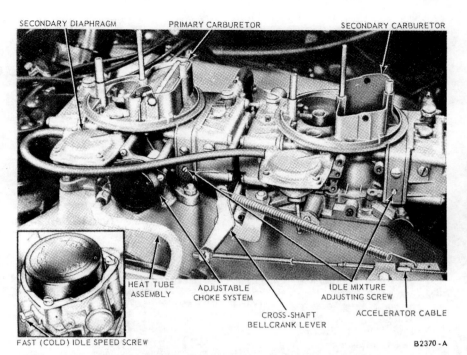

FIG. 15—Holley Dual 4-V Carburetors—Left Side View

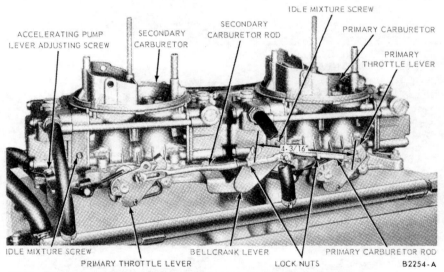

FIG. 16—Holley Dual 4-V Carburetors—Right Side View

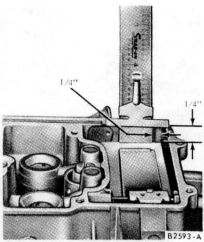

FIG. 17—Fuel Level Float Adjustment (Wet)—Typical For 2-V and 4-V Ford Carburetors

correct fuel level (wet) setting.

5. **If any adjustment is required, stop the engine to minimize the hazard of fire due to fuel spray when the float setting is disturbed.** To adjust the fuel level, bend the float tab (contacting the fuel inlet valve) upward in relation to the original position to raise the fuel level, and downward to lower it. Each time an adjustment is made to the float tab to alter the fuel level, the engine must be started and permitted to idle for at least three minutes to stabilize the fuel level. Check the fuel level after each adjustment until the specified level is achieved.

6. Install a new air horn gasket, the air horn assembly, carburetor identification tag and the retaining screws. Tighten the retaining screws. Install the air cleaner anchor screw.

7. Check the idle fuel mixture, idle speed adjustments and the carburetor dashpot (if so equipped). Adjust the carburetor as required.

8. Install the air cleaner assembly (Part 10-6, Section 2).

Holley 4-V

1. Operate the engine to normalize engine temperatures and place the car on a flat surface, as near level as possible. Stop the engine and remove the air cleaner (Part 10-6, Section 2), if it was not previously removed.

2. Check the fuel level in each fuel bowl separately. **Place a suitable container below the fuel level sight plug in the fuel bowl to collect any spillover of fuel.** Carefully remove the fuel level sight plug and gasket

as possible. Stop the engine.

2. Remove the carburetor air cleaner assembly (Part 10-6, Section 2) and anchor screw, if they have not been previously removed.

3. Remove the air horn retaining screws and the carburetor identification tag. Temporarily place the air horn and gasket in position on the carburetor main body and start the engine. Let the engine idle for several minutes, then rotate the air horn and remove the air horn gasket to provide accessability to the float assembly(ies).

4. While the engine is idling, use a standard depth scale to measure the vertical distance from the top machined surface of the carburetor main body to the level of the fuel in the fuel bowl (Fig. 17). The measurement must be made at least ¼ inch away from any vertical surface to assure an accurate reading, because the surface of the fuel is concave (higher at the edges than in the center). Care must be exercised to measure the fuel level at the point of contact with the fuel. Refer to the specifications (Part 10-9) for the

and check the fuel level (Fig. 18). The fuel level within the bowl should be at the lower edge of the sight plug opening, plus or minus 1/16 inch.

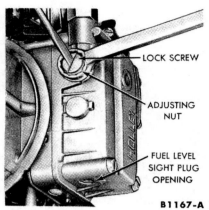

FIG. 18—Fuel Level Float Adjustment (Wet)—Holley 4-V

3. If the fuel level is satisfactory, install the sight plug and gasket.

4. If the fuel level is too high, install the sight plug and gasket. Loosen one lower retaining bolt from the fuel bowl and drain the fuel into a suitable container. **This will eliminate the possibility of foreign material causing a temporary flooding condition. Install and tighten the retaining bolt.**

Start the engine. After the fuel level has stabilized, stop the engine and check the fuel level at the sight plug opening, as outlined in Step 2.

If the fuel level is still too high, it should first be lowered below specifications and then raised until it is just at the lower edge of the sight plug opening. If the fuel level is too low, it is only necessary to raise it to the specified level. Follow the procedure under To Lower Fuel Level or To Raise Fuel Level, whichever is applicable.

To Lower Fuel Level

1. **With the engine stopped,** loosen the lock screw on top of the fuel bowl just enough to allow rotation of the adjusting nut underneath (Fig. 18). **Do not loosen the lock screw or attempt to adjust the fuel level with the sight plug removed and the engine running, because the pressure in the line will spray fuel out and present a fire hazard.**

2. Turn the adjusting nut approximately 1/2 turn in to lower the fuel level below specifications (1/6 turn of the adjusting nut, depending on the direction of rotation, will raise

or lower the float assembly at the fuel level sight plug opening 3/64 inch.

3. Tighten the lock screw and install the fuel level sight plug. Start the engine. After the fuel level has stabilized, stop the engine and check the fuel level at the sight plug opening. The fuel level should be below specified limits. If it is not, repeat the previous steps, turning the adjusting nut an additional amount sufficient to lower the fuel below the specified level.

4. Loosen the lock screw and turn the adjusting nut out in increments of 1/6 turn or less until the correct fuel level is achieved. After each adjustment, tighten the lock screw, install the fuel level sight plug and then start the engine and stabilize the fuel level. Check the fuel level at the sight plug opening. Install the sight plug and gasket.

5. Check the idle fuel mixture and idle speed adjustments. Adjust the carburetor as required.

To Raise Fuel Level. Perform steps 1 through 5 under the procedure To Lower Fuel Level.

IDLE FUEL MIXTURE AND IDLE (HOT ENGINE) SPEED ADJUSTMENTS

It is of utmost importance that the idle fuel system on 2-V and 4-V carburetors be balanced as closely as possible in order to obtain a satisfactory, stable, idle and fuel mixture adjustment. This is achieved by establishing initial idle speed and mixture adjustments before proceeding with the final idle speed and mixture adjustment, and the fast (cold engine) idle speed adjustment.

With the air cleaner removed, make the idle adjustments in the following sequence:

Initial Idle Speed and Fuel Mixture Adjustments—Ford Carburetors. Refer to Figs. 19 and 20 for views of the Ford 1-V carburetor idle fuel mixture and idle (hot engine) speed adjustment screws.

The idle fuel mixture and idle (hot engine) speed adjustment screws for the Ford 2-V and 4-V carburetors are shown in Figs. 21 and 22.

1. Set the initial idle fuel mixture by turning the idle mixture screw(s) (needle) inward (clockwise) until lightly seated; then, turn the screw(s) outward (counterclockwise) the specified turns (Part 10-9). **Do not turn the needle(s) tightly against their seat(s) as they may groove the**

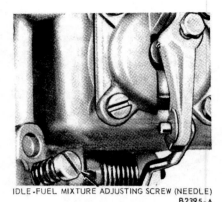

IDLE-FUEL MIXTURE ADJUSTING SCREW (NEEDLE)
B2395-A

FIG. 19—Idle Fuel Mixture Adjustment—Ford 1-V

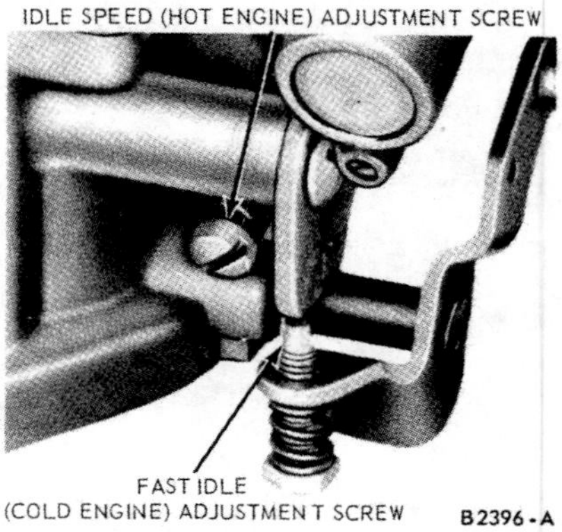

IDLE SPEED (HOT ENGINE) ADJUSTMENT SCREW

FAST IDLE (COLD ENGINE) ADJUSTMENT SCREW
B2396-A

FIG. 20—Idle Speed Adjustments Ford 1-V

ADJUSTING NEEDLES
B2594-A

FIG. 21—Idle Fuel Mixture Adjustments—Typical For Ford 2-V or 4-V

end(s). **If a needle is damaged, it must be replaced before a satisfactory fuel mixture can be obtained.**

2. Position the choke mechanism so that the choke plate is fully open. Seat the throttle plate in the throttle bore. **It may be necessary to back off on the dashpot (if so equipped) adjustment screw to seat the throttle plate in the throttle bore.** Set the idle speed adjustment screw to just

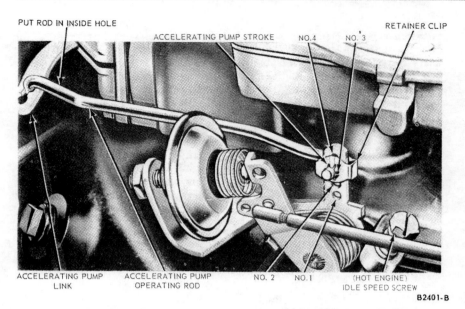

PUT ROD IN INSIDE HOLE   ACCELERATING PUMP STROKE   NO.4   NO. 3   RETAINER CLIP

ACCELERATING PUMP LINK   ACCELERATING PUMP OPERATING ROD   NO. 2   NO. 1   (HOT ENGINE) IDLE SPEED SCREW

B2401-B

FIG. 22—Accelerating Pump Stroke and Idle (Hot Engine) Speed Adjustments—Typical for Ford 2-V and 4-V

make contact with the stop on the carburetor lower body (Ford 1-V) or throttle lever (Ford 2-V or 4-V), and turn the screw inward (clockwise) the specified (Part 10-9) turns.

Initial Idle Speed and Fuel Mixture Adjustments—Holley 4-V Carburetors. The idle fuel mixture is controlled by the idle fuel mixture adjusting screws (needles) located in

the primary metering blocks of the carburetors (Figs. 15, 16 and 23). The idle (hot engine) speed adjusting screw location for each carburetor is shown in Fig. 23.

1. Initially set the idle mixture by turning the idle mixture screws inward until they are lightly seated; then turn the screws outward the specified (Part 10-9) turns. **Do not**

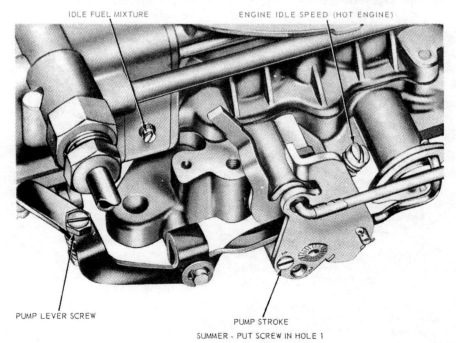

IDLE FUEL MIXTURE   ENGINE IDLE SPEED (HOT ENGINE)

PUMP LEVER SCREW   PUMP STROKE

SUMMER - PUT SCREW IN HOLE 1
WINTER - PUT SCREW IN HOLE 2

B2252-A

FIG. 23—Accelerating Pump, Idle Fuel Mixture and Idle (Hot Engine) Speed Adjustments—Holley Carburetors

turn the needles tightly against the seat as this may groove the ends. If a needle is damaged, it must be replaced before a satisfactory fuel mixture can be obtained.

2. Turn the idle (hot engine) speed screw outward on each carburetor until the throttle plates close tight in the throttle bores. **It may be necessary to back the front carburetor or fast (cold engine) idle adjusting screw (Fig. 15) to close the plates tight in the bores.** Set the idle speed adjustment screws to just make contact with the stops on the carburetor bodies and turn them inward the specified (Part 10-9) turns.

Final Idle (Hot Engine) Speed and Mixture Adjustments. The engine idle speed is adjusted to settings for a hot engine and a cold engine (fast idle speed during choke operation). All final idle speed and mixture adjustments must be made on a hot, normalized engine.

Refer to Figs. 15, 16, 19, 20, 21, 22 and 23 for views of the idle fuel mixture and idle (hot engine) speed screws for the various carburetor applications.

1. Operate the engine until engine temperatures are stabilized. **On a car with an air conditioner, operate the engine for twenty minutes before setting the engine idle speed. The engine idle speed is adjusted with air conditioner operating.**

2. Position the transmission lever in neutral. Allow the throttle to drop back to the normal idle speed position. Attach a tachometer to the engine. Set the parking brake.

On cars equipped with a vacuum release parking brake, remove the vacuum line from the vacuum power unit of the automatic vacuum release parking brake assembly, and plug the vacuum line. Set the parking brake. **It is necessary to inactivate the vacuum power unit to keep the parking brake engaged when the engine is running during the adjustment procedures.**

3. Turn on the headlamps. **It is necessary to place the alternator under a load condition in this manner in order to obtain the specified engine idle speed during the adjustment procedure.**

4. **On a car with a manual shift transmission, the engine idle speed is checked and adjusted with the gear shift lever in neutral position. On a car with an automatic transmission, the engine idle speed is checked and adjusted first with the transmission selector lever in the neutral position**

and adjusted with the transmission selector lever in the drive range position. Adjust and check the engine idle speed. **Be sure the dashpot (if so equipped) is not interfering with the throttle lever or the fast idle screw is not contacting the fast idle cam.**

On carburetors equipped with a hot idle compensator, be sure the compensator is seated to allow for proper idle adjustment.

On Ford carburetors, adjust the engine idle speed to specifications (Part 10-9) by turning the engine idle speed screw (Fig. 20 or 22) inward to increase the speed or outward to decrease the speed.

On the Holley carburetors, adjust the engine idle speed to specifications (Part 10-9) by turning each idle speed adjusting screw (Fig. 23) equally and alternately. **Turn the screws inward to increase the speed and outward to decrease the speed. Be sure the fast idle screw is not touching the fast idle cam when performing this adjustment.**

5. On a Ford carburetor, turn the idle mixture needle(s) (Figs. 19 and 21) inward until the engine rpm begins to drop, due to the lean mixture. Turn the needle(s) outward until the rpm increases and begins to drop. **On cars equipped with a Thermactor exhaust emission system, the outward adjustment of the idle fuel mixture needle(s) is the final fuel mixture needle adjustment required.** On cars without the Thermactor system, turn the idle mixture needle(s) inward for maximum rpm and engine smoothness. Always favor a slightly rich mixture. **On Ford 2-V and 4-V carburetors, the needles should be turned evenly and alternately approximately the same amount. The final setting may vary about ½ turn difference between needles.**

On the Holley carburetors, adjust the idle fuel mixture by turning each idle mixture screw inward (Figs. 15, 16 and 23) evenly and alternately, starting with the front carburetor and finishing with the rear carburetor, until the engine rpm begins to drop (due to the lean mixture). Turn each screw outward until the engine rpm begins to drop (due to the rich mixture); then turn each screw inward for maximum engine rpm and smoothness. **Always favor a slightly rich idle fuel mixture.** Final adjustment of the idle fuel mixture screws should be within ⅛ turn of each other.

6. After the correct engine idle mixture has been obtained, **check the idle speed with the transmission selector lever in neutral and manually opening and closing the throttle.** Adjust the idle speed to specification, if required.

If the car is equipped with an automatic transmission, position the selector lever in drive range to check and adjust the idle speed to specification (Part 10-9), if necessary. **The final engine idle speed may be varied to suit the conditions under which the car is to be operated.**

9. Shut off the engine. Check the fast (cold engine) idle speed.

FAST (COLD ENGINE) IDLE SPEED ADJUSTMENT

On a Ford 1-V carburetor, the fast (cold engine) idle adjustment screw (Fig. 20) is located on the left side of the carburetor.

On a Ford 2-V and 4-V carburetor the fast (cold engine) idle adjustment screw (Fig. 24) is located on the right side of the carburetor.

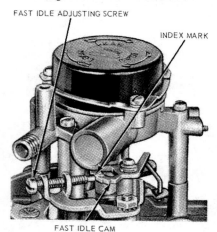

FAST IDLE ADJUSTING SCREW

INDEX MARK

FAST IDLE CAM

B2595-A

FIG. 24—Fast (Cold Engine) Idle Speed Adjustment—Ford 2-V and 4-V

On the Holley carburetor installation, the fast (cold engine) idle speed adjustment is performed on the front (primary) carburetor only. The fast idle speed screw is located on the left side of the front carburetor (Fig. 15).

The fast idle adjusting screw contacts one edge of the fast idle cam. The cam permits a faster engine idle speed for smoother running when the engine is cold during choke operation. As the choke plate is moved through its range of travel from the

closed to the open position, the fast idle cam pick-up lever rotates the fast idle cam. Each position on the fast idle cam permits a slower idle rpm as engine temperature rises and choking is reduced.

Make certain the idle (hot engine) speed and mixture is adjusted to specification before attempting to set the fast idle speed.

1. With the engine operating temperature normalized (hot), air cleaner removed and the tachometer attached, manually rotate the fast idle cam until the fast idle adjusting screw rests adjacent to the shoulder of the highest step (screw aligned with arrow mark) on the cam.

2. Start the engine, and turn the fast idle adjusting screw inward or outward as required to obtain the specified idle rpm (Part 10-9).

3. Place the transmission selector lever in neutral and turn off the engine. Switch off the headlamps and the air conditioner (if so equipped). Remove the tachometer.

On cars equipped with a vacuum release parking brake, connect the vacuum line to the vacuum power unit of the automatic vacuum release parking brake assembly.

4. If the car is equipped with an automatic transmission, check the anti-stall dashpot for proper adjustment.

ANTI-STALL DASHPOT (AUTOMATIC TRANSMISSIONS)

The anti-stall dashpot adjustment is made with the air cleaner removed (Part 10-6, Section 2) from the car.

Ford 1-V

1. Adjust the throttle position to the hot idle setting. Turn the dashpot adjusting screw outward until it is clear of the dashpot plunger assembly (Fig. 25).

2. Turn the dashpot adjusting screw inward until it initially contacts the dashpot plunger assembly; then, turn the adjusting screw inward (clockwise) the specified (Part 10-9) number of turns against the dashpot diaphragm plunger assembly.

3. Check the accelerating pump lever and stroke for proper adjustment, if required. Install the air cleaner (Part 10-6, Section 2).

Ford 2-V and 4-V

1. With the engine idle speed and mixture properly adjusted, and the engine at normal operating tempera-

FIG. 25—Anti-Stall Dashpot Adjustment—Ford 1-V

ture, loosen the anti-stall dashpot lock nut (Fig. 26).

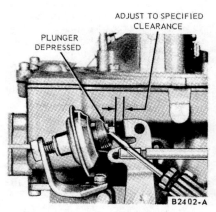

FIG. 26—Anti-Stall Dashpot Adjustment—Typical For Ford 2-V and 4-V

2. Hold the throttle in the closed position and depress the plunger with a screwdriver blade. Check the clearance between the throttle lever and the plunger tip with a feeler gauge of the specified clearance dimension (Part 10-9). Turn the anti-stall dashpot in its bracket in a direction to provide the specified clearance between the tip of the plunger and the throttle lever. Tighten the locknut to secure the adjustment.

3. Check the accelerating pump stroke for proper adjustment, if required. Install the air cleaner assembly (Part 10-6, Section 2).

ACCELERATING PUMP ADJUSTMENTS

Acceleration requirements in various climates are satisfied by controlling the amount of fuel discharged by the accelerating pump. This is accomplished by adjusting the pump clearance to specification; then, adjusting the pump stroke to suit the ambient temperature in which the car is to be operated. **An accelerating pump clearance adjustment is not required on Ford 2-V or 4-V carburetors.**

The accelerating pump adjustments are performed with the carburetor air cleaner removed from the car (Part 10-6, Section 2).

Accelerating Pump Clearance— Ford 1-V.

1. Insert the roll pin in the lower hole (HI) position in the lever stop hole (Fig. 27).

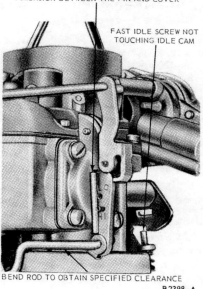

FIG. 27—Accelerating Pump Clearance Adjustment—Ford 1-V

2. Position the throttle and choke linkage so that the throttle plate will seat in the throttle bore. Hold the throttle plates in the closed position. Position a gauge or drill of the specified thickness (Part 10-9) between the roll pin and the cover surface. Bend the accelerating pump actuating rod to obtain the specified gauge or drill clearance between the pump cover and the roll pin in the pump lever (Fig. 27).

Accelerating Pump Clearance— Holly 4-V. Using a feeler gauge and with the primary throttle plates in the wide open position, there should be the specified (Part 10-9) clearance between the accelerating pump operating lever adjusting screw head and the pump arm when the pump arm is fully depressed manually (Fig. 23). Turn the adjusting screw in to increase the clearance and out to decrease the clearance. One-half turn of the adjusting screw is equal to 0.015 inch.

Accelerating Pump Stroke—Ford 1-V. The pump stroke is controlled by changing location of the roll pin in the lever stop hole (Fig. 28).

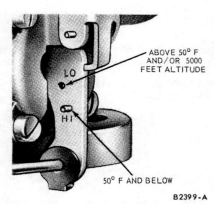

FIG. 28—Accelerating Pump Stroke Adjustment—Ford 1-V

1. For operation in ambient temperatures 50°F. and below, place the roll pin in the lever hole marked HI (lower hole).

For best performance and economy at normal ambient temperatures and high altitude (above 50°F and/or above 5,000 feet altitude), place the roll pin in the LO (upper hole) of the lever.

2. Check the vent valve for proper adjustment.

Accelerating Pump Stroke—Ford 2-V and 4-V. The primary throttle shaft lever (overtravel lever) has 4 holes and the accelerating pump link has 2 holes (Fig. 22) to control the accelerating pump stroke for various ambient temperatures and operating conditions of the engine.

The accelerating pump operating rod should be in the specified (Part 10-9) hole in the overtravel lever and the inboard hole (hole closest to the pump plunger) in the accelerating pump link (Fig. 22).

1. To release the rod from the retainer clip, press the tab end of the clip toward the rod; then, at the

same time, press the rod away from the clip until it is disengaged.

2. Position the clip over the specified (Part 10-9) hole in the over-travel lever. Press the ends of the clip together and insert the operating rod through the clip and the over-travel lever. Release the clip to engage the rod.

Accelerating Pump Stroke—Holley 4-V. To satisfy acceleration requirements in various climates, the accelerating pump discharge can be adjusted. The bottom hole (No. 2) in the cam provides a maximum pump discharge for extreme cold weather and the top hole (No. 1) provides the minimum pump discharge for warm weather operation (Fig. 23).

For summer operation, install the adjustment screw in hole NO. 1. For winter operation, install the adjustment screw in hole NO. 2.

VENT VALVE ADJUSTMENT—FORD 1-V

The vent valve adjustment is always performed after the accelerating pump adjustment has been completed.

1. With the air cleaner removed, set the throttle linkage to the hot idle position. The groove in the vent valve rod should now be even with the open end of the vent (Fig. 29). Bend the arm on the vent valve rod actuating lever (where it contacts the accelerating pump lever) to align the groove with the edge of the bore.

2. Install the air cleaner (Part 10-6, Section 2).

THROTTLE LINKAGE ADJUSTMENT

MANUAL-SHIFT TRANSMISSION

The engine idle speed and fuel mixture must be adjusted to specification prior to performing accelerator linkage adjustments.

1. On all engines except the 427 V-8, disconnect the throttle return spring from the carburetor throttle lever (Fig. 30).

On a 427 V-8 engine, disconnect the throttle return spring from the cross-shaft bellcrank lever.

2. Loosen the accelerator cable mounting bracket adjustment clip retaining bolt.

3. Set the accelerator pedal height by positioning the carburetor throttle lever or the cross-shaft bellcrank lever (427 V-8 engine only) to the wide open throttle position. Depress

NOTCH ON VENT VALVE ROD TO ALIGN WITH EDGE OF HOLE WITH THROTTLE IN HOT IDLE POSITION

BEND LEVER TO OBTAIN CORRECT ROD POSITION

B 2400 - A

FIG. 29—Fuel Bowl Vent Valve Adjustment—Ford 1-V

the accelerator pedal and shaft assembly into contact with the carpet on the dash panel. **If the carpet has been removed, a distance of $1^{3}/_{32}$ inch between the bare metal on the dash panel and the pedal and shaft assembly must be maintained.** Slide the cable conduit rearward (to the left on a 240 six engine) within the cable mounting bracket clip to take up system slack and tighten the adjustment clip.

4. Return the accelerator pedal to its fully released position.

5. On all engines except the 427 V-8, connect the throttle return spring to the carburetor throttle lever.

On a 427 V-8 engine, connect the throttle return spring to the cross-shaft bellcrank lever.

AUTOMATIC TRANSMISSION

The throttle linkage adjustments for the automatic transmissions are covered in Group 7.

CARBURETOR REPAIRS

AIR HORN TO MAIN BODY GASKET REPLACEMENT

Ford 1-V

1. Remove the air cleaner assembly (Part 10-6, Section 2).

2. Disconnect the choke clean air tube and the automatic choke heat

tube from the carburetor. Remove the fast idle cam lever to main body retaining screw. Remove the fast idle cam lever, spring washer and flat washer from the main body.

3. Disconnect the fuel inlet line from the carburetor.

4. Remove the air horn to lower body retaining screws and the carburetor identification tag.

5. Tilt the fuel bowl vent side of the air horn to allow clearance between the float assembly and the air horn. Separate the air horn from the lower body, using a twisting motion to disconnect the fuel vent rod from the actuating lever on the accelerator pump. Remove and discard the air horn to lower body mounting gasket.

6. Install a new gasket on the carburetor lower body. **Make sure all holes in the new gasket have been punched and that no foreign material has adhered to the gasket. Make certain the word Top (inscribed on the gasket) is facing upward.**

7. Insert the fuel bowl vent rod in the actuating lever on the accelerator pump, using a twisting motion, and position the air horn on the mounting gasket. **During the installation, observe the float retaining pin to make certain it does not dislodge.** Install the air horn to lower body retaining screws and the carburetor identification tag. Tighten the screws.

8. Connect the fuel inlet line to the carburetor.

9. Install the flat washer, spring washer, fast idle cam lever and the retaining screw on the main body. Tighten the screw. Connect the automatic choke heat tube and clean air tube to the carburetor.

10. Adjust the idle fuel mixture and engine idle speed as outlined in this section.

Ford 2-V and 4-V

1. Remove the air cleaner assembly (Part 10-6, Section 2). Remove the air cleaner anchor screw.

2. Disconnect the automatic choke clean air tube at the carburetor.

3. Remove the automatic choke plate operating rod to choke lever retainer.

4. Remove the air horn retaining screws and lock washers, and the carburetor identification tag. Remove the air horn and air horn gasket.

5. Install a new air horn to main body gasket. **Make sure all holes in the new gasket have been properly punched and that no foreign material**

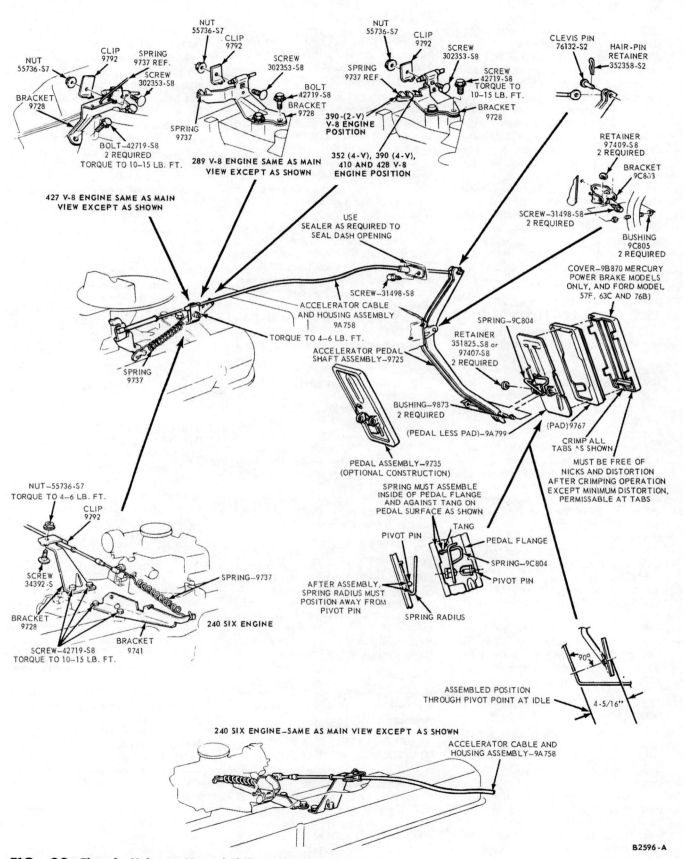

FIG. 30—Throttle Linkage—Manual-Shift Transmission

B2596-A

has adhered to the gasket.

6. Position the air horn on the main body and gasket so that the choke plate operating rod fits into the opening in the choke housing lever. Install the choke plate rod retainer. **On a Ford 4-V carburetor, use care to prevent damage to the secondary throttle control vacuum tubes during the air horn installation.**

7. Install the air horn retaining screws and lock washers and the identification tag. Install the air cleaner anchor screw.

8. Connect the automatic choke clean air tube to the carburetor.

9. Adjust the idle fuel mixture and idle speed and the dashpot as outlined in this section.

10. Install the carburetor air cleaner assembly (Part 10-6, Section 2).

FLOAT OR NEEDLE VALVE REPLACEMENT—FORD 1-V

1. Remove the carburetor air horn body and gasket by following steps 1 through 5 under Air Horn to Main Body Gasket Replacement—Ford 1-V, in this section.

2. Remove the carburetor float shaft and the float assembly. Remove the fuel inlet needle valve.

3. Insert the needle valve into the bore, with the viton tip toward the integral seat in the air horn.

4. Position the float assembly in the air horn, with the tab on the arm located over the needle valve and the hinge of the arm lined up between the hinge bracket holes in the air horn casting. Insert the float shaft through the holes in the air horn and float assembly.

5. Check the float setting. Refer to Float Adjustment—Dry, in this section, for the proper procedure.

6. Install the carburetor air horn and gasket by following steps 6 through 10 under Air Horn to Main Body Gasket Replacement—Ford 1-V, in this section.

MAIN JET REPLACEMENT—FORD 1-V

1. Remove the carburetor upper body and gasket by following steps 1 through 5 under Air Horn to Main Body Gasket Replacement, in this section.

2. Remove and replace the carburetor main jets with a jet wrench or wide bladed screwdriver.

3. Install the carburetor air horn and gasket by following steps 6 through 10 under Air Horn to Main

Body Gasket Replacement—Ford 1-V, in this section.

FLOAT, NEEDLE VALVE AND SEAT, INLET SCREEN, OR MAIN JET REPLACEMENT—FORD 2-V and 4-V

1. Remove the carburetor air horn to main body gasket by following steps 1 through 4 under Air Horn to Main Body Gasket Replacement—Ford 2-V and 4-V, in this section.

2. With the use of a screwdriver, pry the float shaft retainer(s) from the fuel inlet seat(s). Remove the float, float shaft retainer(s) and fuel inlet needle assembly(ies).

3. If required, remove the fuel inlet needle seat(s), filter screen(s) and the main jets with a jet wrench. **Be sure the correct (specified) jets are installed for the primary and secondary (4-V carburetor) systems (Part 10-9).**

4. If required, install the fuel inlet filter(s) in the inlet valve seat bore(s). Install the valve seat(s) and gasket(s). Install the fuel inlet needle valve(s).

5. Slide the float shaft(s) into the float lever(s). Position the float shaft retainer(s) on the float shaft(s).

6. Insert the float assembly(ies) into the fuel bowl(s) and hook the float lever tab(s) under the fuel inlet needle clip(s). Insert the float shaft(s) into the guides at the sides of the fuel bowl(s).

7. With the use of a screwdriver, position the float shaft retainer(s) on the groove of the fuel inlet needle seat(s).

8. Refer to Float Adjustment—Dry, in this section, and perform a dry float fuel level adjustment on the float(s).

9. Install the carburetor air horn and gasket and related parts. Refer to Air Horn to Main Body Gasket Replacement—Ford 2-V and 4-V, Steps 5 through 9, in this section, for the proper procedure.

10. Refer to Fuel Level Float Adjustment—Wet, in this section, and perform the wet fuel level adjustment procedures.

ACCELERATING PUMP DIAPHRAGM REPLACEMENT—FORD 1-V

1. Remove the air cleaner assembly (Part 10-6, Section 2).

2. Depress the tab on the accelerating pump lever to control rod retaining clip with pliers, and slide the rod out of the lever. Remove the clip from the lever.

3. Remove the accelerator pump cover retaining screws. Lift the cover upward and remove the diaphragm and return spring.

4. Position the new diaphragm on the diaphragm cover, with the diaphragm plunger facing the lever, and line up the holes. While holding the diaphragm in place, position the small diameter of the diaphragm return spring on the boss in the accelerator pump chamber; then, position the cover and the diaphragm over the return spring and onto the lower body. Install the cover retaining screws finger-tight.

5. Push the diaphragm inward with the lever and tighten the cover screws.

6. Position the accelerating pump actuating rod retaining clip over the hole in the accelerating pump lever, with the tab side of the clip toward the carburetor barrel. Depress the tab and insert the end of the rod through the lever and clip. Release the tab when the rod is inserted. Perform the Accelerating Pump Adjustments outlined in this section.

7. Install the air cleaner assembly (Part 10-6, Section 2).

ACCELERATING PUMP DIAPHRAGM AND/OR ELASTOMER VALVE REPLACEMENT—FORD 2-V AND 4-V

1. Remove the carburetor air horn to main body gasket by following steps 1 through 4 under Air Horn to Main Body Gasket Replacement—Ford 2-V and 4-V in this section.

2. Remove the accelerating pump operating rod retainer. To release the rod from the retainer, press the tab ends of the clip together; then, at the same time, press the rod away from the clip until it is disengaged. Remove the rod. Remove the accelerating pump cover, diaphragm assembly and spring.

3. If inspection proves it necessary to remove the Elastomer valve, grasp it firmly and pull it out. **If the Elastomer valve tip broke off during removal, be sure to remove the tip from the fuel bowl. An Elastomer valve must be replaced whenever it is removed from the main body.**

4. If the Elastomer valve was removed, lubricate the tip of a new valve and insert the tip into the accelerator pump cavity. Using needle nosed pliers, reach into the fuel bowl and grasp the valve tip. Pull the valve in until it seats, and cut off the tip forward of the retaining shoulder. Remove the tip from the bowl.

5. Position the new accelerating pump diaphragm assembly to the cover and place the cover and diaphragm assembly in position on the return spring and main body. Install the cover screws finger-tight. Push the accelerating pump plunger the full length of its travel and tighten the cover screws.

6. Position the accelerating pump operating rod in the inboard hole (hole closest to the pump plunger).

7. Adjust the accelerating pump stroke to specification (Part 10-9).

8. Install the carburetor air horn and gasket. Refer to the Air Horn to Main Body Gasket Replacement —Ford 2-V and 4-V Carburetor, Steps 5 through 10, in this section for the proper procedure.

SECONDARY DIAPHRAGM REPLACEMENT—FORD 4-V.

1. Remove the carburetor air horn to main body gasket by following steps 1 through 4 under Air Horn to Main Body Gasket Replacement Ford 2-V and 4-V, in this section.

2. Remove the secondary operating rod retainer and remove the rod. Remove the diaphragm cover, return spring Palnut (if so equipped) and diaphragm.

3. Install the new secondary diaphragm and Palnut (if so equipped) on the secondary operating lever. Install the diaphragm return spring on the cover. Install the cover retaining screws finger-tight. With the diaphragm in the extended position, tighten the cover screws.

4. Install the secondary operating rod in the operating lever, and secure the rod to the secondary throttle shaft with the retaining clip.

5. Check the operation and seal of the secondary vacuum system by opening the primary and secondary throttle plates. Hold the secondary throttle plates open. Place a finger over the secondary vacuum inlet hole in the main body and release the secondary throttle plates. **This is a check for vacuum leakage at the diaphragm.** The throttle plates should not close fully. They will move slightly when released, but they must stop and should not move toward the closed position after the initial movement. Replace the diaphragm or tighten the cover

screws as necessary to correct the vacuum leakage.

6. Install the carburetor air horn and gasket by following steps 5 through 10 under Air Horn to Main Body Gasket Replacement—Ford 2-V and 4-V Carburetors, in this section.

ANTI-STALL DASHPOT REPLACEMENT

Diaphragm Replacement— Ford 1-V

1. Remove the air cleaner assembly (Part 10-6, Section 2).

2. Depress the tab on the dashpot lever to control rod retaining clip with pliers and slide the rod out of the lever. Remove the clip from the lever.

3. Remove the dashpot cover retaining screws. Remove the cover, diaphragm and return spring.

4. Position the new diaphragm on the dashpot cover, with the diaphragm plunger facing the lever, and line up the holes. Position the small diameter of the spring on the boss in the dashpot chamber; then, position the cover and diaphragm over the return spring and onto the lower body. Install the cover retaining screws finger-tight.

5. Push the diaphragm inward with the lever and tighten the cover screws.

6. Position the dashpot actuating rod retaining clip over the hole in the accelerating pump lever, with the tab side of the clip toward the carburetor barrel. Depress the tab and insert the end of the rod through the lever and clip. Release the tab when the rod is inserted. Adjust the dashpot. Refer to Anti-Stall Dashpot-Automatic Transmissions, in this section, for the proper adjustment procedure.

7. Install the air cleaner assembly (Part 10-6, Section 2).

Ford 2-V and 4-V

1. Remove the air cleaner assembly (Part 10-6, Section 2).

2. Remove the retaining nut and the dashpot from the mounting bracket.

3. Install the new dashpot and retaining nut on the mounting bracket.

4. Adjust the anti-stall dashpot. Refer to Anti-Stall Dashpot-Automatic Transmissions, in this section for the proper procedure.

5. Install the air cleaner (Part 10-6, Section 2).

THERMOSTATIC CHOKE SPRING HOUSING AND GASKET REPLACEMENT

1. Remove the carburetor air cleaner assembly (Part 10-6, Section 2).

2. Remove the heater hose and mounting bracket from the carburetor.

3. Remove the thermostatic spring housing clamp retaining screws and remove the spring housing and gasket. Discard the gasket.

4. Replace the spring housing, if required.

5. Position the thermostatic choke spring housing gasket on the choke housing. **On a Ford 1-V carburetor, make sure the loop at the end of the thermostatic spring is on the thermostatic spring lever. On a Ford 2-V or 4-V carburetor, make sure the slot in the arm of the thermostatic spring lever is inserted into the loop of the thermostatic spring.** Position the retainer over the thermostatic spring housing and loosely install the retaining screws.

6. Set the thermostatic spring housing to the specified index mark (Part 10-9) and tighten the retaining screws.

7. Install the heater hose mounting bracket, heater hose and the air cleaner assembly (Part 10-6, Section 2) on the carburetor.

THERMOSTATIC CHOKE ASSEMBLY REMOVAL AND INSTALLATION—CLEAN AND OVERHAUL

Ford 1-V

1. Remove the air cleaner assembly (Part 10-6, Section 2).

2. Remove the thermostatic choke spring housing and gasket. To remove the housing, refer to Thermostatic Choke Spring Housing and Gasket Replacement, in this section, and perform steps 1 through 3.

3. Disconnect the clean air heat inlet tube at the choke housing.

4. Remove the choke housing to airhorn (upper body) retaining screws. Remove the choke housing assembly and gasket. Discard the gasket.

5. If it is necessary to clean and overhaul the thermostatic choke housing assembly, remove the automatic choke shaft retaining screw and washer. Remove the choke shaft and retainer assembly, and the lever, link and piston assembly from the choke housing.

If necessary, disassemble the piston lever and link, and remove the retainer from the choke shaft.

6. Clean and inspect the component parts. Refer to Cleaning and Inspection (Part 10-1, Section 3) for the proper procedure.

7. If it was necessary to clean and overhaul the thermostatic choke housing assembly, perform the following procedure:

If necessary, install a new retainer on the choke shaft. If the choke piston lever and link were disassembled, connect the piston lever link to the piston and the choke thermostatic spring lever.

Insert the choke shaft assembly into the rear of the choke housing. Insert the choke piston into the choke housing, and install the choke thermostatic spring lever on the flange of the choke shaft. Install the choke thermostatic spring lever to shaft retaining screw and washer. **Actuate the piston and lever assembly to make certain a binding condition does not exist.**

8. Install the choke control lever on the choke control shaft. Insert the choke housing to upper body retaining screws in the choke housing. Position the choke thermostatic control gasket on the choke housing flange.

9. Hold the choke plate closed and position the choke control lever on the choke shaft. With the choke plate held closed, install the choke housing and gasket assembly on the choke control lever and the upper body flange and tighten the retaining screws. **Make certain the gasket is properly installed.**

10. Connect the choke heat inlet tube to the thermostatic choke housing.

11. Refer to the Automatic Choke Plate Clearance (Pull-Down) and Fast Idle Cam Linkage Adjustment procedures, in this section, and perform steps 2 through 13.

Ford 2-V and 4-V

1. Remove the carburetor air cleaner assembly (Part 10-6, Section 2).

2. Remove the heater hose and mounting bracket from the carburetor. Disconnect the choke heat tube from the carburetor.

3. Remove the fast idle cam retainer.

4. Remove the choke control rod retainer. Remove the choke housing retaining screws. Remove the choke housing assembly, gasket and fast idle cam as a unit. Remove the fast idle cam and rod from the fast idle cam lever.

5. If it is necessary to clean and overhaul the thermostatic choke housing assembly, remove the choke lever retaining screw and washer. Remove the choke piston lever from the housing. If necessary, remove the pin securing the choke piston to the choke lever link. Remove the choke lever and fast idle cam lever from the choke housing.

6. Clean and inspect the component parts. Refer to Cleaning and Inspection (Part 10-1, Section 3) for the proper procedure.

7. If it was necessary to clean and overhaul the thermostatic choke assembly, perform the following procedure:

If the choke piston and link was disassembled, install the choke piston on the choke thermostatic spring lever link and install the retaining pin.

Position the fast idle cam lever on the thermostatic choke shaft and lever assembly. **The bottom of the fast idle lever adjusting screw must rest against the tang on the choke shaft lever.** Insert the choke shaft assembly into the rear of the choke housing. Position the choke shaft lever so that the hole in the lever is to the left side of the choke housing.

Insert the choke piston into the choke housing. Position the choke thermostatic spring lever on the flange of the choke shaft, and install the retaining screw and washer.

8. Install the fast idle cam rod on the fast idle cam lever. Place the fast idle cam on the fast idle cam rod and install the retainer. Place the choke housing vacuum pick-up port to main body gasket on the choke housing flange.

9. Position the choke housing on the main body, and at the same time, install the fast idle cam on the hub of the main body. Position the gasket and install the choke housing retaining screws. Install the fast idle cam retainer.

10. Connect the choke heat inlet tube to the carburetor thermostatic choke housing.

11. Refer to the Automatic Choke Plate Clearance (Pull-Down) and Fast Idle Cam Linkage adjustment procedures, in this section, and perform steps 2 through 13.

VENT VALVE REPLACEMENT —FORD 1-V

1. Remove the air cleaner assembly (Part 10-6, Section 2).

2. Remove the stake marks and the vent rod opening with a scraper or a small file.

3. Remove the roll pin securing the vent rod actuating lever to the accelerator pump cover. **Use pliers to rotate the pin in a direction that will coil the pin to a small diameter. If the pin offers resistance to turning, turn it in the opposite direction.** Remove the lever from the rod.

4. Remove the vent rod assembly by pulling it outward. Remove the return spring.

5. Insert the fuel vent valve return spring in the vent passage. Insert the piston end of the fuel vent rod in the passage.

6. Punch 3 indentations in the vent valve passage opening with a center punch and a hammer. The indentations must distort the inside edge of the opening sufficiently to act as a stop for the piston end of the vent rod.

7. Install the vent rod actuating lever on the vent rod. Position the lever on the accelerator pump cover and install the roll pin with pliers.

8. Perform a Vent Valve Adjustment as outlined in this section of the manual.

9. Install the air cleaner assembly (Part 10-6, Section 2).

SPARK VALVE OR GASKET REPLACEMENT—FORD 1-V

1. Remove the spark valve with a wrench. Remove and discard the gasket.

2. Install a new gasket on the spark valve. Install the spark valve and tighten it securely with a wrench.

POWER VALVE OR GASKETS REPLACEMENT—FORD 4-V

1. Remove the carburetor from the car, Refer to Part 10-4, Section 2 for the proper procedure.

2. Test the power valve. Refer to steps 1 through 4 under Power Valve (Part 10-1, Section 1) for the proper procedure.

3. If it is necessary to replace the cover gaskets or power valve, invert the main body. Remove the power valve cover and gasket. Discard the gasket. Remove the power valve with a box wrench or socket wrench. Discard the power valve gasket.

Install a new gasket on the power valve. Install the power valve and gasket. **Tighten the power valve se-**

curely. Position a new cover gasket on the main body. Install the cover. **Tighten the retaining screws securely.**

4. Install the carburetor assembly on the car. Refer to Part 10-4, Section 2 for the proper procedure.

CARBURETOR SPACER AND GASKETS REPLACEMENT

It is necessary to remove the carburetor from the car to replace a carburetor spacer and gaskets. Refer to the Carburetor Removal and Installation procedure steps in this group that pertain to the type of carburetor installed on the car.

THROTTLE LINKAGE REPAIR— MANUAL SHIFT TRANSMISSIONS

ACCELERATOR CABLE MOUNTING BRACKET REPLACEMENT

1. Loosen the accelerator cable mounting bracket adjustment clip retaining bolt (Fig. 3). Remove the cable from the adjustment clip assembly.

2. On all engines except the 240 six, disconnect the return spring(s) from the carburetor and the accelerator cable mounting bracket.

3. Remove the retaining bolts securing the accelerator cable mounting bracket to the intake manifold.

4. Install the accelerator cable mounting bracket on the intake manifold and torque the retaining bolts to specification.

5. Position the accelerator cable in the mounting bracket adjustment clip. **Do not tighten the clip retaining bolt.**

6. Adjust the accelerator linkage by performing steps 3 and 4 under Accelerator Linkage Adjustment— Manual Transmission, in this section of the manual.

7. On all engines except the 240 six, connect the return spring(s) to the carburetor and the accelerator

cable mounting bracket.

ACCELERATOR PEDAL SHAFT OR PEDAL REPLACEMENT

1. Remove the hairpin clip from the clevis pin attaching the accelerator cable to the accelerator pedal shaft (Fig. 30). Remove the clevis pin and separate the cable from the shaft.

2. Remove the 2 retaining clips from the accelerator pedal shaft pivot pin in the mounting bracket, located on the dash panel. Remove the pivot pin, pedal shaft and 2 nylon bushings.

3. If it is necessary to remove the accelerator pedal, remove the two retaining clips from the accelerator pedal pivot pin. Remove the pivot pin, pedal, spring and the 2 nylon bushings.

4. If the car is equipped with a pedal pad cover, uncrimp the pedal pad cover retaining tabs. Remove the pedal pad and cover.

5. Position the pedal pad on the accelerator pedal. Install the cover, if so equipped, and carefully crimp the retaining tabs to prevent distortion of the tabs and movement of the pad on the pedal.

6. Install the 2 nylon bushings, pedal spring, pin and the 2 pin retaining clips on the accelerator pedal shaft. **Make certain the pedal spring, bushings and retaining clips are properly installed as shown in Fig. 30.**

7. Install the 2 nylon bushings, accelerator pedal shaft, pivot pin and the 2 retainers on the accelerator pedal shaft mounting bracket on the dash panel.

8. Position the accelerator cable in the accelerator pedal shaft and install the clevis pin through the cable and shaft. Install the cotter pin in the clevis pin.

ACCELERATOR CABLE REPLACEMENT

1. Remove the hairpin clip from the clevis pin attaching the accelerator cable to the accelerator pedal

shaft (Fig. 30). Remove the pin and separate the end of the cable from the pedal shaft.

2. Remove the air cleaner, assembly (Part 10-6, Section 2).

3. Remove the 2 screws securing the accelerator cable assembly to the dash panel.

4. Loosen the accelerator cable adjustment clip bolt and remove the cable assembly from the adjustment clip assembly.

5. On all engines except the 427 V-8, disconnect the accelerator cable snap-on fitting from the carburetor throttle lever ball stud.

On a 427 V-8 engine, remove the cotter pin and washer retaining the accelerator cable to the cross-shaft bellcrank lever clevis stud. Disconnect the cable from the clevis stud.

6. Remove the accelerator cable assembly from the car.

7. Position the new accelerator cable through the outside opening in the dash panel. Connect the cable to the accelerator pedal shaft with the clevis pin and hairpin clip.

8. Secure the accelerator cable housing to the dash panel with 2 retaining screws. Apply car body sealer, as required, to the outside edges of the cable housing mounting flange, to seal the dash panel opening.

9. Position the accelerator cable assembly in the adjustment clip and bracket assembly. **Do not tighten the retaining clip bolt.**

10. On all engines except the 427 V-8, connect the accelerator cable snap-on fitting to the carburetor throttle lever ball stud.

On a 427 V-8 engine, connect the accelerator cable to the cross-shaft bellcrank lever clevis stud and install the flat washer and a new cotter pin in the stud. Bend the pin.

11. Adjust the accelerator control linkage as outlined under Throttle Linkage Adjustment, in this section of the manual.

12. Install the air cleaner assembly (Part 10-6, Section 2).

3 CLEANING AND INSPECTION

CARBURETOR

Dirt, gum, water or carbon contamination in the carburetor or the exterior moving parts of the carburetor are often responsible for unsatisfactory performance. For this reason, efficient carburetion depends upon careful cleaning and inspection.

The cleaning and inspection of only those parts not included in the carburetor overhaul repair kit are covered here. All gaskets and parts included in the repair kit should be installed when the carburetor is assembled and the old gaskets and parts should be discarded.

Wash all the carburetor parts (except the accelerating pump diaphragm, the power valve, the secondary operating diaphragm, and the anti-stall dashpot assembly) in clean commercial carburetor cleaning solvent. If a commercial solvent is not available, lacquer thinner or denatured alcohol may be used.

Rinse the parts in kerosene to remove all traces of the cleaning solvent, then dry them with compressed air. Wipe all parts that can not be immersed in solvent with a clean, soft, dry cloth. Be sure all dirt, gum, carbon, and other foreign matter are removed from all parts.

Force compressed air through all passages of the carburetor. **Do not use a wire brush to clean any parts or a drill or wire to clean out any openings or passages in the carburetor.** A drill or wire may enlarge the hole or passage, changing the calibration of the carburetor.

Check the choke shaft for grooves, wear and excessive looseness or binding. Inspect the choke plate for nicked edges and for ease of operation and free it if necessary. Make sure all carbon and foreign material has been removed from the automatic choke housing and the piston. Check the operation of the choke piston in the choke housing to make certain it has free movement.

Check the throttle shafts in their bores for excessive looseness or binding and check the throttle plates for burrs which prevent proper closure.

Inspect the main body, throttle body, metering body and secondary metering block (Holley 4-V carburetor(s), air horn, nozzle bars and booster venturi assemblies (2-V and 4-V carburetors), choke housing and thermostatic spring housing, power valve cover, accelerating pump cover, secondary operating diaphragm cover (4-V carburetors), and the diaphragm housing (Holley 4-V carburetors) for cracks.

On a Ford 1-V carburetor, check the metallic float(s) for leaks by holding them under water that has been heated to just below the boiling point. Bubbles will appear if there is a leak. If a float leaks, replace it.

Replace the float if the arm needle contact surface is grooved. If the floats are serviceable, polish the needle contact surface of the arm with crocus cloth or steel wool. Replace the float shafts if they are worn.

Replace all screws and nuts that have stripped threads. Replace all distorted or broken springs.

Inspect all gasket mating surfaces for nicks and burrs. Repair or replace any parts that have a damaged gasket surface.

On Ford 2-V and 4-V carburetors, inspect the idle tubes in each nozzle bar assembly. If they are plugged,

bent or broken, replace the booster venturi and nozzle bar assembly.

On Holley 4-V carburetors, inspect the main and accelerating pump discharge nozzles and idle restrictions. If any of the openings are blocked, open them with compressed air.

Inspect the rubber boot of the anti-stall dashpot for proper installation in the groove of the stem bushing. Check the stem movement for smooth operation. Do not lubricate the stem. Replace the assembly if it is defective.

FUEL PUMP

On all fuel pumps, except the Carter permanently sealed type, clean the fuel pump body, valve housing and cover. Blow out all body, housing and cover passages. Inspect the pump body, valve housing, cover, rocker arm, spring and pin for cracks or damage and replace them if necessary. If the fuel valves are not serviceable and replacement is necessary, replace the valve housing and valves as an assembly. Inspect the mounting flange for distortion. Remove the pump body or lap the distorted flange if necessary.

On all Carter permanently sealed fuel pumps, clean the fuel pump with a cloth. Inspect the fuel pumps for cracks or damage. Inspect the mounting flange for distortion. Lap the distorted flange, if necessary. Inspect the rocker arm spring, pin and the rocker arm for wear, cracks or damage. **The rocker arm spring, pin and the rocker arm are the only components on the permanently sealed fuel pumps that are replaceable.** If any other fuel pump components are damaged beyond repair, replace the fuel pump.

AIR CLEANER—DRY TYPE

MAINTENANCE

Refer to Group 19 for the recommended air cleaner assembly maintenance mileage interval.

REMOVAL AND INSTALLATION

Refer to Part 10-6, Section 2 for the air cleaner assembly removal and installation procedures.

FILTER ELEMENT

Cellulose fiber filter elements must not be cleaned with a solvent or cleaning solution. Also, oil must not be added to the surfaces of the filter element or air cleaner body.

There are two alternate procedures that can be used to clean the air filter element. One method is performed with the use of compressed air. The other is performed by tapping the element on a smooth horizontal surface.

Compressed Air Method. Direct a stream of compressed air through the element in the direction opposite that of the intake air flow, that is from the inside outward. **Extreme care must be exercised to prevent rupture of the element material.**

Tapping Method. Hold the element in the vertical position and tap it lightly against a smooth, horizontal surface to shake the dust and dirt out. **Do not deform the element or damage the gasket surfaces by tapping too hard.** Rotate the filter after each tap until the entire outer surface has been cleaned.

Inspection. Hold the filter in front of a back-up light and carefully inspect it for any splits or cracks. If the filter is split or cracked, replace it.

BODY AND COVER

Clean the air cleaner body and the cover with a solvent or compressed air. If the air cleaner contains an opening for the crankcase ventilation system air flow, probe the opening to assure removal of deposits. Wipe the air cleaner dry if a solvent is used. Inspect the air cleaner body and cover for distortion or damage at the gasket mating surfaces. Replace the cover or body if they are damaged beyond repair.

AIR CLEANER— OIL BATH TYPE

MAINTENANCE

Refer to Group 19 for the air cleaner assembly recommended maintenance mileage interval.

REMOVAL AND INSTALLATION

Refer to Part 10-6, Section 2 for the air cleaner assembly removal and installation procedures.

AIR CLEANER ASSEMBLY

Drain the air cleaner reservoir. Wash the air cleaner components in cleaning solvent, and dry them with compressed air. Saturate the filter and fill the reservoir to the indicated level with the recommended viscosity oil.

PART 10-2   FORD 1-V CARBURETORS

1   DESCRIPTION AND OPERATION

DESCRIPTION

The carburetor (Figs. 1 and 2) consists of two main assemblies, the main (upper) body and the throttle (lower) body.

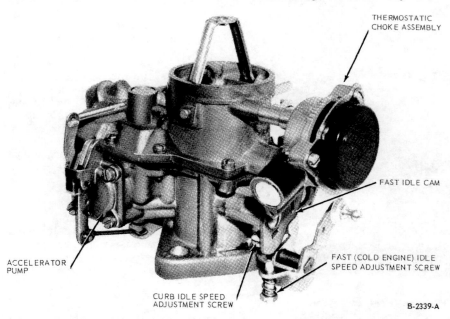

FIG. 1—Ford 1-V Carburetor—Left Rear ¾ View

THERMOSTATIC CHOKE ASSEMBLY

FAST IDLE CAM

FAST (COLD ENGINE) IDLE SPEED ADJUSTMENT SCREW

ACCELERATOR PUMP

CURB IDLE SPEED ADJUSTMENT SCREW

B-2339-A

The upper body (Air Horn) assembly contains the major metering components of the carburetor: the main and idle fuel system, which consists of the power valve, float chamber vent and the fuel inlet system.

The lower body assembly contains: the fuel bowl, accelerating pump assembly, idle mixture adjusting screw (needle) and the spark valve. An hydraulic dashpot is also included in the lower body for use on car models that are equipped with an automatic transmission.

This section applies to all carburetors. Differences in carburetor operation are given when they exist.

OPERATION

The engine speed is regulated and controlled by the proportion of fuel and air delivered to the cylinders for all engine operating conditions. Operation is based on the principle of pressure differences or vacuum.

Air is drawn into the carburetor air horn by manifold vacuum. As the air passes through the carburetor on its way to enter the cylinders, lower pressure is created at the fuel discharge outlets of the carburetor. The fuel bowl is vented to atmospheric pressure and to carburetor air inlet pressure through a vent in the upper body assembly. The high air pressure exerted on the fuel in the bowl forces the fuel to travel up through the fuel discharge channels and out into the air stream passing through the carburetor. The fuel and air is mixed at this point and distributed into the engine cylinders for burning.

FUEL INLET SYSTEM

The fuel inlet system (Fig. 3) of the carburetor maintains a predetermined fuel level in the fuel bowl. **The fuel level in the bowl is extremely important to carburetor calibration.** If the level of the fuel in the bowl is below the specified setting, a lean fuel-air mixture will result. A rich fuel-air mixture will occur from a higher than specified fuel level. The entire calibration of the carburetor is disturbed if the fuel level is not set as specified (Part 10-9).

Fuel enters the fuel bowl through the fuel inlet needle valve and seat assembly. The amount of fuel entering is regulated by the distance the needle valve is moved off the integral seat in the upper body and by fuel pump pressure. **Correct fuel pump pressure is required to maintain the carburetor fuel level within the specified limits.**

The fuel level is maintained at a predetermined level by the float and lever assembly which controls the movement of the needle valve. The needle valve, riding on the tab of the float and lever assembly, reacts

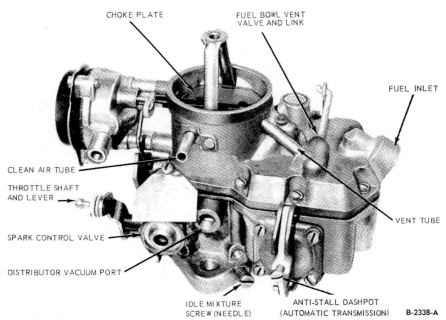

FIG. 2—Ford 1-V Carburetor—Right Side View

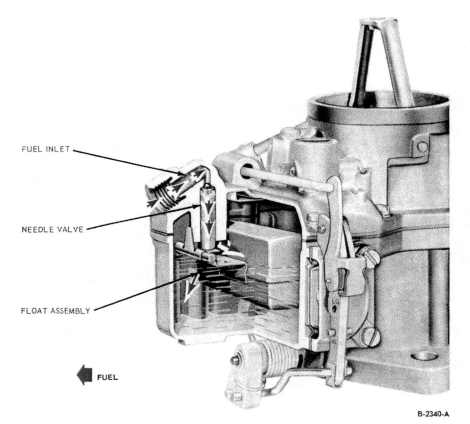

FIG. 3—Fuel Inlet System

to any change in height of the float and the fuel level in the fuel bowl.

IDLE FUEL SYSTEM

The idle system (Fig. 4) functions

when the engine is operating at low rpm. It supplies the fuel-air mixture when the air flow past the carburetor venturi is insufficient to operate the main metering system.

The range of the idle system will

extend into the operation of the main metering system. Fuel flows from the main well, up the idle well and through the calibrated idle jet. Filtered air from the carburetor air horn enters the idle air bleed restriction and mixes with the fuel. The air bleed restriction also serves as a vent to prevent syphoning of fuel at high speeds or when the engine is shut off. The fuel-air mixture then passes down through an idle channel restriction and is transferred to the idle channel in the lower body assembly.

The fuel air mixture passes down the idle channel, past two idle transfer holes, to the idle mixture adjusting screw needle. The idle transfer holes act as additional air bleeds at normal idle. The fuel air mixture flows past the idle adjusting screw needle and seat and is discharged below the throttle plate. The amount of mixture to be discharged is determined by the position of the idle screw needle in relation to the seat in the lower body passage.

During off-idle operation, when the throttle plate is moved past the idle transfer holes, each hole begins discharging fuel as it is exposed to the lower air pressure (manifold vacuum). Continued opening of the throttle plate increases engine rpm and air flow through the carburetor. The greater air flow past the booster venturi causes a pressure drop in the venturi great enough to bring the main fuel metering system into operation as the idle fuel metering system tapers off.

MAIN FUEL METERING SYSTEM

The main fuel metering system (Fig. 5) supplies the fuel required for engine operation during the cruise or part-throttle range. The system begins to function when the air flow through the carburetor venturi creates sufficient vacuum to start fuel flowing in the main system. The vacuum at the discharge nozzle will increase as the air flow increases. The faster the engine operates, the more fuel will flow through the main fuel system.

Fuel entering the main jet, located at the bottom of the main well, flows up toward the main nozzle. A main well tube is inserted within the main well. Air from the high speed bleed channel enters the main well tube through a calibrated restriction at the top of the tube. The air passes through holes spaced along the tube,

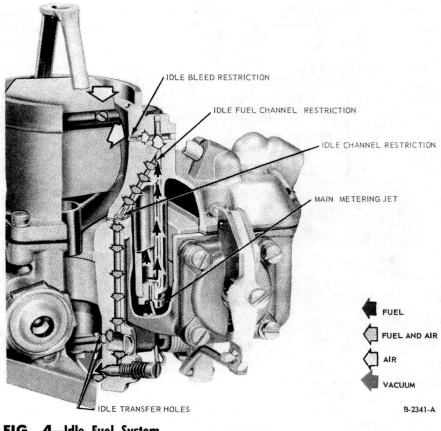

FUEL

FUEL AND AIR

AIR

VACUUM

B-2341-A

FIG. 4—Idle Fuel System

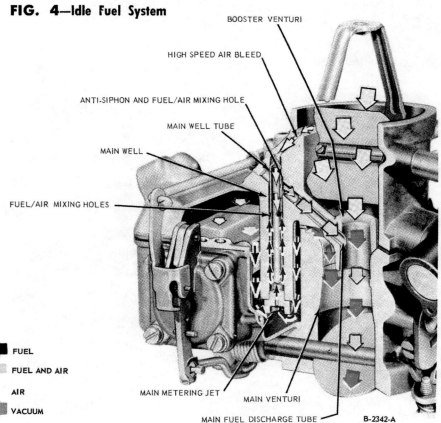

FUEL

FUEL AND AIR

AIR

VACUUM

B-2342-A

FIG. 5—Main Metering System

mixing with the fuel flowing up the main well. The fuel and air mixture being lighter than solid fuel, responds faster to changes in venturi pressures. The mixture continues flowing up the main well to the anti-syphon bleed. More air is introduced at the anti-syphon bleed to the fuel and air mixture which is then discharged from the main nozzle. The fuel is mixed with the filtered air moving past and through the booster venturi.

The anti-syphon bleed acts as a vent to prevent syphoning of fuel at low engine speeds.

ACCELERATING PUMP SYSTEM

Smooth acceleration requires a momentary increase in the supply of fuel. The air flow through the carburetor responds almost immediately to any increase in carburetor throttle valve opening. The fuel within the metering passages will lag momentarily in its response to the pressure difference created by this increased air flow. This lag in fuel response will cause a temporary leanness in the fuel-air mixture that results in a hesitation in engine acceleration. A mechanically operated accelerating pump system (Fig. 6) supplies added fuel to provide a richer fuel-air mixture for this brief period of time.

The accelerating pump, located on the side of the lower body assembly, is actuated by linkage connected to the throttle shaft. When the throttle is opened on acceleraion, the diaphragm forces fuel from the accelerating pump chamber into the discharge channel. The inlet ball check closes to prevent a reverse flow of fuel. Fuel under pressure forces he outlet ball check valve and weight off its seat, allowing fuel to pass up to the discharge nozzle. The fuel is sprayed from the nozzle into the air stream above the main venturi.

When the throttle plate is closed on deceleration, a return spring forces the diaphragm back, drawing fuel through the inlet channel. The inlet ball check opens, allowing fuel to pass into the chamber while the ball check closes, preventing entry of air. A bleed hole is located in the body casting to allow vapor and excess pressure to escape from the diaphragm chamber.

POWER FUEL SYSTEM

When the engine is required to deliver more power to meet an increased road load demand or wide-open throttle operation, the carburetor must deliver a richer fuel-

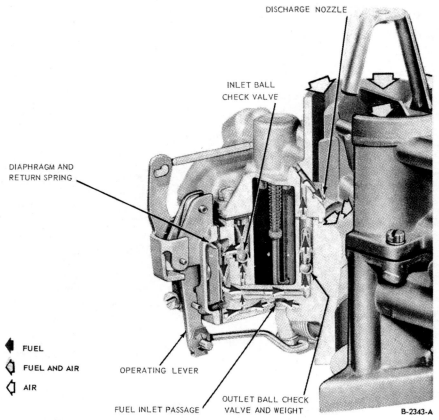

DISCHARGE NOZZLE

INLET BALL
CHECK VALVE

DIAPHRAGM AND
RETURN SPRING

◀ FUEL

◁ FUEL AND AIR

◁ AIR

OPERATING LEVER

FUEL INLET PASSAGE

OUTLET BALL CHECK
VALVE AND WEIGHT

B-2343-A

FIG. 6—Accelerating Pump System

air mixture than supplied during the operation of the main fuel system at cruise or part throttle operation. When the engine is running under a high power demand, intake manifold vacuum is low. The vacuum below the carburetor throttle plate approximates intake manifold vacuum. The carburetor power valve (Fig. 7) will open when the manifold vacuum drops below a predetermined value. The fuel-air mixture is thus automatically enriched to meet the increased engine power demands.

Manifold vacuum is transmitted from an opening below the throttle plate, through a channel to the upper body assembly and to the top of the power valve piston. At idle and normal engine speeds, the manifold vacuum is great enough to hold the power valve piston up.

The power valve rod is connected to the piston. The foot of the rod controls the spring-loaded power valve ball check. With the piston held up by manifold vacuum, the ball check closes the power jet inlet channel.

A power valve spring is located on the rod. The spring is shim calibrated to overcome the vacuum above the piston when manifold vacuum drops

below a predetermined level. Upon demand for more power, the manifold vacuum drops below this level. The spring tension moves the rod down and allows the power valve ball check to open. Air pressure above the fuel bowl forces fuel to flow through the power jet, adding to fuel in the main fuel system, enriching the fuel-air mixture.

As the demand for power decreases and manifold vacuum increases, the vacuum above the piston overcomes the spring tension. The piston and rod move up and the ball check closes the power jet channel.

AUTOMATIC CHOKE SYSTEM

The automatic choke system (Fig. 8), provides the proper choking action required to enrich the fuel air mixture during the engine warm up period.

The choke plate, located, in the air horn of the upper body, when closed, provides a high vacuum above as well as below the throttle plate. With a vacuum above the throttle plate, fuel will flow from the main fuel system as well as from the idle fuel system. This provides the extremely rich fuel mixture necessary for cold engine operation.

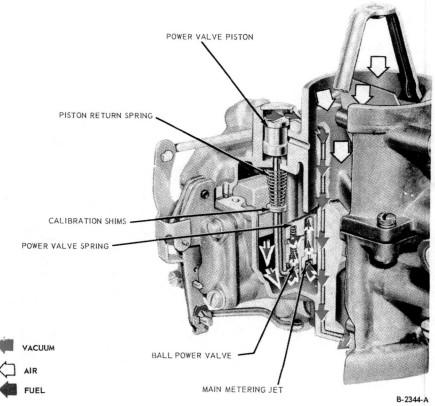

POWER VALVE PISTON

PISTON RETURN SPRING

CALIBRATION SHIMS

POWER VALVE SPRING

◀ VACUUM

◁ AIR

◀ FUEL

BALL POWER VALVE

MAIN METERING JET

B-2344-A

FIG. 7—Power Valve and Fuel Enrichment System

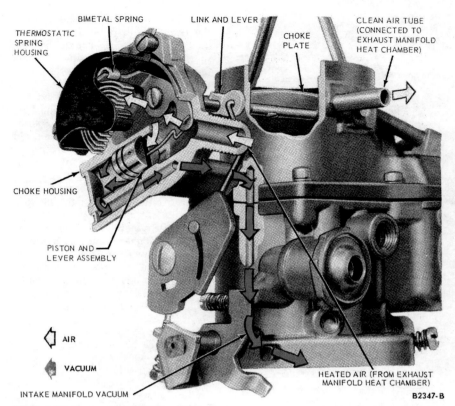

THERMOSTATIC SPRING HOUSING

BIMETAL SPRING

LINK AND LEVER

CHOKE PLATE

CLEAN AIR TUBE (CONNECTED TO EXHAUST MANIFOLD HEAT CHAMBER)

CHOKE HOUSING

PISTON AND LEVER ASSEMBLY

AIR

VACUUM

INTAKE MANIFOLD VACUUM

HEATED AIR (FROM EXHAUST MANIFOLD HEAT CHAMBER)

B2347-B

FIG. 8—Automatic Choke System

The carburetor choke shaft is connected to the thermostatic choke control mechanism by the choke thermostat lever link.

The linkage between the choke shaft and the throttle shaft is designed so that the choke plate will partially open when the accelerator pedal is fully depressed. This permits unloading of a flooded engine.

The automatic choke is equipped with a bi-metal thermostatic spring and a vacuum piston (Fig. 8). The bi-metal thermostatic spring mechanism winds up when cold and unwinds when warm.

When the engine is cold, the thermostatic spring, through attaching linkage, holds the choke piston upward and the choke plate in a closed position prior to engine start.

A cold engine is started by opening the throttle fully to permit the pressure exerted by the bi-metal spring to fully close the choke plate. At the same time, the fast idle cam is also rotated into position by the automatic choke lever link to contact the fast idle adjusting screw. The throttle is returned to a partially opened position and the engine is cranked.

When the engine is started, manifold vacuum (channeled through a passage below the choke piston in the choke housing) acts directly on the piston and draws it downward, exerting an opening force on the choke plate. This force immediately moves the choke plate against the tension of the thermostatic spring to a partially open position to prevent stalling.

As the engine continues to operate, manifold vacuum draws heated air from the exhaust manifold heat chamber. The amount of air entering the choke housing is controlled by restrictions in the air passages in the carburetor.

The warmed air enters the choke housing and heats the thermostatic spring, causing it to unwind. The tension of the thermostatic spring gradually decreases as the temperature of the air from the heat chamber rises, allowing the choke plate to gradually open. The air is exhausted into the intake manifold.

When the engine reaches its normal operating temperature, the thermostatic spring exerts tension on the choke plate, forcing it to the full open position. In this position, the choke piston is at its lowest point in the choke housing cylinder. Slots in the piston chamber wall allow sufficient air to bleed past the piston and

into the intake manifold, causing a continual flow of warm air to pass through the thermostatic spring housing. The spring thus remains heated and the choke plate remains fully open until the engine is stopped and allowed to cool.

The choke control rod actuates the fast idle cam during choking. Steps on the edge of the fast idle cam contact the fast idle adjusting screw, which permits a faster engine idle speed for smoother running when the engine is cold. As the choke plate is moved through its range of travel from the closed to open position, the choke control rod rotates the fast idle cam. Each step on the fast idle cam permits a slower idle rpm as engine temperature rises and choking is reduced.

During the warm-up period, if the engine should reach the stall point due to a lean fuel mixture, manifold vacuum will drop considerably. The tension of the thermostatic spring then overcomes the lowered vacuum acting on the choke piston, and the choke plate will be moved toward the closed position, providing a richer fuel mixture to help prevent stalling.

FUEL BOWL VENT SYSTEM

The fuel bowl requires venting (Fig. 9) to provide proper operation for the various systems. Fuel vapors may form in the fuel bowl when a hot engine is stopped, idling or operating at very low speeds. By venting the fuel bowl to the atmosphere by means of a vent control valve, engine performance is improved. At higher engine speeds, venting to the carburetor air horn prevents calibration changes due to normal air cleaner contamination.

The restriction of air due to air cleaner contamination causes a pressure drop in the carburetor air horn, and a richer air-fuel mixture. The pressure drop will increase as the demand for air (engine speed) is increased.

On all carburetors, a valve connected through linkage to the throttle shaft and located in a bore over the fuel bowl, is at the inward position during closed or part throttle operation. In this position, the valve allows venting only to the atmosphere. At normal or wide-open throttle operation, the valve moves outward sealing the external vent and opening the vent to the carburetor throat.

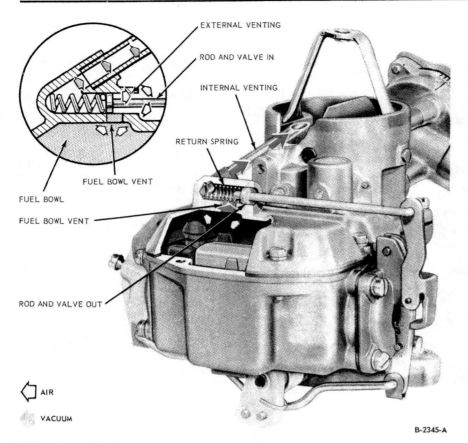

FIG. 9—Fuel Bowl Venting System—Typical

nels. The spark valve is held open by the combination of vacuum and atmospheric pressure acting on the spark valve diaphragm to overcome the tension of a calibrated spring in the spark valve.

Calibrated restrictors in the manifold vacuum channels limit the flow of manifold vacuum to the distributor. Also, during low manifold vacuum periods, the bypass restrictor controls the reduction of venturi vacuum caused by bleed back.

At off-idle engine speeds, vacuum at the throttle edge is high due to a venturi effect created by the position of the throttle plate in the throttle bore. The high vacuum in this area is supplied to the distributor through the manifold vacuum channels for the required increase in distributor spark advance.

Upon acceleration and under wide-open throttle operation, manifold vacuum drops. When the manifold vacuum falls below a predetermined point, the spark valve closes, shutting off the manifold vacuum to the distributor. The drop in distributor vacuum retards the spark advance. Venturi vacuum, now greater than manifold vacuum, supplies vacuum to the distributor, thus preventing a full spark retard.

SPARK (DISTRIBUTOR VACUUM) CONTROL SYSTEM

The degree of spark advance in the distributor is determined by the strength of the vacuum acting on the distributor diaphragm. A high vacuum will increase spark advance. The carburetor is calibrated to provide the required vacuum to the distributor through an interaction of venturi vacuum and manifold vacuum. Venturi vacuum is obtained through the pickup tube in the main venturi and is supplied to the distributor only when it exceeds manifold vacuum (Fig. 10).

Manifold vacuum supplied to the distributor is obtained from a pickup hole at the throttle plate edge (when the throttle is closed) and is metered to the distributor. An additional passage is always open to manifold vacuum. The purpose of the additional passage is to provide a higher spark advance at closed throttle during deceleration to promote complete burning of the fuel and greater efficiency.

Metering of the manifold vacuum to the distributor is accomplished through the use of the spark valve and restrictors in the vacuum chan-

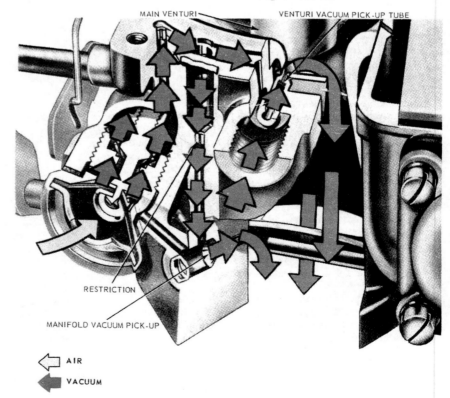

FIG. 10—Spark (Distributor Vacuum) Control System

As the engine load demands decrease, the increase in manifold vacuum will become greater than venturi vacuum. The increased manifold vacuum opens the spark valve and the higher vacuum now supplied to the distributor increases the spark advance for more efficient engine operation.

ANTI-STALL DASHPOT SYSTEM

The low idle rpm setting on automatic transmission equipped units requires a means of control to prevent engine stall upon sudden closing of the throttle plate. This is accomplished by hydraulic dampening of the throttle closing rate.

The dashpot, located on the side of the fuel bowl, is actuated by linkage connected to the throttle shaft (Fig. 11). When the throttle is opened a return spring forces the diaphragm back, drawing fuel through the inlet channel. The inlet ball check opens, allowing fuel to flow into the dashpot chamber.

When the throttle plate is closed, the dashpot actuating lever and adjusting screw moves the diaphragm inward. The diaphragm moving inward seats the inlet ball check, closes the inlet channel and forces fuel through a restriction into the fuel

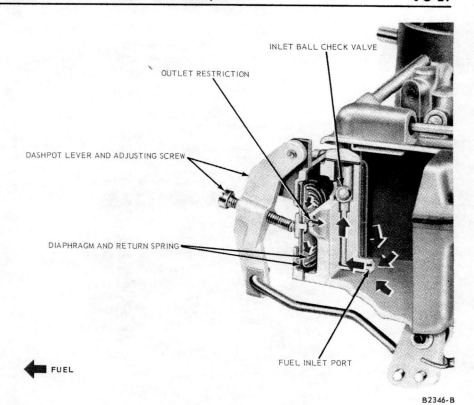

FUEL

FIG. 11—Anti-Stall Dashpot System

outlet channel into the bowl. The discharge restriction limits the flow

of fuel and slows the closing of the throttle plate.

2   REMOVAL AND INSTALLATION

REMOVAL

Flooding, stumble on acceleration and other performance complaints, are, in many instances, caused by the presence of dirt, water, or other foreign matter in the carburetor. To aid in diagnosing the complaint, the carburetor should be carefully removed from the engine without removing the fuel from the bowl. The contents of the bowl may then be examined for contamination as the carburetor is disassembled.

1. Remove the air cleaner assembly from the carburetor (Part 10-6, Section 2).

2. Disconnect the clean air tube, throttle return spring, throttle cable, automatic choke heat tube, in-line fuel filter and distributor vacuum line from the carburetor.

3. Remove the carburetor to intake manifold retaining nuts. Remove the carburetor, upper mounting gasket, spacer and lower mounting gasket from the intake manifold. Discard the gaskets.

INSTALLATION

1. Clean the gasket mounting surface of the carburetor and intake manifold.

2. Position the spacer between 2 new gaskets, and position them on the intake manifold. Install the carburetor and tighten the retaining nuts evenly and alternately to specification (Part 10-9).

3. Connect the distributor vacuum line, fuel inlet line, automatic choke heat tube, clean air tube, throttle cable and throttle return spring to the carburetor.

4. Adjust the idle fuel mixture and engine idle speed. Refer to Common Adjustments and Repair (Part 10-1, Section 2) for the proper procedures.

3   MAJOR REPAIR OPERATIONS

DISASSEMBLY

Use a separate container for the component parts of the various assemblies, to facilitate cleaning, inspection and assembly.

The following is a step by step sequence of operations for completely overhauling the carburetor; however, certain components of the carburetor may be serviced without a complete

disassembly of the entire unit.

A disassembled view of the carburetor is shown in Fig. 13.

AUTOMATIC CHOKE

1. Remove the choke thermostatic

spring housing clamp retaining screws (Fig. 12). Remove the clamp, housing and gasket. Discard the gasket.

the fuel bowl vent side of the upper body to allow clearance between the float assembly and the lower body. Separate the upper body from the

5. If it is necessary to remove the choke plate and shaft, lightly scribe the choke along the choke shaft so that the choke plate can be installed in the same position during installation.

Remove the choke plate screws. The retaining screws are staked in the choke shaft. If the tips of the screws are flared excessively, file off the flared portion to avoid damage to the threads in the choke shaft. Be careful not to damage the choke shaft or venturi while filing the screws. Remove the choke plate from the top of the air horn by sliding the plate out of the shaft. Slide the shaft out of the body.

FUEL VENT VALVE ROD

1. Remove the stake marks at the vent rod opening with a scraper or file.

2. Remove the vent rod assembly and spring by pulling the vent rod outward.

LOWER BODY

1. Depress the tab on the accelerating pump lever to control rod retaining clip with pliers, and slide the rod out of the lever. Remove the clip from the lever.

2. Remove the accelerating pump cover retaining screws. Remove the cover assembly from the lower body. Separate the pump diaphragm and spring from the cover or lower body.

If necessary, remove the fuel vent rod actuating lever to cover retaining pin and the accelerating pump lever to cover retaining pin with pliers. Turn them in a direction that will coil the pins to a smaller diameter. If the pins offer resistance to turning, turn them in the opposite direction. Remove the levers from the cover.

3. If the carburetor is equipped with a dashpot, depress the tab on the dashpot lever and control rod retaining clip, and slide the rod out of the dashpot lever. Remove the dashpot cover retaining screws and remove the cover assembly. Separate the diaphragm and spring from the cover or body.

If necessary, remove the lever to cover retaining pin with pliers. Turn the pin in a direction that will coil the pin to a smaller diameter. If the pin offers resistance to turning, turn it in the opposite direction. Remove *the lever from the cover.*

4. Remove the throttle shaft lever and retaining ring and washer. Remove the lever and overtravel spring

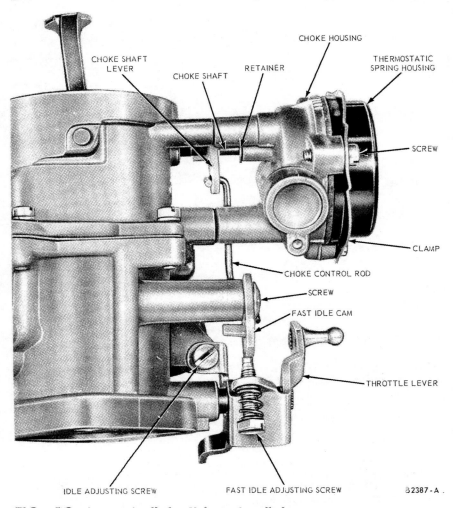

FIG. 12—Automatic Choke Linkage Installed

2. Remove the choke housing to upper body retaining screws. Remove the choke housing assembly and gasket. Discard the gasket.

3. Remove the automatic choke shaft retaining screw and washer. Remove the choke shaft and retainer assembly and the lever, link and piston assembly from the choke housing. If necessary, disassemble the piston lever and link, and remove the retainer from the choke shaft.

4. Remove the fast idle cam lever to main body retaining screw, and remove the lever and choke control rod. If necessary, remove the control rod from the lever.

UPPER AND LOWER BODY

1. Remove the upper (air horn) to lower body retaining screws and the carburetor identification tag. Tilt

lower body, using a twisting motion to disconnect the fuel vent rod from the actuating lever on the accelerator pump. Remove and discard the upper to lower body mounting gasket.

2. Invert the lower body assembly and allow the accelerating pump discharge weight and ball check, accelerating pump inlet ball check, and the dashpot ball check, if so equipped, to fall into the hand.

UPPER BODY (AIR HORN)

1. Remove the float shaft and the float assembly.

2. Remove the fuel inlet needle valve.

3. Remove the main jet.

4. Remove the air cleaner bracket retaining pins with pliers. Pull the retainer out of the retaining channels.

from the throttle shaft. Remove the accelerator pump and dashpot control rods from the lever.

5. Remove the distributor vacuum outlet adapter.

6. Remove the spark valve and gasket.

7. Remove the idle mixture adjusting screw and spring.

8. If it is necessary to remove the throttle plate and shaft, lightly scribe the throttle plate along the throttle shaft so that the throttle plates can be installed in the same position during installation.

Remove the throttle plate retaining screws and slide the plate out of the shaft. For assembly purposes, note that the dimple in the throttle plate is located below the throttle shaft. **The retaining screws are staked in the throttle shaft.** If the tips of the screws are flared excessively, file off the flared portion to avoid damage to the threads in the throttle shaft. **Be careful not to damage the throttle shaft or venturi while filing the screws.**

9. Remove the overtravel spring tension pin from the throttle shaft and slide the shaft out of the body.

CLEANING AND INSPECTION

Clean and inspect the carburetor component parts. Refer to Part 10-1, Section 3, for the proper procedure. Replace all worn or damaged parts.

ASSEMBLY

Make sure all holes in the new gaskets have been properly punched and that no foreign material has adhered to the gaskets.

During assembly of the carburetor, certain adjustments are required. The details of these adjustments are covered in Part 10-1, Section 2, under Common Adjustments and Repairs.

A disassembled view of the carburetor is shown in Fig. 13.

FUEL VENT VALVE ROD

1. Insert the fuel vent valve return spring in the fuel vent passage in the upper body. Insert the piston end of the fuel vent rod in the passage.

2. Punch three indentations in the vent valve passage opening with a center punch and a hammer. The indentations must distort the inside edge of the opening sufficiently to act as a stop for the piston end of the vent rod. Perform a Vent Valve Adjustment after the carburetor is assembled and installed in the car.

UPPER BODY (AIR HORN)

1. If the choke plate and the shaft were removed, insert the choke shaft assembly into the air horn with the flat surface of the shaft facing upward.

Refer to the line previously scribed on the choke plate and insert the choke plate into its original position with the plate indentation facing upward and toward the accelerating pump side of the carburetor. Install the choke plate retaining screws snug, but not tight.

Check for proper plate fit, binding in the air horn and free rotation of the shaft by moving the plate from the closed position to the open position. If it moves freely, tighten the choke plate retaining screws while holding the plate in the fully-closed position. Stake the screws. **When staking the screws, support the shaft and plate on a block of wood or a metal bar to prevent bending of the shaft.**

2. Install the main jet in the main fuel well.

3. Insert the needle valve into the bore, with the viton tip toward the integral seat in the upper body.

4. Insert the air cleaner bracket in the channels of the air horn and install the bracket retaining pins.

5. Position the float assembly in the upper body, with the tab on the arm located over the needle valve and the hinge of the arm lined up between the hinge bracket holes in the upper body casting. Insert the float shaft through the holes in the upper body and float assembly.

6. Check the float setting. Refer to Part 10-1, Section 2 for the proper procedure.

LOWER BODY

1. If the throttle plate and shaft were removed, slide the throttle shaft into the lower body, with the flat surface on the throttle shaft facing toward the bottom surface of the lower body. Install the throttle shaft retaining pin.

Refer to the line previously scribed on the throttle plate and insert the plate through the slot in the throttle shaft. The plate indentations must face the bottom of the body and point toward the accelerator pump side of the lower body. Install the throttle plate screws snug, but not tight.

Rotate the throttle shaft while lightly tapping the throttle plate within the throttle bore. Check for

free rotation of the throttle shaft. Hold the lower body up to the light. **Little, or no light should show between the throttle plate and throttle bore.** When the plate is properly located, hold the throttle plate closed; then, tighten and stake the retaining screws. **When staking the screws, support the shaft and plate on a block of wood or a metal bar to prevent bending of the shaft.**

2. If the lever was removed from the accelerating pump cover, position the top hole of the lever between the top bracket holes in the cover; then, install the retaining roll pin.

Position the vent rod lever over the accelerating pump cover bracket. Line up the hole in the lever with the holes in the bracket and install the retaining roll pin.

Install the roll pin in the "HI" (lower) stop hole in the lever.

Position the small diameter end of the diaphragm return spring in the boss in the accelerating pump chamber. Position the diaphragm assembly in the accelerating pump cover, with the diaphragm plunger facing the lever, and line up the holes. Position the cover and diaphragm over the return spring and onto the body. Install the cover retaining screws finger-tight. Push the diaphragm assembly inward with the lever and tighten the cover retaining screws.

3. If the carburetor is equipped with a dashpot, proceed with the following steps:

If the lever was removed from the dashpot cover, position the hole in the lever between the holes in the bracket on the cover. Install the lever retaining roll pin. Install the adjusting screw in the lever, if necessary.

Position the small diameter of the diaphragm return spring on the boss in the dashpot chamber. Position the diaphragm in the dashpot cover, with the diaphragm plunger facing the lever, and line up the holes. Position the cover and the diaphragm over the return spring and onto the body. Install the cover retaining screws finger-tight. Push the diaphragm assembly inward with the lever and tighten the cover retaining screws.

4. Position the overtravel spring on the accelerating pump lever and hook the tang of the spring on the lever. Position the accelerating pump overtravel lever and spring on the throttle shaft.

5. Install the overtravel lever ten-

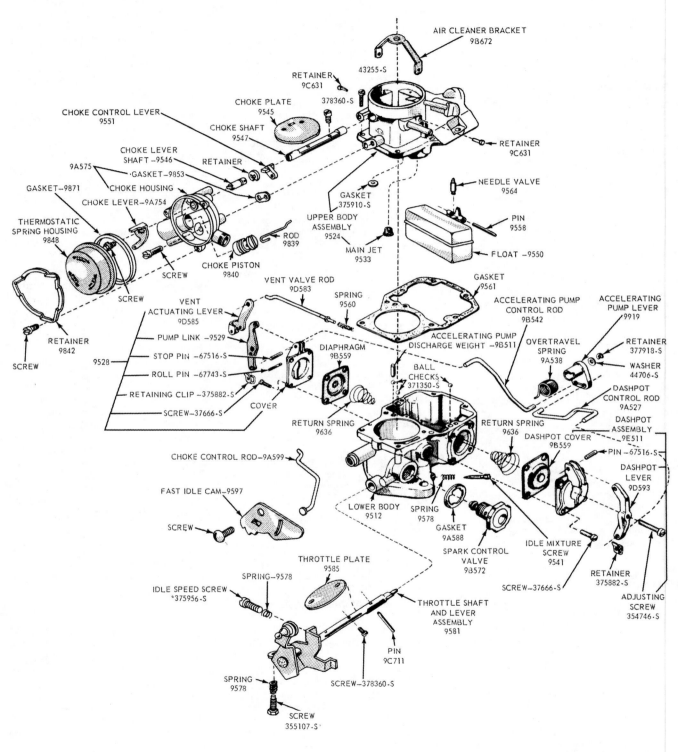

AIR CLEANER BRACKET
9B672

RETAINER
9C631

43255-S

378360-S

CHOKE PLATE
9545

CHOKE CONTROL LEVER
9551

RETAINER
9C631

CHOKE SHAFT
9547

CHOKE LEVER
SHAFT—9546

RETAINER

9A575

·GASKET—9853

NEEDLE VALVE
9564

GASKET—9871

CHOKE HOUSING

GASKET
375910-S

PIN
9558

CHOKE LEVER—9A754

UPPER BODY
ASSEMBLY
9524

THERMOSTATIC
SPRING HOUSING
9848

FLOAT —9550

ROD
9839

MAIN JET
9533

CHOKE PISTON
9840

SCREW

SCREW

VENT VALVE ROD
9D583

GASKET
9561

SCREW

VENT
ACTUATING LEVER
9D585

SPRING
9560

ACCELERATING PUMP
CONTROL ROD
9B542

ACCELERATING
PUMP LEVER
9919

RETAINER
9842

PUMP LINK —9529

ACCELERATING PUMP
DISCHARGE WEIGHT —9B511

OVERTRAVEL
SPRING
9A538

RETAINER
377918-S

SCREW

STOP PIN —67516-S

DIAPHRAGM
9B559

WASHER
44706-S

9528

ROLL PIN —67743-S

BALL
CHECKS
371350-S

DASHPOT
CONTROL ROD
9A527

RETAINING CLIP —375882-S

RETURN SPRING
9636

DASHPOT
ASSEMBLY
9E511

SCREW—37666-S

COVER

RETURN SPRING
9636

DASHPOT COVER
9B559

PIN —67516-S

CHOKE CONTROL ROD—9A599

DASHPOT
LEVER
9D593

FAST IDLE CAM—9597

LOWER BODY
9512

SPRING
9578

SCREW

GASKET
9A588

IDLE MIXTURE
SCREW
9541

RETAINER
375882-S

SPARK CONTROL
VALVE
9B572

SCREW—37666-S

ADJUSTING
SCREW
354746-S

THROTTLE PLATE
9585

SPRING—9578

THROTTLE SHAFT
AND LEVER
ASSEMBLY
9581

IDLE SPEED SCREW
*375956-S

PIN
9C711

SCREW—378360-S

SPRING
9578

SCREW
355107-S

B2388-B

FIG. 13—Ford 1-V Carburetor—Disassembled

sion spring retaining pin in the throttle shaft. Pull the arm of the spring over the retaining pin to apply spring tension to the overtravel lever. Install the washer and retaining clip on the throttle shaft.

6. Insert the keyed end of the accelerating pump actuating rod and the dashpot actuating rod (if so equipped) into the inboard side of the slotted holes in the overtravel lever.

7. Position the accelerating pump actuating rod retaining clip over the hole in the accelerating lever, with the tab side of the clip toward the carburetor barrel. Depress the tab and insert the end of the rod through the lever and clip. Release the tab when the rod is inserted. Perform the Accelerating Pump Adjustments (Part 10-1, Section 2) after the carburetor is assembled.

8. If the carburetor is equipped with a dashpot, position the dashpot actuating rod retaining clip over the hole in the dashpot lever, with the tab side of the clip facing toward the carburetor barrel. Depress the tab and insert the end of the rod through the lever and clip, then release the tab when the rod is inserted. Perform an Anti-Stall Dashpot Adjustment (Part 10-1, Section 2) after the carburetor is assembled.

9. Position the spark valve gasket over the valve and screw the valve into the lower body. Tighten the valve securely. **A loose valve will cause poor engine operation.**

10. Install the idle mixture adjusting screw and spring in the lower body. Perform the Preliminary Idle Mixture Setting (Part 10-1, Section 2) after the carburetor is assembled.

UPPER (AIR HORN) TO LOWER BODY ASSEMBLY

1. Place the ball check and the accelerating pump weight into the lower body accelerating pump outlet passage. Insert a ball check in the accelerating pump inlet passage.

2. If the carburetor is equipped with a dashpot, insert a ball check in the dashpot inlet passage.

3. Install the upper to lower body gasket onto the lower body. **Make certain the word TOP (inscribed on the gasket) is facing upward. Position the upper body on the lower body and gasket. During the installation, observe the float shaft to make certain it does not dislodge.** Install the upper to lower body retaining screws and the carburetor identification tag. Tighten the screws.

AUTOMATIC CHOKE

1. Install the choke control lever on the choke control rod. Install the fast idle cam on the main body and install the retaining screw (Fig. 12).

2. If necessary, install a new retainer on the choke shaft.

3. If the choke piston, lever and link were disassembled, connect the piston lever link to the piston and the choke thermostatic spring lever.

4. Insert the choke shaft assembly into the rear of the choke housing. Insert the choke piston into the choke housing, and install the choke thermostatic spring lever on the flange of the choke shaft. Install the choke thermostatic spring lever to shaft retaining screw and washer. **Actuate the piston and lever assembly to make certain a binding condition does not exist.**

5. Insert the choke housing to upper body retaining screws in the choke housing. Position the choke thermostatic control gasket on the choke housing flange.

6. Hold the choke plate closed and position the choke control lever on the choke shaft. With the choke plate held closed, install the choke housing and gasket assembly on the choke control lever and the upper body flange and tighten the retaining screws. **Make certain the gasket is properly installed.** Perform the Choke Plate Clearance Adjustment (Part 10-1, Section 2).

7. Install a new choke thermostatic spring housing gasket on the choke housing. Position the thermostatic spring housing on the choke housing, making sure the loop at the end of the thermostatic spring is on the choke thermostat lever. **The spring must wind clockwise when viewed from the choke housing side of the carburetor (Fig. 14).**

8. Loosely install the thermostatic spring housing clamp and the retaining screws. Rotate the spring housing in a counterclockwise (rich) direction and align the index mark on the spring housing with the specified index mark (Part 10-9) on the choke housing. Tighten the clamp retaining screws. Perform the Fast Idle Cam Linkage Adjustment (Part 10-1, Section 2).

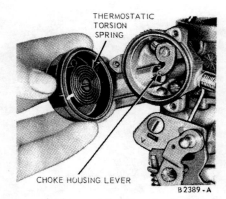

THERMOSTATIC TORSION SPRING

CHOKE HOUSING LEVER

B 2389-A

FIG. 14—Correct Position of Automatic Choke Torsion Spring

PART 10-3

FORD 2-V CARBURETORS

1 DESCRIPTION AND OPERATION

DESCRIPTION

The carburetor (Figs. 1 and 2) have two main assemblies, the air horn and the main body.

housing is attached to the main body.

The two barrels each contain a main and booster venturi, main fuel discharge, accelerating pump dis-

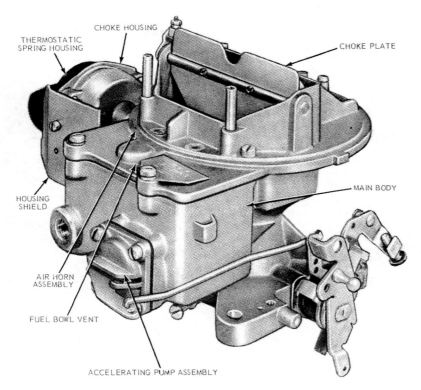

THERMOSTATIC SPRING HOUSING

CHOKE HOUSING

CHOKE PLATE

HOUSING SHIELD

MAIN BODY

AIR HORN ASSEMBLY

FUEL BOWL VENT

ACCELERATING PUMP ASSEMBLY

B2378-B

FIG. 1—Left Front ¾ View

The air horn assembly, which serves as the main body cover, contains the choke plate and the vents for the fuel bowl.

The throttle plate, the accelerating pump assembly, the power valve assembly, and the fuel bowl are in the main body. The automatic choke

charge, idle fuel discharge and a throttle plate.

OPERATION

FUEL INLET SYSTEM

The amount of fuel entering the fuel bowl (Fig. 3) is regulated by the

distance the fuel inlet needle is raised off its seat and by fuel pump pressure. Movement of the fuel inlet needle in relation to the seat is controlled by the float and lever assembly which rises and falls with the fuel level. When the fuel in the fuel bowl reaches a pre-set level, the float lowers the fuel inlet needle to a position where it restricts the flow of fuel, admitting only enough fuel to replace that being used.

An integral retaining clip is attached to the fuel inlet needle assembly. The clip hooks over the tab on the end of the lever of the float assembly. This clip assures reaction of the fuel inlet needle to any downward movement of the float. Downward movement of the float or float drop is controlled by adjustment of the tab end of the float lever.

A wire-type retainer prevents movement of the float shaft within the guides on each side of the fuel bowl. The retainer fits into a groove on the outside of the fuel inlet needle seat. The ends of the retainer are hooked over grooves on opposite ends of the float shaft.

The fuel bowl is internally vented into the air cleaner. It is also externally vented to the atmosphere.

AUTOMATIC CHOKE SYSTEM

The choke plate, located in the air horn above the barrels, when closed, provides a high vacuum above as well as below the throttle plates. With a vacuum above the throttle plates, fuel will flow from the main fuel system as well as from the idle fuel system. This provides the extremely rich fuel mixture necessary for cold engine operation.

The carburetor choke shaft is linked to a thermostatic choke con-

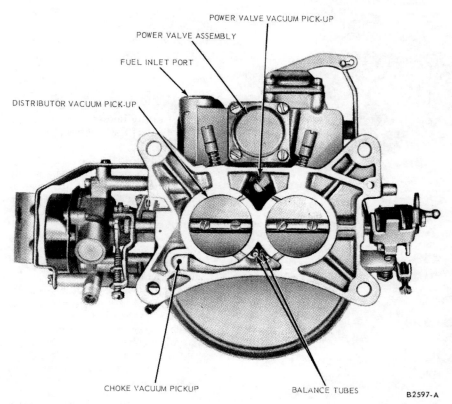

POWER VALVE VACUUM PICK-UP

POWER VALVE ASSEMBLY

FUEL INLET PORT

DISTRIBUTOR VACUUM PICK-UP

CHOKE VACUUM PICKUP

BALANCE TUBES

B2597-A

FIG. 2—Bottom View

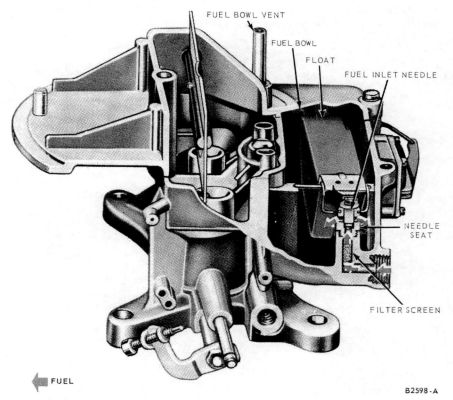

FUEL BOWL VENT

FUEL BOWL

FLOAT

FUEL INLET NEEDLE

NEEDLE SEAT

FILTER SCREEN

FUEL

B2598-A

FIG. 3—Fuel Inlet System

trol mechanism mounted on the main body (Fig. 4).

signed so that the choke plate will partially open when the accelerator pedal is fully depressed. This permits unloading of a flooded engine.

The automatic choke is equipped with a bi-metal thermostatic spring and a vacuum piston (Fig. 4). The bi-metal thermostatic spring mechanism winds up when cold and unwinds when warm. When the engine is cold, the thermostatic spring, through attaching linkage, holds the choke piston upward and the choke plate in a closed position prior to engine start. Manifold vacuum channeled through a passage in the choke control housing draws the choke vacuum piston downward, exerting an opening force on the choke plate.

When the engine is started, manifold vacuum, acting directly on the piston located in the choke housing, immediately moves the choke plate against the tension of the thermostatic spring to a partially open position to prevent stalling.

As the engine continues to operate, manifold vacuum draws heated air from the exhaust manifold heat chamber. The amount of air entering the choke housing is controlled by restrictions in the air passages in the carburetor.

The warmed air enters the choke housing and heats the thermostatic spring, causing it to unwind. The tension of the thermostatic spring gradually decreases as the temperature of the air from the heat chamber rises, allowing the choke plate to open. The air is exhausted into the intake manifold.

When the engine reaches its normal operating temperature, the thermostatic spring exerts tension on the choke plate forcing it to the full open position. In this position, the choke piston is at its lowest point in the cylinder. Slots in the piston chamber wall allow sufficient air to bleed past the piston and into the intake manifold, causing a continual flow of warm air to pass through the thermostatic spring housing. The spring remains heated and the choke plate remains fully open until the engine is stopped and allowed to cool.

The choke rod actuates the fast idle cam during choking. Steps on the edge of the fast idle cam contact the fast idle adjusting screw. This permits a faster engine idle speed for smoother running when the engine is cold. As the choke plate is moved through its range of travel from the closed to the open position, the

The linkage between the choke lever and the throttle shaft is de-

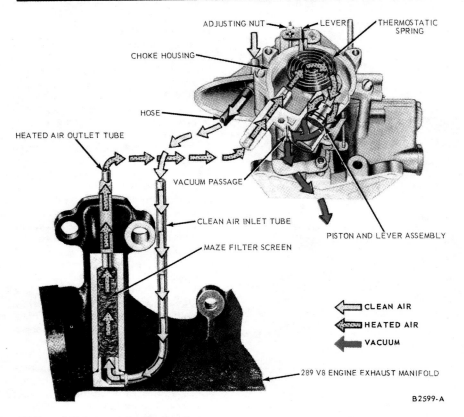

FIG. 4—Automatic Choke System

choke rod rotates the fast idle cam. Each step on the fast idle cam permits a slower idle rpm as engine temperature rises and choking is reduced.

During the warm-up period, if the engine should reach the stall point due to a lean mixture, manifold vacuum will drop considerably. The tension of the thermostatic spring then overcomes the lowered vacuum acting on the choke piston and the choke plate is moved toward the closed position, providing a richer mixture to help prevent stalling.

The linkage between the choke lever and the throttle shaft is designed so that the choke plate will partially open when the accelerator pedal is fully depressed. This permits unloading of a flooded engine.

IDLE FUEL SYSTEM

The difference in pressure between the fuel bowl and the idle discharge port forces fuel through the idle fuel system. Fuel flows from the fuel bowl through the main jet and into the bottom of the main well (Fig. 5).

From the main well, the fuel flows up through the idle tube and through a short diagonal passage in the booster venturi assembly into the idle passage in the main body. A cali-

brated restriction, at the upper tip of the idle tube, meters the flow of fuel.

Air enters the idle system from the air bleed, located directly above the idle tube. The air bleed also acts as a vent to prevent siphoning at off idle or high speeds and when the engine is stopped. Additional air is bled into the system through an air bleed located at the bottom of the diagonal passage in the booster venturi where the fuel enters the idle passage in the main body.

Fuel flows down the idle passage in the main body past three idle transfer holes. The idle transfer holes act as additional air bleeds at curb idle. The Fuel then flows past the pointed tip of the adjusting needle which controls the idle fuel discharge. From the adjusting needle chamber, the fuel flows through a short horizontal passage and is discharged below the throttle plates.

During off idle when the throttle plate is moved slightly past the idle transfer holes, each hole begins discharging fuel as it is exposed to manifold vacuum. As the throttle plate is opened still wider and engine speed increases, the air flow through the carburetor is also increased. This creates a vacuum in the booster venturi strong enough to bring the main fuel system into operation. Fuel flow from the idle fuel system tapers off

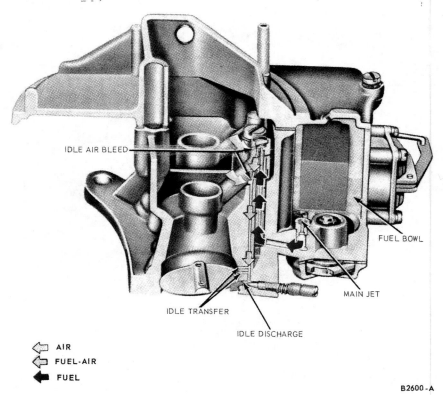

FIG. 5—Idle Fuel System

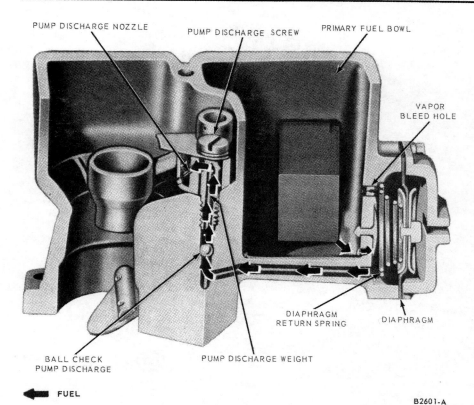

FIG. 6—Accelerating Pump System

as the main fuel system begins discharging fuel.

ACCELERATING SYSTEM

Upon acceleration, the air flow through the carburetor responds almost immediately to the increased throttle opening. There is, however, a brief interval before the flowing fuel, which is heavier than air, can gain the required flow speed to maintain the desired balance of fuel and air. During this interval, the accelerating system (Fig. 6) supplies fuel until the other systems can once again provide the proper mixture.

When the throttle is closed, the diaphragm return spring forces the diaphragm toward the cover, drawing fuel into the chamber through the inlet. The inlet has an Elastomer valve which uncovers the inlet hole to admit fuel from the fuel bowl. The valve covers the inlet hole when the accelerating pump is operated to prevent the fuel from returning to the bowl. A discharge weight and ball check prevents air from entering from the discharge nozzle when fuel is drawn into the diaphragm chamber.

When the throttle is opened, the diaphragm rod is forced inward, forcing fuel from the chamber into

the discharge passage. Fuel under pressure forces the pump discharge

weight and ball off their seat and fuel passes through the accelerating pump discharge screw and is sprayed into each main venturi through discharge ports.

An air bleed in the wall of the accelerating pump fuel chamber prevents vapor entrapment and pressure build-up in the diaphragm chamber.

MAIN FUEL SYSTEM

As engine speed increases, the air passing through the booster venturi creates a vacuum. The amount of vacuum is determined by the air flow through the venturi, which in turn is regulated by the speed of the engine. The difference in pressure between the main discharge port and the fuel bowl causes fuel to flow through the main fuel system (Fig. 7).

At a predetermined venturi vacuum, fuel flows from the fuel bowl, through the main jets, and into the bottom of the main well. The fuel moves up the main well tube past air bleed holes. Filtered air from the high speed air bleed enters the fuel flow in the main well tube through holes in the side of the tube. The high speed air bleed meters an increasing amount of air to the fuel as venturi vacuum increases, maintain-

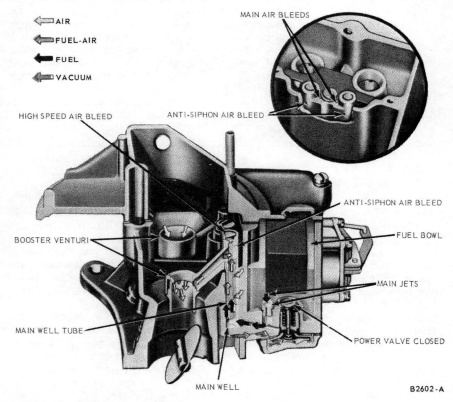

FIG. 7—Main Fuel System

ing the required fuel-air ratio. The mixture of fuel and air is lighter than raw fuel and responds faster to changes in venturi vacuum. It also atomizes more readily than raw fuel. The fuel and air continue up the main well tube past another air bleed which also acts as a vent to prevent siphoning when the engine is shut down. The fuel is discharged into the booster venturi where it is atomized and mixed with the air flowing through the carburetor.

The throttle plate controls the amount of the fuel-air mixture admitted to the intake manifold, regulating the speed and power output of the engine.

A balance tube is located in each barrel directly below the booster venturi. When decelerating, the balance tube siphons off any excess fuel droplets remaining around the edge of the booster venturi and discharges the droplets into the equalizing slots in the base of the carburetor where they are mixed with the idle fuel. The balance tube also acts as an additional air bleed during the idle fuel system operation.

POWER FUEL SYSTEM

During periods of increased road loads or high speed operation, the fuel-air ratio must be increased for added power. The added fuel required during this period is supplied by the power fuel system (Fig. 8).

The power fuel system is controlled by the intake manifold vacuum.

Manifold vacuum is transmitted from an opening in the base of the main body, through a passage in the

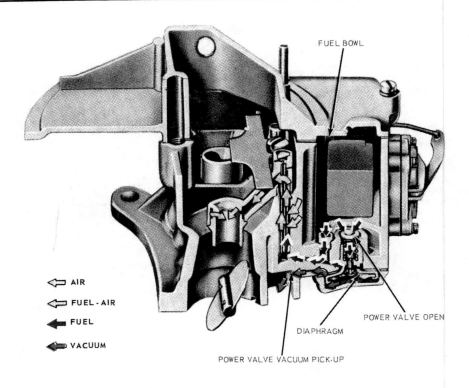

AIR
FUEL-AIR
FUEL
VACUUM

FUEL BOWL

POWER VALVE OPEN

DIAPHRAGM

POWER VALVE VACUUM PICK-UP

B2603-A

FIG. 8—Power Fuel System

main body and power valve chamber to the power valve diaphragm. The manifold vacuum, acting on the power valve at idle speed or normal road load conditions, is great enough to hold the power valve diaphragm down, overcoming the tension of the spring on the valve stem and holding the valve closed. When high power operation places a greater load on the engine and manifold vacuum drops below a predetermined

value, the spring opens the power valve. Fuel from the fuel bowl flows through the power valve and into passages leading to the main fuel well. Here the fuel is added to the fuel from the main fuel system, enriching the mixture.

As engine power demands are reduced, manifold vacuum increases. The increased vacuum overcomes the tension of the valve stem spring and closes the power valve.

2 REMOVAL AND INSTALLATION

REMOVAL

Flooding, stumble on acceleration and other performance complaints are in many instances, caused by the presence of dirt, water or other foreign matter in the carburetor. To aid in diagnosing the cause of complaint, the carburetor should be carefully removed from the engine without removing the fuel from the bowls. The contents of the bowls may then be examined for contamination as the carburetor is disassembled.

1. Remove the air cleaner (Part 10-6, Section 2). Remove the choke

shield retaining screws and remove the hose and shield from the carburetor assembly.

2. Remove the throttle cable from the throttle lever. Disconnect the distributor vacuum line, in-line fuel filter and the choke heat tube at the carburetor.

3. Disconnect the choke clean air tube from the air horn.

4. Remove the carburetor retaining nuts and lockwashers; then remove the carburetor. Remove the carburetor mounting gasket, spacer and lower gasket from the intake manifold.

INSTALLATION

1. Clean the gasket mounting surfaces of the spacer and carburetor. Place the spacer between two new gaskets and position the spacer and gaskets on the intake manifold. Position the carburetor on the spacer and gasket and secure it with the retaining lockwashers and nuts. To prevent leakage, distortion or damage to the carburetor body flange, snug the nuts; then, alternately tighten each nut in a criss-cross pattern to the specified torque (Part 10-9).

2. Connect the in-line fuel filter throttle cable, choke heat tube, and

distributor vacuum line. Position the *heater hose* on the choke shield and install the shield and retaining screws.

3. Connect the choke clean air tube to the air horn.

4. Refer to Part 10-1, Section 2, Common Adjustments and Repairs

and adjust the engine idle speed, the idle fuel mixture, anti-stall dashpot (if so equipped) and the accelerating pump stroke (if required). Install the air cleaner (Part 10-6, Section 2).

3 MAJOR REPAIR OPERATIONS

DISASSEMBLY

To facilitate working on the carburetor, and to prevent damage to the throttle plates, install carburetor legs on the vase. If legs are unavailable, install 4 bolts (about 2¼ inches long of the correct diameter) and 8 nuts on the carburetor base.

Use a separate container for the component parts of the various assemblies to facilitate cleaning, inspection and assembly.

The following is a step-by-step sequence of operations for completely overhauling the carburetor. However, certain components of the carburetor may be serviced without a complete disassembly of the entire unit. For a complete carburetor overhaul, follow all of the steps. To partially overhaul a carburetor or to install a new gasket kit, follow only the applicable steps.

Refer to Fig. 20 for parts identification.

AIR HORN

1. Remove the air cleaner anchor screw.

2. Remove the automatic choke control rod retainer.

3. Remove the air horn retaining screws, lock washers and the carburetor identification tag. Remove the air horn and air horn gasket (Fig. 9).

4. Remove the choke control rod by loosening and turning the choke shaft lever clevis nut counterclockwise. Remove the rod from the air horn. Slide the felt seal and two

washers out of the air horn.

If it is necessary to remove the choke plate, remove the staking marks on the choke plate retaining screws and remove the screws. Remove the choke plate by sliding it out of the shaft from the top of the air horn. Slide the choke shaft out of the air horn.

If the tips of the screws are flared excessively, file off the flared portion to prevent damage to the threads in the shaft.

VACUUM PISTON CHOKE

1. Remove the fast idle cam retainer (Fig. 10).

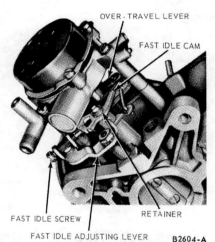

FIG. 10—Fast Idle Cam and Fast Idle Lever

2. Remove the thermostatic choke spring housing retaining screws and remove the clamp, housing and gasket.

3. Remove the choke housing assembly retaining screws. If the air horn was not previously removed, remove the choke control rod retainer. Remove the choke housing assembly, gasket and the fast idle cam. Remove the fast idle cam and rod from the fast idle cam lever.

4. Remove the choke lever retaining screw and washer (Fig. 11). Remove the choke piston lever from

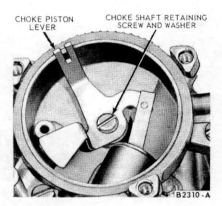

FIG. 11—Choke Shaft and Lever

the housing. If necessary, remove the pin securing the choke piston to the choke lever link. Remove the choke lever and fast idle cam lever from the choke housing.

MAIN BODY

1. With the use of a screwdriver, pry the float shaft retainer from the fuel inlet seat (Figs. 12 and 13). Remove the float, float shaft retainer and fuel inlet needle assembly. Remove the retainer and float shaft from the float lever.

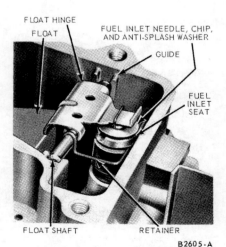

FIG. 12—Float Assembly

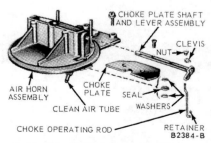

FIG. 9—Air Horn Assembly

FIG. 13—Float Shaft Retainer Removal or Installation

2. Remove the fuel inlet needle, seat, filter screen, and the main jets with a jet wrench (Figs. 14 and 15).

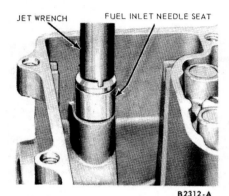

FIG. 14—Fuel Inlet Needle Seat Removal or Installation

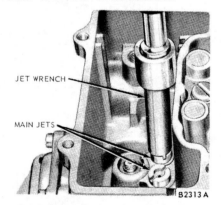

FIG. 15—Main Jet Removal or Installation

3. Remove the accelerator pump discharge screw, air distribution plate (if so equipped), booster venturi and gasket (Fig. 16). Invert the main body and let the accelerating pump discharge weight and ball fall into the hand. Remove the fuel inlet fitting.

4. Remove the accelerator pump operating rod from the over-travel

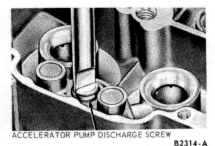

FIG. 16—Booster Venturi Removal or Installation

lever and the retainer. **To release the operating rod from the over-travel lever retainer, press the ends of the retainer together; then, at the same time, press the rod away from the retainer until it is disengaged.** Remove the rod and retainer.

5. Remove the accelerating pump cover retaining screws. Remove the accelerating pump cover, diaphragm assembly and spring (Fig. 17).

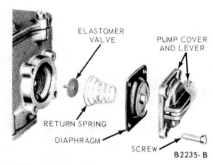

FIG. 17—Accelerating Pump Assembly

6. If it is necessary to remove the Elastomer valve, grasp it firmly and pull it out. If the Elastomer valve tip broke off during removal, be sure to remove the tip from the fuel bowl. **An Elastomer valve must be replaced whenever it has been removed from the carburetor.**

7. Invert the main body and remove the power valve cover and the gasket. Remove the power valve with a box wrench or socket wrench (Fig. 18). Remove the power valve gasket. Discard the gasket.

8. Remove the idle fuel mixture adjusting screws (needles) and the springs.

9. If necessary, remove the nut and washer securing the fast idle adjusting lever assembly to the throttle shaft, and remove the lever assembly (Fig. 10). If necessary, remove the idle screw and the retainer from the fast idle adjusting lever.

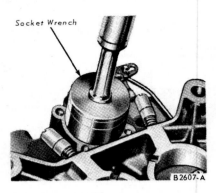

FIG. 18—Power Valve Removal or Installation

10. Remove the anti-stall dashpot, if so equipped.

11. If it is necessary to remove the throttle plates, lightly scribe the throttle plates along the throttle shaft, and mark each plate and its corresponding bore with a number or letter for proper installation (Fig. 19).

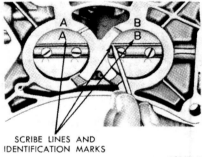

FIG. 19—Throttle Plate Removal

12. Slide the throttle shaft out of the main body.

PARTS REPAIR REPLACEMENT

Clean and inspect the carburetor component parts. Refer to Part 10-1, Section 3 for the proper procedure. Replace all worn or damaged parts.

ASSEMBLY

Make sure all holes in the new gaskets have been properly punched and that no foreign material has adhered to the gaskets. Make sure the accelerating pump diaphragm is not torn or cut.

The carburetor assembly is shown in Fig. 20.

MAIN BODY

1. Slide the throttle shaft assembly into the main body.

2. Refer to the lines scribed on the throttle plates and install the

B2383-B

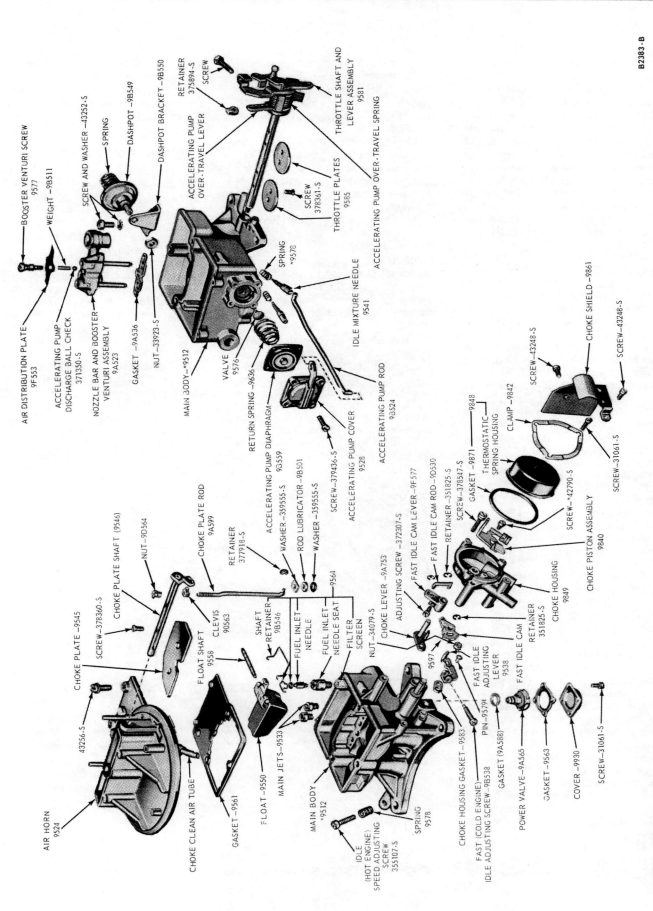

FIG. 20—Carburetor Assembly

throttle plates in their proper location with the screws snug, but not tight.

3. Close the throttle plates. Invert the main body, and hold it up to the light. Little or no light should show between the throttle plates and the throttle bores. Tap the plates lightly with a screwdriver handle to seat them. Hold the throttle plates closed and tighten and stake the retaining screws. **When staking the screws, support the shaft and plate on a block of wood or a metal bar to prevent bending of the shaft.**

4. If necessary, install the fast idle screw pin and the screw on the fast idle adjusting lever.

5. Install the anti-stall dashpot, if so equipped.

6. If the fast idle lever was removed, place the fast idle lever assembly on the throttle shaft and install the retaining washer and nut (Fig. 10).

7. If the Elastomer valve was removed, lubricate the tip of a new Elastomer valve and insert the tip into the accelerator pump cavity center hole. Using a pair of needle nosed pliers, reach into the fuel bowl and grasp the valve tip. Pull the valve in until it seats in the pump cavity wall and cut off the tip forward the retaining shoulder. Remove the tip from the bowl.

8. Install the accelerating pump diaphragm return spring on the boss on the chamber (Fig. 17). Insert the diaphragm assembly in the cover and place the cover and diaphragm assembly into position on the main body. Install the cover screws.

9. Insert the accelerating pump operating rod into the inboard hole of the accelerating pump actuating lever. Position the accelerating pump operating rod retainer over the specified hole (Part 10-9) in the over-travel lever to suit the operating and climatic conditions under which the car is to be operated. Press the ends of the retainer together; then, at the same time, insert the operating rod through the retainer and the hole in the over-travel lever. Release the ends of the retainer to secure the rod.

10. Invert the main body. Install the power valve (economizer valve) and new gasket with a wrench (Fig. 18). **Tighten the valve securely.** Install the power valve cover and new gasket.

11. Install the idle mixture adjusting screws (needles) and springs (Fig. 18). Turn the needles in gently with the fingers until they just touch the seat, then back them off the specified (Part 10-9) turns for a preliminary idle fuel mixture adjustment.

12. Install the main jets and the fuel inlet seat, filter screen, and new gasket, using a jet wrench (Figs. 14 and 15). **Be sure the correct jets are installed.**

13. Install the fuel inlet needle assembly in the fuel inlet seat. The fuel inlet needle and seat are matched assemblies. **Be sure the correct needle and seat are assembled together.**

14. Slide the float shaft into the float lever (Fig. 12). Position the float shaft retainer on the float shaft.

15. Insert the float assembly into the fuel bowl and hook the float lever tab under the fuel inlet needle assembly. Insert the float shaft into its guides at the sides of the fuel bowl.

16. With the use of a screwdriver, position the float shaft retainer in the groove on the fuel inlet needle seat (Fig. 13). Refer to Part 10-1, Section 2 and check the float setting.

17. Drop the accelerating pump discharge ball into its passage in the main body. Seat the ball with a brass drift and a light hammer. **Make sure the ball is free in the bore.** Drop the accelerating pump discharge weight on top of the ball. Position the new booster venturi gasket and the booster venturi in the main body. Install the air distribution plate (if so equipped) and the accelerator pump discharge screw (Fig. 16). Tighten the screw.

VACUUM PISTON CHOKE

1. If the choke piston and link was disassembled install the choke piston on the choke thermostatic spring lever link and install the retaining pin (Fig. 21).

2. Position the fast idle cam lever on the thermostatic choke shaft and lever assembly (Fig. 21). **The bottom of the fast idle cam lever adjusting screw must rest against the tang on the choke lever.** Insert the choke lever into the rear of the choke housing. Position the choke lever so that the hole in the lever is to the left side of the choke housing.

3. Insert the choke piston into the choke housing, and install the choke piston lever on the flange of the choke lever. Install the choke piston lever to choke lever retaining screw and washer (Fig. 11).

4. Install the fast idle cam rod on the fast idle cam lever. Place the

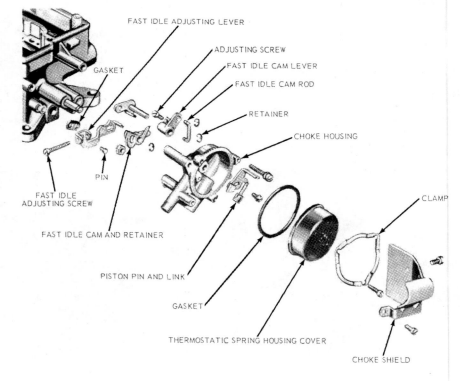

FAST IDLE ADJUSTING LEVER
ADJUSTING SCREW
FAST IDLE CAM LEVER
FAST IDLE CAM ROD
RETAINER
CHOKE HOUSING
GASKET
PIN
FAST IDLE ADJUSTING SCREW
FAST IDLE CAM AND RETAINER
PISTON PIN AND LINK
GASKET
THERMOSTATIC SPRING HOUSING COVER
CLAMP
CHOKE SHIELD

B2608-A

FIG. 21—Choke Housing Assembly

fast idle cam on the fast idle cam rod and install the retainer. Place the choke housing vacuum pick-up port to main body gasket on the choke housing flange. Position the choke housing on the main body and at the same time, install the fast idle cam on the hub on the main body. Position the gasket, and install the choke housing retaining screws. Install the fast idle cam retainer. **The thermostatic spring housing is installed after the choke plate clearance (pull-down) has been adjusted to specification.**

AIR HORN

Refer to Fig. 9 for the correct location of the parts.

1. If the choke plate shaft was removed, position the choke plate shaft in the air horn. Place the choke plate rod seal between the two brass washers and slide them into position on the choke plate rod

seal retainer.

Insert the choke plate rod through the rod seal and the air horn. Insert the choke plate rod into the choke shaft lever clevis nut, and turn the nut clockwise to thread the rod onto the nut.

2. If the choke plate was removed, insert the choke plate into the choke plate shaft. Install the choke plate screws snug, but not tight. Check for proper plate fit, binding in the air horn and free rotation of the shaft by moving the plate from the closed position to the open position. If necessary, remove the choke plate and grind or file the plate edge where it is binding or scraping on the air horn wall. If the choke plate and shaft moves freely, tighten the choke plate screws while holding the choke in the fully-closed position. Stake the screws. **When staking the screws, support

shaft and plate on a block of wood or a metal bar to prevent bending of the shaft.**

3. Position the air horn gasket on the main body, with the fuel bowl vent hole in the gasket located opposite the fuel inlet.

4. Position the air horn over the main body and insert the end of the choke plate rod into the automatic choke lever. Install the air horn retaining screws and the carburetor identification tag. Tighten the retaining screws. Install the choke plate rod retainer. Install the air cleaner anchor screw.

5. Refer to Part 10-1, Section 2 Common Adjustments and Repairs and perform the automatic choke plate clearance (pull-down) and fast idle cam linkage adjustment. Perform a fuel level float adjustment (wet) after the carburetor has been installed on the car.

PART 10-4

FORD 4-V CARBURETOR

1 DESCRIPTION AND OPERATION

DESCRIPTION

The Ford 4-V (venturi) carburetor (Figs. 1,2 and 3) has two main assemblies; the air horn, and the main body.

The air horn assembly, which serves as the main body cover, contains the choke plate, hot idle compensator, vents for the fuel bowls, secondary throttle control vacuum tubes, and the automatic choke clean air pick-up tube. A rubber hose and steel tube connects the clean air pick-up tube to the automatic choke heat chamber in the right exhaust manifold.

The primary and secondary throttle plates, accelerating pump assembly, power valve assembly, secondary operating diaphragm assembly and the fuel bowls are in the main body. The automatic choke housing is attached to the main body.

The two primary (front) barrels each contain a main and booster venturi, main fuel discharge, accelerating pump discharge, idle fuel discharge and a primary throttle plate.

The two secondary (rear) barrels each have a main fuel discharge, and a vacuum operated throttle plate.

OPERATION

FUEL INLET SYSTEM

A separate fuel bowl is provided for the primary and secondary stages (Fig. 4). The fuel enters the primary fuel bowl through the fuel inlet. A drilled passage through the right side of the main body connects the fuel bowls. The pressure in the two fuel bowls is balanced by means of a pressure equalizing chamber built into the left side of the main body. Two baffles in the internal fuel equalizer passage between the primary and secondary fuel bowls permit proper control and balance of the metering forces within each fuel bowl.

The amount of fuel entering a fuel bowl is regulated by the distance the fuel inlet needle is raised off its seat and by fuel pump pressure. Movement of the fuel inlet needle in relation to the seat is controlled by the float and lever assembly which rises and falls with the fuel level. When the fuel in the fuel bowl reaches a pre-set level, the float lowers the fuel inlet needle to a position where it restricts the flow of fuel, admitting only enough fuel thru the filter screen to replace that being used.

A retracting clip is attached to the fuel inlet needle and hooks over the tab on the end of the lever of the float assembly. This clip assures reaction of the fuel inlet needle to any movement of the float. Downward movement of the float or float drop is controlled by the tab end of the float lever.

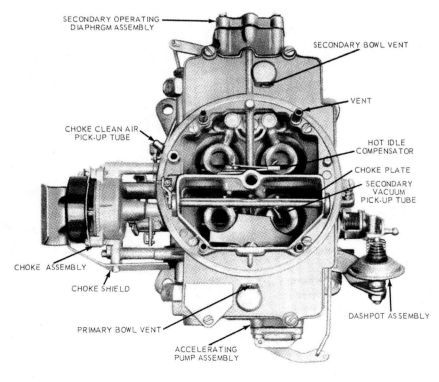

SECONDARY OPERATING DIAPHRGM ASSEMBLY

CHOKE CLEAN AIR PICK-UP TUBE

CHOKE ASSEMBLY

CHOKE SHIELD

PRIMARY BOWL VENT

ACCELERATING PUMP ASSEMBLY

SECONDARY BOWL VENT

VENT

HOT IDLE COMPENSATOR

CHOKE PLATE

SECONDARY VACUUM PICK-UP TUBE

DASHPOT ASSEMBLY

B2609-A

FIG. 1—Top View—Air Horn Installed

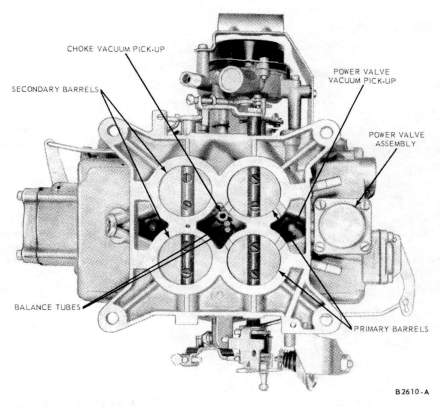

CHOKE VACUUM PICK-UP

SECONDARY BARRELS

POWER VALVE
VACUUM PICK-UP

POWER VALVE
ASSEMBLY

BALANCE TUBES

PRIMARY BARRELS

B2610-A

FIG. 2—Bottom View

A wire-type retainer prevents movement of the float shaft within the guides on each side of the fuel bowl. The retainer fits into a groove on the inlet needle seat. The ends of the retainer are hooked over grooves on opposite ends of the float shaft.

The fuel filter screen, located below the inlet needle seat, prevents the entrance of foreign matter.

The primary and secondary fuel bowls are vented externally at all times. In addition, both the primary and secondary fuel bowls are internally vented into the air cleaner. The standpipe pitot tubes in the primary and secondary internal vent tube openings raise the level of the internal vent openings above the external vent openings. This provides the necessary pressure differential for proper evacuation of the gaseous vapors through the external vent during a hot soak period.

An integral anti-splash washer is located on top of each fuel inlet needle.

AUTOMATIC CHOKE SYSTEM

The choke plate, located in the air horn above the primary barrels, when closed, provides a high vacuum above as well as below the throttle plates. With a vacuum above the throttle plates, fuel will flow

from the main fuel system as well as from the idle fuel system. This pro-

vides the extremely rich fuel mixture necessary for cold engine operation.

The carburetor choke shaft is linked to a thermostatic choke control mechanism mounted on the main body (Fig. 5).

The linkage between the choke lever and the throttle shaft is designed so that the choke plate will partially open when the accelerator pedal is fully depressed. This permits unloading of a flooded engine.

The automatic choke is equipped with a bi-metal thermostatic spring and a vacuum piston (Fig. 5). The bi-metal thermostatic spring mechanism winds up when cold and unwinds when warm. When the engine is cold, the thermostatic spring, through attaching linkage, holds the choke piston upward and the choke plate in a closed position prior to engine start. Manifold vacuum channeled through a passage in the choke control housing draws the choke vacuum piston downward, exerting an opening force on the choke plate.

When the engine is started, manifold vacuum acting directly on the piston, located in the choke housing, immediately moves the choke plate against the tension of the thermostatic spring to a partially open position to prevent stalling.

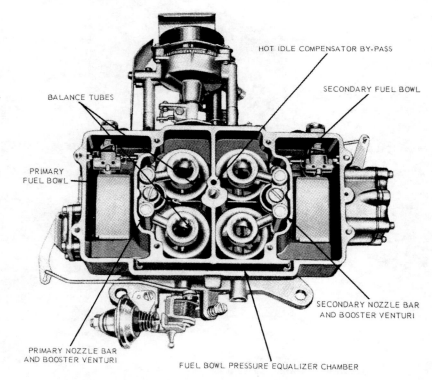

HOT IDLE COMPENSATOR BY-PASS

SECONDARY FUEL BOWL

BALANCE TUBES

PRIMARY
FUEL BOWL

SECONDARY NOZZLE BAR
AND BOOSTER VENTURI

PRIMARY NOZZLE BAR
AND BOOSTER VENTURI

FUEL BOWL PRESSURE EQUALIZER CHAMBER

B2611-A

FIG. 3—Top View—Air Horn Removed

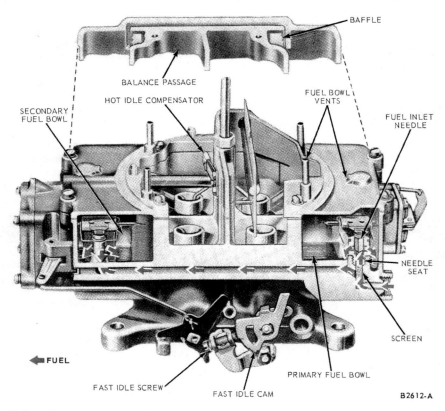

FIG. 4—Fuel Inlet System

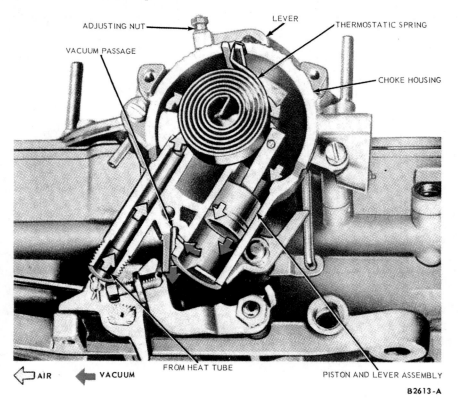

FIG. 5—Automatic Choke System

As the engine continues to operate, manifold vacuum draws heated air from the exhaust manifold heat chamber. The amount of air entering the choke housing is controlled by restrictions in the air passages in the carburetor.

The warmed air enters the choke housing and heats the thermostatic spring, causing it to unwind. The tension of the thermostatic spring gradually decreases as the temperature of the air from the heat chamber rises, allowing the choke plate to open. The air is exhausted into the intake manifold.

When the engine reaches its normal operating temperature, the thermostatic spring exerts tension on the choke plate forcing it to the full open position. In this position, the choke piston is at its lowest point in the cylinder. Slots in the piston chamber wall allow sufficient air to bleed past the piston and into the intake manifold, causing a continual flow of warm air to pass through the thermostatic spring housing. The spring remains heated and the choke plate remains fully open until the engine is stopped and allowed to cool.

The choke rod actuates the fast idle cam during choking. Steps on the edge of the fast idle cam contact the fast idle adjusting screw. This permits a faster engine idle speed for smoother running when the engine is cold. As the choke plate is moved through its range of travel from the closed to the open position, the choke rod rotates the fast idle cam. Each step on the fast idle cam permits a slower idle rpm as engine temperature rises and choking is reduced.

During the warm-up period, if the engine should reach the stall point due to a lean mixture, manifold vacuum will drop considerably. The tension of the thermostatic spring then overcomes the lowered vacuum acting on the choke piston and the choke plate is moved toward the closed position, providing a richer mixture to help prevent stalling.

The linkage between the choke lever and the throttle shaft is designed so that the choke plate will partially open when the accelerator pedal is fully depressed. This permits unloading of a flooded engine.

IDLE FUEL SYSTEM

The difference in pressure between the fuel bowls and the idle discharge ports forces fuel through the primary and secondary stage idle fuel systems.

Primary Stage. Fuel flows from the primary stage fuel bowl through

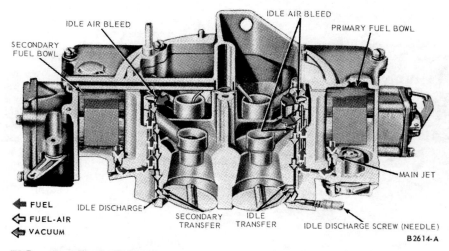

FUEL
FUEL-AIR
VACUUM

B2614-A

FIG. 6—Idle Fuel System

the main jet and into the bottom of the main well (Fig. 6).

From the main well, the fuel flows up through the idle tube and through a short diagonal passage in the booster venturi assembly into the idle passage in the main body. A calibrated restriction, at the upper tip of the idle tube, meters the flow of fuel.

Air enters the system from the air bleed located directly above the idle tube. The air bleed also acts as a vent to prevent siphoning at off-idle or high speeds and when the engine is stopped. The fuel and air pass down a diagonal passage in the booster venturi and through a calibrated restrictor. Additional air is bled into the system through an air bleed located at the bottom of the diagonal passage where the fuel enters the idle passage in the main body.

Fuel flows down the idle passage in the main body past two idle transfer holes. The idle transfer holes act as additional air bleeds at curb idle. The fuel then flows past the pointed tip of the adjusting needle which controls the idle fuel discharge in the primary stage. From the adjusting needle chamber, the fuel flows through a short horizontal passage and is discharged below the primary throttle plates.

During off-idle when the primary throttle plate is moved slightly past the idle transfer holes, each hole begins discharging fuel as it is exposed to manifold vacuum. As the primary throttle plate is opened still wider and engine speed increases, the air flow through the carburetor is also increased. This creates a vacuum in the booster venturi strong enough to bring the primary stage main fuel system into operation. Fuel flow

from the primary idle fuel system begins tapering off as the main fuel system begins discharging fuel.

Hot Idle Compensator System.

A thermostatically controlled hot idle compensator is located on the air horn above the secondary booster venturis (Fig. 7). At carburetor high inlet air temperatures, the hot idle compensator will open and allow air to bypass the throttle plates through a passage in the air horn and main body and enter the intake manifold. This improves idle stability and minimizes the effect of fuel vaporization which results in excessively rich idle mixtures.

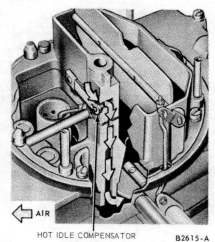

AIR

HOT IDLE COMPENSATOR   B2615-A

FIG. 7—Hot Idle Compensator System

Secondary Stage.

Fuel flows from the secondary stage fuel bowl through the main jet and into the bottom of the main well (Fig. 6).

From the main well, the fuel flows up through the idle tube and through

a short diagonal passage in the booster venturi assembly and then into the idle passage in the main body. A calibrated restriction, at the upper tip of the tube, meters the flow of fuel.

Fuel flows down the idle passage in the main body, past two transfer holes above the closed throttle plate, and flows through a metered restriction into a short horizontal passage where it is discharged into the secondary barrel below the closed throttle plate. The transfer holes act as air bleeds at idle. The secondary idle fuel system continues discharging fuel until the secondary main fuel system comes into operation.

Air is introduced into the secondary stage idle fuel system from the idle air bleed, located directly above the idle tube. The air bleed also acts as a vent to prevent siphoning in the idle fuel system at high speeds and when the engine is stopped.

ACCELERATING SYSTEM

Upon acceleration the air flow through the carburetor responds almost immediately to the increased throttle opening. There is, however, a brief interval before the flowing fuel, which is heavier than air, can gain speed to maintain the desired balance of fuel and air. During this interval, the accelerating system (Fig. 8) supplies fuel until the other systems can once again provide the proper mixture.

When the throttle is closed, the diaphragm return spring forces the diaphragm toward the cover, drawing fuel into the chamber through the inlet. The inlet has an Elastomer valve which uncovers the inlet hole to admit fuel from the fuel bowl. The valve covers the inlet hole when the accelerating pump is operated to prevent the fuel from returning to the bowl. A discharge weight and ball check prevents air from entering from the discharge nozzle when fuel is drawn into the diaphragm chamber.

When the throttle is opened, the diaphragm rod is forced inward, forcing fuel from the chamber into the discharge passage. Fuel under pressure forces the pump discharge weight and ball off their seat and fuel passes through the accelerating pump discharge screw and is sprayed into each main venturi through discharge ports.

An air bleed in the wall of the accelerator pump fuel chamber prevents vapor entrapment and pres-

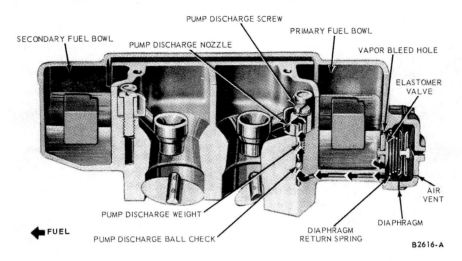

FIG. 8—Accelerating System

sure build-up in the diaphragm chamber.

PRIMARY STAGE MAIN FUEL SYSTEM

As engine speed increases, the air passing through the booster venturi creates a vacuum. The amount of vacuum is determined by the air flow through the venturi, which in turn is regulated by the speed of the engine. The difference in pressure between the main discharge port and the fuel

bowl causes fuel to flow through the main fuel system (Fig. 9).

At a predetermined venturi vacuum, fuel flows from the primary fuel bowl, through the main jets, and into the bottom of the main well. The fuel moves up the main well tube past air bleed holes. Filtered air from the high speed air bleed enters the fuel flow in the main well tube through holes in the side of the tube. The high speed air bleed meters an increasing amount of air to the fuel

as venturi vacuum increases, maintaining the required fuel-air ratio. The mixture of fuel and air is lighter than raw fuel and responds faster to changes in venturi vacuum. It also atomizes more readily than raw fuel. The fuel and air continue up the main well tube past another air bleed which also acts as a vent to prevent siphoning when the engine is shut down. The fuel is discharged into the booster venturi where it is atomized and mixed with the air flowing through the carburetor.

The throttle plate controls the amount of the fuel-air mixture admitted to the intake manifold, regulating the speed and power output of the engine.

A balance tube is located in each primary barrel directly below the booster venturi. When decelerating, the balance tube siphons off any excess fuel droplets remaining around the edge of the booster venturi and discharges the droplets into the equalizing slots in the base of the carburetor where they are mixed with the idle fuel. The balance tube also acts as an additional air bleed during the idle fuel system operation.

POWER FUEL SYSTEM

During periods of increased road loads or high speed operation, the fuel-air ratio must be increased for added power. The added fuel required during this period is supplied by the power fuel system (Fig. 10).

The power fuel system is controlled by manifold vacuum.

Manifold vacuum is transmitted from an opening in the base of the main body, through a passage in the main body and power valve chamber to the power valve diaphragm. The manifold vacuum, acting on the power valve at idle speed or normal road load conditions, is great enough to hold the power valve diaphragm down, overcoming the tension of the spring on the valve stem and holding the valve closed. When high power operation places a greater load on the engine and manifold vacuum drops below a predetermined value, the spring opens the power valve. Fuel from the primary fuel bowl flows through the power valve and into passages leading to both primary stage main fuel wells. Here the fuel is added to the *fuel from the primary stage main fuel system*, enriching the mixture.

As engine power demands are reduced, manifold vacuum increases. The increased vacuum overcomes the

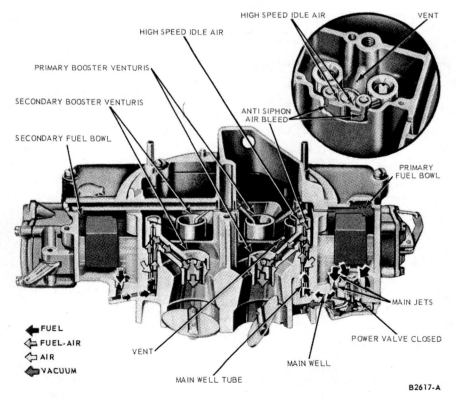

FIG. 9—Primary Stage Main Fuel System

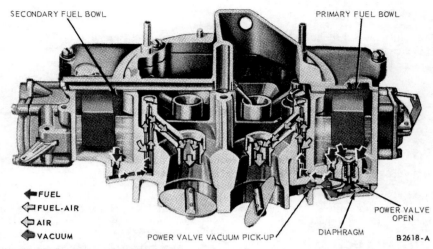

FUEL
FUEL-AIR
AIR
VACUUM

SECONDARY FUEL BOWL
PRIMARY FUEL BOWL
POWER VALVE OPEN
DIAPHRAGM
POWER VALVE VACUUM PICK-UP
B 2618-A

FIG. 10—Power Fuel System

tension of the valve stem spring and closes the power valve.

SECONDARY THROTTLE OPERATION AND MAIN FUEL SYSTEM

To provide sufficient fuel-air mixture to operate the engine at maximum power, the mixture supplied by the primary stage is supplemented by an additional quantity of fuel-air mixture from the secondary stage (Fig. 11).

This additional supply of fuel-air mixture is delivered through the two secondary (rear) barrels of the carburetor. The secondary stage throttle plates are operated by a spring-loaded vacuum diaphragm assembly attached to the main body and linked to the secondary throttle shaft.

Opening of the secondary throttle plates is controlled by vacuum from the left primary booster venturi. The vacuum is transmitted from the secondary throttle control vacuum tube through passages in the air horn, main body, and behind the secondary operating diaphragm.

As the primary throttle plates are opened, primary venturi vacuum increases. When the vacuum reaches a predetermined amount, it starts to act on the secondary stage operating diaphragm, which in turn starts to open the secondary throttle plates.

A ball check, located in the vacuum passage in the diaphragm housing, controls the rate at which the secondary throttle plates are allowed to open. Any rapid increase in vacuum which would tend to open the secondary throttle plates too suddenly holds the ball check against its seat. The opening of the secondary throttle plates is slowed to a rate governed by the amount of vacuum passing through a bleed in the ball seat.

As the secondary throttle plates begin to open, fuel flows from the secondary fuel bowl through the secondary main jets into the bottom of the main well and up the main well tube past air bleed holes. Air is introduced through an air bleed at the top of the tube. When the secondary throttle plates are moved slightly past the secondary transfer holes, each hole begins discharging fuel as it is exposed to manifold vacuum. As secondary venturi vacuum is increased, the fuel is discharged into the secondary booster venturi. Fuel from the transfer holes tapers off and the holes act as additional air bleeds.

When decelerating, vacuum in the primary venturi decreases and the secondary throttle plates begin to close. The ball check in the diaphragm housing passage will unseat when the throttle is closed quickly, allowing the low pressure on the vacuum side of the diaphragm to rapidly return to atmospheric pressure. As the vacuum acting on the diaphragm is lessened, the load on the diaphragm spring will start closing the secondary plates.

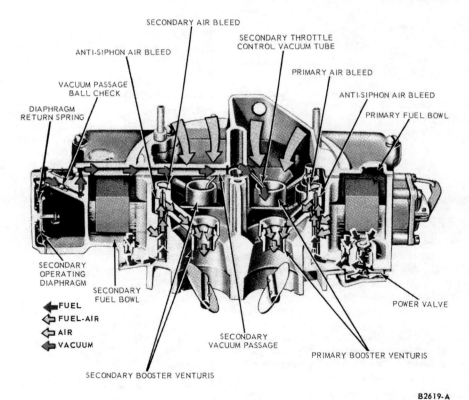

SECONDARY AIR BLEED
ANTI-SIPHON AIR BLEED
VACUUM PASSAGE BALL CHECK
DIAPHRAGM RETURN SPRING
SECONDARY THROTTLE CONTROL VACUUM TUBE
PRIMARY AIR BLEED
ANTI-SIPHON AIR BLEED
PRIMARY FUEL BOWL
SECONDARY OPERATING DIAPHRAGM
SECONDARY FUEL BOWL
POWER VALVE
SECONDARY VACUUM PASSAGE
PRIMARY BOOSTER VENTURIS
SECONDARY BOOSTER VENTURIS

FUEL
FUEL-AIR
AIR
VACUUM

B2619-A

FIG. 11—Secondary Stage Main Fuel System

2 REMOVAL AND INSTALLATION

REMOVAL

Flooding, stumble on acceleration, and other performance complaints are, in many instances, caused by the presence of dirt, water, or other foreign matter in the carburetor. To air in diagnosing the cause of a complaint, the carburetor should be carefully removed from the engine without removing the fuel from the bowls. The contents of the bowls may then be examined for contamination as the carburetor is disassembled.

1. Remove the air cleaner (Part 10-6, Section 2). Remove the bracket that secures the heater hose to the automatic choke. Remove the throttle cable from the throttle lever. Disconnect the distributor vacuum line, in-line fuel filter, choke clean air tube and the choke heat tube at the carburetor.

2. Remove the carburetor retaining nuts and lock washers; then remove the carburetor. Remove the spacer upper gasket. Discard the gasket. **Whenever the carburetor is removed from the engine, care must be exercised to prevent damage to the throttle plates. The lower edges of the throttle plates project below the carburetor body whenever they are open.**

3. Remove the spacer and lower gasket. Discard the gasket.

INSTALLATION

1. Clean the gasket surface of the intake manifold, spacer and carburetor. Place a new gasket above and below the spacer and install the spacer. Position the carburetor on the spacer. Install the carburetor retaining nuts. To prevent leakage, distortion or damage to the carburetor body flange, snug the carburetor retaining nuts; then, alternately tighten the nuts in a criss-cross pattern to the specified torque (Part 10-9).

2. Connect the choke heat tube, in-line fuel filter, choke clean air tube and the distributor vacuum line. Connect the throttle cable to the throttle lever. Refer to Common Adjustments and Repairs (Part 10-1, Section 2) and adjust the accelerating pump stroke (if necessary); the idle fuel mixture and idle speed, and the anti-stall dashpot (if so equipped). Install the air cleaner (Part 10-6, Section 2).

3 MAJOR REPAIR OPERATIONS

DISASSEMBLY

To facilitate working on the carburetor and to prevent damage to the throttle plates, install carburetor legs on the base. If legs are unavailable, install 4 bolts (about 2¼ inches long of the correct diameter) and 8 nuts on the carburetor base.

Use a separate container for the component parts of the various assemblies to facilitate cleaning, inspection and assembly.

For a complete carburetor overhaul, follow all the steps. To partially overhaul the carburetor or to install a new gasket kit, follow only the applicable steps.

Refer to Fig. 24 for parts identification.

AIR HORN

1. Remove the air cleaner anchor screw.

2. Remove the choke plate operating rod to choke lever retainer (Fig. 12).

3. Remove the air horn retaining screws and lock washers and the identification tag. Remove the air horn and air horn gasket.

4. If it is necessary to remove the choke plate rod, seal and washers, remove the choke plate rod by loosening and turning the choke shaft lever clevis nut counterclockwise. Remove the rod from the air horn. Slide the felt seal and two

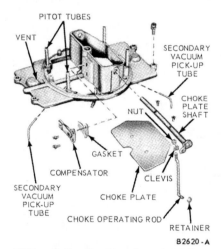

FIG. 12—Air Horn Assembly

washers out of the choke rod seal retainer.

5. If it is necessary to remove the choke plate or choke shaft, remove the staking marks on the choke plate retaining screws and remove the screws. **If the tips of the screws are flared excessively, file off the flared portion to prevent damage to the threads of the shaft.** Remove the choke plate by sliding it out of the shaft, from the top of he air horn. Slide the choke shaft out of the air horn.

6. If it is necessary to remove the secondary throttle control vacuum tubes, pry them out with needle nose pliers. Discard the tubes after removal.

7. If it is necessary to replace the hot idle compensator, remove the staking marks on the retaining screws and remove the hot idle compensator.

VACUUM PISTON CHOKE

1. Remove the fast idle cam retainer (Fig. 13).

2. Remove the thermostatic choke spring housing retaining screws, and remove the clamp, housing and gasket (Fig. 13).

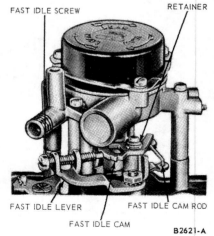

FIG. 13—Fast Idle Cam and Fast Idle Lever

3. Remove the choke housing assembly retaining screws. If the air horn was not previously removed, remove the choke control rod retainer. Remove the choke housing assembly, gasket and the fast idle cam. Remove the fast idle cam and rod from the fast idle cam lever.

4. Remove the choke lever retaining screw and washer (Fig. 14). Remove the choke piston lever from the housing. If necessary, remove the pin securing the choke piston to the choke lever link. Remove the choke lever and fast idle cam lever from the choke housing.

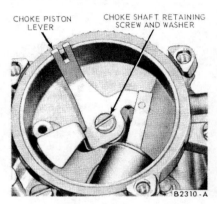

FIG. 14—Choke Shaft and Piston Lever

MAIN BODY

1. With the use of a screwdriver, pry the float shaft retainer from the fuel inlet seat in each fuel bowl (Figs. 15 and 16). Remove the floats, float shaft retainers and fuel inlet needle assemblies. Remove the retainer and float shaft from each float lever.

2. Using a jet wrench, remove the fuel inlet needle seat, gasket and

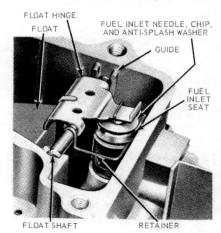

FIG. 15—Float Assembly

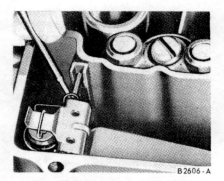

FIG. 16—Float Shaft Retainer Removal or Installation

filter screen from each fuel bowl (Fig. 17).

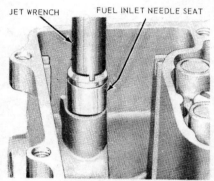

FIG. 17—Fuel Inlet Needle Seat Removal or Installation

3. Remove the primary stage and secondary stage main jets (Fig. 18).

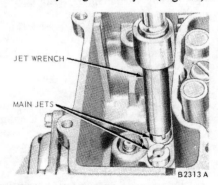

FIG. 18—Main Jet Removal or Installation

4. Remove the primary stage booster venturi assembly and gasket (Fig. 19). Invert the main body and let the accelerating pump discharge weight and ball fall into the hand.

5. Remove the secondary stage booster venturi assembly and gasket.

6. Remove the accelerating pump operating rod retainer. To release

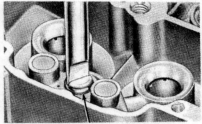

FIG. 19—Booster Venturi Removal or Installation

the rod from the retainer clip, press the tab ends of the clip together; then, at the same time, press the rod away from the clip until it is disengaged. Remove the rod. Remove the accelerating pump cover, diaphragm assembly and spring (Fig. 20).

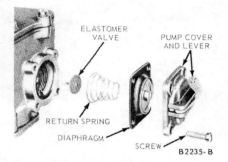

FIG. 20—Accelerating Pump Assembly

If it is necessary to remove the Elastomer valve, grasp it firmly and pull it out. If the Elastomer valve tip broke off during removal, be sure to remove the tip from the fuel bowl. **An Elastomer valve must be replaced whenever it is removed from the main body.**

7. Remove the secondary diaphragm operating rod retainer and remove the rod. Remove the diaphragm cover, return spring, Palnut (if so equipped) and diaphragm (Fig. 21). Invert the main body and let the secondary ball check fall into the hand.

8. Invert the main body and remove the power valve cover and gasket. Using a socket wrench or box wrench, remove the power valve and gasket (Fig. 22).

9. Remove the idle fuel mixture adjusting screws (needles) and springs.

10. Remove the anti-stall dashpot, if so equipped.

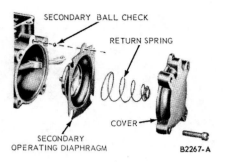

FIG. 21—Secondary Diaphragm Assembly

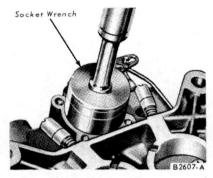

FIG. 22—Power Valve Removal or Installation

11. If necessary, remove the idle (hot engine) adjusting screw and spring, and the nut and washer securing the fast idle adjusting lever assembly to the primary throttle shaft (Fig. 13). Remove the lever assembly.

12. If it is necessary to remove the throttle plates, lightly scribe the primary and secondary throttle plates along the throttle shafts, and mark each plate and its corresponding bore with a number or letter for proper installation (Fig. 23).

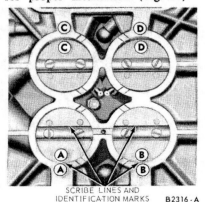

FIG. 23 — Throttle Plate Removal

Remove the staking marks on the throttle plate retaining screws and remove the screws. **If the tips of the**

screws are flared excessively file off the flared portion to prevent damage to the threads of the shaft(s). Do not scratch the edge of the plates or walls of the barrels. Remove the screws and the throttle plates.

Slide the primary and secondary throttle shafts out of the main body.

PARTS REPAIR OR REPLACEMENT

Clean and inspect the carburetor component parts. Refer to Cleaning and Inspection (Part 10-1, Section 3) for the proper procedure. Replace all worn or damaged parts.

ASSEMBLY

Make sure all holes in the new gaskets have been properly punched and that no foreign material has adhered to the gaskets. Make sure the accelerating pump diaphragm and secondary operating diaphragm are not torn or cut. The carburetor assembly is shown in Fig. 24.

MAIN BODY

1. If the throttle plates were removed, slide the primary throttle shaft assembly into the main body.

Refer to the lines and identification marks scribed on the throttle plates (Fig. 23), and install the primary throttle plates in their proper location with the screws snug, but not tight. Invert the main body and hold it up to the light. Little or no light should show between the throttle plates and the throttle bores. Tap the plates lightly with a screwdriver handle to seat them. Tighten and stake the screws.

Slide the secondary throttle shaft into the main body. Refer to the lines scribed on the secondary throttle plates and install the throttle plates in their proper location. To install the plates, follow the procedure given for the primary throttle plates.

Adjust the secondary throttle plates. Refer to Common Adjustments and Repairs (Part 10-1, Section 2) for the proper procedure.

2. Install the idle (hot engine) adjusting screw and spring.

3. If the fast idle lever was removed, place the fast idle lever assembly on the primary throttle shaft, and install the retaining washer and nut (Fig. 13). **Do not install the fast idle cam or retainer at this time.**

4. Install the anti-stall dashpot, if so equipped.

5. If the Elastomer valve was removed, lubricate the tip of a new Elastomer valve and insert the tip into the accelerator pump cavity center hole (Fig. 20). Using a pair of needle nosed pliers, reach into the fuel bowl and grasp the valve tip. Pull the valve in until it seats and cut off the tip forward of the retaining shoulder. Remove the tip from the bowl. Position the diaphragm return spring on the boss in the chamber.

6. Position the accelerator pump diaphragm assembly to the cover and place the cover and diaphragm assembly in position on the return spring and main body. Install the cover screws finger-tight. Push the accelerating pump plunger the full distance of its travel and tighten the cover screws.

7. Install the accelerating pump operating rod. Refer to Common Adjustments and Repairs (Part 10-1, Section 2) and adjust the accelerating pump stroke.

8. Invert the main body. Using a socket wrench or box wrench, install the power valve and new gasket (Fig. 22). **Tighten the power valve securely.** Install the cover and new gasket.

9. Install the idle mixture adjusting screws (needles) and springs. Turn the needles in gently with the fingers until they just touch the seat, then, back them off the specified number of turns (Part 10-9) for a preliminary idle adjustment.

10. Drop the secondary discharge ball check into the passage, in the main body (Fig. 21).

11. Install the secondary operating diaphragm and Palnut (if so equipped) on the secondary operating lever. Install the diaphragm return spring on the cover. Install the cover with the screws finger-tight. With the diaphragm in the extended position, tighten the cover screws. Install the secondary operating rod in the operating lever, and secure the rod to the secondary throttle shaft with the retaining clip.

Check the operation and seal of the secondary vacuum system by opening the primary and secondary throttle plates. Hold the secondary throttle plates open. Place a finger over the secondary vacuum inlet hole in the main body and release the secondary throttle plates. This is a check for vacuum leakage at the diaphragm. The throttle plates should

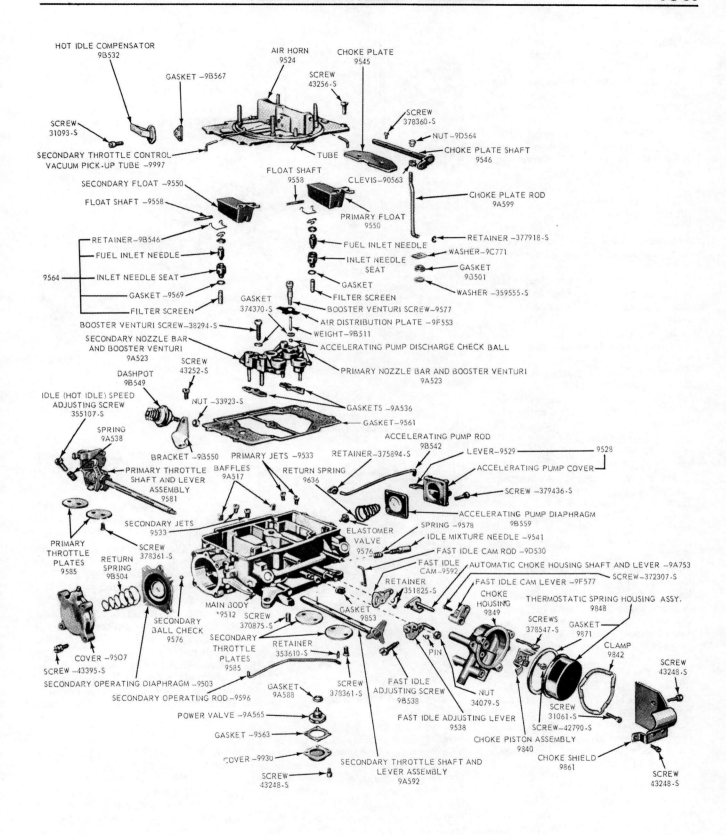

FIG. 24—Carburetor Assembly

B2376-B

not close fully. They will move slightly when released, but they must stop and should not move toward the closed position after the initial movement. Replace the diaphragm or tighten the cover screws as necessary to correct the vacuum leakage.

12. Using a jet wrench, install the primary and secondary main jets (Fig. 18). **Be sure the correct jets are installed for the primary and secondary systems (Part 10-9).**

13. Install the primary and secondary fuel inlet filters in the inlet valve seat mounting bores. Install the valve seats and gaskets (Fig. 17). Install the fuel inlet needle valves (Fig. 15).

14. Slide the primary float shaft into the float lever (Fig. 15). Position the float shaft retainer on the float shaft.

Insert the float assembly into the fuel bowl and hook the float lever tab under the fuel inlet needle clip. Insert the float shaft into its guides at the sides of the fuel bowl.

With the use of a screwdriver, position the float shaft retainer on the groove of the fuel inlet needle seat (Figs. 15 and 16).

15. Repeat step 14 on the secondary stage fuel bowl.

16. Refer to Float Adjustment (Dry) Part 10-1, Section 2, and perform a dry float fuel level adjustment on the primary and secondary floats.

17. Drop the accelerating pump discharge ball into its passage in the primary side of the main body. Seat the ball with a brass drift and a light hammer. **Make sure the ball is free.** Drop the accelerating pump discharge weight on top of the ball. Position the primary booster venturi assembly and gasket in the main body. Install the air distribution plate (if so equipped) and the retaining screw. Tighten the screw securely (Fig. 19). **The primary booster screw is hollow.**

18. Position the secondary booster venturi assembly and gasket in the main body, and install the gasket and retaining screw.

VACUUM PISTON CHOKE

1. If the choke piston and link was disassembled, install the choke piston on the choke thermostatic spring lever link and install the retaining pin (Fig. 25).

2. Position the fast idle cam lever on the thermostatic choke shaft and

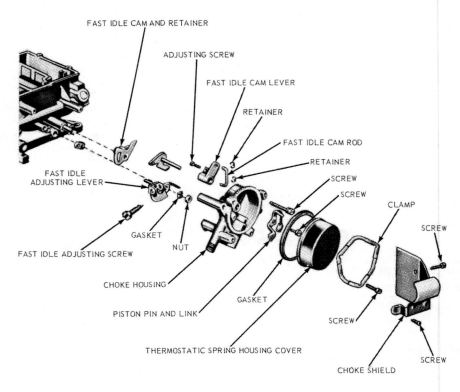

FIG. 25—Choke Housing Assembly

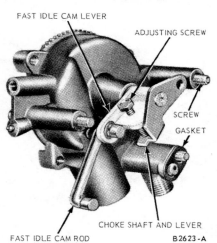

FIG. 26—Choke Linkage Installation

lever assembly (Figs. 25 and 26). **The bottom of the fast idle lever adjusting screw must rest against the tang on the choke shaft lever.** Insert the choke shaft assembly into the rear of the choke housing. Position the choke shaft lever so that the hole in the lever is to the left side of the choke housing (Fig. 26).

3. Insert the choke piston into the choke housing. Position the choke thermostatic spring lever on the

flange of the choke shaft, and install the retaining screw and washer (Fig. 14).

4. Install the fast idle cam rod on the fast idle cam lever (Fig. 26). Place the fast idle cam on the fast idle cam rod and install the retainer.

Place the choke housing vacuum pick-up port to main body gasket on the choke housing flange. Position the choke housing on the main body, and at the same time, install the fast idle cam on the hub of the main body. Position the gasket and install the choke housing retaining screws. Install the fast idle cam retainer. **The thermostatic spring housing is installed after the choke plate clearance (pull-down) has been adjusted (Part 10-1, Section 2) to specification.**

AIR HORN

Refer to Fig. 12 for the correct location of the parts.

1. If the choke plate shaft was removed, position the choke plate shaft in the air horn. Insert the plastic choke pulldown adjusting nut and *swivel into the keyed hole in the* choke shaft lever. Position the felt washer between the two brass washers and slide them into place on the choke control rod seal retainer.

Insert the choke plate rod through the plate rod seal and the air horn. Insert the choke plate rod into the choke shaft lever clevis nut, and turn the nut clockwise to thread the rod onto the nut.

2. If the choke plate was removed, insert the choke plate into the choke plate shaft. Install the choke plate screws snug, but not tight.

Check for proper plate fit, binding in the air horn, and free rotation of the shaft by moving the plate from the closed position to the open position. If necessary, remove the choke plate and grind or file the plate edge where it is binding or scraping on the air horn wall. If the choke plate and shaft moves freely, tighten the choke plate screws while holding the choke in the fully-closed position. Stake the screws. **When staking the screws, support the shaft and plate on a block of wood or a metal bar to prevent bending of the shaft.**

3. If necessary, start new secondary throttle control vacuum tubes into the air horn. **Make certain the tubes are installed in a manner that will insure that the pick-up will face downward toward the primary booster venturi when the air horn is installed.** Drive each tube into

the air horn by grasping it lightly below the shoulder with pliers and striking the pliers with a hammer. Drive each tube in until it stops against its shoulder. **Do not crush or bend the tubes. The tubes should not touch the booster venturi wall when the air horn is installed on the main body. The correct position of each tube is 0.020-0.060 inch from the wall.**

4. If the hot idle compensator was removed, install a new compensator and gasket. Stake the retaining screws.

5. Position the main body gasket on the main body (Fig. 27). Position the air horn on the main body and gasket so that the choke plate rod fits into the opening in the choke housing lever. Install the choke plate rod retainer. **Use care to prevent damage to the secondary throttle control vacuum tubes during the air horn installation.** Install the air horn retaining screws, lock washers and the carburetor identification tag. Tighten the screws.

6. Refer to Part 10-1, Section 2, Common Adjustments and Repairs and perform the automatic choke plate clearance (pulldown) and fast idle cam linkage adjustment.

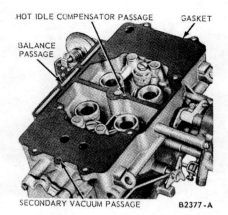

HOT IDLE COMPENSATOR PASSAGE   GASKET
BALANCE PASSAGE
SECONDARY VACUUM PASSAGE   B2377-A

FIG. 27—Main Body Gasket Installation

7. Position the thermostatic choke spring housing on the choke housing. Install the spring housing on the choke housing and gasket, with the slot in the arm of the thermostatic spring lever inserted into the loop of the thermostatic spring. Position the spring housing retainer (clamp) over the spring housing and loosely install the retaining screws.

8. Refer to Common Adjustments and Repairs (Part 10-1, Section 2) and perform the automatic choke spring housing adjustment.

PART 10-5 HOLLEY DUAL 4-V CARBURETOR

1 DESCRIPTION AND OPERATION

DESCRIPTION

The dual 4-V (venturi) carburetor installation for the 427 cubic inch engine consists of two 4-barrel carburetors, mounted on a special aluminum intake manifold. The carburetors are mounted in reverse of the normal manner, with the primary throttles and fuel bowls facing toward the rear of the engine (Fig. 1).

A cross-shaft bellcrank lever assembly is located between the two carburetors. It is mounted on the secondary (rear) carburetor stud bosses (Fig. 1). The bellcrank lever transfers accelerator movement from the left side to the right side of the engine. Adjustable connecting rods transfer the movement from the bellcrank lever to the primary throttle levers of the rear (secondary) and the front (primary) carburetors.

The interconnecting linkage is designed to delay the opening of the throttle on the rear (secondary) carburetor and permit the use of the front (primary) carburetor only for low engine speed driving; however, both carburetors will reach wide open throttle simultaneously.

Due to the progressive opening feature of the rear (secondary) carburetor throttle plates, choking action for cold starting is performed by the front (primary) carburetor only. **A choke system is not used on the rear (secondary) carburetor (Fig. 2).**

OPERATION

The *primary* and secondary carburetors are downdraft two-stage carburetors. Each carburetor can be considered as two dual carburetors; one supplying a fuel-air mixture throughout the entire range of operation (primary stage), and the other

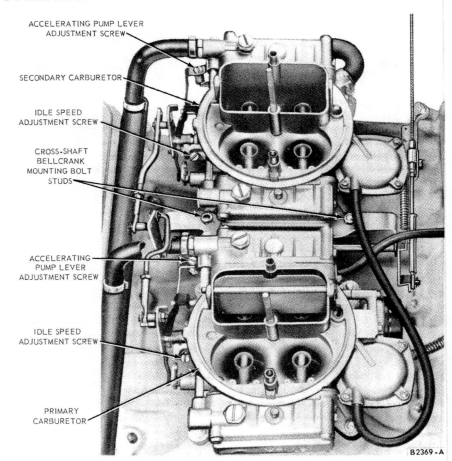

FIG. 1—Dual 4-V Carburetor Installation—Top View

functioning only when a greater quantity of fuel air mixture is required (secondary stage).

The carburetors (Figs. 1 thru 5) contain a primary power system or power valve located within the primary metering blocks only.

Due to the design similarity of the primary and secondary carburetors, the following operating principles apply to both carburetors. Differences in various carburetor items are noted where applicable.

The primary stage of the carburetors contains a fuel bowl, metering block, and an accelerating pump assembly. The primary barrels each contain a primary and booster ven-

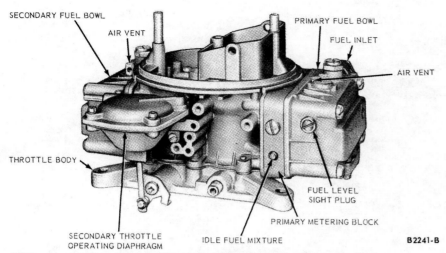

FIG. 2—Dual 4-V Secondary Carburetor—Left Rear ¾ View

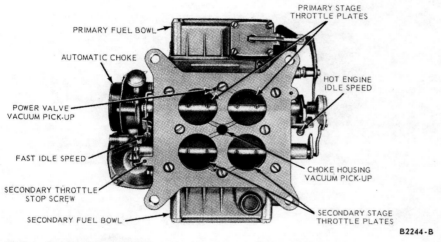

FIG. 3—Dual 4-V Primary Carburetor—Bottom View

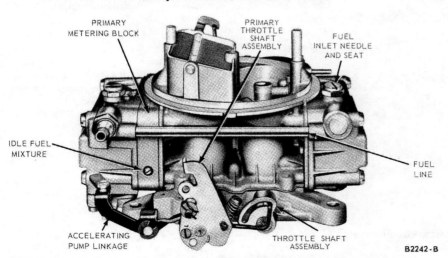

FIG. 4—Dual 4-V Primary Carburetor—Right Rear ¾ View

turi, main fuel discharge nozzle, throttle plate, and an idle fuel passage. The choke plate (if so equipped), mounted in the air horn above the primary barrels, is automatically controlled by an automatic choke mechanism.

The secondary stage of the carburetors contains a fuel bowl, a metering body and the throttle operating diaphragm assembly. The secondary barrels each contain a primary and booster venturi, idle fuel passages, a transfer system, a main secondary fuel discharge nozzle, and a throttle plate.

The carburetors have four primary stage fuel systems, and two secondary stage fuel systems. The primary stage fuel passages are identified in Fig. 6. The secondary stage fuel passages are identified in Fig. 7.

A fuel inlet system for both, the primary, and the secondary stages of the carburetors provides the fuel metering systems with a constant supply of fuel. In addition, a carburetor automatic choke system (primary carburetor only) provides a means of temporarily enriching the fuel mixture to aid in starting and operating a cold engine.

FUEL INLET SYSTEM

A separate fuel inlet system is provided for the primary and secondary stages (Fig. 8). The fuel first enters the primary fuel bowl through a filter screen and then into the fuel inlet needle and seat assembly. A fuel tube at the fuel inlet connects both fuel bowls. The fuel inlet system for the primary and secondary system operates the same.

The amount of fuel entering the fuel bowl is regulated by the distance the fuel inlet needle is lowered off its seat, and by fuel pump pressure. Movement of the fuel inlet needle in relation to the seat is controlled by the float and lever assembly which rises and falls with the fuel level. As the fuel level drops, the float drops, lowering the fuel inlet needle from its seat to allow fuel to enter the fuel bowl.

When the fuel in the fuel bowl reaches a pre-set level, the float raises the fuel inlet needle to a position where it restricts the flow of fuel, admitting only enough fuel to replace that being used. The fuel inlet system must maintain the preset level, because the basic metering systems are calibrated to deliver the proper fuel mixture only when the fuel is at the proper level. A spring, located under the float, assists in keeping the float stable.

The fuel bowls are internally vented by the vent tube at all times. In addition, the primary and secondary fuel bowls are each externally vented by an air vent located at the top of the bowl. The external vent

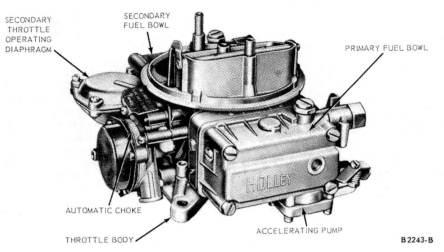

FIG. 5—Dual 4-V Primary Carburetor—Left Rear ¾ View

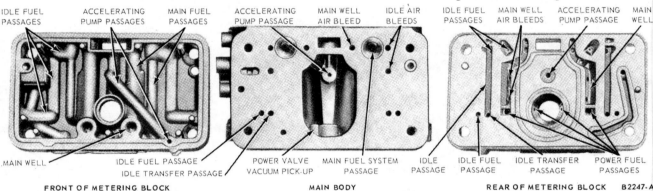

FIG. 6—Primary Fuel Passages Identification

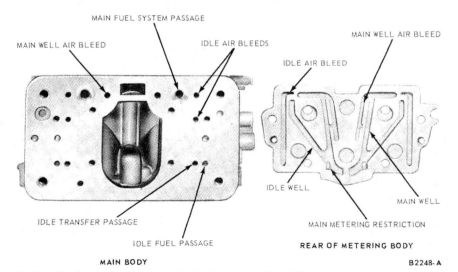

FIG. 7—Secondary Stage Fuel Passages Identification

provides a release of excess fuel vapors from the bowl.

The balance tube (Fig. 8), which connects the primary and secondary fuel bowls, balances the air pressure between the two bowls.

AUTOMATIC CHOKE SYSTEM

The secondary (rear) carburetor does not contain an automatic choke system.

The choke plate, located in the air horn above the primary barrels,

when closed, provides a high vacuum above as well as below the throttle plates. With a vacuum above the throttle plates, fuel will flow from the main fuel system as well as from the idle fuel system. This provides the extremely rich fuel mixture for cold engine operation.

The carburetor choke shaft is linked to a thermostatic choke control mechanism mounted on the main body (Fig. 9).

The automatic choke is equipped with a bi-metal thermostatic spring and a vacuum piston. The bi-metal thermostatic spring mechanism winds up when cold and unwinds when warm. When the engine is cold, the thermostatic spring, through attaching linkage, holds the choke plate in a closed position. Manifold

vacuum, channeled through a passage in the choke control housing, draws the choke vacuum piston downward, exerting an opening force on the choke plate. When the engine is started, manifold vacuum acting directly on the piston located in the choke housing and the flow of air acting on the offset choke plate immediately moves the plate against tension of the thermostatic spring. This action partially opens the choke plate to prevent stalling.

As the engine continues to operate, manifold vacuum draws heated air from the exhaust manifold heat chamber. The amount of air entering the choke housing is controlled by restrictions in the air passages in the carburetor.

The warmed air enters the choke housing and heats the thermostatic spring, causing it to unwind. The *tension of the thermostatic spring* gradually decreases as the temperature of the air from the heat chamber rises, allowing the choke plate to open. The air is exhausted into

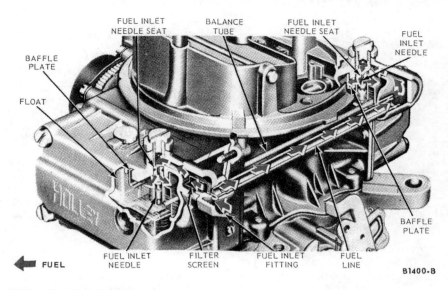

FUEL INLET NEEDLE SEAT — BALANCE TUBE — FUEL INLET NEEDLE SEAT — FUEL INLET NEEDLE

BAFFLE PLATE

FLOAT

HOLLEY

BAFFLE PLATE

← FUEL

FUEL INLET NEEDLE — FILTER SCREEN — FUEL INLET FITTING — FUEL LINE

B1400-B

FIG. 8—Fuel Inlet System

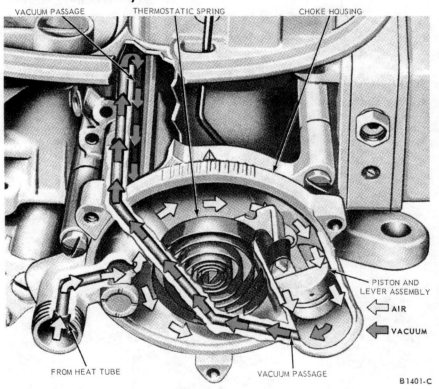

VACUUM PASSAGE — THERMOSTATIC SPRING — CHOKE HOUSING

PISTON AND LEVER ASSEMBLY

⇦ AIR

⇦ VACUUM

FROM HEAT TUBE — VACUUM PASSAGE

B1401-C

FIG. 9—Automatic Choke System

the intake manifold.

When the engine reaches its normal operating temperature, the thermostatic spring no longer exerts an opposing tension on the choke piston, allowing the piston to pull the choke plate to the full open position. In this position, the choke piston is at its lowest point in the cylinder. Slots in the piston chamber will allow sufficient air to bleed past the piston and into the intake manifold,

causing a continual flow of warm air to pass through the thermostatic spring housing. The spring thus remains heated and the choke plate remains fully open until the engine is stopped and allowed to cool.

The choke rod actuates the fast idle cam during choking. Steps on the edge of the fast idle cam contact the fast idle adjusting screw which permits a faster engine idle speed for smoother running when the en-

gine is cold. As the choke plate is moved through its range of travel from the closed to the open position, the choke rod rotates the fast idle cam. Each step on the fast idle cam permits a slower idle rpm as engine temperature rises and choking is reduced.

During the warm-up period, if the engine should reach the stall point due to a lean mixture, manifold vacuum will drop considerably. The tension of the thermostatic spring then overcomes the lowered vacuum acting on the choke piston, and the choke plate will be moved toward the closed position, providing a richer mixture to prevent stalling.

The linkage between the choke lever and the throttle shaft is designed so that the choke plate will partially open when the accelerator pedal is fully depressed. This permits unloading of a flooded engine.

IDLE FUEL SYSTEM

Since the idle fuel system for the primary and secondary carburetor operate in the same manner, only one carburetor is discussed.

At idle and low speed operation, the engine does not draw sufficient air through the primary booster venturi to create a vacuum great enough to operate the main metering system; therefore, an idle fuel system is provided which is not dependent upon venturi-vacuum to discharge fuel.

High manifold vacuum at idle creates a low pressure at the idle discharge port. The pressure in the fuel bowl is near atmospheric pressure. The difference in pressure between the fuel bowl and the idle discharge port forces fuel through the idle fuel system.

The carburetor has identical idle fuel systems (Fig. 10) for each primary barrel, and identical idle fuel systems for each secondary barrel. Idle fuel is discharged into both the primary and secondary barrels. Idle fuel for the primary barrels is drawn from the primary fuel bowl, and idle fuel for the secondary barrels is drawn from the secondary fuel bowl.

Fuel flows from the primary fuel bowl through the main jets into a smaller angular passage (idle feed) that leads across to the idle well.

Fuel flows from the secondary fuel bowl through the main metering restrictions of the rear metering body and into the idle well. The

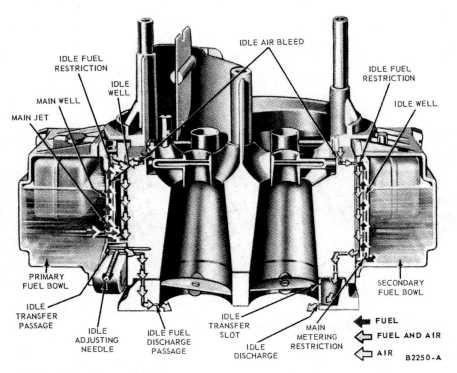

FIG. 10—Idle Fuel System

fuel flows up the idle well, where it is mixed with air from the idle air bleeds.

PRIMARY STAGE

After leaving the idle well, the fuel-air mixture flows through a short horizontal passage and then down another vertical passage. At the bottom of this vertical passage, the fuel-air mixture branches in two directions, one through the idle discharge passage and the other to the idle transfer passage (Fig. 11).

The fuel in the idle discharge passage flows past the idle adjusting needle which controls the fuel discharge at idle. From the idle adjusting needle chamber, the fuel goes through a short passage in the main body and down another passage into the throttle body. The fuel is discharged below the throttle plate.

During off-idle operation when the throttle plate is moved slightly, the fuel flows through the idle transfer passage (Fig. 11) in the metering body and then into the main body through a restriction. From the main body, it flows into a passage in the throttle body. As the idle transfer slot is exposed to manifold vacuum, fuel is discharged.

As the throttle plate is opened still wider and engine speed increases, the air flow through the carburetor is also increased. This creates a vac-

uum in the booster venturi great enough to bring the main fuel system into operation. The flow from the primary stage idle fuel system begins tapering off as the main fuel system begins discharging fuel.

SECONDARY STAGE

After leaving the idle well or idle fuel passage, the fuel-air mixture flows through a short horizontal passage and then down another vertical passage. At the bottom of this passage, the fuel-air mixture flows through a short passage in the main body, and down another passage into the throttle body. The fuel is discharged below the closed throttle plate. A transfer slot acts as an air bleed at idle. The secondary idle fuel system continues discharging fuel until the secondary main fuel system comes into operation.

ACCELERATING SYSTEM

The accelerating system for the primary and secondary carburetors operate in the same manner; therefore, only one carburetor is discussed.

Upon acceleration, the air flow through the carburetor responds almost immediately to the increased throttle opening. There is, however, a brief interval before the fuel, which is heavier than air, can gain speed and maintain the desired balance of fuel and air. During this

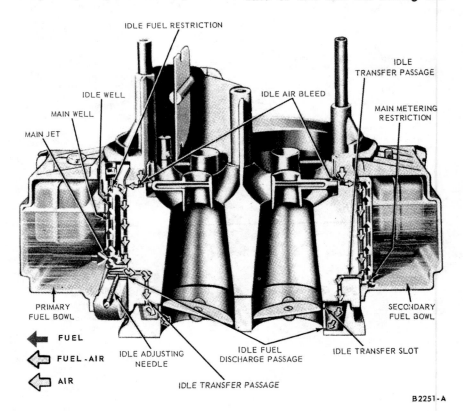

FIG. 11—Idle Transfer System

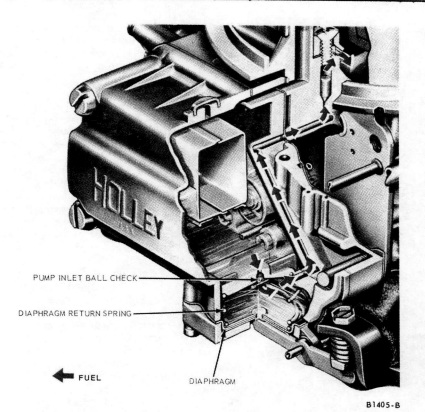

PUMP INLET BALL CHECK

DIAPHRAGM RETURN SPRING

← FUEL

DIAPHRAGM

B1405-B

FIG. 12—Accelerating System

PRIMARY STAGE MAIN FUEL SYSTEM

The primary stage main system for the primary and secondary carburetors operate in the same manner; therefore, only one carburetor is discussed.

When the throttle plate is progressively opened, engine speed increases and the air passing through the booster venturi gradually creates sufficient vacuum to bring the main fuel system into operation and fuel will be discharged through the main discharge nozzle. The difference in pressure between the primary venturi and the fuel bowl causes fuel to flow through the primary stage main fuel system (Fig. 13).

The fuel moves up the main well past the main well air bleeds in the side of the well. Filtered air enters through the main air bleed in the main body and then into the metering block by interconnecting passages. This mixture of fuel and air, being lighter than raw fuel, responds faster to any change in venturi vacuum and atomizes more readily when discharged into the air stream of the venturi. The mixture of fuel and air moves up the main well passage in the metering block and passes into the short horizontal passage

interval, the accelerating pump supplies fuel until the other fuel systems can once again provide the proper mixture (Fig. 12).

The accelerating pump is located in the bottom of the primary fuel bowl. It begins to function when the pump operating lever is actuated by throttle movement. When the throttle is opened, the accelerating pump linkage, actuated by a cam on the primary throttle shaft, forces the pump diaphragm up. As the diaphragm moves up, the inlet ball check is forced onto its seat, preventing fuel from flowing back into the fuel bowl. The fuel flows from the short passage in the primary fuel bowl into the long diagonal passage in the primary metering block. The fuel passes into the main body and then into the pump discharge chamber. The pressure of the fuel raises the discharge needle and fuel is discharged into the venturi from the pump nozzle.

As the throttle is moved toward the closed position, the linkage returns to its original position and the diaphragm spring forces the diaphragm down. As the diaphragm returns to its original position, the pump inlet ball check is moved off

its seat and the diaphragm chamber is filled with fuel from the fuel bowl.

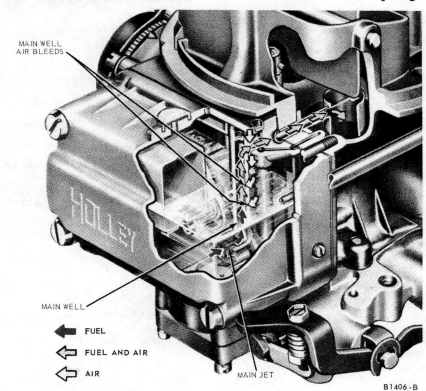

MAIN WELL
AIR BLEEDS

MAIN WELL

← FUEL

⇐ FUEL AND AIR

⇐ AIR

MAIN JET

B1406-B

FIG. 13—Primary Stage Main Fuel System

leading to the main body, then through the horizontal channel of the discharge nozzle. The fuel is discharged into the booster venturi where it is atomized and mixed with air flowing through the carburetor.

POWER FUEL SYSTEM

The primary power fuel systems for the primary and secondary carburetors operate in the same manner; therefore, only one carburetor is discussed.

During periods of increased road loads or high power operation, the carburetor has a tendency to lean out as the air flow is increased. To supplement the primary stage main fuel system, additional fuel is required to maintain the proper fuel-air ratio. The added fuel required during this period is supplied by the power fuel system (Fig. 14).

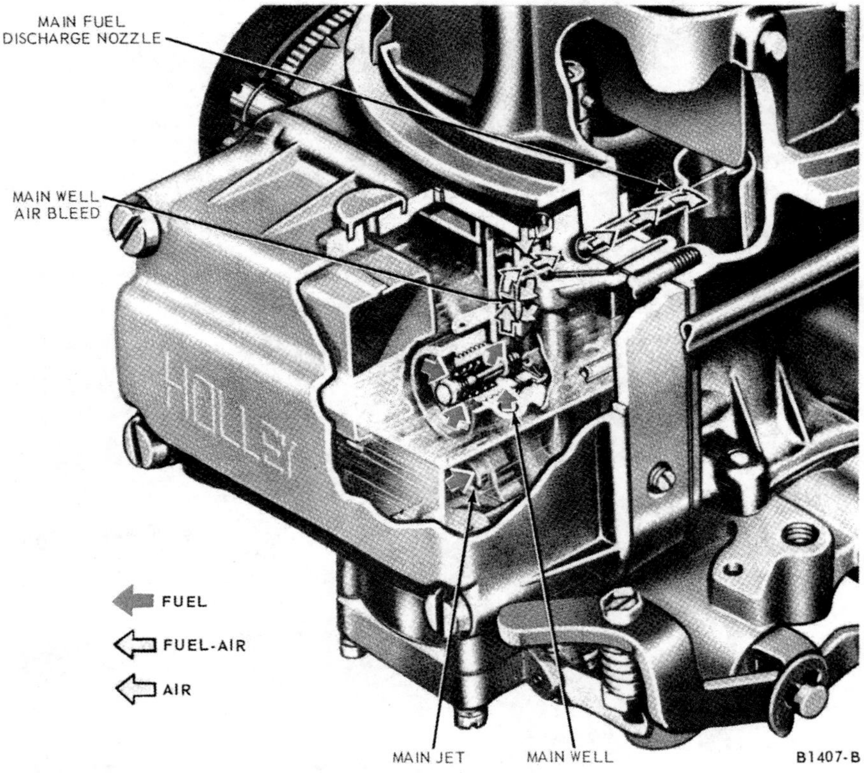

the throttle body and main body to the power valve chamber in the primary metering block. The manifold vacuum, acting on the diaphragm at idle or normal load conditions, is strong enough to overcome the tension of the power valve spring and holds the diaphragm closed. When high power operation places a greater load on the engine and manifold vacuum drops below a predetermined value, the power value spring overcomes the reduced vacuum and opens the power valve. Fuel flows from the fuel bowl through the power valve and through the diagonal restrictions in the metering block into the main well. In the main well, the fuel joins the fuel flow from the primary stage main fuel system, enriching the mixture.

As engine power demands are reduced, manifold vacuum increases.

eration and main fuel systems for the primary and secondary carburetors are the same in operation; therefore, only one carburetor is discussed.

The secondary stage of the carburetor is supplied with fuel from the secondary fuel bowl which receives its fuel through a connecting tube at the fuel inlet fitting on the primary fuel bowl. The secondary fuel inlet system operates the same as the primary fuel inlet system.

The secondary stage throttle plates are operated by a spring-loaded vacuum diaphragm assembly attached to the side of the main body and linked to the secondary throttle shaft (Fig. 15).

Opening of the secondary throttle plates is controlled by vacuum from the right primary and secondary venturis. At high speeds, when engine requirements approach the capacity of the two primary barrels, the increased primary venturi vacuum moves the secondary diaphragm, compressing the diaphragm spring. The diaphragm, acting through the diaphragm link and lever, starts to open the secondary throttle plates. The position of the throttle plates depends upon the strength of the vacuum. This, in turn, is determined by the air flow through the primary barrels. As the secondary throttle plates begin to open, the vacuum in the secondary barrels increases. The increased vacuum in the right secondary venturi assists the primary venturi vacuum in further opening the secondary throttle plates. As top speed is reached, the secondary throttle plates will approach wide open position.

The bleed past the ball check valve in the vacuum passage of the secondary diaphragm housing limits the rate at which the secondary throttle plates will open. Any rapid increases in vacuum, which would tend to open the secondary throttle plates too suddenly, merely holds the ball check valve securely against its seat. The opening of the throttle plates is slowed to a rate governed by the amount of air passing through an air bleed in the ball check valve seat. This allows the vacuum to build up slowly at the diaphragm, which results in a controlled rate of opening for the secondary throttle plates.

When engine speed is reduced, venturi vacuum in the bores becomes weaker. The momentarily stronger vacuum at the secondary throttle operating diaphragm moves the ball

MAIN FUEL
DISCHARGE NOZZLE

MAIN WELL
AIR BLEED

HOLLEY

← FUEL
← FUEL-AIR
← AIR

MAIN JET   MAIN WELL   B1407-B

FIG. 14—Power Fuel System

The power fuel system is controlled by manifold vacuum, which gives an accurate indication of the power demands placed on the engine. Manifold vacuum is highest at idle speed and decreases as the load on the engine is increased.

Manifold vacuum is transmitted from an opening in the base of the throttle body, through a passage in

The increased vacuum overcomes the tension of the power valve spring and draws the valve diaphragm closed. This closes the power valve and shuts off the added fuel supply.

SECONDARY STAGE THROTTLE OPERATION AND MAIN FUEL SYSTEM

The secondary stage throttle op-

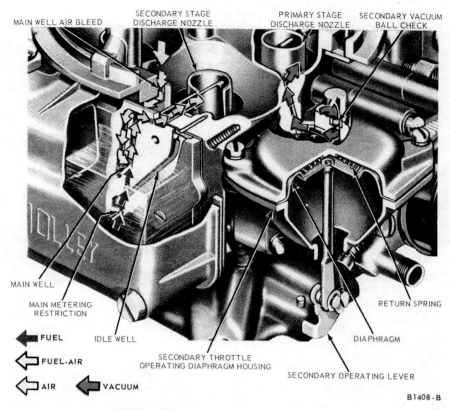

FIG. 15—Secondary Stage Main Fuel System

the diaphragm is lessened, the load on the diaphragm spring will start closing the secondary throttle plates. The diaphragm spring is assisted by the design of the secondary plates. Each secondary plate is slightly off set. When the plates are closing, the combined force of manifold vacuum and the air stream has greater effect on the larger, upstream area of the plates, forcing them to a closed position. The secondary plates are retained in the closed position when primary plates are fully closed by the secondary throttle connecting rod. This rod, which is fastened to the primary throttle lever, rides in a slot in the secondary throttle lever.

A transfer slot or passage begins to function when the secondary throttle plates begin to open. As the plates begin to open, the fuel flows through the main metering restrictions into the transfer passages, which are similar to those in the primary metering block.

When the secondary throttle plates are opened further, the difference in pressure between the secondary booster venturis and the secondary fuel bowl causes the secondary main fuel system to begin discharging fuel. The passages in this system are similar to those in the primary main fuel system.

check valve off its seat in the vacuum passage, permitting an immediate flow of air into the diaphragm chamber. As the vacuum acting on

2 REMOVAL AND INSTALLATION

Flooding, stumble on acceleration, and other performance complaints are, in many instances, caused by the presence of dirt, water, or other foreign matter in the carburetor. To aid in diagnosing the cause of a complaint, the carburetor should be carefully removed from the engine without removing the fuel from the bowls. The contents of the bowls may then be examined for contamination as the carburetor is disassembled.

REMOVAL

A view of the carburetors installed is shown in Fig. 1.

1. Remove the air cleaner assembly and mounting gasket(s). (Part 10-6, Section 2) Disconnect the secondary vacuum hose from the diaphragm(s). Disconnect the fuel inlet hose(s) from the carburetor(s) and discard the retaining clamp(s). **Use care to prevent fuel spillage that could result in a fire.**

2. Disconnect the inter-carburetor linkage at the front (primary) and rear (secondary) carburetor primary throttle levers, and at the bellcrank lever. Disconnect the throttle cable from the cross-shaft bellcrank lever.

3. If the primary carburetor is to be removed, disconnect the choke control heat tube.

4. Remove the carburetor retaining nuts. Remove the carburetor(s) and mounting gasket(s).

INSTALLATION

1. Be sure all old gasket material is removed from the manifold and carburetor mounting flanges. Place a new carburetor mounting gasket(s) on the manifold.

2. Position the carburetor on the intake manifold. If the secondary (rear) carburetor was removed, install the bellcrank assembly on the carburetor. If the primary (front) carburetor was removed, connect the choke heat tube loosely to the

carburetor. Install the carburetor retaining nuts and tighten the nuts evenly and alternately to specification.

3. If the primary (front) carburetor was removed, tighten the choke heat tube fitting at the carburetor. Connect the secondary vacuum hose to the diaphragm(s). Install a new retaining clamp(s) on the fuel inlet hose(s). Install the hose(s) on the fuel inlet fitting(s). Tighten the retaining clamp(s) with the use of Milbar Tool 572 or an equivalent tool.

4. Connect and adjust the carburetor inter-connecting linkage. Refer to Common Adjustments and Repairs (Part 10-1, Section 2) for the proper procedure.

5. Adjust the engine idle speed and idle fuel mixture. Refer to Common Adjustments and Repairs (Part 10-1, Section 2) for the proper procedure.

6. Install the air cleaner and mounting gaskets (Part 10-6, Section 2).

3 MAJOR REPAIR OPERATIONS

DISASSEMBLY

To facilitate working on the carburetor(s), and to prevent damage to the throttle plates, install carburetor legs on the base. If legs are unavailable, install 4 bolts (about 2¼ inches long of the correct diameter) and 8 nuts on the carburetor base.

Use a separate container for the component parts of the various assemblies, to facilitate cleaning, inspection, and assembly.

The following is a step-by-step sequence of operations for completely overhauling the carburetor(s). However, certain components of the carburetor may be serviced without a complete disassembly of the entire unit. For a complete carburetor overhaul, follow all the steps. To partially overhaul the carburetor or to install a new gasket kit, follow only the applicable steps.

Refer to Fig. 23 for identification of the parts used on Holley carburetors.

PRIMARY FUEL BOWL AND METERING BLOCK

Refer to Fig. 16 for the correct location of the fuel bowl parts.

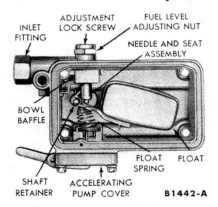

FIG. 16—Primary Fuel Bowl—Typical

1. Remove the fuel bowl and gasket and the metering block and gasket. Discard the gaskets.
2. Remove the fuel line tube and discard the O-ring seal.
3. Remove the balance tube, washer and O-ring seal. Discard the O-ring seal.
4. Remove the idle adjusting needles and gaskets. Discard the gaskets.
5. Using a jet wrench, remove the main jets (Fig. 17).

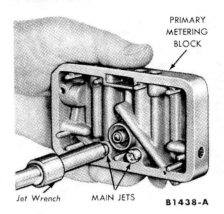

FIG. 17—Main Jet Removal or Installation

6. Using a socket wrench, remove the power valve and gasket (Fig. 18).

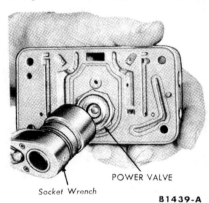

FIG. 18—Power Valve Removal or Installation

7. Remove the fuel level adjustment lock screw and gasket. Turn the adjusting nut counterclockwise and remove the lock nut and gasket. Remove the fuel inlet needle and seat assembly. **Do not disassemble the fuel inlet needle and seat. They are matched assemblies and are replaced as an assembly.**
8. Using needle-nose pliers, remove the float retainer (Fig. 19). Slide the float off the shaft. Remove the spring from the float.
9. Remove the baffle plate from the fuel bowl.
10. Remove the fuel level sight plug and gasket.
11. Remove the fuel inlet fitting, gasket, and filter screen.
12. Invert the fuel bowl and remove the accelerating pump cover, diaphragm, and spring. The acceler-

FIG. 19—Float Shaft Retainer Removal or Installation

ating pump inlet ball check is not removable.

SECONDARY FUEL BOWL AND METERING BODY

1. Remove the fuel bowl. Using a clutch-type screw driver, remove the metering body, plate, and gaskets (Fig. 20). Discard the gaskets.

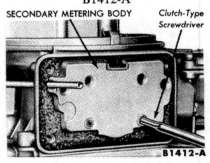

FIG. 20—Secondary Metering Body Removal or Installation

2. Remove the balance tube washer and O-ring seal. Discard the O-ring seal.
3. Disassemble the fuel bowl by following Steps 7 thru 10 under Primary Fuel Bowl and Metering Block Disassembly in this section.

MAIN BODY

1. Remove the air cleaner anchor stud, and remove the secondary diaphragm link retainer.
2. Invert the carburetor and remove the throttle body retaining screws and lock washers. Lift off the throttle body and discard the throttle body gasket.
3. If the carburetor is equipped with an automatic choke, remove the choke rod retainer from the choke housing shaft and lever assembly. Remove *the thermostatic spring housing* and gasket; then, remove the choke housing and gaskets from the main body.

Remove the choke housing shaft nut, lock washer, and spacer; then remove the shaft and fast idle cam. Remove the choke piston and lever assembly.

Remove the choke rod and seal from the main body. If necessary, remove the choke plate from the choke shaft and slide the shaft and lever out of the air horn. **The retaining screws are staked to the choke shaft. If the tips of the screws are flared excessively, file off the flared portion to avoid damage to the threads in the choke shaft. Be careful not to damage the choke shaft or venturi while filing the screws.**

4. Remove the secondary diaphragm housing and gasket from the main body. **The housing must be removed before the cover can be removed.** Remove the diaphragm housing cover; then remove the spring and diaphragm, and the vacuum ball check from the housing.

5. Remove the accelerating pump discharge nozzle screw; then lift the pump discharge nozzle and gaskets out of the main body. Invert the main body and let the accelerating

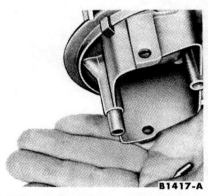

FIG. 21—Accelerating Pump Discharge Needle Removal

pump discharge needle fall into the hand (Fig. 21).

THROTTLE BODY

1. Remove the accelerating pump operating lever retainer.

2. Remove the secondary throttle connecting rod retainers and the connecting rod. Remove the secondary diaphragm lever and the fast idle cam lever retaining screws and washers, and remove the levers.

3. If necessary, remove the throttle stop screw and spring.

4. If it is necessary to remove the throttle plates, lightly scribe the throttle plates along the throttle shaft, and mark each plate and its

corresponding bore with a number or letter for proper installation (Fig. 22). Remove the throttle plates. **The retaining screws are staked to the throttle shaft. If the tips of the screws are flared excessively, file off the flared portion to avoid damage to the threads in the throttle shaft.**

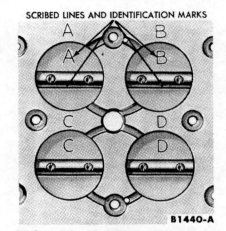

SCRIBED LINES AND IDENTIFICATION MARKS

B1440-A

FIG. 22—Throttle Plate Removal

Be careful not to damage the throttle shaft or venturi while filing the screws.

Remove the fast idle cam lever, and remove the primary throttle shaft return spring from the notch on the throttle shaft lever (Fig. 23). Slide the primary throttle lever and shaft assembly out of the throttle body. Remove the accelerating pump cam.

Slide the secondary throttle shaft out of the main body and remove the bushings from the shaft.

PARTS REPAIR OR REPLACEMENT

Clean and inspect the carburetor component parts. Refer to Cleaning and Inspection (Part 10-1, Section 3) for the proper procedure. Replace all worn or damaged parts.

ASSEMBLY

Make sure all holes in the new gaskets have been properly punched and that no foreign material has adhered to the gaskets. Make sure the accelerating pump and secondary operating diaphragms are not cut or torn.

The carburetor assemblies are shown in Fig. 23.

THROTTLE BODY

Refer to Fig. 23 for the correct location of the parts.

1. If the secondary throttle plates were removed, position the bushings

on the secondary throttle shaft and slide the shaft into the throttle body. Refer to the lines scribed on the throttle plates, then install the plates in their proper location with the screws snug, but not tight.

Close the throttle plates and hold the throttle body up to the light. Little or no light should show between the throttle plates and the throttle bores. If the throttle plates are properly installed and there is no binding when the throttle shaft is rotated, tighten the throttle plate screws. Stake the screws. **When staking the screws, support the shaft and plates on a block of wood or a soft metal bar to prevent bending of the shaft.**

Refer to Common Adjustments and Repairs (Part 10-1, Section 2) for the correct adjustment of the secondary throttle plates.

2. Install the secondary diaphragm lever, lock washer, and screw.

3. If the primary throttle plates were removed place the accelerating pump cam on the primary throttle shaft. Place the end of the throttle connecting rod with the smallest bend in position in the primary throttle lever. Slide the throttle shaft into the throttle body, guiding the throttle connecting rod so that the other end fits into the secondary throttle lever.

4. Position the primary throttle return spring so that the small tang fits into the slot in the throttle lever and the long tang rests against the throttle body stop (Fig. 24).

5. Install a washer on the secondary throttle shaft end of the connecting rod; then, secure both ends of the connecting rod with pin retainers.

6. Install the primary throttle plates, using the same procedures as for the secondary throttle plates.

7. Install the fast idle cam lever, lock washer, and screw.

8. Install the throttle stop screw and spring.

9. Install the accelerating pump operating lever and retainer.

MAIN BODY

1. Drop the accelerator pump discharge needle into its well (Fig. 25). Lightly seat the needle with a brass drift and a hammer. Position the accelerating pump nozzle and gaskets in the main body and install the retaining screw.

2. **The secondary diaphragm housing must be installed before the**

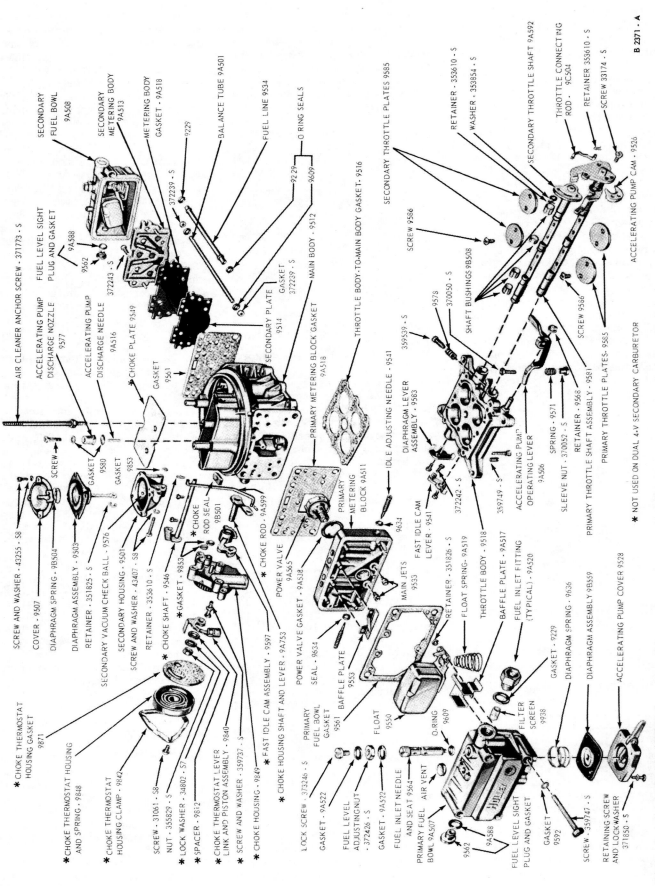

B 2371 - A

* CHOKE THERMOSTAT HOUSING GASKET 9871

* CHOKE THERMOSTAT HOUSING AND SPRING - 9848

* CHOKE THERMOSTAT HOUSING CLAMP - 9842

SCREW - 31061 - S8
NUT - 355829 - S
* LOCK WASHER - 34802 - S7
* SPACER - 9812
* CHOKE THERMOSTAT LEVER LINK AND PISTON ASSEMBLY - 9840
* SCREW AND WASHER - 359737 - S
* CHOKE HOUSING - 9849

* FAST IDLE CAM ASSEMBLY - 9597
* CHOKE HOUSING SHAFT AND LEVER - 9A753

AIR CLEANER ANCHOR SCREW - 371773 - S

ACCELERATING PUMP DISCHARGE NOZZLE 9577

ACCELERATING PUMP DISCHARGE NEEDLE 9A516

SCREW AND WASHER - 43255 - S8
COVER - 9507
DIAPHRAGM SPRING - 9B504
DIAPHRAGM ASSEMBLY - 9503
RETAINER - 351825 - S
SECONDARY VACUUM CHECK BALL - 9576
SECONDARY HOUSING - 9501
SCREW AND WASHER - 43407 - S3
RETAINER - 353610 - S
* CHOKE SHAFT - 9546
* GASKET 9853

SCREW
GASKET 9580
GASKET 9853

CHOKE PLATE 9519

GASKET 9561

SECONDARY PLATE 9514

* CHOKE ROD SEAL 9B501

* CHOKE ROD - 9A599

POWER VALVE 9A565
POWER VALVE GASKET - 9A538
POWER VALVE SEAL - 9634

SECONDARY FUEL BOWL 9A508

SECONDARY METERING BODY 9A513

METERING BODY GASKET - 9A518

9229

372239 - S
9A588
9562
372243 - S

BALANCE TUBE 9A501

FUEL LINE 9534

O RING SEALS
9229
9609

GASKET 372239 - S

MAIN BODY - 9512

THROTTLE BODY-TO-MAIN BODY GASKET - 9516

PRIMARY METERING BLOCK GASKET 9A518

IDLE ADJUSTING NEEDLE - 9541

PRIMARY METERING BLOCK 9A511

SECONDARY THROTTLE PLATES 9585

SCREW 9586

9578

SHAFT BUSHINGS 9B508

370050 - S

SCREW 9586

DIAPHRAGM LEVER ASSEMBLY - 9583

359539 - S

9578

RETAINER - 353610 - S
WASHER - 353854 - S

SECONDARY THROTTLE SHAFT 9A592

THROTTLE CONNECTING ROD - 9C504
RETAINER 353610 - S
SCREW 33174 - S

ACCELERATING PUMP CAM - 9526

372242 - S

359749 - S

ACCELERATING PUMP OPERATING LEVER 9A506

SPRING - 9571
SLEEVE NUT - 370052 - S
RETAINER - 9568

9634

PRIMARY THROTTLE SHAFT ASSEMBLY - 9581
PRIMARY THROTTLE PLATES - 9585

* NOT USED ON DUAL 4-V SECONDARY CARBURETOR

LOCK SCREW - 37324c - S
GASKET - 9A522

FUEL LEVEL ADJUSTINGNUT - 372426 - S
GASKET - 9A522

FUEL INLET NEEDLE AND SEAT 9564

PRIMARY FUEL AIR VENT BOWL 9A507

GASKET 9592
9562
9A588

SCREW - 359747 - S

RETAINING SCREW AND LOCKWASHER 371850 - S

PRIMARY FUEL BOWL GASKET 9561

BAFFLE PLATE 9553

FLOAT 9550

FAST IDLE CAM LEVER - 9541

MAIN JETS 9533

RETAINER - 351826 - S
FLOAT SPRING - 9A519
THROTTLE BODY - 9518
BAFFLE PLATE - 9A517
FUEL INLET FITTING (TYPICAL) - 9A520

O-RING 9609

FUEL LEVEL SIGHT PLUG AND GASKET

GASKET - 9229
DIAPHRAGM SPRING - 9636
DIAPHRAGM ASSEMBLY 9B559
ACCELERATING PUMP COVER 9528

FILTER SCREEN 9938

FUEL LEVEL SIGHT PLUG AND GASKET

FIG. 23—Holley 4-V Carburetor Assembly

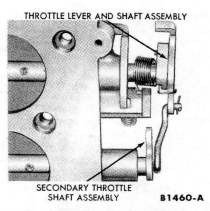

FIG. 24—Throttle Lever and Shaft Assembly Installation

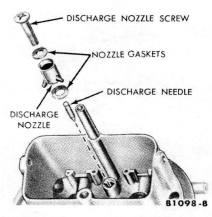

FIG. 25—Accelerating Pump Discharge Assembly

choke housing (if so equipped). Drop the vacuum ball check in the vacuum port of the secondary diaphragm housing; then, position the secondary diaphragm in the housing and place the spring in the cover (Fig. 26). Install the cover and tight-

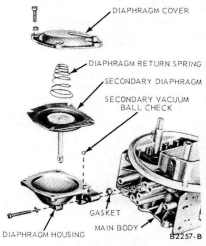

FIG. 26—Secondary Diaphragm Assembly

en the retaining screws finger-tight. Pull the diaphragm rod downward as far as it will go and tighten the cover screws. **The diaphragm housing must be removed from the main body to install the cover.**

3. Place the gasket on the secondary vacuum passage opening on the main body. Place the diaphragm housing in position on the main body and install the lock washers and retaining screws.

4. If the carburetor is equipped with an automatic choke, position the choke plate shaft in the air horn and install the choke plate in the shaft (Fig. 27). Install the rod seal on the choke rod. Slide the U-shaped end of the choke plate rod through the opening in the main body and insert the rod end through the inner side of the bore in the choke lever. The rod end must face outward. Push the rod seal into the

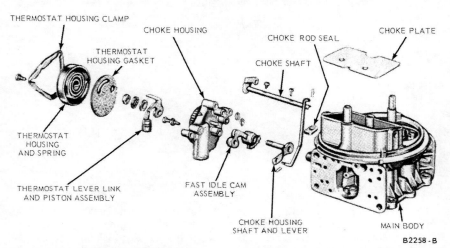

FIG. 27—Choke Plate and Housing Assembly—Primary Carburetor

retaining grooves on the underside of the air cleaner mounting flange.

Position the choke thermostat lever link and piston assembly in the choke housing. Position the fast idle cam assembly on the choke housing and install the choke housing shaft and lever assembly (Fig. 28). Position the lever and piston assembly on the choke housing shaft and lever assembly. Install the spacer, lock washer and nut.

Lay the main body assembly on its side and position the choke housing gaskets on the main body. Insert the choke rod in the choke housing shaft lever as the choke housing is placed into position on the main body. **Be sure the projection on the choke rod is placed under the fast idle cam, so that the cam will be**

lifted **when the choke plate is closed.** Install the choke housing lock washers and screws. Using needle-nose pliers, install the choke rod cotter pin.

Place the thermostatic spring housing gasket into position on the choke housing, engaging the thermostatic spring on the spring lever; then install the housing, clamp and screws. Adjust the thermostatic spring housing by aligning the index mark on the cover with the mid-position mark on the choke housing.

5. Invert the main body and position the throttle body gasket on the main body. Place the throttle body on the main body so that the fuel inlet fitting will be on the same side as the accelerating pump operating lever. Slide the secondary diaphragm rod onto the operating lever as the throttle body is placed into position. Install the throttle body to main

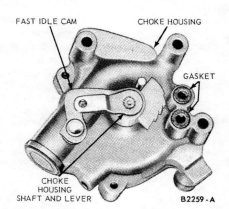

FIG. 28—Choke Housing Linkage Installed

body screws and lock washers. Secure the secondary diaphragm rod with the retainer.

6. Install the air cleaner anchor stud.

PRIMARY FUEL BOWL AND METERING BLOCK

Refer to Fig. 29 for the correct location of the fuel bowl parts.

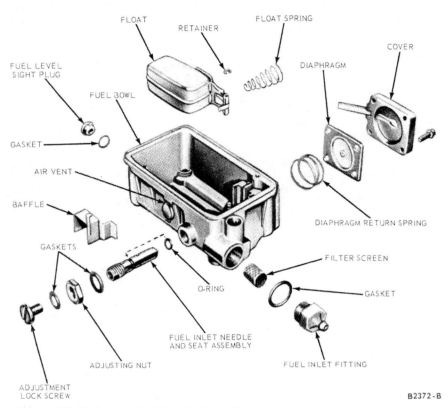

FIG. 29—Primary Fuel Bowl Assembly

1. Place the accelerating pump diaphragm spring and diaphragm in the accelerating pump chamber. The diaphragm must be positioned so that the large end of the lever disc will be against the operating lever. Install the cover and tighten the retaining screws finger-tight. Make sure the diaphragm is centered, then compress the diaphragm with the pump operating lever and tighten the cover screws.

After the carburetor has been assembled, refer to Common Adjustment and Repair (Part 10-1, Section 2) for the correct adjustment of the accelerating pump.

2. Install the filter screen, gasket and fuel inlet fitting.

3. Install the fuel level sight plug and gasket.

4. Slide the baffle plate onto the ridges in the fuel bowl.

5. Install the float spring on the float and slide the float onto the shaft. Be sure the float spring is between the ridges on the boss on the

floor of the fuel bowl. Using needle-nose pliers, install the float retainer.

6. Apply petroleum jelly to a new O-ring seal and slide it on the fuel inlet needle and seat assembly.

7. Position the fuel inlet needle and seat assembly in the fuel bowl, through the top of the bowl. Position the adjusting nut gasket and the nut on the fuel inlet needle and seat assembly. Align the flat on the I.D. of the nut with the flat on the O.D. of the fuel inlet needle and seat assembly. Install the fuel level adjustment lock screw and gasket.

8. As a preliminary float adjustment, refer to Common Adjustments and Repairs (Part 10-1, Section 2) and perform the Float Adjustment—Dry procedure.

9. Using a socket wrench, install the power valve and gasket in the metering block (Fig. 18). **Be sure to install the correct power valve. Refer to the specifications (Part 10-9) for the correct identification number. The number is stamped on a flat on the base of the valve.**

10. Using a jet wrench, install the jets in the metering block (Fig. 17).

11. Using new gaskets, install the idle adjusting needles. Turn the idle adjusting needles in until they just

touch the seat; then, back them off the specified number of turns (Part 10-9) for a preliminary idle adjustment.

12. Slide the balance tube through the holes in the primary side and the secondary side of the main body. Position the balance tube so that the tube protrudes equally at each end. Apply petroleum jelly to a new O-ring seal and slide it on the balance tube, and then slide the washer on the same end of the balance tube (Fig. 30). Push the O-ring seal and washer into the recess in the primary side of the main body.

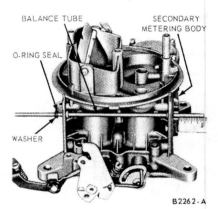

FIG. 30—Balance Tube Adjustment

13. Position the metering block gasket on the dowels located on the back of the metering block. Slide the metering block and gasket onto the balance tube. Position the metering block and gasket on the main body. Position the baffle plate (primary side only) and the gasket on the metering block. Place the retaining screws and new compression gaskets in the fuel bowl. Position the bowl in place on the metering block and tighten the retaining screws.

14. Apply petroleum jelly to the fuel line tube O-ring seal. Place the seal against the flange on one end of the fuel line tube. Install this end of the fuel line tube into the recess in the primary fuel bowl.

SECONDARY FUEL BOWL AND METERING BODY

1. Assemble the secondary fuel bowl and perform a float adjustment —dry by following steps 3 thru 8 under Primary Fuel Bowl and Metering Block Assembly in this section.

2. Apply petroleum jelly to a new balance tube O-ring seal. Slide the O-ring seal on the balance tube, and install the O-ring seal washer on the tube. Push the O-ring seal and washer into the recess in the secondary side of the main body.

3. Slide the metering body gasket (Fig. 31) on the balance tube and into position on the main body. Position the metering plate, gasket, and metering body (Fig. 31) on the main body, and install the retaining screws (Fig. 20). Adjust the balance tube so that the distance from the metering body to the end of the balance tube is one inch (Fig. 30).

4. Apply petroleum jelly to the fuel line tube O-ring seal and position it against the flange on the fuel line tube. Position the fuel bowl on the main body, guiding the fuel line tube into the recess in the bowl. Install the retaining screws with new compression gaskets.

5. Refer to Common Adjustments and Repairs (Part 10-1, Sec-

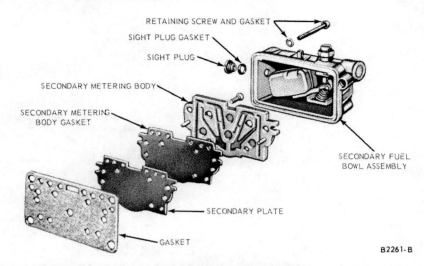

FIG. 31—Secondary Fuel Bowl and Metering Body Assembly

tion 2) and perform the accelerating pump lever, accelerating pump stroke and the automatic choke adjustments.

PART 10-6 AIR CLEANER

1 DESCRIPTION AND OPERATION

CONVENTIONAL DRY-TYPE AIR CLEANER

The 240 Six passenger car engine, 352 and 390 engines with an automatic transmission, and the 410, 427 and 428 engines are equipped with a conventional dry-type carburetor air cleaner that has a replaceable filtering element.

The air cleaner body is mounted on a sealing gasket, located on the carburetor air horn. The air cleaner assembly is retained on the engine by a stud on the carburetor body and a wing nut above the filter cover.

The air from the engine compartment enters the air cleaner assembly through the opening (horn) on the side of the body, into a silencing chamber and passes through the filter element. Dust particles are trapped in the filter element as the air passes through it. After leaving the filter element, the air is deflected down into the carburetor.

DRY-TYPE HOT AND COLD AIR INTAKE AIR CLEANER

All 289 V-8 engines and the 352 and 390 V-8 engines with manual-shift transmissions are equipped with a dry-type carburetor air cleaner assembly and a thermostatically controlled carburetor air inlet duct assembly.

The air cleaner body is mounted on a sealing gasket, located on the carburetor air horn. The air cleaner assembly is retained on the engine by a stud in the carburetor body and a wing nut above the filter cover. The replaceable filter element assembly prevents entry of dirt and unfiltered air into the engine.

On a 289 V-8 engine, the thermostatically controlled air inlet duct and valve assembly is secured to the air cleaner body with 2 wing-type screws.

The thermostatically controlled air inlet duct and valve assembly for 352 and 390 V-8 engines is connected to the air cleaner body by an extension tube. The extension tube is secured to the air cleaner body by 2 wing-type screws. The duct and valve assembly is secured to the extension tube by a wing-type screw and washer.

The duct and valve assembly slips onto the shroud. The shroud is positioned on the right exhaust manifold and is retained by a stud, lockwasher and nut.

The air inlet duct mechanism for the various engines consists of a valve plate, thermostat, adjustable thermostat rod, 2 springs and a retaining clip.

The air received from the air duct passes through a silencing chamber in the air cleaner body and then through the filter element. After leaving the filter element, the air is deflected down into the carburetor. Dust particles and other foreign materials are trapped in the filter element as the air rushes through it.

The temperature of the air entering the air cleaner is thermostatically controlled by the carburetor air duct assembly. Air from the engine compartment, or heated air from a shroud around the exhaust manifold, is available to the engine.

A thermostatic bulb in the air duct is exposed to the incoming air. A spring-loaded valve plate is connected to the thermostatic bulb through linkage. The valve plate spring holds the valve in the closed position (heat on) until the thermostatic bulb overcomes the valve tension.

During the engine warm-up period when the air temperature entering the air duct is less than 75°F, the thermostat is in the retracted position and the valve plate is held in the up position (heat on) by the valve plate spring, thus shutting off the air from the engine compartment. All air is then drawn from the shroud around the exhaust manifold.

As the temperature of the air passing the thermostatic bulb approaches 85°F, the thermostat starts to expand, and pulls the valve plate down. This allows cooler air from the engine compartment to enter the air cleaner. When the temperature of the air reaches approximately 105°F, the valve plate will be in the down position (heat off) so that only engine compartment air is allowed to enter the air cleaner.

OIL BATH AIR CLEANER

The 240 Six Police and Taxi engines are equipped with an oil bath air cleaner, containing an integral wire mesh filter element seated in an oil sump in the air cleaner body.

The air from the engine compartment enters the air cleaner and passes down between the outside wall of the filter element and the wall of the oil reservoir. The air is then deflected by a baffle in the bottom of the oil chamber, up through the filter element. After leaving the filter element, the air flows into the carburetor.

As the air rushes across the oil in the filter, large heavy particles fall into the oil and are entrapped. The smaller dust particles are trapped in the oil dampened filtering element as the air passes through to the carburetor.

CLOSED CRANKCASE VENTILATION SYSTEM AIR CLEANERS

Air is drawn into the crankcase ventilation system at the integral crankcase ventilation air inlet tube of the carburetor air cleaner body, and passes through the connecting rubber hose into the crankcase. On a 427 V-8 engine, a flame arrestor is connected to the hose leading into the base of the air cleaner body.

2 REMOVAL AND INSTALLATION

AIR CLEANER MAINTENANCE

Refer to Group 19 for the air cleaner assembly recommended maintenance mileage interval.

AIR CLEANERS AND FILTER ELEMENTS

REMOVAL

1. On a 240 Six engine, remove the retaining nut(s) securing the air cleaner to the support bracket.

2. Disconnect the crankcase ventilation system hose, if so equipped, from the air cleaner.

3. Disconnect the air intake duct and valve assembly, if so equipped, from the air cleaner body.

4. Remove the wing bolt or nut retaining the air cleaner to the carburetor. Remove the air cleaner assembly from the carburetor. **If the air cleaner is an oil bath type, use care to prevent oil spillage.**

5. On a dry-type air cleaner, remove the air cleaner cover and filter element from the air cleaner body.

On an oil bath air cleaner, remove the wing nut retaining the air cleaner body to the air cleaner duct. Separate the units.

6. Discard the air cleaner to carburetor mounting gasket if it is worn or damaged.

CLEANING AND INSPECTION

Refer to Part 10-1, Section 3 for the recommended cleaning and inspection procedure.

INSTALLATION

1. Install a new air cleaner to carburetor mounting gasket, if required.

2. On an oil bath air cleaner, position the air cleaner body to the duct and install the retaining wing nut. Position the air cleaner assembly on the carburetor and install the wing-type retaining screw. **Use care to prevent oil spillage.**

3. On a dry-type air cleaner, position the air cleaner body and filter element on the carburetor. **If the word TOP is indicated on the filter** **element, make sure the word TOP faces upward. Make sure the filter element is properly seated.** Install the air cleaner cover and retaining wing nut or screw.

4. On a 240 Six engine, secure the air cleaner to the mounting brace with the retaining bolt and nut(s).

5. Connect the air intake duct and valve assembly, if so equipped, to the air cleaner body. Tighten the retaining wing nuts.

6. Connect the crankcase ventilation system hose, if so equipped, to the air cleaner body. Tighten the retaining clamp.

HOT AND COLD AIR INTAKE DUCT AND VALVE ASSEMBLY

The air intake duct thermostatic valve can be adjusted to change the air temperature at which the valve opens. Increasing the thermostatic rod length will move the valve toward the heat-**off** position. Decreasing the rod length will move the valve toward the heat-**on** position. Adjustments must be verified by testing the opening temperature as detailed in Part 10-1, Section 1.

REMOVAL

1. Remove the 2 wing-type retaining screws that secure the air intake duct and valve assembly to the air cleaner.

2. Remove the shroud to exhaust manifold retaining nut and washer. Remove the air intake duct and shroud assembly from the engine.

DIAGNOSIS AND TESTING

Refer to Part 10-1, Section 1 for the air intake duct and valve testing procedures.

INSTALLATION

1. Install the air intake duct and valve assembly shroud on the exhaust manifold. Install the shroud retaining nut and washer. Tighten the nut.

2. Connect the air inlet duct and valve assembly to the air cleaner and tighten the 2 wing-type retaining screws.

DISASSEMBLY

1. On a 352 or 390 V-8 engine, remove the wing-type retaining screw securing the air duct and valve assembly to the extension. Separate the air inlet duct and valve assembly, shroud and extension.

2. If the duct and valve assembly was removed because of a suspected malfunction, check the operation of the thermostat and air duct assembly. Refer to the Air Intake Duct Test (Part 10-1, Section 1) for the proper procedure.

3. If inspection reveals that the valve plate is sticking, or the thermostat is malfunctioning, remove the thermostat and valve plate as follows:

Detach the valve plate tension spring from the valve plate with the use of long-nose pliers. Loosen the thermostat lock nut and unscrew the thermostat from the mounting bracket. Remove the lock nut. Grasp the valve plate and withdraw if from the duct.

ASSEMBLY

1. If it was necessary to disassemble the thermostat and air duct and valve, assemble the unit as follows:

Install the valve plate. Install the lock nut on the thermostat, and screw the thermostat into the mounting bracket. Install the valve plate tension spring on the valve plate and duct.

Check the operation of the thermostat and air duct assembly. Refer to the Air Intake Duct Test (Part 10-1, Section 1) for the proper procedure. Adjust the thermostat as required.

2. On a 352 or 390 V-8 engine, connect the duct and valve assembly to the shroud and the extension tube. Install the duct and valve assembly to extension tube retaining wing-screw and washer. Tighten the retaining screw.

PART 10-7

FUEL PUMP

1 DESCRIPTION AND OPERATION

Single-action fuel pumps are standard equipment for all car models.

The fuel pumps for the 240 Six engines are mounted on the lower, left center of the cylinder block.

On all V-8 engines, the fuel pumps are mounted on the left side of the cylinder front cover.

Table 1 lists the type of fuel pumps and in-line fuel filter applications used on the engines. Refer to Figs. 1 through 5 for views of the fuel pumps and applicable fuel filters.

TABLE 1—Fuel Pump and Fuel Filter Application

ENGINE APPLICATION	FUEL PUMP TYPE		IN-LINE FUEL FILTER	
	Carter*	A/C	Replaceable Element	Replaceable Filter
240 Six		x		x
289, 352, 390 410 and 428 V-8	x			x
427 V-8		x	x	
*Permanently Sealed-Type				

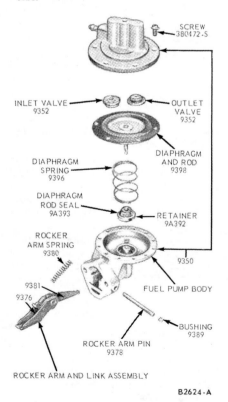

FIG. 1—AC Fuel Pump—240 Six Engine

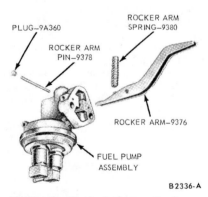

FIG. 2—Typical Carter Fuel Pump—289, 352, 390, 410 and 428 V-8 Engines

The fuel pumps are mechanically actuated by means of the fuel pump rocker arm and an eccentric on the camshaft.

A flexible fuel pump diaphragm is operated by a combination of rocker arm action and calibrated spring tension.

On the fuel intake stroke, the camshaft eccentric causes the rocker arm to lift the fuel pump diaphragm against the diaphragm spring pressure. This action draws fuel through the intake valve into the pump inlet chamber and closes the outlet valve.

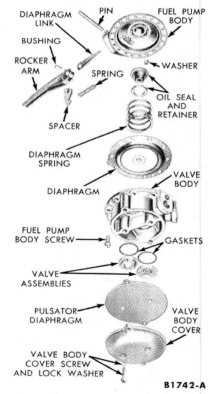

FIG. 3—AC Fuel Pump—427 V-8

At the time, fuel is drawn from the

fuel tank through the fuel intake line to replace the fuel drawn into the chamber.

As the camshaft eccentric continues to rotate, the rocker arm relieves the pressure on the diaphragm spring and allows the spring to move the diaphragm toward the inlet and outlet valves, exerting pressure on the fuel inlet chamber. This pressure causes the pump inlet valve to close and the ensuing pressure build-up opens the outlet valve. The fuel is then forced through the pump outlet to the in-line fuel filter where it is cleansed before entering the car-

buretor. **Fuel is delivered to the carburetor only when the fuel inlet valve in the carburetor is open. The carburetor inlet valve is closed by fuel pressure on the float when the specified fuel level in the carburetor float chamber is reached.**

When there is no demand for fuel from the carburetor, the diaphragm spring tension is not strong enough to force the diaphragm against the fuel pressure built up in the inlet chamber of the pump. Thus, the up and down rocker arm action continues, but the diaphragm remains stationary until pressure against the

carburetor float is relieved by a demand for fuel at the carburetor.

A pulsator diaphragm in the 427 V-8 fuel pumps dampens the effect of fuel pump pressure pulsations on the carburetor fuel inlet needle valve.

The Carter permanently sealed fuel pumps for the V-8 engines contain pressure relief orifices in the inlet and outlet valve cages to prevent pressure build-up in the line to the carburetor during hot soak periods.

The fuel pumps contain a diaphragm rod seal to prevent the entrance of engine oil into the fuel pump.

2   REMOVAL AND INSPECTION

FUEL FILTER MAINTENANCE

The in-line fuel filter used on all engines except the 427 4-8 (Fig. 4) is of one-piece construction and cannot be cleaned. **Replace the filter if it becomes clogged or restricted.**

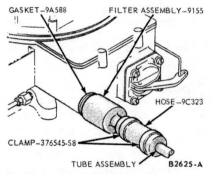

FIG. 4—In-Line Fuel Filter— All Except 427 V-8

The in-line fuel filter for the 427 V-8 engine (Fig. 5) contains a replaceable filter element. Replace the element if it becomes clogged or restricted and also at the recommended maintenance mileage interval (Group 19).

FUEL FILTER OR ELEMENT REPLACEMENT

FUEL FILTERS—ALL EXCEPT 427 V-8

1. Remove the air cleaner (Part 10-6, Section 2).

2. Loosen the retaining clamp securing the fuel inlet hose to the fuel filter (Fig. 4).

3. Unscrew the fuel filter from the carburetor and discard the gasket. Disconnect the fuel filter from the hose and discard the retaining clamp.

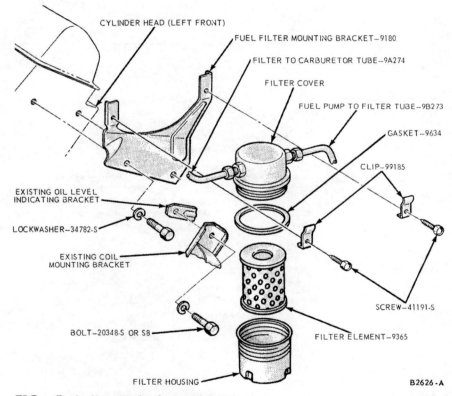

FIG. 5—In-Line Fuel Filter—427 V-8

4. Install a new clamp on the inlet hose and connect the hose to the filter. Place a new gasket on the new fuel filter and screw the filter into the carburetor inlet port. Tighten the filter.

5. Position the fuel line hose clamp and crimp the clamp securely.

6. Start the engine and check for fuel leaks.

7. Install the air cleaner (Part 10-6, Section 2).

FUEL FILTER ELEMENT— 427 V-8

1. Unscrew the filter housing from the fuel filter cover (Fig. 5). Remove and discard the filter element and gasket.

2. Clean the filter housing in solvent.

3. Coat a new gasket with light engine oil and position the gasket on the filter housing. Position a new filter element over the spout on the

cover. **Only a filter element displaying installation instructions should be used. Install the filter element according to the printed instructions on the element.**

4. Screw the filter housing onto the cover. Hand tighten the filter housing until the gasket makes contact with cover; then, advance it ⅛ turn.

5. Start the engine and check for fuel leaks.

FUEL FILTER ASSEMBLY— 427 V-8

1. Remove the retaining screws and clips securing the fuel lines to the fuel filter mounting bracket (Fig. 5).

2. Disconnect the fuel lines from the fuel filter assembly.

3. If required, disassemble the fuel filter. Refer to Fuel Filter Ele-ment—427 V-8 in this section for the proper procedure.

4. If required, assemble the fuel filter. Refer to Fuel Filter Element —427 V-8 in this section for the proper procedure.

5. Position the fuel filter on the engine and connect the fuel lines to the filter.

6. Secure the filter assembly to the fuel filter mounting bracket with the retaining screws and clips.

7. Start the engine and check for leaks.

FUEL PUMP REMOVAL

1. Disconnect the inlet line and the outlet line at the fuel pump.

2. Remove the fuel pump retaining screws and remove the pump and the gasket. Discard the gasket.

FUEL PUMP INSTALLATION

1. If the fuel pump on a 240 Six engine is to be replaced, transfer the fuel pump fitting(s) to the new fuel pump.

2. Remove all the gasket material from the mounting pad and pump. Apply oil-resistant sealer to both sides of a new gasket. Position the new gasket on the pump flange and hold the pump in position against the mounting pad. **Make sure the rocker arm is riding on the camshaft eccentric.**

3. Press the pump tight against the pad, install the retaining screws. and alternately torque them to specifications.

4. Connect the fuel inlet line or hose (use a new clamp on the hose) and the outlet line. If a hose is used at the fuel pump connection, crimp the retaining clamp securely.

5. Operate the engine and check for fuel leaks.

---

3 MAJOR REPAIR OPERATIONS

AC FUEL PUMP—240 SIX

The fuel pump is shown in Fig. 1.

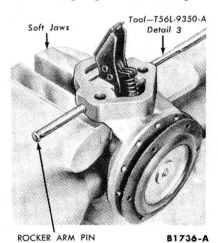

FIG. 6—Rocker Arm Pin Removal or Installation

DISASSEMBLY

1. Scribe a line on the flanges of the pump body and valve housing to identify their original position.

2. Remove the valve housing from the fuel pump body.

3. Remove the staking marks from around the valves and remove both valves from the valve housing. **Carefully note or index the position of the valves in the valve housing** cover, so that new valves can be correctly installed.

4. Using a blunt punch or tool T56L-9350-A, Detail 3, drive the rocker arm pin out of the pump body (Fig. 6).

5. Press the pump diaphragm into the fuel pump body and pull the rocker arm outward to unhook the diaphragm actuating rod from the rocker arm and link assembly (Fig. 7).

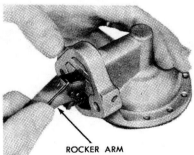

FIG. 7—Fuel Pump Diaphragm Removal

6. Remove the diaphragm and diaphragm return spring, rocker arm and link assembly and the rocker arm return spring from the pump body.

7. Remove the diaphragm actuating rod oil seal from the pump body (Fig. 1).

CLEANING AND INSPECTION

Refer to Part 10-1, Section 3 for the cleaning and inspection procedures. Replace all worn or damaged parts.

ASSEMBLY

1. Immerse the new diaphragm actuating rod oil seal in clean engine oil for 2 minutes prior to installation. Install the oil seal and retainer so that the seal protrudes toward the diaphragm mounting flange (Fig. 1).

2. Seat the oil seal retainer, using tool 9350-C or T56L-9350-A, Detail 1 (Fig. 8). Stake the oil seal retainer in at least 3 places to secure the installation.

3. Install the valves in the valve body so that the valve positions are as shown in Fig. 1.

4. Seat the valves firmly in the valve body, using tool 9350-D or T56L-9350-A, Detail 2. Stake the valves in place.

5. Lubricate the diaphragm actuating rod with lubriplate.

6. Position the fuel pump diaphragm and spring into the pump body as shown in Fig. 9.

7. Hold the diaphragm assembly in the pump body; position the pump body so that the mounting flange faces up. *Apply slightly more pressure to the lower edge of the diaphragm, and insert the rocker arm link assembly with the cam shoe*

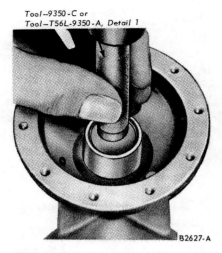

Tool—9350-C or
Tool—T56L-9350-A, Detail 1

B2627-A

FIG. 8—Seating The Oil Seal

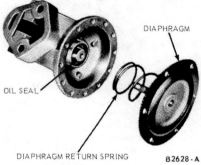

DIAPHRAGM

OIL SEAL

DIAPHRAGM RETURN SPRING   B2628-A

FIG. 9—Diaphragm Installation

facing away from the diaphragm. Hook the rocker arm link to the diaphragm actuating rod.

8. Lift one edge of the diaphragm and observe the positioning of the oil seal. **Make sure the oil seal is fully extended as shown in Fig. 10.** If the oil seal is not properly positioned, push the diaphragm inward as far as possible with a slight twisting motion to the diaphragm. This will assist the oil seal to position itself properly on the diaphragm rod. **Do not twist the diaphragm too severely or the rod may be unhooked from the link.**

9. Install the rocker arm return spring and hold it in place by cocking the rocker arm slightly.

10. Install the rocker arm pin in the pump body.

11. Position the valve body and pump body so that the previously scribed marks are aligned.

12. Install all the screws and the lockwashers until the screws just engage the fuel pump body. **Make sure that all of the screws pass through the holes in the diaphragm without tearing the fabric.**

13. Hold the rocker arm in the

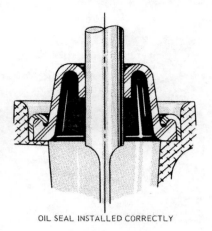

OIL SEAL INSTALLED CORRECTLY

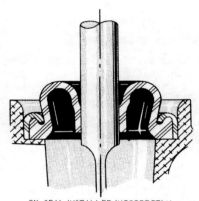

OIL SEAL INSTALLED INCORRECTLY

B2366-A

FIG. 10—Fuel Pump Oil Seal Installation

down position to compress the diaphragm spring and tighten all of the screws, alternately and evenly.

14. Cover all but one vent hole in the pump lower body, using masking tape or a similar material.

15. Using a suitable vacuum source, apply 15 inches of vacuum (Hg.) to the underside of the pump diaphragm at the open vent hole. **Use a suitable rubber tipped probe or hose to assure proper sealing at the vent hole.** Apply vacuum to the diaphragm 2 times for a minimum of one minute each time. This will position the oil seal properly on the diaphragm rod. Remove the sealing tape from the vents.

CARTER PERMANENTLY—SEALED FUEL PUMPS

The fuel pump assemblies are shown in Fig. 2.

DISASSEMBLY

1. Scrape away the staking mark and remove the rocker arm pin seal plug as shown in Fig. 11.

2. Release the tension on the

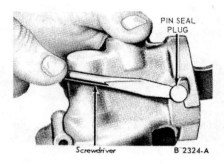

PIN SEAL PLUG

Screwdriver   B 2324-A

FIG. 11—Rocker Arm Pin Seal Plug Removal

rocker arm by pressing the arm downward against the diaphragm and rocker arm spring pressure and allow the rocker arm pin to fall out. If the pin does not come out freely, tap the fuel pump assembly lightly on the bench until the pin sticks out of the bore; then, remove the pin with pliers. Remove the rocker arm and spring.

CLEANING AND INSPECTION

Clean and inspect the fuel pump component parts. Refer to Cleaning and Inspection (Part 10-1, Section 3) for the proper procedure. Replace all worn or damaged parts.

ASSEMBLY

The fuel pump assemblies are shown in Fig. 2.

1. Insert the rocker arm spring into the spring guide bore in the dome of the fuel pump rocker arm cavity.

2. Insert the rocker arm into the cavity and hook it onto the diaphragm rod, directly below the rod flange. Position the rocker arm spring over the spring locater on the rocker arm. Align the rocker arm pin holes and install the rocker arm pin. **Make certain the rocker arm spring is properly positioned on the spring locater on the rocker arm.**

3. Install a new rocker arm pin plug. Stake the plug into position.

AC FUEL PUMP—427 V-8

The fuel pump is shown in Fig. 3.

DISASSEMBLY

1. Scribe marks on the fuel pump body, valve body, and cover so that these parts can be assembled in their original position.

2. Separate the fuel pump body and the valve body.

3. Remove the fuel pump body cover and pulsator diaphragm.

4. Remove the staking marks around the valves, and pry the valves out with a screwdriver. **Note or index the position of the inlet and outlet valves so that the new valves can be installed in the same manner.**

5. Remove the upset on the end of the rocker arm pin. Remove the retaining washer, then drive the pin out using a blunt punch or tool T56L-9350-A, Detail 3, (Fig. 12). Work the fuel pump link out of the diaphragm stem.

Tool—T56L-9350-A, Detail 3   B1468-A

FIG. 12—Rocker Arm Pin Removal or Installation

6. Remove the diaphragm and spring. Remove the diaphragm stem retainer and seal. Discard the seal.

7. Remove the rocker arm and link assembly.

CLEANING AND INSPECTION

Refer to Part 10-1, Section 3 for the cleaning and inspection procedures. Replace all worn or damaged parts.

ASSEMBLY

1. Immerse the new oil seal in clean engine oil for 2 minutes prior to installation. Install the diaphragm rod oil seal and retainer in the fuel pump body (Fig. 13) so that the seal protrudes toward the diaphragm mounting flange. Seat the oil seal retainer using tool T56L-9350-A, Detail 1, or 9350-C. Stake the oil seal

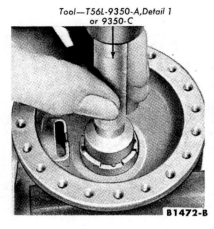

Tool—T56L-9350-A, Detail 1 or 9350-C   B1472-B

FIG. 13—Oil Seal and Retainer Installation

retainer in at least 3 places to secure the installation.

2. Place the link, with the hook up, inside the return spring retainer spacer. Place these parts inside the rocker arm, and install the bushing. The cam contact surface of the rocker arm faces up.

3. Install a washer on each end of the bushing.

4. Place the rocker arm return spring over the boss in the pump body. Place the rocker arm and link assembly in the pump body and hold them in place (Fig. 12).

5. Install the rocker arm pin. Place the retainer washer on the end of the pin. Peen the pin.

6. Lubricate the fuel pump diaphragm rod with Lubriplate. Position the spring on the fuel pump diaphragm rod. Insert the rod through the diaphragm stem oil seal, and hook the stem slot over the short link (Fig. 14).

7. Check the oil seal to make sure it is positioned properly. Refer to step 8 of AC Fuel Pump—240 Six, Assembly in this section for the proper procedure.

8. Install the gaskets and fuel valves in the valve body (Fig. 15), then stake them in place. **Be sure the valves are positioned as noted during removal of the valves.**

9. Position the pulsator diaphragm and cover on the valve body, use the identifying marks made on disas-

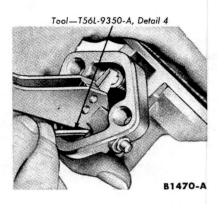

Tool—T56L-9350-A, Detail 4   B1470-A

FIG. 14—Fuel Pump Diaphragm Installation

sembly as guides. Hold the cover against the valve body and install the cover retaining screws. Make sure the diaphragm extends evenly around the edge of the cover. Tighten the screws.

10. Place the fuel pump body on the valve body, aligning the scribed line on the valve body with the line on the fuel pump body. Be sure the diaphragm extends evenly all around the edge of the valve body. Compress the spring with the rocker arm, and install the retaining screws. Tighten the screws evenly, then release the rocker arm.

11. To assure proper installation of the diaphragm rod oil seal, perform step 14 of AC Fuel Pump—240 Six, Assembly in this section.

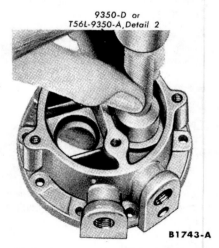

9350-D or T56L-9350-A, Detail 2   B1743-A

FIG. 15—Fuel Pump Valve and Gasket Installation

PART 10-8   FUEL TANK AND LINES

1 DESCRIPTION AND OPERATION

Views of the fuel tank, lines and related parts are shown in Fig. 1. Station wagon models are equipped with a 20 gallon fuel tank. All car models except station wagons are equipped with a 25 gallon fuel tank.

On all models except station wagons, the fuel tank is retained by two steel support straps.

The station wagon fuel tank is held in a vertical position by one steel support strap. The tank is located behind the wheel opening in the left rear quarter panel.

The fuel sender unit is located on the front side of the tank and is accessible from underneath the car.

On station wagons, a fuel tank guard in the wheel well must be removed to gain access to the fuel sender unit.

The fuel outlet line is fastened to a connecting hose attached to a line which enters the fuel tank through the sender unit assembly. A filter is located in the tank on the fuel line pick-up tube. **This filter does not require servicing.**

The fuel tank filler pipe is located behind a door in the left rear quarter panel, just above the rearward of the wheel well opening. The tank is vented through the fuel filler pipe cap.

On station wagons, the filler pipe is an integral part of the tank.

On other models, the filler pipe slides into the fuel tank. An O-ring is used to seal the filler pipe to the tank. The filler pipe is attached to the filler pipe housing with four screws and is sealed to the filler pipe housing with a gasket.

The fuel line is routed from the fuel tank, passing beneath the left side of the underbody, along the left frame rail, then, up the left inner fender well to the fuel pump. The complete fuel line is replaceable as a unit. However, only the damaged segments are usually replaced.

2 REMOVAL AND INSTALLATION

FILLER PIPE

The filler pipe installation is shown in Fig. 1. The fuel filler pipe is removable on all models except station wagons.

REMOVAL

1. Partially drain the fuel tank with a siphon to a level below the filler pipe connection in the tank.
2. Remove the four retaining screws securing the filler pipe to the filler pipe housing.
3. Raise the car on a hoist.
4. Grasp the filler pipe near the fuel tank, rotate the filler pipe and pull it outward to remove it from the fuel tank and filler pipe housing.
5. Remove the O-ring seal from the fuel tank opening.

INSTALLATION

1. Lubricate the O-ring seal and install it in the fuel tank opening.
2. Position the filler pipe in the filler pipe housing and slide the pipe into the fuel tank opening. **Be sure that the O-ring seal is properly seated.**
3. Lower the car.
4. Install and tighten the filler pipe retaining screws.
5. Fill the fuel tank and install the filler cap. Check for fuel leaks.

FUEL TANK

The fuel tank installations are shown in Fig. 1.

REMOVAL

All Except Station Wagons

1. Remove the filler cap. Using necessary precautions, drain the fuel into a suitable container.
2. Remove the four filler pipe to filler pipe housing screws.
3. Raise the vehicle on a hoist.
4. Remove the filler pipe.
5. Disconnect the fuel gauge sending unit wire and fuel line at the sending unit.
6. Remove the two nuts retaining the tank support straps to the body

floor pan at the rear of the tank. Remove the straps and lower the tank.
7. Remove the sending unit from the old tank if a new tank is to be installed.

Station Wagons

1. Remove the filler cap. Using necessary precautions, drain the fuel into a suitable container.
2. Remove the fuel tank filler door.
3. Remove the six boot retainer to body retaining screws and remove the boot and retainer as an assembly.
4. Raise the car on a hoist.
5. Remove the left rear tire.
6. Remove the wheel well splash shield.
7. Disconnect the fuel gauge sending unit wire and fuel line at the sending unit.
8. Remove the nut retaining the tank support strap to the body. Remove the strap and remove the tank.

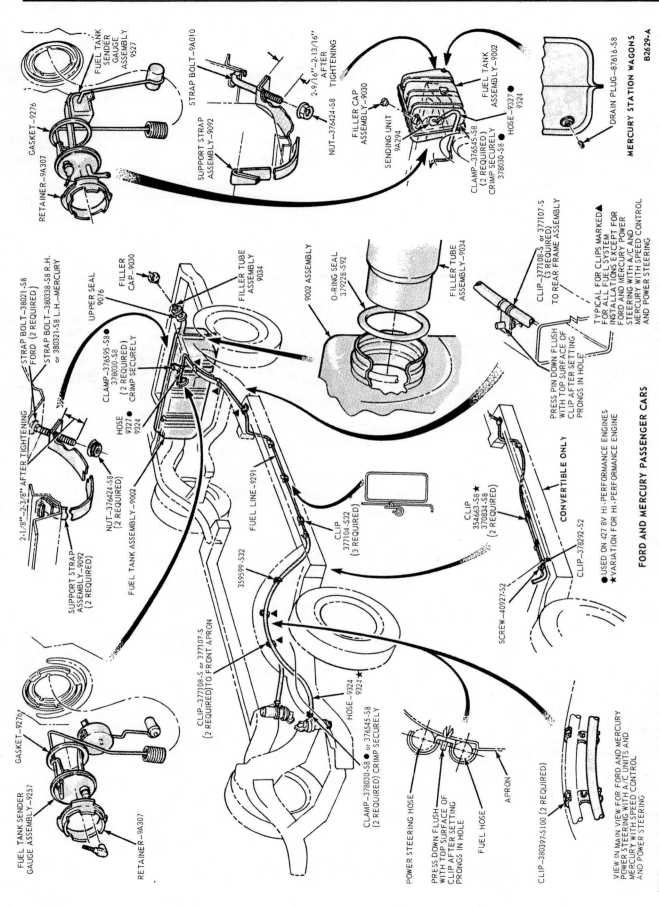

FIG. 1—Fuel Systems—Ford and Mercury

9. Remove the sending unit from the old tank if a new tank is to be installed.

INSTALLATION

All Except Station Wagons

1. If a new tank is to be installed, install the fuel gauge sending unit and a new mounting gasket in the tank. Install the drain plug.

2. Hold the tank in position against the body floor pan. Hook the support straps to the retainers in the floor pan at the front of the tank. Position the straps over the studs, *then install* the nuts retaining the straps to the body floor pan at the rear of the tank.

3. Connect the fuel line and sending unit wire to the sending unit.

4. Lubricate a new O-ring seal and place it in position in the fuel tank opening.

5. Install the filler pipe in the fuel tank. Be sure the O-ring seal is properly seated.

6. Lower the car.

7. Install the four filler pipe retaining screws.

8. Fill the tank and check all connections for leaks.

Station Wagons

1. If a new tank is to be installed, install the fuel gauge sending unit and a new mounting gasket in the fuel tank.

2. Install the drain plug and the filler cap.

3. Hold the tank in position and install the retaining strap.

4. Connect the fuel line and the sending unit wire to the sending unit.

5. Install the wheel well splash shield.

6. Install the left rear wheel and lower the car.

7. Remove the filler cap and install the boot and retainer.

8. Fill the fuel tank and install the filler cap.

9. Check all connections for leaks.

FUEL LINES

The various fuel lines (Fig. 1) are not serviced as assemblies. They must be cut, squared and formed out of rolls of fuel system service tubing and hose material available at dealerships.

A damaged section of **tubing** longer than 12 inches can be cut out of the existing line and replaced by a comparable service **tubing section,** spliced into the line by means of connecting hoses and retaining clamps. **All replacement hoses must be cut to a length that will insure proper clamp retention beyond the flared ends of the connecting tubing.**

REMOVAL

1. Partially drain the fuel tank to a level below the sending unit in the tank.

2. Disconnect the line at the fuel gauge sender unit and the fuel pump. Remove the lines from the holding clips along the underbody. Remove all damaged hose sections and tube sections.

INSTALLATION

1. Cut a new section of tubing to approximately the same length as the section to be replaced. **Allow extra** length for flaring the ends of the tubing. Square the ends of the cut tubing with a file.

2. Ream the inside edges of the cut tubing with the reamer blade on the tube cutter. **Be sure metal chips are removed from inside the tube(s).** Flare the ends of the cut tubing, as required, with a standard tube flaring kit and tool (Fig. 2).

3. Bend the tube section to conform to the contour of the original tube. Cut an ample length of hose to form a coupling between the flared ends of the fuel lines. Connect the hose couplings to the tubing and install the retaining clamps.

4. Position the lines in the underbody clips and tighten the clips. Connect the line to the fuel gauge sender unit and the fuel pump. Fill the tank and check for leaks.

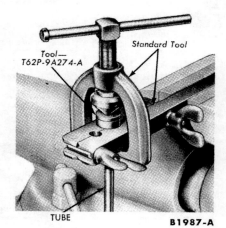

Tool— T62P-9A274-A

Standard Tool

TUBE

B1987-A

FIG. 2—Fuel Line Tube Die

PART 10-9 SPECIFICATIONS

NOTE: All specifications are given in inches unless otherwise noted.

CARBURETORS

The basic part number of all the carburetors is 9510. The part number prefix and suffix appears on the identification tag mounted on the carburetor.

Always refer to the Master Parts Catalog for parts usage and interchangeability before replacing a carburetor, or a component part for a carburetor.

CARBURETOR APPLICATION AND GENERAL INFORMATION

Engine and Trans.	Carb. Part Number (9510)	Carb. Model	Throttle Bore Dia.		Venturi Diameter		Main Metering Jet				Booster Venturi		Power Valve Color		Spark Valve Color	Choke Cover Spring
							Normal		Altitude							
			Pri.	Sec.	Pri.	Sec.	Pri.	Sec.	Pri.	Sec.	Pri.	Sec.	Normal	Altitude		
240-1V Std.	C6AF-R	Ford 1101-A	1.690	—	1.290	—	69F	—	67F	—	—	—	—	—	Plain④	AU
240-1V Std.①	C6AF-V	Ford 1101-A	1.690	—	1.290	—	72F	—	70F	—	—	—	—	—	—	AV
240-1V Std.②③	C6AF-M	Ford 1101-A	1.440	—	1.100	—	59F	—	57F	—	—	—	—	—	—	AV
240-1V Auto.	C6AF-S	Ford 1101-A	1.690	—	1.290	—	68F	—	66F	—	—	—	—	—	Plain④	AR
240-1V Auto.①	C6AF-Y	Ford 1101-A	1.690	—	1.290	—	68F	—	66F	—	—	—	—	—	—	AR
240-1V Auto.②③	C6AF-N	Ford 1101-A	1.440	—	1.100	—	59F	—	57F	—	—	—	—	—	—	AV
289-2V Std.	C6AF-A	Ford 2100-A	1.437	—	1.145	—	51F	—	49F	—	CG	—	Red	Plain	—	TW
289-2V Std.①	C6AF-Z	Ford 2100-A	1.437	—	1.145	—	50F	—	48F	—	P	—	Plain	Green	—	TW
289-2V Auto.	C6AF-B	Ford 2100-A	1.437	—	1.145	—	50F	—	48F	—	CE	—	Green	Yellow	—	TO
289-2V Auto.①	C6AF-AA	Ford 2100-A	1.437	—	1.145	—	49F	—	47F	—	P	—	Plain	Green	—	TO
352-4V Auto.	C6AF-L	Ford 4100-A	1.562	1.562	1.125	1.189	48F	55F	46F	53F	KD	BA	Plain	Green	—	TT
352-4V Auto.①	C6AF-AJ	Ford 4100-A	1.437	1.437	1.080	1.189	47F	45F	59F	57F	D	F	Plain	Green	—	TO
390-2V Std.	C6AF-C	Ford 2100-A	1.564	—	1.231	—	57F	—	55F	—	D	—	Plain	Green	—	TN
390-2V Std.①	C6AF-AH	Ford 2100-A	1.564	—	1.231	—	56F	—	54F	—	P	—	Plain	Green	—	TN
390-2V Auto.	C6MF-A	Ford 2100-A	1.687	—	1.330	—	60F	—	58F	—	D	—	Plain	Green	—	TN
390-2V Auto.①	C6MF-D	Ford 2100-A	1.687	—	1.330	—	60F	—	58F	—	P	—	Plain	Green	—	TN
390-4V Std.	C6AF-E	Ford 4100-A	1.437	1.437	1.080	1.189	49F	67F	47F	65F	D	F	Plain	Green	—	TN
390-4V Std.①	C6AF-AB	Ford 4100-A	1.437	1.437	1.080	1.189	48F	67F	46F	65F	D	F	Plain	Green	—	TN
390-4V Auto.	C6AF-F	Ford 4100-A	1.437	1.437	1.080	1.189	48F	67F	46F	65F	D	F	Plain	Green	—	TO
390-4V Auto.①	C6AF-AC	Ford 4100-A	1.437	1.437	1.080	1.189	47F	67F	45F	65F	D	F	Plain	Green	—	TO
410-4V Std.	C6AF-E	Ford 4100-A	1.437	1.437	1.080	1.189	49F	67F	47F	65F	D	F	Plain	Green	—	TN
410-4V Std.①	C6AF-AB	Ford 4100-A	1.437	1.437	1.080	1.189	48F	67F	46F	65F	D	F	Plain	Green	—	TN
410-4V Auto.	C6AF-F	Ford 4100-A	1.437	1.437	1.080	1.189	48F	67F	46F	65F	D	F	Plain	Green	—	TO
410-4V Auto.①	C6AF-AC	Ford 4100-A	1.437	14.37	1.080	1.189	47F	67F	45F	65F	D	F	Plain	Green	—	TO

① Thermactor Exhaust Emission Control System ② Police ③ Taxi ④ Spark Valve Closes @ 8.500 Inches of Mercury ⑤ Drilled Hole

CARBURETOR APPLICATION AND GENERAL INFORMATION—Continued

Engine and Trans.	Carb. Part Number (9510)	Carb. Model	Throttle Bore Dia.		Venturi Diameter		Main Metering Jet				Booster Venturi		Power Valve Color		Spark Valve Color	Choke Cover Spring
							Normal		Altitude							
			Pri.	Sec.	Pri.	Sec.	Pri.	Sec.	Pri.	Sec.	Pri.	Sec.	Normal	Altitude		
427-4V 4-Speed	C5AF-BC	Holley 4160-C	1.687	1.687	1.312	1.375	68	70⑤	—	—	—	—	85	—	—	—
427-4V 4-Speed	C5AF-BD	Holley 4160-C	1.437	1.437	1.312	1.375	68	70⑤	—	—	—	—	85	—	—	58L-1
428-4V Std.	C6AF-E	Ford 4100-A	1.437	1.437	1.080	1.189	49F	67F	47F	65F	D	F	Plain	Green	—	TN
428-4V Std.①	C6AF-AB	Ford 4100-A	1.437	1.437	1.080	1.189	48F	67F	46F	65F	D	F	Plain	Green	—	TN
428-4V Std.②	C6AF-AF	Ford 4100-A	1.562	1.562	1.125	1.187	52F	68F	50F	66F	DB	FA	Plain	Green	—	TO
428-4V Std.③	C6AF-J	Ford 4100-A	1.562	1.562	1.125	1.187	52F	68F	50F	66F	DB	FA	Plain	Green	—	TO
428-4V Auto.	C6AF-F	Ford 4100-A	1.437	1.437	1.080	1.189	48F	67F	46F	65F	D	F	Plain	Green	—	TO
428-4V Auto.①	C6AF-AC	Ford 4100-A	1.437	1.437	1.080	1.189	47F	67F	45F	65F	D	F	Plain	Green	—	TO
428-4V Auto.②	C6AF-K	Ford 4100-A	1.562	1.562	1.125	1.187	51F	68F	49F	66F	DB	FA	Plain	Green	—	TO
428-4V Auto.③	C6AF-AG	Ford 4100-A	1.562	1.562	1.125	1.187	51F	68F	49F	66F	DB	FA	Plain	Green	—	TO

① Thermactor Exhaust Emission Control System　② Police　③ Taxi　④ Spark Valve Closes @ 8.500 Inches of Mercury　⑤ Drilled Hole

CARBURETOR SETTINGS AND ADJUSTMENTS

Refer to Group 10, Part 10-1, Section 2 of the shop manual for the carburetor adjustment procedures

Carb. Part No. (9510)	Choke Spring Housing Setting	Choke Plate Clearance (Pull-Down)—0.036 Inch Gauge①	Accelerator Pump Setting		Dry Float Setting		Fuel Level (Wet)		Fast Idle RPM	Curb Idle RPM③④	Anti-Stall Dashpot (If So Equipped) Clearance at Curb Idle	Secondary Throttle Plate Setting
			Pump Lever	Throttle Lever	Pri.	Sec.	Pri.	Sec.				
C6AF-R	Index	0.180-0.220	0.210②	②	1.093	—	—	—	1500	500-525	—	—
C6AF-V	Index	0.180-0.220	0.210③	③	1.093	—	—	—	1500	625-650	—	—
C6AF-M	Index	0.180-0.220	0.210②	②	1.093	—	—	—	1500	500-525	—	—
C6AF-S	Index	0.180-0.220	0.210②	②	1.093	—	—	—	1600	500-525	3½ Turns⑥	—
C6AF-Y	Index	0.180-0.220	0.210②	②	1.093	—	—	—	1600	550-575	3½ Turns⑥	—
C6AF-N	Index	0.140-0.160	0.210③	③	1.093	—	—	—	1600	500-525	3½ Turns⑥	—
C6AF-A	Index	0.130-0.150	Inboard	4	0.491	—	0.875	—	1400	575-600	—	—
C6AF-Z	Index	0.130-0.150	Inboard	3	0.371	—	0.750	—	1400	610-635	—	—
C6AF-B	2 Rich	0.110-0.130	Inboard	3	0.491	—	0.875	—	1600	475-500	0.060-0.090	—
C6AF-AA	2 Rich	0.110-0.130	Inboard	3	0.371	—	0.750	—	1600	525-550	—	—
C6AF-L	Index	0.130-0.150	Inboard	3	0.531	0.531	0.910	0.910	1500	475-500	0.060-0.090	1 Turn⑤
C6AF-AJ	1 Rich	0.110-0.130	Inboard	3	0.491	0.621	0.880	1.000	1500	525-550	—	—
C6AF-C	Index	0.190-0.210	Inboard	2	0.491	—	0.880	—	1400⑤	475-500	—	—
C6AF-AH	Index	0.190-0.210	Inboard	3	0.431	—	0.810	—	1500	525-550	—	—
C6MF-A	Index	0.170-0.190	Inboard	3	0.491	—	0.880	—	1400⑤	475-500	0.060-0.090	—
C6MF-D	Index	0.170-0.190	Inboard	3	0.431	—	0.810	—	1500	525-550	—	—
C6AF-E	2 Rich	0.150-0.170	Inboard	3	0.531	0.681	0.910	1.060	1200⑤	575-600	—	1 Turn⑤
C6AF-AB	2 Rich	0.150-0.170	Inboard	3	0.491	0.621	0.880	1.000	1300	610-635	—	—
C6AF-F	1 Rich	0.130-0.150	Inboard	3	0.531	0.681	0.910	1.060	1300⑤	475-500	0.060-0.090	1 Turn⑤
C6AF-AC	1 Rich	0.130-0.150	Inboard	3	0.491	0.621	0.880	1.000	1500	525-550	—	—
C6AF-AF	Index	0.150-0.170	Inboard	3	0.531	0.681	0.910	1.060	1300	610-635	—	—

CARBURETOR SETTINGS AND ADJUSTMENTS—Continued

Carb. Part No. (9510)	Choke Spring Housing Setting	Choke Plate Clearance (Pull-Down)— 0.036 Inch Gauge①	Accelerator Pump Setting		Dry Float Setting		Fuel Level (Wet)		Fast Idle RPM	Curb Idle RPM③④	Anti-Stall Dashpot (If So Equipped) Clearance at Curb Idle	Secondary Throttle Plate Setting
			Pump Lever	Throttle Lever	Pri.	Sec.	Pri.	Sec.				
C6AF-J	Index	0.150-0.170	Inboard	3	0.531	0.681	0.910	1.060	1200⑨	575-600	—	1 Turn⑤
C6AF-H	1 Rich	0.130-0.150	Inboard	3	0.531	0.681	0.910	1.060	1300	475-500	0.060-0.090	1 Turn⑤
C6AF-K	1 Rich	0.130-0.150	Inboard	3	0.531	0.681	0.910	1.060	1300⑨	550-575	0.060-0.090	1 Turn⑤
C6AF-AG	1 Rich	0.130-0.150	Inboard	3	0.531	0.681	0.910	1.060	1500	525-550	0.060-0.090	—
C5AF-BC	—	—	No. 1	—	⑥	⑥	⑦	⑦	—	700-800	—	½ Turn⑤
C5AF-BD	3 Lean	—	No. 1	—	⑥	⑥	⑦	⑦	—	700-800	—	½ Turn⑤

① DECHOKE CLEARANCE—Choke Plate to Air Horn
Ford 1-V . . . . ¹⁄₁₆
Ford 2-V and 4-V . . . . ¹⁄₁₆

② ACCELERATOR PUMP ADJUSTMENTS—FORD 1-V
Accelerator Pump Lever Clearance—Inches
Pin in HI position, throttle plate seated
Accelerator Pump Lever Adjustment—Pin Placement
50° F. or below . . . . HI
Above 50° F. and/or above 5,000 ft. . . . . LO

③ IDLE FUEL MIXTURE ADJUSTMENT—Initial Setting
All Carburetors . . . . 1 to 1½ Turns Open

④ IDLE SPEED ADJUSTMENT—Initial Setting
All Carburetors . . . . : . . . . 1½ Turns Open

⑤ SECONDARY THROTTLE PLATE SETTING
Turns After Screw Contacts Lever.

⑥ DRY FLOAT SETTING
Top of Float Parallel With Top of Fuel Bowl (Bowl Inverted)

⑦ FUEL LEVEL SETTING—WET
Lower Edge of Sight Plug

⑧ ANTI-STALL DASHPOT CLEARANCE—FORD 1-V
Turns in After Initial Contact of Adjusting Screw With Diaphragm Assembly

⑨ For Cold Operation at 0° F. or lower increase the fast idle speed 200 rpm.

AIR CLEANERS

CAR MODEL	ENGINE APPLICATION	COLOR	TYPE
Ford	240 Six—Except Taxi	Red	Dry
Ford	240 Six—Taxi	Black	Oil Bath①
Ford	289 V-8	Gold Bronze	Dry
Ford	352 V-8	Gold Bronze	Dry
Ford	390 V-8	Gold	Dry
Mercury	390 V-8	Red	Dry
Mercury	410 V-8	Red	Dry
Ford	427 V-8	Aluminum	Dry
Mercury	427 V-8	Aluminum	Dry
Ford	428 V-8—Except Police	Gold	Dry
Mercury	428 V-8—Except Police	Red	Dry
Ford	428 V-8—Police	Vermillion	Dry
Mercury	428 V-8—Police	Red	Dry

① Refill Capacity . . . . 1 Pint
Oil Viscosity—Above +32° F. . . . . SAE 30
Oil Viscosity—Below +32° F. . . . . SAE 20

FUEL TANK CAPACITY

CAR
U. S. Measure . . . . 25 Gallons
Imperial Measure . . . . 21 Gallons

STATION WAGON
U. S. Measure . . . . 20 Gallons
Imperial Measure . . . . 16¾ Gallons

SPECIAL TOOLS

TOOL DESCRIPTION	TOOL NUMBER
Choke Plate Staking Pliers	9586
Power Valve Test Fixture	T57L-9904-A
Fuel Pump Overhaul Tools	T56L-9350-A
Float Bending Tool	9564-A
Choke Plate Clearance (Pull-Down) Piston Slot Wire Gauge	0.036
Wire Gauges—Specified Clearance Sizes	As Required
Fuel Line Tube Die	T62P-9A274-A

FUEL PUMP

FUEL PUMP STATIC PRESSURE—Psi @ 500 Engine rpm
240 Six and 289 V-8 . . . . 4.0-6.0
352, 390, 410, 427 and 428 V-8 . . . . 4.5-6.5

MINIMUM FUEL PUMP VOLUME—Flow @ 500 Engine rpm
240 Six . . . . 1 pint in 30 seconds
289, 352, 390, 410, 427 and 428 V-8 . . . . 1 pint in 20 seconds

MINIMUM INTAKE STATIC VACUUM—Inches of Mercury @ 500 Engine rpm
All Engines 6.0

ECCENTRIC TOTAL LIFT
240 Six 0.290-0.310
289, 352, 390, 410, 427 and 428 V-8 . . . . 0.690-0.710

COOLING SYSTEM

GROUP 11

PART 11-1   GENERAL COOLING SYSTEM SERVICE

This part covers general cooling system service. For cooling system component removal, disassembly, assembly, installation and repair procedures and specifications, refer to the pertinent part of this group.

Part 11-5 lists the identification features of radiators; such as, fins per inch, width, depth (thickness) and height. The radiators are listed in relation to the car, engine, cooling requirement, and cooling fan size.

The service part number denotes a replacement radiator.

To check the number of fins per inch, count the total number of fins across 4 inches and divide by the number of inches (4).

1 DIAGNOSIS AND TESTING

DIAGNOSIS

Engine overheating and slow engine warm-up are the two engine troubles most commonly attributed to the cooling system.

Loss of coolant, a thermostat stuck in the closed position, or accumulation of rust and scale in the system are the main causes of overheating. Coolant loss may be due to external leakage at the radiator, radiator pressure cap, water pump, hose connections, heater, or core plugs. Cool-

ant loss may also be caused by internal leakage due to a defective cylinder head gasket, improper tightening of the cylinder head bolts, or warped cylinder head or block gasket surfaces.

Internal leakage can be detected by operating the engine at fast idle and looking for the formation of bubbles in the radiator. Oil in the radiator may indicate leakage in the engine block or a leak in the automatic transmission oil cooler. Water formation on the oil level dipstick

could also be an indication of internal leakage.

Rust and scale that form in the engine water passages are carried into the radiator passages by the circulation of the coolant. This clogs the radiator passages and causes overheating. Rust can be detected by the appearance of the coolant. If the coolant has a rusty or muddy appearance, rust is present.

A defective thermostat that remains open will cause slow engine warm-up.

DIAGNOSIS GUIDE

ENGINE OVERHEATS	Exhaust control valve sticking (except 240 engine). Belt tension incorrect. Radiator fins obstructed. Thermostat stuck closed, or otherwise defective. Cooling system passages blocked	by rust, scale or other foreign matter. Water pump inoperative. Faulty fan drive clutch. Ignition initial timing incorrect. Distributor advance incorrect.
ENGINE FAILS TO REACH NORMAL OPERATING TEMPERATURE OR HAS WRONG INDICATED TEMPERATURE	Thermostat stuck open or of incorrect heat range. Temperature sending unit defective (causing gauge to indicate low engine temperature).	Temperature gauge defective (not indicating true engine temperature) or incorrectly installed. Incorrect temperature gauge indication.
LOSS OF COOLANT	Leaking radiator, radiator supply tank, or transmission oil cooler. Loose or damaged hose connections. Water pump leaking. Cylinder head gasket defective. Improper tightening of cylinder	head bolts. Cylinder block core plugs leaking. Cracked cylinder head or block, or warped cylinder head or block gasket surface. Radiator pressure cap defective or wrong type.

TESTING

COOLING SYSTEM PRESSURE TEST

It is recommended that a cooling system pressure test gauge be used to properly test the system for:

1. Blown or leaking cooling system sealing gaskets.
2. Internal or external coolant leakage.
3. Pressure cap malfunction.

Many types of pressure gauges are available for use. Therefore, it is recommended that the gauge manufacturer's instructions be followed when performing the test. **Never exceed the rated pressure indicated on the pressure cap when performing the pressure test.**

THERMOSTAT TEST— THERMOSTAT INSTALLED

The thermostat can be tested without removing it from the engine, by using the Rotunda Thermostat Tester. The engine should be cool (below 115°F.) when starting to perform this test.

1. Loosen the radiator cap to release any pressure; then re-tighten it.
2. Remove the temperature sending unit from the engine. A small amount of coolant may run out of the threaded opening but it should stop almost immediately. **If it does not stop running out, the pressure cap may be defective and should be tested. Replace it if defective.**
3. Calibrate the Rotunda Thermostat Tester by pressing the control button to the ADJUST position.

While holding the control button in the ADJUST position, turn the adjusting knob until the indicator on the upper meter points to the SET position. Push the control switch to the ON position.

4. Screw the engine test probe into the threaded opening from which the temperature sending unit was removed (the dual fitting arrangement provides for use on any engine).
5. Attach the single connector from the Rotunda Thermostat Tester to the engine test probe and ground the tester by attaching the ground wire clip to any convenient place on the engine which will provide a good ground.
6. Remove the radiator cap, attach the double connector, and place the radiator test probe in the filler opening making certain that the probe is well immersed in the coolant.
7. Turn the heater temperature control to the OFF position, start the engine, and allow it to idle.
8. Watch the lower meter to read the warmup rate. The needle should move through the RED area into the GREEN (normal) area. This indicates that the thermostat is remaining closed allowing proper warmup. **If the needle remains in the RED area it means that the thermostat is stuck in the open position, is defective, and should be replaced.**
9. When the lower meter needle reaches the GREEN area, the upper meter needle will move toward the

opening temperature of the thermostat. When this (upper metering) needle reaches the approximate opening temperature of the thermostat, the lower meter needle should move back through the RED area. When this happens, you can, by observing the upper meter needle, know that the thermostat is functioning and know at what temperature it is opening.

THERMOSTAT TEST— THERMOSTAT REMOVED

It is good practice to test new thermostats before installing them in the engine.

Remove the thermostat and immerse it in boiling water. Replace the thermostat if it does not open more than ¼ inch.

If the problem being investigated is insufficient heat, the thermostat should be checked for leakage. This may be done by holding the thermostat up to a lighted background. Light leakage around the thermostat valve (thermostat at room temperature) is unacceptable and the thermostat should be replaced. It is possible, on some thermostats, that a slight leakage of light at one or two locations on the perimeter of the valve may be detected. This should be considered normal.

FAN DRIVE CLUTCH TEST

1. Run the engine at approximately 1000 rpm until normal operating temperature is reached. This process can be speeded up by block-

ing off the front of the radiator with cardboard. Regardless of temperatures, the unit must be operated for at least five minutes immediately before being tested.

2. Stop the engine and, using a cloth to protect the hand, immediately check the effort required to turn the fan. If considerable effort is required, it can be assumed that the

coupling is operating satisfactorily. If very little effort is required to turn the fan, it is an indication that the coupling is not operating properly, and it should be replaced.

2 MAINTENANCE

COOLANT

Correct coolant level is essential for maximum circulation and adequate cooling. In addition, for the cooling system to perform its function, it must receive proper care. This includes keeping the radiator fins clean and a periodic inspection of the cooling system for leakage.

Use care when removing the radiator cap to avoid injury from escaping steam or hot water.

In production, the cooling system is filled with a long-life coolant mixture which prevents corrosion, keeps the cooling system clean, provides anti-freeze protection to −35° F in winter and provides for summer operation at system temperature up to 250°F without boiling.

For the most effective cooling system operation, this mixture strength should be maintained all year around and in all climates.

All coolant added should be a 50-50 mixture of Rotunda permanent anti-freeze and water.

To avoid possible overheating in very hot weather, do not use mixtures with more than 50% anti-freeze except in areas where anti-freeze protection below −35° is required. In this case, refer to the coolant mixture chart on the Rotunda permanent

anti-freeze container.

A standard ethylene glycol hydrometer can be used to check the protection level of the long-life coolant.

Refer to Group 19 for the recommended cooling system drain interval.

DRAINING AND FILLING THE COOLING SYSTEM

To prevent loss of anti-freeze when draining the radiator, attach a hose on the radiator drain cock and drain the anti-freeze from the radiator into a clean container.

To drain the radiator, open the drain cock located at the bottom of the radiator. The cylinder block of the V-8 engines have a drain plug located on both sides of the block (Fig. 1). The six cylinder engine has one drain plug located at the left rear of the cylinder block.

To fill the cooling system, close the drain cocks or install the plugs in the block and close the radiator drain cock. Fill the system to one inch just below the filler neck. Disconnect the heater outlet hose at the water pump to bleed or release trapped air in the system. When the coolant begins to escape, connect the heater outlet hose. Operate the engine until normal operating temperature has been

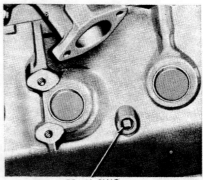

DRAIN PLUG   B1196-A

FIG. 1—Typical Cylinder Block Drain Plug

reached. **After the initial fill, the coolant level may drop approximately 1 quart after the engine has been operated about 20 minutes at 2000 rpm. This is due to the displacement of entrapped air.** Add more coolant to fill the radiator supply tank.

FAN DRIVE BELTS

If the fan drive belt(s) are noisy, check the tension of the belts to make certain they are within specifications. Also, check for misaligned pulleys. If the drive belts are worn or frayed, replace them following the procedures in Part 11-1, Section 3.

3 COMMON ADJUSTMENTS AND REPAIRS

ADJUSTMENTS

DRIVE BELTS

The fan drive belt(s) should be properly adjusted at all times. Loose drive belt(s) cause improper alternator, fan and water pump operation. A belt that is too tight places a severe strain on the water pump and the alternator bearings.

Properly tensioned drive belts minimize noise and also prolong service life of the belt. Therefore, it is recommended that a belt tension gauge be used to check and adjust the belt tension. **Any belt that has operated for a minimum of 10 minutes is con-**

sidered a used belt, and, when adjusted, it must be adjusted to the reset tension shown in the specifications.

Belt Tension

1. Install the belt tension tool on the drive belt (Fig. 2) and check the tension following the instructions of the tool manufacturer.

2. If adjustment is necessary, loosen the alternator mounting and adjusting arm bolts. Move the alternator toward or away from the engine until the correct tension is obtained. Remove the gauge. Tighten the alter-

nator adjusting arm and mounting bolts. Install the tension gauge and check the belt tension.

REPAIRS

FAN REPLACEMENT

6-Cylinder Engine

1. Loosen the fan belt. Remove the capscrews and lock washers retaining the fan to the water pump hub. Remove the fan.

2. Position the fan on the water pump hub. Install the lock washers and capscrews and torque the capscrews to specifications. Adjust the

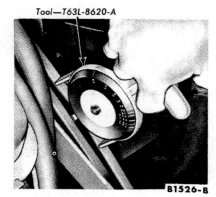
Tool—T63L-8620-A

B1526-B

FIG. 2—Checking Drive Belt Tension

fan belt tension to specifications.

V-8 Engines. On a car with an air conditioner or extra-cooling radiator, a fan drive clutch may be used (see Specifications). Cars without air conditioning utilize a pulley-to-fan spacer.

1. Remove the radiator upper support and fan guard. Loosen the fan belt. Remove the capscrews and lock washers retaining the fan and spacer (or drive clutch) to the water pump hub. Remove the fan and spacer (or drive clutch).

2. If equipped with a fan drive clutch, remove the retaining capscrews and lock washers and separate the fan from the drive coupling. Position the replacement fan on the drive clutch and install the lock washers and capscrews. Torque the capscrews evenly and alternately to specifications.

3. Position the fan and spacer (or drive clutch) on the water pump hub and install the lock washers and capscrews. Torque the capscrews evenly and alternately to specifications. Adjust the fan belt tension to specifications. Then, check the fan drive clutch flange-to-water pump hub for proper mating. Install the radiator upper support and fan guard.

FAN DRIVE BELT REPLACEMENT

6-Cylinder and 289 V-8 Engine

If equipped with power steering, air conditioning and/or Thermactor exhaust emission control system it will be necessary to loosen and remove the drive belts before the fan drive belt can be removed.

1. Loosen the alternator mounting and the adjusting arm bolts. Move the alternator toward the engine. Remove the belt from the alternator

and crankshaft pulleys, and lift it over the fan.

2. Place the belt over the fan and insert it in the water pump and alternator pulley grooves. Adjust the belt tension to specifications.

If equipped with power steering, air conditioning, and/or Thermactor exhaust emission control system, install the belts and adjust the tension to specifications.

352, 390, 410, 427, and 428 V-8

1. On a car with power steering, loosen the power steering pump at the mounting bracket and remove the drive belt.

On a car with an air conditioner, remove the compressor drive belt.

2. Loosen the alternator mounting and adjusting arm bolts. Move the alternator toward the engine. Remove the belt(s) from the alternator and crankshaft pulleys, and lift them over the fan.

3. Place the belt(s) over the fan. Insert the belt(s) in the water pump pulley, crankshaft pulley and alternator pulley grooves. Adjust the belt tension to specifications.

4. On a car with an air conditioner, install and adjust the compressor drive belt to specifications.

5. On a car with power steering, install the power steering pump drive belt and tighten the pump at the mounting bracket. Adjust the drive belt tension to specifications.

RADIATOR HOSE REPLACEMENT

Radiator hoses should be replaced whenever they become cracked, rotted or have a tendency to collapse.

1. Drain the radiator; then loosen the clamps at each end of the hose to be removed. Slide the hose off the radiator connection and the radiator supply tank connection (upper hose) or the water pump connection (lower hose).

2. Position the clamps at least ⅛" from each end of the hose. Slide the hose on the connections. **Make sure the clamps are beyond the bead and placed in the center of the clamping surface of the connections.** Tighten the clamps. Fill the radiator with coolant. Operate the engine for several minutes, then check the hoses and connections for leaks. Check for proper coolant level after the engine has reached normal operating temperature.

THERMOSTAT REPLACEMENT

A thermostat is mounted in a recess in the coolant outlet passage of the intake manifold. When the thermostat is closed, coolant flows to the water pump through a bypass passage at the front of the intake manifold.

The high-temperature thermostat used in production is for use with water or permanent-type anti-freeze. A low-temperature thermostat is available for use with non-permanent-type anti-freeze or water. For operating temperatures, refer to specifications.

Check the thermostat before installing it, following the procedure under "Thermostat Test," Part 11-1, Section 1.

Do not attempt to repair the thermostat. It should be replaced if it is not operating properly.

6-Cylinder and V-8 Engines except Mercury 390 V-8

1. Drain the radiator so that the coolant level is below the thermostat.

2. Remove the coolant outlet housing retaining bolts. Pull the elbow away from the cylinder head sufficiently to provide access to the thermostat. Remove the thermostat and gasket.

3. Clean the coolant outlet housing and cylinder head gasket surfaces. Coat a new gasket with water-resistant sealer. Position the gasket on the cylinder head opening. **The gasket must be positioned on the cylinder head or the intake manifold, before the thermostat is installed.**

4. Install the thermostat in the cylinder head opening, or the intake manifold opening, with the copper pellet or element toward the engine and the thermostat flange positioned in the recess. **If the thermostat is not properly installed it will cause a retarded flow of coolant.**

5. Position the coolant outlet housing against the cylinder head, or the intake manifold. Install and torque the remaining bolts to specifications.

6. Fill the cooling system. Check for leaks and proper coolant level after the engine has reached normal operating temperatures.

Mercury Engines

To remove or install the thermostat, refer to "Radiator Supply Tank Removal or Installation."

Check the thermostat before installing it, following the procedure under Thermostat Test, Part 11-1, Section 1.

4   CLEANING AND INSPECTION

CLEANING COOLING SYSTEM

To remove rust, sludge and other foreign material from the cooling system, use Rotunda Cooling System Cleanser. Removal of such material restores cooling efficiency and avoids overheating.

In severe cases where cleaning solvents will not properly clean the cooling system for efficient operation, it will be necessary to use the pressure flushing method.

Various types of flushing equipment are available.

Always remove the thermostat prior to pressure flushing.

A pulsating or reversed direction of flushing water flow will loosen sediment more quickly than a steady flow in the normal direction of coolant flow.

WATER PUMP

1. Clean the gasket mounting surfaces of the water pump and cylinder block.

2. Clean and inspect the seal seating surface of the water pump.

3. Clean the pump housing and inspect it for cracks, sand holes, improper machining and damaged surfaces. If the water pump housing is damaged beyond repair, replace the complete water pump.

PART 11-2 WATER PUMP

1 DESCRIPTION AND OPERATION

A centrifugal-type water pump is mounted on the front of the cylinder block. On the 289 V-8, the water pump is mounted on the cylinder front cover. The water pump inlet port is connected to the radiator lower header tank to draw coolant from the radiator when the thermostat is open. On the V-8 engines, a bypass port on the water pump is connected to the coolant outlet housing to permit coolant circulation within the engine when the thermo-stat is closed, bypassing the radiator. On the 6-cylinder engine, the water pump bypass passage is aligned with a bypass passage in the cylinder block for coolant circulation in the engine when the thermostat is closed.

A vane-type plastic impeller supplies coolant through centrifugal action to the water pump outlet port on a 6-cylinder engine. On the V-8 engines, the water pump has two outlet ports, one for each cylinder bank, to provide uniform coolant circulation in both banks of the engine.

The water pumps have a sealed bearing integral with the water pump shaft. The bearing requires no lubrication. A bleed hole in the water pump housing allows water that may leak past the seal to be thrown out by the slinger. **This is not a lubrication hole.**

The cooling fan hub is pressed a specified distance onto the water pump shaft.

2 REMOVAL AND INSTALLATION

240 SIX-CYLINDER ENGINE

REMOVAL

1. Drain the cooling system.
On a car with air conditioning, remove the compressor drive belt.

2. Disconnect the radiator lower hose and heater hose at the water pump. Remove the fan, spacer, pulley and drive belt.

3. Remove the four bolts retaining the water pump to the block; then remove the pump and the gasket.

INSTALLATION

Before a water pump is re-installed, check it for damage. If it is damaged and requires repair, replace it with a new pump or install a rebuilt pump obtained from a Ford Authorized Reconditioner.

1. If a new water pump is to be installed, remove the heater hose fitting from the old pump and install it on the new pump. Clean all gasket material from the mounting surfaces of the cylinder block and water pump.

2. Position a new gasket, coated on both sides with sealer, on the cylinder block. Install the pump body on the block. Torque the retaining bolts to specifications.
On a car with air conditioning, install the compressor drive belt. Adjust the belt tension to specifications.

3. Install the pulley, spacer and fan. Install the drive belt and adjust the belt tension. Connect the radiator hose and heater hose. Fill and bleed the cooling system. Operate the engine and check for leaks.

289 V-8 ENGINE
REMOVAL

1. Drain the cooling system.
On a car with power steering, remove the power steering drive belt. Remove the power steering pump.
On a car with an air conditioner, remove the compressor drive belt.

2. Disconnect the radiator lower hose and heater hose at the water pump. Remove the drive belt, fan, fan spacer or fan drive clutch and pulley.

3. Remove the bolts retaining the pump to the cylinder front cover. Remove the pump and gasket. Discard the gasket.

INSTALLATION

Before a water pump is re-installed, check it for damage. If it is damaged and requires repair, replace it with a new pump or install a rebuilt pump obtained from a Ford-Authorized Reconditioner.

1. Remove all gasket material from the mounting surfaces of the cylinder front cover and water pump.

2. Position a new gasket, coated on both sides with sealer, on the cylinder front cover; then install the pump.

3. Install the retaining bolts and torque them to specifications.
On a car with power steering, install the power steering drive belt and adjust the tension to specifications.
On a car with an air conditioner, install the compressor drive belt and adjust the tension to specifications.

4. Install the pulley, spacer or fan drive clutch and fan. Install and ad-

just the drive belt to the specified belt tension. Connect the radiator hose and heater hose.

5. Fill and bleed the cooling system. Operate the engine until normal operating temperatures have been reached and check for leaks.

352, 390, 410, 427 AND 428 V-8

REMOVAL

1. Drain the cooling system.

On a car with power steering, remove the power steering drive belt. Remove the bolts and nuts retaining the power steering pump mounting bracket. Remove the power steering pump and mounting bracket as an assembly, and set to one side.

On a car with an air conditioner, remove the compressor drive belt.

2. Disconnect the radiator lower hose and heater hose at the water pump. Remove the radiator upper support and fan guard. Remove the fan belt(s), fan, fan spacer or fan drive clutch and pulley.

3. Remove the four bolts retaining the pump to the block. Remove the pump and gaskets.

INSTALLATION

Before a water pump is re-installed, check it for damage. If it is damaged and requires repair, replace it with a new pump or install a rebuilt pump obtained from a Ford-Authorized Reconditioner.

1. If a new water pump is to be installed, remove the heater hose fitting from the old pump and install it on the new pump. Remove all gasket material from the mounting surfaces of the cylinder front cover or block and water pump.

2. Position new gasket, coated on both sides with sealer, on the cylinder block; then install the pump.

3. Install the retaining bolts and torque them to specifications.

On a car with power steering, install the power steering pump and bracket assembly, and adjust the power steering drive belt.

On a car with an air conditioner, install and adjust the compressor drive belt.

4. Install the pulley, spacer or fan drive clutch and fan. Torque the capscrews evenly and alternately to specification. Then, check the fan drive clutch flange-to-water pump hub for proper mating. Install the belt(s) and adjust the belt tension. Connect the radiator hose and heater hose. Install the radiator upper support and fan guard.

5. Fill and bleed the cooling system. Operate the engine until normal operating temperatures have been reached and check for leaks.

PART 11-3 RADIATOR AND SUPPLY TANK

1 DESCRIPTION AND OPERATION

RADIATOR

Standard and extra-cooling radiators are available with all engines.

6-CYLINDER AND V-8 ENGINES —EXCEPT MERCURY 390 V-8

The radiators are of the tube and corrugated-fin-core type with the tubes arranged for vertical flow of the coolant. Two header tanks, one on the top and one on the bottom of the radiator, provide uniform distribution of the coolant to the tubes. The radiator outlet port (lower header tank) is connected to the water pump inlet port. The radiator inlet port (upper header tank) is connected to the coolant outlet housing of the engine, thereby permitting coolant circulation through the radiator when the thermostat is open. The radiator bottom header tank on automatic transmission cars contains a heat exchanger for cooling the transmission oil.

MERCURY

The radiator is the tube and corrugated-fin-core type with the tubes arranged horizontally for cross-flow of the coolant. Two header tanks, one on each side of the radiator, provide uniform distribution of the coolant to the cross-flow tubes. The header tank, or chamber, on the left side of the radiator contains a heat ex- changer for cooling the transmission fluid. The radiator outlet port (lower left side) is connected to the water pump inlet port.

SUPPLY TANK—MERCURY

A separate radiator supply tank is connected to the radiator inlet port to serve as an expansion chamber and supply reservoir. The inlet port of the supply tank is connected to the intake manifold coolant passage at the thermostat, thereby permitting coolant circulation through the supply tank and radiator when the thermostat is open.

2 REMOVAL AND INSTALLATION

RADIATOR

REMOVAL

1. Drain the cooling system. Disconnect the radiator upper and lower hoses from the radiator.

On a car with an automatic transmission, disconnect the automatic transmission fluid cooler inlet and outlet lines from the radiator.

2. Remove the radiator upper support retaining bolts and remove the upper support. Remove the radiator.

On a car equipped with an air conditioner, remove the bolts retaining the radiator shroud to the radiator. Remove the radiator upper retaining bolts. Remove the upper support retaining bolts. Remove the radiator. Lift the radiator shroud from the engine compartment.

INSTALLATION

1. If a new radiator is to be installed, remove the drain cock from the old radiator and install it on the new radiator.

On a car equipped with an automatic transmission, transfer the fluid cooler line fittings to the new radiator, using oil resistant sealer.

2. Position the radiator assembly and install (but do not tighten on a car with an automatic transmission) the radiator upper support and bolts.

On a car with an automatic transmission, connect the automatic transmission fluid cooler lines; then tighten the radiator upper support bolts.

On a car with an air conditioner, position the radiator assembly and install the upper support and bolts. Tighten the support bolts and install the shroud to the radiator.

3. Connect the radiator upper and lower hoses. Close the drain cock. Fill and bleed the cooling system.

4. Operate the engine and check for leaks at the hose connections and the automatic transmission fluid cooler lines. Check the automatic transmission fluid level.

RADIATOR SUPPLY TANK

REMOVAL

1. Drain the cooling system so that the coolant level is below the radiator supply tank. Disconnect the radiator upper hose from the radiator supply tank (Fig. 3).

2. Remove the supply tank retaining screws. Remove the supply tank. Remove the thermostat and gasket from the supply tank.

INSTALLATION

1. Remove all the gasket material from the mounting surfaces of the supply tank and intake manifold. Coat a new supply tank gasket with sealer, then position the gasket on the

FIG. 3—Radiator Supply Tank— Typical

intake manifold opening. **The supply tank gasket must be positioned on the manifold before the thermostat is installed.**

2. Install the thermostat in the manifold opening with the copper pellet or element toward the engine. **If the thermostat is improperly installed, it will cause the engine to overheat.**

3. Position the supply tank against the manifold; then install and torque the retaining screws to specifications.

If a new tank is installed, remove the overflow hose from the old tank and install it on the new tank.

4. Connect the radiator upper hose. Fill and bleed the cooling system. Check for leaks and proper coolant level after the engine has reached normal operating temperature.

PART 11-4 FAN DRIVE CLUTCH

1 DESCRIPTION AND OPERATION

The fan drive clutch (Fig. 4) is a fluid coupling containing silicone oil. Fan speed is regulated by the torque-carrying capacity of the silicone oil. The more silicone oil in the coupling the greater the fan speed, and the less silicone oil the slower the fan speed.

FIG. 4—Typical Fan Drive Clutch Installation

Two types of fan drive clutches are available. On one (Fig. 5) a bi-metallic strip and control piston on the front of the fluid coupling regulate the amount of silicone oil entering the coupling. The bi-metallic strip bows

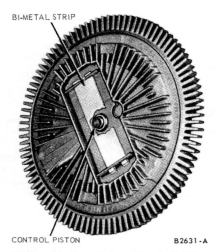

FIG. 5—Fan Drive Clutch With Flat Bi-Metal Spring

outward with an increase in surrounding temperature and allows a piston to move outward. The piston opens a valve regulating the flow of silicone oil into the coupling from a reserve chamber. The silicone oil is returned to the reserve chamber through a bleed hole when the valve is closed.

On the other type of fan drive clutch (Fig. 6) a heat-sensitive, bi-

FIG. 6—Fan Drive Clutch With Flat Coil Bi-Metal Spring

metal spring connected to an opening plate brings about a similar result. Both units cause the fan speed to increase with a rise in temperature and to decrease as the temperature goes down.

In some cases a Flex-Fan is used instead of a Fan Drive Clutch. Flexible blades vary the volume of air being drawn through the radiator, automatically increasing the pitch at low engine speeds.

2 REMOVAL AND INSTALLATION

REMOVAL

1. Remove the radiator upper support and fan guard.
2. Loosen the fan belt. Remove the capscrews retaining the fan drive clutch to water pump hub (Fig. 4). Remove the fan drive clutch and fan as an assembly.

3. Remove the retaining capscrews and separate the fan from the drive clutch.

INSTALLATION

1. Position the fan on the drive clutch. Install the capscrews.
2. Position the fan drive clutch and fan assembly to the water pump

hub (Fig. 4). Install and torque the retaining capscrews evenly and alternately to specifications. Then, check the fan drive clutch flange-to-water pump hub for proper mating. Adjust the fan belt tension to specifications.

3. Install radiator upper support.

PART 11-5   SPECIFICATIONS

DRIVE BELT TENSION

ALL BELTS	LBS.
New	110-140
Used (any belt operated over 10 minutes)	80-110

COOLING SYSTEM CAPACITY

Cooling System	APPROXIMATE CAPACITY① (QUARTS) (U.S. x 0.8325 = IMP.)	
	U.S. Measure	Imperial Measure
Standard		
240	13.0	11.00
289	15.0	12.49
All other Engines	20.5	17.07

① Includes heater. If deleted, subtract one quart.

RADIATOR

Pressure Cap—All Engines	12-15 psi

THERMOSTATS

LOW TEMPERATURE	
Opens °F (289 and 352)	155°-162°
Fully Open	182°
Opens °F 240, 390 and 427	157°-164°
Fully Open	184°-186°
HIGH TEMPERATURE	
Opens °F All Engines	188°-195°
Fully Open	210°-212°

WATER PUMP

WATER PUMP DRIVE ARRANGEMENT
Water pump, fan and alternator belt driven from crankshaft damper.

WATER PUMP PULLEY TO ENGINE RATIO
Standard Cooling and Air-Conditioning-Equipped
- 240 .... 1.08:1
- 289 .... 1.04:1
  - (With Thermactor) 1.13:1
- 352, 390, 410, 427 and 428 .... 0.94:1
- 428 (Police Interceptor) .... .97:1

WATER PUMP ASSEMBLY DIMENSIONS
Front Face of Pulley Hub to Pump Housing Face
- 240 .... 3.60
- 289 .... 5.426
- 352, 390, 410, 427 and 428 .... 7.569

Impeller to Housing Cover Mounting Surface Clearance
- 240 .... 0.10-0.50
- 289 .... 0.030-0.050
- 352, 390, 410, 427 and 428 .... 0.070-0.080

TORQUE VALUES

NOTE: All specifications are given in ft-lbs unless otherwise noted.

Water pump to Cylinder Block (or Cylinder Front Cover)
- 289 12-15
- Other Engines 20-25

Water Outlet Housing
- All Engines 12-15

Fan and Spacer to Pulley Hub
- All Engines 12-18

Fan to Fan Clutch (with a/c)
- All Engines 10-15

Fan Shroud Assembly to Radiator
- Where Applicable 5-7

Radiator Shroud Lower Half to Upper Half
- Where Applicable .... 14-20 in-lbs

Upper Support or Fan Guard to Radiator
- All Engines 5-7

Radiator Brace Rod to Radiator Support
- Where Applicable .... 20-30 in-lbs

Radiator to Engine Hose Clamps
- 240, 289, 352, 390 and 427 .... 1.0-2.5

Transmission Oil Cooler Tubes to Oil Cooler
- All Engines 9-12

Radiator Inlet and Outlet Hose Clamps
- All Engines 1.0-2.5

Fan Drive Clutch to Water Pump Hub 12-18

SPECIAL SERVICE TOOLS

Description	Ford Tool No.	Former Tool No.
Belt Tension Gauge	T63L-8620-A	8620-A

RADIATOR AND COOLING FAN IDENTIFICATION

Radiator dimensions are given for the core only; do not measure mounting flanges or header tanks.

CAR, ENGINE AND COOLING	RADIATOR IDENTIFICATION Dimensions-Inches				TRANS-MISSION		THERMACTOR EQUIPPED		RADIATOR SERVICE PART NUMBER	FANS—DIAMETER X BLADE WIDTH AND NO. BLADES (4)	
	Depth	Height	Width	Fins/In.	Std.	Auto.	No	Yes		W/O Thermactor	W/Thermactor
FORD											
240 Six											
Std. Cool.	1.27	17.38	20.24	10	X	X	X	X	C6AZ-B	18.25 x 1.38 (4)	18.25 x 1.38 (4)
Std. Cool.	1.27	17.38	20.24	11		X	X		C5AZ-C	18.25 x 1.38 (4)	—
Std. Cool.	1.27	17.38	20.24	11		X		X	C6AZ-B	—	18.25 x 1.38 (4)
Ext. Cool.	1.27	17.38	20.24	13		X	X		C5AZ-C	18.25 x 1.38 (4)	—
Ext. Cool.	1.27	17.38	20.24	13	X	X	X	X	C6AZ-B	18.25 x 1.38 (4)	18.25 x 1.38 (4)
Air Cond.	1.27	17.38	23.24	13	X	X	X	X	C5AZ-F	18.25 x 1.75 (7)	18.25 x 1.75 (7)
Air Cond.	1.27	17.38	23.24	13	X	X	X	X	C6AZ-C	18.25 x 1.75 (7)	18.25 x 1.75 (7)
289 V-8											
Std. Cool.	1.27	17.38	20.24	10		X	X	X	C5AZ-B	17.50 x 2.00 (4)	17.00 x 1.75 (4)
Std. Cool.	1.27	17.38	20.24	10	X		X	X	C5AZ-C	17.50 x 2.00 (4)	17.00 x 1.75 (4)
Ext. Cool.	1.27	17.38	20.24	13	X	X	X	X	C5AZ-C	17.50 x 2.00 (4)	17.00 x 1.75 (4)
Air Cond.	1.27	17.38	23.24	10	X	X	X		C5AZ-F	17.00 x 2.00 (5)	
Air Cond.	1.27	17.38	23.24	12	X	X		X	C5AZ-F	—	②18.00 x 2.25 (5)
352 V-8											
Std. Cool.	1.95	17.38	23.24	8		X	X	X	C5AZ-B	18.50 x 2.00 (4)	18.50 x 2.00 (4)
Ext. Cool.	1.95	17.38	23.24	11		X	X	X	C5AZ-B	18.50 x 2.00 (4)	18.50 x 2.00 (4)
Air Cond.	1.95	17.38	23.24	12		X	X	X	C5AZ-B	①18.50 x 2.00 (4) ②19.00 x 2.25 (7)	①17.50 x 2.25 (5) ②19.50 x 2.50 (7)
390 V-8											
Std. Cool.	1.95	17.38	23.24	8	X	X	X	X	C5AZ-B	18.50 x 2.00 (4)	18.50 x 2.00 (4)
Ext. Cool.	1.95	17.38	23.24	11	X	X	X	X	C5AZ-B	18.50 x 2.00 (4)	18.50 x 2.00 (4)
Air Cond.	1.95	17.38	23.24	12	X		X	X	C5AZ-B	①18.50 x 2.00 (4) ②19.00 x 2.25 (7)	①17.50 x 2.25 (5) ②19.50 x 2.50 (7)
Air Cond.	1.95	17.38	23.24	12		X	X	X	C5AZ-F	①18.50 x 2.00 (4) ②19.00 x 2.25 (7)	①17.50 x 2.25 (5) ②19.50 x 2.50 (7)
427 V-8											
Std. Cool.	1.95	17.38	23.24	11	X		X		C5AZ-B	18.00 x 2.00 (7)	
428 V-8											
Std. Cool.	1.95	17.38	23.24	11	X	X	X	X	C5AZ-B	18.50 x 2.00 (4)	18.50 x 2.00 (4)
Air Cond.	1.95	17.38	23.24	12	X	X	X	X	C5AZ-B	①18.50 x 2.00 (4) ②19.00 x 2.25 (7)	①17.50 x 2.25 (5) ②19.50 x 2.50 (7)
MERCURY											
390 V-8											
Std. Cool.	1.95	17.24	22.5	8	X	X	X	X	C5MY-E	18.50 x 2.00 (4)	18.50 x 2.00 (4)
Ext. Cool.	1.95	17.24	22.5	8	X	X	X	X	C5MY-E	18.50 x 2.00 (4)	18.50 x 2.00 (4)
Air Cond.	1.95	17.24	22.5	8	X	X	X	X	C5MY-E	②19.00 x 2.25 (7)	②19.50 x 2.50 (7)
410 V-8											
Std. Cool.	1.95	17.24	22.5	8	X	X	X	X	C5MY-E	18.50 x 2.00 (4)	18.50 x 2.00 (4)
Ext. Cool.	1.95	17.24	22.5	8	X	X	X	X	C5MY-E	18.50 x 2.00 (4)	18.50 x 2.00 (4)
Air Cond.	1.95	17.24	22.5	8	X	X	X	X	C5MY-E	②19.00 x 2.25 (7)	②19.50 s 2.50 (7)
427 V-8											
Std. Cool.	1.95	17.24	22.5	8	X		X	X	C5MY-E		
428 V-8											
Std. Cool.	1.95	17.24	22.5	8	X	X	X	X	C5MY-E	18.50 x 2.00 (4)	18.50 x 2.00 (4)
Ext. Cool.	1.95	17.24	22.5	8	X	X	X	X	C5MY-E	18.50 x 2.00 (4)	18.50 s 2.00 (4)
Air Cond.	1.95	17.24	22.5	8	X	X	X	X	C5MY-E	②19.00 x 2.25 (7)	②19.50 x 2.50 (7)

① Economy   ② Selectaire

EXHAUST SYSTEM

GROUP 12

PART 12-1   GENERAL EXHAUST SYSTEM SERVICE

This part covers general exhaust system diagnosis, tests, adjustment and repair procedures. In addition, the cleaning and inspection procedures are covered.

For exhaust system component removal, disassembly, assembly, installation, major repair procedures and specifications, refer to the pertinent part of this group.

Always refer to the Master Parts Catalog for parts usage and interchangeability before replacing a component part of the exhaust system.

1 DIAGNOSIS AND TESTING

DIAGNOSIS

EXHAUST SYSTEM

Exhaust system performance complaints, such as excessive back pressure or a sticking exhaust control valve, are usually noticeable by their effect on engine performances.

An exhaust control valve that is stuck in the open position will result in poor engine performance during initial warm-up, because the heat passing through the intake manifold heat riser is insufficient for proper fuel atomization.

On V-8 engines, if the valve is stuck in the closed position, the intake manifold will be supplied with excessive heat after the initial warm-up period. This will cause poor acceleration, a lack of power, and poor

high speed performance.

However, other defective, malfunctioning, or improperly-adjusted components have similar effects on engine performance and are characterized by the same symptom or complaint. Thus, for diagnosis of exhaust system problems that affect engine performance, refer to Part 8-1, Section 1.

External leaks in the exhaust system are often accompanied by noises or greyish-white smoke emitted from under the car. Small leaks are usually inaudible and not visible. A visual inspection of the exhaust system usually will show the location of a leak. Look for holes, ruptured

joints and eroded areas in the muffler(s), resonator(s), inlet pipe(s) and outlet pipe(s). Examine joints and connections for greyish white deposits that would be caused by exhaust gas leakage.

A misaligned exhaust system is usually indicated by vibration, grounding, rattling, or binding of the components. Often the associated noise is hard to distinguish from other chassis noises. Look for broken or loose clamps and brackets and replace or tighten as necessary. The exhaust system components should be inspected for proper alignment, and the necessary adjustments should be made to maintain the installation clearances shown in Part 12-3. If this does not eliminate the noise (symptom or complaint), examine the chasis for possible location of the problem. Be sure the noise is isolated to and caused by the exhaust system before replacing any of the components.

DIAGNOSIS GUIDE

THERMACTOR EXHAUST EMISSION CONTROL SYSTEM

A preliminary "Diagnosis Guide" is included below as an aid in trouble shooting the Thermactor exhaust emission control system.

Prior to performing any extensive diagnosis of the Thermactor system, it must be determined that the engine as a unit is functioning properly. Disconnect the anti-backfire valve vacuum sensing and air supply lines at the intake manifold connections. Plug the manifold connections to preclude leakage. Normal engine diagnosis procedures (Part 8-1) can then be performed.

EXCESSIVE BACKFIRE IN EXHAUST SYSTEM	Anti-backfire valve vacuum line collapsed, plugged, disconnected or leaking. Defective or malfunctioning anti-	backfire valve resulting in insufficient air delivery to the intake manifold or air delivery not timed to engine requirement.
EXCESSIVE HESITATION ON ACCELERATION AFTER SUDDEN THROTTLE PLATE CLOSURE (ABOVE 20 MPH)	Intake vacuum leak at anti-backfire valve vacuum line or air outlet line (to intake manifold).	Defective or malfunctioning anti-backfire valve.
AIR SUPPLY HOSE(S) BAKED OR BURNED	Defective check valve on air supply manifold(s).	
NOISY AIR PUMP DRIVE BELT	Drive belt improperly adjusted. Seized or failing air pump.	Misaligned or defective pulleys.
ROUGH ENGINE IDLE	Improper carburetor adjustment—idle speed, idle fuel mixture, automatic choke, etc., (Group 10). Improper initial ignition timing. Intake vacuum leak at the anti-	backfire valve vacuum line or air inlet hose. Anti-backfire valve defective or stuck open.
ENGINE SURGES AT ALL SPEEDS	Anti-backfire valve defective or stuck open. Improper carburetor adjustment—	idle speed, idle fuel mixture, automatic choke, etc., (Group 10).

TESTING

EXHAUST CONTROL VALVE

Check the thermostatic spring of the valve to make sure it is hooked on the stop pin. To check the exhaust control valve on the car, make sure the spring holds the valve closed. Actuate the counterweight by hand to make sure it moves freely through approximately 90° of rotation without binding.

The closed and open positions of the exhaust control valve are shown in Fig. 1 (240 Six engine) and Fig. 2 (390, 410, 427 and 428 V-8 en-gines).

The valve is closed when the engine is cold. However, a properly operating valve will open when very light finger pressure is applied to the counterweight. Rapidly accelerate the engine to make sure the valve momentarily opens. The valve is designed to open when the engine is at normal operating temperature and is operated at high rpm.

THERMACTOR EXHAUST EMISSION CONTROL SYSTEM

The following procedures are recommended for checking and/or verifying that the various components of the Thermactor exhaust emission control system are operating properly. **The engine and all components must be at normal operating temperatures when the tests are performed.**

Prior to performing any extensive diagnosis of the Thermactor system, it must be determined that the engine as a unit is functioning properly. Disconnect the anti-backfire valve vacuum sensing and air supply lines at the intake manifold connections. Plug the manifold connections to preclude leakage. Normal engine

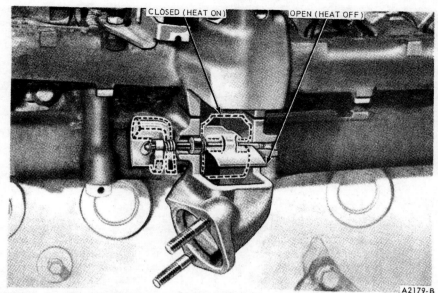

CLOSED (HEAT ON) OPEN (HEAT OFF)

A2179-B

FIG. 1—240 Six Exhaust Control Valve

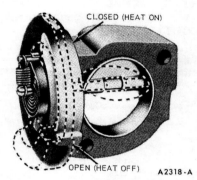

CLOSED (HEAT ON)

OPEN (HEAT OFF)   A2318-A

FIG. 2—V-8 Engine Exhaust Control Valve

diagnosis procedures (Part 8-1) can then be performed.

Check Valve Test

This test can be performed at the same time as the Air Pump Test.

1. Operate the engine until it reaches normal operating temperature.

2. Inspect all hoses and hose connections for obvious leaks and correct as necessary before checking the check valve operation.

3. Disconnect the air supply hose(s) at the check valve on the air manifold(s).

4. Visually inspect the position of the valve plate inside the valve body. It should be lightly positioned against the valve seat—away from the air manifold.

5. Insert a probe into the hose connection on the check valve and depress the valve plate. It should freely return to the original posi-

tion, against the valve seat, when released.

If equipped with two air manifold and check valve assemblies, check both valves for free operation.

6. Leave the hose(s) disconnected and start the engine. Slowly increase the engine speed to 1500 rpm and watch for exhaust gas leakage at the check valve(s). **There should not be any exhaust leakage.** The valve may flutter or vibrate at idle speeds, but this is normal due to the exhaust pulsations in the manifold.

7. If the check valve(s) does not meet the recommended conditions (steps 4, 5 and 6), replace it.

Anti-Backfire Valve Test

1. Operate the engine until it reaches normal operating temperature.

2. Inspect all hoses and hose connections for obvious leaks, and correct as necessary before checking the anti-backfire valve operation.

3. Disconnect the pressure air hose (from air pump) at the anti-back-fire valve. Insert a suitable plug in the hose and fasten it securely with a hose clamp **to prevent air pressure from blowing out the plug.**

4. Connect a vacuum gauge to the air pressure (hose) connection on the anti-backfire valve.

5. Operate the engine at normal idle speed with the transmission in neutral.

6. The vacuum gauge should indicate zero vacuum. If a vacuum is indicated, the anti-backfire valve is not

seating properly and it should be replaced.

7. Open and close the throttle rapidly. The vacuum gauge indicator should move up scale rapidly and slowly settle back to zero. Repeat several times. If the gauge fails to respond, the valve is not functioning properly and should be replaced.

Air Supply Pump Test

1. Assemble a test gauge adapter as shown in Fig. 3, and install a fuel pump test gauge on the adapter. **The test gauge used must be accurate and readable in ¼ psi increments.**

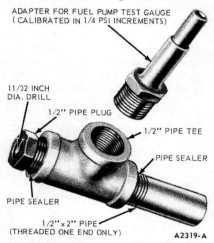

ADAPTER FOR FUEL PUMP TEST GAUGE (CALIBRATED IN 1/4 PSI INCREMENTS)

11/32 INCH DIA. DRILL

1/2" PIPE PLUG

1/2" PIPE TEE

PIPE SEALER

PIPE SEALER

1/2" x 2" PIPE (THREADED ONE END ONLY)   A2319-A

FIG. 3—Air Supply Pump Test Gauge Adapter

2. Operate the engine until it reaches normal operating temperature.

3. Inspect all hoses and hose connections for leaks and correct as necessary before checking the air supply pump.

4. Check the air pump belt tension and adjust to specifications.

5. Disconnect the air supply hose(s) at the air manifold check valve(s). If there are two check valves, close off one hose by inserting a suitable plug in the end of the hose. **Use a hose clamp and secure the plug so it will not blow out.**

6. Insert the open pipe end of the test gauge adapter in the other air supply hose. **Clamp the hose securely to the adapter to prevent it from blowing out.**

Position the adapter and test gauge so that the air blast emitted through the drilled pipe plug will be harmlessly dissipated.

7. Install a tachometer on the en-

gine. Start the engine and slowly increase the engine speed to 1500 rpm. Observe the pressure produced at the test gauge. The air pressure should be one (1) psi or more.

8. If the air pressure does not

meet or surpass the above pressures, disconnect and plug the air supply hose to the anti-backfire valve. Clamp the plug in place, and repeat the pressure test.

If the air pump pressure still

doesn't meet the minimum requirement, install a new air pump filter element and repeat the pump test. Replace the air pump filter element and/or air pump as determined by the result of this test.

2 COMMON ADJUSTMENTS AND REPAIRS

ADJUSTMENTS

The exhaust system must be free of leaks, binds, grounding and excessive vibration.

Exhaust system vibration, grounding or binds are usually caused by: loose, broken or improperly aligned clamps, or brackets, or improperly connected pipes. Any of the aforementioned conditions may cause changes to clearances of the exhaust system components. If any of these conditions exist, the exhaust system components must be checked, adjusted or replaced to make certain the specified clearances (refer to the illustrations in Part 12-2) are maintained.

EXHAUST SYSTEM ALIGNMENT

Refer to the pertinent illustration in Part 12-2 for the clearance specifications and location of components. Perform the following procedure to adjust the exhaust system components:

1. Loosen the pipe connection clamps and the pipe support bracket clamp(s). Loosen the inlet pipe to exhaust manifold retaining nuts.

2. Torque the exhaust manifold to

inlet pipe retaining nuts evenly and alternately to specification to insure uniform pressure on the seal and inlet pipe flange.

3. Work from the front of the car toward the rear and progressively adjust the exhaust system components and clamps at the various pipe connections to relieve binds and improper pipe connections. **Be sure the inlet and outlet pipes and mufflers are aligned so that all clearances are within the limits shown on the illustrations in Part 12-2.** Then torque the clamps to specification.

4. Check the exhaust system for leaks.

REPAIRS

EXHAUST CONTROL VALVE MAINTENANCE

Refer to Group 19 for the recommended maintenance mileage interval.

The exhaust control valve, if the car is so equipped, should be periodically checked to make certain it is operating properly. A valve that is stuck in the open position will result in poor engine performance during initial warm-up, because the heat passing through the intake mani-

fold heat riser is insufficient for proper fuel atomization.

On V-8 engines, if the valve is stuck in the closed position, the intake manifold will be supplied with excessive heat after the initial warm-up period. This will cause poor acceleration, a lack of power, and will cause poor high speed performance in general.

Lubricate the valve with FoMoCo Exhaust Control Valve Solvent (COAA-19A501-A.)

MUFFLERS, INLET PIPES AND OUTLET PIPES

Brackets, clamps and insulators should be replaced if they are defective or become badly corroded. Do not attempt repair of these parts.

THERMACTOR EXHAUST EMISSION CONTROL SYSTEM

Air Nozzles

For cleaning and inspection of the air nozzles, refer to Section 3.

Air Pump Air Cleaner

Replace the air cleaner filter element at the recommended maintenance interval. Refer to the maintenance chart in Group 19.

3 CLEANING AND INSPECTION

EXHAUST SYSTEM

INSPECTION

Inspect the inlet pipe(s), outlet pipe(s), resonator(s) and muffler(s) for cracked joints, broken welds and corrosion damage (holes) that would result in a leaking exhaust system. Inspect the clamps, brackets and insulators for cracks and stripped or badly corroded bolt threads. When pipe clamp(s) are loosened and/or removed to replace a pipe, muffler or resonator, replace the clamp(s), if there is reasonable doubt that its service life is limited.

Check the exhaust control valve. Be sure the thermostatic spring is hooked on the stop pin. Move the

counterweight by hand to make sure it moves freely throughout its normal travel range (approximately 90° of rotation).

THERMACTOR EXHAUST EMISSION CONTROL SYSTEM CLEANING AND INSPECTION

Anti-Backfire Valve

Do not attempt to clean the anti-backfire valve.

Air Pump Air Cleaner

When replacing the air cleaner element, clean the air cleaner body with a low-volatility, petroleum-base solvent, and wipe it dry with a clean, lint-free cloth.

Hoses, Lines and Air Manifolds

Normally, the air hoses, vacuum line and air manifolds should be cleaned only during major engine overhaul. If malfunctions or restrictions occur in the system, these components may require cleaning. Use a low-volatility, petroleum-base solvent and a suitable stiff bristle brush. Dry the cleaned parts, except the check valve, with compressed air. **Do not blow compressed air through the check valve in either direction. Shake it dry.**

Air Nozzles

With the air nozzles removed, clean the nozzle tips with a wire brush. Clean the nozzle air hole with a 5/16-inch-diameter stiff wire brush. Inspect the air nozzles for eroded, burned or damaged tips that would restrict the normal air flow. Inspect the connections for stripped or damaged threads and damaged tube nut seats.

Air supply pump. The air supply pump is protected against the entrance of foreign material by the air cleaner. Thus, it should require cleaning only when it is being overhauled.

Do not immerse the rotor and housing assembly in solvent as the bearing is permanently lubricated.

Clean the vane and bearing assemblies and rotor ring and rear bearing assembly in a clean petroleum-base solvent. **Do not use compressed air to dry the bearings. Shake the bearings to remove excess solvent, and let them drain dry.**

Inspect the bearings for discoloration, uneven rotation or looseness, and replace as required.

Wipe the rotor, housing and cover assembly with a cloth dampened in cleaning solvent. Wipe the parts dry with a clean cloth. Use compressed air to blow all carbon dust out of

the rotor and housing assembly.

Clean the carbon shoes and shoe springs by wiping with a clean, dry cloth.

Inspect the vanes and carbon shoes for grooves or scores that would permit air leakage. Place each vane on the shaft (cover assembly) and check it for loose or worn bearings. Inspect the shaft for grooves and worn areas that might cause early wear on the vane and bearing assemblies.

Replace all worn, defective or broken parts.

PART 12-2

EXHAUST PIPES, MUFFLERS AND CONTROL VALVE

1 DESCRIPTION

The exhaust systems for the various car models are listed in Table 1, and are shown in Figs. 1 thru 5.

The single exhaust system on cars with a 240 Six engine (Fig. 1) consists of a muffler inlet pipe, muffler and muffler outlet pipe.

The single exhaust system on all Ford Models with 289-2V or 390-2V engine and Mercury Models with a 390-2V or 410-4V engine (Figs. 2 and 3) consists of a Y-type muffler inlet pipe, muffler and muffler outlet pipe.

The dual exhaust system (Fig. 4) for cars with a 352, 390-4V, 427 or 428 V-8 engine consists of a welded one-piece H-type inlet pipe assembly, muffler and muffler outlet pipe or welded muffler and outlet pipe assembly.

The exhaust control valve for cars with a V-8 engine (except 289 and 352 V-8) is located between the right exhaust manifold and the attached muffler inlet pipe.

On the 240 Six engine equipped cars, the exhaust gas control valve

is integral with the exhaust manifold.

The location and type of exhaust system gaskets, retaining clamps, and loop-type support brackets are shown in the respective exhaust system illustrations (Figs. 1 thru 4). The loop-type support bracket insulators eliminate tension on the hangers due to thermal expansion of the system.

On cars equipped with Thermactor exhaust emission control system, **special clamps and gaskets may be used.** Refer to the Master Parts Catalog for proper parts usage.

TABLE 1—Exhaust System Application

Car Line	Engine			Type System			Resonator	Exhaust Control Valve
	Cyl.	C.I.D.	Carb.	Sedan	Convertible	Station Wagon		
Ford	6	240	1V	Single	Single	Single	No	Yes
	8	289	2V	Single	Single	Single	No	No
	8	352	4V	Dual	Dual	Single	No	No
	8	390	2V	Single	Single	Single	No	Yes
	8	390	4V	Dual	Dual	Single	No	Yes
	8	427	8V	Dual	Dual	—	No	Yes
	8	428	4V	Dual	Dual	Single	No	Yes
Mercury	8	390	2V	Single	Single	Single	No	Yes
	8	410	4V	Single	Single	Single	No	Yes
	8	428	4V	Dual	Dual	Single	No	Yes

2 REMOVAL AND INSTALLATION

The replacement procedures given apply to all car models and to right and left assemblies on dual and single exhaust systems unless otherwise noted. Typical exhaust systems for the various car models are shown in Figs. 1 through 4.

EXHAUST CONTROL VALVE REPLACEMENT—240 SIX

Normally, the exhaust control valve

does not require replacement unless it becomes inoperative due to excessive corrosion or damage.

The exhaust control valve on this engine is integral with the exhaust manifold. If the exhaust control valve requires replacement, refer to Part 8-2, Section 2 for the manifold replacement procedures, and refer to Part 8-1, Section 2 for the control valve replacement procedures.

EXHAUST CONTROL VALVE ALL V-8 ENGINES EXCEPT 289 AND 352 V-8

SINGLE EXHAUST SYSTEMS

Removal

1. Remove the retaining bolts or clamp securing the muffler to the support bracket and insulator assembly (Figs. 2 and 3).

2. Temporarily support the muffler and inlet pipe with soft wire.

3. Remove the muffler inlet pipe clamp from the body No. 3 crossmember.

4. Remove the nuts securing the inlet pipe to both exhaust manifolds.

5. Pull the inlet pipe rearward and remove the exhaust control valve and all mounting gaskets. Discard the gaskets.

6. Clean the exhaust control valve and the flanges of the exhaust manifolds and inlet pipe. Replace all defective or damaged parts.

Installation

1. Place new gaskets on both sides of the exhaust control valve and position it over the studs of the right exhaust manifold (Figs. 2 and 3). Place a new gasket on the left exhaust manifold flange.

2. Install the muffler inlet pipe on the exhaust manifolds. Install the retaining nuts and torque them to specifications.

3. Install the muffler inlet pipe clamp on the body No. 3 crossmember.

4. Attach the muffler to the support bracket and insulator assembly. Tighten the bolts or clamp to specifications.

5. Remove the temporary support wire.

6. Adjust the exhaust system components to conform to the clearance specifications (Figs. 2 and 3). Properly position the respective clamps and brackets. Working from the front of the exhaust system toward the rear, progressively torque the retaining bolts, nuts and clamps to specifications.

7. Check the exhaust system for leaks.

DUAL EXHAUST SYSTEMS

Removal

1. Remove the retaining bolts or clamps securing the left and right mufflers to the support brackets (Fig. 4).

2. Loosen the clamps on the outlet pipe support brackets.

3. Temporarily support the exhaust system in position with soft wire.

4. Remove the nuts securing the inlet H-pipe to both exhaust manifolds. Pull the inlet H-pipe rearward and remove the exhaust control valve and all mounting gaskets. Discard the gaskets. Temporarily support the exhaust system in position with soft wire.

5. Clean the exhaust control valve and the flanges of the inlet pipe and the exhaust manifolds. Replace all worn or damaged parts.

Installation

1. Place new gaskets on both sides of the exhaust control valve and position it over the studs of the right exhaust manifold.

Position a new gasket on the left exhaust manifold.

2. Install the muffler inlet H-pipe on the exhaust manifolds; then install the retaining nuts and torque them to specification.

3. Install the mufflers on the rear support brackets and torque the retaining bolts or clamps to specification.

4. Remove the temporary support wires.

5. Adjust the exhaust system components to conform to the clearance specifications (Fig. 4). Properly position the respective clamps and brackets. Working from the front of the exhaust system toward the rear, progressively torque the retaining bolts, nuts and clamps to specifications.

6. Check the exhaust system for leaks.

OUTLET PIPES

REMOVAL

1. Remove the bolts or clamp attaching the intermediate support bracket to the muffler or outlet pipe.

If the car is equipped with a welded exhaust system that has not previously had the outlet pipe replaced, cut the outlet pipe with a hacksaw at a point $4^{7}/_{16}$ inches up from the center line of the muffler outlet pipe (See Figs. 1 through 4).

2. Remove the clamp attaching the outlet pipe to the rear support bracket and remove the outlet pipe.

3. Replace any damaged parts.

INSTALLATION

1. Install the outlet pipe onto the muffler and position the muffler to outlet pipe clamp.

2. Postition the outlet pipe to the rear support bracket. **Be sure the slot in the support bracket mates with the stop on the outlet pipe.** Install the retaining clamp and tighten it snug, but not tight.

3. Install the bolts or clamp attaching the intermediate support bracket to the muffler or outlet pipe. Tighten the bolts or clamp snug, but

not tight.

4. Adjust the exhaust system and torque all bolts and clamps to specifications.

5. Start the engine and check the system for leaks.

MUFFLERS

REMOVAL

1. Remove the outlet pipe by following the steps listed under Outlet Pipe Removal.

2. Loosen the clamp at the muffler to inlet pipe connection (Figs. 1 through 4) and slide the clamp forward. Temporarily support the inlet pipe with soft wire. Remove the bolts or clamp securing the muffler or outlet pipe to the intermediate support bracket.

3. Separate the muffler from the inlet pipe and remove the muffler or muffler and outlet pipe assembly.

4. Replace any damaged parts.

INSTALLATION

1. Install the muffler or muffler and outlet pipe assembly to the inlet pipe and properly position the clamp (Figs. 1 through 4). The clamp must be positioned so it is not contacting the locating tab or an exhaust leak will result. Tighten the clamp snug, but not tight. Install the muffler or outlet pipe to intermediate support bracket bolts or clamp finger-tight. Remove the soft wire used to temporarily support the inlet pipe.

2. Install the outlet pipe by following the steps under Outlet Pipe Installation. **Do not torque the retaining clamps, bolts and nuts until the exhaust system has been aligned.**

3. Adjust the exhaust system components to conform to the clearance specifications shown in Figs. 1 through 4. Properly position and torque all retaining clamps and bolts to specifications.

4. Start the engine and check the exhaust system for leaks.

INLET PIPE

REMOVAL

1. Loosen the inlet pipe clamp(s) at the muffler(s) (Figs. 1 through 4).

2. Loosen the clamp attaching the intermediate support bracket assembly to the outlet pipe or remove the bolts attaching the muffler(s) to muffler support bracket(s). Temporarily support the muffler(s) with soft wire.

3. Loosen the clamp(s) attaching the outlet pipe(s) to rear support bracket(s).

4. Slide the muffler(s) off the inlet pipe(s).

5. Remove the inlet pipe clamp(s) from the body No. 3 crossmember.

6. Remove the retaining nuts securing the inlet pipe(s) to the exhaust manifold(s) and remove the inlet pipe(s). Remove the exhaust control valve from the right exhaust manifold, if so equipped.

7. Clean the gasket surfaces of the exhaust manifold(s), inlet pipe(s) and exhaust control valve, if so equipped.

8. Discard the gaskets and replace any damaged parts.

INSTALLATION

1. On all cars except those V-8 engines with an exhaust control valve, install a new gasket(s) on the inlet pipe flange(s) (Figs. 1 through 4). Place a new gasket on each side of the exhaust control valve (if so equipped) and install it on the right exhaust manifold. Install a new gasket on the left exhaust manifold (if required).

2. Install the inlet pipe(s) on the exhaust mainfold(s) and loosely install the retaining nuts on the studs of the manifold(s).

3. Install the inlet pipe clamp(s) on the body No. 3 crossmember.

4. Place the retaining clamp(s) on the inlet pipes). Connect the muffler(s) onto the inlet pipe(s) and position the clamp(s) so it is not contacting the locating tab or an exhaust leak will result.

5. Loosely install the bolts or clamp(s) securing the muffler(s) or outlet pipe to intermediate support bracket(s).

6. Adjust the exhaust system components to conform to the clearance specifications shown in Figs. 1 through 4. Properly position the respective clamps and brackets. Working from the front of the exhaust system toward the rear, progressively torque the retaining bolts, nuts and clamps to specifications. Remove the soft wire used to temporarily support the muffler(s).

7. Start the engine and check the exhaust system for leaks.

A2314-A

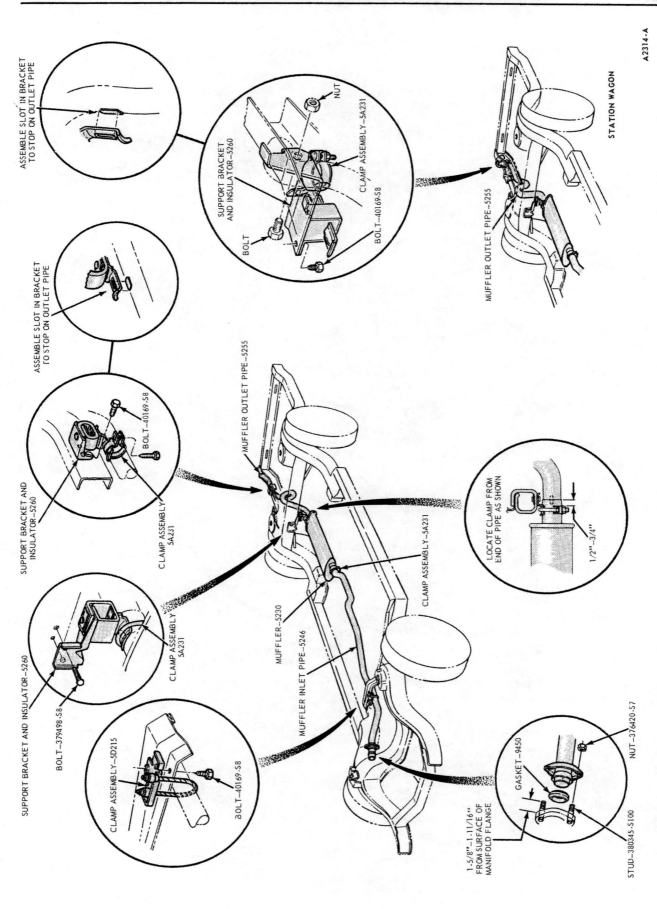

ASSEMBLE SLOT IN BRACKET
TO STOP ON OUTLET PIPE

ASSEMBLE SLOT IN BRACKET
TO STOP ON OUTLET PIPE

SUPPORT BRACKET
AND INSULATOR–5260

BOLT

NUT

CLAMP ASSEMBLY–5A231

BOLT–40169-S8

STATION WAGON

MUFFLER OUTLET PIPE–5255

SUPPORT BRACKET AND
INSULATOR–5260

BOLT–40169-S8

CLAMP ASSEMBLY
5A231

MUFFLER OUTLET PIPE–5255

CLAMP ASSEMBLY
5A231

CLAMP ASSEMBLY–5A231

MUFFLER–5230

MUFFLER INLET PIPE–5246

LOCATE CLAMP FROM
END OF PIPE AS SHOWN

1/2"–3/4"

SUPPORT BRACKET AND INSULATOR–5260

BOLT–379498-S8

CLAMP ASSEMBLY–5D215

BOLT–40169-S8

1-5/8"–1.11/16"
FROM SURFACE OF
MANIFOLD FLANGE

GASKET–9450

NUT–376420-S7

STUD–380345-S100

FIG. 1—240 Six—Single Exhaust System

A2315-A

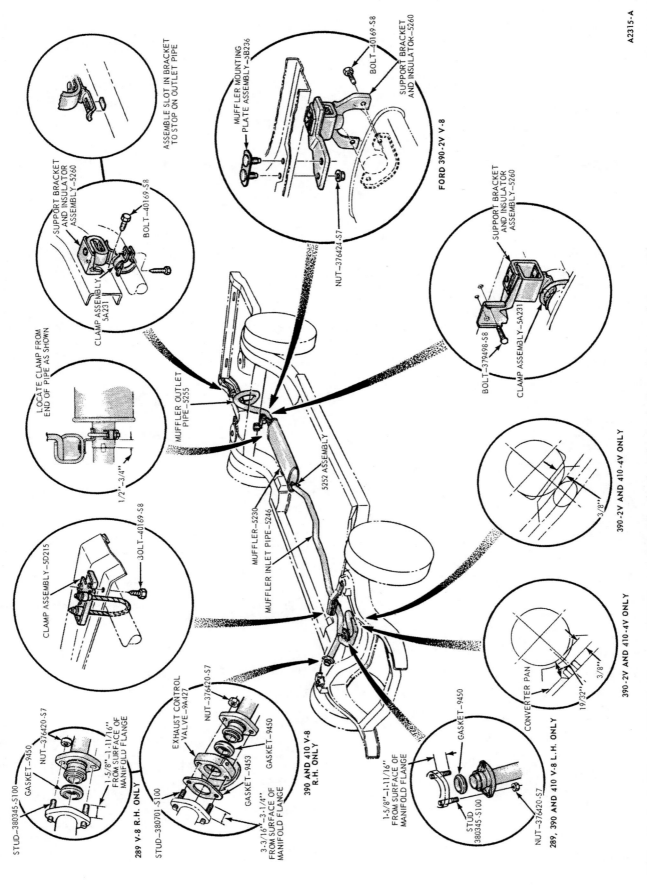

ASSEMBLE SLOT IN BRACKET
TO STOP ON OUTLET PIPE

BOLT—40169-S8

MUFFLER MOUNTING
PLATE ASSEMBLY—5B236

SUPPORT BRACKET
AND INSULATOR—5260

FORD 390-2V V-8

NUT—376424-S7

SUPPORT BRACKET
AND INSULATOR
ASSEMBLY—5260

BOLT—40169-S8

CLAMP ASSEMBLY—5A231

SUPPORT BRACKET
AND INSULATOR
ASSEMBLY—5260

BOLT—379498-S8

CLAMP ASSEMBLY—5A231

LOCATE CLAMP FROM
END OF PIPE AS SHOWN

MUFFLER OUTLET
PIPE—5255

1/2"—3/4"

3/8"

390-2V AND 410-4V ONLY

5252 ASSEMBLY

MUFFLER—5230

MUFFLER INLET PIPE—5246

CLAMP ASSEMBLY—5D215

BOLT—40169-S8

3/8"

19/32"

390-2V AND 410-4V ONLY

CONVERTER PAN

390 AND 410 V-8
R.H. ONLY

GASKET—9450
NUT—376420-S7

STUD—380345-S100

1-5/8"—1-11/16"
FROM SURFACE OF
MANIFOLD FLANGE

289 V-8 R.H. ONLY

EXHAUST CONTROL
VALVE—9A427

NUT—376420-S7

GASKET—9450

GASKET—9453

GASKET—9450

STUD—380701-S100

3-3/16"—3-1/4"
FROM SURFACE OF
MANIFOLD FLANGE

GASKET—9450

STUD
380345-S100

1-5/8"—1-11/16"
FROM SURFACE OF
MANIFOLD FLANGE

NUT—376420-S7

289, 390 AND 410 V-8 L.H. ONLY

FIG. 2—Ford 289 and 390-2V; Mercury 390-2V and 410-4V— Single Exhaust System, Sedan and Convertible

A2316-A

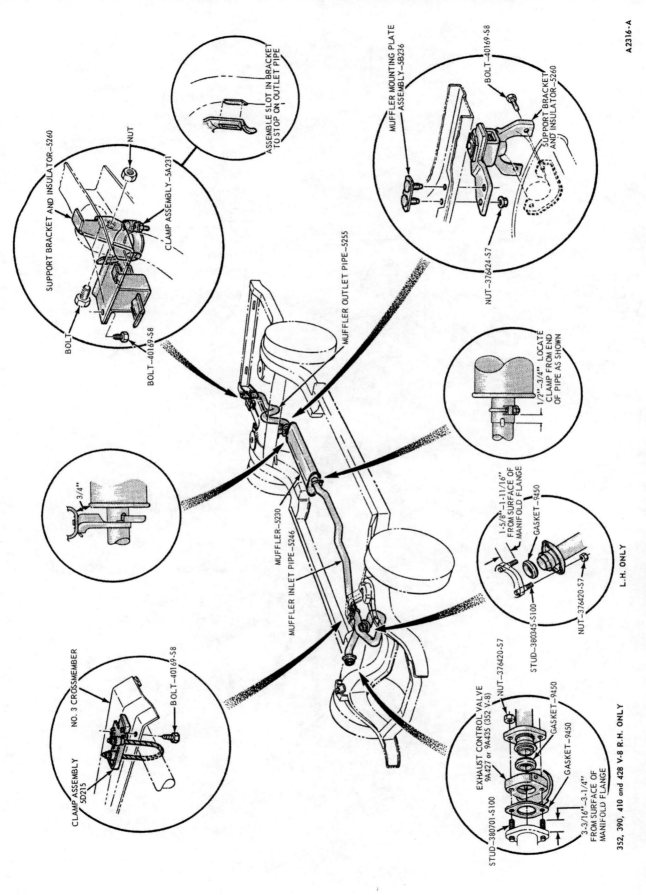

SUPPORT BRACKET AND INSULATOR—5260

NUT

CLAMP ASSEMBLY—5A231

BOLT

BOLT—40169-S8

ASSEMBLE SLOT IN BRACKET TO STOP ON OUTLET PIPE

MUFFLER MOUNTING PLATE ASSEMBLY—5B236

BOLT—40169-S8

SUPPORT BRACKET AND INSULATOR—5260

NUT—376424-S7

MUFFLER OUTLET PIPE—5255

3/4"

1/2"—3/4" LOCATE CLAMP FROM END OF PIPE AS SHOWN

MUFFLER—5230

MUFFLER INLET PIPE—5246

1-5/8"—1-1/16" FROM SURFACE OF MANIFOLD FLANGE

GASKET—9450

GASKET—9450

STUD-380345-S100

NUT—376420-S7

L.H. ONLY

CLAMP ASSEMBLY 5D215

NO. 3 CROSSMEMBER

BOLT—40169-S8

STUD-380701-S100

EXHAUST CONTROL VALVE 9A427 or 9A435 (352 V-8)

NUT—376420-S7

GASKET—9450

GASKET—9450

GASKET—9450

3-3/16"—3-1/4" FROM SURFACE OF MANIFOLD FLANGE

352, 390, 410 and 428 V-8 R.H. ONLY

FIG. 3—Ford and Mercury With V-8 Engines—Single Exhaust System, Station Wagon

A2317-A

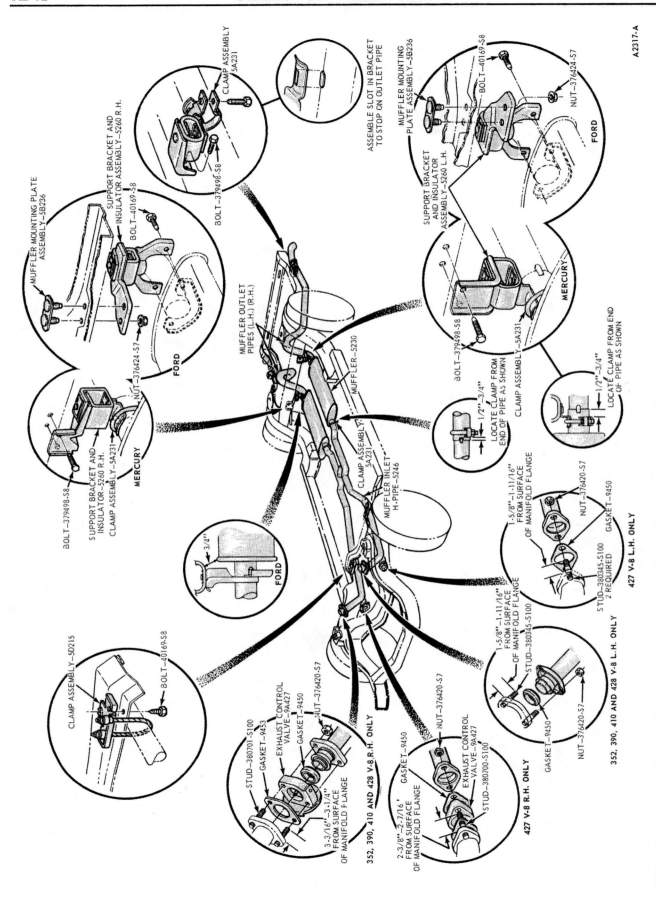

FIG. 4—Ford and Mercury With V-8 Engines (Except 289, 390-2V and 410-4V)—Dual Exhaust System, Sedans and Convertibles

PART 12-3
THERMACTOR EXHAUST EMISSION CONTROL SYSTEM

1 DESCRIPTION AND OPERATION

The Thermactor exhaust emission control system is designed to reduce the hydrocarbon and carbon monoxide content of gasoline engine exhaust gases. By controlling the amount of contaminants emitted through the exhaust system to an acceptable minimum, air pollution is reduced.

Control of exhaust-emitted gases by the Thermactor system is achieved by burning the hydrocarbon and carbon monoxide concentrations in the exhaust ports of the cylinder head(s). To accomplish this burning of the contaminants, air under pressure is injected into the exhaust ports near each exhaust valve. The oxygen in the air plus the heat of the exhaust gases in each exhaust outlet port induces combustion during the exhaust stroke of the piston. The burned gases then flow out the exhaust manifold into the exhaust system.

The Thermactor system consists of: an air supply pump; an air manifold for each cylinder head; an anti-backfire valve; an air cleaner; a check valve on each air manifold; an air nozzle for the exhaust port of each engine cylinder; and the connecting air supply hoses and vacuum sensing line. On some engines, the ignition distributor and carburetor are specially calibrated.

A schematic of the Thermactor system is shown in Fig. 1, and the anti-backfire valve is shown in Fig. 2. Installation drawings for each engine series are included (Figs. 3, 4 and 5).

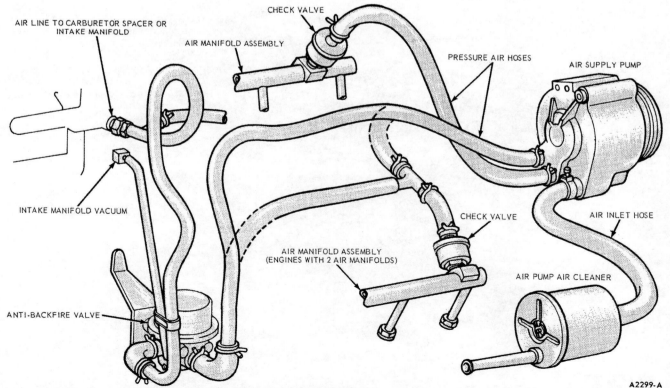

FIG. 1—Thermactor Exhaust Emission Control System Schematic

A2299-A

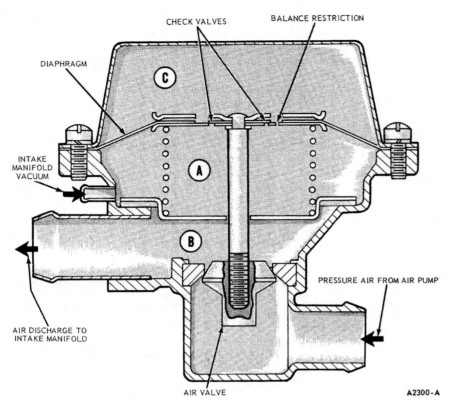

FIG. 2—Anti-Backfire Valve Schematic

Air under pressure from the pump flows through a hose(s) to the air manifold(s) that distributes the air to the air nozzle in each exhaust port. A check valve is incorporated in the inlet air side of the air manifold. The check valve prevents a backflow of exhaust gases into the air pump during operating periods when the exhaust back pressure exceeds the air pump delivery pressure.

The anti-backfire valve operates only during periods of sudden decreases in intake manifold pressure. The valve is necessary, because, immediately following the closing of the throttle after a period of acceleration, a rich fuel mixture is present in the intake manifold. The rich mixture is due to the momentary continuation of fuel flow from the carburetor, or from the boiling of residual fuel in the manifold as a result of the sudden reduction in manifold pressure.

This overly-rich mixture does not burn completely during the normal combustion period, and it is discharged through the engine into the exhaust system. The secondary air being injected into the exhaust ports reduces the rich mixture to a combustible mixture, causing an explosion or backfire in the exhaust system. To prevent this condition and provide a combustible mixture, the anti-backfire valve allows additional fresh air to enter the induction system, whenever intake manifold pressure decreases.

The anti-backfire valve is controlled and operated by intake manifold vacuum as follows:

Assume the vehicle is accelerating

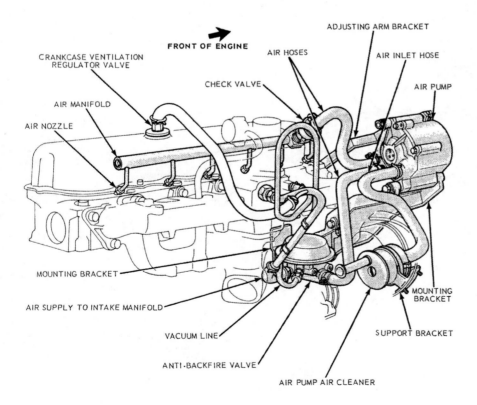

FIG. 3—240 Six Engine With Thermactor Exhaust Emission System

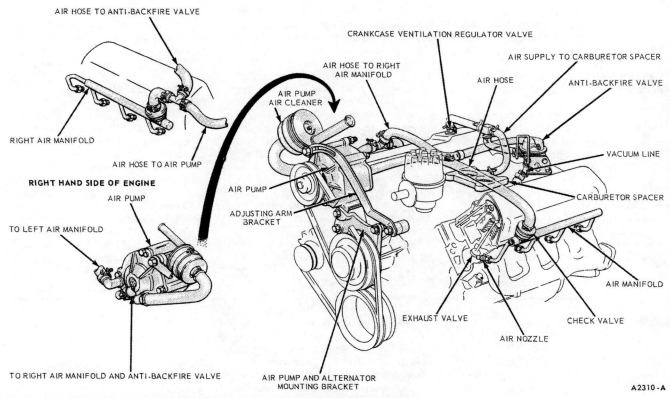

FIG. 4—289 V-8 Engine With Thermactor Exhaust Emission System

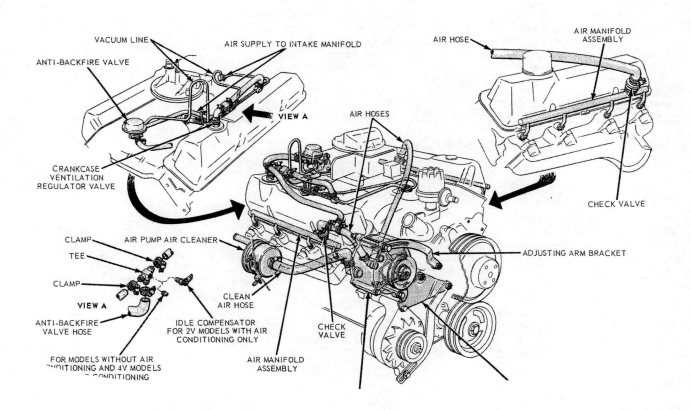

FIG. 5—Thermactor Exhaust Emission System—Typical for 352, 390, 410, 427 and 428 V-8

at a rate to produce 3 inches of Mercury (in. Hg) vacuum in the intake manifold. Then, there must also be 3 in. Hg manifold vacuum in chambers A and B (Fig. 2) since they are both connected to the intake manifold. The vacuum in chamber C is also 3 in. Hg, because it connects to chamber A through a balance restriction in the diaphragm assembly.

Since the vacuum on both sides of the diaphragm assembly is the same, the forces cancel and the diaphragm spring holds the air valve on its seat. Thus, with a steady intake manifold vacuum, the anti-backfire valve remains inoperative (or closed).

When the carburetor throttle plate is closed, or during vehicle deceleration, manifold vacuum rises to about 23 in. Hg. Now, there is 23 in. Hg vacuum in chambers A and B, but

for the moment still 3 in. Hg in chamber C. There is more vacuum on the A chamber side of the diaphragm assembly than on the C chamber side; therefore, the diaphragm moves toward the air valve, compressing the diaphragm spring and lifting the air valve from its seat to an open position. This allows the air pump to force air through the open valve into chamber B and into the intake manifold as a gulp of air.

However, since the balance restriction connects chambers A and C, the vacuum pressures are soon equalized. When this occurs, the spring returns the diaphragm and air valve to its original closed position.

Suppose that during pumping of air into the intake manifold, it is required to accelerate the vehicle. At the moment of acceleration the

valve must close fast, or an unsatisfactory acceleration results, due to the excess air being pumped into the intake manifold. For this reason, a quick return feature has been designed into the valve.

Assume that the gulp is about ½ completed and the vacuum in chamber C has reached an intermediate value between 23 in. and 3 in. Hg (about 10 in. Hg). If at this moment the car is suddenly accelerated and the manifold vacuum in chamber A drops to 3 in. Hg, there is more vacuum in chamber C than in chamber A. Then, the check valves in the diaphragm assembly open immediately, equalizing the vacuum in chambers A and C, and the spring instantly moves the diaphragm closing the air valve.

2   IN-CAR ADJUSTMENTS AND REPAIRS

DRIVE BELT ADJUSTMENT

The air supply pump drive belt should be properly adjusted at all times. A loose drive belt causes improper air pump operation. A belt that is too tight places a severe strain on the air pump bearings.

Properly tensioned drive belts minimize noise and also prolong service life of the belt. Therefore, it is recommended that a belt tension gauge be used to check and adjust the belt tension. **Any belt that has operated for a minimum of 10 min-**

utes is considered a used belt, and, when adjusted, it must be adjusted to the reset tension shown in the specifications.

BELT TENSION

1. Install the belt tension tool (T63L-8620-A) on the drive belt and check the tension following the instructions of the tool manufacturer. Compare the belt tension to the specified belt tension (Part 12-4) and adjust as necessary.

2. If adjustment is necessary,

loosen the air pump mounting and adjusting arm bolts (Figs. 3, 4 or 5). Move the air pump toward or away from the engine until the correct tension is obtained. **Use a suitable bar and pry against the pump rear cover** to hold belt tension while tightening the mounting bolts. **Do not pry against the pump housing.** Remove the gauge. Tighten the air pump adjusting arm and mounting bolts. Install the tension gauge and check the belt tension.

3   REMOVAL AND INSTALLATION

AIR PUMP AIR CLEANER ELEMENT REPLACEMENT

1. Remove the wing nut (Fig. 6) and air horn assembly. Remove the filter element from the air horn assembly.

2. Wipe the air horn assembly and air cleaner with a clean, lint-free cloth to remove any accumulated dirt or foreign matter. Under extremely dirty conditions it may be necessary to wash both the air horn and body in low-volatility mineral spirits. Be sure the parts are dry before installing them.

3. The filter element is not cleanable. Refer to Group 19 for the recommended replacement interval. Place a new filter element on the air

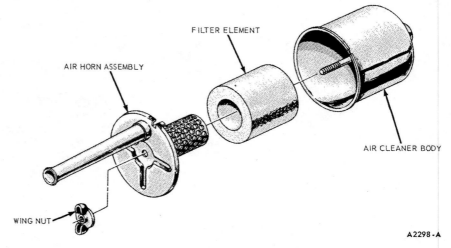

FILTER ELEMENT

AIR HORN ASSEMBLY

AIR CLEANER BODY

WING NUT

A2298-A

FIG. 6—Thermactor Exhaust Emission System Air Cleaner

horn assembly. Position the assembled air horn and filter element in the air cleaner body. **Be sure the tang is fitted in the slot (Fig. 6).** Install the wing nut.

AIR CLEANER

REMOVAL

1. Note the position of the air horn with respect to the car (or engine) and with respect to the air cleaner mounting bracket.

2. Disconnect the air hose from *the air cleaner body.* Remove the air cleaner mounting bracket screws and remove the air cleaner.

INSTALLATION

1. Position the air cleaner and mounting bracket assembly in the same way that it was previously installed, and install the mounting bracket screws.

2. Connect the air hose to the air cleaner body.

DRIVE BELT REPLACEMENT

1. Loosen the air supply pump adjusting arm nut and bolt (Figs. 3, 4 and 5). Loosen the air supply pump to mounting bracket nut and bolt, and push the air pump towards the cylinder block. Remove the drive belt.

2. Install a new drive belt. With a suitable bar, **pry against the rear cover of the air pump** to obtain the specified belt tension (refer to Part 12-4), and tighten the adjusting arm bolt and nut. **Do not pry against the pump housing.** Adjust the belt tension (refer to Section 3) as necessary. **Always use a belt tension gauge (Tool T63L-8620-A) to check belt tension.**

3. Tighten the air supply pump to mounting bracket bolt and nut.

ANTI-BACKFIRE VALVE

REMOVAL

Disconnect the air and vacuum hoses at the anti-backfire valve body (Figs. 3, 4 and 5). Remove the valve to mounting bracket bolts and sep-

arate the valve from the mounting bracket.

INSTALLATION

Position the anti-backfire valve on the mounting bracket, and install the attaching bolts. Be sure the valve is positioned properly (Fig. 3, 4 and 5), and connect the air and vacuum hoses.

CHECK VALVE REPLACEMENT

1. Disconnect the air supply hose at the valve. Use a 1¼ inch crowfoot wrench to unscrew the check valve assembly (the valve has a standard, right-hand pipe thread).

2. Clean the threads on the air manifold adapter with a wire brush. Install the check valve and torque it to specifications. Connect the air supply hose.

AIR MANIFOLD

REMOVAL

1. Disconnect the air supply hose at the check valve and position the hose out of the way.

2. Loosen all of the air manifold to cylinder head tube coupling nuts (compression fittings). Then unscrew each one until it is free of the cylinder head. Grasp the air manifold at each end and pull it away from the cylinder head. Follow the same procedure to remove the other air manifold, if the engine is so equipped.

INSTALLATION

1. Position the air manifold(s) on the cylinder head. Be sure all the tube coupling nuts are aligned with the cylinder head. Screw each coupling nut into the cylinder head 1 to 2 threads. Tighten the tube coupling nuts.

2. Connect the air supply hose to the air manifold.

AIR NOZZLE REPLACEMENT

Normally, air nozzles would be replaced as necessary during cylinder head overhaul. A nozzle may be replaced without removing the cylinder

head by removing the air manifold and using a hooked tool to pull the nozzle.

For cleaning and inspection of the air nozzles, refer to Part 12-1, Section 3. Additionally, the air nozzles could be inspected for badly eroded tips with the aid of a mirror, when the exhaust manifold(s) is removed.

DRIVE PULLEY REPLACEMENT

1. Loosen the air supply pump adjusting arm and mounting bolts and nuts to relieve the belt tension.

2. Remove the drive pulley attaching bolts and pull the drive pulley off the air pump shaft.

3. Position the drive pulley on the air supply pump shaft, and install the retaining bolts. Torque the bolts in sequence, across from each other, to specifications.

4. Position the drive belt and adjust the belt tension (Section 3) to specifications. Tighten the adjusting arm and mounting bolts and nuts.

AIR SUPPLY PUMP

REMOVAL

1. Disconnect the air inlet and outlet hoses at the air pump.

2. Loosen the adjusting arm to air pump and air pump to mounting bracket bolts to relieve the drive belt tension.

3. Disengage the drive belt. Remove the mounting bolts and air pump.

REPAIR

For disassembly and repair procedures, refer to Section 4 of this part.

INSTALLATION

1. Position the air pump on the mounting bracket and install the mounting bolt and nut.

2. Place the drive belt in the pulleys and attach the adjusting arm to the air pump. Adjust the drive belt tension to specifications and tighten the adjusting arm and mounting bolts.

3. Connect the air inlet and outlet hoses to the air pump.

4 MAJOR REPAIR OPERATIONS

AIR SUPPLY PUMP

The air supply pump and component parts are shown in Fig. 7.

DISASSEMBLY

1. Position the air supply pump in

a vise with the pulley hub between the vise jaws and the pump assembly above the vise. **Do not mount the pump housing in a vise.**

2. Remove the cover bolts. Use a plastic (or rawhide hammer to tap

the cover assembly off the dowel pins. Then pull the cover assembly off the pump by hand.

3. Remove the rotor ring screws and remove the rotor ring and bearing assembly. Remove the rear seal.

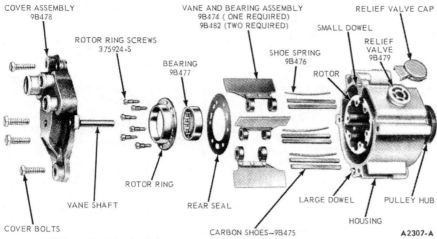

COVER ASSEMBLY
9B478

ROTOR RING SCREWS
375924-S

BEARING
9B477

VANE AND BEARING ASSEMBLY
9B474 (ONE REQUIRED)
9B482 (TWO REQUIRED)

SHOE SPRING
9B476

RELIEF VALVE CAP

SMALL DOWEL

RELIEF
VALVE
9B479

ROTOR

COVER BOLTS

VANE SHAFT

ROTOR RING

REAR SEAL

CARBON SHOES—9B475

LARGE DOWEL

PULLEY HUB

HOUSING

A2307-A

FIG. 7—Air Supply Pump

This is a carbon seal and it should be replaced whenever the pump is disassembled.

4. Locate the vane (Fig. 8) that is attached to the bearing nearest the cover assembly (rear of pump). Grasp it with the fingers and pull it as far as possible out of the rotor. Then pull the other vanes out as far as possible. Alternately pull each vane until they are free of the rotor. If the carbon shoes and shoe springs move out of the rotor as the vanes are being removed, push down on the

carbon shoe next to the shoe spring. Then remove the shoe spring. This will aid in removal of the vanes.

5. **Use a pair of tweezers** to remove the carbon shoes. If needle-nosed pliers are used to remove the carbon shoes, **do not pinch the shoes with the pliers too tightly as the carbon is easily crushed.**

6. If the bearing in the rotor ring requires replacement, position the rotor ring on Tool T66L-9A486-AB with the bearing part number facing upwards. Place Tool T66L-9A486-

AA on the bearing and use an arbor press to remove the bearing.

Further disassembly of the rotor from the housing is not recommended. If any components of the housing assembly require replacement, the entire housing must be replaced.

CLEANING AND INSPECTION

Refer to Part 12-1, Section 3 for the cleaning and inspection procedures.

ASSEMBLY

1. **The rotor ring is a matched assembly with the housing and rotor assembly, thus these parts are replaceable as a unit only.** If the rotor ring bearing was removed, use Tools T66L-9A486-AA and T66L-9A486-AB and press a new bearing into the rotor ring. **The part number side of the bearing should be on the same side of the rotor ring as the flat surface (side towards rotor), and the** bearing should be flush to $1/32$ inch below the surface of the ring.

2. Place the rotor and housing assembly in a vise with the vise jaws gripping the pulley hub. **Do not clamp the housing assembly in a vise.**

3. **Lubricate the vane assembly bearings with only the special air pump bearing lubricant (refer to Part 12-4 for the lube specification) as follows:**

Hold each vane assembly bearing over the vane assembly pin (Tool-T66L-9A486-C) with the pin just engaged in the bearing. Fill the inside of the bearing with bearing lubricant. Cover the open end of the bearing with the thumb or finger, and press the bearing onto the assembly pin. This will force the lubricant into and around the needle rollers of the bearing. Wipe off the excess grease. Repeat the procedure for the other vane bearings.

4. Mesh the bearings of the vane assemblies so that the ends of the vanes are even, and install the vanes in the rotor (Fig. 8).

5. Install the carbon shoes in the rotor. **One side of each shoe is not square with the other sides. The** shoes must be installed with the narrow edge towards the vane bearings as shown in Fig. 8 and the slant side against the vane.

6. *Install the shoe springs between the rotor and shoe in front of the leading (counterclockwise rotation from rear of pump) face of each vane. **The springs must be installed***

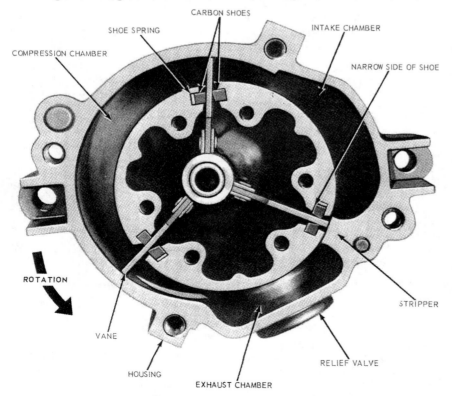

COMPRESSION CHAMBER

SHOE SPRING

CARBON SHOES

INTAKE CHAMBER

NARROW SIDE OF SHOE

ROTATION

VANE

HOUSING

EXHAUST CHAMBER

RELIEF VALVE

STRIPPER

FIG. 8—Vanes, Carbon Shoes and Springs Installed in Rotor

with the tension at the ends of the spring against the rotor and the tension at the center of the spring against the shoe.

Position the vanes with one vane against the stripper part of the housing as shown in Fig. 8.

7. Lubricate the rotor rear bearing (in the rotor ring) with air pumlubricant (refer to Part 12-4 for the specification). Coat the bearing surfaces with lubricant and work it into the bearing with the thumb or finger. Wipe the excess lubricant from the *bearing* and rotor ring assembly.

8. Position a new rear seal and the rotor ring and bearing assembly on the rotor. The rotor ring bolt holes are unevenly spaced to ensure the rotor ring being properly aligned with the rotor. Apply a thin coating of Loctite thread locking compound to the rotor ring attaching screws, and install the ring screws and torque to specifications.

9. Using the vane assembly pin (Tool T66L-9A486-C), align the vane bearings. Remove the alignment tool.

10. Carefully align the cover assembly with the rotor and insert the vane shaft into the vane bearings. **Do not force the shaft into place, or the vanes will become misaligned.** It may be necessary to rotate the cover and shaft and/or wiggle it slightly from side to side while pushing inward.

Rotate the cover to align with the housing dowels, and push it onto the dowels.

11. Install the cover bolts and torque evenly and alternately in sequence to specifications.

RELIEF VALVE REPLACEMENT

Do not disassemble the air pump to replace the relief valve, but remove it from the engine.

1. Position Tool T66L-9A486-D on the air pump and remove the relief valve with the aid of a slide hammer (T59L-100-B).

2. Position the relief valve on the pump housing and hold Tool T66L-9A486-B on the relief valve. Use a hammer to **tap the tool lightly** until the relief valve is seated.

PART 12-4 SPECIFICATIONS

TORQUE LIMITS

EXHAUST SYSTEM — Ft-lbs

Inlet Pipe(s) To Exhaust Manifold(s)—427 V-8 High Performance	40-53
Inlet Pipe(s) To Exhaust Manifold(s)—All Except 427 V-8 High Performance	25-35
Inlet Pipe To Muffler Clamp	14-22
Outlet Pipe To Intermediate (Muffler) Support Bracket Clamp	14-22
Support Bracket and Insulator To Frame Bolts and Nuts	14-22

THERMACTOR EXHAUST EMISSION SYSTEM

Check Valve To Air Manifold	16-19
Air Manifold To Cylinder Head	
Air Pump Drive Pulley To Pump Hub	
Air Pump Mounting Bolts	23-28

LUBRICANTS — Ford Part No.

Exhaust Control Valve Lubricant	COAZ-19A501-A, R-149-A

SEALERS — Ford Part No.

Loctite (thread locking compound)	C3AZ-19554-A

SPECIAL TOOLS

Description	Ford Tool No.	Kent-Moore Tool No.
Rotor Ring Bearing Remover and Installer		T66L-9A486-AA
Rotor Ring Support		T66L-9A486-AB
Relief Valve Installer		T66L-9A486-B
Vane Assembly Pin		T66L-9A486-C
Relief Valve Remover (Use With T59L-100-B)		T66L-9A486-D
Handle Adapter (Use With T66P-9A486-C)	T62L-201-A	
Slide Hammer	T59L-100-B	
Belt Tension Gauge	T63L-8620-A	
Crowfoot Wrench—1¼ inch (Check Valve Removal)		

CHARGING SYSTEM

GROUP 13

PART 13-1

GENERAL CHARGING SYSTEM SERVICE

1 DIAGNOSIS

The charging system consists of an alternator, alternator regulator, battery, charge indicator light or gauge, and the necessary wiring to connect the components (Figs. 1 and 2).

Battery discharge is not always due to charging system defects. Excessive use of lights and accessories while the engine is either off or running at low idle; corroded battery cables and connectors; low water level in the battery; or prolonged disuse of the battery, which would permit self-discharge; are all possible reasons which should be considered when a battery is run down or low in charge.

Charging system troubles such as low alternator output, no alternator output (indicated by the indicator light being on or the indicator gauge showing discharge while the engine is running), or alternator output voltage too high, require testing of both the alternator and the alternator regulator.

Alternator regulator failures are usually not recognized except by the direct effect on the alternator output and, of course, eventual battery discharge. As the regulator is the control valve for the alternator, it acts to protect the battery by preventing excessive voltage output. Discharge of the battery to ground through the alternator is prevented by the diodes of the alternator which permit current flow in one direction (to the battery) only. Proper adjustment of the two units in the alternator regulator (field relay and voltage limiter), is very important.

The road map type of procedures which follow will assist in a logical sequence of pinpointing specific troubles. **Always determine the cause of failure as well as making the repair.**

BATTERY LOW IN CHARGE, HEADLIGHTS DIM AT IDLE

Refer to Fig. 3 for these symptoms.

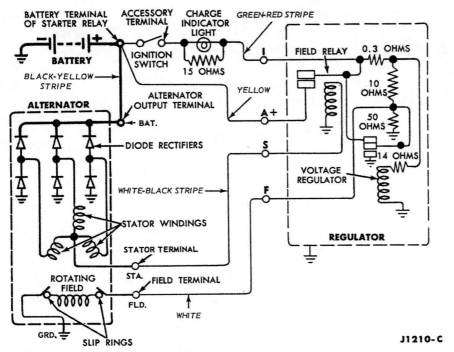

FIG. 1—Autolite Alternator System—Ford

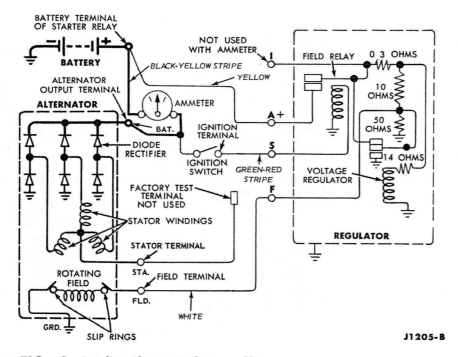

FIG. 2—Autolite Alternator System—Mercury

CHARGE INDICATOR GAUGE— NO READING OR GAUGE OPERATES IN REVERSE

Either of two different type indicator gauges may be encountered. One type of gauge has external loops on the back of the gauge. The gauge wire is routed through these loops with no physical connection to the gauge. The other type gauge uses external terminal post connections. In this case, the gauge wire is connected to the terminal posts.

To test the charge indicator gauge, turn the headlights ON with the engine off. The indicator pointer should move toward the D or discharge portion of the scale. The test for indication in the charge direction is made by first turning on the lights for about two minutes and then running the engine at about 1500 rpm. Turn the lights off and observe the pointer travel. If charge is indicated, the indicator is satisfactory.

If no movement of the needle is obtained, check the loop (or connections) on the rear of the gauge to see if the battery to alternator wire passes inside the loop (or the connections are tight). If the wire is in the loop (or the connections are tight) and the gauge does not indicate a charge or discharge, the gauge is inoperative.

If the pointer moves toward the C or charge portion of the scale when the headlights are first turned ON, the wire passes through the loop in the wrong direction (or the wire connections are reversed). Feed the wire through the loop in the opposite direction (or reverse the wires on the terminals), observing the precaution of disconnecting the battery before working under the instrument panel.

CHARGE INDICATOR LIGHT STAYS ON

Refer to Fig. 4 for this symptom. Other symptoms covered under this heading are: charge indicator gauge indicates constant discharge; battery will not hold charge; alternator has no output; alternator has low output.

NOTE 1

If the owner has had previous difficulty with the battery running down and past history does not indicate that the problem is due to excessive night driving, excessive use of accessories, short trips or extended periods of idle, then it is suggested that the complete charging system be checked.

NOTE 2

Test the alternator output at the battery. With the ammeter in series between the battery cable and battery post, it is necessary to add 2 amperes to the output reading obtained to cover the current draw of the standard ignition system and 6 amperes for the transistor ignition system.

NOTE 3

Check the voltage limiter setting,

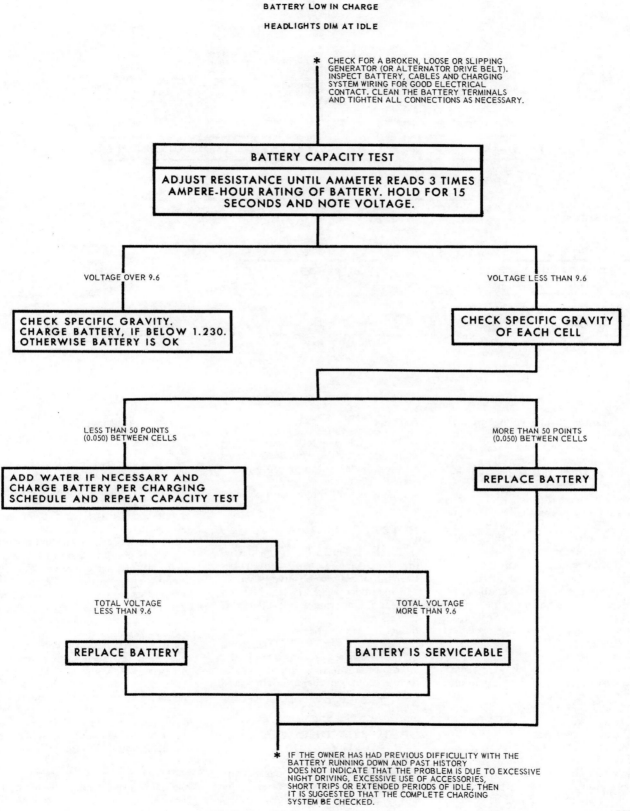

FIG. 3—Battery Low in Charge, Headlights Dim at Idle—Road Map

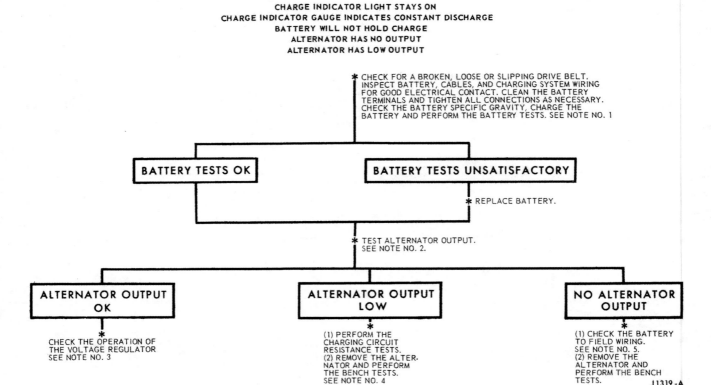

CHARGE INDICATOR LIGHT STAYS ON
CHARGE INDICATOR GAUGE INDICATES CONSTANT DISCHARGE
BATTERY WILL NOT HOLD CHARGE
ALTERNATOR HAS NO OUTPUT
ALTERNATOR HAS LOW OUTPUT

* CHECK FOR A BROKEN, LOOSE OR SLIPPING DRIVE BELT.
INSPECT BATTERY, CABLES, AND CHARGING SYSTEM WIRING
FOR GOOD ELECTRICAL CONTACT. CLEAN THE BATTERY
TERMINALS AND TIGHTEN ALL CONNECTIONS AS NECESSARY.
CHECK THE BATTERY SPECIFIC GRAVITY, CHARGE THE
BATTERY AND PERFORM THE BATTERY TESTS. SEE NOTE NO. 1

BATTERY TESTS OK   BATTERY TESTS UNSATISFACTORY

* REPLACE BATTERY.

* TEST ALTERNATOR OUTPUT.
SEE NOTE NO. 2.

ALTERNATOR OUTPUT OK   ALTERNATOR OUTPUT LOW   NO ALTERNATOR OUTPUT

*
CHECK THE OPERATION OF
THE VOLTAGE REGULATOR
SEE NOTE NO. 3

*
(1) PERFORM THE
CHARGING CIRCUIT
RESISTANCE TESTS.
(2) REMOVE THE ALTER-
NATOR AND PERFORM
THE BENCH TESTS.
SEE NOTE NO. 4

*
(1) CHECK THE BATTERY
TO FIELD WIRING.
SEE NOTE NO. 5.
(2) REMOVE THE
ALTERNATOR AND
PERFORM THE BENCH
TESTS.   J1319-A

FIG. 4—Charge Indicator Light Stays On—Road Map

and check the closing voltage of the field relay (the voltage at which the field relay contacts just make contact). Adjust the voltage limiter if necessary. Adjust the field relay if its setting is out of specification.

On some cars the location of the regulator may prevent adjustment on the car. Remove the regulator to an alternator-regulator test stand if adjustment is necessary.

The field relay used with the transistorized voltage regulator is a sealed unit and is not to be adjusted. To determine its closing voltage, follow the procedure given in Section 2 Testing, under Autolite Regulator and Circuit Tests.

If the regulator was adjusted properly, check the green-red wire from the accessory terminal of the ignition switch through the charge indicator light and 15-ohm resistor to the voltage regulator, and the white-black wire from the voltage regulator to the alternator. Repair or replace as necessary.

With the engine at 1000 rpm, the voltage produced at the STA terminal of the alternator should be 6 volts or more. A voltage less than 6 volts may be caused by an open negative diode.

NOTE 4

An output of 2 to 5 amperes less than that specified usually indicates an open diode. An output of approximately 10 amperes less than that specified usually indicates a shorted diode.

NOTE 5

To check the battery to field wiring, connect the field rheostat between the battery positive terminal and the alternator FLD terminal and arepeat the alternator output test. If the alternator now has good output the wire from the battery terminal of the starer relay to the FLD terminal of the alternator is defective. If the alternator still has no output it is defective. Remove the alternator and perform the bench tests. Replace defective parts.

LIGHTS AND FUSES FAIL PREMATURELY, SHORT BATTERY LIFE

Refer to Fig. 5 for these symptoms. Other symptoms covered under this heading are: battery uses excessive amount of water; burning of distributor points, ignition resistor wire, or coil; high battery charging rate.

ALTERNATOR NOISY

When investigating the complaint of alternator noise, first try to localize the noise area to make sure that the alternator is at fault rather than the alternator belt, water pump, or another part of the vehicle. Start the engine and use a stethoscope or similar sound detector instrument to localize the noise. An alternator bearing, water pump bearing or belt noise is usually evidenced by a squealing sound.

An alternator with a shorted diode will normally whine (magnetic noise) and will be most noticeable at idle speeds. Perform the alternator output test. If the output is approximately 10 amperes less than that specified, a shorted diode is usually indicated.

To eliminate the belt(s) as the cause of noise, check the belt(s) for bumps, apply a light amount of belt dressing to the belt(s). If the alternator belt is at fault, adjust the belt to specification, or replace the belt if necessary.

If the belt(s) is satisfactory and the noise is believed to be in the alternator or water pump, remove the alternator belt. Start the engine and listen for the noise as a double check to be sure that the noise is not

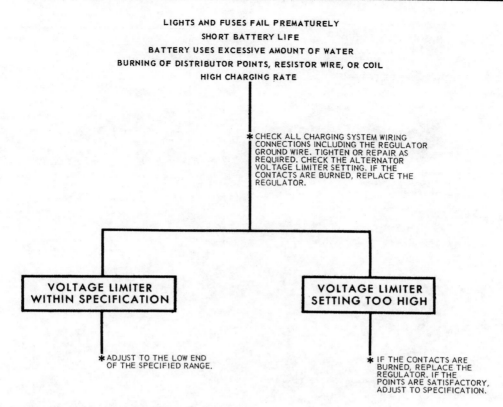

LIGHTS AND FUSES FAIL PREMATURELY
SHORT BATTERY LIFE
BATTERY USES EXCESSIVE AMOUNT OF WATER
BURNING OF DISTRIBUTOR POINTS, RESISTOR WIRE, OR COIL
HIGH CHARGING RATE

* CHECK ALL CHARGING SYSTEM WIRING
CONNECTIONS INCLUDING THE REGULATOR
GROUND WIRE. TIGHTEN OR REPAIR AS
REQUIRED. CHECK THE ALTERNATOR
VOLTAGE LIMITER SETTING. IF THE
CONTACTS ARE BURNED, REPLACE THE
REGULATOR.

VOLTAGE LIMITER
WITHIN SPECIFICATION

VOLTAGE LIMITER
SETTING TOO HIGH

* ADJUST TO THE LOW END
OF THE SPECIFIED RANGE.

* IF THE CONTACTS ARE
BURNED, REPLACE THE
REGULATOR. IF THE
POINTS ARE SATISFACTORY,
ADJUST TO SPECIFICATION.

J1320-A

FIG. 5—Lights and Fuses Fail Prematurely—Road Map

caused by another component. Use this test and the sound detector test to isolate the offending unit. If the noise is traced to the alternator, remove it and inspect the bearings for wear, shaft scoring, or an out-of-round condition.

CHARGE INDICATOR GAUGE FLUCTUATES OR WARNING LIGHT FLICKERS

This condition may be caused by dirty or oxidized regulator contacts, loose or damaged connections in the charging system wiring harness, worn

brushes, or improper brush tension.

At certain engine speeds the ammeter needle will fluctuate to some degree when voltage regulation is just starting, and when the turn signals are in operation, which is normal.

2 TESTING

ALTERNATOR TESTS

Refer to Wiring Diagram Manual Form 7795P-66 for locations of wiring harnesses. Schematics are shown in Group 22 of this manual. **Use care when connecting any test equipment to the alternator system, as the alternator output terminal is connected to the battery at all times.**

ALTERNATOR OUTPUT TEST ON ENGINE

When the alternator output test is conducted off the car, a test bench must be used. Follow the procedure given by the test bench equipment manufacturer. **When the alternator is removed from the car for this purpose always disconnect a battery cable as the alternator output connec-**

tor is connected to the battery at all times.

To test the output of the alternator on the car, proceed as follows:

1. Place the transmission in neutral or park **and apply the parking brake.** Make the connections as shown in Fig. 6 or 7. Be sure that the field resistance control is at the OFF position at the start of this test.

2. Close the battery adapter switch. Start the engine, then open the battery adapter switch.

3. Increase the engine speed to approximately 2000 rpm. Turn off all lights and electrical accessories.

4. Turn the field rheostat clockwise until 15 volts is indicated on the voltmeter. Turn the master control clockwise until the voltmeter indi-

cates between 11 and 12 volts. Holding the master control in this position turn the field rheostat clockwise to its maximum rotation. Turn the master control counterclockwise until the voltmeter indicates 15 volts. Observe the ammeter reading. Add 2 amperes to this reading when the car is equipped with standard ignition or 6 amperes with the transistor ignition system, to obtain total alternator output. If rated output cannot be obtained, increase the engine speed to 2900 rpm and repeat this step.

5. Return the field resistance control to the maximum counterclockwise position, release the master control, and stop the engine. Disconnect the test equipment, if no further tests are to be made.

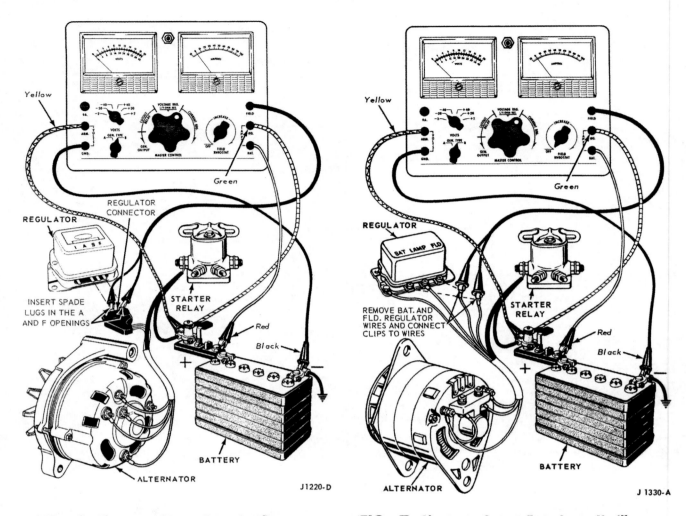

FIG. 6—Alternator Output Test—Autolite

FIG. 7—Alternator Output Test—Leece Neville

An output of 2 to 8 amperes below specifications usually indicates an open diode rectifier. An output of approximately 10 to 15 amperes below specifications usually indicates a shorted diode rectifier. An alternator with a shorted diode will usually whine, which will be most noticeable at idle speed.

AUTOLITE STATOR NEUTRAL VOLTAGE TEST—ON ENGINE

The Autolite alternator STA terminal is connected to the stator coil neutral or center point (see Figs. 1 and 2). The voltage generated at this point is used to close the field relay in the charge indicator light system.

To test for the stator neutral voltage, connect the voltmeter positive lead to the STA terminal and connect the negative lead to ground. Start the engine and run it at 1000 rpm. Turn off all lights and accessories. The voltage indicated on the

meter should be 6 volts or more.

FIELD OPEN OR SHORT CIRCUIT TEST—ON BENCH

Make the connection as shown in Fig. 8. The current draw, as indicated by the ammeter, should be to specifications. If there is little or no current flow, the field or brushes have a high resistance or are open. A current flow considerably higher than that specified above, indicates shorted or grounded turns or brush leads touching. If the test shows that the field is shorted or open and the field brush assembly or slip rings are not at fault, the entire rotor must be replaced.

If the alternator has output at low rpm and no output at high rpm, centrifugal force may be causing the rotor windings to short to ground. Put the alternator on a test stand and repeat the preceding test. Run the alternator at high speed during the test.

DIODE TEST—ON BENCH

Disassemble the alternator and disconnect the diode assembly from the stator and make the test connections as shown in Figs. 10, 11 or 12.

To test the negative diodes contact one probe to the diode plate as shown and contact each of the three stator lead terminals with the other probe. Reverse the probes and repeat the test. Test the positive diodes in the same way.

All of the diodes should show a low reading of approximately 60 ohms in one direction and infinite reading (no needle movement) with the probes reversed. **Be sure to use the Rotunda ohmmeter with the multiply-by knob at 10.**

OPEN OR GROUNDED STATOR COIL TESTS—ON BENCH

These tests are made to verify that the stator coil is defective. Disassemble the stator from the alternator and rectifier assembly for these tests.

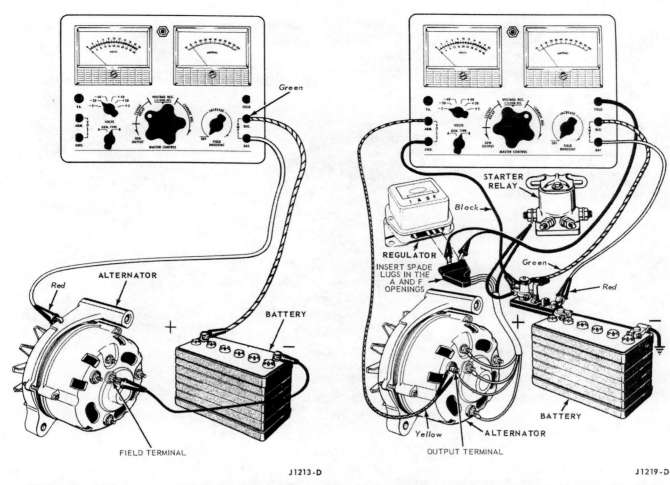

J1213-D

FIG. 8—Field Open or Short Circuit Test—Typical

J1219-D

FIG. 9—Autolite Voltage Drop Test—Alternator to Battery Positive Terminal

Open Stator Test——On Bench. Set the Rotunda ohmmeter multiply-by knob at 1. Connect the ohmmeter between each pair of stator leads. If the ohmmeter does not show equal readings between each pair of stator leads, the stator is open and must be replaced.

Grounded Stator Test——On Bench. Set the Rotunda ohmmeter multiply-by knob at 1000. Connect the ohmmeter between one of the stator leads and the stator core. Be sure that the test lead makes a good electrical connection to the core. The ohmmeter should not show any continuity, if it does, the stator winding is grounded and must be replaced.

ALTERNATOR REGULATOR AND CIRCUIT TESTS

CIRCUIT RESISTANCE TESTS

For the purpose of this test, the resistance values of the circuits have been converted to voltage drop readings for a current flow of 20 amperes.

Alternator to Battery Positive Terminal. To check the alternator to battery positive terminal voltage drop, make the connections as shown in Fig. 9 or 13. Turn off all electrical accessories and lights. Close the battery adapter switch, start the engine, then open the battery adapter switch. Increase the engine speed to 2000 rpm. Adjust the field rheostat until the ammeter indicates 20 amperes. Note the voltmeter reading at this point. The voltage reading should be no greater than 0.3 volt on a car with a charge indicator light and 0.5 volt on a car with an ammeter.

These voltage drops have been computed for a standard car. The current used by any auxiliary, continuously operating, heavy-duty equipment will not show on the ammeter and will have to be taken into account when making this test.

Alternator to Battery Ground Terminal. To check the alternator to

battery ground terminal voltage drop, make the connections as shown in Figs. 14 or 15. Close the battery adapter switch, start the engine and open the adapter switch. Maintain the engine speed at 2000 rpm. Adjust the field rheostat until the ammeter indicates 20 amperes. The voltage indicated on the voltmeter should be less than 0.1.

REGULATOR TESTS

Voltage Limiter Test. Voltage limiter calibration tests must be made with the regulator cover in place and the regulator at normal operating temperature (equivalent to the temperature after 20 minutes of operation on the car with the hood down).

For accurate voltage limiter testing, the battery specific gravity must be at least 1.225. If the battery is low in charge, either charge it to 1.225 specific gravity or substitute a fully charged battery, before making a voltage limiter test.

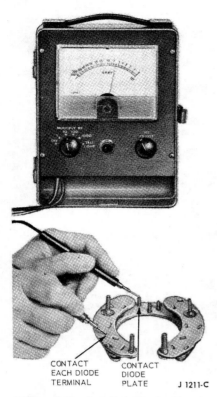

CONTACT
EACH DIODE
TERMINAL

CONTACT
DIODE
PLATE   J 1211-C

FIG. 10—Autolite Diode Test

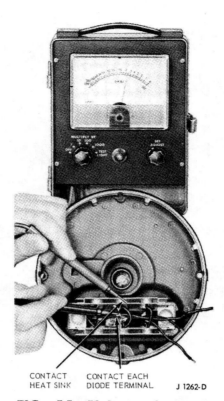

CONTACT   CONTACT EACH
HEAT SINK   DIODE TERMINAL   J 1262-D

FIG. 11—53-Ampere Leece Neville Diode Test

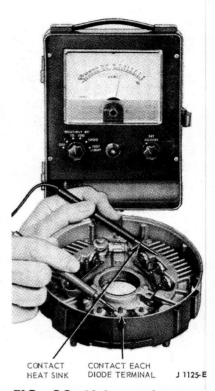

CONTACT   CONTACT EACH
HEAT SINK   DIODE TERMINAL   J 1125-E

FIG. 12—60-Ampere Leece Neville Diode Test

To test the voltage regulator on the car, make the test connections to the battery as shown in Fig. 16. Turn all accessories off, including door operated dome lights. Close the battery adapter switch, start the engine, then open the adapter switch. Attach a voltage regulator thermometer to the regulator cover. Operate the engine at approximately 2000 rpm for 5 minutes.

When the battery is charged, and the voltage regulator has been temperature stabilized, the ammeter should indicate less than 10 amperes with the master control set at the ¼ —OHM position.

Cycle the regulator as follows (mechanical regulators only): turn the ignition key to OFF to stop the engine, close the adapter switch, start the engine, and open the adapter switch. Allow the battery to normalize for a few seconds, then read the voltmeter. Read the thermometer, and compare the voltmeter reading with the voltage given in Table 1 for the ambient temperature indicated on the thermometer. If the regulated voltage is not within specifications, make a voltage limiter adjustment. After each adjustment, be sure to cy-

cle the regulator before each reading (mechanical regulator only). **The readings must be made with the cover in place (mechanical regulator only).**

On some cars the location of the regulator may prevent adjustment on the car. Remove the regulator to an alternator-regulator test stand if adjustment is necessary.

TABLE 1—Voltage Limiter Setting Versus Ambient Air Temperature (Mechanical or Transistor Regulator)

Ambient Air Temperature °F	Voltage Limiter Setting (Volts)
50	14.3-15.1
75	14.1-14.9
100	13.9-14.7
125	13.8-14.6

Field Relay Test—Mechanical Regulator. Remove the regulator

from the car, and remove the regulator cover. Make the connections as shown in Fig. 17, 19, or 20. Slowly rotate the field rheostat control clockwise from the maximum counterclockwise position until the field relay contacts close. Observe the voltmeter reading at the moment that the relay contacts close. This is the relay closing voltage. If the relay closes immediately, even with the field rheostat close to the maximum counterclockwise position, push the red button between the two meters, and repeat the test. If the closing voltage is not to specifications, adjust the relay (Part 13-3).

Field Relay Test—Transistor Regulator. Disconnect the relay connector plug. Make the connections as shown in Fig. 18. Slowly rotate the field rheostat control clockwise from the maximum counterclockwise position until the test light comes on. Observe the voltmeter reading at the moment that the light comes on. This is the relay closing voltage. If the relay closes immediately, even with the field rheostat close to the maximum counterclockwise position, push the red button between the two meters, and repeat the test. If the closing

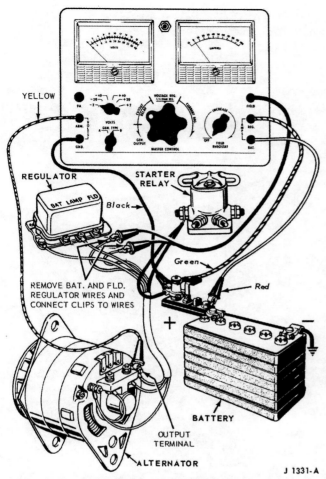

FIG. 13—Leece Neville Voltage Drop Test—Alternator to Battery Positive Terminal

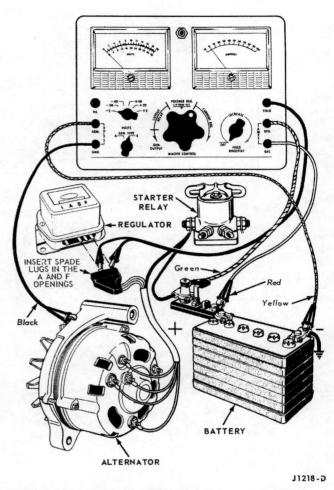

FIG. 14—Autolite Voltage Drop Test—Alternator to Battery Ground Terminal

voltage is not to specification, replace the relay.

BATTERY TESTS AND CONCLUSIONS

Tests are made on a battery to determine the state of charge and also the condition. The ultimate result of these tests is to show that the battery is good, needs recharging, or must be replaced.

If a battery has failed, is low in charge, or requires water frequently, good service demands that the reason for this condition be found. It may be necessary to follow trouble shooting procedures to locate the cause of the trouble (Section 1 in this part).

Hydrogen and oxygen gases are produced during normal battery operation. This gas mixture can explode if flames or sparks are brought near the vent openings of the battery. The sulphuric acid in the battery electrolyte can cause a serious burn if spilled

on the skin or spattered in the eyes. It should be flushed away with large quantities of clear water.

Before attempting to test a battery, it is important that it be given a thorough visual examination to determine if it has been damaged. The presence of moisture on the outside of the case and/or low electrolyte level in one or more of the cells are indications of possible battery damage.

The Ford and Mercury batteries incorporate a single one-piece cover which completely seals the top of the battery and the individual cell connectors. This cover must not be pierced with test probes to perform individual cell tests.

A battery can be tested by determining its ability to deliver current. This may be determined by conducting a Battery Capacity Test. Fig. 3 shows the battery capacity test in outline form.

BATTERY CAPACITY TEST

A high rate discharge tester (Battery-Starter Tester) in conjunction with a voltmeter is used for this test.

1. Turn the control knob on the Battery-Starter Tester to the OFF position.

2. Turn the voltmeter selector switch to the 16 or 20-volt position.

3. Connect both positive test leads to the positive battery post and both negative test leads to the negative battery post. **The voltmeter clips must contact the battery posts and not the high rate discharge tester clips. Unless this is done the actual battery terminal voltage will not be indicated.**

4. Turn the load control knob in a clockwise direction until the ammeter reads three times the ampere hour rating of the battery. (A 45 ampere-hour battery should be tested at 135 amperes load.)

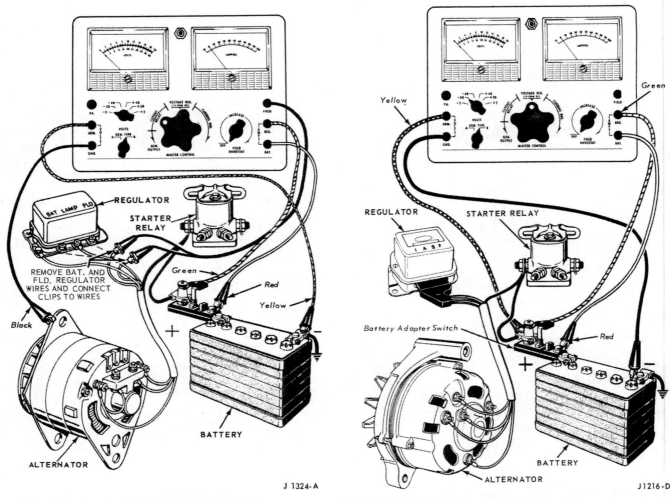

FIG. 15—Leece Neville Voltage Drop Test—Alternator to Battery Ground Terminal

FIG. 16—Voltage Limiter Test—Typical

5. With the ammeter reading the required load for 15 seconds, note the voltmeter reading. **Avoid leaving the high discharge load on the battery for periods longer than 15 seconds.**

6. If the voltmeter reading is 9.6 volts or more, the battery has good output capacity and will readily accept a charge, if required. Check the specific gravity. If the specific gravity reading is 1.230 or below, add water if necessary and charge the battery until it is fully charged.

The battery is fully charged when the cells are all gassing freely and the specific gravity ceases to rise for three successive readings taken at hourly intervals. Additional battery testing will not be necessary after the battery has been properly charged.

7. If the voltage reading obtained during the capacity test is below 9.6 volts, check the specific gravity of each cell.

8. If the difference between any two cells is more than 50 points

(0.050), the battery is not satisfactory for service and should be replaced.

9. If the difference between cells is less than 50 points (0.050) the battery should be charged according to the charging schedule in Table 2. In

TABLE 2—Allowable Battery High Rate Charge Time Schedule

Specific Gravity Reading	Charge Rate Amperes	Battery Capacity—Ampere Hours			
		45	**55**	**70**	**80**
1.125-1.150①	35	65 min.	80 min.	100 min.	115 min.
1.150-1.175	35	50 min.	65 min.	80 min.	95 min.
1.175-1.200	35	40 min.	50 min.	60 min.	70 min.
1.200-1.225	35	30 min.	35 min.	45 min.	50 min.
Above 1.225	5	②	②	②	②

①If the specific gravity is below 1.125, use the indicated high rate of charge for the 1.125 specific gravity, then charge at 5 amperes until the specific gravity reaches 1.250 at 80°F.

②Charge at 5 ampere rate **only** until the specific gravity reaches 1.250 at 80°F.

At no time during the charging operation should the electrolyte temperature exceed 130° F.

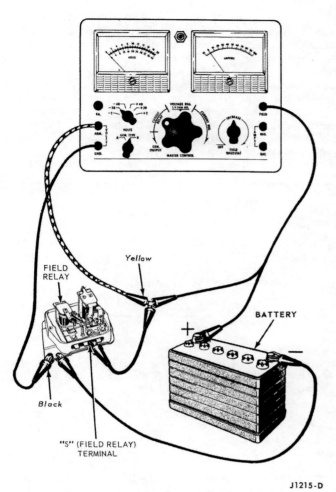

FIG. 17—Autolite Field Relay Test—Mechanical Regulator

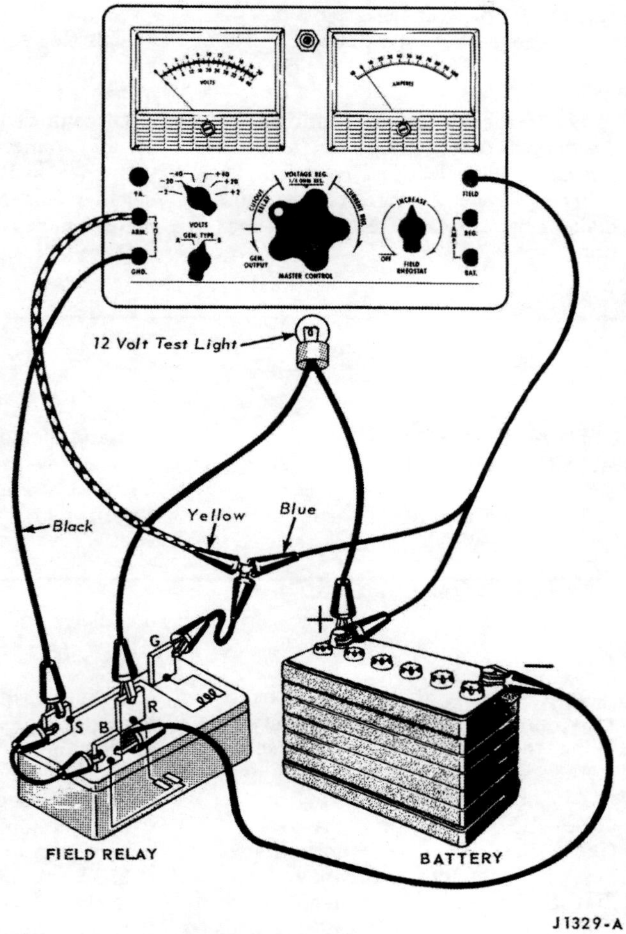

FIG. 18—Autolite Field Relay Test—Transistor Regulator

some cases the electrolyte level may be too low to obtain a specific gravity reading. In such cases water should be added until the electrolyte level just covers the ring in the filler well, then charge the battery at 35 amperes for the maximum charging time indicated in Table 2, for capacity of the battery being tested.

10. After the battery has been charged, repeat the capacity test. If the capacity test battery voltage is

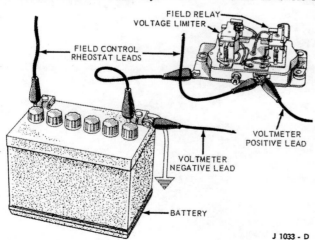

FIG. 19—Leece Neville Field Relay Test—Light Circuit

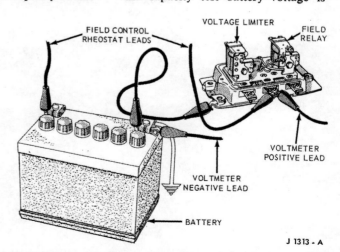

FIG. 20—Leece Neville Field Relay Test—Ammeter Circuit

still less than 9.6 volts, replace the battery. If the voltage is 9.6 volts or more, the battery is satisfactory for service.

11. If the battery is found to be discharged only, check for a loose fan belt, loose electrical connections, charging system performance, and make a battery drain test (in this section).

BATTERY DRAIN TEST

This test will determine if there is any external load that would cause unwanted battery discharge.

Disconnect the battery ground cable and connect the positive lead of a voltmeter to the cable. Connect the negative lead of the voltmeter to the battery negative post.

With all circuits off, the meter should read zero. Any battery external load will cause the voltmeter to read full battery voltage.

If the car is equipped with an electric clock, momentarily connect the battery ground cable to the battery negative post to make certain that the clock is wound. When the clock runs down at the end of approximately 2 minutes the voltmeter will show full battery voltage.

3   COMMON ADJUSTMENTS AND REPAIRS

BELT ADJUSTMENT— ALTERNATOR

1. Loosen the alternator mounting

bolt and the adjusting arm bolts.

2. Apply pressure on the alternator front housing only and tighten the adjusting arm to alternator bolt.

3. Check the belt tension using tool T63L-8620-A. Adjust the belt for specified tension.

4. Tighten all mounting bolts.

4   CLEANING AND INSPECTION

1. The rotor, stator, and bearings must not be cleaned with solvent. Wipe these parts off with a clean cloth.

2. Rotate the front bearing on the drive end of the rotor drive shaft. Check for any scraping noise, looseness or roughness that will indicate that the bearing is excessively worn. Look for excessive lubricant leakage. If any of these conditions exist, replace the bearing.

3. Inspect the rotor shaft at the rear bearing surface for roughness or severe chatter marks. Replace the rotor assembly if the shaft is not smooth.

4. Place the rear end bearing on the slip-ring end of the shaft and ro-

tate the bearing on the shaft. Make the same check for noise, looseness or roughness as was made for the front bearing. Inspect the rollers and cage for damage. Replace the bearing if these conditions exist, or if the lubricant is lost or contaminated.

5. Check the pulley and fan for excessive looseness on the rotor shaft. Replace any pulley or fan that is loose or bent out of shape. Check the rotor shaft for stripped or damaged threads. Inspect the hex hole in the end of the shaft for damage.

6. Check both the front and rear housings for cracks. Check the front housings for stripped threads in the mounting ear. Replace defective housings.

7. Check all wire leads on both the stator and rotor assemblies for loose soldered connections, and for burned insulation. Resolder poor connections. Replace parts that show burned insulation.

8. Check the slip rings for nicks and surface roughness. Nicks and scratches may be removed by turning down the slip rings. Do not go beyond the minimum diameter limit of 1.22 inches. If the slip rings are badly damaged, the entire rotor will have to be replaced, as it is serviced as a complete assembly.

9. Replace any parts that are burned or cracked. Replace brushes and brush springs that are not to specification.

PART 13-2   AUTOLITE ALTERNATORS

1   DESCRIPTION AND OPERATION

The alternator charging system is a negative (—) ground system, and consists of an alternator, a regulator, a charge indicator, a storage battery and associated wiring. Refer to Wiring Diagram Manual Form 7795P-66 for locations of wiring harnesses. Schematics are shown in Group 22 of this manual.

ALTERNATOR

The alternator is belt driven from the engine. The mechanical construction of the alternator differs from a generator in that the field rotates, and the generating windings are stationary. Energy is supplied from the alternator-regulator system to the rotating field through two brushes to two slip rings. The slip rings are mounted on the rotor shaft (Fig. 2), and are connected to the field coil.

The alternator produces power in the form of alternating current. The alternating current is rectified to direct current by six diodes (Fig. 6) for use in charging the battery and supplying power to the electrical system.

2   REMOVAL AND INSTALLATION

REMOVAL

1. Disconnect the battery ground cable, then raise the car on a hoist.
2. Loosen the alternator mounting bolts and remove the adjustment arm to alternator bolt.
3. Disengage the alternator belt. Remove the alternator mounting bolt, disconnect the alternator wiring harness and remove the alternator.

INSTALLATION

1. Attach the alternator wiring harness (Fig. 1). Position the alternator to the engine, and install the alternator mounting bolt finger-tight.
2. Install the adjustment arm to alternator bolt.
3. Adjust the belt tension using tool T63L-8620-A. **Apply pressure on the alternator front housing only, when tightening the belt.** Tighten the adjusting arm bolts and the mounting bolt.
4. Lower the car and connect the battery ground cable.

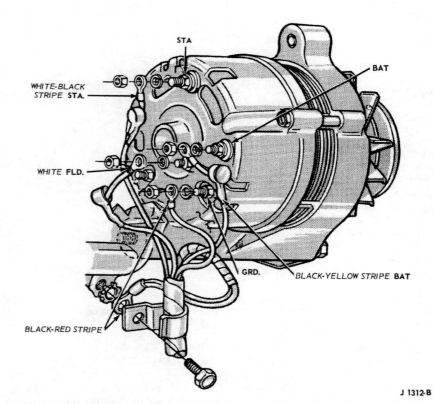

FIG. 1—Wiring Harness Connections—Typical

J 1312-B

3   MAJOR REPAIR OPERATIONS

DISASSEMBLY

Fig. 2 shows a disassembled view of the Ford alternator.

1. Mark both end housings and the stator with a scribe mark for assembly.

2. Remove the three housing through bolts.
3. Separate the front end housing

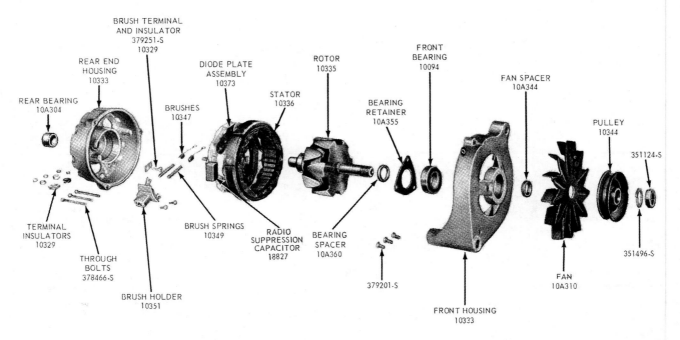

FIG. 2—Disassembled Alternator

and rotor from the stator and rear end housing.

4. Remove all the nuts and washers from the rear end housing and remove the rear end housing from the stator and diode plate assembly.

5. Remove the brush holder mounting screws and remove the holder, brushes, brush springs, insulator and terminal.

6. If replacement is necessary, press the bearing from the rear end housing, supporting the housing on the inner boss.

7. If the diode plate assembly is being replaced, unsolder the stator leads from the printed-circuit board terminals, and separate the stator from the diode plate assembly. Use a 100-watt soldering iron.

8. If the printed-circuit board is being replaced, cut the printed-circuit board into six separate pieces and unsolder each piece from the diode it is attached to. Remove and discard the roll pins from the diode plates.

9. Remove the drive pulley nut, lockwasher, pulley, fan, fan spacer, rotor and rotor stop. (Fig. 3).

10. Remove the three screws that hold the front end bearing retainer, and remove the retainer. Support the housing close to the bearing boss, and press out the old bearing from the housing, only if the bearing is defective or has lost its lubricant.

11. Perform a diode test and a

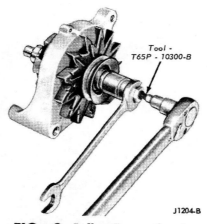

FIG. 3—Pulley Removal

field open or short circuit test (Part 13-1).

**PARTS REPAIR
OR REPLACEMENT**

Nicks and scratches may be removed from the rotor slip rings by turning down the slip rings. Do not go beyond the minimum diameter limit of 1.22 inches. If the slip rings are badly damaged, the entire rotor must be replaced as it is serviced as an assembly. The diode plate assembly is serviced as an assembly. However the printed circuit board is serviced separately.

ASSEMBLY

1. Press the front end bearing in the bearing boss and install the bearing retainer.

2. If the stop-ring on the rotor drive shaft was damaged, install a new stop-ring. Push the new ring on the shaft and into the groove. **Do not open the ring with snap ring pliers as permanent damage will result.**

3. Position the rotor stop on the drive shaft with the recessed side against the stop-ring.

4. Position the front end housing, fan spacer, fan, pulley and lock washer on the drive shaft and install the retaining nut (Fig. 3), to specified torque.

5. If the rear end housing bearing was removed, support the housing on the inner boss and press in a new bearing flush with the outer end surface.

6. Place the brush springs, brushes, brush terminal and terminal insulator in the brush holder and hold the brushes in position by inserting a piece of stiff wire in the brush holder as shown in Fig. 4.

7. Position the brush holder assembly in the rear end housing and install the mounting screws. Position the brush leads in the brush holder as shown in Fig. 5.

8. If a new diode plate or printed-circuit board is being installed, po-

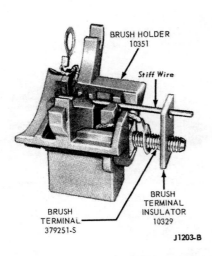

FIG. 4—Brush Holder Assembly

BRUSH HOLDER
10351

Stiff Wire

BRUSH TERMINAL
INSULATOR
10329

BRUSH TERMINAL
379251-S

J1203-B

FIG. 5—Brush Lead Positions

J1206-B

sition the diode plate so that the diode leads go through the three holes in the printed-circuit board. Install the terminal bolt and insulator. Install new roll pins to maintain the ½-inch insulator spacing between the printed-circuit board and the diode plate. Install a small tinned washer and a solder ring on each diode lead and solder the diode leads to the printed-circuit board. Use a 100-watt iron. Avoid excess heat on the printed-circuit board so as not to loosen the printed-circuit wiring from the board.

9. Wrap the three stator winding leads around the printed-circuit board terminals and solder them. Use a 100-watt soldering iron and rosin-core solder. Position the stator neutral lead eyelet on the stator terminal screw and install the screw in the diode assembly (Fig. 6).

10. Install the STA and BAT terminal insulators (Fig. 6). Position the stator and diode plate assembly in the rear end housing. Position the STA (black), BAT (red) and FLD (white) insulators, on the terminal bolts, and install five retaining nuts (Fig. 7).

11. Wipe the rear end bearing *surface* of the rotor shaft with a clean lint-free rag.

12. Position the rear end housing and stator assembly over the rotor and align the scribe marks made during disassembly. Seat the machined portion of the stator core into the step in both end housings. Install the housing through bolts. Remove the brush retracting rod, and put a daub of waterproof cement over the hold to seal it.

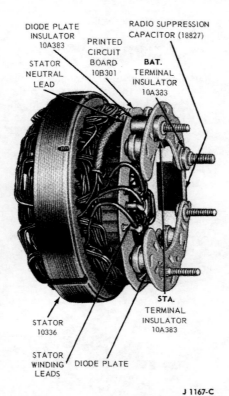

DIODE PLATE
INSULATOR
10A383

STATOR
NEUTRAL
LEAD

PRINTED
CIRCUIT
BOARD
10B301

RADIO SUPPRESSION
CAPACITOR (18827)

BAT.
TERMINAL
INSULATOR
10A383

STA.
TERMINAL
INSULATOR
10A383

STATOR
10336

STATOR
WINDING
LEADS

DIODE PLATE

J 1167-C

FIG. 6—Stator Lead Connections

STA

BAT

FLD

GRD

J1221-D

FIG. 7—Alternator Terminal Locations

PART 13-3

AUTOLITE ALTERNATOR REGULATORS

1 DESCRIPTION AND OPERATION

MECHANICAL VOLTAGE REGULATOR

The alternator regulator is composed of two control units, a field relay and a voltage limiter, mounted as an assembly (Fig. 1). Because the reverse current through the rectifier is small, a reverse current cutout relay is not needed. The alternator is self current limiting, thus a current limiter is not needed. Refer to Wiring Diagram Manual Form 7795P-66 for locations of wiring harnesses. Schematics are shown in Group 22 of this manual.

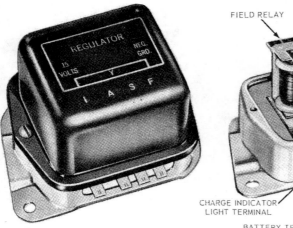

FIG. 1—Alternator Regulator

FIELD RELAY

The field relay serves to connect charging system voltage to the field circuit when the engine is running.

CHARGE INDICATOR CIRCUIT—LIGHT

When the ignition switch is closed, battery current flows through the charge indicator light and 15-ohm

parallel resistor, and through the regulator voltage limiter contacts to the field coil. This small current is enough to allow the alternator to start generating, and is necessary, as residual magnetism in the alternator is usually too small to start voltage build-up. The charge indicator light is shunted with a 15-ohm resistor to supply adequate starting field current.

When the alternator builds up enough voltage to close the field relay contacts, full voltage is applied to the field, and the charge indicator light goes out.

CHARGE INDICATOR CIRCUIT —AMMETER

When the ignition switch is closed, the field relay is energized. Closing of the relay contacts connects the battery and alternator output to the field through the voltage limiter contacts.

VOLTAGE LIMITER

The temperature compensated

voltage limiter is a double contact unit. Limiting is accomplished by controlling the amount of current supplied to the rotating field.

When the upper contacts are closed, full system voltage is applied to the field and maximum field current will flow. When the limiter armature floats between the contacts, field current is reduced by flowing through the field resistor. When the limiter lower contacts are closed, zero current flows to the field. At low engine speed and with a load applied, the armature vibrates on the upper contact. At high engine speed and light or no load the armature vibrates on the lower contact.

A 50-ohm resistor is connected from the field terminal to ground to absorb electrical surges in the alternator circuits as the voltage limiter armature vibrates on the contacts.

TRANSISTORIZED VOLTAGE REGULATOR

The transistorized voltage regulator (Fig. 2), controls the alternator voltage output in a similar manner to a mechanical voltage regulator, by regulating the alternator field current. The regulation is accomplished electronically with the use of transistors and diodes rather than by a vibrating armature relay. The voltage sensing element is a zener diode which has the characteristic of suddenly changing its resistance when a specified voltage is reached. The field relay (Fig. 3) is still used, but it is mounted separately from the voltage regulator.

Figs. 4 and 5 show schematics of the transistorized voltage regulator system. When the engine is started, battery current is supplied to the field through the field relay, field current

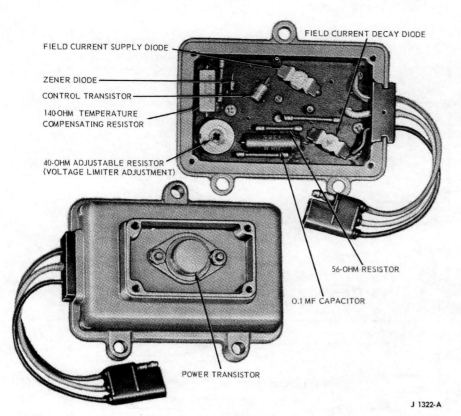

FIELD CURRENT SUPPLY DIODE

FIELD CURRENT DECAY DIODE

ZENER DIODE

CONTROL TRANSISTOR

140-OHM TEMPERATURE COMPENSATING RESISTOR

40-OHM ADJUSTABLE RESISTOR (VOLTAGE LIMITER ADJUSTMENT)

56-OHM RESISTOR

0.1 MF CAPACITOR

POWER TRANSISTOR

J 1322-A

FIG. 2—Transistorized Voltage Regulator

J 1323-A

FIG. 3—Field Relay

supply diode, and the power transistor.

As the alternator begins to supply current, the battery voltage will increase. When the battery voltage reaches approximately 14.5 volts, the zener diode (Figs. 4 and 5), due to its characteristics, suddenly reduces its resistance and lowers the voltage at point B on the control transistor. The control transistor then acting as a switch applies battery voltage to point B on the power transistor. The power transistor also acting as a switch then opens, cutting off battery current to the field. The battery voltage drops slightly, the zener diode increases its resistance, opening the control transistor, which in turn closes the power transistor and battery current again flows to the alternator field.

This sequence of events repeats itself at an approximate rate of 2000 times per second, which is faster than the rate that a mechanical regulator interrupts the field current.

The field current supply diode is used to protect the power transistor.

The field current decay diode performs the same function as the resistors in a mechanical regulator, providing a path to ground for the energy from the field when the field current is interrupted.

The 140 ohm resistor is made of a special material that changes its resistance with temperature in such a manner that during cold weather the battery charging voltage is increased. This resistor performs the same function as the bimetal hinge on the voltage limiter armature of a mechanical regulator.

The alternator output voltage is adjusted by varying the 40-ohm adjustable resistor (Fig. 2). Varying the adjustable resistor performs the same function as adjusting the voltage limiter armature spring tension on a mechanical regulator.

The 0.1 microfarad capacitor in series with the 56-ohm resistor causes the control transistor and the power transistor to switch on and off faster providing better control of the field current.

The remaining resistors in the unit provide proper operating voltages for the zener diode and the two transistors.

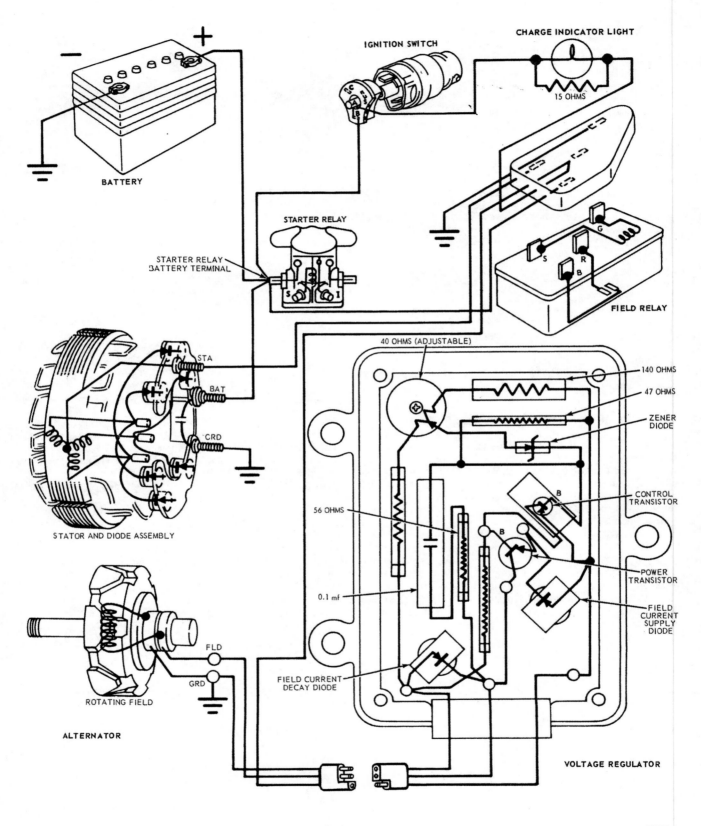

IGNITION SWITCH

CHARGE INDICATOR LIGHT

15 OHMS

BATTERY

STARTER RELAY

STARTER RELAY
BATTERY TERMINAL

FIELD RELAY

STA

BAT

CRD

40 OHMS (ADJUSTABLE)

140 OHMS

47 OHMS

ZENER
DIODE

CONTROL
TRANSISTOR

56 OHMS

B

B

POWER
TRANSISTOR

FIELD
CURRENT
SUPPLY
DIODE

0.1 mf

STATOR AND DIODE ASSEMBLY

FIELD CURRENT
DECAY DIODE

FLD

GRD

ROTATING FIELD

ALTERNATOR

VOLTAGE REGULATOR

J1326-A

FIG. 4—Alternator System With Transistor Voltage Regulator and Charge Indicator Light

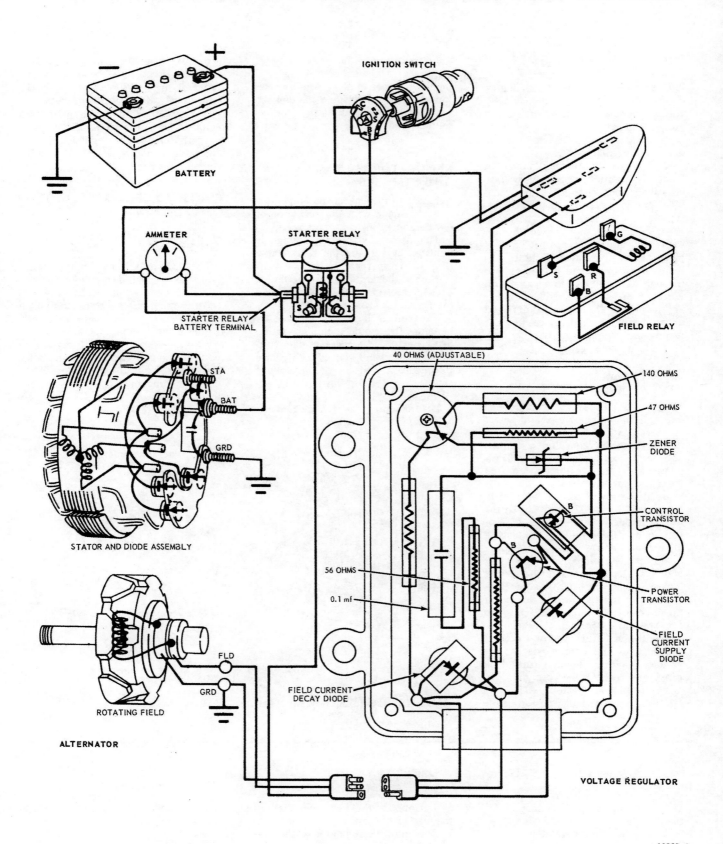

J1321-A

FIG. 5—Alternator System With Transistor Voltage Regulator and Ammeter

2   IN-CAR ADJUSTMENTS AND REPAIRS

MECHANICAL REGULATOR ADJUSTMENTS

Erratic operation of the regulator, indicated by erratic movement of the voltmeter pointer during a voltage limiter test, may be caused by dirty or pitted regulator contacts. **Vehicle ammeter pointer waver at certain critical engine speeds and electrical loads, is normal.** Use a very fine abrasive paper such as silicon carbide, 400 grade, to clean the field relay and the voltage limiter contacts. Wear off the sharp edges of the abrasive by rubbing it against another piece of abrasive paper. Fold the abrasive paper over and pull the paper through the contacts to clean them. Keep all oil or grease from contacting the points. Do not use compressed air to clean the regulator. When adjusting the gap spacing use only hospital clean feeler gauges.

REGULATOR GAP ADJUSTMENTS

Voltage Limiter. The difference between the upper stage and lower stage regulation (0.3 volt), is determined by the voltage limiter contact and core gaps. Make the gap adjustment with the regulator removed from the car.

Bend the lower contact bracket to obtain 0.017 to 0.022-inch gap at the lower contacts with the upper contacts closed. Maintain the contacts in alignment.

Adjust the core gap with the upper contacts closed. Loosen the center lock screw ¼ turn. Use a screwdriver blade in the adjustment slot under the lock screw. Adjust the core gap for 0.049 to 0.056-inch clearance between the armature and the core at the edge of the core closest to the contact points. Tighten the lock screw and recheck the core gap.

Field Relay. Place a 0.010 to 0.018-inch feeler gauge on top of the coil core closest to the contact points. Hold the armature down on the gauge. Do not push down on the contact spring arm. Bend the contact post arm (Fig. 6) until the bottom contact just touches the upper contact.

REGULATOR VOLTAGE ADJUSTMENTS

Final adjustment of the regulator must be made with the regulator at normal operating temperature.

The field relay closing voltage is adjusted by bending the relay frame (Fig. 6). To increase the closing voltage, bend the armature frame down. To decrease the closing voltage, bend the frame up.

The voltage limiter is adjusted by bending the voltage limiter spring arm (Fig. 6). To increase the voltage setting, bend the adjusting arm downward. To decrease the voltage setting, bend the adjusting arm upward.

Before setting the voltage and before making a final voltage test, the alternator speed must be reduced to zero and the ignition switch opened momentarily, to cycle the regulator.

On some cars the location of the regulator may prevent adjustment on the car. Remove the regulator to an alternator-regulator test stand if adjustment is necessary.

TRANSISTORIZED REGULATOR ADJUSTMENTS

REGULATOR VOLTAGE LIMITER ADJUSTMENTS

The only adjustment on the transistorized alternator regulator is the voltage limiter adjustment.

Adjustment of the transistor voltage limiter must be made with the regulator at normal operating temperature. Remove the regulator mounting screws and remove the bottom cover from the regulator. The voltage setting may be moved up or down by adjusting the 40-ohm adjustable resistor (Fig. 2).

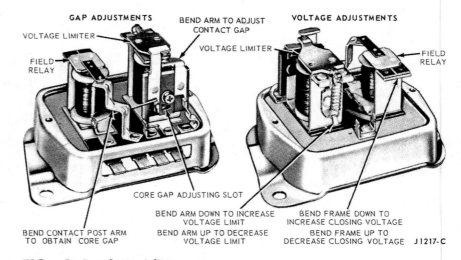

FIG. 6—Regulator Adjustments

3   REMOVAL AND INSTALLATION

1. Remove the battery ground cable.
2. Remove the regulator mounting screws.
3. Disconnect the regulator from the wiring harness.

4. Connect the new regulator to the wiring harness.
5. Mount the regulator to the regulator mounting plate. The radio suppression condenser mounts under one mounting screw. The ground lead mounts under the other mounting screw.

6. Connect the battery ground cable, and test the system for proper voltage regulation.

PART 13-4 — 53-AMPERE LEECE NEVILLE ALTERNATOR

1 DESCRIPTION AND OPERATION

The operation and general electrical description of the Leece Neville 53-ampere alternator is similar to that of the Autolite alternators. (Part 13-2). The field brushes are mounted in an insulated brush holder which is mounted in the brush end housing (Fig. 2).

The drive end bearing is a sealed ball bearing. The brush end bearing is a needle type bearing and is not sealed. The Alternator mountings are shown in Fig. 1.

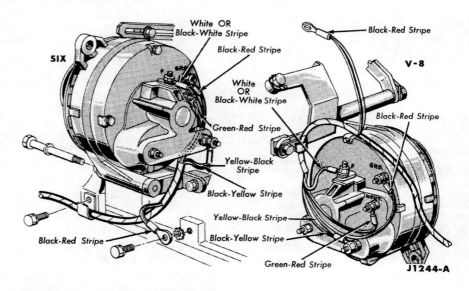

FIG. 1—Alternator Mounting—Typical

2 REMOVAL AND INSTALLATION

REMOVAL

1. Disconnect the battery ground cable.
2. Loosen the alternator mounting bolts and remove the adjustment arm to alternator bolt.
3. Disengage the alternator belt. Remove the alternator mounting bolt, disconnect the alternator wiring and remove the alternator.

INSTALLATION

1. Attach the alternator wiring. Position the alternator to the engine, and install the alternator mounting bolt finger-tight (Fig. 1).
2. Install the adjustment arm to alternator bolt.
3. Adjust the belt tension using tool T63L-8620-A. Apply pressure on the alternator drive end housing only. Tighten the adjusting arm bolts and the mounting bolt.
4. Connect the battery ground cable.

3 MAJOR REPAIR OPERATION

DISASSEMBLY

1. Remove the brush holder and the brushes (Fig. 2). Scribe the end housings for reference in assembly.
2. Remove the alternator housing through bolts, and separate the drive end housing and rotor from the stator and brush end housing.
3. Press the rotor shaft out of the drive end housing only if the rotor or bearing are being replaced. Remove the bearing spacer.
4. Remove the bearing retainer, support the housing around the bearing pocket to prevent damage to the housing, and press the bearing from the drive end housing. Remove the bearing only if replacement is required.
5. Remove the BT, Neut., and ground terminal nuts and washers, and remove the brush end housing from the stator and diode rectifier assembly.
6. If the diode plates or stator are being replaced, carefully unsolder the three stator leads from the diode connector eyelets, and separate the leads from each other. Clean the solder from the eyelets.
7. Press the brush end housing bearing from the housing only if it is being replaced.

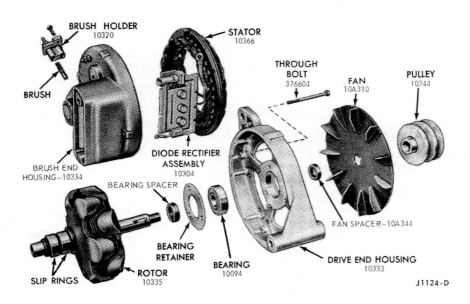

FIG. 2—Disassembled 53-Ampere Leece Neville Alternator

PARTS REPAIR OR REPLACEMENT

Nicks and scratches may be removed from the rotor slip rings by turning down the slip rings. Remove only enough to clean up the surface. If the slip rings are badly damaged, they should be replaced. Repair any broken lead wires.

ASSEMBLY

1. If the drive end bearing was removed, press the new bearing into the drive end housing putting pressure on the outer race only. Install the bearing retainer.

2. Place the bearing spacer on the drive end shaft and press the drive

end bearing on the shaft tight against the spacer. Put pressure on the inner race only.

3. If the brush end housing bearing was removed, press a new bearing into the housing flush with the outer surface of the housing.

4. Position the two diode plate assemblies together with the insulators and terminal bolts as shown in Fig. 3. The positive diode plate is positioned closest to the outside.

5. Position the eyelets over the diode leads, insert the three stator leads in the eyelets and solder them in position.

6. Position the brush end housing over the diode plate assembly and install the insulators, washers and terminal nuts. The condenser ground lug is mounted under the ground terminal nut. Make certain that the stator leads are positioned out of the way of the rotor (Fig. 4).

7. Position the rotor and drive end housing and the stator and brush end housing together. Align the housing scribe marks and install the housing through bolts.

8. Install the slip ring brushes and brush holder.

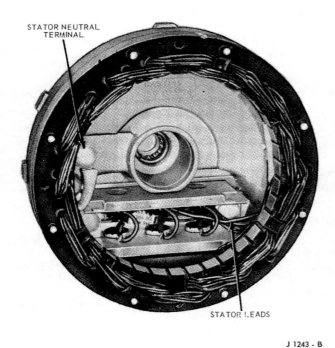

FIG. 3—Diode Plate and Star Assembly

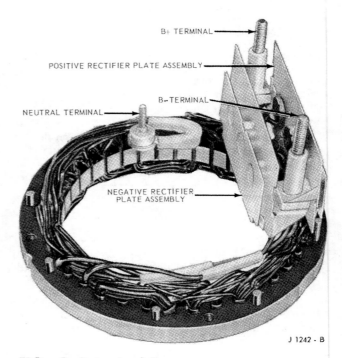

FIG. 4—Stator Lead Dress

PART 13-5 60-AMPERE LEECE NEVILLE ALTERNATOR

1 DESCRIPTION AND OPERATION

The operation and general electrical description of the 60-ampere alternator is the same as that for the Autolite alternator (Part 13-2). The field brushes of the 60-ampere alternator are mounted in a sealed brush holder on the brush end housing. (Fig. 2). Two shielded and sealed ball bearings support the rotor in both end housings.

Refer to Wiring Diagram Manual Form 7795P-66 for locations of wiring harnesses. Schematics are shown in Group 22 of this manual.

2 REMOVAL AND INSTALLATION

1. Disconnect the battery ground cable.

2. Loosen the mounting bolts and the adjusting arm to alternator bolt, and remove the drive belt.

3. Remove the mounting bolts and the adjusting arm bolt, disconnect the alternator wires and remove the alternator.

4. Connect the alternator wires (Fig. 1), position the alternator in the mounting bracket and install the mounting bolts and adjusting bracket bolt finger-tight.

5. Adjust the belt tension (Section 3, Part 13-1), tighten the mounting bolts, and check the operation of the alternator.

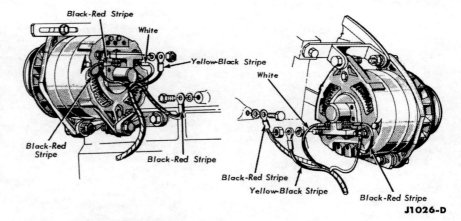

FIG. 1—Alternator Mounting

3 MAJOR REPAIR OPERATIONS

A disassembled view of the alternator is shown in Fig. 2.

DISASSEMBLY

1. Remove the pulley nut and washer, remove the pulley with a gear puller, and remove the shaft key and spacer.

2. Remove the brushes and terminal insulator, and remove the brush holder assembly from the brush end housing.

3. Remove the through bolts and separate the brush end housing and

stator assembly from the alternator.

4. Remove the nuts from the three AC terminals. Remove the stator from the end housing.

5. Remove the rotor from the drive-end housing using a gear puller or an arbor press only if the bearing is defective and must be replaced.

6. Unsolder the field leads from the slip rings, and remove the slip rings and the bearing from the slip ring end of the rotor shaft, only if the bearing is defective and must be replaced. Use a gear puller. **Use care**

in removing the slip rings, so as not to damage them. If they are cracked or broken during disassembly, they must be replaced.

7. Remove the bearing retainer from the drive-end housing and press out the old bearing from the housing, only if the bearing is defective and must be replaced.

8. Remove the rectifier assembly mounting bolts, terminals, and insulators and remove the rectifier assemblies. Remove the stator terminal insulator.

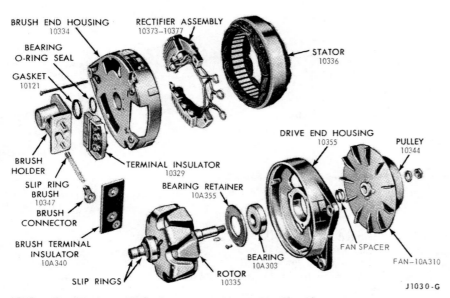

FIG. 2—Disassembled 60-Ampere Leece Neville Alternator

PARTS REPAIR
OR REPLACEMENT

Nicks and scratches may be removed from the rotor slip rings by turning down the slip rings. Remove only enough to clean up the surface. If the slip rings are badly damaged, they should be replaced.

ASSEMBLY

1. Press the new bearing onto the slip-ring end of the rotor shaft. **Put pressure on the inner race only.** Heat the slip rings so that the insulation will not split, carefully press the slip rings on the shaft and solder the field wires to the rings.

2. Press the new bearing into the drive end housing, and install the bearing retainer. **Put pressure on the outer race only.**

3. Place the slip-ring end of the shaft firmly on a flat plate in an arbor press, and assemble the drive end housing and bearing on to the drive end of the shaft. **Use a tube or pipe so as to put pressure on the bearing inner race only.**

4. Install the stator insulator. Put the rectifier insulators in position. Place the rectifier assemblies in the

housing and install the mounting screws and terminals. Make certain that the rectifier assemblies are insulated from the end frame. Position the three rectifier terminals to the terminal studs. Position the wires under the tabs extending from each

heat sink to prevent interference with the rotor (Fig. 3).

5. Place the stator in position (Fig. 3), and line up the end-housing through bolt holes to match those in the stator. Position the three stator terminals over the three rectifier terminals, and install the terminal nuts (Fig. 3).

6. Place the brush end housing and stator assembly into position over the rotor. Use the housing through bolts to line up the two housings and the stator. Tighten the housing through bolts.

7. Install the brush holder with the O-ring between the holder and the frame (Fig. 2). Place the brushes and springs in the holder with the extruded portion of the brush connectors against the terminal screw shoulders. Hold the brush connectors in position with a machinists steel scale until the terminal insulator is installed. Install the brush terminal insulator, and withdraw the steel scale.

8. Use a spacer that will provide $1/16$ inch clearance between the fan fins and the drive end housing. Install the fan spacer, shaft key, fan, pulley, and lock washer and nut. Tighten the mounting nut to 40 ft.-lbs. torque.

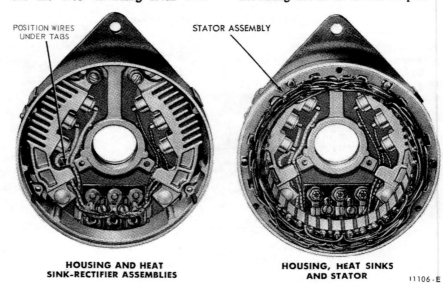

FIG. 3—Slip-Ring End Housing, Rectifier, and Stator Assembly

PART 13-6 LEECE-NEVILLE ALTERNATOR REGULATORS

1 DESCRIPTION AND OPERATION

The alternator regulators are composed of two control units mounted as an assembly (Fig. 1). The units are similar in operation to those used on the standard alternator regulator and consist of a double-contact voltage limiter and a field relay.

Two regulators are used. The regulator used with an ammeter charge indicator has three terminals, battery (BAT), ignition (IGN), and field (FLD). The regulator used with the charge indicator light has four terminals; three on the front, battery (BAT), Light (LAMP), and field (FLD); one on the back, neutral (NEUT). The replacement regulator

FIG. 1—Leece Neville Alternator Regulator

has five terminals including an ignition terminal (IGN).

Refer to Wiring Diagram Manual Form 7795P-66 for locations of wiring harnesses. Schematics are shown in Group 22 of this manual.

FIELD RELAY

The field relay (Fig. 1) is controlled by the ignition switch, on cars with an ammeter, and by alternator neutral junction voltage on cars with a charge indicator light. The field relay connects the battery to the alternator field through the voltage limiter contacts.

VOLTAGE LIMITER

The voltage limiter holds the alternator voltage within a predetermined range by controlling the amount of current supplied to the rotating field.

2 IN-CAR ADJUSTMENTS AND REPAIRS

REGULATOR ADJUSTMENTS

Final checking of the regulator must be made with the regulator at normal operating temperature and the cover in place. For any of the adjustments given below, remove the cover by removing the two mounting screws.

REGULATOR GAP ADJUSTMENTS

Make the regulator gap adjustments with the regulator removed from the car.

Voltage Limiter. Adjust the contact gap adjusting arm lock screw (Fig. 2), and adjust the contact gap to specification (Part 13-7). Tighten the lock screw. Adjust the core gap with the lower contacts closed. Loosen the core gap lock screw and move the contact insulator up or down until the specified core gap is arrived at between the coil core and the armature. Tighten the lock screw.

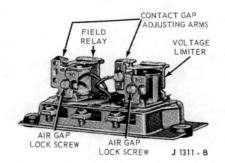

FIG. 2—Regulator Gap Adjustments

Field Relay. Adjust the core gap first. Loosen the field relay air gap lock screw and move the contact insulator up or down until the specified core air gap is arrived at between the coil core and the armature. Tighten the lock screw. Put the blade of a small screw driver in the field relay adjusting arm slot (Fig. 2), and bend

the arm to obtain the specified contact gap (Part 13-7).

REGULATOR VOLTAGE ADJUSTMENTS

Voltage Limiter. To increase the voltage setting, bend the adjusting arm downward (Fig. 3). To decrease the voltage setting, bend the adjusting arm upward (Fig. 3). **Before ad-**

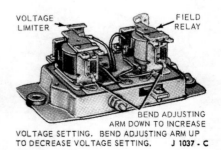

VOLTAGE LIMITER FIELD RELAY
BEND ADJUSTING ARM DOWN TO INCREASE VOLTAGE SETTING. BEND ADJUSTING ARM UP TO DECREASE VOLTAGE SETTING. J 1037 - C

FIG. 3—Alternator Regulator Adjustments—Typical

justing the voltage, and before making a final voltage reading with the cover in place, cycle the alternator. Reduce the alternator speed to zero and turn the ignition switch to OFF momentarily. This procedure must be repeated each time an adjustment is made.

Field Relay. The field relay cut-in voltage is increased by bending the adjusting arm downward, or decreased by bending the adjusting arm upward (Fig. 3).

3 REMOVAL AND INSTALLATION

1. Disconnect the battery ground cable.

2. Remove the wires from the regulator.

3. Remove the regulator mounting screws and the regulator.

4. Position the regulator and install the mounting screws. Mount the black-red stripe ground wire lug under the mounting screw at the ground strap end of the regulator. (Fig. 4 or 5).

5. Connect the remaining regulator wires (Fig. 4 or 5).

6. Connect the battery ground cable and check the regulator operation.

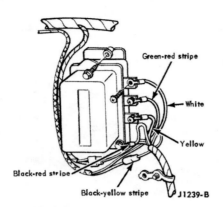

FIG. 4—Regulator Mounting Ammeter Circuit

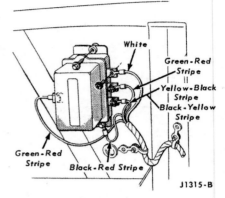

FIG. 5—Regulator Mounting—Indicator Light

PART 13-7

SPECIFICATIONS

ALTERNATOR

Supplier	Stamp Color	Rating		Field Current Amps @ 12V	Cut-In Speed (Engine r.p.m.)	Rated Output Speed (Engine r.p.m.)	Slip-Ring Turning (Inches)		Brush Length (Inches)		Pulley Nut Torque (ft.-lbs.)	Belt Tension (lbs.)	
		Amperes @ 15V	Watts @ 15V				Min. Dia.	Max. Runout	New	Wear Limit		6 Cyl.	8 Cyl.
Autolite	Orange	42	630	2.9	400	1600 Cold 2900 Hot	1.22	0.0005	½	5/16	60-100	60-90	80-110
Autolite	Black	45	675	2.9	400	1700 Cold 2900 Hot	1.22	0.0005	½	5/16	60-100	60-90	80-110
Autolite	Red	55	825	2.9	400	1400 Cold 2900 Hot	1.22	0.0005	½	5/16	60-100	60-90	80-110
Leece-Neville	—	53	795	2.9	400	1700 Cold 2100 Hot	Light Cut	0.002	⅝	⅜	30-50	60-90	80-110
Autolite	Green	60	840	4.6	400	2000 Cold 2900 Hot	1.22	0.0005	½	5/16	60-100	60-90	80-110
Leece-Neville	—	60	840	2.9	400	1600 Cold 2000 Hot	Light Cut	0.002	½	9/32	30-50	60-90	80-110

①Used Belt. New Belt 110-140. A used belt is one that has been in operation more than 10 minutes. Ford Alternator Pulley nut Torque 60-100 foot pounds.

REGULATOR

Vendor	Current Reading	Lower Stage Voltage Regulation @ 75° F.	VOLTAGE LIMITER			FIELD RELAY		
			Contact Gap (Inches)	Core Air Gap (Inches)	Contact Gap (Inches)	Core Air Gap (Inches)	Closing Volts	
Autolite	Used With Ford Alternators	14.1-14.9	0.017-0.022	0.049-0.056	———	00.010-0.018	2.5-4	
Autolite	Transistor Regulator Used With 42, 45, 55 and 60 Ampere Alternators	14.1-14.9	———	———	———	———	2.5-4	
Leece-Neville Indicator Light Circuit	Used With 53 Ampere Leece-Neville Alternator	14.1-14.9	0.018-0.020 With Lower Contacts Closed	0.042-0.052 With Lower Contacts Closed	0.018-0.020	0.009-0.011 With Contacts Touching	1.6-2.6	
Leece-Neville Ammeter Circuit	Used With 53 and 60-Ampere Leece-Neville Alternator	14.1-14.9	0.018-0.020 With Lower Contacts Closed	0.042-0.052 With Lower Contacts Closed	0.024-0.026	0.011-0.013 With Contacts Touching	6.2-7.2	

①See table on this page for voltage settings at other temperatures.
②Silver stamp color is used with 38 and 42-ampere alternators.
  Yellow stamp color is used with 45 and 55-ampere alternators.

VOLTAGE REGULATION SETTING

Ambient Temperature °F.	All Alternator Regulators
50	14.3-15.1
75	14.1-14.9
100	13.9-14.7
125	13.8-14.6

BATTERY

Filler Cap Color	Number of Plates	Amp. Hours
Yellow	54	45
Red	66	55
Gray	66	70
Black	78	80
Black	90	85

ALLOWABLE BATTERY HIGH RATE CHARGE TIME SCHEDULE

Specfic Gravity Reading	Charge Rate Amperes	BATTERY	CAPACITY	AMPERE	HOURS
		45	55	70	80
1.125-1.150*	35	65 min.	80 min.	100 min.	115 min.
1.150-1.175	35	50 min.	65 min.	80 min.	95 min.
1.175-1.200	35	40 min.	50 min.	60 min.	70 min.
1.200-1.225	35	30 min.	35 min.	45 min.	50 min.
Above 1.225	5	**	**	**	**

*If the specific gravity is below 1.125, use the indicated high rate of charge for the 1.125 specific gravity, then charge at 5 amperes until the specific gravity reaches 1.250 at 80° F.

Charge at 5 ampere rate **only until the specific gravity reaches 1.250 at 80°F.

At no time during the charging operation should the electrolyte temperature exceed 130°F.

BATTERY FREEZING TEMPERATURES

Specific Gravity	Freezing Temp.
1.280	—90°F.
1.250	—62°F.
1.200	—16°F.
1.150	+ 5°F.
1.100	+19°F.

TOOLS

Ford Tool No.	Former No.	Description
Tool T63L-8620-A	8620 BT-33-73-F	Belt Tension Gauge

STARTING SYSTEM

GROUP 14

GENERAL STARTING SYSTEM SERVICE

1 DIAGNOSIS AND TESTING

The starting system includes the starting motor and drive, the battery, the starter relay, the starter (ignition) switch, and the necessary cables and wiring to connect the components. Vehicles equipped with an automatic transmission employ a neutral-start switch in the system which prevents operation of the starter in all selector positions except N (neutral) and P (park).

A schematic diagram of the starting circuit is shown in Fig. 1.

The majority of starting problems usually fall into one of the following situations: the starter will not crank the engine; the engine will crank at normal speed but will not start; and the starter cranks the engine very slowly.

If the engine will crank but will not start, the trouble is usually in the engine, fuel system or ignition system rather than in the starting system.

Following are road map type charts which may be followed to determine the cause of the difficulty and the corrective action.

ROAD SERVICE

On road service calls, connect a booster battery to the system for

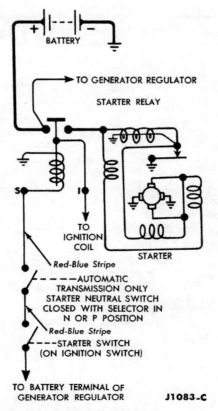

FIG. 1—Starting Circuit

BATTERY

TO GENERATOR REGULATOR

STARTER RELAY

S   I

TO IGNITION COIL

STARTER

Red-Blue Stripe

— — —AUTOMATIC TRANSMISSION ONLY STARTER NEUTRAL SWITCH CLOSED WITH SELECTOR IN N OR P POSITION

Red-Blue Stripe

- - -STARTER SWITCH (ON IGNITION SWITCH)

TO BATTERY TERMINAL OF GENERATOR REGULATOR   J1083-C

cases of a starter that will not crank the engine or a starter that cranks the engine very slowly. If the starter turns the engine over, but the engine still will not start, even with the booster battery attached, refer to the following charts. **Be certain that correct battery polarity is observed when using a booster battery; positive to positive, and negative to negative connection of the auxiliary cables.**

STARTER WILL NOT CRANK THE ENGINE

Refer to Fig. 2 for this symptom.

NOTE 1—NEUTRAL START SWITCH TEST

On vehicles equipped with an automatic transmission, apply the brakes and attempt to start the engine while moving the selector lever through all ranges. This may determine if the problem is caused by a maladjusted or defective neutral-start switch. Refer to Group 7 Part 3 for the adjustment of this switch.

NOTE 2

Connect a heavy jumper cable from the battery terminal of the relay

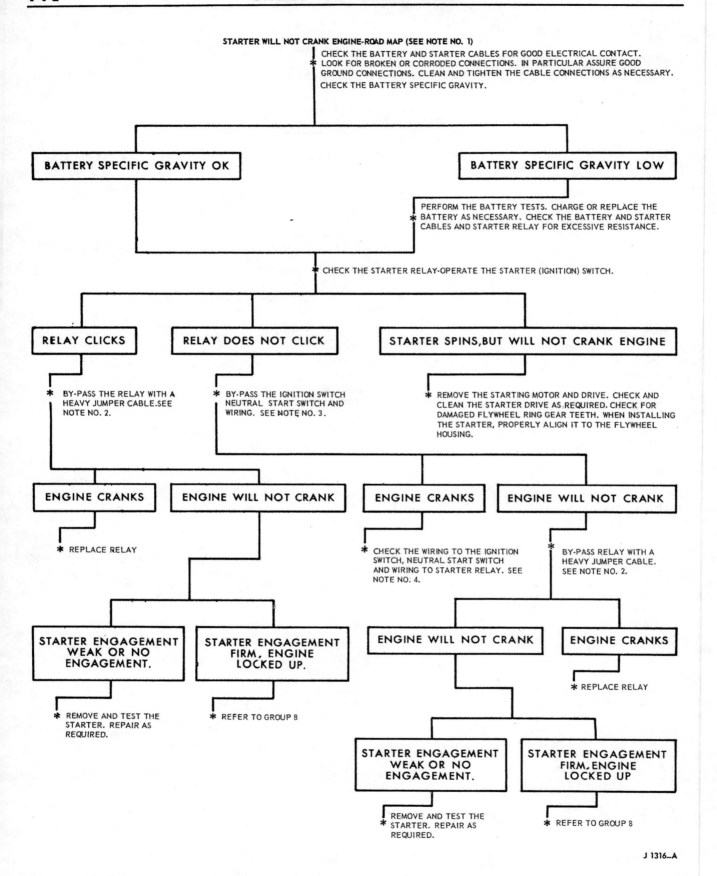

STARTER WILL NOT CRANK ENGINE-ROAD MAP (SEE NOTE NO. 1)

* CHECK THE BATTERY AND STARTER CABLES FOR GOOD ELECTRICAL CONTACT. LOOK FOR BROKEN OR CORRODED CONNECTIONS. IN PARTICULAR ASSURE GOOD GROUND CONNECTIONS. CLEAN AND TIGHTEN THE CABLE CONNECTIONS AS NECESSARY. CHECK THE BATTERY SPECIFIC GRAVITY.

BATTERY SPECIFIC GRAVITY OK

BATTERY SPECIFIC GRAVITY LOW

* PERFORM THE BATTERY TESTS. CHARGE OR REPLACE THE BATTERY AS NECESSARY. CHECK THE BATTERY AND STARTER CABLES AND STARTER RELAY FOR EXCESSIVE RESISTANCE.

* CHECK THE STARTER RELAY-OPERATE THE STARTER (IGNITION) SWITCH.

RELAY CLICKS

RELAY DOES NOT CLICK

STARTER SPINS, BUT WILL NOT CRANK ENGINE

* BY-PASS THE RELAY WITH A HEAVY JUMPER CABLE. SEE NOTE NO. 2.

* BY-PASS THE IGNITION SWITCH NEUTRAL START SWITCH AND WIRING. SEE NOTE NO. 3.

* REMOVE THE STARTING MOTOR AND DRIVE. CHECK AND CLEAN THE STARTER DRIVE AS REQUIRED. CHECK FOR DAMAGED FLYWHEEL RING GEAR TEETH. WHEN INSTALLING THE STARTER, PROPERLY ALIGN IT TO THE FLYWHEEL HOUSING.

ENGINE CRANKS

ENGINE WILL NOT CRANK

ENGINE CRANKS

ENGINE WILL NOT CRANK

* REPLACE RELAY

* CHECK THE WIRING TO THE IGNITION SWITCH, NEUTRAL START SWITCH AND WIRING TO STARTER RELAY. SEE NOTE NO. 4.

* BY-PASS RELAY WITH A HEAVY JUMPER CABLE. SEE NOTE NO. 2.

STARTER ENGAGEMENT WEAK OR NO ENGAGEMENT.

STARTER ENGAGEMENT FIRM, ENGINE LOCKED UP.

ENGINE WILL NOT CRANK

ENGINE CRANKS

* REPLACE RELAY

* REMOVE AND TEST THE STARTER. REPAIR AS REQUIRED.

* REFER TO GROUP 8

STARTER ENGAGEMENT WEAK OR NO ENGAGEMENT.

STARTER ENGAGEMENT FIRM, ENGINE LOCKED UP

* REMOVE AND TEST THE STARTER. REPAIR AS REQUIRED.

* REFER TO GROUP 8

J 1316—A

FIG. 2—Starter Will Not Crank Engine—Road Map

to the starter terminal of the relay (Fig. 3, connection No. 1).

NOTE 3—STARTER RELAY TEST

Connect a jumper from the battery terminal of the relay to the starter (ignition) switch terminal of the relay (Fig. 3, connection No. 2). If the engine does not crank, the starter relay probably is at fault.

NOTE 4—STARTER CONTROL CIRCUIT TEST

On vehicles equipped with an automatic transmission, if the engine cranks, connect a jumper from the battery terminal of the relay to the relay side of the neutral-start switch (Fig. 3, connection No. 3). If the engine does not crank, the wiring between the neutral-start switch and the relay is at fault. If the engine cranks, connect a jumper from the battery terminal of the relay to the starter (ignition) switch side of the neutral-start switch (Fig. 3, connection No. 4). If the engine does not crank, the neutral-start switch is out of adjustment or defective. If the engine cranks, check for voltage at the battery terminal of the starter (ignition) switch wiring harness connec-

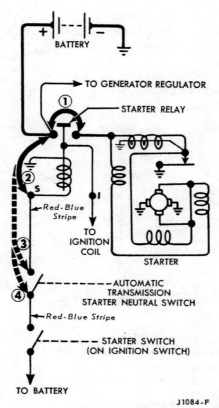

FIG. 3—Starting Control Circuit Tests

tor with a test light or a voltmeter. If voltage is not available, the wiring between the battery terminal of the starter relay and the battery terminal of the starter (ignition) switch is at fault. If voltage is available, substitute an ignition switch from stock. If the engine cranks, replace the ignition switch. If the engine still will not crank, the trouble is in the wiring or connections between the ignition switch and the starter-neutral switch.

STARTER CRANKS ENGINE SLOWLY

Refer to Fig. 4 for this symptom.

ENGINE WILL CRANK AT NORMAL SPEED BUT WILL NOT START

Refer to Group 8 for this symptom.

STARTER LOAD TEST

Connect the test equipment as shown in Fig. 5. Be sure that no current is flowing through the ammeter and heavy-duty carbon pile rheostat portion of the circuit (rheostat at maximum counterclockwise position).

Crank the engine with the ignition OFF, and determine the exact reading on the voltmeter. This test is ac-

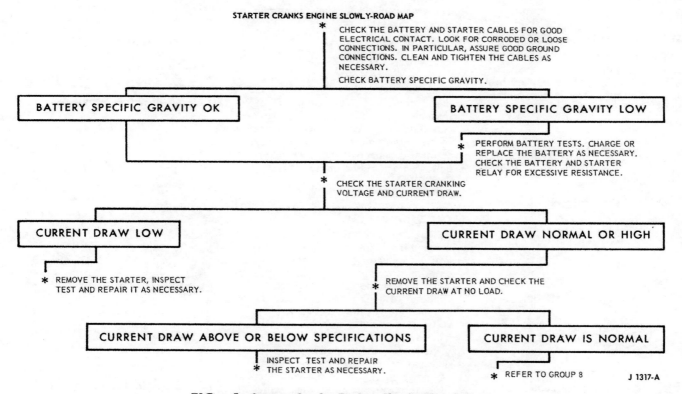

FIG. 4—Starter Cranks Engine Slowly—Road Map

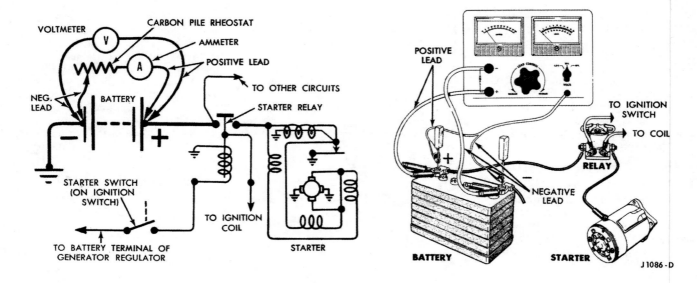

FIG. 5—Starter Load Test

complished by disconnecting and grounding the high tension lead from the spark coil, and by connecting a jumper from the battery terminal of the starter relay to the ignition switch terminal of the relay.

Stop cranking the engine, and reduce the resistance of the carbon pile until the voltmeter indicates the same reading as that obtained while the starter cranked the engine. The ammeter will indicate the starter current draw under load.

STARTER NO-LOAD TEST

The starter no-load test will uncover such faults as open or shorted windings, rubbing armature, and bent armature shaft. The starter can be tested, at no-load, on the test bench only.

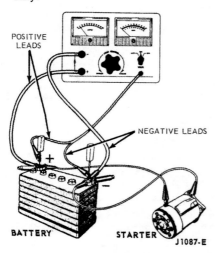

FIG. 6—Starter No-Load Test on Test Bench

Make the test connections as shown in Fig. 6. The starter will run at no-load. Be sure that no current is flowing through the ammeter (rheostat at maximum counterclockwise position). Determine the exact reading on the voltmeter.

Disconnect the starter from the battery, and reduce the resistance of the rheostat until the voltmeter indicates the same reading as that obtained while the starter was running. The ammeter will indicate the starter no-load current draw.

ARMATURE OPEN CIRCUIT TEST—ON TEST BENCH

An open circuit armature may sometimes be detected by examining the commutator for evidence of burning. The spot burned on the commutator is caused by an arc formed every time the commutator segment, connected to the open circuit winding, passes under a brush.

ARMATURE AND FIELD GROUNDED CIRCUIT TEST— ON TEST BENCH

This test will determine if the winding insulation has failed, permitting a conductor to touch the frame or armature core.

To determine if the armature windings are grounded, make the connections as shown in Fig. 7. If the voltmeter indicates any voltage, the windings are grounded.

Grounded field windings can be detected by making the connections as shown in Fig. 8. If the voltmeter indicates any voltage, the field windings are grounded.

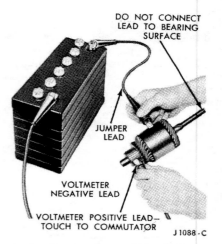

FIG. 7—Armature Grounded Circuit Test

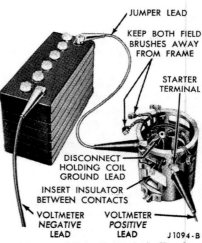

FIG. 8—Field Grounded Circuit Test

STARTER CRANKING CIRCUIT TEST

Excessive resistance in the starter circuit can be determined from the results of this test. Make the test connections as shown in Fig. 9. Crank the engine with the ignition OFF. This is accomplished by disconnecting and grounding the high tension lead from the spark coil and by connecting a jumper from the battery terminal of the starter relay to the ignition switch terminal(s), of the relay.

The *voltage drop* in the circuit will be indicated by the voltmeter (0 to 2 volt range). Maximum allowable voltage drop should be:

1. With the voltmeter negative lead connected to the starter terminal and the positive lead connected to the battery positive terminal (Fig. 9, connection ①) .... 0.5 volt.

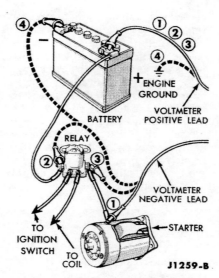

FIG. 9—Starter Cranking Circuit Test

2. With the voltmeter negative lead connected to the battery terminal of the starter relay and the positive lead connected to the positive terminal of the battery (Fig. 9, connection ②) .... 0.1 volt.

3. With the voltmeter negative lead connected to the starter terminal of the starter relay and the positive lead connected to the positive terminal of the battery (Fig. 9, connection ③) .... 0.3 volt.

4. With the voltmeter negative lead connected to the negative terminal of the battery and the positive lead connected to the engine ground (Fig. 9, connection ④) .... 0.1 volt.

---

2 COMMON ADJUSTMENTS AND REPAIRS

STARTER DRIVE REPLACEMENT

1. Loosen and remove the brush cover band and the starter drive plunger lever cover.

2. Loosen the through bolts enough to allow removal of the rear end housing and the starter drive plunger lever return spring.

3. Remove the pivot pin retaining the starter drive plunger lever and remove the lever.

4. Remove the drive gear stop ring retainer and stop ring from the end of the armature shaft and remove the drive gear assembly.

5. Apply a thin coating of Lubriplate 777 on the armature shaft splines. Install the drive gear assembly on the armature shaft and install a new stop ring.

6. Position the starter gear plunger lever on the starter frame and install the pivot pin. **Be sure that the plunger lever properly engages the starter drive-assembly.**

7. Install a new stop-ring retainer. Position the starter drive plunger lever return spring and rear end housing to the starter frame, and then tighten the through bolts to specifications (55-75 inch pounds).

8. Position the starter drive plunger lever cover and the brush cover band, with its gasket, on the starter. Tighten the brush cover band retaining screw.

BRUSH REPLACEMENT

Replace the starter brushes when

they are worn to ¼ inch. Always install a complete set of new brushes.

1. Loosen and remove the brush cover band, gasket, and starter drive plunger lever cover. Remove the brushes from their holders.

2. Remove the two through bolts from the starter frame.

3. Remove the rear end housing, and the plunger lever return spring.

4. Remove the starter drive plunger lever pivot pin and lever, and remove the armature.

5. Remove the front end plate.

6. Remove the ground brush retaining screws from the frame and remove the brushes (cut the ground brush nearest the starter terminal from the brush terminal block, as close to the brush lead terminal as possible).

7. Cut (or unsolder) the insulated brush leads from the field coils, as close to the field connection point as possible.

8. Clean and inspect the starter motor.

9. Replace the front end plate if the insulator between the field brush holder and the end plate is cracked or broken.

10. Position the new insulated field brushes lead on the field coil terminal. Install the clip provided with the brushes to hold the brush lead to the terminal. Solder the lead, clip, and terminal together, using rosin core solder (Fig. 4, Part 14-2). Use a 300-watt iron.

11. Install the ground brush leads to the frame with the retaining screws.

12. Clean the commutator with #00 or #000 sandpaper.

13. Position the front end plate to the starter frame, with the end plate boss in the frame slot.

14. Position the fiber washer on the commutator end of the armature shaft and install the armature in the starter frame.

15. Install the starter drive gear plunger lever to the frame and starter drive assembly, and install the pivot pin.

16. Position the return spring on the plunger lever, and the rear end housing to the starter frame. Install the through bolts and tighten to specified torque (55-75 inch pounds). Be sure that the stop ring retainer is seated properly in the rear end housing.

17. Install the commutator brushes in the brush holders. Center the brush springs on the brushes.

18. Position the plunger lever cover and the brush cover band, with its gasket, on the starter. Tighten the band retaining screw.

19. Connect the starter to a battery to check its operation.

ARMATURE REPLACEMENT

1. Loosen the brush cover band retaining screw and remove the brush cover band, gasket, and the starter drive plunger lever cover. Remove

the brushes from their holders.

2. Remove the through bolts, the rear end housing, and the drive plunger lever return spring.

3. Remove the pivot pin retaining the starter gear plunger lever, and remove the lever.

4. Remove the armature. If the starter drive gear assembly is being reused, remove the stop ring retainer and the stop ring from the end of the armature shaft, and remove the assembly.

5. Place the drive gear assembly

on the new armature with a new stop ring.

6. Install the fiber thrust washer on the commutator end of the armature shaft and install the armature.

7. Position the drive gear plunger lever to the frame and drive gear assembly and install the pivot pin.

8. Position the drive plunger lever return spring, the rear end housing, and the front end plate to the starter frame, and then install and tighten the through bolts to specification. Be sure that the stop ring retainer is

seated properly in the drive gear housing. If the starter has needle bearings apply a small amount of grease to the needles before installing the starter ends.

9. Place the brushes in their holders, and center the brush springs on the brushes.

10. Position the plunger lever cover and the brush cover band, with its gasket, and then tighten the retaining screw.

11. Connect the starter to a battery to check its operation.

3 CLEANING AND INSPECTION

1. Use a brush or air to clean the field coils, armature, commutator, armature shaft, front end plate, and rear end housing. Wash all other parts in solvent and dry the parts.

2. Inspect the armature windings for broken or burned insulation and unsoldered connections.

3. Check the armature for open circuits and grounds.

4. Check the commutator for run-out (Fig. 10). Inspect the armature shaft and the two bearings for scoring and excessive wear. On a starter with needle bearings apply a small amount of grease to the needles. If

the commutator is rough, or more

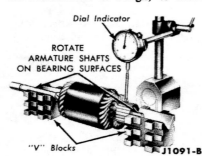

FIG. 10—Commutator Runout Check

than 0.005 inch out-of-round, turn it down.

5. Check the brush holders for broken springs and the insulated brush holders for shorts to ground. Tighten any rivets that may be loose. Replace the brushes if worn to ¼ inch in length.

6. Check the brush spring tension. Replace the springs if the tension is not within specified limits (40 ounces minimum).

7. Inspect the field coils for burned or broken insulation and continuity. Check the field brush connections and lead insulation.

PART 14-2 STARTER

1 DESCRIPTION AND OPERATION

The function of the starting system is to crank the engine at high enough speed to permit it to start. The system includes the starter motor and drive, the battery, a remote control starter switch (part of the ignition switch), the neutral-start switch, the starter relay, and heavy circuit wiring. The starter mounting is shown in Fig. 1.

Turning of the ignition key to the START position actuates the starter relay, through the starter control circuit. The starter relay then connects the battery to the starter.

Cars equipped with an automatic transmission have a neutral-start switch, in the starter control circuit, which prevents operation of the start-

FIG. 1—Starter Mounting

er if the selector lever is not in the N (neutral) or P (park) position.

The starter utilizes an integral positive-engagement drive (Fig. 2).

When the starter is not in use, one of the field coils is connected directly to ground through a set of contacts. When the starter is first connected to the battery a large current flows through the grounded field coil, actuating a movable pole shoe. The pole shoe is attached to the starter drive plunger lever and thus the drive is forced into engagement with the flywheel.

When the movable pole shoe is fully seated, it opens the field coil grounding contacts and the starter is then in normal operation. A holding coil is used to maintain the movable pole shoe in the fully seated position, during the time that the starter is turning the engine.

2 REMOVAL AND INSTALLATION

1. Raise the car on a hoist.
2. Disconnect the starter cable at the starter terminal.
3. Remove the starter mounting

bolts. Remove the starter assembly.

4. Position the starter assembly to the flywheel housing, and start the mounting bolts.

5. Snug all bolts, then torque them to specification.
6. Connect the starter cable.
7. Lower the car.

3 MAJOR REPAIR OPERATIONS

Use the following procedure when it becomes necessary to completely overhaul the starter. Fig. 2 illustrates a partially disassembled starter.

DISASSEMBLY

1. Loosen the brush cover band retaining screw and remove the brush cover band and the starter drive plunger lever cover. Observe the lead positions for assembly and then remove the commutator brushes from the brush holders.

2. Remove the through bolts, starter rear end housing, and the starter drive plunger lever return spring.

3. Remove the pivot pin retaining the starter gear plunger lever and remove the lever and the armature.

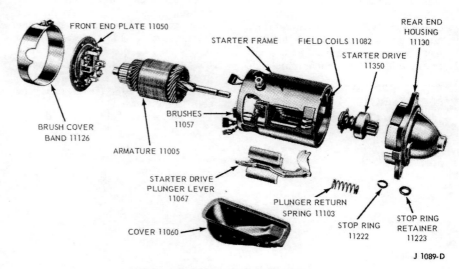

FIG. 2—Starter Disassembled

4. Remove the stop ring retainer. Remove and discard the stop ring retaining the starter drive gear to the end of the armature shaft, and remove the starter drive gear assembly.

5. Remove the front end plate.

6. Remove the two screws retaining the ground brushes to the frame.

7. On the field coil that operates the starter drive gear actuating lever, bend the tab up on the field retainer and remove the coil retainer.

8. Remove the three coil retaining screws, using tool 10044-A and an arbor press (Fig. 3). The arbor press prevents the wrench from slipping out of the screw. Unsolder the field coil leads from the terminal screw, and remove the pole shoes and coils from the frame (use a 300-watt iron).

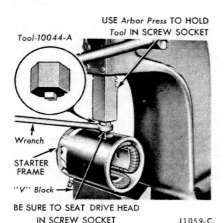

Tool-10044-A

USE *Arbor Press* TO HOLD
Tool IN SCREW SOCKET

Wrench

STARTER
FRAME

"V" *Block*

BE SURE TO SEAT DRIVE HEAD
IN SCREW SOCKET   J1059-C

FIG. 3—Pole Shoe Screw Removal

9. Cut (or unsolder) the insulated brush leads from the field coils, as close to the field connection point as possible.

10. Remove the starter terminal nut, washer, insulator and terminal from the starter frame. Remove any excess solder from the terminal slot.

PARTS REPAIR OR REPLACEMENT

Nicks and scratches may be re-

moved from the commutator by turning it down. A brush kit and a contact kit are available. All other assemblies are to be replaced rather than repaired. If the starter has needle bearings, apply a small amount of grease to the needles before assembly.

ASSEMBLY

1. Install the starter terminal, insulator, washers, and retaining nut in the frame (Fig. 4). Be sure to posi-

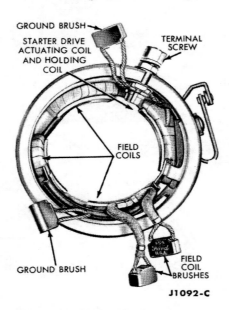

GROUND BRUSH

STARTER DRIVE
ACTUATING COIL
AND HOLDING
COIL

TERMINAL
SCREW

FIELD
COILS

GROUND BRUSH

FIELD
COIL
BRUSHES

J1092-C

FIG. 4—Field Coil Assembly

tion the slot in the screw perpendicular to the frame end surface.

2. Position the coils and pole pieces, with the coil leads in the terminal screw slot, and then install the retaining screws (Fig. 3). As the pole shoe screws are tightened, strike the frame several sharp blows with a soft-faced hammer to seat and align the pole shoes, then stake the screws.

3. Install the solenoid coil and retainer and bend the tabs to retain the coils to the frame.

4. Solder the field coils and sole-

noid wire to the starter terminal using rosin core solder. Use a 300-watt iron.

5. Check for continuity and grounds in the assembled coils.

6. Position the new insulated field brushes lead on the field coil terminal. Install the clip provided with the brushes to hold the brush lead to the terminal. Solder the lead, clip, and terminal together, using rosin core solder (Fig. 4). Use a 300-watt iron.

7. Position the solenoid coil ground terminal over the nearest ground screw hole.

8. Position the ground brushes to the starter frame and install the retaining screws (Fig. 4).

9. Position the starter brush end plate to the frame, with the end plate boss in the frame slot.

10. Apply a thin coating of Lubriplate 777 on the armature shaft splines. Install the starter motor drive gear assembly to the armature shaft and install a new retaining stop ring. Install a new stop ring retainer.

11. Position the fiber thrust washer on the commutator end of the armature shaft and position the armature in the starter frame.

12. Position the starter drive gear plunger lever to the frame and starter drive assembly, and install the pivot pin.

13. Position the starter drive plunger lever return spring and the rear end housing to the frame and install and tighten the through bolts to specification (55-75 inch pounds). **Do not pinch the brush leads between the brush plate and the frame.** Be sure that the stop ring retainer is seated properly in the drive housing.

14. Install the brushes in the brush holders. **Be sure to center the brush springs on the brushes.**

15. Position the drive gear plunger lever cover on the starter and install the brush cover band with a gasket. Tighten the band retaining screw.

16. Check the starter no-load amperage draw.

PART 14-3 SPECIFICATIONS

Vendor	Current Draw Under Normal Load (Amperes)	Normal Engine Cranking Speed (rpm)	Minimum Stall Torque @ 5 Volts (Foot Pounds)	Maximum Load (Amperes)	No-Load (Amperes)	Brushes		
						Mfg. Length (Inches)	Wear Limit (Inches)	Brush Spring Tension (Ounces)
Ford Positive Engagement 4.5 inch Diameter	250	250-290	15.5	670	70	0.5	0.25	40

Maximum commutator runout in inches is 0.005.
Maximum starting circuit voltage drop (battery + terminal to starter terminal @ normal engine temperature) 0.5 volt.
Starter through-bolt torque 55-75 inch pounds.
Starter mounting-bolt torque ⅜-inch bolt two-hole mounting 15-20 foot pounds, 5/16-inch bolt three-hole mounting 12-15 foot pounds.

SPECIAL TOOLS

Ford Tool No.	Former No.	Description
TOOL 10044-A	10044-A	Generator Pole Screw Wrench

LIGHTING SYSTEM, HORNS, AND INSTRUMENTS

GROUP 15

PART 15-1 GENERAL LIGHTING SYSTEM, HORNS, AND INSTRUMENTS SERVICE

LIGHTING TROUBLE DIAGNOSIS GUIDE

ALL HEADLIGHTS DO NOT LIGHT	1. Loose battery cable. 2. Loose quick disconnect or broken wire from the battery to the headlight switch. 3. Defective headlight switch. 4. Disconnected or broken wire from the headlight switch to the beam selector switch.	5. Loose or broken wire to the bulbs. 6. Defective beam selector switch. 7. All headlight bulbs burned out. This may be caused by a defective or improperly adjusted alternator voltage regulator (Group 13).
INDIVIDUAL LIGHTS DO NOT LIGHT	1. Burned out bulb. 2. Loose or broken wires to the	bulb. 3. Poor ground.
LIGHTS BURN OUT REPEATEDLY	1. Loose or corroded electrical connections. 2. Excessive vibration.	3. Improperly adjusted or defective alternator voltage regulator (Group 13).

LIGHTING TROUBLE DIAGNOSIS GUIDE (Continued)

BOTH LOW BEAM HEADLIGHTS DO NOT LIGHT	1. Defective beam selector switch. 2. Loose or broken wire to the bulbs.	3. Both low beam filaments burned out.

INSTRUMENT TROUBLE DIAGNOSIS GUIDE

OIL PRESSURE INDICATOR LIGHT INOPERATIVE—FORD	1. Indicator bulb burned out. 2. Loose or broken wire from the light to the indicator switch.	3. Defective oil pressure indicator switch.
CHARGE INDICATOR LIGHT INOPERATIVE—FORD	1. Burned out bulb. 2. Loose or broken wires to the armature terminal of the voltage regulator, or to the accessory terminal of the ignition switch.	3. Generator armature not grounded. 4. Generator regulator malfunction.
CHARGE INDICATOR LIGHT STAYS ON AT IDLE	1. Idle speed too low 2. Parallel resistance wire burned out.	
OIL PRESSURE INDICATOR GAUGE INOPERATIVE—MERCURY	1. Loose or broken wire from the constant voltage regulator to the oil gauge. 2. Grounded or broken wire from	the engine oil pressure sending unit. 3. Defective gauge. 4. Defective oil pressure sending unit.
CHARGE INDICATOR GAUGE INOPERATIVE—MERCURY	1. Defective gauge. 2. Loose or broken wires.	3. Alternator system malfunction.
FUEL GAUGE ERRATIC OR INOPERATIVE	1. Loose or broken wire from the constant voltage regulator to the fuel gauge. 2. Defective fuel gauge. 3. Loose, broken, or shorted wire from fuel gauge to the fuel tank sending unit.	4. Defective constant voltage regulator. 5. Defective fuel tank sending unit. 6. Poor ground between fuel tank and body.
TEMPERATURE GAUGE ERRATIC OR INOPERATIVE—MERCURY	1. Loose or broken wire from constant voltage regulator to the temperature gauge. 2. Defective temperature gauge. 3. Loose or broken wire from the	temperature sending unit to the temperature gauge. 4. Defective temperature sending unit.
BOTH FUEL AND TEMPERATURE GAUGES ERRATIC	1. Loose or corroded constant voltage regulator ground. 2. Defective constant voltage regulator.	3. Broken or loose wire from or to the constant voltage regulator. 4. Defective ignition switch.

HORN TROUBLE DIAGNOSIS GUIDE

HORNS DO NOT SOUND	1. Loose connection at horn button contact. 2. Open wire (yellow-green stripe) from horn to horn button. 3. Open wire (yellow) from horn button to circuit breaker in head-	light switch. 4. Horns defective or out of adjustment. 5. Defective relay on cars so equipped. 6. Horns not properly grounded.

HORN TROUBLE DIAGNOSIS GUIDE (Continued)

ONE HORN FAILS TO OPERATE	1. Broken or loose wire to the horn. (Black wire.) 2. Horn not properly grounded.	3. Horn defective or out of adjustment.
HORNS OPERATE CONTINUOUSLY	1. Horn button defective. 2. Shorted relay on cars so equipped.	

TURN INDICATOR TROUBLE DIAGNOSIS GUIDE

TURN INDICATOR LIGHTS INOPERATIVE	1. Burned out bulbs, or loose sockets. 2. Burned out fuse. 3. Loose or broken wire from ignition switch to flasher. 4. Defective flasher.	5. Loose or broken wire from flasher to turn indicator switch. 6. Defective turn indicator switch. 7. Broken, shorted, or loose wires from switch to lights.
TURN INDICATOR LIGHTS OPERATE INCORRECTLY	1. Loose, broken, or shorted wires from switch to light. 2. Defective indicator switch.	3. Defective flasher. 4. Burned out bulb.
TURN INDICATOR CANCELS IMPROPERLY	1. Cam improperly positioned on steering wheel hub.	2. Coil spring on switch plate assembly loose or weak.

WINDSHIELD WIPER TROUBLE DIAGNOSIS GUIDE

INOPERATIVE OR SLOW WIPER	1. Binding linkage. 2. Defective switch. 3. Defective wiper motor.	4. Defective wiring or circuit breaker.
CONTINUOUS WIPER ACTION WITH SELECTOR AT INTERMITTENT POSITION—MERCURY	1. Loose, broken, or plugged vacuum hose from engine to control to governor. 2. Ruptured governor or governor	switch diaphragm. 3. Defective control selector switch.
EXCESSIVE DWELL TIME DURING INTERMITTENT OPERATION—MERCURY	1. Pinched hose from lower governor fitting to control switch rear fitting.	2. Plugged orifice in control selector dwell regulator.

TESTING

Refer to Wiring Diagram Manual Form 7795P-66 for locations of wiring harnesses. Schematics are shown in Group 22 of this manual.

HORN TEST

The only test necessary on the horns is for current draw.

Connect a voltmeter and ammeter to the horn and to a voltage supply as shown in Fig. 1. The normal current draw for the horns at 12 volts is 4.0-5.0 amperes.

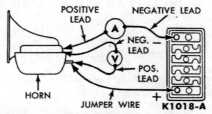

FIG. 1—Horn Current Draw Test

HEADLIGHT AND BEAM SELECTOR SWITCH TESTS

The following tests may be made

to determine whether a headlight switch or a beam selector switch is defective:

Set the headlight switch to the headlight position, and operate the beam selector switch. If none of the headlights turn on when the beam selector switch is operated, yet the instrument panel lights operate, the headlight switch or the red-yellow stripe wire from the headlight switch to the beam control switch is probably defective. Substitute a known good switch for the suspected switch to determine whether the switch or the wiring is at fault.

If the headlights operate only with the beam control switch in one position, the switch or the wiring from the switch to the headlight is defective. Substitute a known good switch for the suspected switch to determine whether the switch or the wiring is at fault.

CONSTANT VOLTAGE REGULATOR TEST

Turn the ignition switch ON. Check for voltage at the gauge feed wire. The voltage should oscillate between zero and about 10 volts. If it does not, the constant voltage regulator is defective, or there is a short to ground between the voltage regulator and the gauges.

If the gauge unit is inaccurate or does not indicate, replace it with a new unit. If the gauge unit still is erratic in its operation, the sending unit or wiring to the sending unit is faulty.

If the fuel gauge, the temperature gauge and the oil pressure gauge indicate improperly and in the same direction, the constant voltage regulator could be defective, as it supplies the three gauges.

FUEL GAUGE AND FUEL LEVEL SENDING UNIT TEST

Disconnect the wire at the fuel level sending unit and connect it to a known good sending unit. Connect a jumper wire from the sending unit mounting plate to ground or the car frame. Raise the float arm to the upper stop. The instrument panel gauge should read full. Lower the float arm to the bottom stop, the gauge should read empty.

If the gauge reads properly the sending unit in the gas tank is defective.

If the gauge unit still indicates improperly or is erratic in its operation, the gauge unit or the wiring to the gauge unit is faulty, repair the wire or replace the gauge unit.

LOW FUEL LEVEL WARNING SYSTEM TEST

A thermistor assembly is attached to the fuel sender outlet tube and is kept cooled when covered with gasoline. However, the thermistor will heat up when the fuel gets low enough to expose the thermistor to air. The thermistor resistance then drops and allows current to flow

through a warning signal relay. The relay contacts then close to light the warning light.

The low fuel warning light circuit is tested each time the ignition switch is turned to the start position. When the ignition switch is turned from ON to START, the warning light is illuminated. This proves that both the light circuit and the light are functioning properly.

The system consists of three components: the fuel sender assembly, the warning relay, and the warning light. In the event of system failure, the following tests can be made:

1. Check to see that the bulb lights with the switch in the start position.

2. Check for loose connections, broken wires, or a blown fuse.

3. With the ignition switch on ACC or ON position, disconnect the wiring at the sender assembly and ground the relay to thermistor wire (green, white stripe). If the warning light lights, replace the sender assembly. If the warning light does not light, replace the relay.

TEMPERATURE INDICATOR LIGHT TEST—FORD

This test must be performed only when the engine is cool. Turn the ignition switch to the ON position. The blue light should flash on. If the blue light does not flash on, remove the wire (white-green stripe) from the temperature sending unit and ground it to the engine. If the blue light now flashes on, the temperature sending unit is defective, or it was not properly sealed to the engine. **Be sure to use an electrically conductive sealer C3AZ-19554-B.** If the blue light does not flash on, the bulb or the wiring is defective.

Turn the ignition switch to the start position momentarily. The red light should flash on. If the red light does not flash on, remove the wire (red-white stripe) from the temperature unit and ground it to the engine. If the red light now flashes on, the red light prove out portion of the ignition switch is defective. If the red light does not flash on, the bulb or the wiring is defective.

TEMPERATURE GAUGE TEST —MERCURY

Start the engine and allow it to run until it has reached normal operating temperature. Place a thermometer in the coolant at the radiator filler cap. The temperature should read close to the temperature range

of the coolant thermostat that is being used. The gauge in the instrument panel should indicate within the normal band.

If the gauge does not indicate, momentarily short the temperature sender unit terminal wire to ground (ignition switch on). If the gauge now indicates, the sender unit is defective or it was not properly sealed to the engine. **Be sure to use an electrically conductive sealer C3AZ-19554-B.** If the gauge does not indicate, the gauge, the wires leading to the gauge or the constant voltage regulator are at fault. **Do not leave the sender wire grounded longer than necessary to make the test, as the gauge may be damaged.**

OIL PRESSURE INDICATOR LIGHT TEST—FORD

To test the indicator light, turn on the ignition switch. Do not start the engine. The light should come on. Start the engine. The light should go out, indicating that the oil pressure has built up to a safe value.

To test the oil pressure switch on the engine, turn the ignition switch on, engine not running, the indicator light should come on. If the indicator light does not come on, short the terminal of the oil pressure switch unit to ground. If the light now comes on, the oil pressure switch is defective, or not properly sealed to the engine. **Be sure to use electrically conductive sealer C3AZ-19554-B.** If the light still does not come on, the bulb is burned out or the wires from the bulb to the ignition switch and oil pressure switch are defective.

OIL PRESSURE INDICATOR GAUGE TEST—MERCURY

Remove the oil pressure sender unit and temporarily attach an oil pressure gauge in its place. Operate the engine to determine the oil pressure. If the oil pressure is normal, the gauge should indicate within the normal band.

If the gauge did not indicate, momentarily short the oil pressure sender wire to ground. If the gauge now indicates, the sender unit is defective or it was not properly sealed to the engine. **Be sure to use electrically conductive sealer C3AZ-19554-B.** If the gauge does not indicate, the gauge, the wires leading to the gauge or the constant voltage regulator are at fault. **Do not leave the sender wire grounded longer** than necessary to make the test, as the gauge may be damaged otherwise.

CHARGE INDICATOR LIGHT TEST—FORD

To test the charge indicator light, turn the ignition switch on with the engine stopped. The light should come on. If it does not, the bulb is burned out, or the wiring to the light is defective.

An open resistor wire in the Ford alternator charging system wiring harness will usually cause the charge indicator light to stay on until the engine speed is increased to several thousand rpm. This effect will be noticed each time the engine is started. In some cases the light will not go out at all.

The charge indicator light may be tested with the use of a test light containing a trade number 67 or 1155 bulb.

Disconnect the regulator plug from the regulator. Turn the ignition switch to the ACC position. Touch one test probe from the test light to the ignition terminal and the other to the regulator base. The test light will come on if the circuit is in proper working order. If the 15 ohm resistor or circuit is open, the indicator light will operate at full brightness and the test light will be out.

AMMETER TEST—MERCURY

To test the ammeter, turn the headlights ON with the engine stopped. The meter pointer should move toward the D or discharge scale. If no movement of the needle is observed, check the rear of the meter housing to see if the battery to circuit breaker wire connections are loose. If the connections are tight, and the meter does not indicate a discharge, the meter is inoperative. **If the meter pointer moves toward the C or charge scale when the headlights are turned ON, the wire connections at the meter are reversed.**

SPEEDOMETER TESTS

To test the odometer accuracy, drive the car over a measured mile. Speedometer accuracy can be checked by comparing the speedometer in question against one known to be accurate, while two cars are moving at the same speed, or by timing the car on a measured mile. The Ford Car Master Parts Catalog and the Lincoln Mercury Parts and Accessories Catalog show the proper speedometer gears to use for various rear axle and tire size combinations.

2 COMMON ADJUSTMENTS AND REPAIRS

HORN ADJUSTMENT

The current is adjusted by changing the contact tension. Connect the horn as shown in Fig. 1. Turn the self-locking adjusting nut until the current is within the limits for the horn being adjusted.

NEUTRAL START SWITCH ADJUSTMENT

See Part 7-2 on cars equipped with an automatic transmission.

3 CLEANING AND INSPECTION

SINGLE-SPEED ELECTRIC WIPER MOTOR

1. Clean the gear housing of all old grease. **Do not allow any cleaning fluid to contact the armature shaft and output shaft bearings.**
2. Wipe all other parts with a clean cloth.
3. Cover the motor housing bearing, and blow out any dust from the housing with compressed air.
4. Inspect the armature for burned commutator bars and loose connections. Check all shafts, bushings, and gears for scored surfaces. Check the thrust ball for pitting or discoloration due to heat. Make sure that the output gear is not loose on the output

shaft, and that the cam surface is not worn. Replace any defective parts.
5. Check the armature for grounds with a test light. Replace the armature if it is grounded.
6. Inspect the brush plate assembly for cracks or distortion. The brush holders should be securely fastened to the brush plate. Inspect the contact points for burned or pitted surfaces. Replace defective parts.
7. Inspect the motor housing and magnet assembly. Replace the assembly if it has a cracked magnet, or if the thrust button is hollowed out to a diameter greater than $1/32$ inch.

8. Replace the brushes if they are worn to $5/16$ inch. Replace distorted or burned brush springs.

TWO-SPEED ELECTRIC WIPER MOTOR—FORD

1. Clean the gear housing of all old grease. **Do not allow any cleaning fluid to contact the armature shaft and output shaft bearings.**
2. Wipe all other parts with a clean cloth.
3. Inspect the gear housing for cracks or distortion. Replace a cracked or distorted housing.
4. Check all shafts, bushings, and gears for scored surfaces. Replace defective parts.

PART 15-2   LIGHTING SYSTEM AND HORNS

1   DESCRIPTION AND OPERATION

Refer to Wiring Diagram Manual Form 7795P-66 for locations of wiring harnesses. Schematics are shown in Group 22 of this manual.

HEADLIGHTS

Four sealed-beam headlights are used on the Mercury. The two outboard lights have two filaments each for low beam and high beam, and are marked by a numeral 2 molded in the glass lens. Locating tabs molded in the glass allow the mounting of the No. 2 lights in the outboard headlight support frames only. The low beams are used for city driving, when meeting oncoming traffic on the highway, and for No. 2 headlight alignment.

The inboard headlights with a numeral one molded in the glass lens have only one filament and are used for highway driving along with the high beams of the No. 2 headlights. Locating tabs molded in the glass allow the mounting of the No. 1 lights in the inboard headlight support frames only.

On the Ford, the sealed beam headlights are mounted with the No. 1 lights in the lower position and the No. 2 lights in the upper position.

A conventional beam control switch is located on the floor board near the left cowl trim panel. Quick disconnect terminals are provided at the left and right of the radiator support assembly. The terminals are color coded. Like colored terminals are connected together.

HORNS

All cars are equipped with a pair of tuned horns. The horn button switch closes the circuit to the horns without the use of a relay. One of the horns has a high-pitched tone; the other has a low-pitched tone.

Cars equipped with a tilt steering column have a relay in the circuit.

CORNERING LIGHTS—MERCURY

A continuous turning light is provided in the Mercury, located in each side of the front fenders.

The lights operate through the turn signal lever-switch through a relay that holds the circuit in a continuous closed position as long as the turn signals are on.

2   IN-CAR ADJUSTMENTS AND REPAIRS

HEADLIGHT ALIGNMENT

All headlight adjustments should be made with a half-full fuel tank plus or minus one gallon, with a person seated in the driver's seat, and a person seated in the right front passenger seat, the car unloaded and the trunk empty except for the spare tire and jacking equipment, and recommended pressure in all tires. Before each adjustment, bounce the car by pushing on the center of both the front and rear bumpers, to level the car.

To align the No. 1 headlights by means of a wall screen, select a level portion of the shop floor. Lay out the floor and wall as shown in Fig. 1. Establish the headlight horizontal centerline by subtracting 20 inches from the actual measured height of the headlight lens center from the floor and adding this difference to the 20-inch reference line obtained by sighting over the uprights to obtain dimension B (upper diagram

Fig. 2), low, and parallel to the headlight horizontal centerline. Then draw the headlight vertical centerlines on the screen as measured on the car (dimension A, upper diagram Fig. 2).

NO. 1 HEADLIGHT ADJUSTMENT—MERCURY INNER LIGHTS, FORD LOWER LIGHTS

Adjust each No. 1 headlight beam as shown in Fig. 2. **Cover the No. 2**

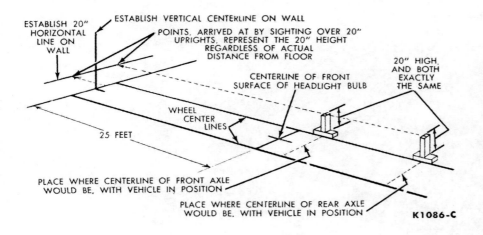

FIG. 1—Floor and Wall Layout

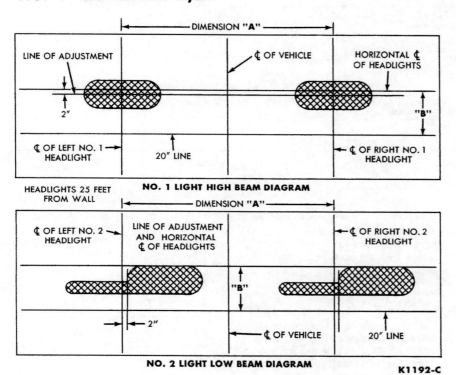

FIG. 2—Headlight Wall Screens

lights when making this adjustment.

Some states may not approve of the 2-inch dimension for the No. 1 headlights. Check the applicable state law, as a 3-inch dimension may be required.

NO. 2 HEADLIGHT ADJUSTMENT—MERCURY OUTER LIGHTS

To align the No. 2 headlights (outer lights) a different wall chart (lower diagram Fig. 2) is used. Dimension B for the No. 2 lights is the same as B for the No. 1 lights. Dimension A is as measured on the car. Note that the line of adjustment of the No. 2 lights is the horizontal centerline of the No. 2 lights. Turn the headlights to low beam and adjust each No. 2 light as shown in Fig. 2.

Each headlight can be adjusted by means of two screws located under the headlight trim ring as shown in Fig. 3. Always bring each beam into final position by turning the adjusting screws clockwise so that the headlights will be held against the tension

springs when the operation is completed.

NO. 2 HEADLIGHT ADJUSTMENT—FORD UPPER LIGHTS

To align the Ford No. 2 headlights (upper lights), a new wall chart is used. Dimension B for the No. 2 lights will be different than B for the No. 1 lights, but dimension A which is measured on the car will be the same as for the No. 1 lights. Note that the line of adjustment of the No. 2 lights is the horizontal centerline of the No. 2 lights. Turn the headlights to low beam and adjust each No. 2 light as shown in Fig. 2.

Each headlight can be adjusted by means of two screws located under the headlight trim ring (Fig. 4). Always bring each beam into final position by turning the adjusting screws clockwise so that the headlights will be held against the tension springs when the operation is completed.

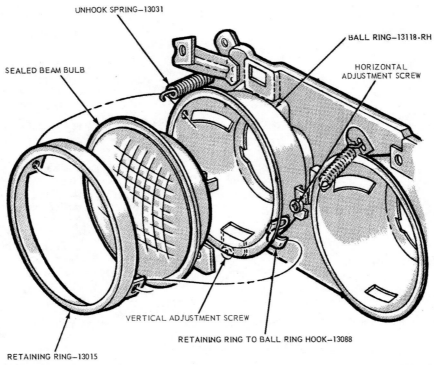

UNHOOK SPRING—13031

SEALED BEAM BULB

BALL RING—13118-RH

HORIZONTAL
ADJUSTMENT SCREW

VERTICAL ADJUSTMENT SCREW

RETAINING RING TO BALL RING HOOK—13088

RETAINING RING—13015

FIG. 3—Headlight Adjustment—Typical

K1520-D

3 REMOVAL AND INSTALLATION

HEADLIGHTS

1. Remove the screws and remove the headlight trim ring.

2. Place a hand over the headlight assembly and unhook the spring from the retaining ring.

3. Remove the retaining ring by unhooking the ring from the clip located directly across the bulb from the spring hook (Fig. 3).

4. Pull the headlight bulb forward and disconnect the wiring assembly plug.

5. Plug in the new bulb and place it in position, locating the bulb glass tabs in the positioning slots.

6. Hook the retaining ring over the clip, then over the bulb, and secure it with the existing ball-ring spring.

7. Align the bulb with the wall screen.

8. Install the trim ring in position and install the retaining screws.

PARKING LIGHT—FORD

To replace the bulb in the parking light, raise the hood, remove the bulb socket by pulling straight out, then remove the bulb.

PARKING LIGHT—MERCURY

To replace the bulb in the parking light remove the two retaining screws and the lens, then remove the bulb.

TAIL, STOP, BACK-UP AND LICENSE PLATE LIGHTS—FORD

From inside the luggage compartment remove the four retaining screws. Pull the light assembly back from the car, snap out the socket and remove the bulb. On station wagons the retaining screws are removed from outside the vehicle.

To remove the bulb in the license plate light, remove the lens retaining screw, remove the lens, then remove the bulb.

TAIL, STOP, BACK-UP AND LICENSE PLATE LIGHTS— MERCURY

To replace a bulb in the upper rear lights, open the deck lid, remove the socket and bulb from the tail light body, then remove the bulb.

To replace a bulb in the lower rear lights, remove the lens retaining screws, remove the lens, then remove the bulb.

To remove the bulb in the license plate light, remove the lens retaining screw, remove the lens, then remove the bulb.

DOME LIGHT

Remove the two screws retaining the dome light lens and bezel. Remove the lens and bezel, then replace the bulb.

INSTRUMENT LIGHT

The instrument panel light bulbs can be replaced by pulling out the individual light sockets from the rear of the instrument panel.

HORNS

The horns are mounted on the horizontal fender and radiator support in the engine compartment. Disconnect the horn wire at the terminal, remove the mounting bracket support retaining screw and remove the horn from the support.

To install, place the horn in position, and install the retaining screw. Install the horn wire.

HORN RING—FORD

1. Disconnect the horn wire connector, that has a yellow and a yellow-green wire in it, under the instrument panel, to the left of the steering column.

2. Press down evenly on the horn ring and turn counterclockwise until it lifts out from the steering wheel.

3. Remove the horn ring and spring.

4. The horn ring contacts are integral with the turn signal switch and are removed with the switch.

5. *Install the horn ring spring and ring.*

6. Connect the horn wire connector under the instrument panel.

HORN BUTTON—MERCURY

1. Disconnect the horn wires at the connector at the lower end of the steering column.

2. Remove the hub from the steering column by pressing it down and rotating it counterclockwise.

3. Remove the screws from the center retaining the wires.

4. Remove the screws from the center, retaining the ring to the column and from end of the ring to the steering wheel. Remove the ring. A spring will fall out from under each button.

5. Position the springs under the buttons. Position the ring assembly to the wheel and install the center screws. Install the ring to the steering column, securing it with a screw at each end of the buttons, located in the steering spokes.

6. Install the screws in the center retaining the wires.

7. Install the hub.

8. Connect the electrical plug at the lower end of the steering column.

PART 15-3
SWITCHES, CIRCUIT BREAKERS, AND FUSES

1 DESCRIPTION AND OPERATION

Refer to Wiring Diagram Manual Form 7795P-66 for locations of wiring harnesses. Schematics are shown in Group 22 of this manual.

HEADLIGHT SWITCH

A combination headlight switch, dome light switch, and two circuit breakers is used (Fig. 1). The 18-ampere circuit breaker protects the headlight circuit. The 15-ampere circuit breaker protects the tail, park, license plate light, and horn circuits.

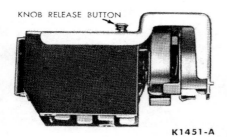

KNOB RELEASE BUTTON

K1451-A

FIG. 1—Headlight Switch

FUSES

The fuse panel is mounted on the dash panel near the brake pedal. Fig. 2 shows the fuse values and locations.

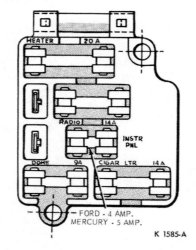

K 1585-A

FIG. 2—Fuse Panel

MECHANICAL STOP LIGHT SWITCH

The mechanical stoplight switch differs from the hydraulic switch formerly used. The switch assembly is installed on the pin of the brake pedal arm so that it straddles the master cylinder push rod (Fig. 3). The switch assembly is a slip fit on the pedal arm pin and thus the switch assembly moves with the pedal arm whenever the brake pedal is depressed.

The brake pedal arm pin has a designed-in clearance with the eye of the master cylinder push rod (Fig. 3). Because of this clearance, whenever the brake pedal is pushed forward, the stop light switch contacts, moving with the pedal arm, are actually pushed against the end of the master cylinder push rod, through the switch actuating pin. It is this movement of the switch with respect to the actuating pin and master cylinder push rod that closes the switch contacts completing the circuit to the stoplights.

When the brake pedal is released, the spring in the stop light switch returns the actuating pin to its normal position and the circuit to the stop lights opens.

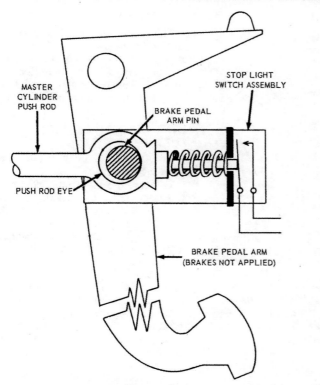

FIG. 3—Mechanical Stop Light Switch Operation

2 REMOVAL AND INSTALLATION

SWITCHES

Before removing any switch, disconnect the battery ground cable from the battery.

HEADLIGHT SWITCH

1. Remove the control knob and shaft by pressing the knob release button on the switch housing (Fig. 1), with the knob in the full ON position. Pull the knob out of the switch.

2. Unscrew the mounting nut, remove the switch and disconnect the wiring connector.

3. To install the switch, attach the wiring connector, insert the switch in the instrument panel, and install the mounting nut.

4. Install the knob and shaft assembly by inserting it all the way into the switch until a distinct click is heard. In some instances it may be necessary to rotate the shaft slightly until it engages the switch-contact carrier.

HEADLIGHT BEAM SELECTOR SWITCH

Lay the floor mat back from the area of the switch, and remove the mounting screws (Fig. 4). Disconnect the wire terminal block from the switch.

To install the switch, connect the terminal block to the switch and install the switch to the floor. Replace the floor mat.

FIG. 4—Headlight Beam Selector Switch

STOP LIGHT SWITCH

1. Disconnect the wires at the connector.

2. Remove the hairpin retainer, slide the stoplight switch, the push rod and the nylon washers and bushing away from the pedal, and remove the switch (Fig. 5).

3. Position the switch, push rod, and bushing and washers on the brake pedal pin, in the order shown in Fig. 5, and install the hairpin retainer.

4. Connect the wires at the connector, and install the wires in the retaining clip (Fig. 5).

TURN INDICATOR SWITCH AND WIRE ASSEMBLY

1. Disconnect the battery ground cable.

2. Remove the horn button.

3. Remove the steering wheel retaining nut.

4. Remove the steering wheel from the worm shaft.

5. Remove the turn indicator handle.

6. Remove the screws and turn indicator switch from the steering column tube.

7. Disconnect the connector blocks at the column. Release the tabs one at a time and remove the wires from the block connectors.

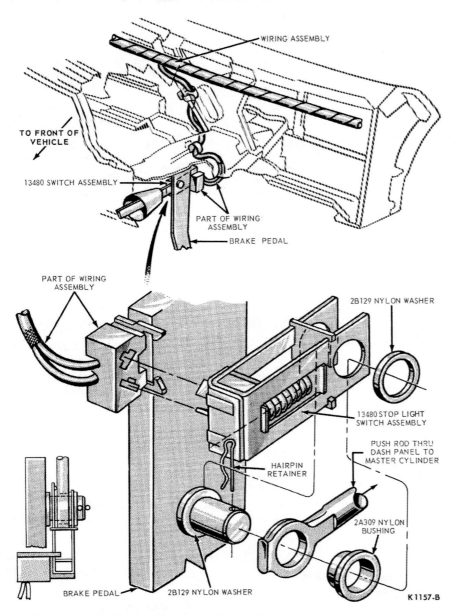

FIG. 5—Typical Stop Light Switch

8. From the lower portion of the column remove the cover from the wiring assembly and tie a cord to the wire ends. Remove the switch from the top of the column feeding the wire and cord up the column.

9. Attach the wire ends of a new turn indicator switch to the cord and feed the wires down through the steering column. Remove the cord and install the wire assembly cover.

10. Install the connector blocks in the column. Plug in the electrical leads and position the wiring assembly in the retaining clip.

11. Install the screws securing the turn indicator switch to the steering column tube and install the turn indicator handle.

12. Install the steering wheel on the worm shaft. Install the retaining nut, torque it and install the stake nut.

13. Install the horn button.

14. Connect the battery ground cable.

15. Check the operation of the turn indicator and horn.

DOME LIGHT SWITCH

The dome light switch is a part of the headlight switch. It is actuated by rotating the switch control knob to the maximum counter-clockwise position. The dome light and headlight switch is replaced as a unit (Fig. 1).

IGNITION SWITCH AND LOCK CYLINDER

1. Disconnect the negative cable from the battery.

2. Turn the ignition key to the accessory position. Slightly depress the release pin, turn the key counterclockwise, and pull the key and lock cylinder out of the switch assembly. If only the lock cylinder is to be replaced, proceed to step 8.

3. Unscrew the bezel from the ignition switch and remove the switch from the instrument panel.

4. Remove the insulated plug and wires from the rear of the switch.

5. If a new ignition switch as well as the lock cylinder is to be installed, insert a screwdriver into the lock opening of the ignition switch and turn the slot in the switch to a full counterclockwise position.

6. Connect the insulated plug and accessory wires to the back of the ignition switch.

7. Place the bezel and switch in the switch opening and install the bezel nut.

8. If a new lock cylinder is to be installed, insert the key in the cylinder and turn the key to the accessory position. Place the lock and key in the ignition switch, depress the release pin slightly and turn the key counterclockwise. Push the lock cylinder into the switch. Turn the key to check the lock cylinder operation.

9. Connect the battery cable and check the ignition switch operation.

NEUTRAL START SWITCH

See Part 7-2 for replacement of the neutral start switch on cars equipped with automatic transmissions.

BACK-UP LIGHT SWITCH

On cars equipped with the steering column standard shift, the switch is located on the lower end of the steering column.

On cars equipped with a shift lever directly over either the standard or automatic transmissions, the back-up light switch is located on the transmission.

PART 15-4

INSTRUMENTS

1 DESCRIPTION AND OPERATION

CONSTANT VOLTAGE REGULATOR

The constant voltage regulator (Fig. 1) used with the fuel, temperature, and oil gauges maintains an average value of 5.0 volts at the gauge terminals.

The regulator operates by means of a bimetallic arm and a heating coil. When the ignition switch is turned on, the heating coil (Fig. 1) heats the bimetallic arm causing it to bend and break the contacts, disconnecting the voltage supply from the heating coil. The bimetallic arm then cools and brings the contacts together again. The making and breaking of the contacts, causes a pulsating voltage, with an effective

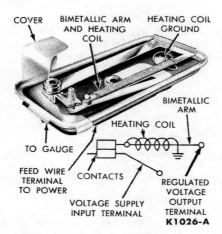

FIG. 1—Constant Voltage Regulator

average value of 5.0 volts to be supplied to the gauges. Although these pulsations are quite rapid, there is in each gauge a bimetallic arm which changes temperature quite slowly, assuring steady average readings.

To prevent the pulsating voltage from causing radio interference, a radio suppression choke is connected in series with the constant voltage regulator supply wire.

FUEL GAUGE

The fuel gauge consists of a sending unit, located on the gas tank, and a remote register unit (fuel gauge) mounted in the instrument cluster. The remote register unit pointer is controlled by a bimetallic arm and heating coil. The sending unit is a rheostat that varies its resistance depending on the amount of fuel in the tank. The rheostat is operated by a float control. As the fuel level rises or falls the float control arm moved by the float, varies the resistance.

TEMPERATURE INDICATING LIGHTS—FORD

The temperature indicating system consists of a sending unit mounted in the cylinder head and remote registering units (temperature indicating lights) mounted on the instrument panel (Fig. 2). When the engine is cold and the ignition switch is in the ACC or IGN position, the blue light flashes on. When the temperature of the engine coolant reaches approximately 125° F., the blue light will go out. Should the temperature of the engine coolant reach approximately 245° F., the red light will flash on indicating a malfunction in the engine cooling system. These lights are controlled by the temperature sending unit, which through a bimetallic arm completes the circuit to ground. With the ignition switch in the start position, the red light should flash on even though the engine is cold, thus proving that the red light is operable (Fig. 2). A set of contacts in the ignition switch completes the proving circuit to ground.

TEMPERATURE GAUGE—MERCURY

The temperature gauge consists of a sending unit mounted in the cylinder head, and a remote register unit (temperature gauge) mounted on the instrument panel. Changes of engine temperature vary the resistance of the sending unit which in turn operates the temperature gauge.

CHARGE INDICATOR LIGHT —FORD

A red alternator charge indicator light is used. This light flashes on if the battery is discharging and the alternator is not supplying current.

When the ignition switch is closed, battery current flows through the charge indicator light and 15-ohm parallel resistor, and through the regulator voltage limiter contacts to the field, and the light flashes on.

When the alternator builds up enough voltage to close the field relay contacts, full voltage is applied to the field and the charge indicator light goes out.

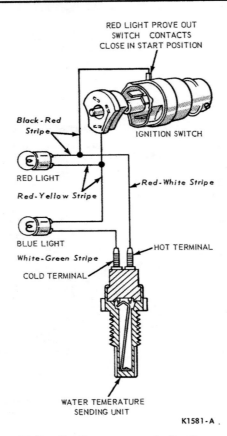

FIG. 2—Temperature Indicating System—Ford

CHARGE INDICATOR GAUGE—MERCURY

The charge indicator gauge is an ammeter which indicates whether the battery is being charged or discharged. The ammeter is non-adjustable and should be replaced. If proved to be defective.

OIL PRESSURE INDICATOR LIGHT—FORD

All models are equipped with a red indicator light which flashes on when the oil pressure is below a safe value. The light should come on when the ignition switch is first turned on, and it should go out when the engine comes up to speed. The light is connected between the oil pressure switch unit and the accessory terminal of the ignition switch.

OIL PRESSURE INDICATOR GAUGE—MERCURY

A meter-type oil pressure gauge is used. The gauge consists of a sending unit on the engine and a remote register unit in the instrument cluster.

OIL TEMPERATURE WARNING LIGHTS

The oil temperature warning sys-

tem (Fig. 3) when installed on Ford cars, uses the oil pressure indicator light as a temperature warning light. This light continues to serve as a low pressure warning light, flashing on if the pressure goes down.

If the temperature goes up to approximately 315° the light will flash on and off and continue to do so until the temperature drops to less than approximately 315°F.

When installed on Mercury cars the temperature warning light is not used for pressure warning purposes, as Mercury cars have an oil pressure gauge as standard equipment.

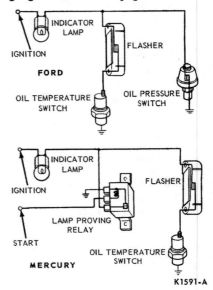

FIG. 3—Oil Temperature Warning System

TURN INDICATOR

The turn indicator uses the dual filament parking lights as indicator lights. The flasher is located on the back of the instrument cluster.

EMERGENCY WARNING FLASHER SYSTEM

The emergency warning flasher system is controlled by a combination switch and flasher assembly. All turn signal lights can be made to flash at the same time by closing the switch of the switch-flasher assembly.

SPEEDOMETER

The speedometer is connected to the output shaft of the transmission by means of a flexible shaft, and a drive gear located inside the transmission. The flexible shaft drives the speedometer which registers speed in miles per hour and also drives an odometer which records distance traveled in miles and tenths of a mile.

WINDSHIELD WIPER—MERCURY

The Mercury wiper provides high speed (65 to 75 cycles per minute) constant wiping action, and also intermittent low speed (5-30 cycles per minute), intermittent wiping action. This low speed operation is based not on a low speed wiping stroke but on an adjustable dwell period in the park position.

The intermittent wiper is operated through the use of a dual knob. The outer or large knob, when in the center *position*, turns the system off. When turned fully clockwise, the wiper is in the constant high speed setting. When turned fully counterclockwise, the wiper goes on the intermittent lower speed range. The intermittent wiper action is controlled by the inner, or small knob.

The intermittent wiper control is an electro-pneumatic system, a governor located in the engine compartment, that allows selection of either varying dwell between wipe cycles or continuous wiper action thru application of variable opposing vacuum and pressure within the system.

With the control selector in the instrument panel turned to intermittent wiper control, engine manifold vacuum is applied to the upper chamber of the governor (Sketch I, Fig. 4). Atmospheric pressure in the lower chamber then moves the diaphragm upward. Simultaneous rotation of the governor valve cam thru the spiral action of the follower applies manifold vacuum to the diaphragm of the normally closed electrical switch. The switch diaphragm is moved downward compressing the diaphragm spring and moving the switch into the park position. The wiper blades then move to the park position and remain there. (Sketch II, Fig. 4).

Rotation of the governor valve cam that applied vacuum to the governor switch also opened the upper governor chamber to atmosphere. The compressed diaphragm spring applies downward pressure to the diaphragm creating super atmosphere in the lower chamber. This is allowed to bleed off thru a variable orifice in the control selector. The size of this orifice is determined by the position of the intermittent selector (inner knob) and establishes the length of wiper cycle dwell (Sketch II, Fig. 4).

As the diaphragm moves downward, the governor valve cam is rotated thru the spiral action of the cam follower, opening the lower chamber of the electrical switch diaphragm to atmosphere. The compressed diaphragm spring moves the switch into the closed position, actuating the wiper motor. Simultaneously, the rotational movement of the valve cam applies manifold vacuum to the upper chamber of the governor, thus beginning a new cycle.

If the engine is subjected to sudden acceleration as in passing, the available manifold vacuum will be greatly reduced. When the vacuum loss becomes sufficient to allow the electrical switch diaphragm spring to overcome the vacuum, the switch will be moved to the closed position providing continuous wiper operation. This will continue until the engine has returned to an operating condition that will provide normal manifold vacuum. The wipers will then return to whatever wiper cycle dwell had been previously selected.

In the same manner as above, under engine acceleration, if any loss of vacuum or pressure in the intermittent control system occurs due to a mechanical failure or malfunction, the wipers will automatically shift to continuous operation, thereby rendering the system fail safe. (Sketch III, Fig. 4).

K 1633-A.

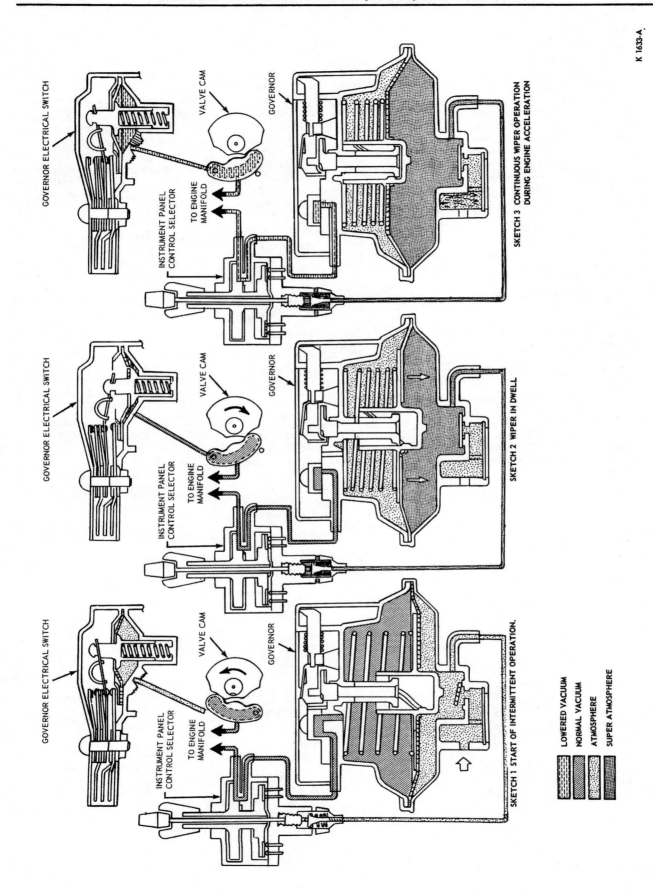

FIG. 4—Electro-Pneumatic Governor Intermittent Windshield Wiper

2   IN-CAR ADJUSTMENT AND REPAIR

WINDSHIELD WIPER BLADE ADJUSTMENT

Turn the ignition switch to the accessory position momentarily, with the wiper control off. After bringing the pivot shafts to their rest positions, install the wiper blades so that they lie flat against the lower edge of the windshield.

CLOCK ADJUSTMENT

Adjustment of the clock is automatic. If the clock runs slow or fast, merely reset the clock to the proper time. This action adjusts the clock automatically. Turning the knob clockwise, the clock will go faster. By turning the knob counterclockwise the clock will go slower.

The clock fuse is in the fuse panel which is mounted on the dashboard above and to the right of the brake pedal.

3   REMOVAL AND INSTALLATION

INSTRUMENTS

On Mercury cars, the design of the instrument panel permits the removal and installation of any of the various instruments individually once the instrument cluster center finish panel has been removed.

INSTRUMENT CLUSTER CENTER FINISH PANEL—MERCURY

Removal

1. Disconnect the battery ground cable.
2. From inside the car remove the headlight control knob and bezel nut.
3. Remove the wiper control knob and bezel nut.
4. Remove the rear window control or convertible top control bezel nut.
5. Remove the air conditioner and heater control knobs.
6. Remove the radio knobs.
7. Remove the retaining screws from the instrument cluster center finish panel.
8. Cover the steering column to protect it.
9. Position the finish panel out from the instrument panel, disconnect the wires from the air conditioner and heater switches, and remove the finish panel.

Installation

1. Position the finish panel near the instrument panel mask and connect the wires.
2. Position the finish panel to the mask and install the retaining screws.
3. Install the radio knobs.
4. Install the air conditioner and heater control knobs.
5. Install the wiper control knob and bezel nut.
6. Install the rear window control or convertible top control bezel nut.
7. Install the headlight control knob and bezel nut.
8. Connect the battery ground cable.

CONSTANT VOLTAGE REGULATOR

Remove the instrument cluster center finish panel and the oil pressure-ammeter unit. Disconnect the wires from the regulator, loosen one screw and remove the constant voltage regulator.

FUEL GAUGE—MERCURY

Remove the instrument cluster center finish panel and the fuel gauge retaining screws. Disconnect the wires and remove the fuel gauge.

FUEL GAUGE—FORD

Removal

1. Disconnect the battery ground cable.
2. Cover the steering column to protect it.
3. Remove the four retaining screws and remove the instrument panel cluster hood.
4. Remove the retaining screws and remove the lower instrument panel cluster cover.
5. Remove the retaining screws and remove the upper instrument panel cluster cover.
6. Remove the radio knobs.
7. Remove the friction pins retaining the instrument cluster lens and mask, and remove the lens and mask.
8. Remove the left standoffs and the speedometer retaining screws.
9. Remove the screws retaining the fuel gauge, pull back on the left side of the speedometer head and ease out the fuel gauge, remove the wires and remove the gauge.

Installation

1. Position the fuel gauge, connect the wires, reposition the gauge and install the gauge retainer screws.
2. Install the speedometer retainer screws and install the standoffs.
3. Position the cluster assembly lens and mask and install the retainer pins.
4. Install the radio knobs.
5. Position the upper instrument panel cluster cover, and install the retaining screws.
6. Position the lower instrument panel cluster cover, and install the retaining screws.
7. Position the instrument panel cluster pad and retainer and install the retaining screws.
8. Remove the cover from the steering column.
9. Connect the battery ground cable.

AMMETER OIL PRESSURE GAUGE—MERCURY

The ammeter and oil pressure gauge are removed as a unit. Remove the instrument cluster center finish panel and the retaining screws holding the ammeter-oil pressure gauge unit to the mask. Disconnect the wires and remove the unit.

TEMPERATURE INDICATOR GAUGE—MERCURY

Remove the instrument cluster center finish panel and the screws retaining the temperature indicator. Disconnect the wires and remove the temperature gauge.

TEMPERATURE SENDING UNIT

1. Disconnect the temperature sending unit wire(s) at the sending unit.
2. Prepare the new temperature sending unit for installation by applying a small amount of water resistant **electrically conductive** sealer C3AZ-19554-B to the threads.
3. Remove the temperature send-

ing unit from the cylinder head and immediately install the new temperature sending unit.

4. Connect the wire(s) to the temperature sending unit.

5. Start the engine and check the sending unit operation.

OIL PRESSURE SENDER—FORD

The oil pressure switch used with the indicator light unit is mounted to the rear of the oil filter on the 289 engine, on top of the oil filter on the 352, 390, 410, 427 and 428 engines (Fig. 5), and on the right side of the engine just above the starter on the Mileage Maker Six engine.

FIG. 5—Oil Pressure Switch—Ford

OIL PRESSURE SENDER—MERCURY

The oil pressure sender used with the oil pressure gauge is mounted on the left side of the engine to the rear of the fuel pump (Fig. 6).

FUEL SENDING UNIT

1. Remove the fuel tank filler cap and siphon the fuel from the tank.

2. Disconnect the fuel gauge sending unit wire at the sending unit.

3. Loosen the hose clamp and disconnect the tank line at the sending unit.

4. On station wagons remove the splash shield or drop the gas tank.

5. Remove any dirt that has accumulated around the sending unit so that it will not enter the tank.

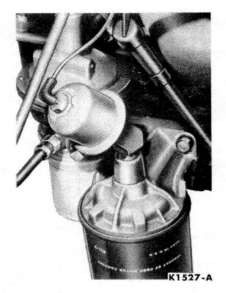

FIG. 6—Oil Pressure Sender—Mercury

6. Turn the sending unit retaining ring counterclockwise and remove the unit, retaining ring, and mounting gasket.

7. Clean the fuel gauge sending unit mounting surface at the fuel tank.

8. Position the sending unit and mounting gasket to the fuel tank, and secure it with the retaining ring.

9. Connect the sending unit wire and fuel tank line.

10. Fill the tank with the fuel removed and install the filler cap.

11. Check the fuel gauge operation and check for leaks.

TURN INDICATOR SWITCH

1. Disconnect the negative (ground) cable from the battery.

2. Remove the steering wheel hub and steering wheel retaining nut.

3. Remove the steering wheel from the shaft.

4. Disconnect the two wire-connector blocks at the dash panel above the steering column.

5. Remove the wires and terminals from the connector blocks. This can be done by depressing the tab on the wire terminal with an awl; then, pull the wire and terminal from the connector block. **Record the color code and location of each wire before removing it from the connector block.** Tape the wires together and attach a piece of heavy cord to the wires to help pull the wires through the steering column during installation.

6. Remove the turn indicator handle from the side of the steering column.

7. Remove 3 bearing retainer attaching screws and remove the bearing retainer and turn indicator switch and wires from the steering column. Disconnect the heavy cord from the switch wires.

8. Tape the ends of the switch wires together and attach the cord to the wires.

9. Pull the wires down through the steering column with the cord, and position the switch to the steering column hub.

10. Install the bearing retainer and attaching screws.

11. Install the turn indicator switch lever.

12. Press the switch wires into the connector blocks in their correct location recorded during removal. Plug the connector blocks together with the mating connector blocks at the dash panel.

13. Install the steering wheel on the shaft.

14. Install the steering wheel retaining nut and hub.

15. Connect the battery ground cable and check the operation of the turn signal switch and horns.

TURN INDICATOR FLASHER

From behind the instrument cluster, disconnect the wires from the flasher unit terminals and pull the flasher from its retaining clip. Observe the color code and number on the cover of the flasher. **Be certain to replace it with a new flasher with the same color code and number on the cover.**

EMERGENCY WARNING FLASHER

Pull the flasher from the retaining clip, and disconnect the wires (Fig. 7).

EMERGENCY WARNING FLASHER SWITCH

Disconnect the battery ground cable. Remove the retaining nut, then lift the switch out from behind the instrument panel. Disconnect all of the wires and remove the flasher (Fig. 7).

SPEEDOMETER—MERCURY

Disconnect the speedometer cable. Remove the instrument cluster center finish panel. Remove the speedometer retaining screws and remove the speedometer.

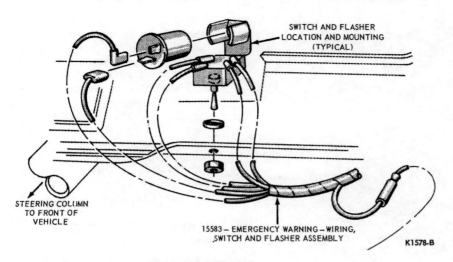

STEERING COLUMN
TO FRONT OF
VEHICLE

SWITCH AND FLASHER
LOCATION AND MOUNTING
(TYPICAL)

15583 – EMERGENCY WARNING – WIRING,
SWITCH AND FLASHER ASSEMBLY

K1578-B

FIG. 7—Emergency Warning Flasher Lights

SPEEDOMETER—FORD

Removal

1. Disconnect the battery ground cable.

2. Cover the steering column to protect it.

3. Remove the retaining screws from the instrument panel cluster pad and retainer.

4. Remove the retaining screws from the lower instrument panel cluster cover, and remove the cover.

5. Remove the retaining screws from the upper instrument panel cluster cover and remove the cover.

6. Remove the radio knobs.

7. Remove the friction pins retaining the instrument cluster lens and mask.

8. Disconnect the speedometer cable.

9. Remove the clock.

10. Remove the retaining screws from the speedometer retaining bracket, and remove the bracket.

11. Remove the screws retaining the speedometer head, remove the standoffs from the locating posts and remove the speedometer head.

Installation

1. Position the speedometer head, then install the standoffs and the retainer screws.

2. Position the speedometer retaining bracket and install the retainer screws.

3. Install the clock.

4. Install the speedometer cable.

5. Position the cluster assembly lens and mask and install the retainer pins.

6. Install the radio knobs.

7. Position the upper instrument

panel cluster cover and install the retainer screws.

8. Position the lower instrument panel cluster cover and install the retainer screws.

9. Position the instrument panel cluster pad and retainer and install the retainer screws.

10. Remove the cover from the steering column.

11. Connect the battery ground cable.

SPEEDOMETER CABLE REPLACEMENT

To replace the speedometer drive cable, disconnect the cable housing at the speedometer, and pull the cable out of the housing. Wipe off all of the old lubricant. Lubricate the new cable with cable lubricant B5A-19581-A (do not over lubricate), insert it all the way into the housing, and twist it slightly to make sure that the squared drive is en-

gaged in the speedometer driven gear. **If a speedometer cable is broken, it will be necessary to disconnect both ends of the cable housing in order to remove the broken sections.** See torque specifications Figs. 8 and 9.

The speedometer driven gear is held on to the speedometer cable by a retainer clip. See proper installation (Fig. 8). When replacing the driven gear, make certain that the gear is secure by placing the gear in position before inserting the retainer clip through the gear slots.

SPEEDOMETER CABLE AND HOUSING ROUTING ON CARS EQUIPPED WITH A STANDARD TRANSMISSION

1. Remove the hex nut from the speedometer head.

2. Remove the cable-housing assembly from the dash panel clip and align it for pulling from the underside.

3. Raise the car and remove the mounting bolt from the clip to transmission.

4. Remove the cable-housing assembly from the transmission and remove the assembly from the car.

5. Route the cluster end of the cable-housing assembly through the opening of the dash panel and seat the gromet halfway in the hole (Fig. 9).

6. From the inside of the body, route the cable up the dash panel (inboard of the brake pedal support) and through the opening of the pedal support brace.

7. Position the cable-housing assembly to the speedometer and secure the hex nut finger tight. Then tighten

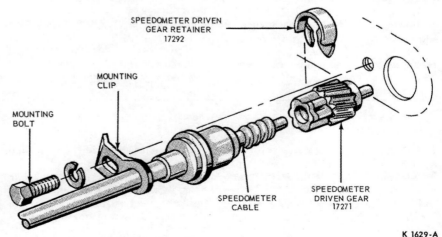

SPEEDOMETER DRIVEN
GEAR RETAINER
17292

MOUNTING
CLIP

MOUNTING
BOLT

SPEEDOMETER
CABLE

SPEEDOMETER
DRIVEN
GEAR
17271

K 1629-A

FIG. 8—Speedometer Driven Gear Retainer and Mounting

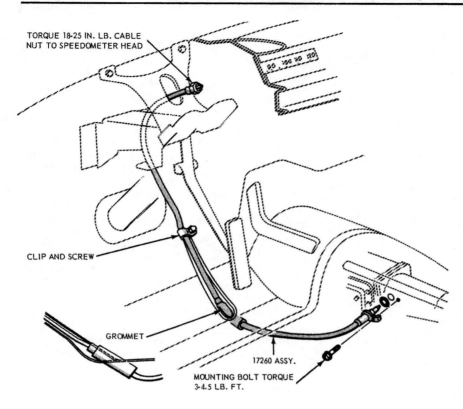

TORQUE 18-25 IN. LB. CABLE
NUT TO SPEEDOMETER HEAD

CLIP AND SCREW

GROMMET

17260 ASSY.

MOUNTING BOLT TORQUE
3-4.5 LB. FT.

FIG. 9—Speedometer Cable Routing On Standard Transmission Equipped Cars

the nut with a torque wrench to 18 to 25 inch pounds.

8. Secure the assembly to the dash panel with one clip and one screw.

9. Dip the cleaned driven gear and end of cable into graphite grease to cover at least two thirds of the gear and roll the grease into the teeth.

10. Assemble the gear to the speedometer plug with a retainer clip (Fig. 8).

11. Remove the dirt seal from the transmission and discard.

12. Assemble the cable and gear to the transmission by slightly turning the drive shaft to align the gears.

13. Secure the cable with a mounting screw and torque the screw to 3 to 4½ foot pounds. Check the

cable to avoid any sharp bends of the assembly in the installation.

WINDSHIELD WIPER MOTOR

When removing the windshield wiper motor, note the sequence in which the wiper links and washers are installed on the motor output arm pins. Assemble them in the same position when installing the motor. This will eliminate binding or noisy wiper linkage after the motor has been installed.

To remove the wiper motor, proceed as follows:

1. Remove the cowl intake screen.

2. Disconnect the wiper links at the motor output arm pin.

3. Disconnect the motor harness connector and remove the motor.

4. Remove the bolts retaining the wiper motor and bracket assembly and lower the motor.

5. Assemble the new motor to the bracket assembly.

6. Connect the motor harness connector to the new motor.

7. Position the motor and install the retaining bolts.

8. Connect the wiper links at the motor output arm pin.

9. Check the wiper operation.

WINDSHIELD WIPER PIVOT SHAFT AND LINK

Removal

1. Remove the wiper arms and blades.

2. Remove the retaining screws, then remove the cowl top ventilator grille, hood pad and the windshield washer nozzles.

3. Through the cowl opening remove the clip retaining the wiper arms to the motor drive arm.

4. Remove the retaining screws, then remove the pivot and arms as an assembly from the right side of the cowl opening.

5. Remove the arm to pivot retaining clip.

Installation

1. Install the new arm or pivot, and install the retaining clip.

2. Position the pivot-arm assembly through the right side of the cowl opening and install the retaining screws.

3. Position the wiper arm to the motor drive arm and install the retaining clip.

4. Install the windshield washer nozzles, position the cowl top hood pad and grille, and install the retaining screws.

5. Install the wiper arms and blades.

4   MAJOR REPAIR OPERATIONS

DISASSEMBLY—PERMANENT MAGNET TYPE SINGLE OR TWO-SPEED ELECTRIC WIPER MOTOR

1. Remove the gear cover retaining screws, ground terminal and cover. (Fig. 10).

2. Remove the gear and pinion retainer.

3. Remove the idler gear and pinion and thrust washer.

4. Remove the motor through bolts, motor housing, switch terminal insulator sleeve, and armature. **Do not pound the motor housing magnet assembly as the ceramic magnets may be damaged.**

5. Mark the position of the out-

put arm with respect to the output shaft, for assembly. Remove the output arm retaining nut, output arm, spring washer, flat washer, output gearshaft assembly, thrust washer, and parking switch lever and parking switch lever washer.

6. Remove the brushes and brush springs.

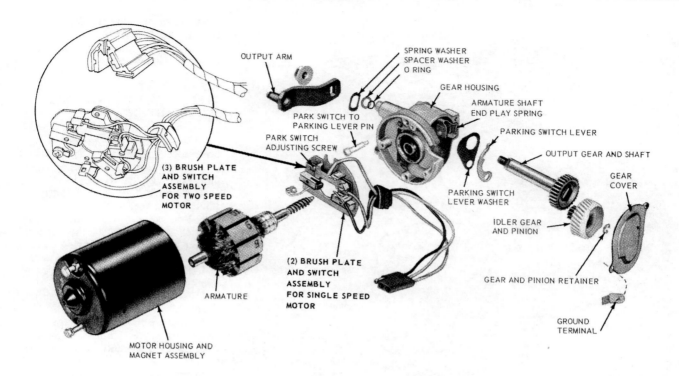

OUTPUT ARM

SPRING WASHER
SPACER WASHER
O RING

GEAR HOUSING

ARMATURE SHAFT
END PLAY SPRING

PARK SWITCH TO
PARKING LEVER PIN

PARK SWITCH
ADJUSTING SCREW

PARKING SWITCH LEVER

OUTPUT GEAR AND SHAFT

GEAR
COVER

(3) BRUSH PLATE
AND SWITCH
ASSEMBLY
FOR TWO SPEED
MOTOR

PARKING SWITCH
LEVER WASHER

IDLER GEAR
AND PINION

(2) BRUSH PLATE
AND SWITCH
ASSEMBLY
FOR SINGLE SPEED
MOTOR

ARMATURE

GEAR AND PINION RETAINER

GROUND
TERMINAL

MOTOR HOUSING AND
MAGNET ASSEMBLY

K 1632 - A

**FIG. 10—Disassembled Single or Two-Speed Wiper Motor—Permanent
Magnet Type**

7. Remove the brush plate and switch assembly, and remove the switch contact to parking lever pin from the gear housing.

PARTS REPAIR OR REPLACEMENT

All parts on both the single-speed and two-speed wiper are replaced and not repaired.

ASSEMBLY—PERMANENT MAGNET TYPE SINGLE OR TWO-SPEED ELECTRIC WIPER MOTOR

1. Install the parking switch lever washer.

2. Install the parking switch lever on the gear and pinion shaft with the cam rider pointing toward the gear housing output shaft hole. Make certain that the lever bottoms against the casting.

3. Apply a film of Sun Prestige grease to the output gear teeth and shaft bearing surface. Insert the shaft in the bearing. Make certain that the parking switch lever is clear of the cam and gear assembly.

4. Place the spacer washer and spring washer on the shaft, position the output arm on the shaft in the marked position from which it was

removed, and install the mounting nut.

5. Position the brush springs and brushes in the holders and wrap wire around them to hold them in the fully retracted position. Push the insulated brush connector onto the switch terminal.

6. Place the switch-contact to parking-lever pin in the gear housing. Position the brush plate assembly to the housing and install the mounting screws.

Make the park switch contact points adjustment covered under **Windshield Wiper Motor Park Switch Test and Adjustment—Single and Two-Speed Permanent Magnet Type** in this section.

7. Apply Sun Prestige grease to the ball bearing in the end of the armature shaft. Position the armature shaft in the gear housing and remove the brush retracting wires.

8. Holding the armature in position, install the terminal insulating sleeve, motor housing and magnet assembly, and through bolts. Seal the area where the terminal insulator sleeve seats against the motor and gear housings.

9. Apply Sun Prestige grease to the worm gear and idler gear, and

install the idler gear, thrust washer and retainer.

10. Apply a generous amount of Sun Prestige grease to the area around the end of the armature shaft. Install the gear housing cover and ground terminal.

WINDSHILD WIPER MOTOR PARK SWITCH TEST AND ADJUSTMENT—SINGLE AND TWO-SPEED PERMANENT MAGNET TYPE

With jumper wires connected as shown in Fig. 11, the motor should move to the park position. If it does, the motor is all right and the fault lies in the panel switch or wiring. If the motor does not park, proceed with the following park switch adjustment (Figs. 10, 11 and 12).

Remove the motor thru bolts and remove the motor cup and armature.

Rotate the output shaft until the park switch lower contacts are firmly closed as shown.

Rotate the adjusting screw clockwise until the park switch lower contacts just open.

Rotate the adjusting screw counterclockwise one full turn.

Check the bridge to assure that the legs are contacting the brush

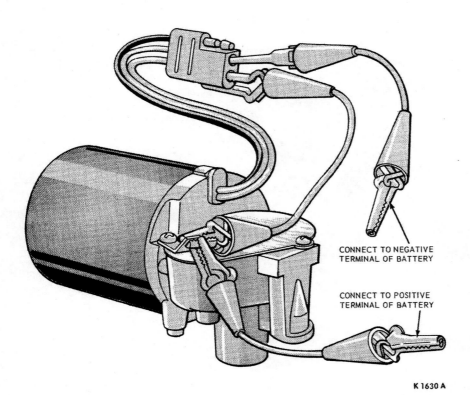

CONNECT TO NEGATIVE
TERMINAL OF BATTERY

CONNECT TO POSITIVE
TERMINAL OF BATTERY

K 1630 A

FIG. 11—Windshield Wiper Motor Park Switch Test

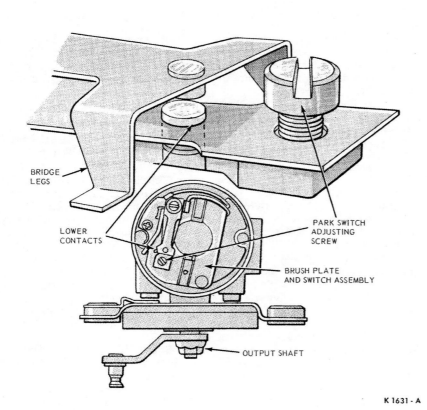

BRIDGE
LEGS

LOWER
CONTACTS

PARK SWITCH
ADJUSTING
SCREW

BRUSH PLATE
AND SWITCH ASSEMBLY

OUTPUT SHAFT

K 1631 - A

FIG. 12—Windshield Wiper Motor Park Switch Adjustment

plate when the lower contacts are closed.

Install the armature, motor cup and thru bolts.

DISASSEMBLY—OSCILLATING TYPE TWO-SPEED ELECTRIC WIPER MOTOR

The two-speed electric motor may be disassembled for service of the drive mechanism parts.

1. Remove the gear housing cover plate and gasket (Fig. 13).

2. Remove the output shaft retainer and spacer washer.

3. Remove the crankpin bearing retainer and remove the spacer washer and cam return spring assembly.

4. Remove the arm and link assembly.

5. Remove the crankpin bearing cam.

6. Remove the input gear retainer and outer spacer shim, and remove the input gear and inner spacer shim.

7. Remove the wiper arm lever nut and lock washer.

8. Remove the wiper arm lever and spacer, and remove the output shaft and gear assembly from the housing.

9. The output gear may be removed from its shaft by tapping with a fiber hammer. Be careful not to damage the end of the shaft.

The worm drive gear and armature assembly is not serviced.

PARTS REPAIR OR REPLACEMENT

All parts on both the single-speed and the two-speed electric wipers are replaced and not repaired.

ASSEMBLY—OSCILLATING TYPE TWO-SPEED ELECTRIC WIPER MOTOR

1. Tighten the motor cover. Adjust the motor shaft end play to 0.000-0.005 inch by turning the shaft stop screw. Measure with a feeler gauge between the stop screw and the motor shaft.

2. Install the input gear shim on the input gear shaft and install the gear in the housing. Adjust the end play to 0.005 to 0.010 inch by adding or removing shims under the input gear retainer. Install the retainer.

3. Install the output gear on the output shaft. Make sure that the gear is bottomed on the shaft.

4. Install the output shaft and gear assembly into the housing with

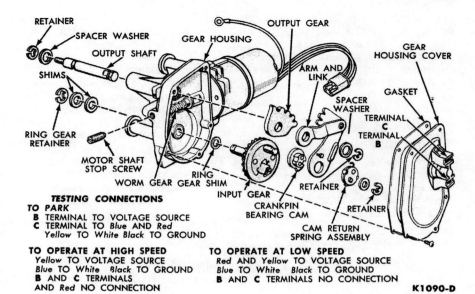

TESTING CONNECTIONS

TO PARK
B TERMINAL TO VOLTAGE SOURCE
C TERMINAL TO *Blue* AND *Red*
Yellow TO *White Black* TO GROUND

TO OPERATE AT HIGH SPEED
Yellow TO VOLTAGE SOURCE
Blue TO *White Black* TO GROUND
B AND **C** TERMINALS
AND *Red* NO CONNECTION

TO OPERATE AT LOW SPEED
Red AND *Yellow* TO VOLTAGE SOURCE
Blue TO *White Black* TO GROUND
B AND **C** TERMINALS NO CONNECTION

K1090-D

FIG. 13—Two-Speed Wiper Motor—Oscillating Type

the gear teeth facing the motor. Install one spacer washer to the outside end of the output shaft and assemble the wiper arm lever to the output shaft, with the linkage studs facing away from and above the shaft. Secure the lever with a lock washer and nut.

5. Place the bearing cam on the crankpin with the small diameter portion of the cam facing outward.

6. Install the arm and link assembly to the bearing cam. As the arm is placed on the shaft, the gears must be meshed and the link which is riveted to the arm must be installed to the output shaft at the same time. Proper gear indexing is obtained when the bottom tooth of the arm and gear segment will be in mesh with the bottom valley of the output shaft gear.

7. Install the output shaft spacer washer and retainer. Check the end play of the output shaft (0.005-0.010 inch). Remove or install spacer washers under the shaft retainer to adjust the end play.

8. Install the cam return spring assembly.

9. Install the bearing spacer and retainer. If the retainer cannot be installed, one or more coils of the spring clutch are probably out of place. If the bearing has excessive end play on the crankpin, the projection of the bearing may ride out of the semi-circular slot in the end plate. Add spacer washers under the re-retainer if necessary.

10. Apply generous amounts of Sun Prestige grease to all moving

parts. Install the gear housing cover plate.

When operating the unit on the bench, do not place hands or fingers between the wiper lever and the case, or inside the gear housing, as considerable power is developed by the gear reduction.

ELECTRO-PNEUMATIC GOVERNOR AND CONTROL SELECTOR SWITCH—MERCURY

The electro-pneumatic governor and the control selector switch are serviced as assemblies only. Should any internal component become defective the complete assembly must be replaced.

In the event of suspected partial or total blockage of internal passages, light air pressure may be applied in an attempt to remove the cause of blockage.

Although the vacuum hoses are an integral part of the wiring harness assembly, individual hoses may be replaced if required.

SPEEDOMETER DIAGNOSTIC PROCEDURES

Speedometer system complaints are generally the result of a visible or audible defect in the system. It is imperative that the specific defect be determined prior to attempting any physical repairs to preclude unnecessarily disassembling system components. The following suggestions are intended to aid in quick and accurate system problem diagnosis.

VISIBLE DEFECTS

Slight Needle Waver or Severe Needle Fluctuation (No Noise)

1. Loose cable nut.
2. Defective speedometer head.
3. Bent cable core at attaching nut.
4. Kinked or pinched cable housing.
5. Excessive grease in the speedometer head.

INOPERATIVE

1. Broken cable core.
2. Defective drive and/or driven gear.
3. Defective speedometer head.

AUDIBLE DEFECTS

Clicking or Ticking (With Needle Waver), Grinding or Ringing

1. Loose cable nut.
2. Defective drive and/or driven gear.
3. Defective speedometer head.
4. No lube on the cable.
5. Defective drive and/or driven gear.
6. Defective speedometer head.

SPEEDOMETER REPAIR PROCEDURES

LOOSE CABLE ATTACHING NUTS

1. Cable nuts should be tightened with pliers to approximately 18 to 25 in-lbs.
2. Cable nuts should start and run up freely by hand for at least three to four turns.
3. A loose cable nut can cause a bent cable core. Tightening will not always correct the problem.

DEFECTIVE CABLE CORE AND HEAD

Before removing a speedometer head, disconnect the cable at the head and insert a short section of cable core in the head. Rotate the section of core to check for any dragging or noise. The speedometer shaft should turn freely and evenly.

DEFECTIVE CABLE CORE AND HOUSING

1. To check for a kinked cable core remove and wipe dry. Lay the core out straight on a flat surface

and roll it back and forth. Any kinks or damage will be seen. Then take an end in each hand, allowing core to hang in approximately a 9-inch loop. Rotate both ends to be sure core turns evenly.

2. Routing of the cable housing is particularly important where the cable leaves the speedometer head. The optimum routing would provide that the cable and housing take virtually no change of direction for at least a length of 8 inches from the speedometer head.

3. When installing a new cable and housing it is necessary that the new assembly be guided and routed properly to eliminate any kinks.

4. Proper lubrication of the cable core is accomplished by a light application of B5A-19581-A lubricant after the cable has been wiped clean. A light film is all that is required.

DEFECTIVE DRIVE AND DRIVEN GEARS

1. A score, nicked or gouged driven gear is usually indicative of a defective drive gear on those vehicles that have the drive gear integral with the transmission output shaft. The output shaft should be carefully inspected for imperfections and replaced if necessary.

2. A driven gear with two or three adjoining teeth badly scored is indicative of improper assembly procedure. The gear should be inserted in the transmission while simultaneously turning the drive shaft. This will insure initial gear engagement and prevent gear damage. Force should never be used.

3. Whenever a drive gear is replaced, a new driven gear should also be installed, regardless of its apparent condition.

PART 15-5 SPECIFICATIONS

CIRCUIT PROTECTION

CIRCUIT	CIRCUIT PROTECTION		LOCATION
	RATING	TRADE NO.	
Headlamp Circuit:			
Headlamps	18 Amp. C.B.		Integral With Lighting Switch.
High Beam Indicator Lamp	18 Amp. C.B.		
Rear Lamps (Tail Lights & Stop Lights)	15 Amp. C.B.		
Front Parking Lamps			
Ignition Switch Lamp			
License Lamp			
Horns			
Dome Lamp Circuit:			
Dome Lamp	9 Amp. Fuse	SFE 9	On Fuse Panel (Dome Socket).
Courtesy Lamps			
Cargo Lamp			
Map Lamp (Mercury)			
Glove Compartment Lamp			
Luggage Compartment Lamp			
Clock			
Tachometer (Mercury)			
Instrument Panel Illumination:			
Ford	4 Amp. Fuse	AGA 4	Fuse Panel (Instrument Panel Socket).
Mercury	5 Amp. Fuse	AGA 5	This Circuit is Connected into the Light Switch Rheostat.
Clock Light			
Instrument Cluster Lights			
Ash Tray Light			
PRNDL—Console or Column Light			
Radio Light			
Heater Control Lights			
Medallion Lamp (No Clock on Parklane) (Mercury)			
Heater Circuit:			
Heater and Defroster Motor	20 Amp. Fuse	SFE 20 or AGC 20	Fuse Panel (Heater Socket).
Safety Convenience Panel Lamps:			
Low Fuel Warning			
Seat Belt Warning			
Door Ajar Warning			
Door Unlock Warning			
Cornering Lamps (Mercury)			
Power Antenna			
Station Wagon Under Seat Heater			
Open Door Warning (Ford-Taxi, Merc.-Police)			
Cigar Lighter Circuit:			
Cigar Lighter	14 Amp. Fuse	SFG 14	Fuse Panel (Cigar Lighter Socket).
Cigar Lighter Plus	20 Amp. Fuse (Replaces 14 Amp. Cigar Fuse).	SFE 20	
Emergency Warning Option (Hang-On or Convenience Panel)			
Radio Circuit:			
Radio	14 Amp. Fuse	SFE 14	Fuse Panel (Radio Socket).
Back-Up Lamps			
Single Speed Washers			
Intermittent Speed Washers (Mercury)			
Turn Signal Circuit			(After Fuse Flasher Protects Circuit for Turn Signal).
Windshield Wipers:			
Single Speed Wipers	6 Amp. C.B.		Integral with Windshield Wiper Switch.
Dual Speed Wipers and Washers (Ford)	12 Amp. C.B.		
Intermittent Wipers (Mercury)	6 Amp. C.B. (Single Speed) 7 Amp. C.B. (Two-Speed)		

CIRCUIT PROTECTION (Continued)

CIRCUIT	CIRCUIT PROTECTION		LOCATION
	RATING	TRADE NO.	
Power Assists: Convertible Top Circuit	14 Gage Wire Fuse Link	(C6AB-14A094-A)	In Wiring near Starter Relay
Convertible Top with Power Option(s)	20 Amp. C.B. Replaces Fuse Link		On Starter Relay
Power Windows Including Backlite & Tailgate	20 Amp. C.B.		
Power Seats (Four- and Six-Way)	20 Amp. C.B.		
Air Conditioning Circuit: Air Conditioner (Economy)	15 Amp.	AGC 15	Fuse Cartridge in Feed Wire
Air Conditioner (Selectair)	25 Amp. C.B.		On Back of Ignition Switch at Accessory Terminal.
Miscellaneous Circuits: Overdrive (Ford)	20 Amp. Fuse	AGC 15	On Overdrive Relay
Transistorized Ignition (Ford)	2 Amp. Fuse	AGA 2	Fuse Cartridge in Feed Wire
Speed Control	14 Amp. Fuse	SFE 14	
Spotlight	7.5 Amp. Fuse	SFE 7.5	
Automatic Headlamp Dimmer	4 Amp. Fuse	AGA 4	
Seat Belt Warning and Parking Brake Warning	No Protection		
Gage Circuits: Charge Indicator Oil Pressure Indicator Engine Water—Cold Engine Water—Hot	No Protection		
Motors: Windshield Wiper Motor Convertible Top Motor Power Window Motor Power Seat Motor	Circuit Breaker		Integral with Motor

SPEEDOMETER

Transmission Mounting Clip Bolt Torque ....3-4½ Ft. Lbs.

Cable Nut at Speedometer Head .... 18-25 In. Lbs.

FORD BULB CHART

Unit	①Candela Or Wattage	Trade Number
Standard Equipment		
Headlamp		
Hi-Lo Beam	37.5 & 50 Watts	4002
Hi Beam	37.5 Watts	4001
Front Parking and Turn Indicator	4-32 C.	1157
Rear Lamp and Stop and Turn (Sedan)—	4-32 C.	1157
Indicator (Sta. Wag.)—	4-32 C.	1157
License Plate Lamp	4 C.	1155
Courtesy Lamp (Convertible)	6 C.	631
Dome Lamp	15 C.	1003
Courtesy Lamp (Door Mounting)	15 C.	1003
Courtesy Lamp ("C" Pillar)	15 C.	1003
Console Lamp	6 C.	631
Courtesy Lamp	12 C.	211
Instrument Panel		
Instruments	2 C.	1895
Indicator Hi Beam	2 C.	1895
Warning Lights (Oil & Generator Temperature Hot/Cold)	2 C.	1895
Park Brake Rel. Warning Light	2 C.	1895

FORD BULB CHART (Continued)

Unit	①Candela Or Wattage	Trade Number
Heater Control Panel (Fresh Air)	3 C.	1895
L & R Turn Indicator	2 C.	1895
Accessory Equipment		
Back-up Lamps	32 C.	1156
Radio Pilot Light	2 C.	1891
Spotlight 4.4" Diameter	30 Watts	4405
Clock	3 C.	1816
Automatic Transmission	1 C.	161
Luggage Compartment	15 C.	93
Cigar Lighter	2 C.	1895
Engine Compartment	6 C.	631
Tachometer	2 C.	1895
Trans. Control Selector Indicator	1.5 C.	1445
Safety Package		
Door Lock	2 C.	1895
Low Fuel	2 C.	1895
Door-Warning Open	2 C.	1895
Emergency Flasher	2 C.	1895
Seat Belt	2 C.	1895

①Candela is the new International term for candlepower

MERCURY BULB CHART

Unit	①Candela Or Wattage	Trade Number
Standard Equipment		
Headlamps		
Hi-Lo Beam	37.5 & 50 Watts	4002
Hi-Beam	37.5 Watts	4001
Front Park and Turn Signal Lamp	4-32 C.	1157
Rear Lamp and Stop and Turn Signal (Pass. Car)	4-32 C.	1157
Dome Lamp	15 C.	1003
License Lamp	4 C.	1155
Courtesy Lamp (Convertible)	6 C.	631
Cargo Lamp (Sta. Wag. 77B)	15 C.	1003
Back-Up Lamp (Sta. Wag. & Pass. Car)	21 C.	1141
Rear, Stop and Turn (Station Wagon)	4 & 32 C.	1157
Courtesy Lamp (Door Mounting)	15 C.	1003
Auto. Trans. Selector	2 C.	1895
Instrument Panel		
Medalion Light	1.5 C.	1445
Gages, Speedometer	2 C.	158
Hi-Beam Indicator	2 C.	158
L & R Signal Indicator	2 C.	158
Glove Compartment	2 C.	1895
Automatic Transmission	1 C.	161
Control Nomenclature	2 C.	1895
Speedometer Pointer	1.5 C.	1445
Rear Window/Top Nomenclature	2 C.	1895
W/S Wiper Nomenclature	2 C.	1895
Lights Nomenclature	2 C.	1895

MERCURY BULB CHART (Continued)

Unit	①Candela Or Wattage	Trade
Instrument Panel (Continued)		
Dome Lamp—Swivel	15 C.	1003
Dome Lamp—Swivel	6 C.	631
Courtesy Lamp ("C" Pillar Reverse Back)	15 C.	1003
Courtesy Lamp ("C" Pillar, Fastback)	6 C.	631
Cornering Lamp	50 C.	1195
Heater Control	2 C.	1895
Accessory Equipment		
Warning Indicator Panel	2 C.	1895
Warning Indicator Panel	1.6 C.	257
Clock	3 C.	1816
Engine Compartment Lamp	15 C.	93
Radio Pilot Light	1.9 C.	1893
Radio On-Off Light (AM-FM only)	1.3 C.	1892
Instrument Warning Lamp Kit	2 C.	1895
Luggage Compartment Lamp	6 C.	631
Spotlamp (4.40 diameter)	30 Watts	4405
Air Conditioner	2 C.	1895
Cargo Lamp (Station Wagon)	15 C.	1003
Parking Brake Warning	1.6 C.	257
Back-up Lamp	21 C.	1141
Courtesy Lamp (Instrument Panel)	6 C.	631
Oil Temp. Warning	1.6 C.	257
Cigar Lighter	2 C.	1895
Tachometer	2 C.	1895
Trans. Control Selector Indicator	1.5 C.	1445

①Candela is the new International term for candlepower

VENTILATING, HEATING, AND ACCESSORIES

GROUP 16

PART 16-1   VENTILATING SYSTEM AND HEATER

1 DESCRIPTION AND OPERATION—VENTILATING SYSTEM

FRONT AIR VENTS

The ventilation air ducts are located in the right and left cowl panels and are accessible for service by removing the cowl trim panels. The air vent grilles are an integral part of the trim panels.

When the car is in motion, outside air enters the vehicle through the cowl air intake immediately forward of the windshield, down the right and left cowl side panels and through the air ducts, into the passenger compartment.

The vent air valves are balanced doors in the side cowl assemblies, controlled by Bowden cables. Pull the control knobs for outside air; push in to close the vents. The location of the vents and control knobs is shown in Figs. 1 and 2.

REAR VENT

The rear vent (Fig. 3) on the hardtop models is opened and closed by a vacuum control switch on the instrument panel, which governs the operation of the two vacuum actuators. Operation of the rear vent system allows quiet window-up driving in most conditions wet or dry. Smoke

and interior odors can also be exhausted through this system when the car is in motion. Some aid to rear window fogging is also accomplished.

On 240 and 289 CID engine installations, a vacuum supply tank located near the battery provides a positive vacuum source for the vacuum actuators. A check valve is built into the supply tank to help maintain a steady source of vacuum.

On 352, 390 and 427 CID engine installations, the vacuum is supplied directly from the engine with a positive check valve in the supply line.

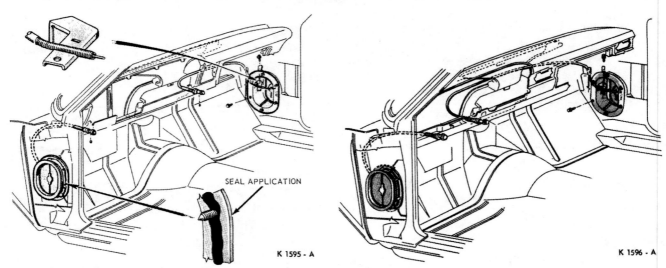

FIG. 1—Vent Air Ducts—Ford

FIG. 2—Vent Air Ducts—Mercury

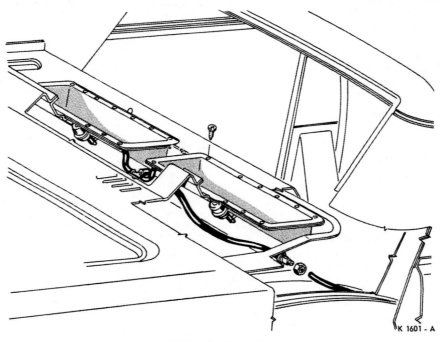

FIG. 3—Rear Vent

2   DESCRIPTION AND OPERATION—HEATING SYSTEM

Refer to Wiring Diagram Manual Form 7795P-66 for locations of wiring harnesses. Schematics are shown in Group 22 of this manual.

FRESH AIR HEATER

The Ford and Mercury heater is a blend air system connected directly to an opening in the right air intake. The heater housing assembly is located on the right side of the dash panel in the engine compartment

and includes the blower motor and wheel, temperature air valve or door, and heater core. The heater hose routings are shown in Fig. 4.

The plenum chamber is attached to the dash panel beneath the instrument panel and a single defroster nozzle leads to two slots in the forward instrument panel garnish moulding.

Outside air is drawn into the blower housing, forced through and/or

around the heater core, mixed, and then discharged through the outlets in the plenum chamber or defroster outlets. The air temperature is controlled by the position of the temperature air valve or door located between the blower and heater core in the heater housing. A heater air valve, *referred to as the heat-defrost door is located in the plenum chamber to control the discharge air between heat and defrost (Fig. 5).*

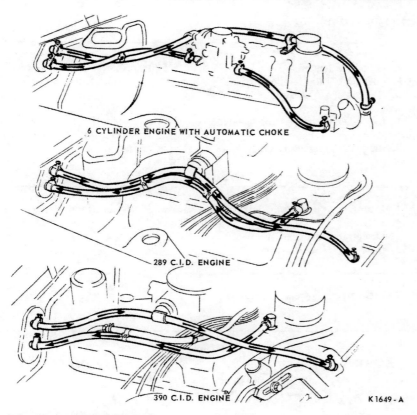

6 CYLINDER ENGINE WITH AUTOMATIC CHOKE

289 C.I.D. ENGINE

390 C.I.D. ENGINE

K 1649 - A

FIG. 4—Heater Hose Routings

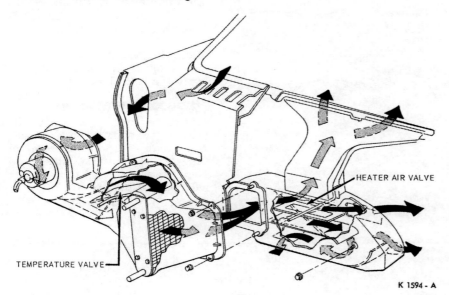

HEATER AIR VALVE

TEMPERATURE VALVE

K 1594 - A

FIG. 5—Heater and Defroster System

The air temperature is controlled by the location of the upper lever in the heater control. As the lever is moved from left to right, a Bowden cable moves the temperature valve in the heater housing from minimum heat to full heat position to modulate the air flow through and/or around the heater core. The air through the core and the air through the by-pass chamber is then mixed as it enters the plenum chamber.

The lower heat-defrost lever actuates a Bowden cable connected to the heater air valve in the plenum chamber. Air flow through the plenum is directed, as required by the operator, through the discharge air outlets in the plenum, in the heat position, or through the defrosters, in the defrost position. The air flow can also be modulated by setting the controls in any position between heat and defrost. When the lower lever is at the extreme left, the heater is in the off position.

The Ford controls are illuminated with two light bulbs; the Mercury controls with one. Three speeds are provided for the blower fan with a four position switch in the control assembly and a resistor assembly located to the right of the heater core in the heater housing. The resistor in the blower motor circuit controls the low and medium blower motor speeds.

3 DIAGNOSIS AND TESTING

VENTILATING AND HEATING DIAGNOSIS GUIDE

| INSUFFICIENT OR NO HEAT | 1. Burned out fuse or loose wires to the heater blower. 2. Defective motor ground, or defective blower motor. 3. Fan loose on motor shaft or motor stalled. |

VENTILATING AND HEATING DIAGNOSIS GUIDE (Continued)

INSUFFICIENT OR NO HEAT (Con't)	4. Defective heater blower switch. 5. Defective blower motor. 6. A kinked, clogged, or collapsed water hose. 7. Improperly connected heater hoses. 8. Plugged heater core, or air outlet.	9. Improperly installed or defective engine thermostat. 10. Incorrectly installed and adjusted control cables. 11. Air leaks in the body. 12. Improper installation of heater to dash panel.
INSUFFICIENT OR NO DEFROSTING	1. Improperly adjusted defroster control cable. 2. Disconnected defroster hose. 3. Binding defroster valve.	4. Plugged or loose defroster nozzle. 5. Obstructed defroster openings at windshield.
TOO MUCH HEAT	1. Incorrectly adjusted blend-air valve.	

TESTING

Refer to Wiring Diagram Manual Form 7795P-66 for locations of wiring harnesses. Schematics are shown in Group 22 of this manual.

The following tests may be made on the heater: Burned out fuses, loose wire connections, defective wires, collapsed hoses, loose defroster hoses and air leaks in the body may be determined by visual inspection of the parts.

HEATER CURRENT DRAW TEST

This test will determine if the blower motor is defective. Connect a 0-50 ammeter as shown in Fig. 6. The blower motor will operate independently of the control switch, and the current drawn by the motor will be indicated on the ammeter.

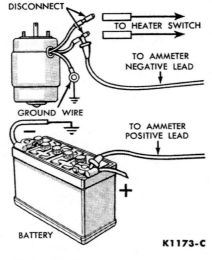

FIG. 6—Heater Motor Current Draw Test

Current draw should be to specifications.

LOOSE MOTOR FAN

Turn on the heater switch, and listen for the sound of the motor. If only a hum is heard, the fan is loose on the motor shaft.

BLOWER SWITCH

Substitute a known good blower switch for the suspected switch.

PLUGGED HEATER CORE

Start the engine and temporarily remove the outlet hose from the heater core (the hose that leads to the water pump). Very little or no flow of water from the core outlet indicates that the core is plugged or kinked. Make certain that water is being supplied to the core inlet.

---

4 COMMON ADJUSTMENTS AND REPAIRS—VENTILATING SYSTEM

Bowden cable operated vents and air inlets are adjusted so that the vents are tightly closed when the control knobs are all the way in.

Loosen the Bowden cable retaining screw at the vent control arm, move the cable housing back and forth

until the vent is closed when the knob is $1/16$-$1/8$ inch from the in position, then tighten the retaining screw.

---

5 COMMON ADJUSTMENTS AND REPAIRS—HEATING SYSTEM

HEATER CONTROL ADJUSTMENT

The Bowden cables can be ad-

justed at the control head or at the heater. Adjustments are made with the controls in the off position. Prop-

er cable routing must be maintained to insure against binding or kinked cables (Figs. 8 and 9).

6 REMOVAL AND INSTALLATION

HEATER CORE

Drain the cooling system and re-move the heater hoses at the core. Remove the retaining screws, heater core cover and seal from the plenum. Remove the heater core from the plenum. Before installing the new core apply a thin film of silicone lubrication to the pads (Fig. 7).

HEATER BLOWER MOTOR

REMOVAL

1. Remove the hood.

2. Remove the retaining bolts and nut, and remove the right hood hinge support bracket.

3. Remove the retaining bolts and remove the right hood hinge and support as an assembly.

4. Disconnect the heater motor wires.

5. Remove the heater blower mounting screws and remove the motor and blower wheel assembly.

6. Loosen the Allen set screw, and remove the blower wheel.

7. Remove the two retaining nuts and remove the mounting plate from the motor.

INSTALLATION

1. Position the mounting plate to the new blower motor and install the retaining nuts.

2. Position the blower wheel and tighten the Allen set screw.

3. Position the motor and blower wheel assembly and install the mounting screws.

4. Connect the heater motor wires.

5. Position the right hood hinge and support and install the retaining bolts.

6. Position the right hood hinge support bracket and install the retaining bolts and the nut.

7. Install the hood.

HEATER CONTROL—FORD

The heater control is mounted in the instrument panel, to the right of the steering column. To remove the control assembly, remove the knobs, remove the two nuts retaining the assembly to the instrument panel. Disconnect the cables, the switch wires, and the pilot light wire from its connector. The blower switch can be removed from the heater control by removing one screw (Fig. 8).

HEATER CONTROL—MERCURY

REMOVAL

1. Remove the battery ground ca-ble.

2. Remove the control knobs from the instrument cluster.

3. Remove the front main bezel (Group 15).

4. Disconnect the blower motor switch wires.

5. Loosen the heater control as-sembly.

6. Remove the radio (Part 16-6 in this group).

7. Remove the retaining nuts and remove the heater control mounting plate.

8. Lower the control, and discon-nect the Bowden cables, and the light bulb wires and remove the con-trol head (Fig. 9).

INSTALLATION

1. Position the control and con-nect the wires and the Bowden ca-bles.

2. Position the control to the con-trol mounting plate and install the retaining nuts.

3. Install the radio (Part 16-6 in this group).

4. Tighten the heater control as-sembly.

5. Connect the blower motor switch wires.

6. Install the front main bezel (Group 15).

7. Install the control knobs on the instrument cluster.

8. Connect the battery ground terminal.

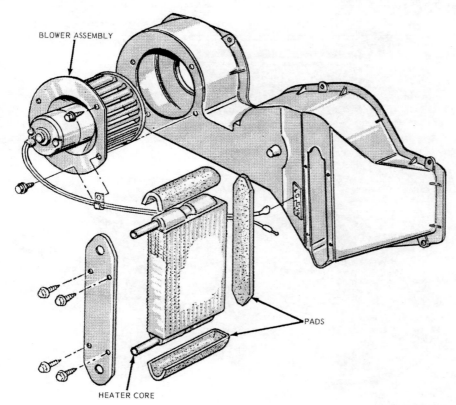

BLOWER ASSEMBLY

PADS

HEATER CORE

K 1615 - A

FIG. 7—Heater Components

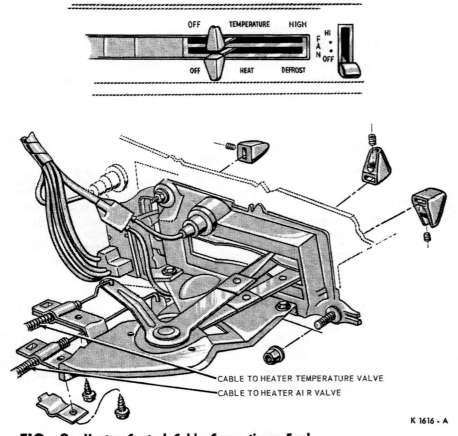

FIG. 8—Heater Control Cable Connections—Ford

CABLE TO HEATER TEMPERATURE VALVE
CABLE TO HEATER AIR VALVE

K 1616 - A

3. Remove the trim panel at the wheel housing and screws.

4. Remove the screws retaining the package tray and remove the tray to a bench.

5. Remove the screws retaining the vent register assembly to the package tray shelf. Disconnect the hose and remove the assembly.

6. Remove the screws from the vacuum actuator mounting bracket, and the actuator linkage. Disconnect the hose and remove the actuator.

7. Position and adjust the new actuator to the mounting bracket and secure it with screws. Screw the actuator to the arm. Connect the hose.

8. Install the register assembly to the package tray shelf and connect the vacuum hose.

9. Position the package tray and secure it with screws.

10. Install the trim at the wheel housing with screws.

11. Install the right and left roof quarter mouldings.

12. Check the operation of the actuator, and install the rear seats.

REAR VENT

REMOVAL

1. Remove the rear seat cushion.
2. Remove the rear seat back.
3. Remove the right and the left horizontal quarter trim mouldings.
4. Remove the package tray.
5. Remove the retaining screws and remove the right and the left register assemblies.

INSTALLATION

1. Position the right and the left register assemblies and install the mounting screws.
2. Install the package tray.
3. Install the right and the left horizontal quarter trim mouldings.
4. Install the rear seat back.
5. Install the rear seat cushion.

VACUUM ACTUATOR—SILENT FLOW VENT

1. Remove the rear seats.
2. Remove the right and left roof quarter mouldings and screws.

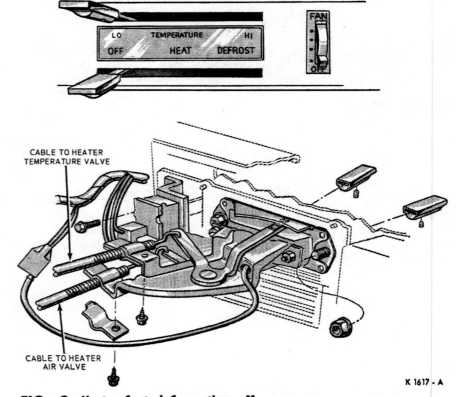

CABLE TO HEATER TEMPERATURE VALVE

CABLE TO HEATER AIR VALVE

K 1617 - A

FIG. 9—Heater Control Connections—Mercury

PART 16-2   AIR CONDITIONING

1 DESCRIPTION AND OPERATION

Refer to Wiring Diagram Manual Form 7795P-66 for locations of wiring harnesses. Schematics are shown in Group 22 of this manual.

The Ford and Mercury air conditioning and heating system is an integral system connected directly to an opening in the cowl air intake on the right side of the dash panel (Fig. 1). The heater core housing is connected directly over the cowl air intake opening on the extreme right side of the dash panel under the right fender.

The blower motor and evaporator case assembly is located on the engine side of the dash panel between the right hood hinge and the centerline of the vehicle. The air conditioner-heat distribution door is located midway between the blower and evaporator core inside the housing and routes the air through the evaporator core in the air conditioning position, or into the plenum chamber in the heat position.

The evaporator core is located midway through the dash panel between the evaporator case and the plenum chamber and is serviced

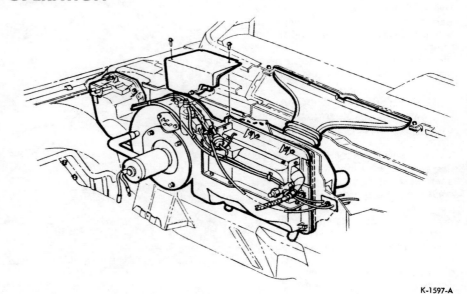

K-1597-A

FIG. 1—Heater-Air Conditioner System

through the cover plate on the evaporator case.

The plenum chamber, located under the instrument panel on the dash includes the outside air door, recirculating air door and heat-defrost door. The air conditioner air distribution outlet duct on the face of the plenum chamber is a separate piece. The duct for the Ford differs from the Mercury. A single defroster nozzle attaches directly to an opening in the top of the plenum and leads to openings in the forward instrument panel garnish moulding.

Outside air is drawn into the system from the cowl air intake directly into the heater core by the blower; forced through the blower housing into the plenum chamber through the outside air door; past the recirculating air door, in the closed position; through the air conditioner-heat door in the evaporator case; through and/or around the evaporator core and discharged through the air conditioner, heat or defrost outlets in the plenum chamber, depending on the position of the control setting. Air flow diagrams are shown in Figs. 2 and 3.

Three speeds are provided for the blower fan with a four position switch in the control assembly and a resistor assembly located in the blower housing. The resistor in the blower motor circuit controls the low and medium blower motor speeds.

CONTROLS

The air temperature is controlled by the location of the upper lever in the control assembly. As the lever is moved from left (cooler) to the right (warmer) a Bowden cable actuates the air conditioner thermostatic switch from maximum cooling to minimum cooling. At the same time, a link between the switch and heater temperature sending unit moves the temperature sending unit from minimum to maximum heat position (Fig. 4).

Air distribution is controlled by the lower control lever in the control panel assembly and the blower switch setting. The lower lever actuates a vacuum selector switch on the control assembly which in turn operates vacuum actuators at the air conditioner-heat door, outside air door, recirculating air door and heat-defrost door. For example, with the lever set at the NORMAL position, vacuum is applied to the outside air door to open the door; the air conditioner-heat door is in the air conditioning position (no vacuum); the recirculating air door is closed with vacuum, and the heat-defrost door is in the heat position (no vacuum). See Chart I for individual settings.

The blower switch must be on to engage the compressor clutch for air conditioning. With the lower lever in either air conditioning position, the air conditioner-heat door is in the

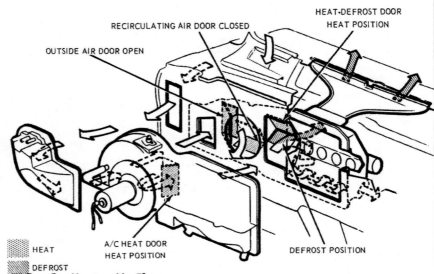

FIG. 2—Heater Air Flow

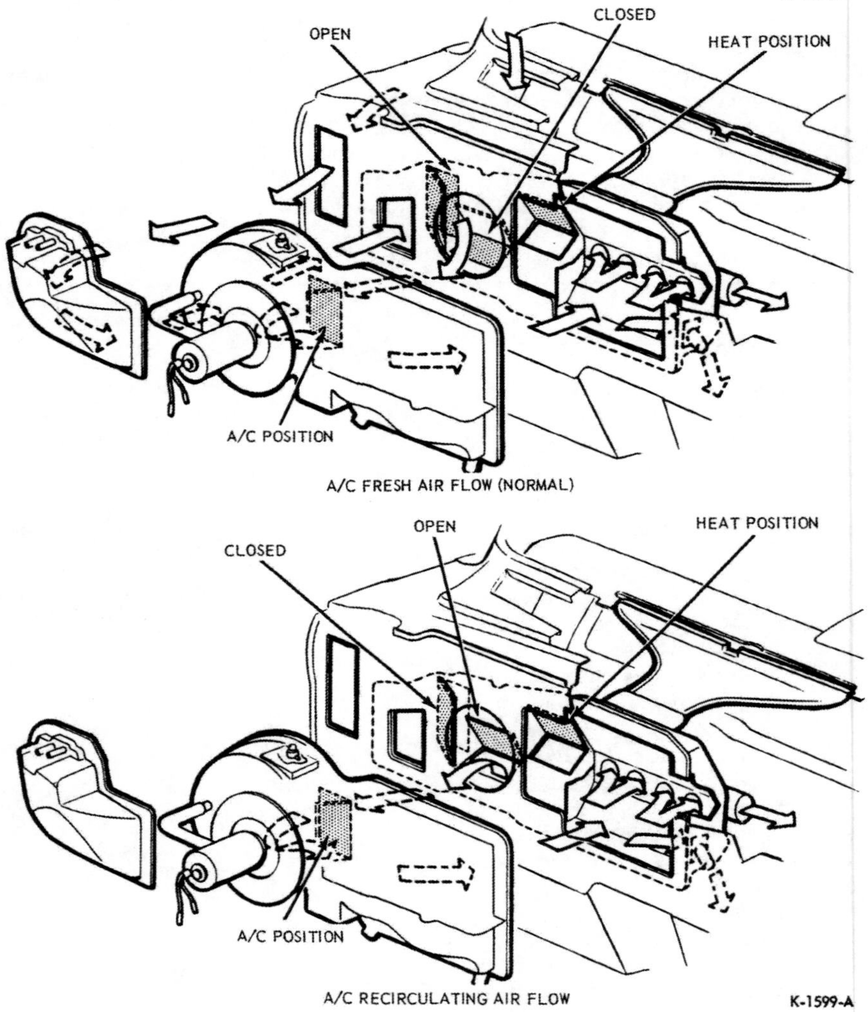

K-1598-A

A/C FRESH AIR FLOW (NORMAL)

FIG. 3—Air Conditioner Recirculating Air Flow

K-1599-A

air conditioning position (no vacuum) and pressure is applied to the compressor clutch switch to close the circuit and engage the clutch.

DISCHARGE AIR

The air discharge outlet duct on the face of the plenum chamber is unique for Ford and Mercury. The

CHART 1—TEMPERATURE AND AIR CONTROL LEVER CHART

		TEMP. CONTROL LEVER (UPPER)	FUNCTIONAL CONTROL LEVER (LOWER)				
			A/C Normal	A/C Recirc.	Off	Heat	Defrost
A I R D O O R S	**Outside Air**		Open V	Closed NV	Closed NV	Open V	Open V
	A/C Heat		A/C Pos. NV	A/C Pos. NV	Heat Pos. V	Heat Pos. V	Heat Pos. V
	Recirc.		Closed V	Open NV	Open NV	Closed V	Closed V
	Heat Defrost		Heat Pos. NV	Heat Pos. NV	Heat Pos. NV	Heat Pos. NV	Defrost Pos. V
S W I T C H	**A/C**	Cooler	On Max.	On Max.	Off	Off	Off
		Modulated	On Mod.	On Mod.	Off	Off	Off
		Warmer	On Min.	On Min.	Off	Off	Off
	Clutch	Cooler	On	On	Off	Off	Off
		Modulated	On	On	Off	Off	Off
		Warmer	On	On	Off	Off	Off
	Blower	Cooler	Man. On L-M-H	Man. On L-M-H	Man. Off	Man. On—L-M-H Off—RAM	Man. On L-M-H
		Modulated	Man. On L-M-H	Man. On L-M-H	Man. Off	Man. On—L-M-H Off—RAM	Man. On L-M-H
		Warmer	Man. On L-M-H	Man. On L-M-H	Man. Off	Man. On—L-M-H Off—RAM	Man. On L-M-H
Temperature Sending Unit		Cooler	Off	Off	Off	On Min.	On Min.
		Modulated	Off	Off	Off	On Mod.	On Mod.
		Warmer	Off	Off	Off	On Max.	On Max.
Water Valve		Cooler	Off	Off	Off	On Min.	On Min.
		Modulated	Off	Off	Off	On Mod.	On Mod.
		Warmer	Off	Off	Off	On Max.	On Max.

L—Low   Min.—Minimum   V—Vacuum
M—Medium   Mod.—Modulated   NV—No Vacuum
H—High   Max.—Maximum   Pos.—Position
          Man.—Manually

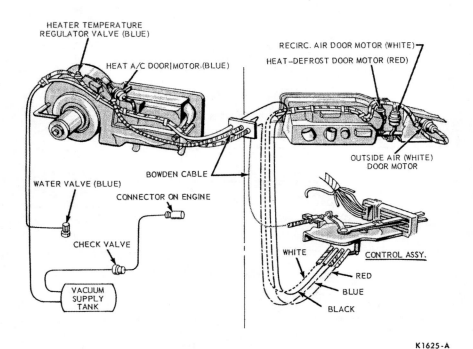

FIG. 4—Air Conditiong and Heater Vacuum Hose and Bowden Cable Routing and Color Coding

Ford duct consists of three round and one rectangular outlets to attach the flexible hoses. The duct for the Mercury consists of four round outlets. Two registers are located in the instrument cluster and two in the lower instrument panel; one near the centerline and one on the extreme right side.

Two floor cooler tubes on the plenum chamber assembly are used to discharge cold air to the floor on each side of the floor tunnel. Deflectors on each tube can be positioned manually for driver or passenger comfort.

The Ford registers are barrel type registers that can be moved up and down and the vertical vanes are positioned by moving a horizontal wheel within the assembly. The Mercury registers are positioned by moving a swivel knob or lever in the center of the registers and controls both horizontal and vertical vanes in the assembly.

The two outboard registers in the Ford system can be closed with a push-pull knob and lever that actuates a balanced door behind the registers. All four registers in the Mercury system are closed in the same manner.

RECEIVER UNIT

The air cooling system stores the liquid Refrigerant-12 under pressure in a combination receiver and dehydrator. The pressure in the receiver normally varies from about 80 to 300 psi, depending on the surrounding air temperature and compressor

speed. The receiver and condenser comes charged and marked with the total weight, so that any leak, indicated by a loss in weight, can be detected before assembly.

The dehydrator serves the purpose of removing any traces of moisture that may have accumulated in the system. Even small amounts of moisture will cause an air cooling unit to malfunction. A fusible plug is screwed into the receiver. This will release the refrigerant before the refrigerant temperature exceeds 212°F.

EVAPORATOR UNIT

When the cooling system is in operation (Fig. 5), the liquid Refrigerant-12 flows from the combination receiver and dehydrator unit through a flexible hose to the evaporator (cooling unit Fig. 5), where it is allowed to evaporate at a reduced pressure. In an integral air conditioning and heating unit, the evaporator core is located midway through the dash panel.

EXPANSION VALVE

The rate of refrigerant evaporation is controlled by an expansion valve, which allows only enough refrigerant to flow into the evaporator to keep the evaporator operating efficiently, depending on its heat load.

The expansion valve consists of the valve and a temperature sensing capillary tube, bulb, and sight glass (Fig. 6). However the sight glass may be located anywhere in the high pressure line between the condenser

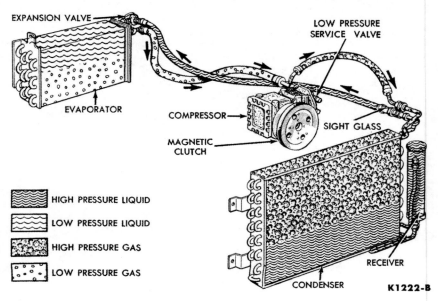

HIGH PRESSURE LIQUID
LOW PRESSURE LIQUID
HIGH PRESSURE GAS
LOW PRESSURE GAS

FIG. 5—Air Conditioning System

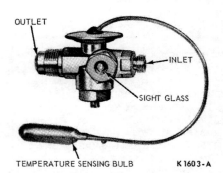

FIG. 6—Expansion Valve and Sight Glass

and the evaporator. The bulb is clamped to the outlet pipe of the evaporator. Thus, the operation of the valve is controlled by the temperature of the refrigerant at the point where it leaves the evaporator or cooling unit.

The restricting effect of the expansion valve at the evaporator causes a low pressure on the low pressure side of the system.

The sight glass is used to check whether or not there is enough refrigerant in the system. Foam seen in the sight glass while the compressor is operating, is an indication of loss of refrigerant. However, foam or bubbles will appear at start up and should disappear if properly charged.

COMPRESSOR UNIT

The evaporated refrigerant leaving the evaporator (now in the form of a gas), at a pressure of 12-50 psi is pumped by the compressor, located on the engine, into the top of the condenser (Fig. 5), located in front of the radiator.

The compressor maintains a pressure on its high pressure side of from 80-300 psi, depending on the surrounding air temperature and compressor speed.

As the heated and compressed refrigerant gas flows down through the condenser, it is cooled by air passing between the sections of the condenser. The cooled, compressed refrigerant gas condenses to liquid refrigerant which then flows into the receiver.

MAGNETIC CLUTCH

It is necessary to control the amount of cooling that the system produces. To accomplish this, the compressor is electrically cut in and out of operation by the use of a magnetic clutch pulley mounted on the compressor crankshaft (Fig. 5). The magnetic clutch is controlled by a thermostatic switch which has its temperature sensing tube inserted in the fins of the evaporator core.

THERMOSTATIC SWITCH

The thermostatic switch controls the operation of the compressor by controlling the compressor magnetic clutch. The temperature sensing tube of the switch is placed in contact with the evaporator fins. When the temperature of the evaporator becomes too cold, the thermostatic switch opens the magnetic clutch electrical circuit disconnecting the compressor from the engine. When the temperature of the evaporator rises to the upper limit at which the thermostatic switch is set, the thermostatic switch closes and energizes the magnetic clutch. This connects the compressor to the engine and cooling action begins again.

When the ignition switch is off, or the cooling control thermostatic switch is in the OFF position, the magnetic clutch is not energized, and the cooling system can not operate.

When the ignition switch is on, (engine running), and the cooling control is in the cooling range, and the blower is in operation, the magnetic clutch is energized, the compressor is connected to the engine and the cooling system is in operation.

The thermostatic switch may be adjusted to maintain an average evaporator temperature of from 30°-60°F. The thermostatic switch operating differential temperature at any one setting is 6°F. The switch is controlled by the cooling control.

SERVICE VALVES

The service valves on the compressor are used to test and service the cooling system (Fig. 7). The high pressure service valve, mounted at the outlet to the compressor, allows access to the high pressure side of the system for attaching a pressure gauge, or a servicing hose.

The low pressure valve, mounted at the inlet to the compressor, allows access to the low pressure side of the system for attaching a pressure gauge, or a servicing hose.

Both service valves may be used to shut off the rest of the system from the compressor during compressor service.

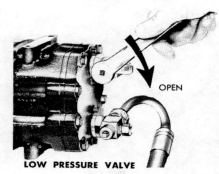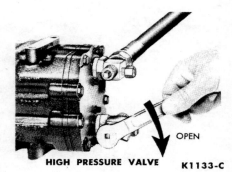

FIG. 7—Opening Service Valve and Gauge Ports

2 DIAGNOSIS AND TESTING

AIR CONDITIONING DIAGNOSIS GUIDE

INSUFFICIENT OR NO COOLING

1. Inoperative magnetic clutch.
2. Inoperative blower motor, or switch.
3. Obstructed air passages.
4. Complete loss of charge. (No bubbles in sight glass at system start up.)
5. Partial loss of charge. (Continuous bubbles in sight glass after start up.)

AIR-CONDITIONING DIAGNOSIS GUIDE (Continued)

INSUFFICIENT OR NO COOLING (Con't)	6. Service valves improperly set (should be maximum counterclockwise). 7. Inoperative vacuum servo. 8. Compressor defective, or loose or broken compressor belt. 9. Vacuum lines kinked, clogged, loose, or off. 10. A/C thermostat defective. 11. Clutch lead disconnected or broken. 12. Expansion valve inoperative—	stays open or closed. 13. Plugs left in compressor under service valve (both gauges indicate the same pressure). 14. Moisture in system. 15. Vacuum lines kinked, clogged, loose, or off. 16. Inoperative vacuum selector valve. 17. Improper installation to the dash panel.
NOISY COMPRESSOR	1. Loose, torn, or misaligned belt. 2. Loose clutch. 3. Foreign material or damaged	parts in compressor. 4. Compressor loose on bracket.
COMPRESSOR VIBRATION	1. Broken or loose mounting bracket, or compressor brace.	2. Loose clutch. 3. Loose belt.

TESTING

Obstructed air passages, broken belts, disconnected or broken wires, loose clutch, loose or broken mounting brackets may be determined by visual inspection of the parts.

CHECKING FOR LEAKS

Attach the manifold gauge set (Fig. 8). Leave both manifold gauge valves at the maximum clockwise position. Set both service valves at the center position. Both gauges should now show approximately 60 to 80 pounds pressure at 75°F. If very little or no pressure is indicated, leave the vacuum pump valve closed, open the Refrigerant-12 tank valve, and set the low pressure manifold gauge valve to the counterclockwise position. This opens the system to tank pressure. Check all connections, and the compressor shaft seal for leaks, using a flame-type leak detector (Fig. 9). Follow the directions with the leak detector. The smaller the flame the more sensitive it is to leaks. Therefore, to insure accurate leak indication keep

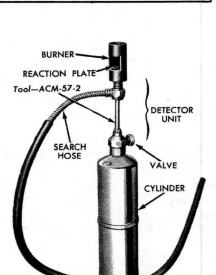

BURNER
 REACTION PLATE
 Tool—ACM-57-2
 DETECTOR UNIT
 SEARCH HOSE
 VALVE
 CYLINDER

K1548-A

FIG. 9—Torch Type Leak Detector

the flame as small as possible. The copper element must be red hot. If it is burned away, replace the element. Hold the open end of the hose at each suspected leak point for two or three seconds. The flame will normally be almost colorless. The slightest leak will be indicated by a bright green blue color to the flame. Be sure to check the manifold gauge set and hoses for leaks as well as the rest of the system.

If the surrounding air is contaminated with refrigerant gas, the leak detector will indicate this gas all the time. Good ventilation

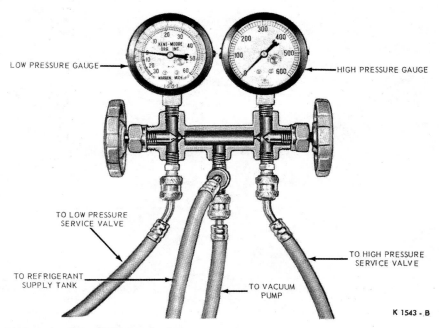

LOW PRESSURE GAUGE
 HIGH PRESSURE GAUGE
 TO LOW PRESSURE SERVICE VALVE
 TO HIGH PRESSURE SERVICE VALVE
 TO REFRIGERANT SUPPLY TANK
 TO VACUUM PUMP

K 1543 - B

FIG. 8—Manifold Gauge Set

is necessary to prevent this situation. A fan, even in a well ventilated area, is very helpful in removing small traces of refrigerant vapor.

USE OF SIGHT GLASS

When observing the sight glass for foam, run the engine at 1500 rpm with the thermostatic switch control lever set for maximum cooling, and the blower on high. Foam in the sight glass indicates an undercharge of refrigerant. Check the system for leaks, repair if necessary and charge the system with the proper amount of Refrigerant-12.

No foam in the sight glass will indicate either a full charge or a complete loss of refrigerant. Clean the sight glass. If the system is fully charged, the sight glass will be perfectly clear and the discharge air should be cool. If the system is completely empty of refrigerant, the sight glass will look oily and will not be as clear as when refrigerant is flowing through it.

When the compressor is not operating and when the system is completely charged, an occasional large bubble of Refrigerant-12 vapor will normally be seen in the sight glass.

Under conditions of extremely high temperatures occasional foam or bubbles may appear.

CHECKING SYSTEM PRESSURES

The pressures developed on the high pressure and low pressure side of the compressor indicate whether or not the system is operating properly.

Attach the manifold gauge set (Fig. 8). It will not be necessary to attach the Refrigerant-12 tank unless refrigerant is to be added to the system. Set both manifold gauge valves at the maximum clockwise, or closed, position. Set both service valves at the center position.

Check the system pressures with the engine running at 1500 rpm, all controls set for maximum cooling, and the front of the car at least 5 feet from any wall.

The actual pressures indicated on the gauges will depend on the temperature of the surrounding air and the humidity. Higher air temperatures along with low humidity, will give higher system pressures. The lowest figures given are for an ambient (surrounding air) temperature of 75°F., 50% relative humidity.

The low pressure gauge should indicate a pressure of from 12-50 pounds. The high pressure gauge should indicate a pressure 6 or 7 times the low pressure of 80-300 pounds.

At idle speed and a surrounding air temperature of 100°-110°F., the high pressure may go as high as 300 pounds or more. If it becomes necessary to operate the air conditioner under these conditions, keep the high pressure down with a fan directed at the condenser and radiator.

INTERPRETING ABNORMAL SYSTEM PRESSURES

Low pressure below normal, high pressure normal. These pressures indicate a restriction between the receiver and the expansion valve or between the expansion valve and the low pressure service valve. If the low pressure is actually a vacuum, the expansion valve is probably closed tightly. Shut the system down and allow it to warm to room temperature. Start the engine and if the evaporator will now become cool, the expansion valve was frozen because of moisture in the system. Release the refrigerant, replace the dryer-receiver assembly, check for leaks, then evacuate and charge the system.

Whenever the system has been opened three times the receiver dryer should be replaced as a precaution against internal icing of the expansion valve.

Check the system between the receiver outlet and the low pressure service valve for restrictions, by feeling all of the connections and components. Any portion that is cold to the touch or that frosts up, with the pressures as indicated here, is restricting the refrigerant flow.

Low Pressure Above Normal, High Pressure Normal. Observe both pressure gauges. If the low pressure is above normal (12-50 pounds) and the high pressure is at or near normal (80-300 pounds), the expansion valve is not operating properly. This condition may cause the compressor to receive slugs of liquid and thus to be very noisy. Also, the suction side of the compressor and the crankcase and head will be colder than normal and will frost up.

The expansion valve will allow too much liquid refrigerant to flow to the compressor if it is defective or, if the temperature sensing element is not making close contact with the evaporator outlet pipe. Make sure that the element is securely

clamped to the outlet pipe, and properly covered.

High Pressure Below Normal, Low Pressure Above Normal. If the two pressures are equal or within 30 pounds of each other, the compressor may be defective. Perform a compressor volumetric efficiency test. Repair or replace the compressor as needed.

High Pressure Above Normal. High compressor head pressures are caused by an overcharge of refrigerant, condenser air passages clogged, a restriction between the condenser inlet and the receiver, or high surrounding air temperatures. High head pressures are generally evidenced by a noisy compressor.

Discharge excess refrigerant until foam is seen in the sight glass (system operating at 1500 engine rpm), then add ½ pound of refrigerant.

THERMOSTATIC SWITCH TEST

The switch must be removed for this test. Move the switch arm to the coldest temperature setting by holding the arm against the stop nearest to the vacuum actuator. At room temperature the switch should be closed. Use a self-powered test light or ohmmeter connected to the switch leads to check whether or not the switch is closed. Release the switch arm. The switch should be open.

MAGNETIC CLUTCH

Disconnect the magnetic clutch wire at the bullet connector, and connect it to the negative lead of an ammeter. Connect the positive lead of the ammeter to the battery positive terminal. The magnetic clutch should pull in with a distinct click and the current reading on the ammeter should be to specification.

BLOWER MOTOR

Disconnect the blower motor wire at the bullet connector, and connect it to the negative lead of an ammeter. Connect the positive lead of the ammeter to the battery positive terminal. The motor should operate and the reading on the ammeter should be to specification.

EXPANSION VALVE

Remove the expansion valve from the evaporator. Connect the Refrigerant-12 supply hose to the expansion valve inlet with a suitable adapter. Open the refrigerant supply valve slightly. Refrigerant gas should come out of the expansion valve outlet. If no gas comes out of the outlet, the temperature sensing element has lost its charge and the expansion valve must be replaced.

COMPRESSOR VOLUMETRIC EFFICIENCY TEST

Malfunction of the compressor can be isolated by checking the compressor volumetric efficiency with a special tool. Make the test with the car in a clean dry atmosphere.

Run the engine at 1500 rpm with all controls at maximum cooling for at least 10 minutes. Adjust the engine idle with a tachometer to exactly 515 rpm with the compressor clutch engaged. Turn the engine off and set the cooling control to the OFF position. Isolate the compressor, then remove both high and low pressure service valve gauge port caps, allowing the gas in the compressor to escape.

Attach the special tool (calibrated orifice with gauge attached) to the high pressure service valve gauge port (Fig. 10). Start the engine. Engage the magnetic clutch for 15 second intervals, by moving the cooling control from the OFF position to the maximum cooling position,

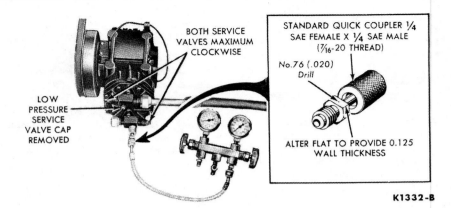

FIG. 10—Volumetric Efficiency Test

and observe the maximum gauge pressure at the end of each 15 second interval. **Be sure to allow the gauge pressure to drop to zero between the 15 second intervals.** Stop the engine.

A good compressor will bring the pressure to 200 psi in 15 seconds. If the pressure does not come up to 200 psi, in 15 seconds, clean the compressor intake screen. If the intake screen is clean, remove and inspect the valve plate. Most of the failures to come up to the 200 psi

specification will be caused by small foreign particles under the valve plate leaves or a defective valve plate. Clean the valve plate and assemble it to the compressor using new gaskets. If this does not effect a cure, replace the valve plate or the compressor as required.

If no further work is to be done on the system after making the volumetric efficiency test, disconnect the orifice tool and gauge, evacuate the compressor and connect it back into the system.

3 COMMON ADJUSTMENTS AND REPAIRS

SAFETY PRECAUTIONS

The refrigerant used in the air conditioner system is Refrigerant-12. Refrigerant-12 is nonexplosive, noninflammable, noncorrosive, has practically no odor, and is heavier than air. Although it is classified as a safe refrigerant, certain precautions must be observed to protect the parts involved and the person who is working on the unit.

Use only Refrigerant-12. Liquid Refrigerant-12, at normal atmospheric pressures and temperatures, evaporates so quickly that it tends to freeze anything that it contacts. For this reason, extreme care must be taken to prevent any liquid refrigerant from coming in contact with the skin and especially the eyes.

Refrigerant-12 is readily absorbed by most types of oil. It is therefore recommended that a bottle of sterile mineral oil and a quantity of weak boric acid solution be kept nearby when servicing the air conditioning system. Should any liquid refrigerant get into the eyes, use a few drops

of mineral oil to wash them out, then wash the eyes clean with the weak boric acid solution. Seek a doctor's aid immediately even though irritation may have ceased.

Always wear safety goggles when servicing any part of the refrigerating system.

The Refrigerant-12 in the system is always under pressure. Because the system is tightly sealed, heat applied to any part would cause this pressure to build up excessively.

To avoid a dangerous explosion, never weld, use a blow torch, solder, steam clean, bake body finishes, or use any excessive amount of heat on or in the immediate area of any part of the air cooling system or refrigerant supply tank, while they are closed to the atmosphere whether filled with refrigerant or not.

The liquid refrigerant evaporates so rapidly that the resulting refrigerant gas will displace the air surrounding the area where the refrigerant is released. To prevent possible suffocation in enclosed areas, always dis-

charge the refrigerant from an air cooling system into the garage exhaust collector. Always maintain good ventilation surrounding the work area. **If the car is to be undercoated, make certain that the under coating does not plug the evaporator drain tubes.**

Although Refrigerant-12 gas, under normal conditions, is nonpoisonous, the discharge of refrigerant gas near an open flame can produce a very poisonous gas. This gas will also attack all bright metal surfaces. This poisonous gas is generated when the flame-type leak detector is used. Avoid inhaling the fumes from the leak detector. **Make certain that Refrigerant-12 is both stored and installed in accordance with all state and local ordinances.**

When admitting Refrigerant-12 gas into the cooling unit, always keep the tank in an upright position. If the tank is on its side or upside down, liquid Refrigerant-12 will enter the system and damage the compressor. **In surrounding air temperatures** above 90°F., prolonged engine idle will result in excessively high compressor pressures.

DISCHARGING THE SYSTEM

Discharge the refrigerant from the system before replacing any part of the system, except the compressor.

To discharge the system, connect the manifold gauge set to the system. Do not connect the manifold center connection hoses to the Refrigerant-12 tank, or vacuum pump. Place the open end of these hoses in a garage exhaust outlet. Set the high pressure *manifold* gauge valve at the maximum counterclockwise or open position. Open the high pressure service valve a slight amount (Fig. 7) and allow the refrigerant to discharge slowly from the system.

Do not allow the refrigerant to rush out, as the oil in the compressor will be forced out along with it.

EVACUATING THE SYSTEM

Attach the manifold gauge set, a tank of Refrigerant-12 and a vacuum pump to the system. Make certain that the Refrigerant-12 tank valve is tightly closed. Set both service valves to the mid-position. Open both manifold valves. Release any

pressure in the system. Open the vacuum pump valve and run the pump until the low pressure gauge reads at least 25 inches, and as close to 30 inches of vacuum as possible. Continue vacuum pump operation for 20 to 30 minutes to boil any moisture out of the system. Close the pump valve. Turn off the pump.

MAKING A PARTIAL CHARGE

Attach the manifold gauge set and hoses (Fig. 11). Open both manifold valves. Close the vacuum pump valve. Open the Refrigerant-12 tank valve. Purge the air from the high pressure hose by loosening the high pressure hose at the service valve, for a few seconds. Tighten the connections and set the high pressure manifold gauge valve at the maximum clockwise position. Loosen the low pressure gauge hose slightly at the low pressure service valve, for a few seconds, to purge the air from the hose. Tighten the connection. Set both service valves at the center position.

Run the engine at 1500 rpm with all controls at the maximum cold position. Charge the system until all foam disappears from the sight glass, then add ½ pound of Refrig-

erant-12. Shut the Refrigerant-12 tank valve.

It may be necessary to place the Refrigerant-12 tank in a container of hot water at about 150°F. to force the gas from the tank during charging.

Never heat the Refrigerant-12 tank with a torch. A dangerous explosion may result.

Set both service valves at the maximum counterclockwise position.

Remove the gauge set, and cap the service valve gauge ports and valve stems.

MAKING A COMPLETE CHARGE

Check for leaks first (See Diagnosis and Testing in this part), release the pressure, then evacuate the system. Leave both service valves at the mid-position and the vacuum pump valve closed. Leave the low pressure manifold gauge valve at the maximum counterclockwise or open position. Set the high pressure manifold gauge valve at the maximum clockwise or closed position. Set all controls to the maximum cold position.

Open the Refrigerant-12 tank valve. Run the engine at 1500 rpm. Charge the system until the weight

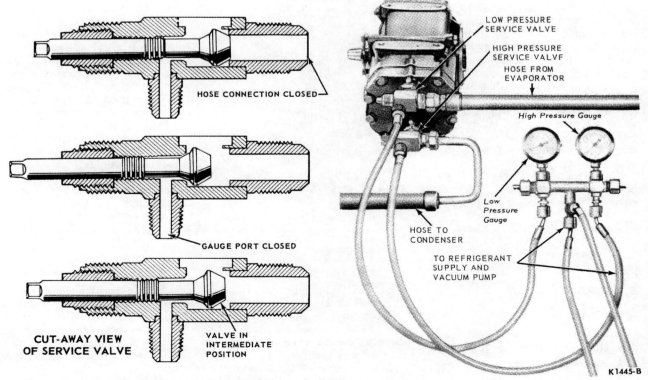

FIG. 11—Charging the Air Conditioning System

of refrigerant is to specification. During the charging, the high pressure may build up to an excessive value. This can be caused by an overcharge of refrigerant, or an overheated engine, in combination with high surrounding temperatures. Never allow the high pressure to exceed 240 pounds while charging. Stop the engine, determine the cause, and correct it.

After the proper charge has been made, close the Refrigerant-12 tank valve, and check the system pressures for proper operation. Set both service valves at the maximum counterclockwise position. Remove the gauge set, and cap the service valve gauge ports and valve stems.

CHARGING FROM SMALL CONTAINERS

Refrigerant-12 is available in one-pound cans. A scale is not necessary if these small containers are used instead of a tank.

Attach the hose that would normally go to the large tank to the special valve that is provided for the small cans. Close the valve (maximum clockwise position) and follow the procedure for leak testing, evacuating and charging the system as previously given.

For charging, attach a one-pound can of Refrigerant-12 to the special valve, and open the valve. Keep the can in an upright position. When the can is empty (no frost showing), close the valve, remove the empty can, attach a new one, and open the valve again.

Allow only ½ of the third can of refrigerant to be pumped into the system by closing the valve at the can when the frost line has reached ½ way down the can. The system will then have been charged with 2½ pounds of refrigerant.

Check the system pressures, set both service valves at the maximum counterclockwise position. Remove

the gauge set, and cap the service valve gauge ports and valve stems.

COMPRESSOR OIL LEVEL CHECK

Under normal conditions, when the air cooling system is operating satisfactorily, the compressor oil level need not be checked. There is no place for the oil to go except inside the sealed system. When the car is first started, some of the oil will be pumped into the rest of the system. After 15 minutes of operation, most of the oil is returned to the compressor crankcase.

Check the compressor oil level only if a portion of the refrigerant system is being replaced, or if there was a leak in the system and the refrigerant is being replaced.

Check the oil after the system has been charged and has been operating at an engine speed of 1500 rpm for 15 minutes in 60°F. surrounding air temperature or above. Turn off the engine, and isolate the compressor. Remove the oil filler plug from the compressor; insert a flattened ⅛-inch diameter rod (Fig. 12) in the oil filler

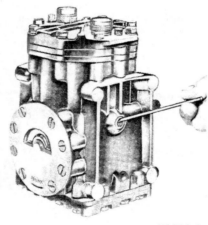

K1544-A

FIG. 12—Compressor Oil Level Check

hole until it bottoms. The rod should show ⅞ inch of oil. This is equivalent to 11 ounces of oil on Tecumseh compressors. On York compressors, the measurement should be ¾ inch. This is equivalent to 10 ounces of oil. It may be necessary to rotate the compressor crankshaft slightly (by hand) so that the dip rod will clear the crankshaft. If additional oil is needed in the compressor, add Suniso 5 or Capella E refrigerator compressor oil or equivalent.

If more than ⅞ inch of oil is indicated, as might happen if a new compressor is installed and oil already in the system is pumped back to the compressor, draw out the excess oil until the proper quantity is indicated.

Replace the oil filler plug, then evacuate and connect the compressor back into the system. Be sure to check the compressor filler opening for leaks.

ISOLATING THE COMPRESSOR

This procedure is used when checking the compressor oil level and when it is desired to replace the compressor without losing the refrigerant charge.

To isolate the compressor from the system, turn both the high and the low pressure service valves to the extreme clockwise position. Loosen the cap on the high pressure service valve gauge port, and allow the gas to escape until the compressor is relieved of refrigerant pressure. **Loosen the cap a small amount only, and do not remove it until the pressure is completely relieved.**

To connect the compressor back into the system, evacuate the compressor at the high pressure service valve gauge port, close the vacuum pump valve, turn both service valves to the maximum counterclockwise position, and cap the high pressure service valve gauge port and service valve stems.

4   REMOVAL AND INSTALLATION

EVAPORATOR CORE

REMOVAL

1. Discharge the refrigerant into the garage exhaust system.

2. Remove the air cleaner.

3. Remove the insulation at the expansion valve and the hose ends.

4. Remove the high and low pressure hoses at the evaporator core.

5. Remove the retaining nuts and remove the evaporator heat door vacuum actuator from the evaporator case, and position it to one side.

6. Carefully draw the thermostatic switch capillary tube out of the evaporator fins.

7. Remove the retaining screws and nuts and remove the evaporator core cover.

8. Remove the retaining screws from the bottom of the evaporator case and remove the evaporator (Fig. 13).

9. Remove the retaining screw and the clamp holding the expansion

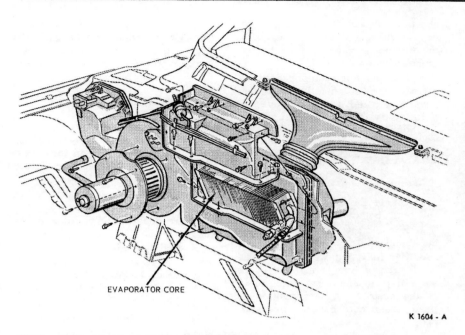

EVAPORATOR CORE

K 1604 - A

FIG. 13—Evaporator Core Removal

valve temperature bulb to the evaporator core.

10. Remove the expansion valve from the core.

INSTALLATION

1. Install the expansion valve on the new evaporator core.

2. Position the temperature bulb and the clamp to the core and install the retaining screw.

3. Position the evaporator core in the evaporator case, and install the retaining screws.

4. Clean off any remaining old sealer from the evaporator case and from the cover.

5. Apply new sealer.

6. Position the cover and install the retaining screws and nuts.

7. Wipe off excess sealer.

8. Position the evaporator heat door vacuum actuator to the evaporator case and install the retaining nuts. Make certain that the vacuum line is properly connected.

9. Through the top of the evaporator case install the capillary tube between the fins of the evaporator core.

10. Install the high and the low pressure hoses on the evaporator.

11. Install the insulation on the expansion valve and on the end fittings of the hoses.

12. Leak test, evacuate and charge the system.

13. Install the air cleaner and test the air conditioning system.

CONDENSER

REMOVAL

1. Drain the cooling system.

2. Remove the radiator (Group 12).

3. Make sure that there is no refrigerant in the system, then disconnect the compressor to condenser hose at the condenser, and disconnect the expansion valve to condenser hose at the condenser.

4. Remove the shroud from the car.

5. Remove the power boost fan assembly at the water pump.

6. Remove the condenser to mounting bracket bolts and remove the condenser.

INSTALLATION

1. Transfer the receiver from the old condenser to the new condenser.

2. Position the condenser assembly to the mounting bracket and install the mounting bolts.

3. Install the power boost fan assembly to the water pump.

4. Position the fan shroud over the water pump.

5. Connect both refrigerant hoses to the condenser.

6. Install the radiator and shroud. Fill the cooling system.

7. Leak test, evacuate and charge the air conditioning system. Check the operation of the system.

COMPRESSOR

REMOVAL

1. Isolate the compressor (See

Common Adjustments and Repairs) and disconnect the two service valves and hoses from the compressor (Fig. 14). Energize the clutch and loosen and remove the clutch mounting bolt.

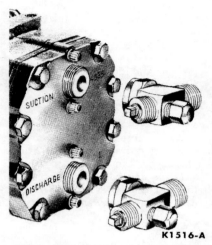

SUCTION

DISCHARGE

K1516-A

FIG. 14—Compressor Service Valves Removed

2. Install a ⅝-11 bolt in the clutch drive shaft hole. With the clutch still energized, tighten the bolt to loosen the clutch from the shaft. Disconnect the clutch wire at the bullet connector.

3. Loosen the idler pulley and remove the drive belt and the clutch and then remove the mounting bolts and the compressor.

4. With the compressor on the work bench, remove the key from the shaft.

INSTALLATION

Before installing the compressor, see Cleaning and Inspection in this part.

1. Mount the clutch on the shaft and install the mounting screw and washer finger-tight. Place the compressor on the mounting bracket and install the four mounting bolts finger-tight.

2. Connect the clutch wire, energize the clutch and torque the clutch mounting bolt to specification. **If the new compressor was shipped with a bolt and washer in the end of the crankshaft, remove and discard the bolt and use a bolt with a nylon insert in it.** Install and tighten the mounting bolts to specification. Do not exceed torque specifications as misalignment can result.

3. Install the belt and adjust and tighten the idler pulley.

4. Install the service valves on the compressor using new seals. Be cer-

tain to remove the rubber shipping plugs first. Tighten the service valve nuts to specification. Do not over tighten. The new ROTO-LOK service valves can be rotated slightly on their seat without breaking the high pressure seal. This is not an indication of a loose valve. Leak test the compressor, then evacuate it and connect it back into the system.

5. Check the oil level in the compressor and add or remove oil if necessary. (See Cleaning and Inspection in this part.)

COMPRESSOR COMPONENTS

All compressor removal and installation operations, except belt replacement, can be performed only after the unit has been isolated from the rest of the system. (See Common Adjustments and Repairs.)

VALVE PLATE

Removal

1. Isolate the compressor and disconnect the service valves. Remove the head bolts.

2. Remove the cylinder head and valve plate from the top of the compressor body (Fig. 15). Do not tap or hit the head with any hard tool, as damage could result. (York compressors are aluminum.)

3. Remove and discard all gaskets, and be sure to clean gasket shreds from all gasket surfaces. Examine the cylinders and top of the pistons, particularly in case of valve breakage. If there are score marks, replace the compressor assembly.

4. If the cylinders and pistons are in good condition, check the valve plate and valve reeds for damage. If the valve assembly is in good condition, it can be used again. If the valve plate is damaged, install the entire replacement kit which includes the valve plate, valve reeds, and the two gaskets (Fig. 15).

5. When the valve plate assembly is reused, wash it in clean solvent and dry in dry air. Check the oil for dirt. If the system is not clean, replace the oil.

Installation

1. Starting with the valve plate gasket, assemble the parts in the order shown in Fig. 15. Insert the cylinder head bolts carefully to avoid damaging the gaskets. Before assembly apply a film of new refrigeration oil to both sides of both gaskets.

2. Tighten all bolts finger-tight, then torque the bolts a quarter turn at a time to specification. Tighten the bolts in sequence so those diagonally opposite are evenly drawn to the required torque.

3. Connect the compressor into the system. Check the oil level in the compressor, and add or remove oil if necessary. (See Cleaning and Inspection in this part.)

CRANKSHAFT SEAL

Removal

1. Isolate the compressor, loosen and remove the belt.

2. Remove the clutch and remove the Woodruff key.

3. Carefully remove all accumulated dirt and foreign material from the seal plate and surrounding area of the compressor, and position a small drain pan beneath the seal plate.

4. Remove the seal plate bolts, and remove the plate and gasket. Do not mar the sealing surfaces, or the polished shaft surface.

Remove the carbon seal ring and seal housing assembly from the crankshaft. A disassembled view of the crankshaft seal assembly is included in Fig. 15.

6. Clean all old gasket material from the seal plate and the compressor. Make certain that the shaft, the seal plate and the compressor gasket surfaces are completely clean before installing the new seal.

Installation

1. Lubricate the new shaft seal parts in clean compressor oil. Position the seal assembly on the crankshaft, with the carbon ring toward the seal plate.

2. Position the new gasket on the compressor, and install the seal plate.

3. Torque the bolts to specification.

4. Make certain that there are no burrs or dirt on the compressor shaft, then install the key and the clutch.

5. Install and adjust the belt.

6. Check the oil level (See Common Adjustments and Repairs).

EXPANSION VALVE

1. Discharge the air conditioning system.

2. Remove the insulation from the expansion valve and hose ends.

3. Loosen the clamp screw retaining the temperature sensing bulb to the evaporator pipe. Pull the bulb from the clamp.

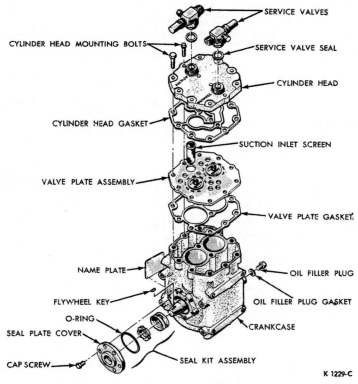

SERVICE VALVES
CYLINDER HEAD MOUNTING BOLTS
SERVICE VALVE SEAL
CYLINDER HEAD
CYLINDER HEAD GASKET
SUCTION INLET SCREEN
VALVE PLATE ASSEMBLY
VALVE PLATE GASKET
NAME PLATE
OIL FILLER PLUG
FLYWHEEL KEY
OIL FILLER PLUG GASKET
O-RING
CRANKCASE
SEAL PLATE COVER
CAP SCREW
SEAL KIT ASSEMBLY

K 1229-C

FIG. 15—Cylinder Head and Valve Assembly

4. Remove the high pressure hose from the expansion valve and remove the valve from the evaporator.

5. Connect the new expansion valve to the evaporator, slide the temperature sensing bulb in the clamp and tighten the mounting screw.

6. Connect the high pressure hose to the expansion valve and leak test the valve connections.

7. Install the insulation on the expansion valve and hose ends.

8. Evacuate and charge the system.

THERMOSTATIC SWITCH

1. Remove the Bowden cable from the switch.

2. Disconnect the switch wires. Disconnect the switch to temperature valve arm, carefully pull the sensing tube from the evaporator and remove the switch.

3. Feed the sensing tube of the new switch into the evaporator and mount the switch to the case.

4. Position the temperature valve arm to the switch, position the control cable in the mounting and install the mounting clip and screw. Install the spring clip retaining the control arm to the switch.

5. Connect the wires to the switch and check the switch operation.

CLUTCH

1. Loosen and remove the belt.

2. Energize the clutch and loosen and remove the clutch mounting bolt.

3. Install a ⅝-11 bolt in the clutch drive shaft hole. With the clutch still energized, tighten the bolt to loosen the clutch from the shaft, then remove the magnetic clutch.

4. Install the clutch, the clutch mounting bolt, and the washer.

5. Energize the clutch, and torque the bolt to specification.

6. Install and adjust the belt.

BLOWER MOTOR

The blower motor is accessible from the engine compartment. Remove the protective cover, remove the mounting plate to dash attaching screws, disconnect the motor wires and remove the motor assembly. Transfer the blower wheel and mounting plate to the new motor before installing it.

BELT

1. Loosen the idler pulley and remove the belt.

2. Place the new belt in position, and adjust the belt tension to specification, then tighten the idler pulley.

3. Check the belt alignment, and adjust it if necessary.

5   CLEANING AND INSPECTION

On compressor clutch installations, carefully remove any burrs or dirt that may be on the compressor shaft. The shaft must be dry and brightly polished. Then install the key in the shaft.

When the compressor is disassembled, completely clean all surfaces of gasket shreds and foreign objects.

Make certain that the brushes and brush slip rings are clean and free of oil or grease.

If the compressor shaft seal is being replaced, inspect the compressor internally and clean out dirt or chips as required.

PART 16-3 SPEED CONTROL—FORD

1 DESCRIPTION AND OPERATION

The speed control system is a driver-operated regulating device which is used as an automatic throttle control for vehicle speeds from 25 to 80 miles per hour. Although the system actually maintains speed, it is not a governor since it does not restrict available engine rpm or performance. The system is controlled by vehicle speed and can be overridden by applying normal pressure to the accelerator pedal. The system will maintain the selected speed up and down hills as well as on a level road.

The major components of the speed control system are: actuator head assembly, vacuum bellows, brake release switch and engagement relay, metering valve and vacuum valve and inhibitor switch, and sensor pump.

ACTUATOR HEAD ASSEMBLY

The speed control actuator head assembly is mounted on the instrument panel (Fig. 1). The operation of the speed control depends on the position of the selector dial which sets the speed at which control is desired, and the switch button which has the positions of OFF and ON. The switch button is held in the ON position magnetically. Turning the selector dial rotates a cam in the metering valve which varies the spring pressure exerted on the pilot valve.

RESUME SPEED BUTTON   ACTUATOR HEAD ASSEMBLY

SELECTOR DIAL   SWITCH BUTTON   K 1654-A

FIG. 1—Actuator Head Assembly

The selector dial is numbered with speed settings from 30 mph to 80 mph (10 mph increments). Setting the selector dial between the indicated increments will produce a corresponding intermediate speed. When the switch button is in the OFF position, the system is inoperative and has no effect at any speed. When the RESUME button is pressed, it energizes the system resulting in the vehicle accelerating to the preset speed without using the accelerator pedal. The RESUME feature operates only at vehicle speeds above 20 mph.

VACUUM BELLOWS

The vacuum bellows is located under the instrument panel and is connected to the accelerator pedal arm with a ball chain through a pulley (Fig. 2). As vacuum is metered to the bellows, it collapses and pulls on the chain which holds the accelerator linkage open and maintains the set speed.

BRAKE RELEASE SWITCH AND ENGAGEMENT RELAY

The brake release switch and engagement relay are located under the instrument panel on the brake pedal

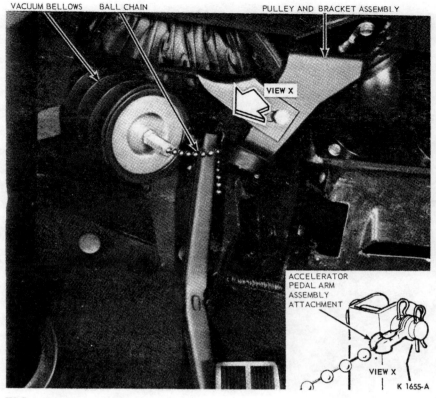

VACUUM BELLOWS   BALL CHAIN   PULLEY AND BRACKET ASSEMBLY

VIEW X

ACCELERATOR
PEDAL ARM
ASSEMBLY
ATTACHMENT

VIEW X

K 1655-A

FIG. 2—Vacuum Bellows

and support assembly (Fig. 3). When the brake pedal is lightly depressed, the brake release switch is opened which disengages the speed control system. The brake release switch is a normally closed switch.

The engagement relay is energized when the contacts in the metering valve close as the vehicle is accelerated to slightly over the present speed setting, or by pressing the resume speed button. An audible click can be heard when the relay closes. The closing of the relay supplies power to the vacuum valve which opens to supply vacuum to the metering valve. When the brake release switch is opened the engagement relay is de-energized closing the vacuum valve, thereby, dropping out the automatic control.

METERING VALVE, VACUUM VALVE AND INHIBITOR SWITCH

The metering valve, vacuum valve and inhibitor switch are mounted in the engine compartment on a com-

mon bracket (Fig. 4). The metering valve is connected to the actuator head assembly by a control cable. As the vehicle is accelerated to slightly above the set speed, pressure from the sensor pump increases to balance the spring pressure exerted on the pilot valve and closes the contact points. When the points close, the engagement relay is energized which in turn opens the vacuum valve allowing manifold vacuum to be metered to the vacuum bellows by the pilot valve. As the pilot valve is now in the equilibrium position, the vacuum bellows does not move the throttle. When climbing a hill the vehicle speed and the sensor pump pressure are reduced. This reduces the pressure on the pilot valve. The spring force, which is constant for the set speed, moves the pilot valve which meters more vacuum to the vacuum bellows. The vacuum bellows opens the throttle and accelerates the vehicle until the equilibrium point is again reached. On a downgrade the same principle applies, reversing the action. As the vehicle speed rises, so does the pressure from the sensor pump causing the pilot valve to overpower the set speed spring force, allowing the pilot valve to vent to the atmosphere. Less vacuum is therefore available to the vacuum bellows and the throttle closes slightly until the pilot valve forces are again equalized. The inhibitor switch prevents the use of the resume-speed feature below 20 mph. This is a safety feature to prevent accidental acceleration from a stop before it is desired. As the vehicle accelerates, pressure from the sensor pump increases, and at 20 mph the pressure is sufficient to close the inhibitor switch. With the inhibitor switch closed the resume-speed feature is operative. Pressing the resume-speed button grounds the system artificially, which energizes the engagement relay and activates the rest of the system in the same manner as bringing the vehicle up to the selected speed, which closes the points in the metering valve, grounding the system.

SENSOR PUMP

The sensor pump is a low friction pump, driven by the speedometer cable, which converts road speed to pressure which applies a balancing force to the pilot valve and closes the inhibitor switch when a speed of 20 mph is attained (Fig. 5). The sen-

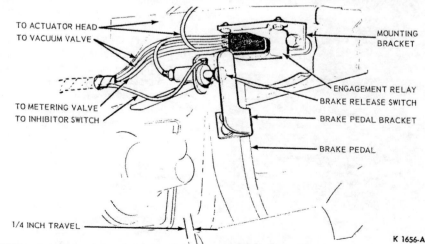

TO ACTUATOR HEAD
TO VACUUM VALVE

MOUNTING
BRACKET

TO METERING VALVE
TO INHIBITOR SWITCH

ENGAGEMENT RELAY
BRAKE RELEASE SWITCH

BRAKE PEDAL BRACKET

BRAKE PEDAL

1/4 INCH TRAVEL

K 1656-A

FIG. 3—Brake Release Switch and Engagement Relay

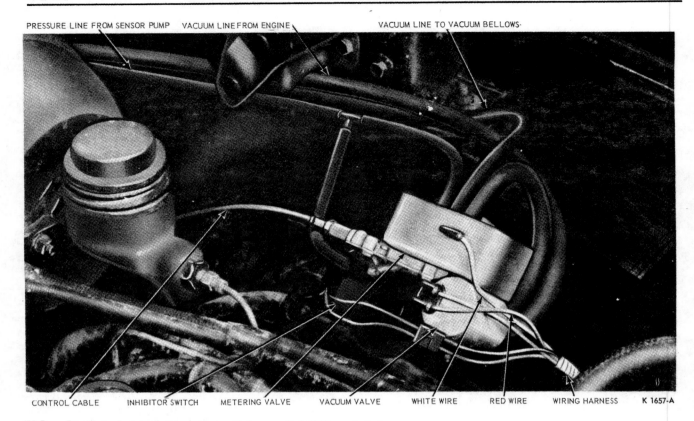

PRESSURE LINE FROM SENSOR PUMP   VACUUM LINE FROM ENGINE   VACUUM LINE TO VACUUM BELLOWS

CONTROL CABLE   INHIBITOR SWITCH   METERING VALVE   VACUUM VALVE   WHITE WIRE   RED WIRE   WIRING HARNESS   K 1657-A

FIG. 4—Metering Valve, Vacuum Valve and Inhibitor Switch

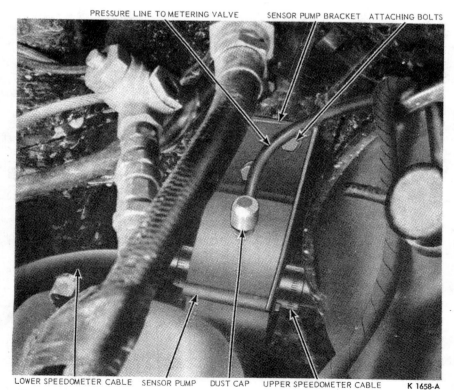

PRESSURE LINE TO METERING VALVE   SENSOR PUMP BRACKET   ATTACHING BOLTS

LOWER SPEEDOMETER CABLE   SENSOR PUMP   DUST CAP   UPPER SPEEDOMETER CABLE   K 1658-A

FIG. 5—Sensor Pump

sor pump operates whenever the vehicle is in motion, whether or not

the speed control is energized and in operation. The pump is a sealed unit

containing a non-volatile fluid with stable viscosity.

The automatic throttle control feature is for use on turnpikes, expressways or other open road operation. To use the speed control system as an automatic throttle control, start the engine, pull out the switch button to the ON position, and select the speed at which you wish to travel by adjusting the selector dial. The unit is now under automatic control and as the vehicle is accelerated to slightly above the selected speed a click will be heard from the engagement relay and the system will lock-in automatically. The system will also bring the vehicle to the selected speed by pressing the resume-speed button when a speed of approximately 20 miles per hour is reached. The speed control system will automatically operate the throttle without the need for foot pressure on the accelerator pedal to maintain the selected speed. The speed of the vehicle can be changed while the speed control system is operating automatically by slowly moving the selector dial to the new *desired* speed.

When under automatic control, always rotate the dial slowly when increasing or decreasing vehicle speed

to prevent sudden acceleration or deceleration.

The vehicle speed can be increased at any time by pushing on the accelerator pedal with normal pressure. Release the pressure on the accelerator pedal and the vehicle will return to the pre-selected speed.

The speed control system may be disengaged at any time by a slight depressing of the brake pedal. It may be re-engaged again by increasing the vehicle speed to slightly above that selected, until the click is heard from the engagement relay. If above 20 miles per hour, the resume-speed button may be pressed which will automatically bring the vehicle up to the selected speed.

Since the speed control system is an electrically actuated device, receiving its power from the battery through the ignition switch, automatic control is cancelled each time the ignition switch is turned to the OFF position as well as when the switch button is pushed to the OFF position.

2   DIAGNOSIS AND TESTING

When diagnosing and trouble shooting the speed control system, first obtain all the facts from the owner concerning his problem and then road test the vehicle with the owner. In this manner you will be assured that the owner is operating the speed control system properly and you will be able to verify the complaint should one exist.

The usage of the service adjustments are covered in the following list of common speed control problems, their possible cause and corrective action.

SPEED CONTROL DIAGNOSIS GUIDE—FORD

TROUBLE	POSSIBLE CAUSE	CORRECTIVE ACTION
SPEED CONTROL SWITCH BUTTON WON'T STAY OUT, SYSTEM IS INOPERATIVE	1. Blown fuse. 2. Wire off back of switch or ignition, or wiring is defective. 3. Switch button burned out.	1. Replace fuse. Check wiring for possible grounding condition (Fig.8). 2. Install plug connector tightly. Check wiring for continuity (Fig. 8). 3. Replace actuator head assembly (Fig. 7).
SPEED CONTROL SWITCH BUTTON STAYS OUT, BUT SYSTEM IS INOPERATIVE	1. Any of the system components.	1. Perform electrical check.
SPEED CONTROL ENGAGES BELOW DESIRED SPEED	1. Resume-speed switch shorted. 2. Metering valve points shorted. 3. Wiring shorted.	1. Replace actuator head assembly. 2. Perform contact points adjustment, or replace metering valve. 3. Check wiring for grounding condition (Fig. 8).
SPEED CONTROL WILL NOT RESUME WHEN RESUME-SPEED SWITCH IS ACTIVATED	1. Resume-speed switch defective. 2. Switch not properly grounded. 3. Wire off back of switch or defective wiring.	1. Replace actuator head assembly. 2. Artificially ground actuator head assembly. If still no operation, replace actuator head assembly (Fig. 7). 3. Install plug connector tightly. Check wiring for continuity (Fig. 8).
SPEED CONTROL WILL NOT DISENGAGE WHEN BRAKE PEDAL IS DEPRESSED	1. Brake switch improperly adjusted or defective.	1. Perform brake switch adjustment.
SPEED CONTROL INOPERATIVE AND SPEEDOMETER DOES NOT REGISTER	1. Broken speedometer cable between transmission and sensor pump.	1. Replace speedometer lower cable.

SPEED CONTROL DIAGNOSIS GUIDE—FORD (Continued)

TROUBLE	POSSIBLE CAUSE	CORRECTIVE ACTION
SPEED CONTROL OPERATES BUT SPEEDOMETER DOES NOT REGISTER	1. Broken speedometer cable between sensor pump and speedometer. 2. Inoperative speedometer mechanism.	1. Replace speedometer upper cable. 2. Replace speedometer head.
SYSTEM HUNTS (SPEED CONTINUOUSLY CHANGES UP AND DOWN)	1. Vacuum hose split between engine intake manifold and vacuum valve, vacuum valve and metering valve or metering valve and vacuum bellows. 2. Ruptured vacuum bellows. 3. Defective metering valve. 4. Sticky carburetor or accelerator linkage.	1. Inspect all vacuum hoses and cut off end and reinstall or replace as required (Fig. 6). 2. Replace vacuum bellows. 3. Replace metering valve. 4. Check for binding conditions and oil connections.
SYSTEM SLUGGISH, WILL NOT HOLD SPEED ON HILLS	1. Ball chain between vacuum bellows and accelerator not properly adjusted. 2. Defective sensor pump. 3. Sticky carburetor or accelerator linkage. 4. Vacuum leak in hoses. 5. Leak in vacuum bellows.	1. Perform accelerator linkage adjustment. 2. Refill or replace sensor pump. 3. Check for binding conditions. Oil all connections. 4. Inspect all vacuum hoses and cut off end and reinstall or replace as required (Fig. 6). 5. Replace vacuum bellows.
ENGINE WILL NOT RETURN TO NORMAL IDLE	1. Throttle linkage improperly adjusted. 2. Speed control accelerator linkage misadjusted.	1. Perform throttle linkage adjustment (Group 7). 2. Perform accelerator linkage adjustment.
WHILE OPERATING, VEHICLE OVER-SPEEDS SPEED SETTING	1. Pressure hose between sensor pump and metering valve leaking. 2. Defective metering valve diaphragm. 3. Vacuum hoses to metering valve reversed.	1. Inspect hose and cut off ends and reinstall or replace as required (Fig. 6). 2. Replace metering valve. 3. Install vacuum hoses as shown in Fig. 6.
INCREASE IN MINIMUM CONTROLLABLE SPEED	1. Loss of fluid from sensor pump.	1. Refill or replace sensor pump.
SELECTOR DIAL SPEED SETTING DOES NOT CORRESPOND TO SPEED INDICATED ON SPEEDOMETER	1. Improper control cable adjustment.	1. Perform control cable adjustment.
HIGH ENGAGEMENT SPEED OVER SET SPEED	1. Contact points in metering valve too far apart.	1. Perform contact points adjustment, or replace metering valve.
SYSTEM RESUMES SPEED AFTER DEPRESSING AND RELEASING BRAKE PEDAL OR RESUMES SPEED WELL BELOW THE SET SPEED	1. Metering valve contact points too close or fused together. 2. Shorted resume-speed button or wiring.	1. Perform contact points adjustment, or replace metering valve. 2. Check resume-speed button for continuous continuity and replace acuator head assembly. Check wiring for continuity and replace as required (Fig. 8).

K 1659-A

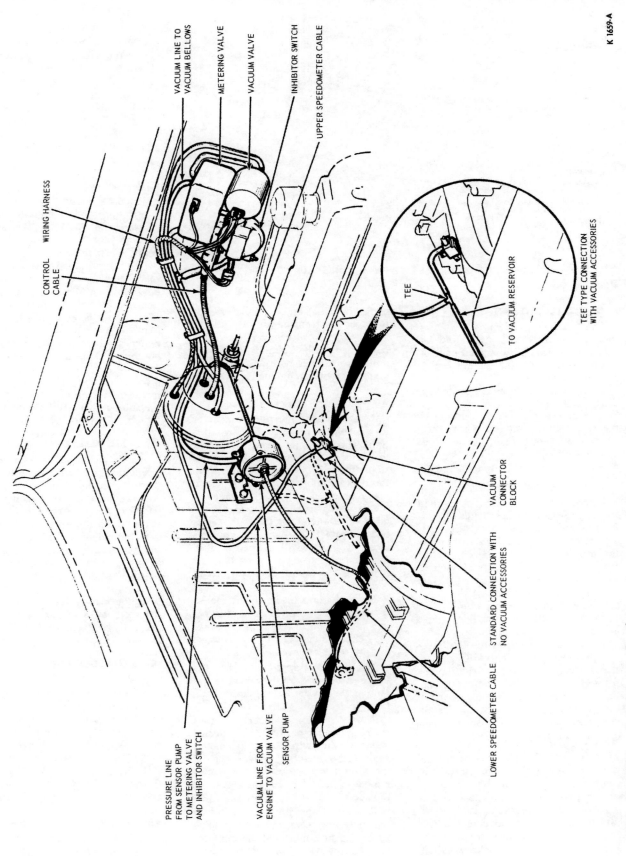

VACUUM LINE TO VACUUM BELLOWS
METERING VALVE
VACUUM VALVE
INHIBITOR SWITCH
UPPER SPEEDOMETER CABLE

WIRING HARNESS

CONTROL CABLE

TEE

TO VACUUM RESERVOIR

TEE TYPE CONNECTION WITH VACUUM ACCESSORIES

VACUUM CONNECTOR BLOCK

PRESSURE LINE FROM SENSOR PUMP TO METERING VALVE AND INHIBITOR SWITCH

VACUUM LINE FROM ENGINE TO VACUUM VALVE

SENSOR PUMP

LOWER SPEEDOMETER CABLE

STANDARD CONNECTION WITH NO VACUUM ACCESSORIES

FIG. 6—Engine Compartment Routing

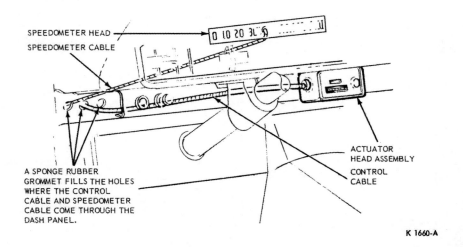

SPEEDOMETER HEAD
SPEEDOMETER CABLE

A SPONGE RUBBER
GROMMET FILLS THE HOLES
WHERE THE CONTROL
CABLE AND SPEEDOMETER
CABLE COME THROUGH THE
DASH PANEL.

ACTUATOR
HEAD ASSEMBLY
CONTROL
CABLE

K 1660-A

FIG. 7—Control Cable and Speedometer Upper Cable Routing

ELECTRICAL CHECKS

The following electrical checks should be performed to determine the cause and correction of speed control trouble and to eliminate unnecessary service work.

1. Turn the ignition switch to the ACC position.

2. Pull out the switch button. If the switch button does not stay out, check for a blown fuse or a wire off at the back of the switch button, or a defective switch button.

INHIBITOR SWITCH

Disconnect the inhibitor switch from the wiring harness (Figs. 4 and 8). Ground one lead of a test light and attach the other lead to one of the terminals on the plug connector from the inhibitor switch. Attach a hot lead to the other terminal in the plug connector. Disconnect the pressure line from the sensor pump (Fig. 5). Blow into the pressure line to apply pressure to the inhibitor switch. The pressure will close the inhibitor switch and the test light will light. If the test light fails to light the inhibitor switch is defective and must be replaced. Reconnect the plug connector to the inhibitor switch and install the pressure line to the sensor pump.

BRAKE RELEASE SWITCH

Disconnect the plug connector to the inhibitor switch and install a jumper wire (Figs. 4 and 8). Remove the plug connector from the vacuum valve. Ground one lead of a test light and touch the other lead to the red wire. The test light will come on indicating that the brake release switch is good. If the test light does not

come on, the brake release switch may require replacement or adjustment (Fig. 3). Reconnect the plug connector to the vacuum valve. Remove the jumper wire and reconnect inhibitor switch plug connector.

METERING VALVE

1. Disconnect the plug connector to the inhibitor switch and install a jumper wire (Figs. 4 and 8). Rotate the selector dial to the low speed stop. Remove the pressure line from the sensor pump and blow into it to apply pressure to the diaphragm in the metering valve. This will lift the pilot valve thereby closing the electrical contacts. When the contacts close, a thump will be heard from the vacuum valve indicating that the metering valve and electrical circuit is good.

Re-applying pressure to the metering valve will result in no thump being heard. If a thump is again heard the engagement relay is defective and must be replaced.

This is a one application test, the brake pedal must be depressed to unground the system before the test can be repeated.

2. If no thump is heard, remove the plug connector from the metering valve (white wire) and ground it against the metering valve case. If the thump is now heard, the metering valve is defective and must be replaced.

Reconnect the plug connector to the metering valve, the pressure line to the sensor pump, and the inhibitor valve to the wiring harness plug connector.

VACUUM VALVE

If no thump is heard in step 2 under Metering Valve, remove the plug connector from the vacuum valve (Figs. 4 and 8). Attach a hot lead to the terminal to which the red wire was connected, with a jumper wire. Ground the other terminal. A thump will now be heard. If no thump is heard, the vacuum valve is defective and must be replaced. Reconnect the plug connector to the vacuum valve.

ENGAGEMENT RELAY

Install a jumper wire across the plug connector to the inhibitor switch (Figs. 4 and 8). With a known good vacuum valve, and when no thump is heard when the metering valve wire (white) is grounded, the engagement relay may be defective. Check the plug connector for proper installation and artificially ground the relay. If a thump is now heard, the relay may be improperly grounded, so a better ground must be provided. If no thump is heard, the engagement relay is defective and must be replaced. Reconnect the plug connector to the metering valve and remove the jumper wire and connect the inhibitor switch to the wiring harness.

RESUME BUTTON

Install a jumper wire across the plug connector to the inhibitor switch (Fig. 8). Pushing the resume button will ground the system and a thump will be heard from the metering valve. If no thump is heard, remove the plug connector (black wire) from the actuator head and ground it. If a thump is now heard, the resume button is defective and the actuator head must be replaced. If no thump is again heard, the wiring may be defective or a check of each part needs to be performed to determine the problem area.

LOSS OF SENSOR PUMP FLUID

Loss of fluid from the sensor pump will result in an increase in the minimum engagement speed and erratic operation. The lowest controllable speed will increase until the system becomes inoperative (Fig. 9).

1. Remove the rubber tubing from the sensor pump. Check the tubing carefully for any indication of pump fluid. The fluid has a pungent odor *which is easily detected.*

2. If fluid is detected, reinstall the rubber tubing to the sensor pump and remove the tubing from the me-

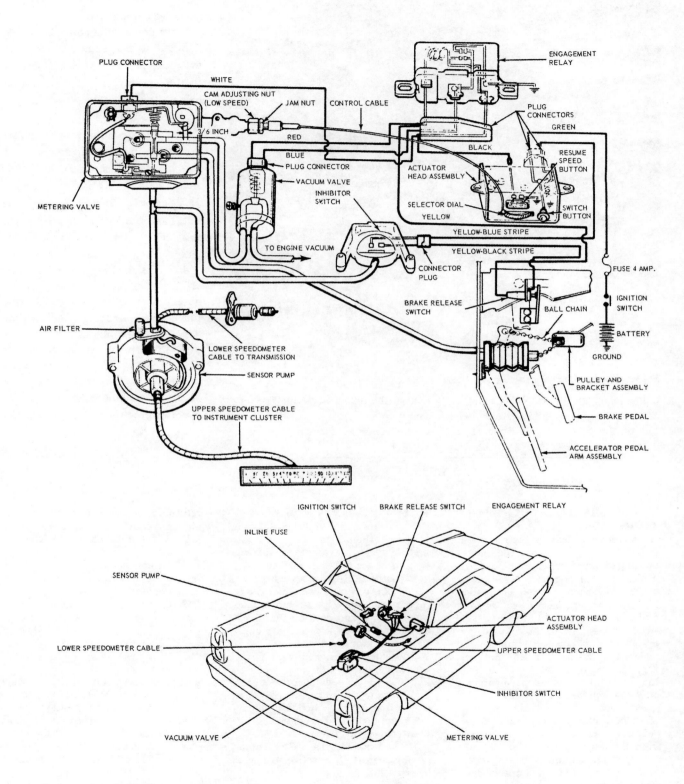

PLUG CONNECTOR
WHITE
CAM ADJUSTING NUT (LOW SPEED)
JAM NUT
CONTROL CABLE
3/6 INCH
RED
BLUE
PLUG CONNECTOR
VACUUM VALVE
INHIBITOR SWITCH
METERING VALVE
TO ENGINE VACUUM
CONNECTOR PLUG
BRAKE RELEASE SWITCH
ENGAGEMENT RELAY
PLUG CONNECTORS
GREEN
BLACK
RESUME SPEED BUTTON
ACTUATOR HEAD ASSEMBLY
SELECTOR DIAL
YELLOW
SWITCH BUTTON
YELLOW-BLUE STRIPE
YELLOW-BLACK STRIPE
FUSE 4 AMP.
IGNITION SWITCH
BALL CHAIN
BATTERY
GROUND
AIR FILTER
LOWER SPEEDOMETER CABLE TO TRANSMISSION
SENSOR PUMP
UPPER SPEEDOMETER CABLE TO INSTRUMENT CLUSTER
PULLEY AND BRACKET ASSEMBLY
BRAKE PEDAL
ACCELERATOR PEDAL ARM ASSEMBLY

IGNITION SWITCH
BRAKE RELEASE SWITCH
ENGAGEMENT RELAY
INLINE FUSE
SENSOR PUMP
ACTUATOR HEAD ASSEMBLY
LOWER SPEEDOMETER CABLE
UPPER SPEEDOMETER CABLE
INHIBITOR SWITCH
VACUUM VALVE
METERING VALVE

K 1661-A

FIG. 8 — Schematic Diagram

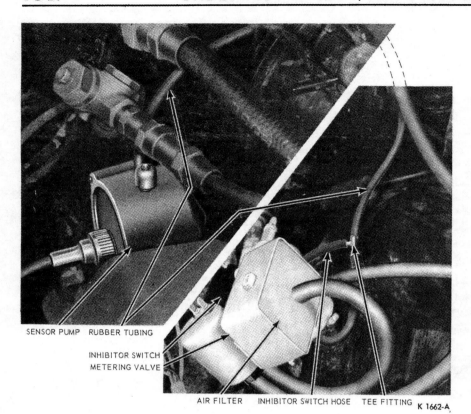

SENSOR PUMP   RUBBER TUBING

INHIBITOR SWITCH
METERING VALVE

AIR FILTER   INHIBITOR SWITCH HOSE   TEE FITTING   K 1662-A

FIG. 9—Loss of Sensor Pump Fluid

tering valve, and the inhibitor switch hose from the tee fitting. Hold the end of the tubing up to drain any fluid in the tubing back into the sensor pump.

The sensor pump, metering valve, inhibitor switch, and tubing form a closed system so that the fluid should never leave the pump.

When liquid is found in the tubing it is due to a leaking diaphragm in the metering valve, a leak at one of the tubing fittings, or driving the vehicle with the rubber hose disconnected.

3. To check for a leaking metering valve diaphragm, remove the two vacuum hoses and air filter. Examine the diaphragm from inside the metering valve, if it is found to be wet, there is a leak in the diaphragm and the metering valve must be replaced.

4. If the diaphragm is found to be dry, check all tubing connections and on any that do not fit tight, cut the tubing back ½ inch and reinstall the tubing to the fitting.

5. Test drive the vehicle to be sure that the speed control is functioning properly. If high engagement speeds or erratic operations are found, follow the procedure for refilling the sensor pump.

3   COMMON ADJUSTMENTS

BRAKE RELEASE SWITCH ADJUSTMENT

The brake release switch located inside the vehicle, above the brake pedal pad must be adjusted so that it will break the electrical circuit and cancel the speed control within the first ¼ inch of free travel of the brake pedal pad. If the brake release switch is too close to the brake pedal bracket, the switch will remain open and the speed control will not engage. If the brake release switch is too far from the brake pedal bracket, the switch will stay closed and the speed control will remain engaged after the brakes are applied (Fig. 3).

1. Remove the plug connector from the inhibitor switch and install a jumper wire. Remove the plug connector from the vacuum valve. Ground one lead of a test lamp and touch the other lead to the red wire from the vacuum valve.

2. Turn the ignition switch to the ACC position. Pull out the switch button to the ON position.

3. Depress the brake pedal, the test light should go out within the first ¼ inch of travel measured at the bottom of the brake pedal pad.

4. If the test light does not go out in ¼ inch of brake pedal pad travel, loosen the brake pedal bracket attaching bolts and position the bracket so that it just clears the plunger of the brake release switch.

5. Vehicles equipped with power brakes should have the engine started and the brake pedal depressed several times to assure correct operation of the brake release switch with vacuum applied to the power brake booster.

If the brake release switch cannot be adjusted, it is defective and must be replaced.

ACCELERATOR LINKAGE ADJUSTMENT

Improper accelerator linkage adjustment can result in the engine not returning to normal idle, the unit not allowing control at high speeds, or a lag in response to speed changes (Fig. 2).

1. Disconnect the ball chain from the accelerator pedal arm assembly attachment.

2. Check the throttle linkage adjustment being sure that the linkage is against the normal idle adjusting screw, with the engine stopped.

3. With the vacuum bellows in the released position, hold the ball chain taut to the accelerator pedal arm assembly attachment. Hold the attachment up in its normal position.

4. Allow one-half to one ball slack in the chain. Cut off the extra chain and reconnect the ball chain to the accelerator pedal arm assembly attachment. If the ball chain is too short, a new chain must be installed.

CONTROL CABLE ADJUSTMENT

1. Remove the two vacuum hoses

and the air filter from the metering valve (Fig. 10).

2. Loosen the jam nut from the cam adjusting nut. Rotate the selector dial against the low speed stop.

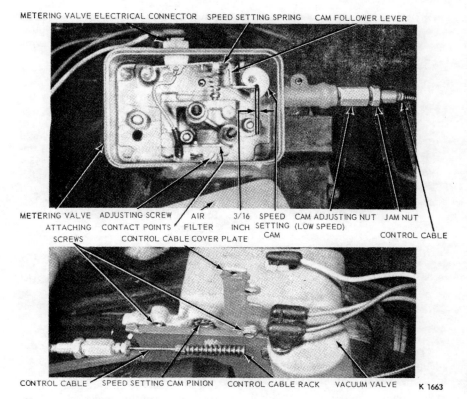

FIG. 10—Control Cable Adjustment

3. Rotate the cam adjusting nut until the clearance between the cam follower lever and the speed setting cam is $3/16$ inch.

4. Tighten the jam nut snugly against the cam adjusting nut. The cam adjusting nut is designed to be loose in the metering valve, it cannot be held tight.

5. Install the air filter and the two vacuum hoses.

INSUFFICIENT THREAD FOR ADJUSTMENT, WHEN INSTALLING NEW METERING VALVE

1. Remove the two vacuum hoses and the air filter from the metering valve. Remove the first screw from the control cable cover plate and loosen the other screw. Rotate the cover plate so that it faces upward.

2. Remove the control cable rack from the speed setting cam pinion.

3. Replace the metering valve if required, as indicated by previous diagnosis.

4. Position the speed-setting cam

to provide approximately $3/16$ inch clearance to the cam follower lever. The selector dial is to be rotated against the low speed stop.

5. Loosen the jam nut. Position

the jam nut so that there are three threads visible beyond the jam nut. Position the cam adjusting nut against the jam nut.

6. Install the control cable rack onto the speed setting cam pinion. Try to maintain approximately $3/16$ inch clearance. With the cam adjusting nut in its groove, lower the control cable cover plate and install and tighten the attaching screws.

7. Final control cable adjustment is made by following steps 2 through 5 under control cable adjustment.

REFILLING SENSOR PUMP

A container of fluid (C5AZ-19577-A), has been released to be used in refilling sensor pumps. The fluid is not to be used to refill a pump that has lost fluid through leakage. Under these conditions, the pump must be returned to the vendor for replacement. The fluid may only be used to refill a pump that has lost fluid by accidental spillage or when the fluid has been pumped from the sensor pump because of a

leak in the rubber tubing or metering valve diaphragm. The following is the procedure to be used when refilling a sensor pump (Fig. 11).

1. It must first be established that loss of fluid is due to accidental spillage and not the result of fluid leakage.

2. When fluid loss is due to leakage, the pump must be returned to the vendor and not refilled.

3. When some fluid has been lost by spillage, the pump is then to be completely emptied. Remove the dust shield from the pump using a pair of channel-lock pliers. The dust shield has a press fit to the sensor pump nipple. Turn the sensor pump upside down and shake it to be sure that all fluid is removed.

4. Place the sensor pump in a vise with the nipples in the upright position. Hold the fluid container in a level position and check to see that the fluid is at the mark on the container. If not at the indicated level, the container is not to be used to refill a sensor pump. Remove the cap from the fluid container (C5AZ-19577-A), turn it upside down and place it to the hole in the sensor pump.

Do not squeeze the container when placing it to the hole in the pump or fluid will be lost.

5. Hold the container tightly against the pump nipple during filling or fluid will be lost. Gently squeeze the container to force some of the fluid into the sensor pump and then release it so air can be sucked back into the container. Repeat this procedure until all the fluid has been transferred to the sensor pump.

6. Carefully assemble the sensor pump to the bracket, being sure that the pump is held in the upright position when being moved. Replace the dust shield onto the sensor pump. Cut the rubber hose back $1/2$ inch and install it onto the sensor pump nipple. Attach the speedometer cables to the sensor pump.

7. Test drive the vehicle to make sure that the speed control unit is functioning properly after the repair.

METERING VALVE CONTACT POINT ADJUSTMENT

The contact point adjustment should not be attempted until all other items have been corrected. Misadjusted contact points can result in the system resuming speed after the brake pedal has been depressed and released, or require going higher

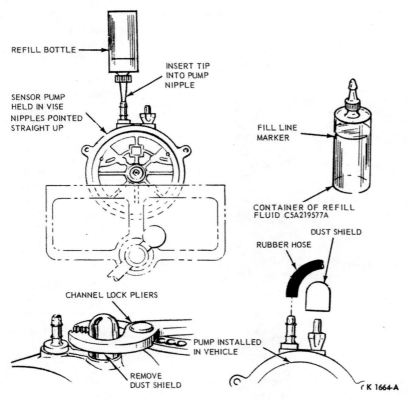

REFILL BOTTLE

INSERT TIP INTO PUMP NIPPLE

SENSOR PUMP HELD IN VISE NIPPLES POINTED STRAIGHT UP

FILL LINE MARKER

CONTAINER OF REFILL FLUID C5A219577A

DUST SHIELD

RUBBER HOSE

CHANNEL LOCK PLIERS

PUMP INSTALLED IN VEHICLE

REMOVE DUST SHIELD

K 1664-A

FIG. 11—Refilling Sensor Pump

above the selected speed than normal to engage the system. **Extreme care must be exercised in making the adjustment because movements of a degree or less of the adjusting screw will make a large change in the distance between the points with a corresponding large change in engagement speed.**

The adjustment of the contact points can only be made with the metering valve on the vehicle. The contact points should be adjusted to close approximately two miles per hour above the set speed (Fig. 10).

1. Remove the two vacuum hoses and the air filter from the metering valve. Connect the two vacuum hoses.

2. Observe the position of the slot in the adjusting screw. It will be at approximately 11 o'clock when correctly adjusted. Place the adjusting screw at this position if it is located at another position. The final adjustment can only be made by driving the vehicle.

3. Drive the vehicle at a steady 35 miles per hour with the speed control system engaged. Depress the brake pedal slightly to disengage the speed control. Allow the speed to drop to about 25 miles per hour, and then gradually increase the speed until the click is heard from the engagement relay. Note the speed at which the click is heard.

4. If the click was heard at less than the set speed, rotate the adjusting screw counterclockwise to open the contact points. If the click was heard at more than two miles per hour above the set speed, rotate the adjusting screw clockwise to close the points. **Rotate the screw only one or two degrees because the adjustment is very critical.**

5. Repeat steps 3 and 4 until the click is heard at about two miles per hour above the set speed.

However, if it becomes very difficult to adjust the contact points properly the metering valve should be changed.

6. Remove the two vacuum hoses. Install the air filter and the two vacuum hoses.

4 REMOVAL AND INSTALLATION PROCEDURES

SENSOR PUMP

Whenever a faulty sensor pump is removed, the vehicle can be driven with the speedometer operating, by removing the sensor pump speedometer cable assemblies from the speedometer head and transmission and by installing a standard speedometer cable assembly between the transmission and speedometer head (Fig. 5).

1. Disconnect the pressure output rubber hose.
2. Disconect the speedometer cables.
3. Remove the two bolts attaching the mounting bracket to the dash panel.
4. Remove the sensor pump from the vehicle. Care must be taken to keep the sensor pump in the upright position or the special fluid in the sensor pump will be spilled.

VACUUM BELLOWS

1. Disconnect the ball chain attaching the vacuum bellows to the accelerator pedal arm assembly and remove chain from pulley (Fig. 2).
2. Disconnect the vacuum hose.
3. Remove the bolts attaching the vacuum bellows to the brake pedal support.
4. Remove the vacuum bellows from the vehicle.
5. Perform the accelerator linkage adjustment after installing the vacuum bellows.

METERING VALVE AND VACUUM VALVE ASSEMBLY

1. Remove the two screws from the control cable cover plate and disengage the control cable rack from the speed setting cam pinion (Fig. 4).
2. Disconnect the vacuum hoses and plug connectors from the metering valve and vacuum valve assembly.
3. Remove the two bolts attaching the metering valve and vacuum valve assembly to the mounting bracket.
4. Remove the metering valve and vacuum valve assembly from the vehicle.
5. After installing the metering valve and vacuum valve assembly,

perform the required control cable adjustment. Check for proper hose routing. Perform the electrical check to assure proper operation.

ENGAGEMENT RELAY

1. Disconnect the plug connector and check for rubber flash at the terminals (Fig. 3).

2. Remove the two screws attaching the relay to the brake pedal support bracket.

3. Remove the engagement relay from the vehicle.

4. After the engagement relay is installed, make sure that all terminals are properly entered into the plug connector.

BRAKE RELEASE SWITCH

1. Disconnect the plug connectors (Fig. 3).

2. Remove the brake pedal bracket.

3. Remove the two bolts attaching the mounting bracket to the brake pedal support. Remove the mounting bracket and brake release switch.

4. After installing the brake release switch, perform the brake release switch adjustment.

ACTUATOR HEAD ASSEMBLY

1. Remove the two screws attaching the actuator head assembly to the instrument panel (Fig. 1).

2. Disconnect the plug connectors.

3. Disconnect the control cable from the metering valve.

4. Remove the actuator head assembly from the vehicle.

5. When installing the control cable during actuator head installation, perform the control cable adjustment procedure.

PULLEY AND BRACKET ASSEMBLY

1. Disconnect the ball chain from the accelerator pedal arm assembly.

Remove the ball chain from the pulley (Fig. 2).

2. Remove the screws attaching the pulley and bracket assembly to the instrument panel.

3. After installing the pulley and bracket assembly, perform the accelerator linkage adjustment.

INHIBITOR SWITCH

1. Disconnect the pressure input hose at the plastic tee (Fig. 4).

2. Disconnect the plug connector.

3. Remove the two bolts attaching the inhibitor switch to the metering valve bracket and remove it from the vehicle.

4. After installing the inhibitor switch, perform the required electrical check.

After servicing the speed control system, the vehicle should be road tested for proper operation in the automatic throttle control position. The speed control system cannot be tested with the vehicle on a hoist or jack.

PART 16-4

SPEED CONTROL—MERCURY

1 DESCRIPTION AND OPERATION

The speed control system is a driver-operated regulating device which may be used either as a speed reminder, or as an automatic throttle control for vehicle speeds from 25 mph to 80 mph. Although the system actually maintains speed, it is not a governor since it does not restrict available engine rpm or performance. The system is controlled by vehicle speed and can be overridden by applying added pressure to the accelerator pedal. The system will maintain the selected speed up and down hills as well as on a level road.

The major components of the speed control system are: actuator head assembly, regulator assembly, and brake release switch.

ACTUATOR HEAD ASSEMBLY

The speed control actuator head assembly is mounted on the instrument panel (Fig. 1). The operation of the speed control depends on the position of the selector dial which sets the speed at which control is desired, and the slide switch which has the positions of OFF, ON, and

AUTO. The ON position places the unit in operation as a speed reminder, and a brief actuation of the slide switch to the AUTO position activates the automatic throttle control feature. An amber light will glow when the system is under automatic control. When the slide switch is in the OFF position, the regulator assembly is disengaged and has no effect at any speed.

The selector dial is numbered with speed markings from 30 mph to 80 mph (10 mph increments). Setting the selector dial between the indicated increments will produce a corresponding intermediate speed. The selector dial incorporates a slip clutch to allow the dial numbers to be adjusted to correspond to the speed indicated on the speedometer.

REGULATOR ASSEMBLY

The speed control regulator assembly is mounted in the engine compartment (Fig. 2). The regulator assembly is mechanically driven and electrically operated. The regulator assembly is driven by a conventional speedometer drive cable

from the transmission. A second speedometer cable assembly, from the regulator assembly to the speedometer head, operates the speedometer assembly. The speed control actuator head assembly is connected to the regulator assembly by a control cable. Mechanical linkage connects the regulator assembly to the carburetor.

A reversible electric motor in the regulator assembly activates the mechanical linkage between the regulator assembly and the carburetor. Motor feed points for forward and reverse energizing of the motor are closed and opened by a governor, under control of a governor spring that is compressed or relaxed to calibrated positions, corresponding to selected speeds actuated by the control cable leading to the selector dial.

BRAKE RELEASE SWITCH

The brake release switch is located under the instrument panel on the brake pedal and support assembly (Fig. 3). When the brake pedal is lightly depressed, the brake release switch is opened which disengages the speed control system. The brake release switch is a normally closed switch.

The speed reminder feature is primarily for use as a safety feature in urban or congested areas to aid in strict attention to speed regulations. To use the speed control system as a speed reminder, move the slide switch to the ON position and rotate the selector dial to the speed which you do not wish to exceed. When the selected speed is reached, a marked increase in accelerator pedal back pressure will be felt. Additional

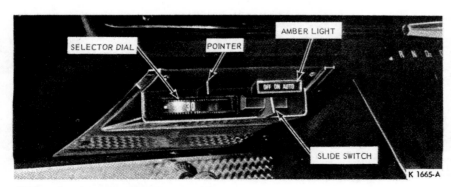

FIG. 1—Actuator Head Assembly

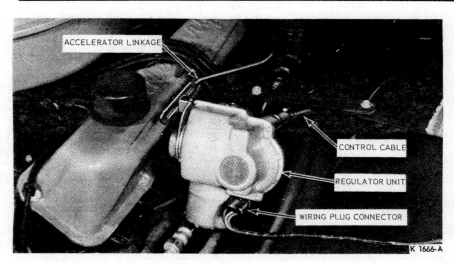

FIG. 2—Regulator Assembly

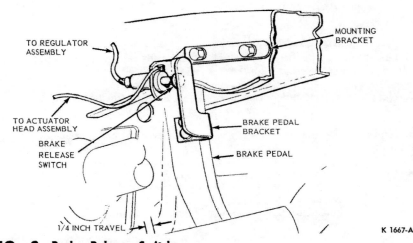

FIG. 3—Brake Release Switch

effort will overcome this back pressure for passing or other required accelerations. The back pressure position will vary with the road grade. The speed setting may be changed while driving by rotating the selector dial to the new desired speed.

The automatic throttle control feature is for use on turnpikes, expressways, and other open road operation. To use the speed control system as an automatic throttle control, push the slide switch momentarily to the AUTO position and then allow it to return to the ON position. Select the speed at which you wish to travel by adjusting the selector dial. An amber light in the actuator head assembly will be lighted whenever the automatic throttle control feature is in operation. The system is now under automatic control and as the vehicle is accelerated to the selected speed and the back-pressure

is felt, the system locks in automatically.

The speed control system will automatically operate the throttle without the need for foot pressure on the accelerator pedal to maintain the predetermined speed. The speed of the vehicle can be changed while the speed control is operating automatically by slowly moving the selector dial to the newly desired speed.

When under automatic control, always rotate the dial slowly when increasing or decreasing vehicle speed, to prevent sudden acceleration or deceleration.

The vehicle speed can be increased at any time by pushing on the accelerator pedal and over-riding the back pressure. Release the pressure on the accelerator pedal and the vehicle will return to the pre-selected speed. The speed control system may be disengaged at any time by a slight depressing of the brake pedal. The

system may be engaged again by increasing the speed until the back pressure is again felt. Since the speed control system is an electrically actuated mechanical device, receiving its power from the battery through the ignition switch, automatic control is cancelled each time the ignition switch is turned to the OFF position as well as when the slide switch is pushed to the OFF position.

The lower speedometer cable drives a governor located inside the regulator assembly. Loading on the governor is from spring pressure controlled by the location of the selector dial. When the vehicle reaches the selected speed, the force of rotation of the governor weights is balanced by the governor spring pressure. When balanced, the contact arm attached to the governor weights is centered between the motor contact points No. 1 and No. 2 located on the magnet assembly.

When the system is unbalanced, the contact arm will move into contact with one of the motor contact points and actuate a 12-volt reversible motor that rotates a drive screw. When the drive screw rotates, a nut on the screw moves the entire magnet assembly to the position where equilibrium is again reached between the governor weights and the governor spring and the contact arm is centered between the motor contact points.

When the vehicle tends to go slower than the pre-selected speed, as would be the case in going up a hill, the force from the governor weights becomes less, resulting in the spring force pushing down on the contact arm and bringing it in contact with motor contact point No. 1. The motor now rotates and moves the magnet assembly to open the throttle and maintain the selected speed.

When the vehicle travels downhill, tending to go faster than the selected speed, the force from the governor weights increases. The increased force over-powers the governor spring, lifting the contact arm and bringing it in contact with motor contact point No. 2. The motor rotates in the opposite direction and moves the magnet assembly to close the throttle and maintain the selected speed.

The regulator assembly is serviced as a complete assembly and no internal repairs, lubrication, or adjustments are to be performed.

2 DIAGNOSIS AND TESTING

When diagnosing and trouble shooting the speed control system, first obtain all the facts from the owner concerning his problem and then road test the vehicle with the owner. In this manner you will be assured that the owner is operating the speed control system properly and you will be able to verify the complaint should one exist.

The usage of the service adjustments are covered in the following list of common speed control problems, their possible cause and corrective action.

SPEED CONTROL DIAGNOSIS GUIDE—MERCURY

TROUBLE	POSSIBLE CAUSE	CORRECTIVE ACTION
BLOWING FUSES	1. Short or ground in the wiring circuit. 2. Defective regulator assembly.	1. Perform electrical check. 2. Replace regulator assembly.
SELECTOR DIAL SPEED SETTING DOES NOT CORRESPOND TO SPEED INDICATED ON SPEEDOMETER	1. Improper selector dial adjustment. 2. Improper accelerator linkage adjustment.	1. Perform selector dial adjustment. 2. Perform accelerator linkage adjustment.
NO AUTOMATIC CONTROL WHEN UNIT IS SET FOR AUTOMATIC	1. Driver riding the brake pedal or driver is not accelerating to the selected speed. 2. No current at terminal No. 2 of regulator assembly plug connector. 3. Improper brake release switch adjustment or wiring. 4. Defective regulator assembly.	1. Instruct owner in proper operation of speed control system. 2. Perform electrical check. 3. Perform brake release switch adjustment. Check wiring for continuity (Fig. 6). 4. Replace regulator assembly.
PULSATING ACCELERATOR PEDAL	1. Speedometer upper or lower cable assembly kinked or poorly lubricated. 2. Improper accelerator linkage adjustment. 3. Defective regulator assembly.	1. Lubricate, replace or reroute cables as required (Fig. 4). 2. Perform accelerator linkage adjustment. 3. Replace regulator assembly.
SPEED CONTROL DOES NOT OPERATE	1. Improper brake release switch adjustment. 2. Accelerator linkage is broken or disconnected. 3. Speedometer lower cable broken or disconnected. 4. Blown fuse. 5. Loose connections or broken wires. 6. Defective regulator assembly.	1. Perform brake release switch adjustment. 2. Check accelerator linkage for proper assembly (Fig. 9). 3. Reconnect or replace speedometer lower cable as required (Fig. 4). 4. Perform electrical check. 5. Check all connections and check wiring for continuity. (Fig. 6). 6. Replace regulator assembly.
SPEED CONTROL DOES NOT OPERATE AND SPEEDOMETER DOES NOT REGISTER	1. Speedometer lower cable assembly broken or disconnected. 2. Speedometer drive gear in transmission damaged.	1. Reconnect or replace speedometer cable as required (Fig. 4). 2. Replace drive gear.
SPEED CONTROL OPERATES BUT SPEEDOMETER DOES NOT REGISTER	1. Speedometer upper cable assembly broken or disconnected. 2. Defective speedometer head.	*1. Reconnect or replace speedometer cable as required (Fig. 4).* 2. Replace speedometer head.

SPEED CONTROL DIAGNOSIS GUIDE—MERCURY (Continued)

TROUBLE	POSSIBLE CAUSE	CORRECTIVE ACTION
CONSTANT PRESSURE ON ACCELERATOR PEDAL REGARDLESS OF SELECTOR DIAL SETTING	1. Blown fuse. 2. No current at terminal No. 1 and No. 2. 3. Defective control cable or actuator head. 4. Defective regulator assembly.	1. and 2. Perform electrical check. 3. Replace actuator head assembly. 4. Replace regulator assembly.
AUTOMATIC CONTROL REMAINS ENGAGED *WHEN BRAKE PEDAL IS DEPRESSED*	1. Brake release switch improperly adjusted. 2. Defective brake release switch.	1. Perform brake release switch adjustment. 2. Replace brake release switch.
UNIT DOES NOT REMAIN INOPERATIVE WHEN THE SLIDE SWITCH IS IN THE OFF POSITION	1. Defective actuator head assembly, wiring, or regulator assembly.	1. Perform electrical check and replace parts as required.
CARBURETOR DOES NOT RETURN TO IDLE	1. Improper accelerator linkage adjustment. 2. Improper accelerator cable adjustment.	1. Perform accelerator linkage adjustment. 2. Perform accelerator cable adjustment (Group 7).

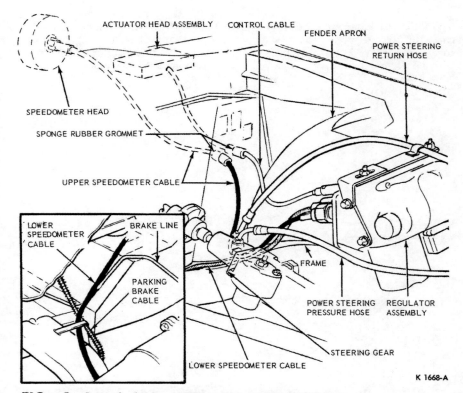

ACTUATOR HEAD ASSEMBLY   CONTROL CABLE

FENDER APRON

POWER STEERING RETURN HOSE

SPEEDOMETER HEAD

SPONGE RUBBER GROMMET

UPPER SPEEDOMETER CABLE

LOWER SPEEDOMETER CABLE

BRAKE LINE

PARKING BRAKE CABLE

FRAME

POWER STEERING PRESSURE HOSE

REGULATOR ASSEMBLY

STEERING GEAR

LOWER SPEEDOMETER CABLE

K 1668-A

FIG. 4—Control Cable and Speedometer Cable Routing

ELECTRICAL CHECK

The following electrical checks should be performed to determine the cause and correction of speed control trouble and to eliminate unnecessary service work on the power unit (Figs. 5 and 6).

1. Disconnect the multiple connector at the regulator assembly.

2. Turn the ignition switch to the ACC position.

3. Push the slide switch to the OFF position. Using a test lamp, ground one test lamp lead and touch the other lead to terminal No. 1 (green-violet wire). The test lamp should light. If the lamp fails to light, check for a blown fuse, defective vehicle wiring, or defective wiring in the actuator head assembly.

Touch the test lamp to terminals No. 2, No. 3 and No. 4. The test lamp should not light. If the lamp lights, check for defective vehicle wiring and defective wiring in the actuator head assembly.

4. Push the slide switch to the ON position. Ground one test lamp lead, touch the other lead to terminal No. 2 (white wire). The test lamp should light. If the lamp fails to light, check for defective wiring in the actuator head assembly, or defective vehicle wiring.

Touch the test lamp to terminals No. 1, No. 3 and No. 4. The test lamp should not light. If the lamp lights, check for defective vehicle wiring and defective wiring in the actuator head assembly.

5. Ground one test lamp lead and touch the other lead to terminal No. 3 (red wire). Push the slide switch to the AUTO position and allow the switch to come back to the ON po-

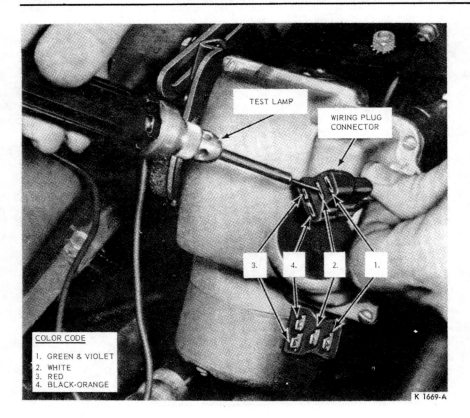

TEST LAMP

WIRING PLUG CONNECTOR

3. 4. 2. 1.

COLOR CODE
1. GREEN & VIOLET
2. WHITE
3. RED
4. BLACK-ORANGE

K 1669-A

FIG. 5—Electrical Check

sition. The test lamp and indicator light should light when the slide switch reaches the AUTO position, and then should go out when the slide switch returns to the ON position.

tion. If the test lamp (and indicator light) fail to operate as described above, check for defective vehicle wiring, defective wiring in the actuator head assembly or burned out indicator bulb.

6. Ground one test lamp lead and touch the other lead to terminal No. 4 (black-orange wire). Push the slide switch to the AUTO position and manually hold the slide switch in the AUTO position. The test lamp should be lighted. The test lamp should go out when the brake pedal is depressed approximately ¼ inch and then come on again when the brake pedal is released. If the test lamp fails to operate as described above, check for improperly adjusted or a defective brake release switch, defective vehicle wiring or defective wiring in the actuator head assembly. Allow the slide switch to return to the OFF position.

Vehicles with power brakes should have the engine running and transmission in park when checking the brake release switch adjustment. The brake pedal height may change with vacuum applied to the brake booster.

7. Remove the test lamp and turn the ignition switch to the OFF position.

8. Connect the multiple connector at the regulator assembly.

9. If the above electrical checks in steps 3 through 8 fail to correct the speed control trouble, check the selector dial adjustment, and the accelerator linkage adjustment before removing the regulator assembly.

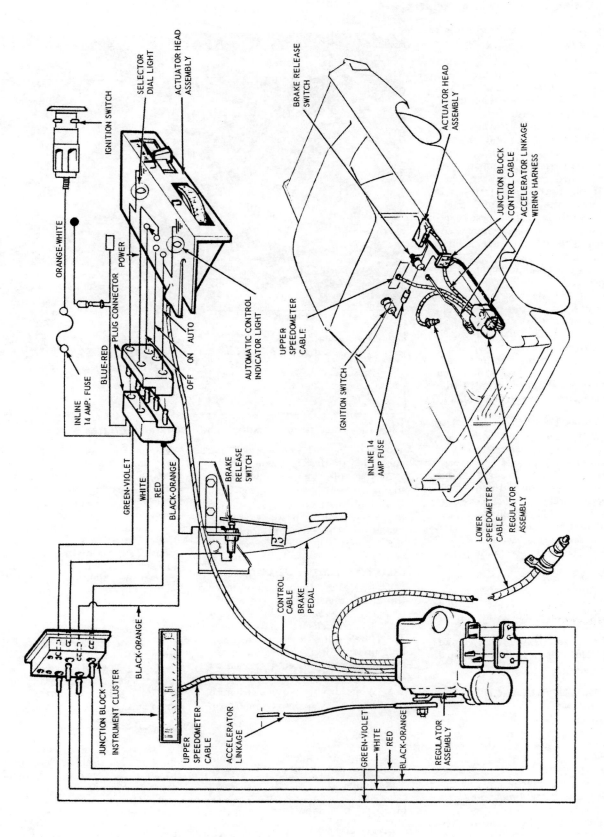

FIG. 6—Schematic Diagram

3 COMMON ADJUSTMENTS

BRAKE RELEASE SWITCH ADJUSTMENT

The brake release switch located inside the vehicle, above the brake pedal pad must be adjusted so that it will break the electrical circuit and cancel the speed control within the first ¼ inch of free travel of the brake pedal pad. If the brake release switch is too close to the brake pedal bracket, the switch will remain open and the speed control will not engage. If the brake release switch is too far from the brake pedal bracket, the switch will stay closed and the speed control will remain engaged after the brakes are applied (Fig. 3).

1. Turn the ignition switch to the ACC position.

2. Push the slide switch to the AUTO position and manually hold it in this position.

3. Remove the plug connector from the regulator assembly. Using a test lamp, ground one test lead, and touch the other lead to terminal No. 4 (black-orange wire) of the plug connector. The test lamp should light.

4. Depress the brake pedal. The test light should go out within the first ¼ inch of travel measured at the bottom of the brake pedal pad.

5. If the test light does not go out in ¼ inch of brake pedal pad travel, loosen the brake pedal bracket attaching bolts and position the bracket so that it just clears the plunger of the brake release switch.

6. Vehicles equipped with power brakes should have the engine started and the brake pedal depressed several times to assure correct operation of the brake release switch with vacuum applied to the power brake booster.

If the brake release switch cannot be adjusted, it is defective and must be replaced.

ACCELERATOR LINKAGE ADJUSTMENT

Improper linkage adjustment can cause the accelerator pedal to pulsate and/or prevent the carburetor from returning to the normal idle position (Fig. 7).

1. Loosen the attaching nut securing the accelerator linkage rod to the exterior arm.

2. With the engine at normal operating temperature, adjust the engine idle speed to specification. Be

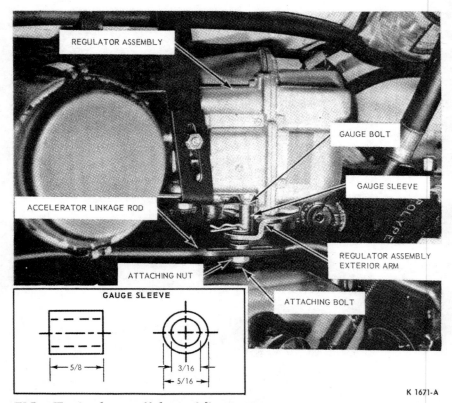

FIG. 7—Accelerator Linkage Adjustment

sure that the fast idle screw is not contacting the fast idle cam.

3. With the engine stopped, place the gauge sleeve over the gauge bolt.

4. With the linkage loose, allow it to seek a neutral position and retighten the bolt in the exterior arm.

5. Remove the gauge sleeve.

SELECTOR DIAL ADJUSTMENT

The selector dial incorporates a slip clutch that is to be used to correct any difference between speedometer and selector dial reading. The clutch will slip when a force of four to seven inch-pounds above the normal operating force is exerted on the dial (Fig. 1).

1. While driving the vehicle, push the slide switch to the AUTO position.

2. Rotate the selector dial to 40 mph.

3. Bring the vehicle speed up until the speed control unit engages.

4. Rotate the selector dial to bring the vehicle to a steady speed of 50 mph, as shown on the speedometer.

5. With the speedometer indicating a vehicle speed of 50 mph, the

50 numeral should be centered below the pointer.

6. If the speedometer and selector dial readings agree, the selector dial is properly adjusted. If the readings do not agree, the selector dial may be adjusted as follows:

Put the slide switch in the OFF position. If the dial reading is on the low side, rotate the selector dial against the high speed stop. If the dial reading is on the high side, rotate the selector against the low speed stop. Rotate the selector beyond the stop, the amount necessary to correct the selector dial setting.

Repeat Steps 1 through 6 of the adjustment procedure until the reading on the selector dial agrees with the reading on the speedometer.

CONTROL CABLE REMOVAL

The control cable requires no adjustment, it simply snaps into the nylon retainer in the regulator assembly (Fig. 8).

1. Remove the screw from the dust shield (View A, Fig. 8).

2. Rotate the dust shield counterclockwise and slide it from the regulator assembly.

3. Press the end of the control cable wire in so that it can be removed from the nylon retainer (View B, Fig. 8).

4. Reverse the above procedure to install the control cable to the regulator assembly.

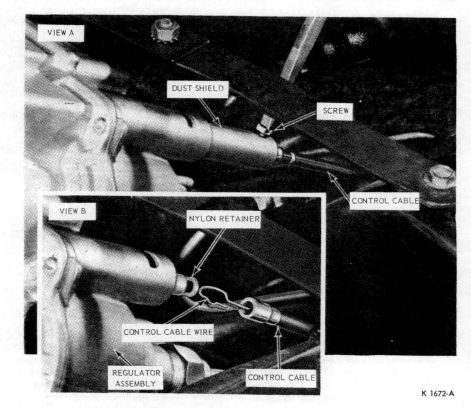

FIG. 8—Control Cable Removal

4   REMOVAL AND INSTALLATION PROCEDURES

REGULATOR ASSEMBLY

Whenever a faulty regulator assembly is removed, the vehicle can be driven with the speedometer operating, by removing the speed control speedometer cable assemblies from the speedometer head and transmission and installing a standard speedometer cable assembly between the transmission and speedometer head (Fig. 2).

1. Disconnect the plug connector from the regulator assembly.

2. Remove the attaching nut from the stud in the exterior arm and remove the accelerator linkage.

3. Disconnect the control cable.

4. Disconnect the speedometer cable assemblies.

5. Remove the two bolts securing the regulator assembly to the mounting bracket.

6. Remove the regulator assembly from the vehicle.

7. After installing the regulator assembly, perform the accelerator linkage adjustment. Check the selector dial adjustment.

ACTUATOR HEAD ASSEMBLY

1. Disconnect the control cable from the regulator assembly. Remove the dust shield from the control cable.

2. Remove the four screws attaching the actuator head assembly to the instrument panel (Fig. 1).

3. Disconnect the plug connector from the actuator head assembly.

4. Carefully remove the actuator head and control cable assembly from the vehicle.

5. When installing the actuator head, refer to Fig. 4 for proper routing of the cables.

6. Perform the electrical check.

Check the selector dial adjustment.

BRAKE RELEASE SWITCH

1. Disconnect the plug connectors (Fig. 3).

2. Loosen the brake pedal bracket.

3. Remove the two bolts attaching the mounting bracket to the brake pedal support. Remove the mounting bracket and brake release switch.

4. After installing the brake release switch, perform the brake release switch adjustment.

After servicing the speed control system, the vehicle should be road tested for proper operation in both the speed reminder and automatic throttle control positions. The speed control system cannot be tested with the vehicle on a hoist or jack.

PART 16-5

HEADLIGHT DIMMER

1 DESCRIPTION AND OPERATION

Refer to Wiring Diagram Manual Form 7795P-66 for locations of wiring harnesses. Schematics are shown in Group 22 of this manual.

The automatic headlight dimmer, which automatically switches the headlight beam in response to light from an approaching car, consists of four individual units: a phototube unit, an amplifier unit, a combination dimmer over-ride-type foot switch and a power relay (Fig. 1).

Headlights are automatically controlled only in one position of the foot switch. Headlights change from automatic operation to full time lower-beam when the foot switch is fully depressed. To obtain momentary highway upper-beam for signaling oncoming drivers, when using automatic control, or for checking automatic position of the foot switch, depress the foot switch about 1/8 inch to a detent.

When a car approaches within a proper distance, light from its headlights, striking the phototube unit, causes the headlights to dim or switch to lower beam. At this time, if the approaching car's headlights were on upper beam, the driver would normally switch to lower-beam, which would greatly reduce the amount of light striking the phototube unit. The automatic headlight dimmer is designed to maintain or hold its vehicle headlights on a lower beam, even with this reduction in light. When light is removed from the phototube unit, the headlights switch back to upper-beam.

A sensitivity control knob, located at the back of the phototube unit, (Fig. 2), gives the driver a limited range of control over the sensitivity of the headlight dimmer. A detent position is provided in the center of the control range for normal sensitivity as adjusted at the factory. When the control is in the detent position, the knob pointer should be

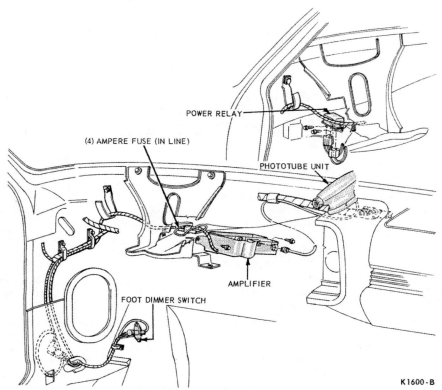

FIG. 1—Automatic Headlight Dimmer

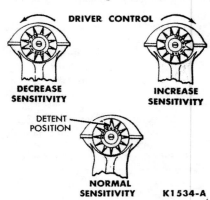

FIG. 2—Driver Control Knob

pointing up. Rotating the knob clockwise (the word FAR moves down), increases sensitivity. In this position, the headlight dimmer will switch the headlights to lower beam when an approaching car is farther away than normal. Rotating the control counterclockwise (the word NEAR moves down), decreases the sensitivity, thus allowing an approaching car to approach nearer before switching occurs.

PHOTOTUBE UNIT

The phototube unit uses a single-stage phototube for sensing light, and is mounted on the top-center of the instrument panel upper-cover. The amber colored lens picks up light from approaching headlights and focuses it through a filter and mask onto the phototube. The phototube converts the light into an electrical signal that can be used by the amplifier unit.

AMPLIFIER UNIT

The amplifier unit supplies voltage to the phototube unit and operates the power relay in response to a signal from the phototube unit. The unit is located at the right side of the steering column bracket support.

A heavy duty power relay, with special alloy contacts for switching the headlights between upper and lower beam, is located at the left side of the steering column bracket support.

FOOT CONTROL SWITCH

The foot switch is a special dimmer over-ride type that provides either automatic or low-beam control of the headlights. It also acts as an over-ride for obtaining an overriding high-beam when in automatic position. The over-ride section of the foot switch functions only when the switch is in automatic position.

A slight downward pressure on top of the switch provides upper-beam, regardless of light on the phototube unit. This arrangement permits signaling the approaching driver if he fails to switch to lower-beam and also provides a simple test for automatic position of the foot switch. Street lights, encountered in the city, are usually sufficient to maintain the vehicle headlights on lower-beam; however, the upper-beam may be obtained when needed by holding foot pressure in the over-ride position.

In the lower-beam position of the foot switch, the automatic headlight dimmer is not an active part of the headlight circuit. However, it is not turned off. It continues to function as long as the headlights are turned on and is ready to provide automatic control whenever the foot switch is returned to the automatic position.

2 DIAGNOSIS AND TESTING

AUTOMATIC HEADLIGHT DIMMER TROUBLE DIAGNOSIS GUIDE

HEADLIGHTS DIM AT WRONG DISTANCE OCCASIONALLY	1. Lights of approaching cars incorrectly adjusted. 2. Fog, or snow.	3. Flashing traffic lights or brightly lighted intersections.
HEADLIGHTS DIM AT WRONG DISTANCE REPEATEDLY	1. Driver control knob not properly adjusted (Fig. 2).	

TESTING

1. Pull the headlight switch to the full ON position. (Allow about 30 seconds for the headlight dimmer to warm up.) With the car in a lighted area, the lights should be on low-beam regardless of the position of the foot switch. (If upper-beam is obtained in one position of the foot switch, check the fuse.)
2. Depress the foot switch about ⅛-inch to the detent. The lights should change to the upper-beam

and then change back to the lower-beam when the foot switch is released, if the foot switch is in the automatic position. If not, cycle the foot switch to obtain the automatic position.
3. Place a hand or a dark cloth over the phototube unit. The lights should switch to the upper-beam. Remove the cloth or hand. The lights should change back to the lower-beam. The unit will not go to upper-beam if the phototube unit temperature is above 90° F. Therefore, check to see if the phototube is hot. If it is, allow it to cool and repeat the above checks.

If the headlights operate as explained in steps 1, 2, and 3, the device should operate correctly with the proper aiming and sensitivity adjustments. If the lights do not operate as described in the above steps, refer to Figs. 3 and 4.

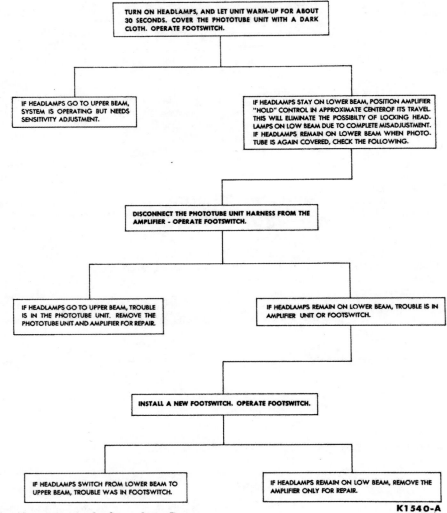

FIG. 3—Trouble Shooting—Locked on Low Beam

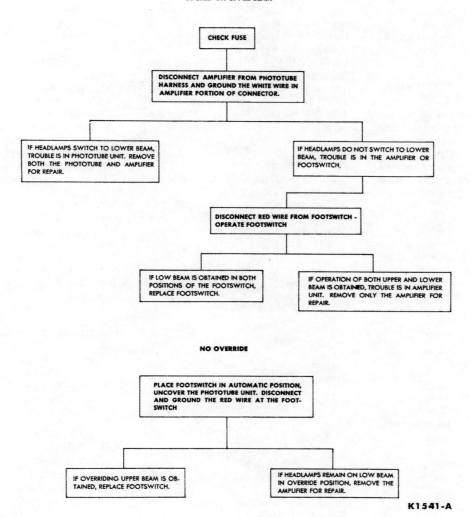

FIG. 4—Trouble Shooting—Locked on Upper Beam

3 COMMON ADJUSTMENTS AND REPAIRS

Be certain that headlights and windshield are free of snow and dirt for proper operation of the automatic headlight dimmer.

PHOTOTUBE UNIT VERTICAL AIMING PROCEDURE

The phototube unit must be accurately aimed vertically. If the unit is aimed too low, back reflections from the headlights which are being controlled, will lock the amplifier on lower-beam. However, the unit must be aimed as low as possible to provide maximum tolerance for car loading.

1. Phototube unit vertical aiming should be done with the car unloaded, trunk empty except for spare tire, gas tank at least half full, and with tires at the correct pressure.

2. Locate the car on a level floor (level within ¼ inch fore and aft of the car).

3. Rock the car sideways to equalize the springs.

4. Install the aiming device, part of the tester on the phototube unit (Fig. 5). **The three points on the aiming device must be resting on top of the phototube unit, and the aiming device must be touching the front of the phototube unit.**

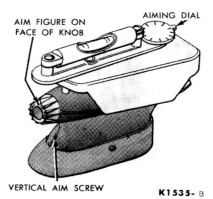

AIM FIGURE ON FACE OF KNOB AIMING DIAL

VERTICAL AIM SCREW K1535-B

FIG. 5—Vertical Aiming Device

5. Adjust the aiming dial until the numeral six is under the pointer.

6. Adjust the vertical aim screw on the phototube unit until the bubble is centered in the level.

HOLD AND DIM SENSITIVITY ADJUSTMENTS ON CAR

Hold sensitivity must be properly adjusted before adjusting Dim sensitivity. The phototube unit must be covered with a black cloth during adjustments. Adjustments should be made with the phototube unit temperature below 90°. If the car has been in the sun immediately prior to checking, allow it to cool in a covered place for approximately one hour before the adjustment is actually made.

PREPARATION FOR ADJUSTMENT

1. Set the driver control to the Detent position.

2. Install the tester lamp (Fig. 6). Cover the tester lamp and phototube with the black cloth furnished.

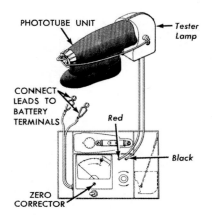

PHOTOTUBE UNIT — Tester Lamp

CONNECT LEADS TO BATTERY TERMINALS

Red

Black

ZERO CORRECTOR

K1536-B

FIG. 6—Dim and Hold Sensitivity Tester

3. Start the engine and operate it at fast idle while making adjustments.

4. Turn the headlights on and wait at least five minutes for the amplifier unit to stabilize. Place the foot switch in the automatic position.

5. Turn the zero corrector, on the face of the meter, until the meter pointer is on the zero set line.

6. Turn the tester intensity control counterclockwise.

7. Connect the battery leads of the tester to the battery terminals (red lead to the positive terminal and black lead to the negative terminal).

HOLD SENSITIVITY ADJUSTMENT

1. Rotate the amplifier Hold control completely clockwise.

2. Rotate the tester intensity con-trol all the way clockwise.

3. Turn the dim-hold switch momentarily to the Dim position to switch the lights to lower-beam, then switch back to the Hold position. **If the lights do not switch to lower-beam, the amplifier dim control must be turned completely clockwise and then readjusted after the Hold adjustment is correct.**

4. Adjust the tester intensity control counterclockwise until the meter pointer is on the Hold sensitivity adjustment line.

5. Turn the amplifier Hold control slowly counterclockwise, just to the point where the headlights switch to upper-beam. **Do not go beyond this setting.**

6. Turn the tester intensity control all the way clockwise.

7. Turn the Dim-Hold switch to Dim position and back to Hold position to obtain a lower beam.

8. Slowly turn the intensity control counterclockwise just to the point where headlamps switch to upper-beam. The meter pointer should now read in the green Hold sensitivity range on the meter scale (Fig. 6). If not, return to step 1 and repeat all steps.

DIM SENSITIVITY ADJUSTMENT

Dim sensitivity should not be adjusted until after the Hold sensitivity is properly adjusted.

1. Rotate the amplifier Dim control completely counterclockwise.

2. Rotate the tester intensity control completely counterclockwise.

3. Momentarily turn the Dim-Hold switch on the tester to Hold, then back to the Dim position to obtain upper-beam.

4. Adjust the tester intensity control until the meter pointer is at the Dim sensitivity adjustment line.

5. Slowly rotate the amplifier Dim control clockwise, just to the point where the headlights switch to lower-beam. **Do not go beyond this setting.**

6. Rotate the tester intensity control completely counterclockwise.

7. Turn the Dim-Hold switch to Hold, then back to Dim to obtain the upper-beam.

8. Slowly rotate the tester intensity control clockwise just to the point where the headlights switch to upper-beam. The meter pointer

should now read in the Dim sensitivity range on the meter scale. If not, return to step 1 and repeat all steps.

9. If the adjustment is correct, turn off the headlights and disconnect the tester.

10. Remove the tester lamp from the phototube unit.

4 REMOVAL AND INSTALLATION

If the automatic headlight dimmer malfunctions and cannot be removed for repair immediately, manual operation of the headlights may be obtained at the foot switch, in most cases, by removing the fuse from the fuse holder. The fuse holder is located in the amplifier wiring harness, just a few inches from the amplifier unit.

Should the car have to be driven with the amplifier removed, manual operation of the foot switch may be obtained by replacing the dimmer over-ride type foot switch with a standard foot switch, and plugging the standard car wiring to it.

PHOTOTUBE

REMOVAL

1. Disconnect the negative (ground) cable from the battery.

2. Remove the screws retaining the upper section of the instrument panel.

3. Remove the garnish molding from the windshield pillars.

4. Carefully lift up the rear end of the panel and pull it away from the windshield.

5. Disconnect the phototube unit plug from the amplifier harness. Remove the top panel and phototube unit.

6. Remove the phototube unit from the top panel.

INSTALLATION

1. Install the phototube unit on the top panel.

2. Position the top panel and phototube to permit connecting the phototube plug to the amplifier harness. Then make the connection, pushing the plug down through the hole in the speaker mounting plate.

3. Carefully position the top panel and install the retaining screws.

4. Replace the garnish moldings on the windshield pillars.

5. Connect the negative (ground) cable to the battery.

6. Check the aim and sensitivity adjustments (See Common Adjustments and Repairs in this part).

AMPLIFIER UNIT AND HARNESS

REMOVAL

1. Disconnect the negative (ground) cable from the battery.

2. Disconnect the amplifier wiring harness from the relay (above the amplifier), from the foot switch, and from the headlight wiring harness.

3. Remove the two amplifier unit mounting screws. Lower the amplifier and disconnect the phototube to amplifier cable.

INSTALLATION

1. Connect the phototube to amplifier cable, position the amplifier, and install the mounting screws.

2. Connect the amplifier unit to the relay, to the foot switch, and to the headlight wiring harness.

3. Connect the negative (ground) cable to the battery.

4. Check the Dim and Hold sensitivity adjustments (See Common Adjustments and Repairs in this part). If the car is to be driven without the automatic headlight dimmer, install a standard foot switch and connect the car headlight harness to it.

FOOT DIMMER SWITCH

REMOVAL

1. Disconnect the negative (ground) cable from the battery. **Very important.**

2. Position the left side of the floor mat back away from the area of the switch.

3. Remove two screws attaching the switch to the floor pan. Lift the switch from the floor pan.

4. Disconnect the wiring connectors from the switch.

INSTALLATION

1. Connect the wiring connectors to the switch.

2. Position the switch on the floor pan, and drive in the two mounting screws.

3. Position the floor mat in the area of the switch.

4. Connect the negative (ground) cable to the battery. **Should installation of a standard foot switch be necessary, remove the left side cowl trim panel, and connect the car headlight wiring harness to the foot switch.**

PART 16-6

STEREO TAPE PLAYER AND RADIO

1 DESCRIPTION AND OPERATION

STEREO TAPE PLAYER

The stereo tape player is an independently operating unit. It is located below the center of the instrument panel. To utilize the tape player, place the tape cartridge, open end first and labeled side up, in the slot and push it in until the cartridge stops. The unit will play the selections on the inserted tape.

ON-OFF SWITCH

The left knob on all units is an on-off switch and volume control. Turn the unit on by rotating the knob to the right. Turning the knob clockwise increases volume and counter-clockwise decreases volume. Turning the knob completely to the left turns off the set.

TONE CONTROL

The ring knob located behind the on-off switch controls the tone of the unit. Turning the ring knob clockwise increases the treble range and counter-clockwise increases the bass range.

CHANNEL SEPARATION

Distribution of sound between the left and right speakers is determined by a ring knob located behind the manual tuning control (inner right knob). Rotate the knob clockwise to increase sound to the right speakers and counter-clockwise to increase sound to the left speakers.

FADER CONTROL

Distribution of sound between the front and rear speakers is accomplished by a fader control located on the instrument panel to the right of the steering column. Set the control in the mid-position for equal distribution of sound. Rotate the control clockwise or counter-clockwise to distribute sound to the front or rear speakers in any proportion desired. **Do not store tape cartridges in areas subjected to high temperatures, such as on the top of the instrument panel, or the top of the rear package tray.**

RADIO

Refer to Wiring Diagram Manual Form 7795P-66 for locations of wiring harnesses. Schematics are shown in Group 22 of this manual.

An AM and an AM/FM radio are available. Both radios have push button tuning as well as manual tuning. The antenna is mounted on the right fender.

The types of radios and the cars for which they are available are as follows:

Car	Manufacturer and Type	Model Number
Ford	Motorola—AM	6TMF
	Motorola—AM with electric antenna	E6TMF
	Motorola—AM/FM	F6TBF
	Bendix—AM	6TBF
	Bendix—AM/FM	F6TBF
	Bendix—AM with electric antenna	EF6TBF
	Philco—AM	6TPF
	Philco of Canada—AM	CE6TPF
Mercury	Motorola—AM	6TMM
	Motorola—AM with electric antenna	F6TMM
	Bendix—AM/FM	F6TBM
	Bendix—AM/FM with electric antenna	EF6TBM

2 DIAGNOSIS AND TESTING

RADIO DIAGNOSIS GUIDE

NO RECEPTION	1. Burned out fuse. 2. Reversed battery polarity. 3. Defective antenna. 4. Shorted speaker lead or defective speaker. Be sure that proper voltage is	available at the set then substitute the known good antenna and speaker. **Be sure to turn off the radio befor removing or installing the speaker.**
NOISY OR ERRATIC RECEPTION	**NOISY RECEPTION—ENGINE NOT RUNNING** 1. Loose connections. **NOISY RECEPTION—ENGINE RUNNING** 1. Defective suppression equipment. 2. Suppression condensers not properly grounded.	3. The receiver not properly grounded to the instrument panel. **NOISY RECEPTION—CAR IN MOTION** 1. Loose or broken lead-in cable. 2. Loose or defective radio antenna. 3. Defective wheel static collectors.
DISTORTED OR GARBLED SOUND	1. Voice coil rubbing on center pole piece of speaker magnet (either front or rear speaker). 2. Torn speaker cone.	3. Foreign material on cone. 4. Bent or twisted speaker mounting.
WEAK RECEPTION	1. Beyond normal reception distance from station (FM only). 2. Defective antenna. If FM reception is poor be sure that the antenna is at 30 to 32 inch height before trying a new antenna.	
NO SOUND FROM ONE SPEAKER	1. One speaker defective. 2. Wiring to dead speaker defective. Operate the fader to determine the speaker at fault.	

ELECTRIC ANTENNA DIAGNOSIS GUIDE

MOTOR DOES NOT OPERATE	1. Burned out fuse. 2. Defective switch or wiring.	3. Poor ground. 4. Defective motor.
MOTOR OPERATES IN ONLY ONE DIRECTION	1. Defective switch or wiring. 2. Defective motor.	
MOTOR RUNS BUT WANDS DO NOT MOVE	1. Bent or corroded wands. 2. Defective drive assembly.	

TESTING

Tests for any of the components in the radio system may be made by substituting known good parts. In the case of an antenna or speaker, it will not be necessary to remove the suspected antenna or speaker. Disconnect the antenna or speaker at the radio and plug in the known good unit. Check the antenna with the car outside of the garage. Plug the antenna lead into the antenna socket in the radio, and extend the antenna wand through the open window of the car.

3 COMMON ADJUSTMENTS AND REPAIRS

PUSH BUTTON ADJUSTMENT

Turn the radio on, and allow it to warm up for 15 minutes. Extend the antenna to a height of approximately 33 inches. Pull out the desired push button and reduce the volume to a low value.

FORD

AM Push Buttons

Press in firmly any one of the

push buttons which has been pre-set to the AM position. Pull out the push button to be set to unlock the push button mechanism. If the red bar on the push button face is down, pull out the push button approximately $1/10$ inch further until the button is free to rotate and rotate the button 180° to the bar-up position. Carefully tune in the desired AM station with the manual tuning knob. After the station is clearly tuned in, push the button straight in until it stops, and then release it. Repeat this procedure for the remaining buttons.

FM Push Buttons

Press in firmly any one of the push buttons which has been pre-set to the FM position. Pull out the push button to be set to unlock the push button mechanism. If the red bar on the push button face is up, pull out the push button approximately $1/10$

inch further until the button is free to rotate and rotate the button 180° to the bar-down position. Carefully tune in the desired FM station with the manual tuning knob. After the station is clearly tuned in, push the button straight in until it stops and then release it. Repeat this procedure for the remaining buttons.

MERCURY

AM Push Buttons

Place the band selector switch to the AM position. Pull out the push button to be set to unlock the push button mechanism. The letters AM must appear at the top of the push button face. If the letters FM appear, pull the push button out approximately $1/10$ inch further until the push button is free to rotate and rotate the push button 180° to the AM position. Carefully tune in the desired AM station with the manual

tuning knob. After the station is clearly tuned in, push the button straight in until it stops and then release it. Repeat this procedure for the remaining buttons.

FM Push Buttons

Place the band selector switch to the FM position. Pull out the push button to be set to unlock the push button mechanism. The letters FM must appear at the top of the push button face. If the letters AM appear, pull the push button out approximately $1/10$ inch further until the push button is free to rotate and rotate the push button 180° to the FM position. Carefully tune in the desired FM station with the manual tuning knob. After the station is clearly tuned in, push the button straight in until it stops and then release it. Repeat this procedure for the remaining buttons.

4 REMOVAL AND INSTALLATION

RADIO
REMOVAL

1. Disconnect the battery ground cable.
2. On cars with air conditioning, disconnect the air conditioning ducts from the plenum and remove the nozzle adapter plate.
3. On Mercury cars with air conditioning, remove the ash tray and slide bracket.
4. Loosen the radio knob set screws and remove the knobs. On Mercury cars equipped with electric antennas, only the left knob has a set screw, the other knobs pull off.
5. Remove the nut retaining the bracket to the radio and position the bracket away from the radio. On cars with air conditioning remove the bracket.
6. Disconnect the antenna, speaker, power and pilot light leads from the radio.
7. On the Ford, remove the two radio to mounting plate mounting bolts from under the instrument panel.
8. On the Mercury, remove the two mounting nuts and washers.
9. Carefully remove the radio from under the instrument panel. Be careful not to damage the radio pointer on the sub dial on the Ford or the dial lens on the Mercury.

INSTALLATION

1. Carefully position the radio to the instrument panel and install the mounting screws (Ford) or mounting washers and nuts (Mercury).
2. Connect the antenna, speaker, power and pilot light leads to the radio.
3. Install the support bracket.
4. Install the radio knobs.
5. Install the ash tray and slide bracket, if it was removed.
6. On cars with air conditioning, install the nozzle adapter plate and the air conditioning ducts.
7. Connect the battery.

MANUAL ANTENNA—FORD

1. Disconnect the antenna lead from the side of the radio chassis and feed the lead out through the dash opening into the engine compartment.
2. Open the hood and disconnect the antenna lead from the three retaining clips.
3. Remove the antenna snap-on base cap at the fender mounting with a small screwdriver.
4. Remove the four mounting screws from the antenna base and remove the antenna assembly.
5. To install the antenna, feed the antenna lead through the fender opening.

6. Position the mounting pad and fasten the antenna base in position with the four mounting screws. Torque the four mounting screws to specification.
7. Snap the base cap into position.
8. Position the antenna lead in the retaining clips along the top of the dash and feed the antenna lead through the dash opening.
9. Plug the antenna lead into the radio chassis.

MANUAL ANTENNA—MERCURY

1. Disconnect the antenna lead from the radio receiver and feed the lead out through the right cowl top panel.
2. Remove the antenna snap-on base cap at the fender mounting with a small screwdriver.
3. Remove the mounting screws from the antenna base and remove the antenna assembly and mounting pad.
4. To install, position the mounting pad over the antenna mounting holes in the fender.
5. Insert the antenna lead into the hole through the fender and through the hole in the cowl top panel. Install the antenna base in position with the trailing edge of the

air foil toward the rear of the vehicle.

6. Route the antenna lead under the dash over the glove compartment and insert it into the antenna receptacle in the radio chassis.

POWER ANTENNA— MERCURY

1. Open the rear deck lid and disconnect the antenna power leads.
2. Disconnect the antenna coaxial lead.
3. Remove the bolt retaining the antenna to the floor pan bracket.
4. Remove the antenna-to-fender nut and spacer, and remove the antenna from the vehicle.
5. Transfer the antenna-to-fender lower spacer and the upper portion of the lower bracket to the new antenna.
6. Position the antenna to the fender and install the spacer and nut.
7. Install the antenna-to-floor pan retaining bracket bolt.
8. Connect the antenna lead, and the power leads.
9. Check the antenna operation.

SPEAKER—FORD

1. Remove the ash try and slide bracket.
2. Disconnect the speaker lead from the radio.
3. Reaching through the ash tray opening, remove the radio speaker and mounting bracket.
4. Install the speaker through the ash tray opening.
5. Connect the radio speaker and mounting bracket by reaching through the ash tray opening.
6. Connect the speaker lead.
7. Install the ash tray and slide bracket.

REAR SPEAKER—STATION WAGON

1. Remove the spare tire cover.
2. Remove the wheel housing cover.

3. Through the tire opening remove the speaker mounting wing nuts.
4. Position the speaker out of the wheel housing and disconnect the speaker leads.
5. Position the new speaker to the wheel housing area and connect the speaker leads.
6. Install the wheel housing cover.
7. Install the spare tire cover.

ROOF QUARTER SPEAKER— MERCURY

1. Remove the light assembly mounting screws, position the light out, disconnect the leads and remove the light.
2. Remove the two mouldings, snap out the trim panel, and remove the speaker retaining screws. Position the speaker out.

3. Open the rear deck and disconnect the speaker leads. Tie a string to the speaker leads.
4. From inside the car remove the speaker and lead.
5. Tie the string to the new speaker leads and pull the speaker leads into the luggage compartment and connect them.
6. Install the speaker, and snap the trim panel in place.
7. Install the two mouldings.
8. Connect the light lead and install the light assembly.

INTERFERENCE SUPPRESSION

Interference suppression items are shown in Figs. 1 and 2. A radio capacitor is installed within the alternator assembly.

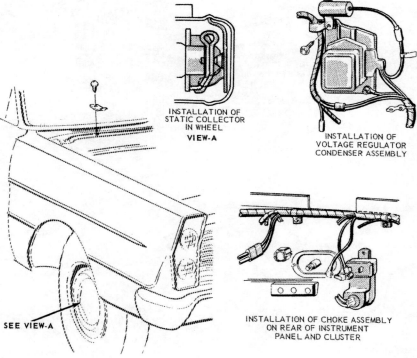

FIG. 1—Radio Interference Suppression

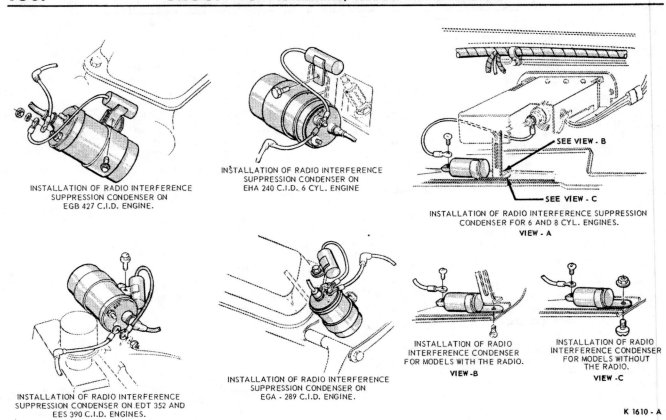

INSTALLATION OF RADIO INTERFERENCE
SUPPRESSION CONDENSER ON
EGB 427 C.I.D. ENGINE.

INSTALLATION OF RADIO INTERFERENCE
SUPPRESSION CONDENSER ON
EHA 240 C.I.D. 6 CYL. ENGINE

SEE VIEW - B

SEE VIEW - C

INSTALLATION OF RADIO INTERFERENCE SUPPRESSION
CONDENSER FOR 6 AND 8 CYL. ENGINES.
VIEW - A

INSTALLATION OF RADIO INTERFERENCE
SUPPRESSION CONDENSER ON EDT 352 AND
EES 390 C.I.D. ENGINES.

INSTALLATION OF RADIO INTERFERENCE
SUPPRESSION CONDENSER ON
EGA - 289 C.I.D. ENGINE.

INSTALLATION OF RADIO
INTERFERENCE CONDENSER
FOR MODELS WITH THE RADIO.
VIEW -B

INSTALLATION OF RADIO
INTERFERENCE CONDENSER
FOR MODELS WITHOUT
THE RADIO.
VIEW -C

K 1610 - A

FIG. 2—Radio Highway Suppression

PART 16-7   SPECIFICATIONS

BLOWER MOTOR CURRENT DRAW

At Low Speed	2-4	Amperes at 12 volts
At Medium Speed	4-6	Amperes at 12 volts
At High Speed	6-8	Amperes at 12 volts①

①When in A/C position 8.4-8.9 Amperes at 12 volts on Select-Aire and Deluxe Air Conditioner. 6.5-7.5 Amperes at 12 volts on Ford and Mercury Air Conditioners.

AIR CONDITIONING COMPRESSOR

Location	Torque (ft-lbs)	
	Tecumseh	York
Cylinder Head	20-24	14-18
Front Seal Plate	6-10	13-17
Service Valve (Rotolock)	35 Max.	35 Max.
Mounting Bolt	14-17	14-17
Oil Filler Plug	18-22	18-22
Clutch Mounting	15-22	15-22
Base Plate		7-11
Back Plate		7-10

Oil Capacity Tecumseh ⅞ inch (11 ounces)
York ¾ inch (10 ounces)
Use Suniso #5, or Capella E, or equivalent.
Refrigerant Capacity 2½ pounds.

CIRCUIT PROTECTION

Heater	AGC-20 Fuse
Air Conditioner	25 Amp. C.B.
Automatic Headlight Dimmer	4 Amp. Fuse

RADIO

Radio Current Draw . . . 1 ampere max. @ 12 volts	
Location	Torque (ft.-lbs.)
Radio to Instrument Panel	25-35
Mounting Plate Nuts	25-35
Antenna to Fender	17-23①

①Inch-pounds.

DRIVEN BELT TENSION

Between Fan Pulley and Air Conditioner Compressor
All Engines . . . . New 120-150
Used① 90-120

①Belt operated for a minimum of 10 minutes is considered a used belt.

SPEED CONTROL

BRAKE PEDAL RELEASE SWITCH
Adjustment Nut Torque . . . . .48-60 in-lbs.

BODY, DOORS, AND WINDOWS

GROUP 17

PART 17-1 GENERAL BODY SERVICE

1 DIAGNOSIS AND TESTING

DUST AND WATER LEAKS

Sealer locations should be considered when checking for dust or water leaks. It should be remembered that the forward motion of the car creates a slight vacuum within the body, particularly if a window or ventilator is partially open. Any unsealed crevice or small opening in the lower section of the body will permit air to be drawn into the body. If dust is present in the air, it will follow any path taken by the air from the point of entry into the passenger and luggage compartments. Opening the ventilator air ducts, will equalize these pressures. Dust may work its way into the hollow, box-type, rocker panel which extends along the edge of the floor below the doors. Dust accumulates in the rocker panel, and may eventually work its way to the kick-up or the rear body pillar, and

follow the contour of the wheelhouse into the luggage compartment.

To eliminate dust leakage, determine the exact point at which the dust enters. As explained above, the point of entry is often deceptive in that the dust may enter at one point then follow the passages, formed by interior trim, to another point.

Under certain conditions, water can enter an automobile body at any point where dirt or dust can enter. Any consideration of water leakage must take into account all points covered under dust leaks.

To determine the exact location of a dust leak, remove the following trim from the car:
1. Cowl side trim panel.
2. Quarter trim panel.
3. Rear seat back and seat cushion.
4. Luggage compartment floor

mats, spare wheel, and side trim panel.
5. Center pillar trim on 4-door models.
6. Scuff plates.

After removing the trim, the location of most leaks will be readily evident. Seal these leaks, and road test the car on a dusty road to make sure that all leaks are sealed. The entrance of dust is usually indicated by a pointed shaft of dust or silt at the point of entrance.

After the road test, check for indications of a dust pattern around the door openings, cowl panel, lower part of the quarter panel, and in the luggage compartment.

Sometimes leaks can be located by putting bright lights under the car, with the above components removed, and checking the interior of the body joints and weld lines. The light will show through where leaks exist.

2 COMMON ADJUSTMENTS AND REPAIRS

TYPES OF SEALERS AND APPLICATION

Since many sealers are used in manufacturing assembly, the all purpose sealers described below have been selected for service use. The method and points of application (Figs. 1 through 3) are given under each sealer type.

RUBBER CEMENT— 8A-19552-B

This quick-drying, strong, adhesive cement is designed to hold weatherstripping on doors, bodies, deck lids, cowl ventilators, and the surrounding metal.

Clean all grease, dirt, and old sealer from the surfaces to be cemented.

SILICONE LUBRICANT— COAZ-19553-A (JELLY) OR COAZ-19553-C (SPRAY)

This lubricant can be used on the door upper weatherstrips of convertible and hardtop models. Its use makes the doors easier to close, avoids weatherstrip squeaks, retards excess weatherstrip wear chafing be-

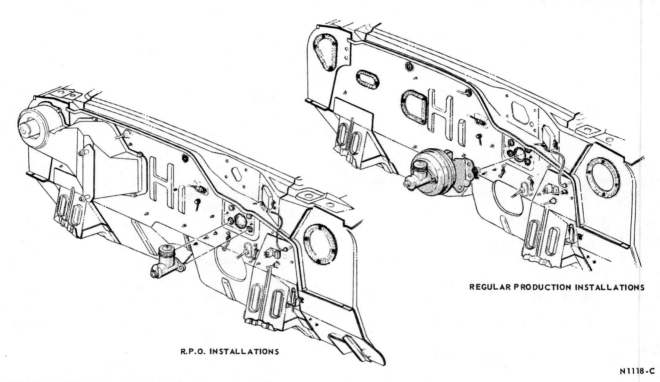

REGULAR PRODUCTION INSTALLATIONS

R.P.O. INSTALLATIONS

N1118-C

FIG. 1—Dash Panel Sealer Locations—Typical

CAULKING CORD— AB-19560-A

This sealer has a plastic base with an asbestos filler, is heavy bodied, and is commonly known as permagum. It is used on spotweld holes, around moulding clips, or between two surfaces not properly sealed by a gasket. Apply the sealer with a putty knife.

TRIM CEMENT— C2AZ-19C525-A

This cement is specially recommended for instrument panel safety pads. It is also useful for repair or replacement of other vinyl and rubber trim.

Wash the surfaces thoroughly with a rag moistened with clean gasoline or cleaner's naphtha. For best results, apply a medium coat of cement to both surfaces, allow it to dry until tacky, and then press both surfaces firmly together.

CLEANING SOLVENT— B7A-19520-A OR B7A-19521-A

Prevent either of these cleaners from contacting either vinyl or leather.

This general clean-up solvent cleans off cement smears, wax, tars, oils, grease, caulk and sealer. It can also be used to thin caulk and sealer. It is harmless to cured paint, and is useful in new car pre-delivery.

tween the door glass upper frame and the weatherstrip, and helps to retain door window alignment by reducing friction between the glass frame and the rubber weatherstrip.

BODY ALIGNMENT

When checking alignment of a badly damaged body, be sure that all necessary frame corrections have been made before attempting to align the body.

Rough out badly damaged areas before taking measurements for squaring up a body. Remove the glass to prevent breakage. In severe cases, reinforcement brackets and other inner construction may have to be removed or cut to permit restoration of the outer shell and pillars without excessive strain on the parts. Straighten, install, and secure all

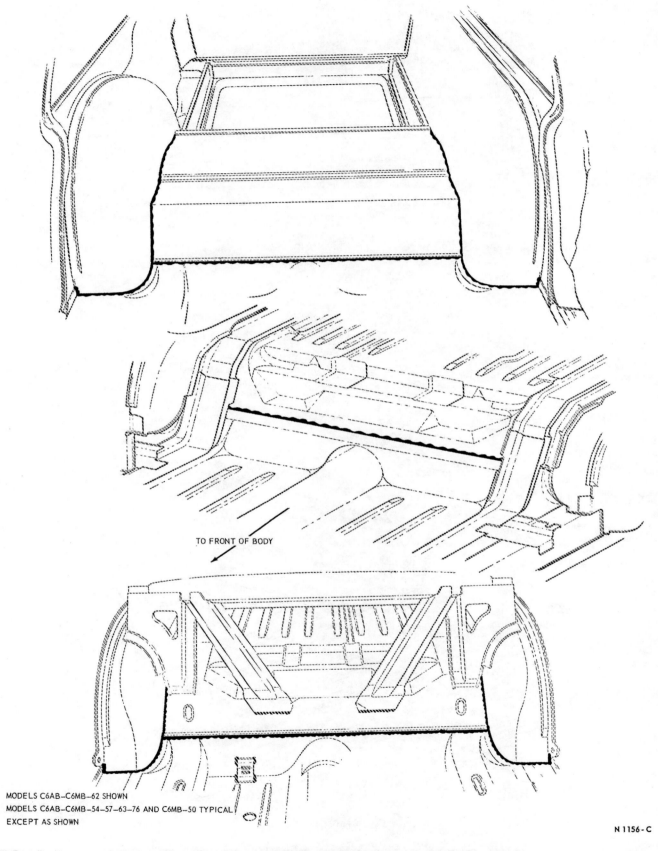

TO FRONT OF BODY

MODELS C6AB–C6MB–62 SHOWN
MODELS C6AB–C6MB–54–57–63–76 AND C6MB–50 TYPICAL
EXCEPT AS SHOWN

N 1156-C

FIG. 2—Front and Center Floor Pan Sealer Application—Body Types 54 and 71—Typical

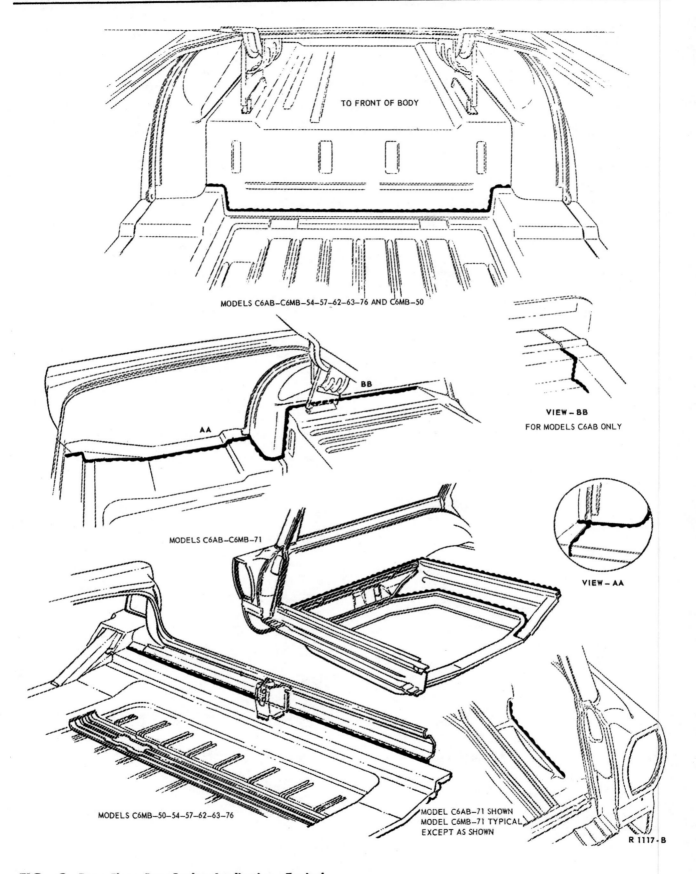

TO FRONT OF BODY

MODELS C6AB–C6MB–54–57–62–63–76 AND C6MB–50

BB

AA

VIEW – BB

FOR MODELS C6AB ONLY

MODELS C6AB–C6MB–71

VIEW – AA

MODELS C6MB–50–54–57–62–63–76

MODEL C6AB–71 SHOWN
MODEL C6MB–71 TYPICAL
EXCEPT AS SHOWN

R 1117-B

FIG. 3—Rear Floor Pan Sealer Application—Typical

parts in place before attempting to align the body.

In cases of severe or sharp bends, it may be necessary to use heat. Any attempt to cold-straighten a severely bent bracket may cause ruptures of the welds (if any) and may also cause cracks in the bent part. Never heat the area more than enough to give a dull red.

CHECKING BODY FOR MISALIGNMENT

To align or square up a body, take two opposite diagonal measurements between the front, center, or rear pillars. Take the measurements between reference points such as crease lines or weld joints which are diagonally opposite each other on the two pillars being measured. Since all measurements should be made from the bare metal, remove all interior trim from the checking points.

Do not attempt to correct any serious misalignment with one jacking operation. This is particularly true if other sections of the body also require aligning. Align each section proportionately until the proper dimensions are obtained. If frame alignment is questionable, see Figs. 7 and 8.

FRAME ALIGNMENT

Frame misalignment can affect front wheel alignment, body alignment, and the operation of the chassis parts. Window glass cracks, door and window opening troubles, and air or water leaks at the doors are often caused by improperly tightened body bolts (Figs. 4 and 5), or frame misalignment.

Before checking frame alignment, inspect all frame members for cracks, twists, or bends. Check all welded connections for cracks. Inspect the bolts and body support brackets for looseness. Make any necessary repairs or replacements.

The conventional frame and convertible frame dimensions are shown in Figs. 4 and 5.

FRAME REPAIRS

To prevent internal stresses in the metal, frame straightening should be limited to parts which are not severely bent. If heat is needed to straighten a frame member, keep the temperature below 1200°F. Excessive heat may weaken the metal in the frame members and cause permanent damage.

Electric welding equipment should be used for all frame welding and **heat should be kept to a minimum area** so that the hardness of the metal will not be affected.

When a reinforcement is to be welded to a frame side member, run the welds lengthwise along the side of the reinforcement.

If a damaged frame member is to be replaced, use the same method of attachment as on the original frame member. New bolts, required for replacement of parts, should be of the same specifications as the original bolts.

PAINT REFINISHING

PAINT DAMAGES AND PROCEDURES FOR REPAIR

Paint Repairs on Galvanized Metals

If for any reason it becomes necessary to perform paint repairs on galvanized rocker panels or any other galvanized steel surfaces, care must be exercised in preparing the bare galvanized surface to properly accept paint, and the best possible paint products must be employed to insure satisfactory adhesion to the metal and to give a good color match with acceptable durability. Most of the approved paint suppliers for refinishing materials agree on the procedure for metal preparation but use different primer recommendations. The methods involving the use of DuPont Preparakote and Ditzler Zinc Dust Primer are indicated here and it is important that either one be employed exactly as directed. No short cuts nor any inter-mixing should be attempted.

METAL PREPARATION FOR GALVANIZED STEEL

1. Strip, sand-off or otherwise remove all paint from the affected galvanized steel panel.

2. Wire-brush or steel-wool the entire metal surface and remove all grease or oil by wiping with a clean solvent.

3. Wipe the panel using a clean cloth or sponge with Lithofoam No. 2 (distributed by the Neilson Chemical Division of Amchem Products, Inc.) or Bonderite No. 34 (distributed by Parker Rustproof). The work should be kept completely wet for at least three minutes and the metal should be thoroughly etched. If any bright metal remains the treatment should be repeated.

4. Rinse the area with clean water and blow off with compressed air, and tack the surface clean.

5. The dried surface must be primed immediately. Then succeeding coats and color as required must be applied according to the vendor's directions. Examples such as the DuPont and Ditzler systems are given as follows:

SYSTEM FOR USING DuPONT PREPARAKOTE

1. Spray Preparakote over properly prepared metal. Force-dry with radiant heat or air-dry overnight. This primer must be dried hard enough to sand wet or dry.

2. Sand the Preparakote very carefully, perferably with 400 paper so as to avoid cutting through to bare metal. Blow off and tack clean.

3. Spray two coats of No. 22 clear sealer and allow it to air-dry for thirty minutes.

4. Spray on matching Acrylic repair paint as directed. Then air-dry or force-dry until the paint is hard enough to be polished.

5. Polish the paint as recommended by the supplier.

SYSTEM FOR USING DITZLER ZINC DUST PRIMER

1. Prime the galvanized area with DPE659 Zinc Dust Primer. This is a two-component product and the zinc must be carefully mixed with the vehicle as directed. A recommended film thickness of one mil may be recoated with a lacquer base primer surface such as DZL3200 in about twenty minutes. Do not sand DPE659.

2. Spray primer surfacer DZL-3200 reduced as directed to a film thickness of about two mils.

3. After drying the primer surfacer about thirty minutes, carefully sand with No. 360 or No. 400 silicon carbide paper, wet or dry, so as not to cut through the zinc dust primer coat. Blow off and tack clean.

4. Apply matching acrylic lacquer as directed, and after drying, polish as required. **Sufficient curing according to supplier recommendations, must be obtained before any polishing operations.**

All material coatings may be force-dried. Careful manipulation is recommended.

Acrylic Enamels

Acrylic enamels exhibit better hardness, mar resistance and gloss re-

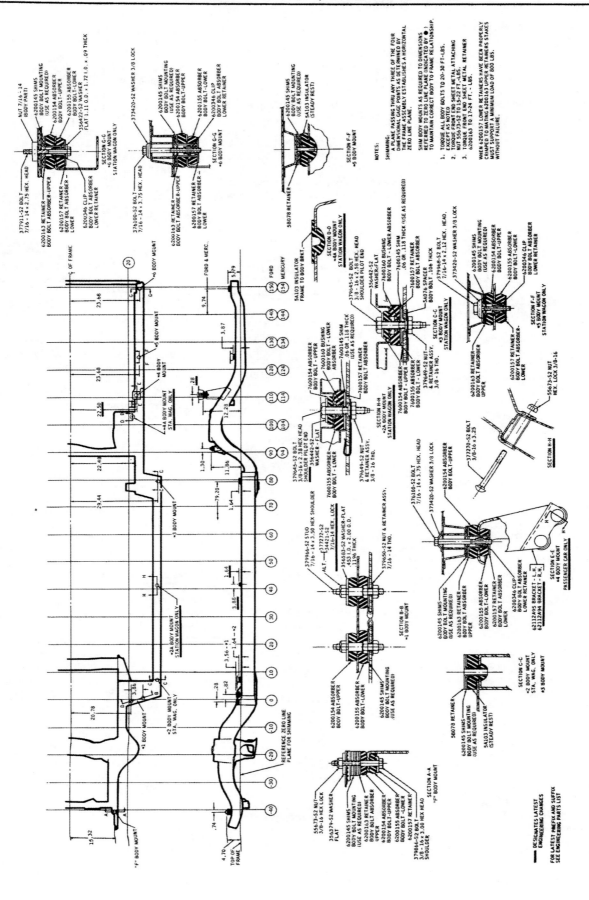

FIG. 4—Conventional Frame and Body Bolts

M1050-D

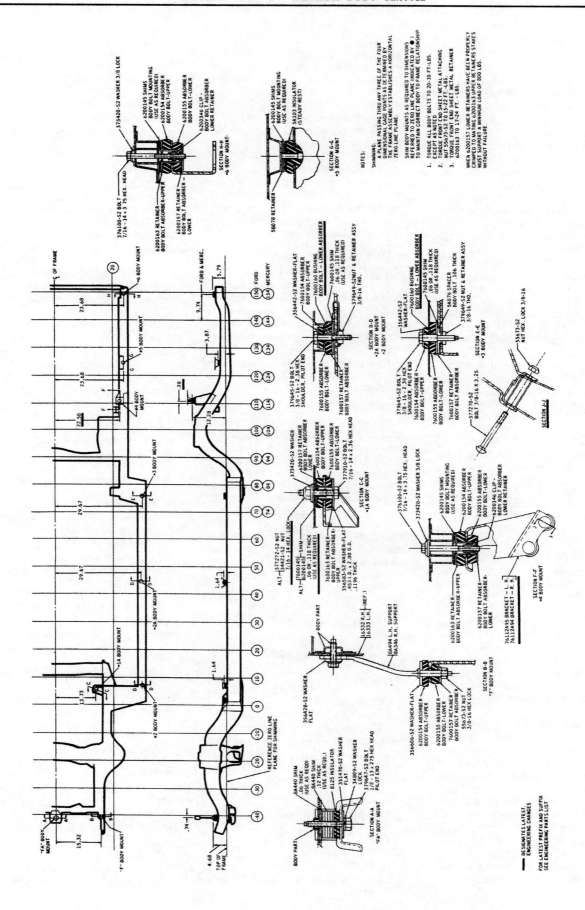

FIG. 5—Convertible Frame and Body Bolts

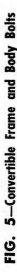

tention in metallic colors than the ordinary enamels. Acrylic enamels also possess the property of good polish-ability.

Following are recommended repair procedures for acrylic enamels:

Repair By Polishing. Repair of minor dirt or fallout, sags, mars, scratches, dry spray, overspray, and orange peel can be accomplished by machine or hand polishing or by both sanding and polishing without the necessity of repainting. Repairs of this type should apply to an entire panel while spot repairs should be attempted only in isolated areas.

The suggested polish repair procedure consists of:

1. Remove the defect by oil sanding with 600 grit paper, using water or mineral spirits as a lubricant.

2. Apply a white or light colored medium grit machine polishing compound (Sno-Flake No. 16 or equivalent) to the painted surface with a brush.

3. Polish the entire panel surface using an 1850 rpm wheel and a carpet pad approximately (⅝-inch nap) or lambswool pad.

4. Buff the surface with a clean lambswool pad.

Normally, acrylic enamels do not need polishing to improve their gloss; however, the foregoing procedure can be used to restore the original luster to the film after weathering, or to improve the surface smoothness of the finish on the entire car.

Repair by Repainting. Acrylic enamels should be repaired by repainting with acrylic repair paint, particularly metallic colors. The use of acrylic repair paint results in a better color match. Spot repairs should not be attempted. Only panel repairs are permissible. Both the original finish and the repair can be polished to provide the same luster, and the air dry acrylic repair lacquer will provide better durability in service than air dry enamels. **Do not use Nitrocellulose lacquers for exterior repairs.**

Before sanding the surface to be painted, remove all traces of wax, polish or grease with a good silicone remover such as DL-60-3721-A. It is extremely important that a thorough sanding of the original finish be accomplished using No. 400 grit paper. Care should be exercised to insure that all surfaces, including edges and areas adjacent to applied mouldings, are thoroughly sanded in order to provide adhesion of the repair top coat. Areas sanded to the base metal (cut through) should be treated with an acid cleaner such as Metalprep (distributed by Amchem Products Inc.). Follow the directions of the supplier as stated on the container.

After sanding, proceed with the application of a primer surfacer reduced according to the supplier's recommendations to any bare metal spots that have been exposed. After the recommended air dry time, sand the primer surfacer with No. 400 grit paper before application of the repair material. The lacquer or enamel used should be reduced as recommended by its supplier.

PAINT DEFECTS AND REPAIR PROCEDURES

Listed here are some of the abnormal paint conditions that may be encountered. It is very important to identify the paint condition correctly so that the proper repair procedure may be followed. For each of the following paint conditions described, the recommended repair procedure will be indicated.

BLISTERING

Blistering is the formation of bubbles or pin points on the surface of the finished work (Fig. 6). Unless inspected by a magnifying glass, this condition is very hard to identify. In some instances, this complaint may be confused with dirt in the paint. To verify blistering, prick the suspected areas, and note whether a hole exists under the bubble. This condition is caused by rust, moisture, or oil between the coats, metal not properly cleaned, or uneven temperatures between the metal and the paint being sprayed.

Acrylic Enamel

Repair by repainting (color coat). Priming procedure must first be followed if defect is due to poor metal preparation.

CHECKING

Line checking has the appearance of thin, straight lines criss-crossing each other (Fig. 6). These lines may be from one-half inch to four inches or longer, increasing in length as the finish ages.

Acrylic Enamel

Refinish panel. (Color coat—primer if damaged.)

CHIPPING AND STONE BRUISES

Chipping occurs when the surface of the finish coat of paint has been broken by a sharp blow, and small particles of paint have flaked off (Fig. 6). Frequently, stone bruises result in chipping (Fig. 6).

Acrylic Enamel

Refinish panel. Paint may be spotted if in isolated areas. (Prime it to bare metal.)

CRACKING

Cracking is evidenced by the paint curling. Frequently, cracking starts at the edge of the panel (Fig. 6). This is caused by poor mixing of paint or by temperature changes during the various painting stages.

Acrylic Enamel

Refinish panel. (Prime if both color and primer are cracking.)

CROW FOOTING

Crow footing may be described as small lines branching off from a point in all directions and giving the appearance of a crow's foot (Fig. 6). Crow footing is usually caused by spraying a second coat before the first coat is dry, by spraying an excessively thick coat, or by thinners which evaporate too fast.

Acrylic Enamel

Refinish panel. (Color coat.)

DIRT IN PAINT

Patches where dirt appears (Fig. 6) are sometimes confused with blistering. To verify the condition, prick the suspected areas, and note whether there is foreign material under the surface.

Acrylic Enamel

Polish repair procedure will be effective in most cases. (Color coat.)

MILDEW

Mildew growth, which occurs along radial lines (Fig. 6) is most commonly found in a very dark gray or black color.

Acrylic Enamel

Repair by polishing.

OFF-COLOR

The term off-color is applied to adjacent areas on which the colors do not match (Fig. 6). It may also appear when making spot repairs.

Acrylic Enamel

Refinish panel if polishing does not correct condition. (Color coat.)

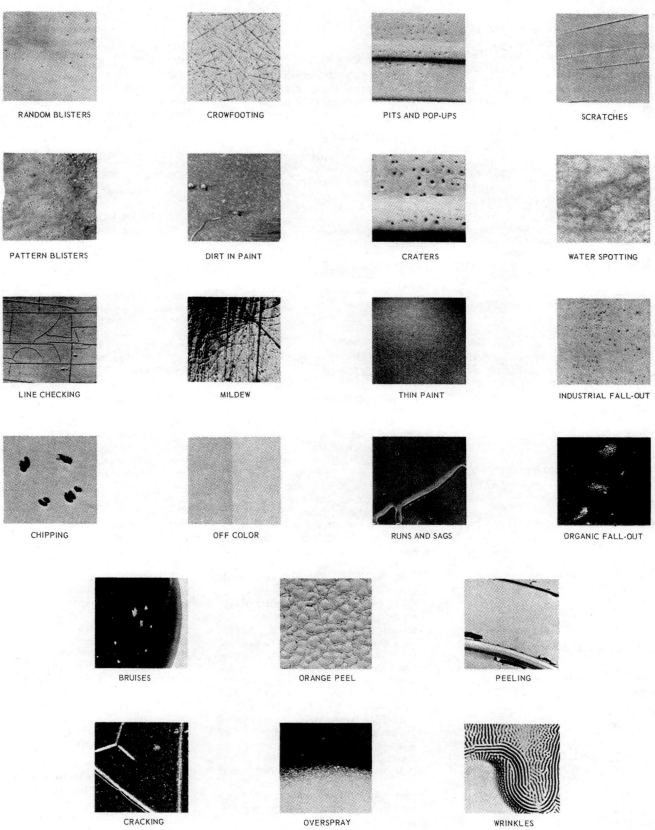

FIG. 6—Paint Defects

ORANGE PEEL

Orange peel is a term used to describe an uneven, mottled appearance on the paint surface (Fig. 6). This is usually caused by improper thinning of the paint.

Acrylic Enamel

Refinish panel if polishing does not correct condition. (Color coat.)

OVERSPRAY

Overspary is evidenced by a rough, dull finish in the area surrounding the paint repair (Fig. 6).

PEELING

Peeling occurs when large areas of the finish or primer coat separate from the metal or prime coat (Fig. 6). This is usually caused by wax, grease, rust, or oil under the paint. Do not confuse with orange peel.

PITS AND POP-UPS

Pits and craters may be identified by the appearance of small round depressions in the paint (Fig. 6). These may be caused by not allowing the first coat to dry sufficiently before applying the second coat or from failure to remove silicone polishes before repainting.

Acrylic Enamel

First use polish repair procedure, refinish panel if necessary. (Color coat.)

THIN PAINT

The primer will show through the finish coat as a result of an excessively thin color coat, or application of the color coat before the surface is dry (Fig. 6).

Acrylic Enamel

Refinish panel. (Color coat.)

RUNS AND SAGS

The uneven collections of paint on the finish surface are referred to as runs or sags (Fig. 6). The collections may appear in the form of tear drops or sagging lines. Usually these lines are quite soft and sometimes they may be wrinkled (Fig. 6). This is usually caused by over-application of paint or hesitation in the stroke of the gun.

Acrylic Enamel

Use polish repair procedure.

SCRATCHES

Scratches are thin marks or tears that may partially or completely penetrate the surface of the finish coat of paint (Fig. 6).

Acrylic Enamel

Use polish repair procedure for shallow penetration. Refinish panels to correct conditions of deep penetration.

SPOT DISCOLORATION

This is evidenced by brown spots or stains on the surface. Stains or spots can be caused by road tar, acid or alkali-bearing water from the streets.

Acrylic Enamel

Use polish repair procedure.

WATER SPOTTING

Water spotting is evidenced by a milky pattern where water drops have fallen (Fig. 6).

Acrylic Enamel

Use polish repair procedure.

INDUSTRIAL FALL-OUT

Industrial fall-out is the result of particles being exhausted into the air by the various processes of heavy industry, or in areas where there is a concentration of industry.

Industrial fall-out particles appear to the eye as tiny rust-colored dots on the paint film and the surface will feel rough to the touch (Fig. 6). Some of the particles have excellent adhesion and are difficult to remove. However the following procedure has proven effective in the removal of this fall-out:

1. Wash the car with car wash compound (COAA-19B521-A) to remove loose dirt. Rinse well and examine painted surfaces for iron base fall-out particles. If there is a significant quantity of fall-out not removed by ordinary washing, the oxalic treatment should then be used. All cracks, ledges, grooves, etc., where fall-out has accumulated, should be cleaned by wiping or by air blow-off.

2. Dissolve six to eight ounces of oxalic acid (dry) in one gallon of warm water and add one to two tablespoonsful of a non-alkaline detergent such as car wash compound (COAA-19B521-A). This acid detergent solution must be prepared and kept in a clean non-metallic container.

Apply this solution liberally to all affected surfaces of the car with a large sponge. Use a broad wiping stroke and keep the work completely wet for about 15 minutes, or until the operator can no longer feel any surface roughness or even isolated gritty particles with bare or gloved finger tips. If this is not done thoroughly, rust staining may soon redevelop. Be sure that the entire acid cleaning procedure is performed in a sheltered area so that the work will be kept as cool as possible to prevent rapid evaporation of water and consequent surface drying. **Do not work in the sun.**

3. Rinse with clear water. This must be done very thoroughly to prevent possible corrosion.

No traces of acid should be left on any surface. Bright trim parts, particularly anodized aluminum and stainless steel, may be stained by prolonged contact with the cleaning solution. Painted areas also can be spotted by prolonged exposure. It is also important to keep the oxalic acid cleaner solution from leaking to the inside of the car because some fabrics might be bleached or discolored by the solution.

If the fall-out is not completely removed or is deeply imbedded in the paint film, cleaning with the acid detergent mixture must be repeated. This may be aided by using a fine scrub brush, possibly a nylon bristle type. Make sure that the light scrubbing required does not scratch the paint. It is sometimes helpful to briskly rub the work with a mixture of equal parts of oxalic acid cleaner and FoMoCo cleaner wax polish (8A-19519-A) using a piece of heavy toweling. **Again, a thorough water rinsing is extremely important.**

Sometimes small black spots remain after the oxalic cleaning has removed all iron based fall-out. Such deposits might be asphaltic or they might be over-spray. These usually can be removed by rubbing vigorously with a cloth saturated with a mixture of kerosene and Actusol (about five parts of kerosene to one part of Actusol). Any residue of this solvent mixture may be readily flushed off with water.

ORGANIC FALL-OUT

Organic fall-out may result from parking cars under trees, or from the air under certain atmospheric conditions (Fig. 6).

Acrylic Enamel

Refinish damaged panels. (Color coat and primer.)

INTERIOR PAINT REPAIRS

The proper matching of colors can be obtained if the following procedures are carefully adhered to:

1. Clean the surface to be painted with wax and silicone remover.

2. Feather-edge the damaged area with 400 grit wet or dry sandpaper. (Prime all areas of bare metal with M-6J-12S Primer.)

3. Mix the paint per instructions on the can and spray several light coats.

Allow the paint to become tacky between coats.

4. Spray the entire area sparingly with B7A-645-S Lacquer Leveler which will blend the repaired area with existing painted surfaces.

PAINT REPAIR OF VINYL ORGANOSOL PAINTED LOAD FLOOR AREAS —STATION WAGONS

The paint is available in the following colors (part numbers in parenthesis): Light Aqua Metallic (VO-1830-C), Red Metallic (VO-1968-C), Parchment (VO-1969-C), Light Aqua (VO-1985-C) and Red (VO-1986-C).

1. Before sanding the surface of the panel to be repainted (either a damaged or service replacement panel), remove all traces of wax or grease using a good silicone remover such as DL-60-3721-A.

2. For minor repairs, scuff sand the panel surface adjacent to the damaged area. For service replacement panels, thoroughly dry sand the entire surface of the panel including edge flanges, preferably using a No. 400 grit paper. In either case, care should be taken not to sand through to bare metal.

3. Wash off the area to be painted with a naphtha dampened cloth. Blow off with clean compressed air, and then tack off.

4. Apply synthetic vinyl enamel paint in the desired color. To obtain proper hiding power and durability on service replacement panels, the dry film thickness should be at least 0.0010 to 0.0015 inch in depth.

5. In areas of minor paint repair, the paint can be air dried. Paint applied to service replacement panels must be cured by baking for approximately 20 minutes at 150° to 190°F. Durability of the paint will be adversely affected if baking is not performed as specified.

6. If conventional baking facilities are not available, a bank of heat lamps set approximately 15 inches from the panel can be used as a substitute to obtain the required temperatures. A portable unit such as a Fostoria Corporation, Fostoria, Ohio— Model 80-448, or a DeVilbiss Company, Toledo, Ohio Model 1RP-510, will give satisfactory results.

3 CLEANING AND INSPECTION

FLOOR PAN PLUGS AND GROMMETS

Many plugs and grommets are used in the floor pan and dash panel. The floor pan plugs seal the various body bolt access holes. If any plugs are missing or improperly installed, a dust or water leak may result. This also applies to the grommets used on the dash panel. When dust or water leaks are evident, these plugs and grommets should be checked for proper installation.

DRAIN AND DUST VALVES

Drain and dust valves are provided in the bottom of each door, in each rocker panel, and in each quarter panel. These valves are located in the lowest points in the panels. The weight of the water will open the valve and allow the water to escape from the panel. After the water has drained, the valve will close and prevent the entry of dust. The drain valves should be inspected periodically to make sure that they are not obstructed.

BODY MAINTENANCE

Regular body maintenance preserves the car's appearance and reduces the cost of maintenance during the life of the car. The following steps are suggested as a guide for regular body maintenance.

1. Vacuum the interior thoroughly and wash the car.

2. Check all openings for water leaks, and seal where necessary.

3. Replace all weatherstrips which are unfit for service. Apply silicone lubricant to the weatherstripping.

4. Replace all cracked, fogged, or chipped glass.

5. Align hood, doors, and deck lid if necessary.

6. Inspect windshield wiper blade and replace them if necessary.

7. Tighten the sill plate and garnish moulding screws.

8. Clean the seats, door trim panels, and headlining.

9. Touch-up or paint chipped or scratched areas.

10. Drain holes, located on the underside of each rocker panel, quarter panel, and door, should be cleared periodically.

RATTLE ELIMINATION

Most rattles are caused by a loose bolt or screw. Foreign objects such as nuts, bolts, or small pieces of body deadener in the door wells, pillars, and quarter panels are often the source of rattles. Door wells can be checked by carefully striking the underside of the door with a rubber mallet. The impact made by the mallet will indicate if loose objects are in the door well.

All bolts and screws should be tightened periodically. In the event that tightening the bolts and screws, located on such assemblies as the doors, hood, and deck lid, does not eliminate the rattles, the trouble is probably caused by misalignment. If this is the case, follow the adjustment and alignment procedures for these assemblies.

Rattles and squeaks are sometimes caused by weatherstripping and anti-squeak material that has slipped out of position. Apply additional cement or other adhesive, and install the material in the proper location to eliminate this difficulty.

EXTERIOR CLEANING

The outside finish should be frequently washed. Never wipe the painted surfaces with a dry cloth. Dusting the finish when it is dry tends to rub the dust and dirt into the baked enamel, and leaves a sandpaper effect on the surface. To keep the finish bright and attractive, and eliminate the necessity of using polish, wash the car whenever it has accumulated a moderate amount of dirt and road salt.

The bright metal parts of the car require no special care. Periodic cleaning will preserve the beauty and life of these finishes. Wash with clear water or if the parts are very dirty use COAA19B521-A Cleaning Compound. Using a clean soft cloth or a sponge and water, rinse and wipe the parts dry. FoMoCo Chrome Cleaner may be used sparingly to remove rust or salt corrosion from chrome plated parts. Do not scour chrome finished parts with steel wool or polish them with products containing abrasives. A FoMoCo Polish will provide excellent protection for all bright metal parts.

INTERIOR CLEANING

Use a vacuum cleaner to remove dust and dirt from the upholstery or floor covering. Vinyl and woven plastic trim that is dusty can usually be cleaned with a damp cloth. **Do not use cleaning materials containing kerosene, naphtha, toluol, xylol 10°, lacquer thinners, cellulose acetate, butyl cellulose, carbon tetrachloride, body polish, battery acid, anti-freeze, gasoline, motor oils or other type lubricants.**

Approved cleaners B8A-19523-A or B, B5A-19525-A, COAZ-19526-A or B (soft trim cleaners) and CIAZ-19C507-A (convertible back window cleaner) are available for service. Instructions for the use of these cleaners are included with their containers.

CARE OF WOOD GRAIN PANELING

Washing

Never wipe the panels or trim rails with a dry cloth. This method of cleaning tends to rub dust particles into the finished surface and leave fine scratches. Flush off all loose dirt and other elements, and wipe the body panels and rails with a sponge and plenty of cold water. If desired, a mild soap may be used. Rinse thoroughly with clear water, and wipe dry.

Glass Fiber Trim Rail Removal and Installation

The glass fiber trim rails are serv-iced with the woodgrain already applied. To remove the body trim rails, remove the cap over each trim rail screw to gain access to the screws. Remove the screws and the trim rail assembly.

When installing the body side trim rail, apply sealer (AB-19560-A) around each mounting hole. Install the cap retainer, screw, and cap.

Application of Wood-Grain Transfers

Wood-Grain transfers are available for application to the panels. The materials necessary to apply the transfers are a bonding coat (M-4584, 20% transfer solution of M-5412-A) and clear spar varnish.

If the surface on which the transfer is to be applied is damaged, repair and metal finish first.

1. Mask off the area where the transfer is to be applied.

2. Before sanding, remove all traces of wax, polish, and grease with a good silicone remover, such as DL-60-3721-A.

3. Prime-coat all bare metal areas, and wet sand. Also, wet or dry sand the entire area where the transfer is to be applied.

4. Wipe off the area with a naphtha dampened cloth. Blow off with clean compressed air, and then tack off.

5. Spray the surface with transfer bonding coat (M-4584). This coat is the binder for the transfer adhesive.

6. Allow the binding coat to air-dry for one hour, or heat-dry (160°) for 20 minutes.

7. Lightly wet-sand the bonding coat, and wipe it dry, carefully removing all dust and sanding particles.

8. Make a paper template of the damaged area, and cut the new transfer to size, using the template as a guide. Leave about ½ inch of extra material around the edge of the transfer to allow for matching and trimming.

9. Mix a solution of one part M-5412-A transfer solution and four parts water. This solution permits shifting of the transfer after it has been applied, so that the graining can be matched. Try a sample of the transfer and solution on an old piece of metal or fender. **If the transfer cannot be pulled off after two minutes the solution is too strong and must be diluted with more water.**

10. Soak the transfer in lukewarm water for one minute to loosen the paper backing. **Do not remove the backing until the transfer is applied.** Allow the excess water to drain off of the transfer before application to the panel.

11. Using a cheese cloth pad, apply the previously mixed 1 to 4 M-5412-A transfer solution and water to the panel. **Any excess solution that runs down on adjacent panels must be wiped off immediately.**

12. Place the wet transfer on the panel, paper side out. Adjust the transfer to match the graining on adjacent panels, and carefully remove the paper backing.

13. Sponge the transfer with clean water to remove all traces of the paper backing adhesive.

14. Remove all air bubbles and wrinkles with a squeegee.

15. Wash the transfer with clear water and dry it with a chamois.

16. Pierce any blisters or small air bubbles as they appear, and press down the area with a finger to remove the air and excess solution.

17. Allow the panel to air-dry for one hour, or heat dry (160°) for 20 minutes.

18. When the panel is dry, spray two coats of clear spar varnish over the transfer. **Do not use clear lacquer or shellac.**

PART 17-2
FRONT SHEET METAL, BUMPERS AND EXTERIOR MOULDINGS

1 IN-CAR ADJUSTMENTS AND REPAIRS

HOOD ADJUSTMENTS

The hood is provided with fore-and-aft, side-to-side, and vertical adjustments (Fig. 1). These directions

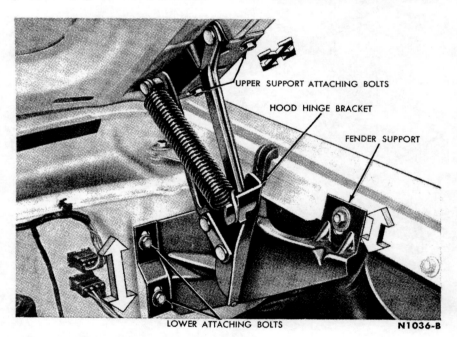

FIG. 1—Hood Hinge Adjustment—Typical

refer to the position of the hood when it is fully lowered. The elongated horizontal bolt slots in the hood hinge provide fore-and-aft adjustment. The elongated bolt slots used to attach the hood hinge bracket to the hood provide the adjustment side-to-side. Vertical adjustment is made in the elongated bolt slots provided in the hood bracket.

HOOD LOCK ADJUSTMENT —FORD

Before adjusting the hood lock mechanism, make certain that the hood is properly aligned. The hood lock can be moved from side-to-side and fore-and-aft to align it with the lock dowel.

1. Loosen the hood lock attaching bolts. Move the lock as required to align it with the lock dowel on the hood.

2. Tighten the four attaching bolts.

3. Loosen the lock nut on the hood lock dowel and turn the dowel inward to adjust the hood tighter or outward to loosen the adjustment.

4. The lock dowel is adjusted correctly when the top of the hood is flush with the fenders, when locked.

5. Tighten the dowel lock nut after adjusting the lock dowel.

HOOD LOCK ADJUSTMENT —MERCURY

Before adjusting the hood lock mechanism, make certain that the hood is properly aligned. The hood locks can be moved from side-to-side for proper alignment with the lock dowels.

1. Loosen the hood lock attaching bolts. Move them as required to align with the lock dowels. Tighten the attaching bolts.

2. Loosen the lock nut on the hood lock dowel and turn the dowel clockwise to pull the hood tighter or counterclockwise to loosen it. The proper height is when the top of the hood is flush with the fenders.

3. Tighten the dowel lock nut after the proper adjustment has been obtained.

2 REMOVAL AND INSTALLATION

HOOD HINGE

1. Prop the front of the hood in the open position and cover the fender and cowl panel.

2. Remove the hinge-to-hood retaining bolts, the retaining bolts at the fender apron and cowl (Fig. 1), and remove the hinge.

3. Position the hood hinge on the

body and install the hinge retaining bolts.

4. Adjust the hood for proper fit.

GRILLE—FORD

1. Remove the screws securing the right and left headlight doors to the headlight housing assembly.

2. Remove the bolts securing the grille to the right and left headlight housings, right and left grille brackets, and front bumper stone deflector. Remove the grille from the car (Figs. 2 and 3).

nectors, remove the grille and headlight assemblies from the car.

2. Remove the headlight doors.

3. Remove the springs retaining the headlights and headlight body assemblies to the grille and remove the headlight and body assemblies.

4. Remove the bolts, washers and nuts retaining the two sections of the grille together (Fig. 4).

5. Remove the headlight adjusting screws, retainers, the Tinnerman nuts and springs from each grille outer section.

opening and tighten the bolts and nuts.

6. For correct headlight aiming refer to Group 15. Install the headlight doors.

FRONT BUMPER

1. Remove the nuts, bolts and washers securing the front bumper inner and outer arm to the frame.

2. Remove the bumper from the car and lay it on a bench.

3. Transfer the inner and outer arms to the new bumper (Fig. 5).

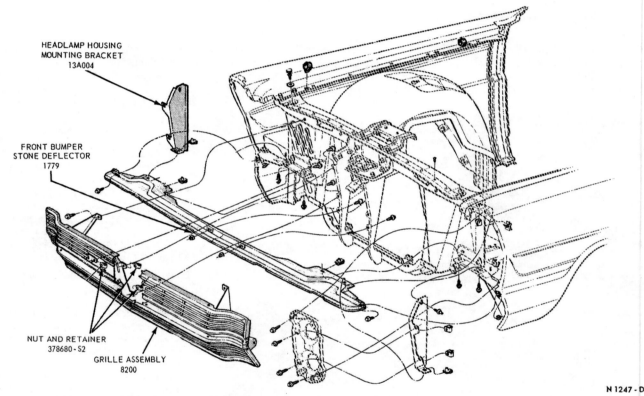

HEADLAMP HOUSING MOUNTING BRACKET 13A004

FRONT BUMPER STONE DEFLECTOR 1779

NUT AND RETAINER 378680-S2

GRILLE ASSEMBLY 8200

N 1247-D

FIG. 2—Grille Installation—Ford (Base Series)

3. Transfer the clips from the old grille to the new grille.

4. Place the new grille into position and start the bolts into their respective locations until they are finger tight.

5. Using a suitable tool, tighten each bolt securing the grille to the car and install the right and left headlight doors.

GRILLE—MERCURY

REMOVAL

1. Remove both front fender front extension assemblies (Fig. 4). Remove the seven bolts and two nuts retaining the grille to its brackets. Disconnect the headlight wiring con-

INSTALLATION

1. Install the headlight adjusting screws, retainers, Tinnerman nuts and springs in each new outer grille section.

2. Position the two grille sections together and install the retaining bolts, washers and nuts.

3. Install the headlight and body assemblies in the grille sections and connect the retaining springs.

4. Position the grille and headlight assembly on the car and connect the headlight wiring connectors.

5. Loosely install the seven bolts and two nuts retaining the grille. Align the grille assembly in the grille

Tighten the mounting bolts finger tight.

4. Transfer the license plate and front bumper lower extension as an assembly to the new bumper.

5. Transfer the rubber bumper located behind the license plate to the new bumper.

6. Place the new bumper assembly into is respective mounting position and install it to the frame using the original bolts, washers, and nuts. Tighten the mounting bolts finger tight.

7. Adjust the bumper assembly in moving it up or down or by adding shims beneath the outer arms. Tighten all mounting bolts.

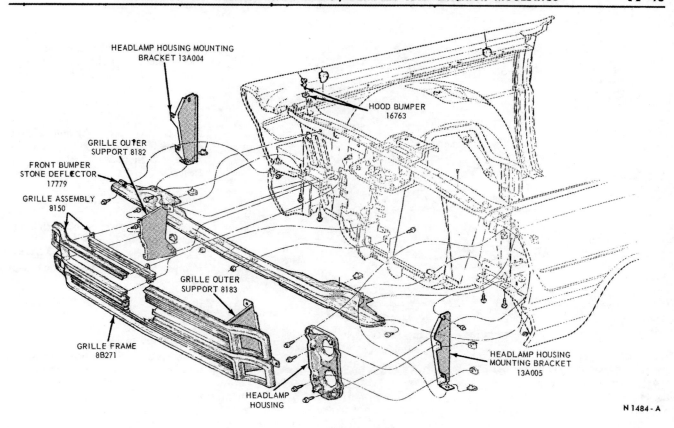

N 1484 - A

FIG. 3—Grille Installation—Ford (High Series)

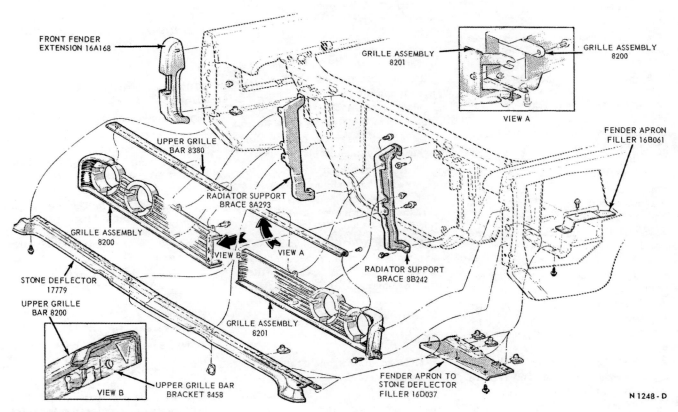

N 1248 - D

FIG. 4—Grille Installation—Mercury

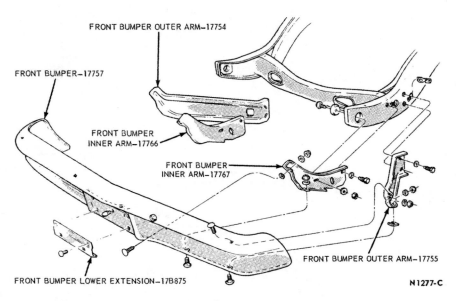

FRONT BUMPER OUTER ARM—17754

FRONT BUMPER—17757

FRONT BUMPER INNER ARM—17766

FRONT BUMPER INNER ARM—17767

FRONT BUMPER OUTER ARM—17755

FRONT BUMPER LOWER EXTENSION—17B875

N 1277-C

FIG. 5—Front Bumper Installation—Typical

REAR BUMPER IMPACT BAR AND/OR IMPACT BAR EXTENSIONS—MERCURY

REMOVAL

1. Disconnect the right and left taillight and backup light wires inside the luggage compartment. Push the wires and grommets out through the back panel.

2. Disconnect the license plate wire. Push the wire and the grommet out through the back panel.

3. Remove the right and left taillight assemblies to provide access to the outer bumper-to-body retaining bolts.

4. Remove the right and left outer bumper-to-body bolts, working from inside the outer bumper.

5. Raise the vehicle on a hoist and remove the nuts, bolts, and washers securing the bumper outer and inner bumper arms to the frame. Remove the rear bumper and place it on a bench (Fig. 6).

6. Remove the license plate.

7. Remove the end arms from the old bumper.

8. Remove the right and left bar extensions from each end of the bumper. **One outer bumper arm is attached to each bar extension.**

9. Remove the right and left back-up light assemblies and remove the arm from each bar extension.

10. Remove the reinforcement impact bar as an assembly.

INSTALLATION

1. Install the inner arm and reinforcement bar to the new bumper.

2. Install the right and left backup light assemblies to the bumper.

3. Install the right and left bar extensions to the bumper and install the right and left outer arms to the bar extensions.

4. Install the right and left bumper end arms.

5. Install the license plate and place the rear bumper in its respective mounting position. Snug the bumper outer and inner arm bolts and nuts to the frame of the car.

6. Adjust the rear bumper and tighten all retaining nuts and bolts.

7. Lower the hoist and install the right and left taillight assemblies. Connect the taillight wires and insert the wire grommets into the back panel.

8. Route the license plate light wire into the back panel and connect it to the light assembly. Insert the grommet into the back panel.

REAR BUMPER—FORD

REMOVAL

1. Open the luggage compartment and disconnect the license light wire.

2. Remove the four nuts retaining the bumper and arms to the frame side rails (Fig. 7).

3. Place a stand under one end of the bumper to hold the bumper in place and tap out the bumper arm-to-frame side rail bolts.

4. Remove the bumper assembly and place it on a bench.

5. Remove the right and left outer arm-to-bumper retaining bolts and remove the left and right outer arms (Fig. 7).

6. Remove the inner arms and reinforcement bar retaining bolts and remove the inner arms and reinforcement as an assembly (includes the license light).

7. Remove the license plate and bumper lower extension as an assembly.

INSTALLATION

1. Install the license plate and bumper lower extension.

2. Position the reinforcement bar and bumper inner arms to the bumper impact bar and install the retaining bolts.

3. Install the left and right outer arms on the bumper impact bar.

4. With the aid of an assistant, position the bumper assembly to the car. Install and tighten the bumper arm-to-frame side rail retaining bolts, washers and nuts.

5. Route the license light wire through the lower back panel and connect it to the wiring connector.

STATION WAGON REAR BUMPER—FORD

1. Remove the license plate and bumper lower extension.

2. Remove the bolts, spring washers, and nuts securing the rear bumper and foot pads to the bumper arms.

3. Transfer the rubber foot pads, license plate and rubber bumper to the new bumper. Use caulking to hold the spring washers on the bumper arms.

4. Install the rear bumper using the old nuts and bolts.

EXTERIOR MOULDINGS REMOVAL AND INSTALLATION

Before removing exterior mouldings, it should be determined by the type of retainer used whether a respective door, quarter or luggage compartment trim panel must first be removed to provide access. Refer to Figures 8 through 19.

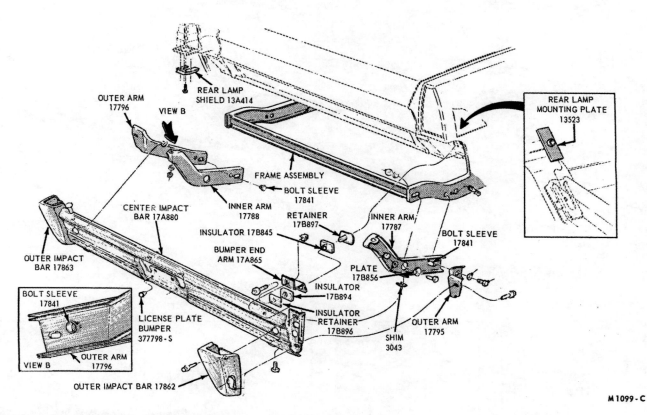

FIG. 6—Rear Bumper Installation—Mercury

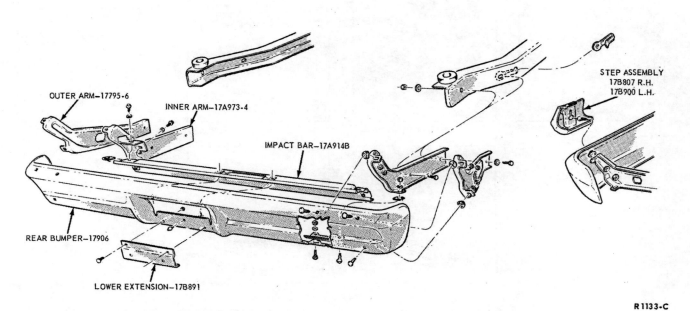

FIG. 7—Rear Bumper Installation—Ford

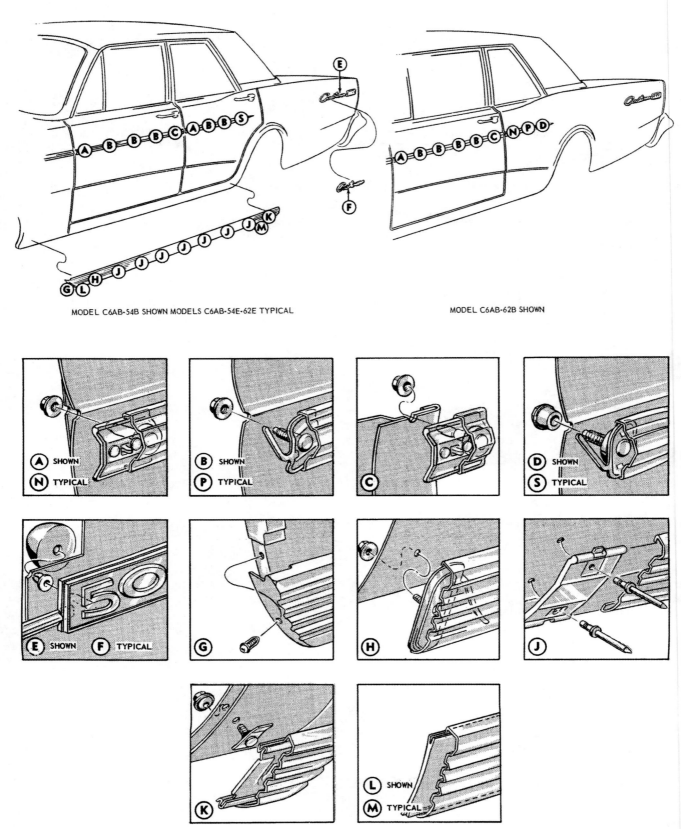

MODEL C6AB-54B SHOWN MODELS C6AB-54E-62E TYPICAL   MODEL C6AB-62B SHOWN

N 1332-C

FIG. 8—Exterior Mouldings—Ford Models 54B, 54E, 62B, 62E

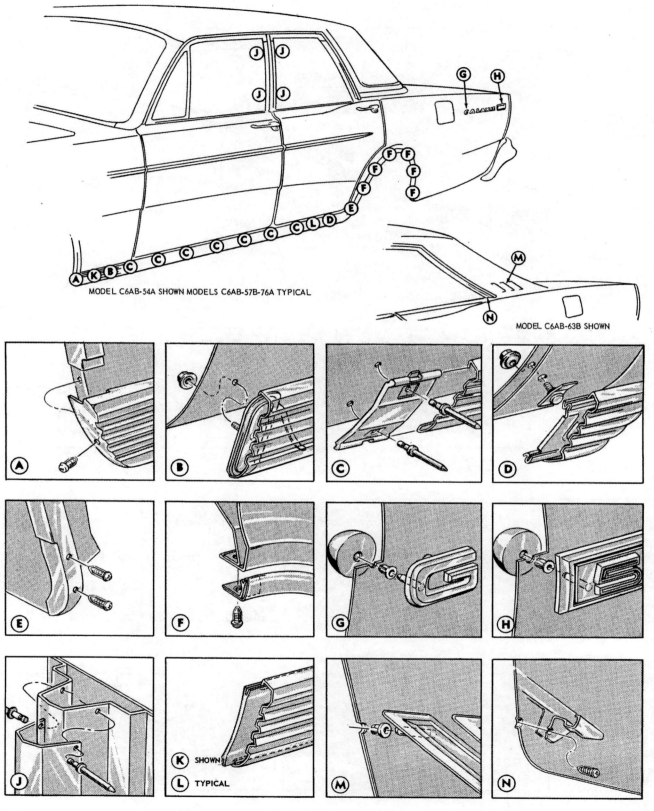

MODEL C6AB-54A SHOWN   MODELS C6AB-57B-76A TYPICAL

MODEL C6AB-63B SHOWN

N 1333-C

FIG. 9—Exterior Mouldings—Ford Models 54A, 57B, 63B, 76A

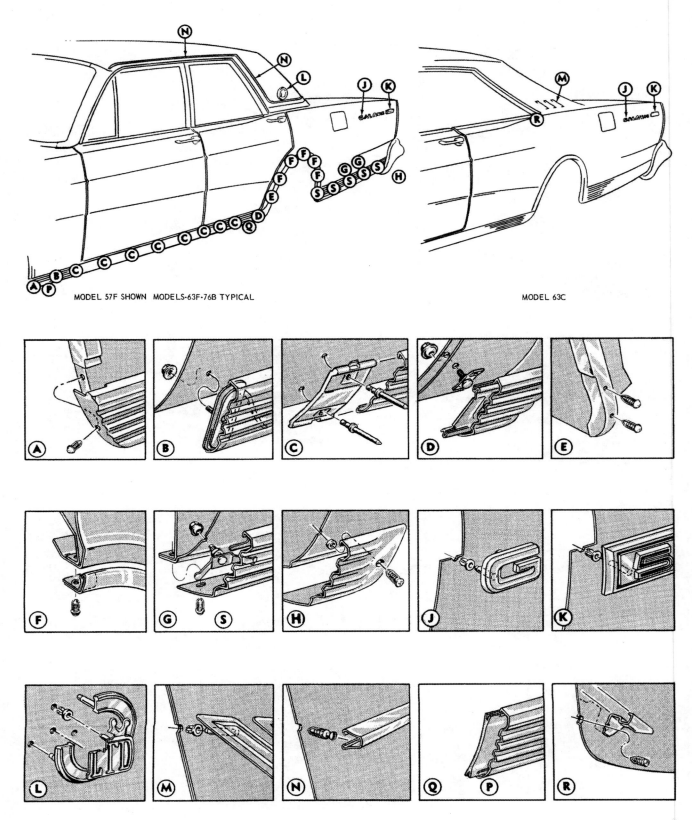

FIG. 10—Exterior Mouldings—Ford Models 57F, 63C, 63F, 76B

N 1334-C

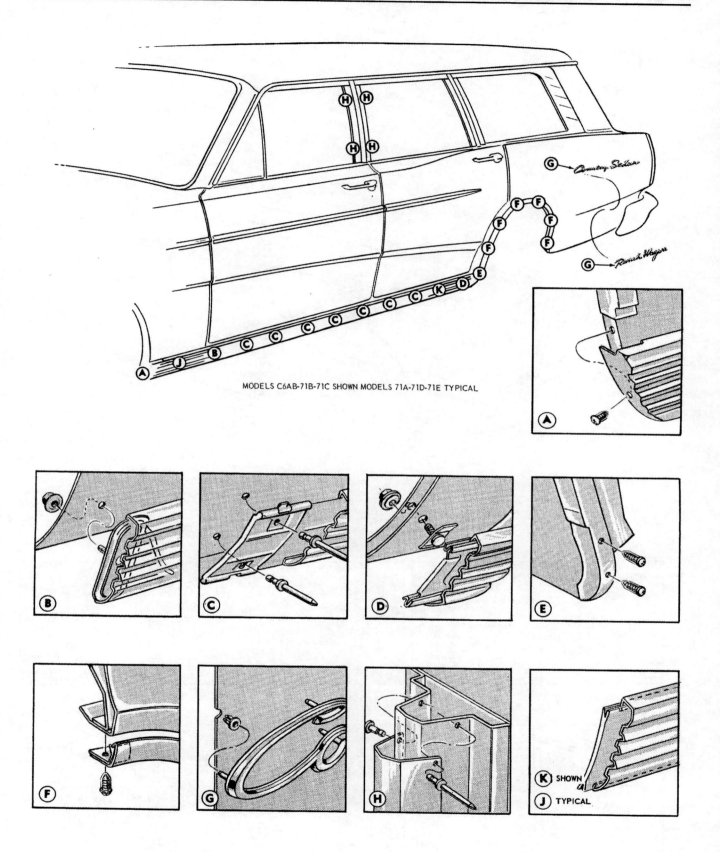

MODELS C6AB-71B-71C SHOWN MODELS 71A-71D-71E TYPICAL

N 1335-C

FIG. 11—Exterior Mouldings—Ford Models 71A, 71B, 71C, 71E

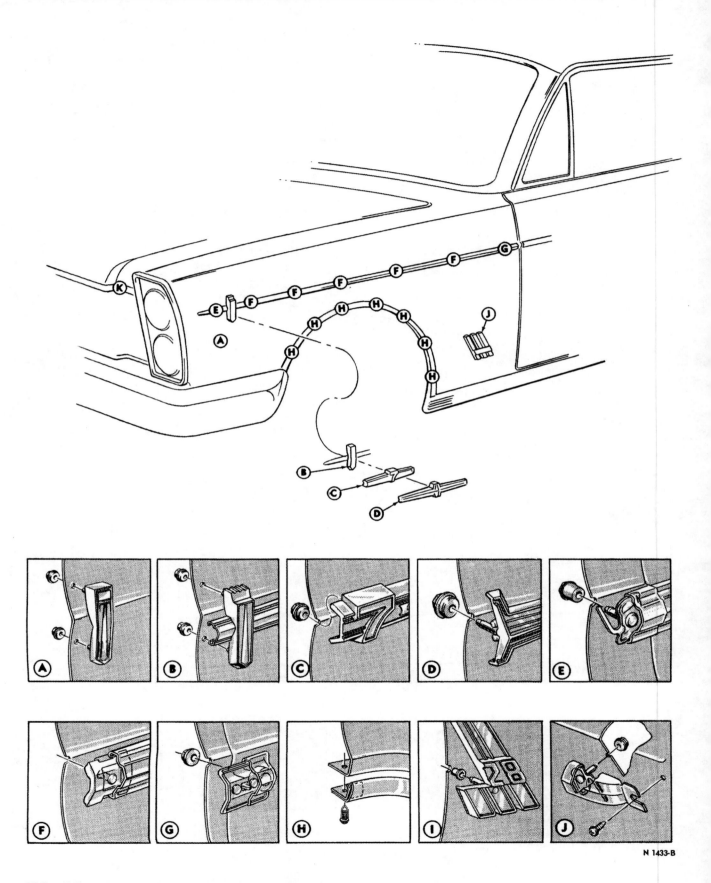

N 1433-B

FIG. 12—Exterior Front Mouldings—Ford Models

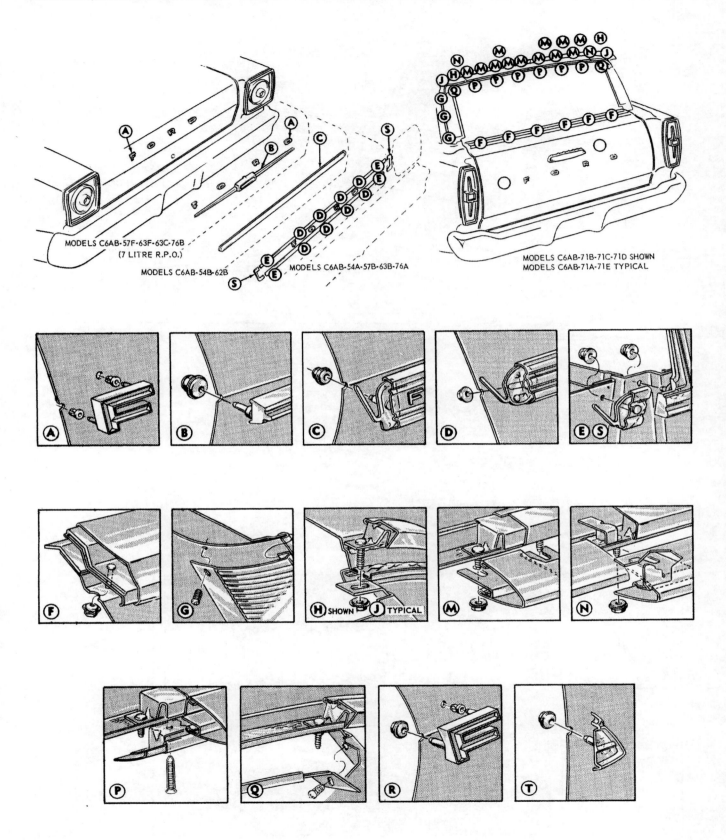

MODELS C6AB-57F-63F-63C-76B
(7 LITRE R.P.O.)

MODELS C6AB-54B-62B

MODELS C6AB-54A-57B-63B-76A

MODELS C6AB-71B-71C-71D SHOWN
MODELS C6AB-71A-71E TYPICAL

N 1336-C

FIG. 13—Exterior Rear Mouldings—Ford Models (ALL)

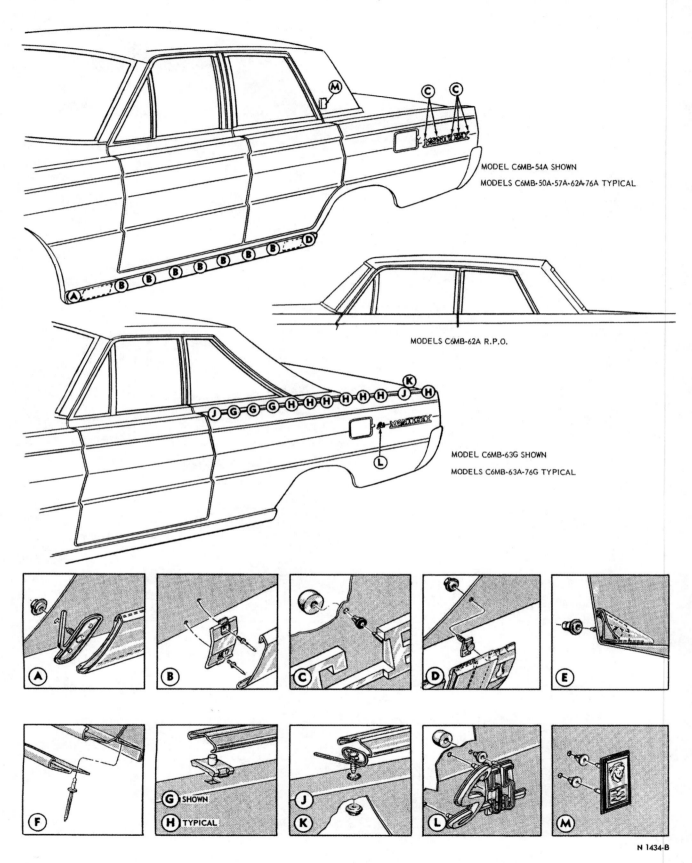

MODEL C6MB-54A SHOWN

MODELS C6MB-50A-57A-62A-76A TYPICAL

MODELS C6MB-62A R.P.O.

MODEL C6MB-63G SHOWN

MODELS C6MB-63A-76G TYPICAL

G SHOWN

H TYPICAL

N 1434-B

FIG. 14—Exterior Mouldings—Mercury Models 50A, 54A, 57A, 62A, 63A, 63G, 76A, 76G

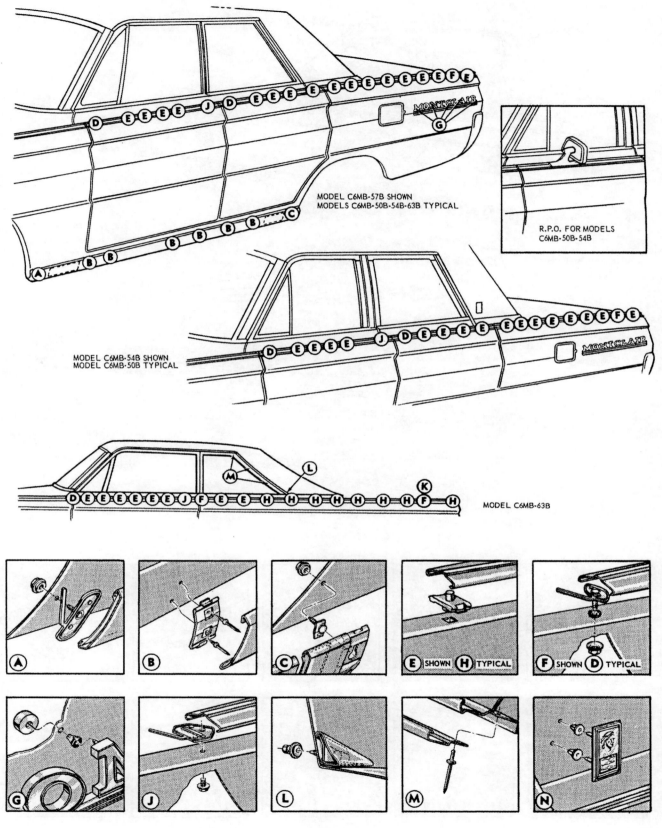

N 1435-B

FIG. 15—Exterior Mouldings—Mercury Models 50B, 54B, 57B, 63B

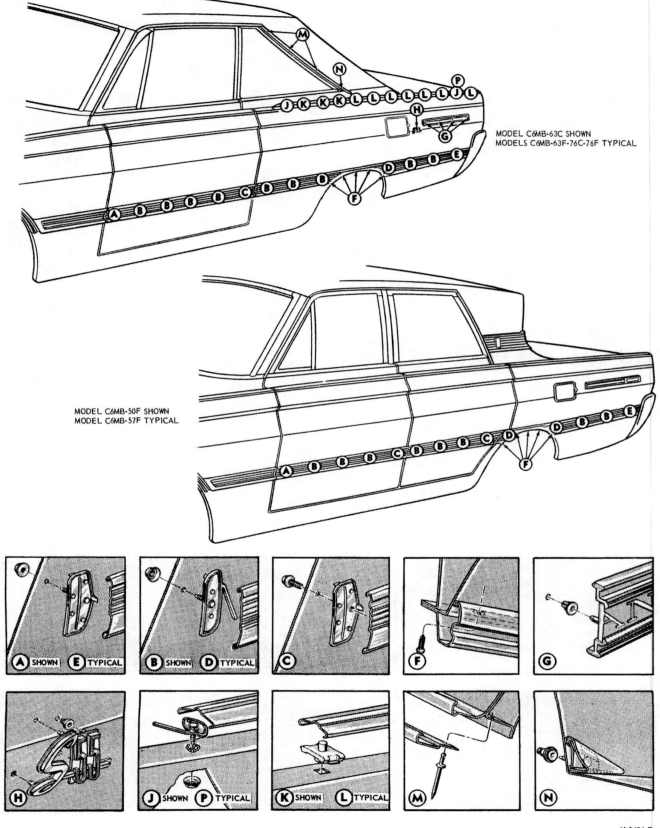

FIG. 16—Exterior Mouldings—Mercury Models 50F, 57F, 63C, 63F, 76C, 76F

N 1436-B

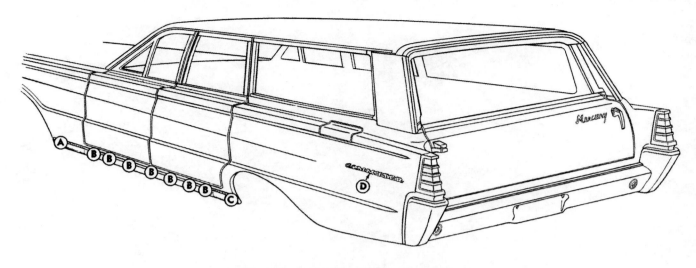

MODELS C6MB-71B-71C SHOWN   MODELS C6MB-71A-71E TYPICAL

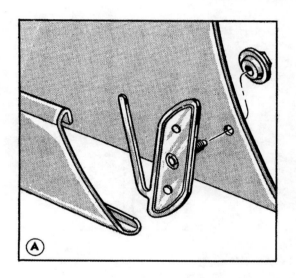

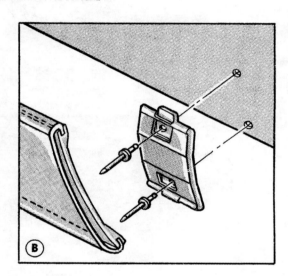

N 1437-B

FIG. 17—Exterior Mouldings—Mercury Model 71

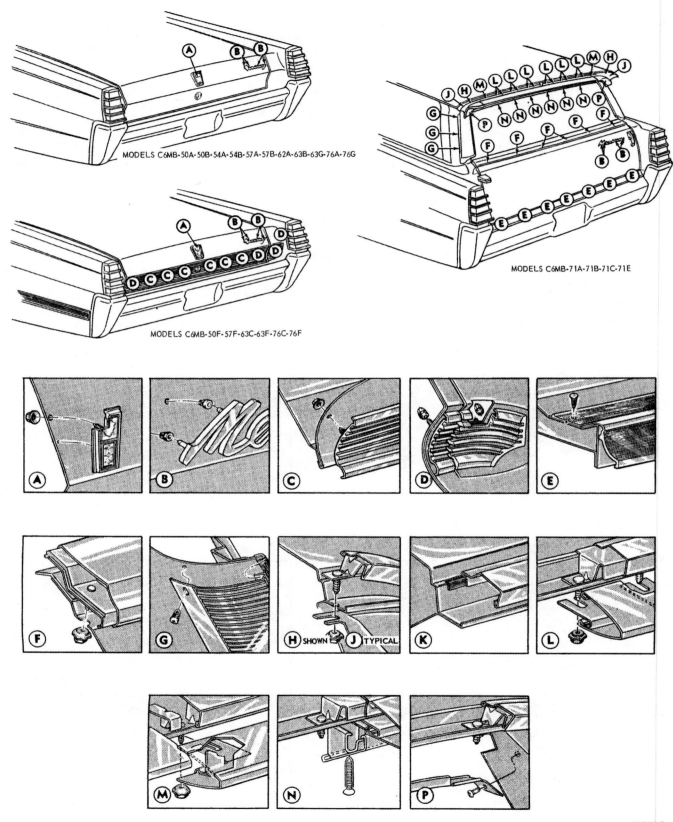

MODELS C6MB-50A-50B-54A-54B-57A-57B-62A-63B-63G-76A-76G

MODELS C6MB-50F-57F-63C-63F-76C-76F

MODELS C6MB-71A-71B-71C-71E

N 1438-B

FIG. 18—Exterior Rear Mouldings—Mercury Models (ALL)

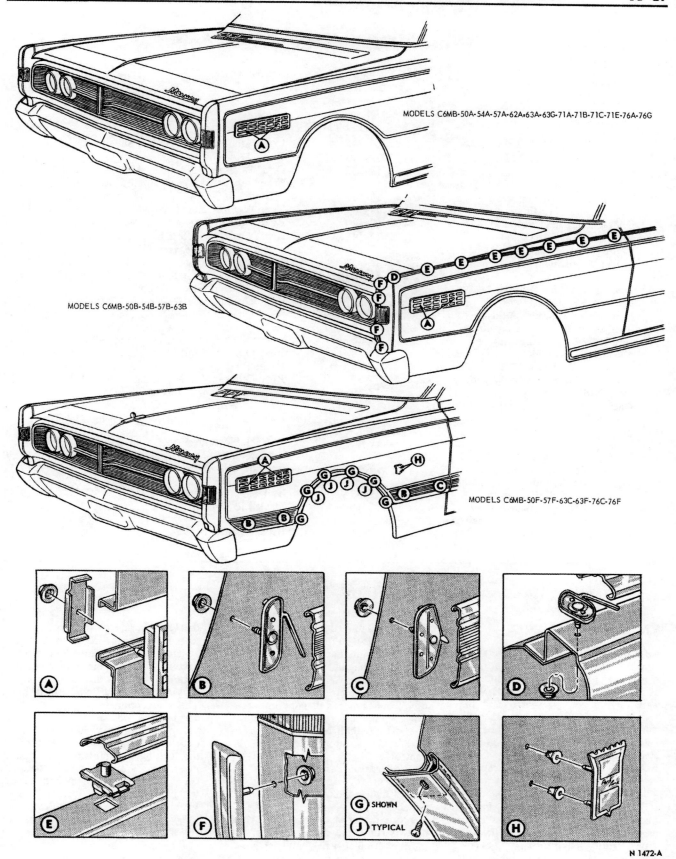

MODELS C6MB-50A-54A-57A-62A-63A-63G-71A-71B-71C-71E-76A-76G

MODELS C6MB-50B-54B-57B-63B

MODELS C6MB-50F-57F-63C-63F-76C-76F

N 1472-A

FIG. 19—Exterior Front Mouldings—Mercury Models (ALL)

PART 17-3 DOORS, WINDOWS, TAILGATE AND DECK LID

1 DESCRIPTION AND OPERATION

VACUUM DOOR LOCKS

The system is composed of vacuum hoses which connect the functioning elements of the system, a reservoir assembly, a control valve assembly, a control switch and the locking mechanism actuators. All vacuum hoses are black, rubber or nylon; but are identified by a colored stripe. Hereafter, the hoses will be indicated by the color of the stripe. A hose not designated by a color will be black.

Vacuum from the engine intake manifold is routed to the reservoir assembly which is located in the left front fender cavity. The reservoir contains a one-way valve which will hold vacuum for approximately 4 complete cycles of operation with the engine not running (Fig. 14).

From the reservoir, a green vacuum hose runs back along the fender, across the dash to a hole where it enters the driver compartment under the instrument panel. This green hose connects to and supplies vacuum to the control valve assembly. A red hose then connects the vacuum from the control valve to the control switch.

The control switch is located on the instrument panel or on the Safety and Convenience Package control panel.

From the control switch, a white hose is routed to the unlocking side of the control valve and a green hose is routed to the locking side of the control valve. On two-door models, an orange hose is routed from the locking side of the control valve to the unlocking side of the actuator at each door. On four-door models, vacuum for the rear door control is obtained by inserting a tee connection into the front door control hose. This connection is made in the hose at the cowl side area.

In the door, a vacuum controlled door locking actuator is attached to the locking mechanism bellcrank. A green hose is also connected between the lock side of the switch to the locking side of the control valve. From the control valve, yellow hoses are routed to each door of the car following the same routing as the orange hose. The yellow hose is attached to the locking side of the vacuum controlled door locking actuator.

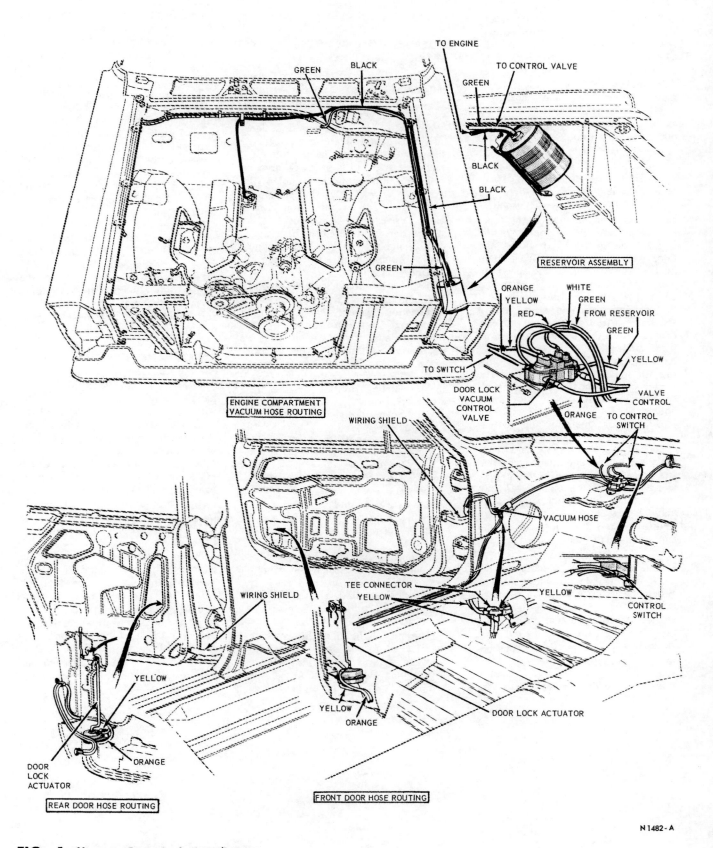

FIG. 1—Vacuum Door Lock Installation

ROLLING DOOR LOCKS

The rolling door lock is an accessory safety item which automatically locks the rear doors of the vehicle when a speed of approximately 8 to 10 mph is reached. The doors remain locked until the vehicle speed drops below the valve actuating speed, at which time they may be manually unlocked by raising the inside door lock knob.

The system is vacuum actuated and controlled by a valve which is operated by the transmission speedometer cable drive (Fig. 2).

The rolling door locks system is composed of a vacuum hose which is routed from the engine down the engine side of the dash under the floor pan to a control valve located on the transmission at the speedometer cable connection. The valve is connected into the transmission and the speedometer cable is attached to the valve. Another vacuum hose is routed from the control valve forward under the floor pan, up the dash and through the dash to a venting tee located on the dash at the center behind the instrument panel, to two vacuum hoses. One hose routes to each rear door vacuum lock actuator assembly. The actuator is connected to the rear door lock bell crank assembly and locks the door when vacuum is applied to the actuator. The venting tee is necessary to allow the air to leak into the vacuum hose after the control valve closes, thus releasing the actuator so that the lock mechanism can be manually actuated.

Vacuum from the engine is controlled by a valve attached to the transmission speedometer drive. When the vehicle reaches a speed of 8 to 10 mph the valve opens and the vacuum then actuates the locking mechanism on the rear doors.

When the vehicle speed drops below the control valve operating speed, the valve closes and vacuum is released from the locking mechanism through the venting tee. The doors can then be unlocked manually.

DUAL ACTION STATION WAGON TAILGATE

The dual action design allows the tailgate to be lowered in the normal manner to a horizontal dropgate position as an extension to the floor cargo area. The dual action design also allows the tailgate to be opened sideways as a door, to provide direct access to the floor cargo area.

To accomplish the dual action of the tailgate assembly, the principal components are an upper and lower hinge, upper and lower locks and strikers, an inside lift type handle to control the assembly as a drop gate and an outside handle to control the assembly as a door.

The lower hinge, located on the left hand side of the vehicle, is a dual action assembly having a horizontal and a vertical pivot pin. When the tailgate is moved to or from a horizontal position, it pivots on the horizontal pin of the lower hinge; and at the same time the lower lock, in the latched position around the striker pin, functions as a hinge and pivot point on the right hand side of the vehicle.

The upper hinge, located on the left hand side of the vehicle, is designed in two separated parts and performs two functions. It functions as a hinge when the tailgate is operated as a door and as a lock when the tailgate is in a fully closed position. A spring loaded latch located in the hinge-on-gate part of the upper hinge, secures the two parts of the hinge together when the tailgate is operated as a door or in the fully closed position, and releases the two parts when the tailgate is operated as a dropgate.

The part of the upper hinge which is attached to the body pillar contains a vertical pivot pin with a rectangular extension on top of the pin. The part of the upper hinge which is attached to the gate is slotted on the underside to accept the rectangular extension of the pivot pin. When the tailgate is operated as a door, it pivots on the upper hinge pivot pin and the vertical pivot pin of the lower hinge.

To open the tailgate to a horizontal position, roll the window to the full down position and lift up on the inside handle. This will disengage the upper lock from the striker pin and the latch from the upper hinge pivot extension allowing the tailgate to pivot on the lower hinge horizontal pivot pin and the lower lock striker pin.

To open the tailgate as a door, roll the window to the full down position and turn the outside handle clockwise. This will disengage both the upper and lower locks from the striker pins allowing the tailgate to pivot on the upper hinge pivot pin and the lower hinge vertical pivot pin.

SAFETY AND CONVENIENCE FEATURES

1. Neither the inside nor outside handle can be actuated unless the window is in the full down position.

2. The inside handle will not actuate when the tailgate is open or being opened as a door.

3. The outside handle will not actuate when the tailgate is open or being opened as a dropgate.

4. A pop-open assist, located in the upper lock assembly, functions when the tailgate is being opened in either direction.

5. The lower hinge assembly incorporates a door check to provide a hold-open feature when the tailgate is operated as a door.

6. A tailgate check cable is provided for stabilization when the tailgate is lowered to the horizontal position.

7. A torsion rod is utilized to assist in lifting the tailgate from the horizontal position.

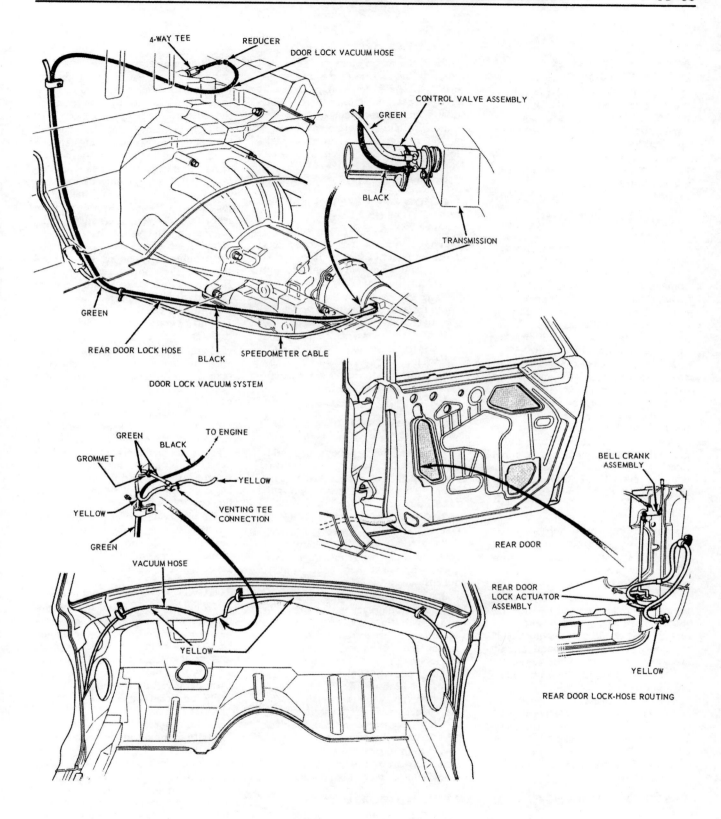

FIG. 2—Rolling Door Lock Installation

2 DIAGNOSIS AND TESTING

DOOR AND QUARTER POWER WINDOWS

Before making any of the following trouble checks, make sure that the battery is fully charged, and turn the ignition switch to the accessory position.

Refer to Wiring Diagram Manual Form 7795P-66 for locations of wiring harnesses. Schematics are shown in Group 22 of this manual.

ALL WINDOWS DO NOT OPERATE

1. Connect a voltmeter or test light from a ground to the power window relay black wire which is connected to the 20-ampere circuit breaker attached to the battery terminal of the starting motor relay. If no voltage is available, repair or replace the 20-ampere circuit breaker or the connecting black wire.

2. Connect a voltmeter from a ground to the red wire terminal of the power window relay. If no voltage is available, repair or replace the ignition switch or the red wire from the ignition switch to the relay.

3. Connect a voltmeter from a ground to the remaining terminal (black-white wire) of the power window relay. If no voltage is available, replace the power window relay.

4. Check the black-white wire at the master control switch for voltage. If no voltage is available, repair or replace the black-white wire from the master control switch to the power window relay.

5. At this point the trouble causing all windows not to operate should have been found and corrected. The chances of having all of the control switches, ground circuit breakers, switch to motor wires, or motors defective at the same time are very remote.

The power window, power seat, and convertible top electrical systems are connected through the same 20-ampere circuit breaker. If failure occurs in all the systems at the same time, the 20-ampere circuit breaker is probably defective.

ONE WINDOW DOES NOT OPERATE

1. Activate the switch and listen for the motor running free. If the motor runs and the window does not move, the rubber coupling or gear teeth have failed.

2. If the motor does not run, disconnect the wires at the motor in order to check for voltage at each feed wire while actuating the window switch at the door or from the master switch. If there is no voltage at the motor feed terminals, check for voltage at the switch feed wire. If there is voltage at the switch, replace the switch.

WINDOW OPERATES IN ONE DIRECTION ONLY

1. Check the operation with the individual and master switches. Replace a defective switch if the window operates normally from one and not from the other.

2. If the window will not function correctly from either switch, check for defective wiring between the switch disconnects and the motor. If the wiring leads are open, replace the wiring.

3. If the window operates normally in one direction, the motor is not defective.

WINDOW OPERATES SLUGGISHLY

1. Check the regulator and window runs for binding. Adjust the runs, repair and lubricate the regulator. Lubricate the runs with silicone lubricant.

2. Check for frayed insulation where the window wires may partially ground. Check for loose connections which will cause high resistance, and make sure that paint is not insulating the ground wires.

3. Check motor current draw during operation (place an ammeter in series with the ground lead of the battery). Motor current draw should not exceed 12 amperes during normal operation and should exceed 20 amperes at stall. If the current draw is above 12 amperes during operation of the window, readjust the glass mechanism. If the stall current is below 20 amperes at stall, look for poor electrical connections.

4. Motor current draw when disconnected from the regulator plate should not exceed 5 amperes.

VACUUM DOOR LOCKS

Problems in the system may develop in the following areas:
Hoses and connections
Reservoir and check valve
Control switch
Control valve

Actuator assemblies

Leaks in the hoses or a disconnection can usually be discovered by listening for a hissing sound along the hose routings.

Door actuators may be checked by connecting a hose between the reservoir and the hose at the control valve. Remove the orange and yellow hoses from the side of the control valve which controls the actuator being checked. Apply vacuum from the reservoir alternately to the orange and the yellow hoses. If the actuator locks and unlocks properly, the trouble may be in the control valve or the control switch system. If the actuator does not operate properly, the hose system and actuator must be checked. If the actuator fails to operate properly, it must be replaced.

If the system from the control valve to the door lock actuators is operating properly, the control valve can be checked by removing the control switch hoses from the control valve. Then, alternately connect the red connector on the valve to the white and green connections. If the systems do not operate, the valve is defective. Replace the valve. If the systems operate properly, the trouble is in the control switch. Replace the control switch.

These service operations are based on the premise that the hoses are not kinked, do not leak, and are properly connected to the appropriate connector.

ROLLING DOOR LOCKS

Trouble in the system will be noticeable in two ways. First, the doors will not lock and second, the engine will have a tendency to be rough at low speeds. Causes for malfunction are:
Inoperative control valve
Disconnected hoses
Kinked hoses
Leaking hoses
Malfunctioning door lock actuator
Binding door lock mechanism

If the doors do not lock automatically, manually check the locking mechanism to determine if it is operating satisfactorily. Adjust or repair any malfunction of the locking linkage.

A disconnected or leaking hose can be detected by a hissing noise. With the engine idling, listen for vacuum leaks at the connections. A leak at any point in the system will cause malfunction.

An inoperative valve can be detected with the rear wheels raised so that they are free to turn. Check for vacuum at the control valve and

then check for valve operation as the speed is increased to 10 mph. If the valve does not operate properly, replace the valve.

If all other parts of the system are operating properly and there is vac-

uum at the actuator assembly but the actuator does not operate, the actuator is defective. Replace the actuator. The door trim panel must be removed to make the actuator accessible.

3 IN-CAR ADJUSTMENTS AND REPAIRS

FRONT DOOR HINGE REPLACEMENT AND/OR ADJUSTMENT

REMOVAL

1. Remove the lower front fender to rocker panel retaining bolt and lower fender to cowl panel retaining bolts.

2. Remove the hood rear bumper

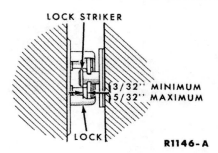

FIG. 3—Door Lock Striker Adjustment

assembly and the hood hinge bracket to fender retaining bolts.

3. Remove the fender to cowl retaining bolt located in the hinge area.

4. If the front hinges are being replaced, brace the door so that it will not fall when the hinge bolts are removed.

5. Mark the present hinge location on the pillar and on the door face. Remove the hinge-to-door bolts.

6. Pull the fender away from the body and block it in place.

7. Remove the hinge-to-body bolts and remove the hinge.

INSTALLATION

1. Install the new hinge and hinge-to-body bolts. Align the hinge with the old hinge locating marks located on the front body pillar and on the door face.

2. Align the door and tighten the hinge-to-door bolts. Remove the braces from the door.

3. Install the fender retaining bolts which secure the fender to the cowl.

4. Install the hood hinge bracket to the fender and install the hood bumper.

5. Install the lower front fender-to-rocker panel retaining bolts.

DOOR ALIGNMENT PROCEDURE

1. Determine which hinge bolts must be loosened to move the door in the desired direction.

2. Loosen the hinge bolts enough to permit movement of the door with a **padded** pry bar.

3. Move the door the distance estimated to be necessary.

4. Tighten the hinge bolts and check the door fit.

5. Repeat the operation until the desired fit is obtained. Then check the alignment between the lock rotor and striker plate for proper door closing. The door locking mechanism consists of the door lock and rotor, lock cylinder, inside and outside handles, striker plate, and the linkage connecting these parts. Improperly aligned doors cause the major portion of lock failures by putting excessive strain on the striker plate and rotor. **Do not attempt to correct door misalignment with a striker plate adjustment.**

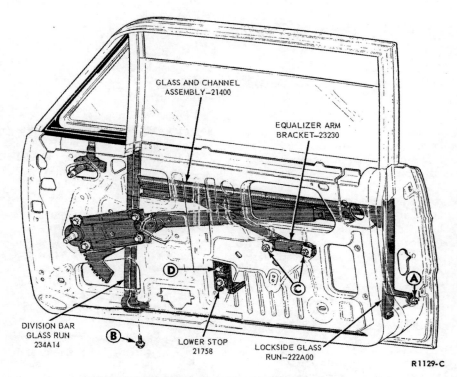

FIG. 4—Front Door Window Models 50, 54, 62 and 71

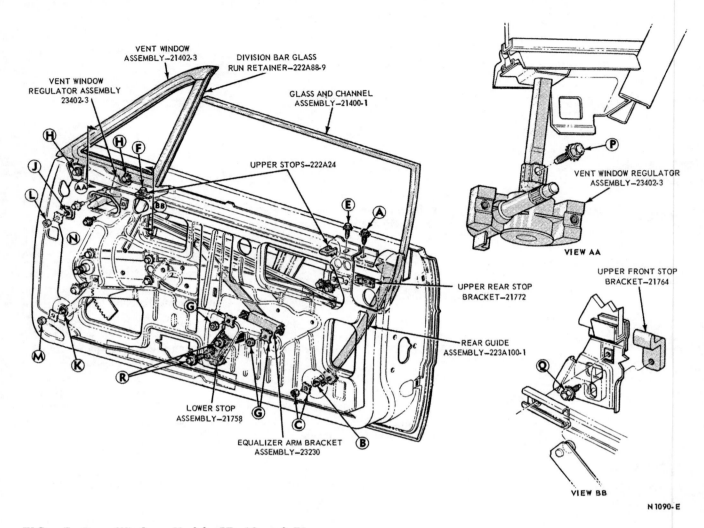

FIG. 5—Door Window—Models 57, 63 and 76

LOCK STRIKER ADJUSTMENT

The striker pin can be adjusted laterally and vertically as well as fore and aft. **The lock striker should not be adjusted to correct door sag.** The lock striker should be shimmed to get the clearance shown in Fig. 3 between the lock striker and the lock. To check this clearance, clean the lock jaws and the striker area, and then apply a thin layer of dark grease to the lock striker. As the door is closed and opened, a measurable pattern will result. Move the striker assembly laterally to provide a flush fit at the door and the pillar or quarter panel.

FRONT DOOR WINDOW ADJUSTMENT—MODELS 50, 54, 62, 71

1. Remove the door trim panel and peel back the watershield to provide access.

2. To properly align the run and retainer assemblies with the door window frame and vent window division bar so that the window does not bind, yet maintain a snug fit, loosen the screw and washer assemblies A and B and nuts C (Fig. 4).

3. Lower the window so that the top of the glass is approximately four inches above the belt line, thus permitting the assemblies to seat.

4. Tighten the screw and washer assemblies A, B and C (Fig. 4).

5. Adjust the lower stop up or down by loosening the screw and washer D, in order to obtain a flush condition between the top edge of the glass and channel assembly and the belt line, when the window is in the down position. After the adjustment, tighten the screw and washer D.

DOOR WINDOW ADJUSTMENTS—MODELS 57, 63, 76

1. Remove the door trim panel and peel back the watershield to provide access.

2. Temporarily loosen all attaching screws and nuts (Fig. 5).

3. Cycle the window to its up position and manually position the window assembly inboard or outboard as required for proper alignment to the outside belt weatherstrip. Then, tighten the screw and washer assembly A (Fig. 5).

4. To obtain a parallel relation-

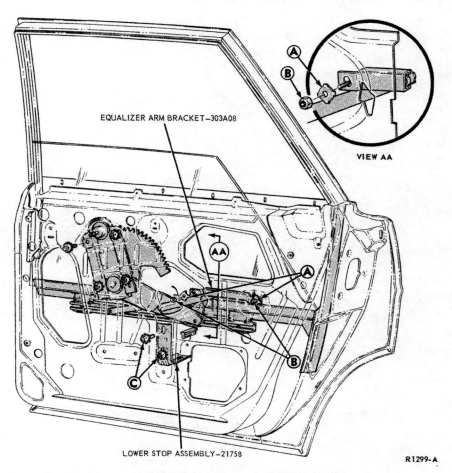

EQUALIZER ARM BRACKET—303A08

VIEW AA

LOWER STOP ASSEMBLY—21758

R1299-A

FIG. 6—Rear Door Window—Models 50, 54 and 71

ship between the top of the window and the roof rail weatherstrip, tilt the window fore or aft as required. This also properly positions the rear guide assembly (Fig. 5). Tighten nut C temporarily.

5. Adjust the upper stops inboard or outboard as required and the upper stop brackets as necessary to maintain equal engagement with the window channel. Then, tighten the screw and washer assemblies D, Q, E, and F securely (Fig. 5).

6. Position the equalizer arm bracket down snugly against the regulator roller. Then tighten the nuts and washers G (Fig. 5) securely.

7. VENT WINDOW: To align the vent window and division bar glass run with the door window assembly and maintain a parallel relationship of the vent assembly and the front body pillar, tilt the vent as-

sembly fore or aft as required. Tighten the screw and washer assemblies H securely. **Be careful not to create a binding condition between the door window glass and the vent window division bar glass run.**

8. To provide a seal (interference fit) between the door window and vent assembly and the roof rail weatherstrip, tilt the window assembly inboard or outboard as required by turning screws B, J and K clockwise or counterclockwise as necessary. Then, tighten locknuts C, L and M securely.

9. Secure the vent window regulator assembly by tightening the screw and washer assemblies N. Tighten the vent window regulator-to-shaft coupling retaining screw P.

10. Cycle the door window to the down position. Adjust the lower stop so that the top of the window is flush

with the belt line and then tighten the lower stop retaining screw and washer assemblies R.

REAR DOOR WINDOW ADJUSTMENT—MODELS 50, 54, 71

1. Remove the door trim panel and peel back the watershield to provide access.

2. With the window fully raised, position the equalizer arm bracket (Fig. 6) at the mid-point of the slotted holes. Tighten the nuts and washers B and A securely.

3. Position the lower stop assembly (Fig. 6) at the bottom of the slotted hole. Tighten the screw and washer assemblies C.

REAR DOOR WINDOW ADJUSTMENT—MODEL 57

1. Remove the door trim panel and peel back the watershield to provide access.

2. Temporarily loosen all attaching screws and nuts (Fig. 7).

3. Tilt the window assembly fore or aft as necessary for parallel alignment with the front door window and the roof rail. Then, tighten the screw and washer assemblies D to secure the window guide panel.

4. Position the front and rear upper stops against the stop brackets and tighten the screw and washer assemblies A, B and C (Fig. 7).

5. Press the window regulator bracket assembly down firmly against the regulator roller and tighten the nuts and washers H and J.

6. Tighten the guide adjusting bracket-to-window guide screw and washer assemblies E.

7. Tilt the window guide panel (Fig. 7) inboard or outboard as required to obtain a good seal between the front and rear door windows and to obtain an interference fit with the roof side rail weatherstrip. Tighten the guide adjusting bracket screw and washer assemblies F.

8. Cycle the window to its down position and adjust the lower stop so that the top of the window is flush with the belt line. Tighten the lower stop retaining screws and washer assemblies G.

9. Raise and lower the window assembly several times to be sure that it maintains proper adjustment. Then, install the watershield and door trim panel.

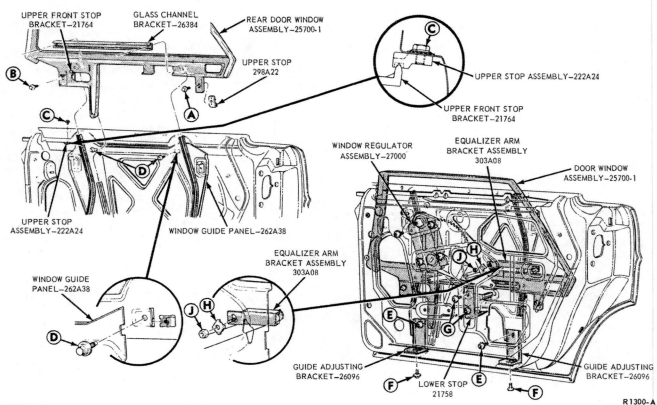

FIG. 7—Rear Door Window—Model 57

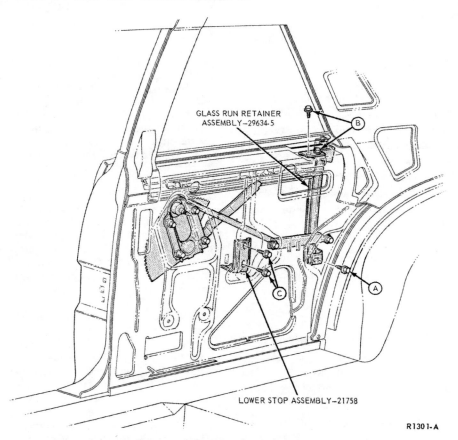

FIG. 8—Quarter Window Adjustment—Model 62

QUARTER WINDOW ADJUSTMENTS—MODEL 62

1. Remove the quarter trim panel and watershield.

2. Lower the window to its full down position. Loosen the lower run retainer retaining screw A (Fig. 8). Move the run retainer against the window and tighten the screw and washer A, finger-tight.

3. Raise the window to its full up position. Loosen the screw and washer assemblies B (Fig. 8). Move the upper portion of the run retainer assembly against the window glass. Then, tighten the screw and washer assemblies A and B (Fig. 8).

4. With the window in the full down position, loosen the lower stop retaining screw and washer assemblies C (Fig. 8). Adjust the lower stop against the lower edge of the window channel. Then, tighten the lower stop retaining screw and washer assemblies C.

5. Cycle the window up and down *several times to insure* that proper adjustment has been made. Install the watershield and quarter trim panel.

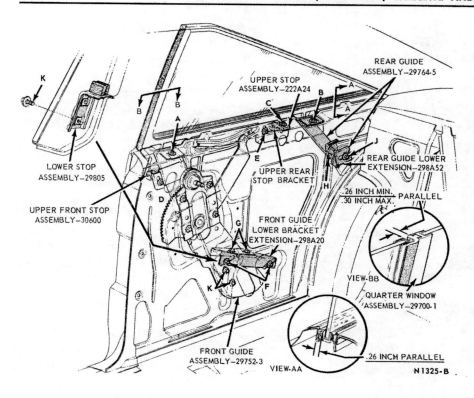

FIG. 9—Quarter Window—Model 63

QUARTER WINDOW ADJUSTMENT—MODEL 63

1. Remove the quarter trim panel and watershield.

2. Loosen the screw and washer assemblies A, B, C, D, E, F and G (Fig. 9).

3. Position the window assembly to obtain a ¼ inch to 5/16 inch parallel dimension between the front edge of the quarter window frame and the rear edge of the door window frame (sectional view BB, Fig. 7). At the same time, the ¼ inch parallel dimension between the door glass lower channel and the inner lip of the door outside panel (view CC, Fig. 9) should be obtained.

4. Temporarily secure the front and rear guides by tightening the screw and washer assemblies A and B finger tight. Tighten the upper stop retaining screws and washers C, D and E. Tighten the front guide retaining screws and washers F (Fig. 9).

5. Tilt the front guide inboard or outboard as required to obtain alignment of the quarter window with the door window and an interference fit

with the roof side rail weatherstrip. Then, tighten the screw and washer assemblies G (Fig. 9).

6. Loosen the screw and washer assemblies H, J and K (Fig. 9). Cycle the window to its down position, flush with the top of the quarter panel. This will locate the rear guide and rear guide lower extension in its proper position. Tighten the screw and washer assemblies J and H. Position the lower stop firmly against the bottom edge of the quarter window and tighten the screw and washer assembly K (Fig. 9).

7. Cycle the window assembly to its full up position and tighten the screw and washer assemblies A and B securely.

QUARTER WINDOW ADJUSTMENT—MODEL 76

1. Remove the quarter trim panel and watershield.

2. To align the quarter window with the door window, loosen the guide assembly retaining screw at point A (Fig. 10), the equalizer bracket retaining screws C, and the

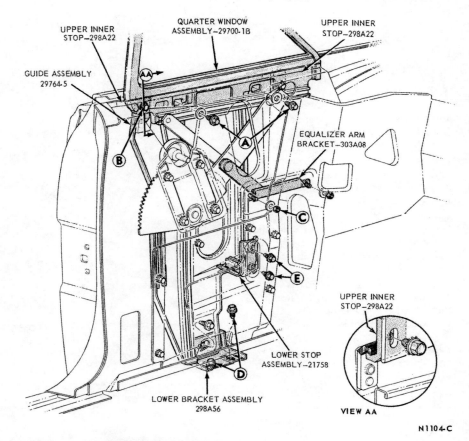

FIG. 10—Quarter Window—Model 76

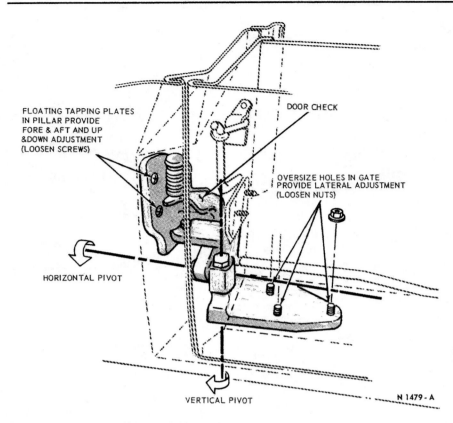

FLOATING TAPPING PLATES IN PILLAR PROVIDE FORE & AFT AND UP &DOWN ADJUSTMENT (LOOSEN SCREWS)

DOOR CHECK

OVERSIZE HOLES IN GATE PROVIDE LATERAL ADJUSTMENT (LOOSEN NUTS)

HORIZONTAL PIVOT

VERTICAL PIVOT

N 1479 - A

FIG. 11—Lower Left Hinge Assembly

upper inner stop retaining screws points B.

3. Adjust the window fore or aft, or tilt, to the best alignment position. Adjust the upper stops up firmly against the window channel and tighten the screw and washer assemblies B, A and C (Fig. 10).

4. To obtain an interference fit between the top edge of the window and the roof side rail for proper sealing, loosen the guide lower bracket retaining screws and washers D. Adjust the guide assembly towards the inside or outside of the body as necessary. Then, tighten the lower guide bracket retaining screws D.

5. Cycle the window to its down position. Loosen the lower stop retaining screws E (Fig. 10). Adjust the window assembly and lower stop to maintain a flush condition between the top edge of the window and the belt line. Tighten the lower stop retaining screws E.

6. Cycle the window assembly up and down several times to check adjustment. Then, install the quarter trim watershield and quarter trim panel.

TAILGATE EMERGENCY OPENING PROCEDURE

Should failure occur on the power operated tailgate window in the up position, entry can be accomplished by disconnecting the window regulator arms from the glass assembly. Use the following procedure:

Carefully insert a hooked tool or wire between the outer weatherstrip and the tailgate window. Locate the window regulator arm rollers. Insert the hooked tool into the roller retaining spring clip and remove the clip from the roller. Hold the tailgate window firmly and pry the regulator arms off of the two rollers, carefully lower the window into the tailgate, then open the tailgate.

TAILGATE ADJUSTMENTS

While full adjustments are provided for the dual action tailgate, no unique methods are employed. The following information will assist in locating and performing the adjustments.

The fore-and-aft and up-and-down-adjustment of the tailgate is

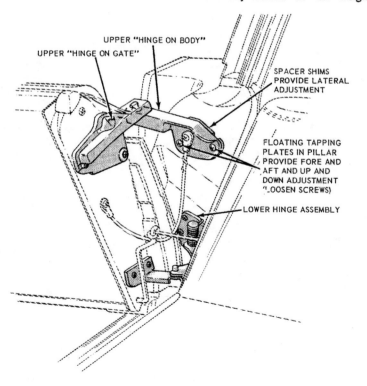

UPPER "HINGE ON BODY"

UPPER "HINGE ON GATE"

SPACER SHIMS PROVIDE LATERAL ADJUSTMENT

FLOATING TAPPING PLATES IN PILLAR PROVIDE FORE AND AFT AND UP AND DOWN ADJUSTMENT (LOOSEN SCREWS)

LOWER HINGE ASSEMBLY

N 1480 - A

FIG. 12—Upper Left Hinge Assembly

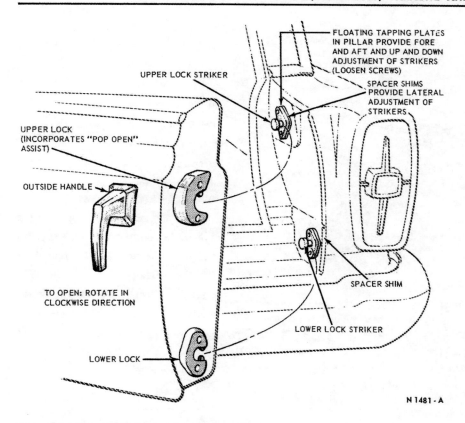

FIG. 13—Tailgate Lock Striker Adjustment

accomplished at the hinge side by means of square holes in the body pillar, backed by floating tapping plates, at the upper and lower hinge attachments (Figs. 11 and 12).

Lateral adjustment of the tailgate is accomplished at the upper hinge by adding or removing spacer shims between the hinge on the body and the pillar. Lateral adjustment at the lower hinge is accomplished by means of oversize holes in the tailgate at the hinge on the gate attachment (Figs. 11 and 12).

Fore-and-aft and up-and-down adjustment of the strikers is accomplished by means of square holes in the pillar backed by floating tapping plates. Lateral adjustment is accomplished by adding or removing shims (Fig. 13).

STATION WAGON TAILGATE WINDOW ADJUSTMENTS

1. To adjust the tailgate window forward or rearward for proper alignment with the window glass run channels on the body and/or to eliminate a binding condition of the windows in the tailgate glass run side channel(s), loosen the lower at-

taching bolt at the tailgate lock pillar, move the lower end of the run(s) forward or rearward as required. Align the glass runs of these items by using a straight edge within the channel of the run(s) in such a way as to assure that the runs line up in the same parallel plane.

2. To correct a condition where the tailgate glass is cocked in the glass run channels, loosen the window regulator attaching screws (Fig. 14), rotate the regulator assembly clockwise or counterclockwise, as required, to eliminate the cocked position.

DECK LID ALIGNMENT

1. To adjust the deck lid forward or rearward, or from side-to-side in the body opening, loosen both hinge strap attaching bolts and adjust the lid as required; then tighten the bolts (Fig. 15).

2. To adjust the deck lid at the hinge area up or down, install shims between the lid inner panel and the hinge straps as follows:

To raise the front edge of the lid at the hinge area, place a shim be-

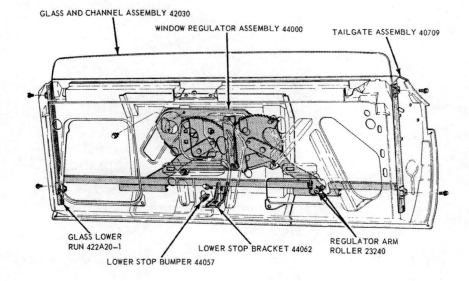

FIG. 14—Tailgate Window Mechanism

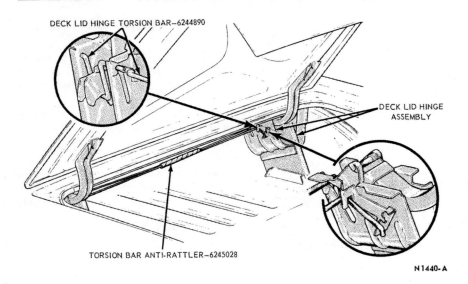

FIG. 15—Luggage Compartment Hinge and Torsion Bar Assembly

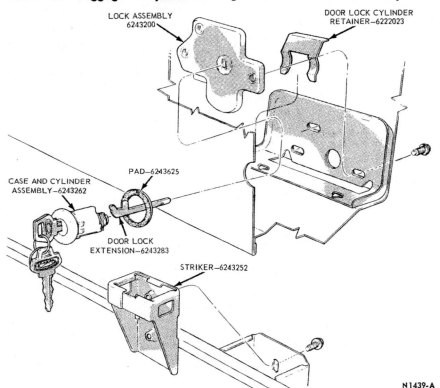

FIG. 16—Luggage Compartment Lock Mechanism

tween the lid inner panel and forward portion of one or both hinge straps.

To lower the front edge of the lid at the hinge area, place a shim between the lid inner panel and rearward portion of one or both hinge straps.

DECK LID LOCK AND STRIKER ADJUSTMENT

Since the rear deck lid lock frame acts as a guide when entering the striker, make sure that the rear deck lid is properly positioned in the body opening before performing a striker alignment check. To check for proper engagement of the rear deck lid lock with the striker, see the following procedures:

1. Insert a small quantity of modeling clay to each side of the lock assembly (Fig. 16). Close the lid with moderate force.

2. Open the lid and check the amount of engagement of the striker with the lock frame as indicated by the compression of the clay. The striker assembly impressions in the clay should be even on both sides of the lock frame. If the impressions in the clay are not even, adjustment is required.

3. To adjust, loosen the striker or lock attaching screws, adjust the lock sideways or the striker up or down to obtain proper engagement, then, tighten the screws.

4 REMOVAL AND INSTALLATION

FRONT DOOR

REMOVAL

1. Remove the trim panel, the water shield, and all usable outside mouldings and clips (if the door is to be replaced).

2. Remove the hinge attaching bolts from the door.

3. Slide the door off the hinges.

4. If a hinge is damaged, remove the pillar attaching bolts, and replace the hinge.

INSTALLATION

1. Drill holes as necessary for attaching the outside mouldings. Install *the door* weatherstrips in proper position.

2. If the hinges were removed, install them in the front pillar.

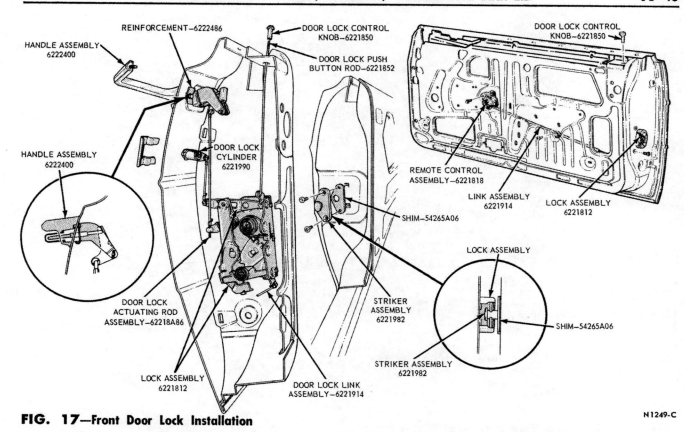

FIG. 17—Front Door Lock Installation

N1249-C

3. Position the door on the hinges, partially tighten the bolts, align the door, and tighten the bolts securely.

4. Install the lock mechanism, the window mechanism, glass, vent window assembly, and the weatherstripping. It may be necessary, at this time, to perform a final door alignment to obtain a satisfactory weatherseal at the windshield pillar and/ or the roof rail.

5. Install the exterior trim, garnish mouldings, water shield, and interior trim.

REAR DOOR

REMOVAL

1. Remove the trim panel, the water shield, and all usable outside mouldings and clips.

2. Brace the door so that it will not fall to the floor when the hinge attaching bolts are removed. Remove the bolts and remove the door.

3. If a hinge is damaged, remove the hinge attaching bolts from the pillar, and replace the hinge.

INSTALLATION

1. Drill holes as necessary for attaching the outside mouldings. Install the door weatherstrips in position.

2. If the hinges were removed, install them in the center pillar.

3. Position the door on the hinges, partially tighten the bolts, align the door, and tighten the bolts securely.

4. Install the window and lock mechanisms, the door glass, and the weatherstripping. Make all necessary adjustments. Final door alignment may be necessary for a satisfactory door weatherseal.

5. Install the exterior trim, garnish mouldings, water shield, and interior trim.

FRONT DOOR LOCK

REMOVAL

1. Remove the door trim panel.

2. Remove the water shield from the door inner panel.

3. Disconnect the remote control link from the remote control and from the lock.

4. Disconnect the door lock actuating rods (Fig. 17) from the door lock.

5. MODELS 54, 62 and 71. Remove the lower window guide retaining bolt.

6. Remove the three screws and lock washers that attach the door lock to the inner panel.

7. Remove the lock through the access hole in the inner panel.

INSTALLATION

1. Apply a film of sealer to the door lock mounting surface.

2. Working through the access hole in the door inner panel, hold the lock in position and secure it in place with three screws and lock washers.

3. Connect the two door lock actuating rods to the lock.

4. Connect the remote control rod to the door lock and to the remote control.

5. MODELS 54, 62 and 71: Install the window lower guide retaining bolt.

6. Check the door locking and window mechanism to make sure that they function properly.

7. Cement the watershield to the door inner panel.

8. Install the trim panel and hardware.

REAR DOOR LOCK

REMOVAL

1. Remove the door trim panel.

2. Remove the water shield from the door inner panel.

3. Disconnect the remote control link from the remote control and the lock.

4. Disconnect the lock control rod from the bellcrank and from the lock (Fig. 18).

5. Remove the three screws and washers that secure the lock to the inner panel.

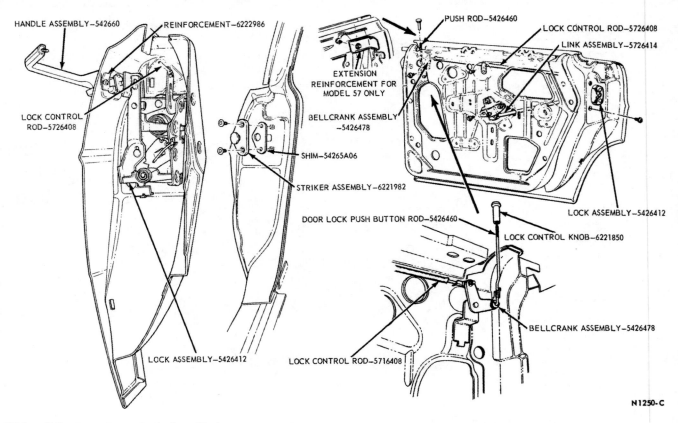

HANDLE ASSEMBLY—542660
REINFORCEMENT—6222986
PUSH ROD—5426460
LOCK CONTROL ROD—5726408
LINK ASSEMBLY—5726414
EXTENSION REINFORCEMENT FOR MODEL 57 ONLY
LOCK CONTROL ROD—5726408
BELLCRANK ASSEMBLY—5426478
SHIM—54265A06
STRIKER ASSEMBLY—6221982
LOCK ASSEMBLY—5426412
DOOR LOCK PUSH BUTTON ROD—5426460
LOCK CONTROL KNOB—6221850
LOCK ASSEMBLY—5426412
LOCK CONTROL ROD—5716408
BELLCRANK ASSEMBLY—5426478
N1250-C

FIG. 18—Rear Door Lock Installation

6. Remove the lock through the access hole in the inner panel.

INSTALLATION

1. Apply a film of sealer to the door lock mounting surface.

2. Working through the access hole in the door inner panel, hold the lock in position and secure it in place with three screws and lock washers.

3. Connect the lock control rod to the bellcrank and lock. Insert the rod in the retaining clip on the inner door panel.

4. Connect the remote control link to the lock and to the remote control.

5. Check the operation of the door lock and window mechanism. Make the necessary adjustments.

6. Cement the water shield to the door inner panel.

7. Install the door trim panel and hardware.

DOOR LOCK CYLINDER

The key code is stamped on the lock cylinder to assist in replacing lost keys.

When a lock cylinder is replaced, both door lock cylinders and the ignition lock cylinder should be replaced in a set. This will avoid car-

rying an extra key which will fit only one lock.

1. Remove the door trim panel. Disconnect the lock actuating rod from the cylinder.

2. Pull the door lock cylinder retainer rearward to release the cylinder (Fig. 17). Pull the lock cylinder out from the door.

3. Transfer the lock cylinder arm and lock actuating rod retaining clip to the new lock cylinder.

4. Position the lock cylinder in the door, and install the lock cylinder retainer (Fig. 17). Connect the lock cylinder to the actuating rod.

5. Install the door trim panel.

DOOR HANDLE PUSH BUTTON

1. Remove the door trim panel, and loosen the water shield enough to reveal the access holes.

2. Remove the two handle retaining nuts, and remove the handle (Fig. 17 or 18). To remove the front door handle, it will be necessary to disconnect the lock actuating link.

3. To replace the push button, remove the retaining plate screw, retaining plate, spring, push button, and rubber seal from the handle.

4. Install the push button assembly

if it was removed, and install the handle assembly. Connect the lock actuating link if it was disconnected.

5. Cement the water shield in place, and install the door trim panel.

VENT WINDOW REGULATOR

1. Remove the door trim panel.

2. Remove the cap screw and lock washer that secures the vent glass regulator to the vent glass lower pivot.

3. Remove the two cap screws that secure the regulator to the door inner panel.

4. Remove the regulator through the opening in the inner panel.

5. Rotate the vent regulator handle shaft until the flat on the regulator shaft is at a 90° angle to the handle shaft.

6. Hold the regulator in place on the door inner panel and install but do not tighten the two attaching screws.

7. Secure the regulator shaft to the vent window pivot with a cap screw and lock washer.

8. Tighten the regulator-to-panel attaching screws.

9. Install the door trim panel and hardware.

VENT WINDOW AND/OR WEATHERSTRIP—MODELS 63 AND 76

REMOVAL

1. Remove the the door trim panel and watershield.

2. Drill out the vent window pivot rivet.

3. Remove the bolt retaining the vent window regulator to the vent window shaft.

4. Remove the vent window assembly from the door.

5. Remove the division bar run retainer screw and pull the weatherstrip down to the belt line.

6. Remove the weatherstrip from the door.

INSTALLATION

1. Apply silicone lubricant to the weatherstrip.

2. Position the weatherstrip in the vent frame.

3. Grip the division bar and weatherstrip with a shop towel and vise grip pliers. Use a drift punch and peen the weatherstrip retainer rivets in the division bar.

4. Install the division bar run.

5. Position the vent assembly in the door.

6. Install the regulator shaft retaining bolt.

7. Position a new rivet in the pivot brackets and crimp it with a vise grip pliers.

8. Install the door watershield and trim panel.

FRONT DOOR GLASS—MODELS 54 AND 71

REMOVAL

1. Remove the door trim panel and peel back the watershield.

2. Remove the rear run retainer.

3. Remove the lower window stop retaining screws and remove the lower stops.

4. Lower the window one third of the way down.

5. Remove the screw retaining the regulator guide channel to the window frame and move the channel forward.

6. Move the window down in the door, tilt it nearly 90 degrees forward and remove it up and out of the window opening while tilting it slightly inward.

7. Remove the lower frame from the glass using a removal tool such as shown in Fig. 19.

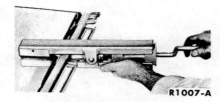

FIG. 19—Glass Channel Replacement

INSTALLATION

1. Install the lower frame to the glass using a tool such as shown in Fig. 19.

2. Position the glass assembly in the door.

3. Position the regulator channel to the lower window frame and install the regulator channel retaining screws.

4. Install the rear run retainer.

5. Install and adjust the lower window stop.

6. Install the watershield and door trim panel.

FRONT DOOR GLASS—MODELS 57 AND 76

REMOVAL

1. Remove the door trim panel and watershield.

2. Remove the front and rear upper stops.

3. Remove the screws retaining the glass channel bracket.

4. Remove the rear glass run retaining bolts and adjusting nut. Position the run in the bottom of the door. **Do not disturb the adjusting screw position.**

5. Lift the glass up and out of the door.

6. Remove the channel-to-frame retaining screws and remove the glass from the channel.

INSTALLATION

1. Install the glass into the glass channel and frame.

2. Position the glass in the door and install the glass channel bracket on the lower glass channel.

3. Install the rear glass run retaining bolts and adjusting nut finger tight.

4. Install the upper stop retaining screws loosely.

5. Close the door and check the window assembly for proper adjustment. Then, tighten all retaining screws and nuts.

6. Install the watershield and door trim panel.

DOOR WINDOW REGULATOR—MODELS 63 AND 76

REMOVAL

1. Open the door. Remove the door trim panel and watershield.

2. Wedge the glass in its full up position.

3. Remove the nut retaining the front glass run at the base. Disconnect the motor wiring if so equipped. Remove the screw retaining the motor to the door inner panel.

4. Remove the four regulator retaining bolts.

5. Disengage the regulator arms from the equalizer and window channel brackets. Remove the regulator assembly from the door.

6. POWER WINDOWS: Place the regulator and motor assembly in a vise and remove the motor to regulator retaining screws. Remove the motor from the regulator.

INSTALLATION

1. POWER WINDOWS: With the regulator assembly held in a vise, position the motor to the regulator and install the motor-to-regulator retaining screws.

2. Position the regulator assembly in the door, connect the regulator arms to the channel rollers and install the regulator retaining bolts.

3. Remove the wedge from the window.

4. POWER WINDOWS: Connect the motor wiring connectors if so equipped and install the front run retaining nut and regulator motor retaining screw.

5. Install the door watershield and trim panel.

FRONT AND REAR DOOR WINDOW REGULATOR—MODELS 50, 54 AND 71

REMOVAL

1. Remove the door trim panel and watershield.

2. Remove the screws retaining the glass channel bracket to the lower glass channel and prop the window in its up position.

3. POWER WINDOWS: Disconnect the motor wiring connector.

4. Remove the screw retaining the motor to the door inner panel. Remove the bolt from the front run retainer.

5. Remove the four regulator assembly-to-door inner panel retaining bolts and remove the regulator assembly.

6. POWER WINDOWS: Place the regulator assembly in a vise. Remove the three motor-to-regulator retaining screws and remove the motor.

INSTALLATION

1. POWER WINDOWS: Place the regulator assembly in a vise. Position the motor and drive assembly to the regulator and install the three retaining screws.

2. Position the regulator assembly in the door and install the four retaining bolts.

3. POWER WINDOWS: Install the regulator motor retaining screw and connect the motor wiring connector.

4. Remove the prop used to hold the window in its up position and install the screws retaining the glass channel bracket to the window lower channel.

5. Install the door watershield and trim panel.

VENT WINDOW REGULATOR MOTOR

REMOVAL

1. Remove the door trim panel.

2. Disconnect the motor wiring connector.

3. Remove the bolt retaining the vent glass pivot to the motor and drive assembly.

4. Remove the two bolts retaining the motor and drive assembly to the door panel. Remove the motor and drive assembly (door window in the up position).

INSTALLATION

1. Position the motor and drive assembly in the door and install the two motor and drive assembly retaining bolts.

2. Install the vent-pivot-to-motor and drive-assembly retaining bolt.

3. Connect the motor wiring connector.

4. Install the door watershield and trim panel.

REAR DOOR GLASS— MODELS 54 AND 71

REMOVAL

1. Remove the door trim panel and watershield.

2. Remove the lower window stop.

3. Remove the screws retaining the glass channel bracket to the glass channel.

4. Tilt the forward edge of the glass assembly up and remove the glass assembly from the door.

5. Using a tool such as shown in Fig. 19, remove the channel assembly from the glass.

INSTALLATION

1. Apply new glass tape to the lower edge of the glass.

2. Install the glass into the channel, using a tool such as shown in Fig. 19.

3. Position the glass and channel assembly into the door.

4. Position the channel bracket to the glass channel and install the channel-bracket-to-channel retaining screws.

5. Install and adjust the lower glass stop.

6. Install the door watershield and trim panel.

FRONT DOOR VENT RETAINER AND DIVISION BAR—MODELS 54 AND 71

REMOVAL

1. Remove the door trim panel and watershield.

2. Remove the vent window regulator.

3. Remove the front run retaining bolt.

4. Remove the window lower stop and lower the window.

5. Remove the three vent window assembly retaining screws and remove the vent window frame assembly from the door.

6. Remove the front run from its retainer.

7. Remove the run retainer from the vent frame.

8. Remove the rivet retaining the vent window pivot bracket and remove the vent window.

9. Remove the rubber weatherstrip from the vent window frame and pop out the four rivets.

INSTALLATION

1. Lubricate the weatherstrip with silicone lubricant, position the weatherstrip in the vent window frame and peen the retaining rivets.

2. Install the run retainer in the vent frame.

3. Install the front run in its retainer.

4. Position the vent window in the frame and install the pivot retaining rivet.

5. Position the vent window and run assembly in the door.

6. Install the retainer screws in the vent frame.

7. Install the lower run retainer retaining bolt.

8. Install and adjust the window lower stop.

9. Install the vent window regulator.

10. Install the door watershield and trim panel.

FRONT DOOR VENT RETAINER AND DIVISION BAR—MODEL 76

REMOVAL

1. Remove the door trim panel and watershield.

2. Remove the vent window regulator.

3. Remove the two vent window retainer bolts.

4. Remove the vent window and run retainer adjusting studs. Remove the stud retainer nuts.

5. Remove the vent window assembly and run retainer from the door.

6. Remove the run from the retainer and the retainer from the division bar.

7. Drill out the vent window pivot rivet.

8. Remove the vent window weatherstrip.

INSTALLATION

1. Apply silicone lubricant to the weatherstrip, and position the weatherstrip in the new vent frame. Crimp the retainer rivets.

2. Position the vent window in the retainer.

3. Position a new rivet in the pivot bracket and crimp it with vise grip pliers.

4. Position the run retainer in the division bar and install the run in the retainer.

5. Position the vent assembly and run retainer in the door, and install the vent retainer bolts loose.

6. Install the vent run adjusting studs.

7. Install the nuts on the studs, and align and adjust the vent window and front run. Tighten the stud and nuts.

8. Install the vent window regulator.

9. Install the door watershield and trim panel.

REAR DOOR WINDOW— MODEL 57

REMOVAL

1. Remove the door trim panel and watershield.

2. Remove the upper stops from the lower glass channel.

3. Remove the two retaining screws from the glass channel bracket and remove the glass assembly from the door (leave the channel bracket attached to the regulator arm rollers).

4. Remove the weatherstrip retaining screw from the front of the glass assembly and remove the weatherstrip.

5. Remove the two retaining screws from the rear lower edge of the upper glass frame, and two retaining screws from the top front edge of the lower glass frame and channel. Remove the glass from the channel, using a tool such as shown in Fig. 19.

INSTALLATION

1. Position new glass tape on the glass and install the frame and frame retaining screws on the glass.

2. Install the weatherstrip on the front of the glass.

3. Position the glass assembly in the door and install the glass channel bracket.

4. Install and adjust the window upper stop.

5. Install the door watershield and trim panel.

REAR DOOR WINDOW REGULATOR—MODEL 57
REMOVAL

1. Remove the rear door trim and watershield. Remove the two rear glass up stops.

2. Remove two screws from the glass channel bracket and remove the door glass from the door. Leave the bracket on the rollers.

3. Remove the four retaining bolts from the guide and remove the rear door guide panel.

4. Remove the five screws retaining the regulator and motor. Remove the assembly from the door.

5. Clamp the regulator assembly in a vise and remove the drive motor. Remove the bracket from the motor.

INSTALLATION

1. Position the motor to the regulator and install the retainer screws.

2. Install the regulator in the door and install the retainer screws.

3. Connect the wires to the regulator motor.

4. Position the door glass in the door and install the channel bracket screws.

5. Install the window up stops and leave the stop bolts snug.

6. Adjust the stops and the guide and tighten all retaining bolts.

7. Install the rear door watershield and panel.

REAR QUARTER GLASS—MODEL 63
REMOVAL

1. Remove the quarter trim panel and watershield.

2. Remove the regulator access hole cover.

3. Remove the two mounting bolts on the rear upper stop and remove the stop.

4. Remove the bolt from the front upper stop and remove the stop.

5. Remove two screws from the regulator channel bracket at the window frame and remove the channel bracket.

6. Remove three bolts and drop the front window guide assembly down.

7. Remove the quarter window assembly from the quarter and place it on a bench.

8. Remove one screw from the weatherstrip and remove the weatherstrip.

9. Remove three screws retaining the window top frame and remove the top frame.

10. Using the tool shown in Fig. 19, remove the glass from the lower side frame.

INSTALLATION

1. Install the glass in the frame using the tool shown in Fig. 19 using new glass tape.

2. Install the top glass frame and install the retainer screw.

3. Install the weatherstrip and screw.

4. Position the quarter window in the guide and install the front guide retainer bolts snug.

5. Install the window regulator channel to glass frame.

6. Install the front and rear upper stops snug.

7. Raise the window to the up position, adjust the front guide and tighten the bolts on the guide.

8. Close the front door, align the quarter window to the door window and tighten the upper stop bolts.

9. Install the regulator access hole cover.

10. Install the quarter watershield and the trim panel.

REAR QUARTER GLASS —MODEL 76
REMOVAL

1. Lower the convertible top.

2. Remove the rear seat cushion, seat back and the rear quarter trim panel and watershield.

3. Remove the quarter window regulator access panel.

4. Remove the two upper window stops.

5. Remove the two screws retaining the regulator channel to the window frame and remove the window assembly.

6. Remove the quarter window weatherstrip.

7. Remove the four screws retaining the upper glass frame to the lower glass frame and separate the frames from the glass.

INSTALLATION

1. Position the seal to the glass and install the frames.

2. Install the frame retainer screws.

3. Install the weatherstrip and retainer screw.

4. Position the window assembly in the quarter panel.

5. Install the regulator channel to the window frame.

6. Lower the top and latch it.

7. Install and align the window upper stops.

8. Install the regulator access panel.

9. Install the watershield and trim panel.

10. Install the rear seat back and seat cushion.

REAR QUARTER GLASS—MODEL 62
REMOVAL

1. Remove the quarter trim panel and watershield.

2. Remove the two screws retaining the quarter window channel bracket to the lower window channel.

3. Roll the regulator assembly to its down position.

4. Tilt the window slightly in the window opening and remove the window assembly.

5. Remove the glass from the window channel, using a tool such as shown in Fig. 19.

INSTALLATION

1. Install the glass in the lower channel, using new glass tape.

2. Position the glass and channel assembly in the window opening.

3. Install the channel bracket to the lower window channel and roll the window assembly up.

4. Install the watershield and door trim panel.

REAR QUARTER WINDOW REGULATOR—MODEL 62
REMOVAL

1. Remove the quarter trim panel and watershield.

2. Prop the quarter window in the up position.

3. Remove two screws retaining the quarter window glass channel bracket and remove the channel.

4. Remove four bolts retaining the regulator to the quarter and remove the regulator from the quarter.

INSTALLATION

1. Position the regulator in the quarter and install the regulator retaining bolts.

2. Position the quarter window glass channel bracket in the quarter and install the two retaining screws.

3. Remove the prop and install the quarter watershield and trim panel.

REAR QUARTER WINDOW REGULATOR—MODEL 63

REMOVAL

1. Remove the quarter trim panel and watershield.

2. Remove the quarter window regulator access hole cover.

3. Remove the four regulator retaining bolts.

4. With the window in the up position, move the regulator out of the mounting holes. Lower the window gradually and ease the regulator arm out of the channel, and remove the regulator assembly.

INSTALLATION

1. Install lubricant on the new regulator arm roller.

2. Position the regulator assembly to the window, and raise the window gradually and position it to the mounting holes.

3. Install the regulator retaining bolts.

4. Install the quarter window regulator access hole cover.

5. Install the quarter watershield and trim panel.

REAR QUARTER WINDOW REGULATOR—MODEL 76

1. Remove the quarter trim panel and watershield.

2. Prop up the window.

3. Remove the four screws retaining the regulator, and ease the regulator arms out of the roller channels. Remove the regulator from the door.

4. Position the regulator in the door and the arm rollers in the channels.

5. Install the regulator retainer screws.

6. Install the watershield and trim panel.

PANEL REAR DOOR GUIDE

1. Remove the rear door trim panel and watershield.

2. Remove the two rear door glass up stops.

3. Remove the two screws from the glass channel bracket and remove the door glass from the door (leave the bracket on the rollers).

4. Remove the four retaining bolts from the guide and remove the rear door guide panel.

5. Position the guide in the door and install the retaining bolts snug.

6. Position the door glass in the door and install the channel bracket screws.

7. Install the window up stops and leave the stop bolts snug.

8. Adjust the stops and the guide and tighten all retaining bolts.

9. Install the rear door watershield and trim panel.

REAR QUARTER WINDOW GUIDE—MODEL 76

REMOVAL

1. Remove the quarter trim panel and watershield.

2. Lower the top assembly.

3. Remove the lower regulator access panel.

4. Remove both upper window stops.

5. Remove two screws retaining the regulator channel bracket to the window lower channel and remove the window assembly.

6. Remove the three screws retaining the guide panel and remove the guide panel.

INSTALLATION

1. Position the guide panel in the quarter panel and loosely install the three retaining screws.

2. Position the window assembly in the quarter panel and guide.

3. Install the regulator channel bracket on the window lower channel.

4. Raise and latch the top assembly.

5. Align the window with the top side rail weatherstrip and front door window. Tighten the guide panel retaining screws.

6. Install the window upper stops.

7. Install the watershield and quarter trim panel.

QUARTER WINDOW FRONT GUIDE—MODEL 63

REMOVAL

1. Remove the quarter trim panel and watershield.

2. Remove the upper front stop.

3. Remove the front guide assembly retaining screws.

4. Remove the window lower stop.

5. Move the guide assembly towards the rear of the door and remove it through the access hole.

6. Remove the two screws retaining the guide lower bracket extension to the guide lower bracket.

INSTALLATION

1. Apply Lubriplate to the guide channels.

2. Position the lower stop and snugly install the stop retaining screws.

3. Install the guide lower extension bracket and retaining screws finger right.

4. Position the guide assembly in place and install the retaining screws finger tight.

5. Position the front upper stop in place and install the retaining screw finger tight.

6. Align the quarter window and tighten all retaining screws.

7. Install the watershield and quarter trim panel.

QUARTER WINDOW REAR GUIDE—MODEL 63

1. Remove the quarter trim panel and watershield.

2. Remove the two capscrews retaining the rear guide to the door panel and remove the guide.

3. Position the guide in the door panel. Adjust the guide, and tighten the two retaining screws.

4. Install the watershield and quarter trim panel.

REAR QUARTER WINDOW AND/OR WEATHERSTRIP— STATION WAGONS

REMOVAL

1. Open the tailgate and remove the following quarter window interior mouldings: front garnish moulding, upper garnish moulding, rear upper corner garnish moulding, rear corner upper finish moulding, rear garnish moulding and the back window upper corner garnish moulding.

2. Remove the quarter upper front trim panel.

3. Remove the front, center and rear (left side only) quarter trim panel retainers.

4. Remove the quarter trim panels.

5. Remove the spare tire cover (right side only).

6. Remove the outside front moulding retaining screws and remove the moulding.

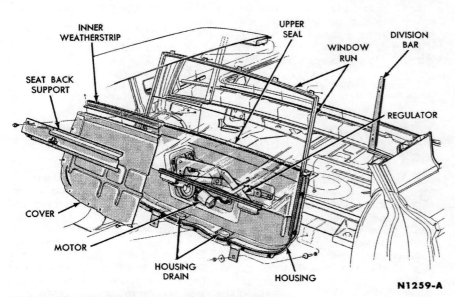

FIG. 20—Retractable Rear Window Installation

7. Remove the outside upper and lower moulding retaining nuts.

8. Remove the outside lower, upper and rear mouldings, using tool T64P-42430-R or L to release the mouldings from the moulding retaining clips.

9. With the aid of an assistant, push the window and weatherstrip assembly out of the window opening. Place the window and weatherstrip assembly on a bench.

10. Remove the weatherstrip from the glass.

INSTALLATION

1. Clean old sealer from the weatherstrip and from the window opening.

2. Apply a bead of sealer around the quarter glass body opening.

3. Apply sealer in the glass groove of the weatherstrip and position the weatherstrip on the glass.

4. Install a pull cord (1/8-inch sash cord) around the body opening groove of the weatherstrip.

5. Position the window and weatherstrip assembly in the window opening. With an assistant applying pressure from the outside, use the pull cord to pull the lip of the weatherstrip over the pinch-weld flange.

6. Install the outside mouldings and moulding retaining nuts.

7. Install the quarter trim panels and retainers.

8. Install the interior garnish mouldings.

9. Clean the glass and mouldings.

RETRACTABLE REAR WINDOW OR MOTOR——MERCURY

REMOVAL

1. Remove the seat cushion and the seat back.

2. Remove the two screws from each division bar moulding and remove the two mouldings.

3. Remove the six screws from the lower garnish moulding and remove the moulding.

4. Remove the six cap screws that secure the seat back support (Fig. 20) to the body and remove the support.

5. Remove the five screws that secure the inner weatherstrip to the cover and remove the weatherstrip.

6. Remove the eleven screws that secure the cover to the housing and remove the cover.

7. Remove the two nuts that at-

tach the window side channel to one side of the housing (Fig. 21).

8. Remove the hairpin clip from each of the rollers in the glass channel.

9. Press the regulator arms to the rear to free them from the two rollers.

10. Lift the side channel off the two studs and allow the window to slide to the lower end of the channels.

11. Remove the window from the housing.

12. Working from inside of the luggage compartment, disconnect the motor wires from the main harness.

13. Remove the four cap screws that secure the regulator to the housing.

14. Slide the regulator arm and roller out of the equalizer bracket.

15. Turn the motor shaft coupling manually until the regulator gear is free of the pinion.

16. Remove the two nuts that secure the motor to the regulator and disconnect it from the shaft coupling.

INSTALLATION

1. Engage the motor shaft to the coupling and secure the motor to the regulator with two nuts and lock washers.

2. Compress the regulator arm until the large gear contacts the pinion. Then, rotate the motor coupling manually until the gear is in the approximate position shown in Fig. 21.

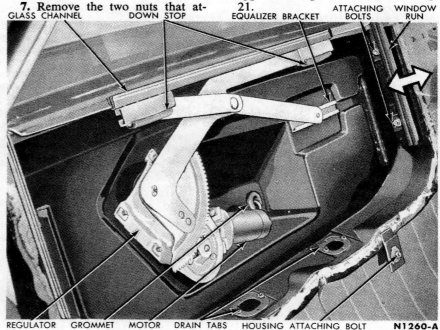

FIG. 21—Retractable Rear Window Motor and Regulator

3. Lubricate the equalizer bracket with Lubriplate or equivalent.

4. Connect the equalizer arm and roller on the regulator to the equalizer arm bracket.

5. Working from inside the luggage compartment, secure the regulator to the housing with four cap screws.

6. Connect the motor wires to the main harness.

7. Lubricate the window channel roller surface with Lubriplate or equivalent. Install the hairpin clip in each roller and install the two roller assemblies in the channel.

8. Insert the glass in the lower end of the side channels and carefully raise it into place. Insert the two regulator pins into the rollers. Make sure that the hair pin clips snap into the retaining groove of the pins.

9. Secure the lower end of the side channel to the housing with two nuts.

10. Coat the housing flange (Fig. 21) with sealer. Secure the cover to the housing with eleven screws.

11. Secure the inner weatherstrip (Fig. 20) to the cover with five screws. Make sure that the weatherstrip contacts the window before tightening the screws.

12. Secure the seat back support to the body with six cap screws.

13. Secure the lower garnish moulding with six screws.

14. Secure each division bar moulding with two screws.

TAILGATE HINGES

UPPER LEFT HINGE

1. Open the tailgate (horizontally, as a dropgate) and scribe a location mark around that part of hinge to be replaced.

2. Remove the hinge retainer screws.

3. Position the hinge to the scribe marks and install the retainer screws.

LOWER LEFT HINGE

1. Open the tailgate (horizontally, as a dropgate) and position a support under the hinge side of the gate.

2. Remove the tailgate door check. Raise the tailgate partially and remove the torsion bar retainer link from the body.

3. Scribe the hinge location on the body and the tailgate. Remove the hinge retainer screws and remove the hinge.

4. Position the hinge to the body and tailgate scribe marks and install the hinge retainer screws.

5. Close the tailgate and check for proper lower hinge alignment. Adjust the hinge if necessary.

6. Open the tailgate partially and install the torsion bar retainer link to the body.

7. Install the tailgate door check.

TAILGATE LOCKS

RIGHT LOWER LOCK

1. Open the tailgate (side opening). Remove the tailgate trim panel, watershield and access panel.

2. Disconnect the linkage from the lock. Remove the three retaining screws and remove the lock.

3. Transfer the linkage retainer clips to the new lock. Position the lock in the gate and install the retainer screws.

4. Install the linkage to the lock. Install the access cover, watershield and trim panel.

RIGHT UPPER LOCK

1. Open the tailgate (side opening). Remove the tailgate trim panel, watershield and access panel.

2. Engage the upper lock pawl to the closed position and raise the window partially out of the gate. Remove the regulator arms from the window regulator channel and remove the window assembly.

3. Disconnect the linkage at the upper lock. Remove the wire connector from the upper lock safety switch.

4. Remove the right guide upper retainer bolt. Remove the three screws retaining the lock and remove the lock assembly.

5. Transfer the linkage retainer clips and the safety switch to the new lock assembly.

6. Position the lock in the gate and install the lock retainer screws. Install the window guide upper retainer bolt.

7. Connect the wire connector to the switch and connect the linkage to the lock.

8. Position the window assembly in the gate and install the regulator arms to the regulator channel. Close the lock pawl to engage the switch and lower the window into the tailgate.

9. Install the tailgate access panel, water shield, and trim panel. Open the upper lock and close the tailgate. Check the lock alignment to the striker. Adjust the lock striker if necessary.

TAILGATE TORSION BAR

REMOVAL

1. Remove the tailgate trim panel, watershield and access cover.

2. Move the tailgate glass out partially by closing the right upper lock pawl and turning the key in the tailgate cylinder.

3. Remove the lock control bellcrank assembly and window lower stop.

4. Loosen the window regulator motor harness to gain slack at the tailgate-to-body location.

5. Raise the tailgate partially and remove the torsion rod retainer link from the body (2 screws).

6. With an assistant, remove the left lower hinge pivot bolt. Unlock the right lower lock, remove one check cable retainer screw from each side and move the tailgate assembly away from the body opening. Place the tailgate on an appropriate stand approximately bumper high.

7. Remove the torsion bar retainer bracket and remove the torsion bar from the left side of the gate (Fig. 22).

INSTALLATION

1. Place the torsion bar in its respective mounting position and install the torsion bar right retainer bracket.

2. With an assistant, position the tailgate assembly to the body opening. Engage the right lower lock to the striker plate. Install the left hinge pivot bolt and install the check cable retainer screws.

3. Install the torsion bar retainer link to the body.

4. Position the motor wiring harness in its original position.

5. Install the window lower stop and lock the bellcrank assembly.

6. Lower the window in the tailgate to where the top edge of the glass is even with the weatherstrip and adjust the lower stop if necessary.

7. Install the tailgate access cover, watershield and trim panel.

DECK LID TORSION BARS

1. Open the deck lid and remove the spare tire.

2. Secure the deck lid open with a suitable prop.

3. To remove either the left or right torsion bar, both bars must be released at the adjustment end. This is accomplished by using a pair of vise grip pliers.

4. Remove either the left or right torsion bar by lowering the bar at

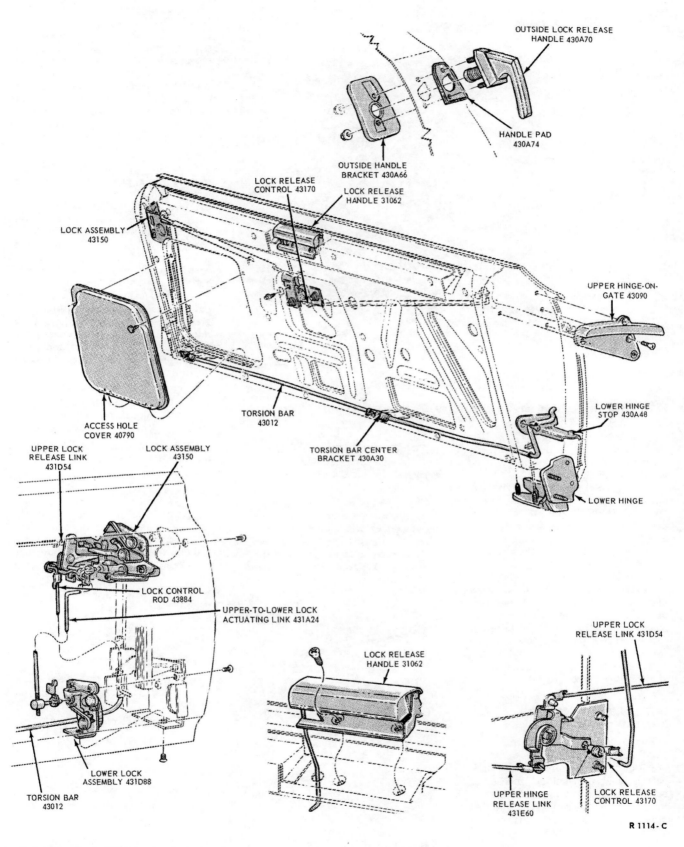

FIG. 22—Tailgate Lock Mechanism

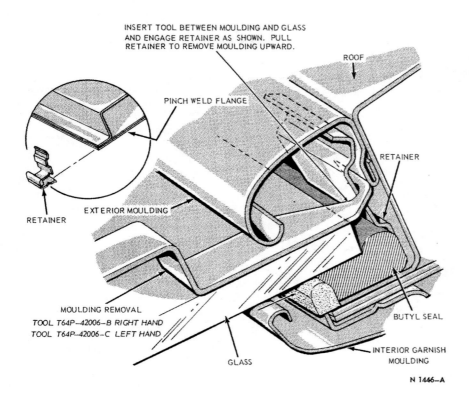

INSERT TOOL BETWEEN MOULDING AND GLASS AND ENGAGE RETAINER AS SHOWN. PULL RETAINER TO REMOVE MOULDING UPWARD.

ROOF

PINCH WELD FLANGE

RETAINER

EXTERIOR MOULDING

RETAINER

MOULDING REMOVAL
TOOL T64P–42006–B RIGHT HAND
TOOL T64P–42006–C LEFT HAND

GLASS

BUTYL SEAL

INTERIOR GARNISH MOULDING

N 1446–A

FIG. 23—Windshield or Back Window Moulding Removal

the adjustment end. Twist the bar until the U portion clears the back section of the hinge assembly, and work it from the car.

5. Install the torsion bar by working it back into the hinge assembly and placing the U shaped portion of the rod over the back section of the hinge assembly.

6. Install both rods in their respective adjustment mountings and adjust as required.

Torsion bars should be adjusted enough to pop the deck lid open two or three inches and to counter balance the door in any raised position. When altering the adjustment of the torsion bars to increase windup, the ends of both torsion bars must be positioned the same.

WINDSHIELD AND/OR BACK WINDOW

For field service replacement of windshields and back windows which are installed with butyl tape, an adhesive sealer (Polysulfide) method is recommended. An adhesive sealer kit (part number C4AZ-19562-A) which includes general instructions for its use, is released for this purpose.

Following are detailed instructions for windshield and/or back window removal and installation using the adhesive sealer kit C4AZ-19562-A.

REMOVAL

1. Place protective covers over interior and exterior body surfaces adjacent to glass.

2. Remove interior garnish mouldings. Remove back window exterior

mouldings or windshield upper exterior moulding using the special tool (T64P-42006-B or C) shown in Fig. 23. Remove the windshield exterior side moulding retaining screws. Remove the cowl top ventilator panel retaining screws and the cowl top ventilator panel to provide access to the windshield outside lower belt moulding retaining screws. Remove the outside lower belt moulding retaining screws and remove the moulding.

3. If the glass has been broken, remove loose glass fragments from vehicle. Beginning at a corner, peel the butyl tape seal away from the body pinch weld flange, then grasp the seal near the flange and pull directly away (Fig. 24). If glass is not broken, insert 2 lengths of the piano wire between the pinch weld flange and the glass. With the aid of an assistant, and using a see-saw motion, cut the seal all the way around the glass. Then remove the glass. **Care must be used to prevent cutting the rubber tip on the retainers and spacers. Remove window from the body opening.**

4. Clean up body flanges thoroughly by removing all butyl tape and if Landau model, remove any excess vinyl top cement in the seal area.

5. Perform sheet metal and paint repairs, if necessary.

INSTALLATION

1. Check all moulding retainers, replace or repair retainers to insure adequate moulding retention. **On Landau Model: Apply masking tape or other protective material over**

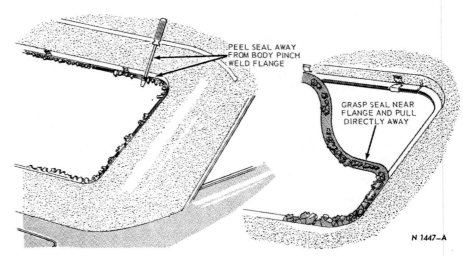

PEEL SEAL AWAY FROM BODY PINCH WELD FLANGE

GRASP SEAL NEAR FLANGE AND PULL DIRECTLY AWAY

N 1447–A

FIG. 24—Butyl Tape Removal

1. PULL OUT DASHER ROD 2½" AS SHOWN

2. INSERT RAM INTO END OF DASHER ROD. PUSH RAM DOWNWARD UNTIL IT STOPS OR BOTTOMS OUT. REMOVE AND DISCARD. THE CURING AGENT IS NOW DISPERSED INTO THE BASE MATERIAL AND IS READY FOR MIXING.

3. TO MIX, PLACE CARTRIDGE VERTI-CALLY ON A BENCH AND HOLD FIRMLY. PUSH DASHER ROD TO THE BOTTOM OF CAR-TRIDGE AND BEGIN STROKING IN A SPIRAL CLOCKWISE MOTION FROM TOP TO BOTTOM OF CAR-TRIDGE. APPROXI-MATELY 50 STROKES ARE REQUIRED.

4. ON THE LAST STROKE DASHER ROD SHOULD BE FULLY INSERTED IN CARTRIDGE. GRIP CARTRIDGE JUST ABOVE BOTTOM CAR AND UN-SCREW DASHER ROD BY ROTATING COUNTER-CLOCKWISE. REMOVE AND DISCARD DASHER ROD.

5. SCREW NOZZLE INTO CARTRIDGE AND REMOVE BOTTOM CAP.

PLACE CARTRIDGE IN SEALANT GUN AND PUMP OUT A ¼" TO 5 6" DIAMETER BEAD FOR AN ORIGINAL INSTALLATION AND A 1/8" TO 3/16" DIAMETER BEAD WHEN SOME OF THE ADHESIVE-SEALER REMAINS FROM THE PREVIOUS INSTALLATION.

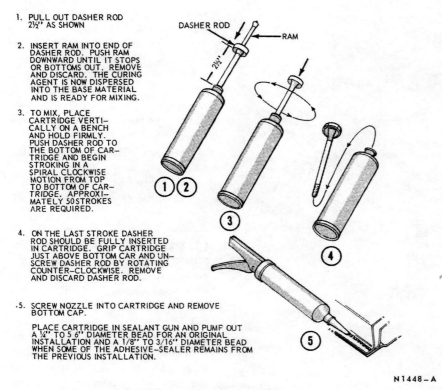

DASHER ROD

RAM

2½"

N1448–A

FIG. 25—Adhesive Mixing and Application

Landau roof cover in area of the glass opening to aid in clean-up operations after installation.

2. Make certain the retainers and spacers around the body opening are in place. Repair or replace any if necessary to insure adequate moulding retention.

3. Temporarily position replacement glass in opening and adjust to the best glass to body pinch weld overlap position. Mark this location with a crayon. Remove the glass and clean thoroughly.

4. To obtain adhesion between the glass and the adhesive-sealer, apply glass primer (ESB-M2G107-A, part of Kit C4AZ-19562-A) around the perimeter of the glass on the inside surface approximately ⅜-inches wide.

5. To obtain adhesion between the paint on the body glass opening pinch weld flange and the adhesive-sealer, apply metal primer (ESB-M2G105-A, part of Kit C4AZ-19562-A) to the pinch weld flange.

6. Prepare the adhesive-sealer as indicated in Fig. 25.

7. Place cartridge in pressure seal-

ant gum and pump out a ¼-inch to 5/16-inch diameter bead, along the facing of the pinch weld flange (Figs. 26 and 27).

8. Apply approximately a ¼-inch bead of sealer around the flange surface of the glass, then place glass in position using the crayon mark on the glass to locate the glass in the body opening. Make certain the glass is contacting the retainer spacers as shown in Fig. 23. **A side window should be opened and left open for at least one-half hour after repair so the new glass is not forced out of position if the doors are slammed shut.**

9. Clean excessive adhesive sealer from the glass with a razor blade and wipe off with a clean cloth dampened with a glass cleaner such as Bon-Ami, Glass Wax or a similar product.

10. Visually inspect appearance of adhesive-sealer through the glass. Dull spots indicate areas where adhesive-sealer is not contacting the glass surface. Repair these areas by applying additional adhesive-sealer or use black sealer (Part Number C3AZ-19562-A) or equivalent.

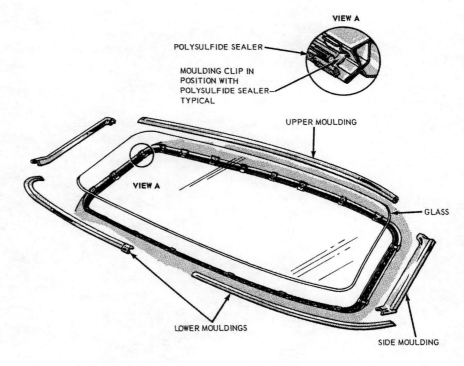

VIEW A

POLYSULFIDE SEALER

MOULDING CLIP IN POSITION WITH POLYSULFIDE SEALER—TYPICAL

UPPER MOULDING

VIEW A

GLASS

LOWER MOULDINGS

SIDE MOULDING

N 1449–A

FIG. 26—Typical Windshield Installation

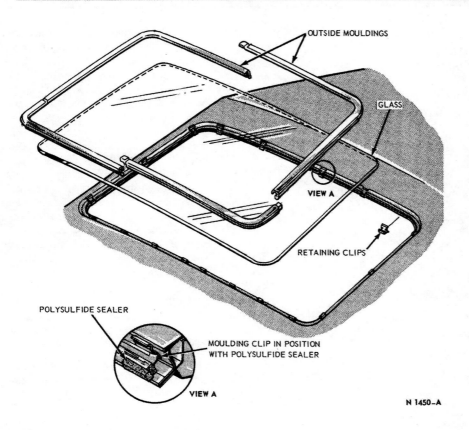

FIG. 27—Typical Back Window Installation

11. Allow the adhesive-sealer to cure before reinstalling any mouldings to avoid cementing the mouldings to the adhesive-sealer, then reinstall the mouldings. **Cure time is three hours, after mixing, in temperatures over 70°F and six hours in temperatures under 70°F. The temperature of the area where this work is performed should be at least 55°F to insure satisfactory curing of the adhesive-sealer.**

Subsequent replacements of glass can be made in the following manner:

When a windshield glass or a back window glass which had been installed using adhesive-sealer is removed, it is not necessary to remove all the adhesive-sealer from the body glass opening. The remaining film of adhesive-sealer on the body flange can be used as a base for the new adhesive-sealer material. Metal primer is not required in this case unless the base of adhesive-sealer was removed for flange repair and new paint applied.

TRIM, SEATS, AND CONVERTIBLE TOP

GROUP 18

PART 18-1

INTERIOR TRIM AND LANDAU TOP COVER

1 DOOR AND QUARTER TRIM PANELS

REMOVAL AND INSTALLATION

Basically, all door and quarter panels are retained in the same manner. In view of this, one removal and installation procedure will cover all models.

1. Unscrew the door lock push button.

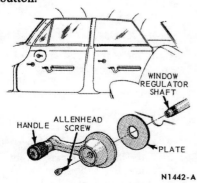

FIG. 1—Handle Installation

2. Remove the Allen screws from the door remote control and window regulator handles (Fig. 1).

3. Remove any screws retaining the trim panel to the inner panel, such as the arm rest retaining screws and lower edge moulding screws. On a car with arm rests, remove the arm rests.

4. With a putty knife, pry the trim panel retaining clips out of the inner panel at each side.

5. Carefully loosen the water shield, if necessary. If the door has electric windows, disconnect the door switch wire connector from the switch lead wire, and remove the trim panel.

6. Place a daub of AB-19560-A sealer over each trim retaining clip hole to seal the retaining clips when they are pushed into the door. Also, apply this sealer around the door handle, regulator shafts, and other existing holes.

7. If the door has electric windows, connect the switch wires. Fasten the water shield to the inner panel with sealer (Figs. 2 and 3). Install the handle shaft springs.

8. Make sure that all the retaining clips are installed in the trim panel, place the upper portion of the door trim panel over the top edge of the door inner panel. Push the retaining clips into the holes in the inner door panel.

9. Install the trim moulding along the bottom of the door and install the arm rest assembly.

10. Roll the window completely shut and install the window handle in the horizontal position with the handle facing forward. Close the vent regulator to the closed position and install the handle in the horizontal position facing rearward as indicated in Fig. 1.

11. Screw the door lock push button on the rod.

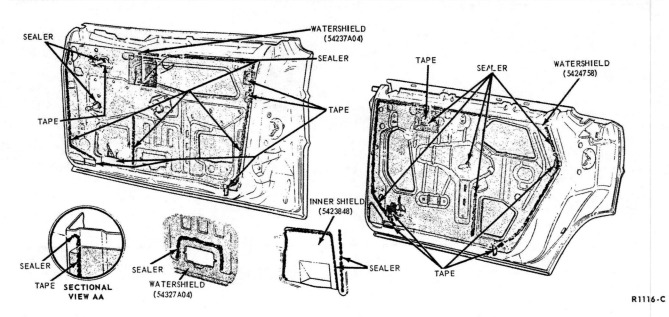

FIG. 2—Door Watershields—Typical

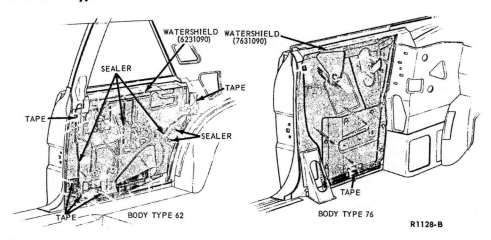

FIG. 3—Quarter Panel Water Shields—Typical

2 ROOF HEADLINING REMOVAL AND INSTALLATION

HEADLINING—SEDANS AND HARDTOPS

Service installation does not require the removal of the windshield or back glass. Removal of a windshield or glass could create problems such as water leaks and/or glass breakage. Service installation differs from production in that the headlining is cemented around its entire perimeter and around the windshield and back glass openings. On models other than 54 and 62 the headlining is tacked around the windshield and back glass opening, and does not require windshield or back glass removal.

The following headlining removal and installation procedures generally apply to all models. If some of the steps do not apply to the particular model being serviced, proceed to the next step.

REMOVAL

1. Remove the sun visor assemblies, side rail mouldings, and coat hanger hooks.
2. Remove the upper windshield garnish mouldings, visor arm clip brackets, and windshield pillar garnish mouldings.
3. Remove the rear seat cushion and back assembly (Part 18-2).
4. Remove the side rail rear inner mouldings and back window corner garnish mouldings.
5. Remove the package tray side mouldings.
6. Remove the back window lower garnish moulding, right and left upper back window garnish mouldings, and back window side garnish mouldings.
7. Remove the quarter trim panels and package tray.
8. Remove the quarter headlining panels and dome light assembly.
9. Cut the headlining around the rear window and pry the headlining loose at the windshield header, side-

rails, quarter sections, and other glued areas. Remove the headliner with the bows intact from the car.

INSTALLATION

1. Unpackage the new headlining and lay it out on a bench.

2. Trim the listings on the new headlining on the approximate length of those on the old one. Remove the bows from the old headlining and install them in the same relative bow listings of the new headlining. **Roof bows are color coded at each end. When ordering new roof bows, be sure to note the color at each end of the bow.**

3. Position the headlining to the roof top and secure the ends of the bows.

4. Staple the headlining around the back window (Fig. 4).

garnish moulding, right and left upper back window garnish mouldings and back window lower garnish moulding.

10. Install the package tray side mouldings.

11. Install the back window corner garnish mouldings and side rail rear inner mouldings.

12. Install the rear seat back assembly and rear cushion.

13. Install the windshield pillar garnish mouldings, visor arm clip brackets, and upper windshield garnish mouldings.

14. Install the coat hanger hooks, side rail mouldings, and sun visor assemblies.

**HEADLINING—
STATION WAGONS**

The following headlining removal

2. Remove the rear view mirror assembly.

3. Remove the right and left, top and rear, windlace assemblies.

4. Remove the front upper corner garnish corner mouldings from around the quarter window.

5. Remove the windlace from around the top of the rear door and remove the coat hooks located above each rear door.

6. Remove the dome light lens.

7. Remove the tailgate opening upper corner, upper, and side garnish mouldings.

8. Remove the rear quarter panel upper mouldings.

9. Remove the right and left quarter window upper garnish mouldings.

10. Remove the staples from the headlining around the tailgate open-

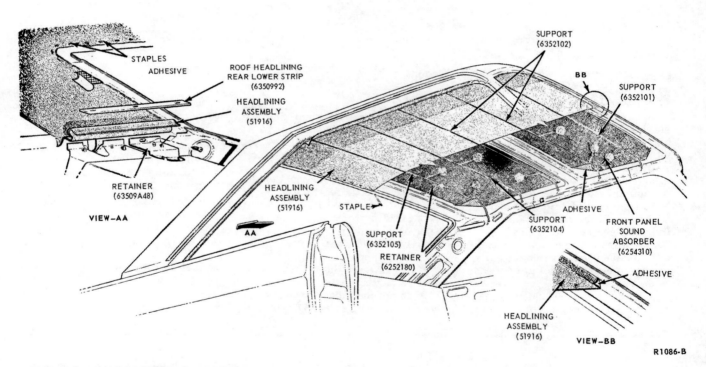

FIG. 4—Typical Headlining—Sedans

5. Pull the headlining forward and stretch and glue the headlining along the side rails working from the front to the back.

6. Cut a hole in the headlining around the dome light fixture.

7. Install the dome light assembly and quarter headlining panels.

8. Install the quarter trim panels and package tray.

9. Install the back window side

and installation procedures generally apply to all model station wagons. If some of the steps do not apply to the particular model being serviced, proceed to the next step.

REMOVAL

1. Remove the sun visors, windshield side garnish mouldings, and right and left upper garnish moulding assemblies.

ing and unhook the headlining at the quarter panels.

11. Remove the staples from the headlining at the quarter windows.

12. Remove the glued portion of the headlining from the top of the windshield, over the front door openings, B pillar, and rear door openings (Fig. 5).

13. Unhook the bows and remove the headlining from the car.

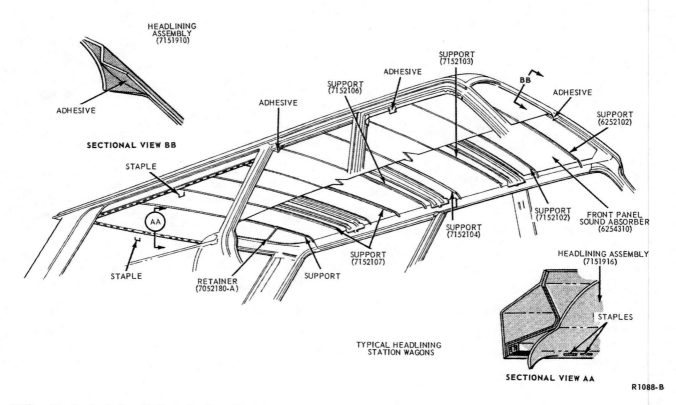

FIG. 5—Typical Headlining—Station Wagons

INSTALLATION

1. Unpackage the new headlining and lay it out on a flat surface. Mark and trim the new headlining using the old one as a pattern.

2. Trim the listings on the new headlining to the approximate length of those on the old one. Remove the bows from the old headlining and install them in the same relative bow listings of the new headlining.

Roof bows are color coded at each end. When ordering new roof bows, be sure to note the color at each end of the bow.

3. Position the headlining to the roof and secure the ends of the bows.

4. Staple the headlining across the top of the tailgate opening and trim the excess material (Fig. 5).

5. Hook the headlining at the quarter panels and trim the excess material.

6. Cement the headlining to the windshield header; over the top of the front door openings, to the B pillar; and over the top of the rear door openings (Fig. 5).

7. Install the right and left quarter window upper garnish mouldings.

8. Install the right and left upper quarter panels.

9. Install the tailgate opening upper and side garnish mouldings.

10. Install the windlace across the top of the rear doors.

11. Install the right and left quarter window front and front corner garnish mouldings.

12. Install the coat hangers above each rear door.

13. Cut the headlining around the dome light and install the dome light lens assembly.

14. Install the rear view mirror assembly.

15. Install the windshield upper and side garnish mouldings.

16. Install the right and left sun visors.

3   INSTRUMENT PANEL SAFETY PAD

FORD

REMOVAL

1. Remove the instrument cluster pad and retainer.

2. Remove the windshield side garnish mouldings on sedans, hard-tops and station wagons. On convertibles, remove the upper inside windshield garnish mouldings, sun visors and brackets, then remove the windshield side garnish mouldings.

3. Remove the windshield lower garnish mouldings and lower garnish moulding retainer clips (Fig. 6).

4. Remove the glove compartment liner, ash tray assembly, and retainer bracket.

5. Remove the nuts securing the pad to the instrument panel. Unhook the pad from the tabs, loosen the glued areas, and remove the pad assembly.

INSTALLATION

1. Unpack the new pad and using the old pad as a template trim the excess material from the pad.

2. Transfer the studs to the new pad and apply adhesive to the leading edge of the pad.

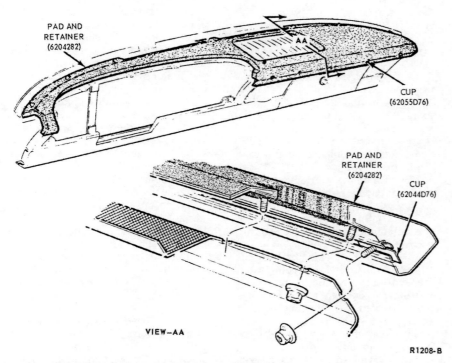

PAD AND RETAINER (6204282)

CUP (62055D76)

PAD AND RETAINER (6204282)

CUP (62044D76)

VIEW—AA

R1208-B

FIG. 6—Instrument Panel Pad Installation—Ford

3. Position the pad in its respective mounting position. Install the leading edge on the tabs and press the cemented areas to the instrument panel.

4. Install the pad retainer nuts, ash tray, retainer bracket, and glove box liner.

5. Install the lower windshield moulding retainer clips and lower windshield garnish mouldings.

6. Install the windshield side garnish mouldings. On convertibles, install the sun visors and brackets and upper windshield garnish mouldings.

7. Install the instrument cluster pad and retainer.

MERCURY

REMOVAL

1. Disconnect the battery.

2. Remove the upper inside windshield garnish moulding.

3. Remove the sun visors and brackets.

4. Remove the windshield side garnish mouldings.

5. Remove the windshield lower garnish mouldings.

6. Remove the right and left side cowl trim panels.

7. Disconnect the left and right air duct cables at the ducts.

8. Remove two bolts retaining the steering column to the instrument panel. Allow the column to rest down.

9. Disconnect the speedometer cable.

10. On vehicles equipped with an automatic head-lamp dimmer, disconnect the sensor at the amplifier.

11. Disconnect the turn signal wiring connector at the steering column.

12. Remove the two screws retaining the fuse panel to the dash panel.

13. Disconnect the wiring at the stop light switch.

14. Remove the two bolts and nuts retaining the instrument panel to the brake support.

15. Remove the parking brake to instrument panel retaining bolt.

16. Remove the one bolt and nut retaining the instrument panel to the left side cowl panel.

17. Disconnect the two multiple wiring connectors at the dash panel. From the engine compartment, push the connectors through the dash. Also, disconnect the wiper motor wiring connectors.

18. Disconnect the air conditioner temperature control cable (if so equipped) at the thermostatic switch. Disconnect the heater control cables at the heater plenum.

19. Remove the bolt and nut retaining the instrument panel to the right side cowl.

20. Disconnect the heater or air conditioner ducts at the plenum and at the defroster duct nozzles.

21. Cover the steering column.

22. Remove the seven screws retaining the instrument panel to the dash panel.

23. Remove the bolt from the top of the dash at the windshield which retains the brace and instrument panel to the dash panel.

24. Allow the instrument panel to rest down. Disconnect all necessary wiring at the instrument panel, dimmer switch and door pillar switches. Disconnect the heater wiring and antenna lead. On heater-air conditioner equipped cars, disconnect the vacuum hoses at the control.

25. Remove the instrument panel and place it on a bench.

26. Remove the speaker grille.

27. Remove the nuts retaining the safety cover to the instrument panel and the instrument panel brace.

28. Remove the windshield moulding clips.

29. Loosen the brace from the left corner to the center of the instrument panel.

30. Remove the nuts retaining the cluster assembly to the instrument panel. Remove the radio support nut.

31. With a large screw driver, pry the left corner of the instrument panel up to gain access to the left cluster nut.

32. Position the cluster assembly forward to gain access to two screws in the left corner which retain the safety cover to the instrument panel.

33. Remove the moulding above the right side of the glove box.

34. Remove the two nuts retaining the left instrument panel moulding and remove the moulding.

35. Remove the two lower screws retaining the cover to the instrument panel. Remove the sensor if so equipped.

36. Remove the cover assembly.

37. Clean excess cement from the instrument panel.

INSTALLATION

1. Apply trim cement to the top edge of the instrument panel.

2. Position a new cover to the instrument panel. Install the two left corner screws, and the two right side lower screws.

3. Install the nuts retaining the left instrument panel moulding.

4. Install the right instrument panel moulding and retaining nuts.

5. Position the cluster assembly to the instrument panel and install the retaining nuts.

6. Position the instrument panel brace to the instrument panel. Install the retaining nuts. Extend the left corner to center of instrument panel brace, and install the nuts retaining the safety cover.

7. Install the radio speaker grille.

8. Install the windshield moulding clips.

9. Install the radio rear support nut.

10. Position the instrument panel in the car.

11. Connect the right door pillar button wiring.

12. From the engine compartment, feed mechanics wire through the dash and panel and tie it to the heater leads. Pull the leads through the dash. Remove the mechanics wire and connect the leads at the heater.

13. Feed the air conditioner temperature control cable (on vehicles so equipped) through the dash panel. Route the right and left air duct cables to the ducts.

14. On heater-air conditioner equipped vehicles connect the vacuum hoses to the control. Connect the antenna lead. Connect the two wiring connectors at the left side of the dash panel support.

15. Position the instrument panel to the dash panel. Install the brace support bolt at the windshield.

16. Install eight screws retaining the instrument panel to the dash panel.

17. Install the right instrument panel support bolt and nut to the cowl.

18. Connect the right air duct cable and adjust it.

19. Install the defroster duct. (Remove the ash tray to gain access on air conditioner equipped cars.)

20. Connect the four air conditioner ducts on units so equipped.

21. Install the ash tray.

22. Position the steering column to its support and install the two bolts loosely.

23. Install the brace from the cowl mounting brace to the steering column support.

24. Install the parking brake to instrument panel retaining bolt. Install the two bolts and nuts retaining the instrument panel to the brake support. Tighten the steering column bolts.

25. Connect the left air vent cable to the air duct and adjust it.

26. Connect the turn signal wiring, stop light switch and dimmer switch wiring connectors. Route the wiper motor wires through the dash panel. Assemble the main wiring connectors in the dash panel. Connect the left door pillar button wiring. Position the fuse panel to the dash panel and install the retaining screws.

27. Connect the main wiring connectors at the dash panel in the engine compartment. Connect the wiper motor wiring connectors.

28. On vehicles so equipped, connect the temperature cable to the thermostatic switch and adjust it.

29. Install the cowl side trim panels.

30. Connect the speedometer cable.

31. Connect the sensor lead to the amplifier.

32. Install the lower windshield garnish mouldings.

33. Install the windshield side garnish mouldings.

34. Install the sun visors and brackets.

35. Install the upper windshield garnish mouldings.

36. Position the sensor to the instrument panel. Install the two retaining screws. Position the upper half of the sensor and install the pivot pin. Connect the amplifier.

37. Connect the battery.

38. Connect the heater control cables to the plenum chamber and adjust the controls.

39. Check the operation of all gauges and instruments.

4 CONSOLE

REMOVAL

1. Remove the console top finish panel and the screws securing the shift indicator dial assembly to the console.

2. Pull the carpets away from the console mouldings and remove the console retainer screws (Fig. 7).

3. Disconnect the light-wire harness and remove the console from the car.

4. Remove the screws securing the console top to the mouldings and retainer brackets.

INSTALLATION

1. Position the console top to the retainer bracket and install the screws. Align the top as required.

2. Place the console in its respective moulding position in the car and connect the light-wiring harness. Install the console retainer screws.

3. Tuck the carpet under the console mouldings and install the shift indicator assembly to the console.

4. Install the console top finish panel.

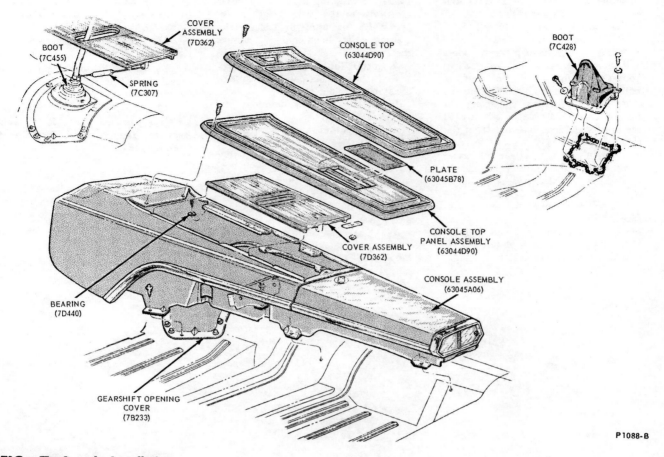

FIG. 7—Console Installation

5   LANDAU TOP COVER

REMOVAL

1. Remove the sun visors and the windshield garnish mouldings.

2. Remove the windshield wiper arm and blade assemblies.

3. Remove the cowl top grille.

4. Remove the windshield and outside moulding retainers.

5. Remove the belt side and belt back mouldings and retainers.

6. Remove the back outside mouldings.

7. Remove the package tray and back window garnish mouldings and remove the back window.

8. Remove the back window outside moulding retainer clips and the clips across the windshield header.

9. Remove the quarter courtesy light bezels and lenses.

10. Remove the roof side rear trim covers.

11. Remove the drip rail mouldings, and remove the sealer from the drip rails.

12. Using a 0.128 to 0.132-inch diameter drill, remove the rivets from the drip rail retainers and discard the retainers.

13. Remove and discard all roof assembly retaining staples. Remove and discard the cover assembly.

14. Remove all old sealer and/or cement from the roof panel and drip rail areas with naphtha solvent or equivalent. **It is extremely important that the entire roof and drip rails are thoroughly cleaned.**

INSTALLATION

It is recommended that a ⅛-inch oval head blind rivet (Part No. 378527-S, Pop Rivet) be substituted for the screw and the drive nail. The rivet and installing pliers (Mfg. Part No. PRP-26-A) can be procured from: POP Rivet Division, United Shoe Machinery Corp., Sheldon, Connecticut, or from their local distributor.

Wherever possible, use the existing drive nail or screw holes. Therefore, each location should be identified on the pinch weld flange with a wax crayon.

Seal all unused holes with either C1AZ-19627-A Pressure Sensitized Tape or AB-19560-A Sealer.

1. Carefully position the outside cover on the roof panel. (Fore-and-aft center punch marks have been provided in the cover for centering purposes.)

2. With the cover properly positioned and temporarily secured, apply an even coating of trim cement C2AZ-19C525-A to the roof panel and a like amount to the corresponding area of the roof outside cover assembly. For best results, secure limited sections at a time. **Make certain that the adhesive is not lumpy as it will be objectionable from an appearance standpoint.**

3. Using a 0.128 to 0.132-inch

diameter drill, pierce the vinyl material at the existing drive nail or screw hole locations. Install POP rivets in each of the holes.

4. Position both drip rail retainers and, using the same drill referred to above, pierce the vinyl at each of the holes. Install the POP rivets from the underside of the drip rail except at the extreme rear hole in which case the rivet should be inserted from the retainer side.

5. Trim excess cover material from around the entire perimeter.

6. Apply sealer C3AZ-19562-A (for white tops) or C3AZ-19562-B (for black tops) over the entire surface of the drip rail retainers. With the drip rail properly sealed, a minimum depth of ⅛ inch should be retained for adequate water drainage.

Place the masking tape on the cover assembly for the entire length of the drip rail before applying sealer. After the sealer has been applied, remove the tape.

7. Install the drip rail mouldings.

8. Install the back window outside moulding retainer clips.

9. Install the back window and windshield.

10. Reposition and secure the headlining.

11. Install the roof side rear trim covers.

12. Install the courtesy light lenses and bezels.

13. Install the back window and package tray garnish mouldings.

14. Apply an ample amount of caulking cord AB-19560-A around the entire outer perimeter of the

back window, between the weatherstrip and the recess of the body opening.

15. Install the back window outside mouldings.

16. Install the back belt side and back moulding retainers and mouldings.

17. Apply caulking cord AB-19560-A to each roof side rail weatherstrip retainer before installing the retainer (Fig. 8).

18. Install the roof side rail weatherstrip.

19. Install the windshield outside moulding retainers and mouldings.

20. Install the cowl top grille.

21. Install the wiper arms and blades.

22. Install the sun visors.

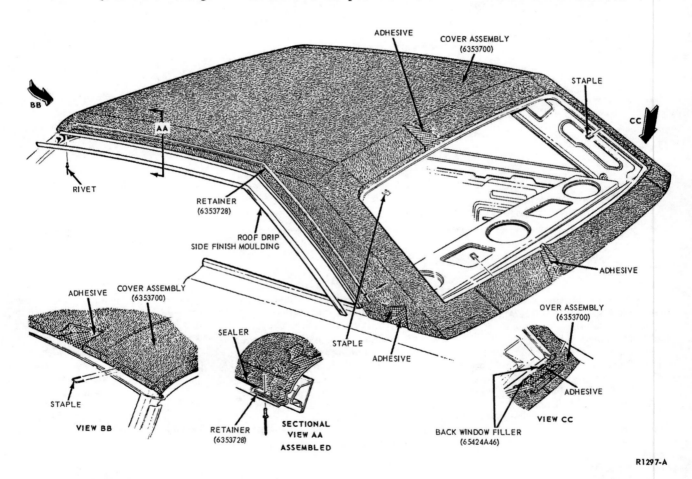

FIG. 8—Landau Top Cover Installation—Typical

PART 18-2 SEATS

1 MANUAL SEATS

FRONT SEAT AND/OR TRACK REMOVAL AND INSTALLATION

Work other than that of minor nature is more easily performed when the front seat assembly is removed from the car.

1. Remove the bolts retaining the seat tracks to the floor pan, and lift the seat assembly from the car. Remove the right and left cushion side shields (if so equipped).

2. Remove the bolts and lockwashers retaining each seat track to the seat (Fig. 1), and disconnect the seat track tie rod and front seat track adjusting spring as the track assembly is removed.

3. On a car with a one-piece seat back, remove the bolts and washers attaching the seat back.

On a car with a split seat back, remove the screw from the center bracket cover, and remove the hairpin clips from the seat back studs.

4. Remove the seat back from the seat.

5. Position the seat back assembly on the seat. On a car with the split seat back, install the hairpin clips and attach the center bracket cover screw and washer.

6. On a car with a one-piece seat back, install the bolts and washers attaching the seat back to the seat.

7. Connect the seat track tie rod as the seat track is positioned; then install the bolts and lockwashers re-

taining the seat track to the seat assembly.

8. Position the seat assembly in the car and install the retaining bolts and nuts. Position the cushion side shields (if so equipped) and install the retaining screws.

TIE ROD ADJUSTMENT

Tie rod adjustment will affect only the passenger side of the seat. In case the latch retaining the track fails to release, turn the adjusting turnbuckle (Fig. 1) clockwise enough to shorten the tie rod travel and release the track latch. If the latch fails to secure the seat travel, turn the adjusting turnbuckle counterclockwise enough to allow the latch to snap into locking position.

SEAT CUSHION, BACK, AND/OR COVER REMOVAL AND INSTALLATION

Standard or custom seat cushion and seat back assemblies are available in kits. A typical covered seat is shown in Fig. 2. The covers are serviced separately to match the trim in a given car. A damaged frame, spring, or pad requires a complete frame and spring kit for repair. A damaged or worn cover can be replaced separately. The following procedure for seat back or cushion replacement includes steps necessary for cover replacement, and is applicable to most kits.

1. Remove the seat or back as-

sembly from the car and remove the cover and/or the pad. If working on a seat cushion, remove the tracks and any operating mechanism from the frame.

2. Position the frame and spring right side up on a clean working surface.

3. Carefully center the pad support and the pad(s) in the order shown in Fig. 2.

4. Insert the listing wire(s) in the cover.

5. Center the cover on the pad, and draw the cover over the corners, working out any wrinkles.

6. Carefully turn the frame bottom side up, being careful not to disturb the pads and cover.

7. Working on the edge of the cover with the listing wire(s), start at the center and use hog rings to fasten the cover to the frame. Work alternately toward the corners and along each side, installing the rings about four inches apart.

8. Fasten the other long edge of the cover to the frame, using hog rings about four inches apart. Work alternately to each corner from the center.

9. Install the seat tracks and any operating mechanism that was previously removed.

10. After applying Lubriplate to the track slides and to the seat back pivots, install the complete assembly in the car.

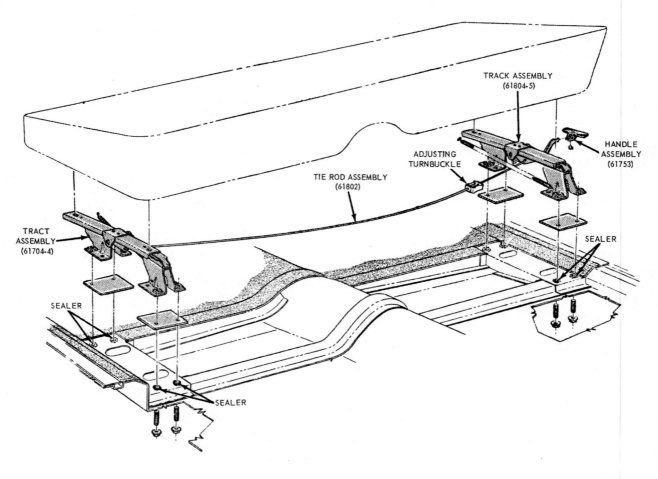

TRACK ASSEMBLY
(61804-5)

HANDLE
ASSEMBLY
(61753)

ADJUSTING
TURNBUCKLE

TIE ROD ASSEMBLY
(61802)

TRACT
ASSEMBLY
(61704-4)

SEALER

SEALER

SEALER

R1034-B

FIG. 1—Manual Front Seat Mechanism

REAR SEAT CUSHION AND/OR BACK—2-DOOR SEDAN

REMOVAL AND INSTALLATION

1. Lift the rear seat cushion and pull it forward to remove it from the car.

2. Remove one rear seat arm rest.

3. Remove 2 rear seat back attaching screws located at the bottom of the seat back.

4. Lift up on the seat back to disengage the seat from the upper hooks and remove the seat back from the car.

5. Position the seat back in the car and engage the seat with the upper hooks.

6. Install the seat back lower retaining screws and the removed arm rest. Then, install the rear seat cushion.

REAR SEAT—SIX PASSENGER STATION WAGON

REMOVAL AND INSTALLATION

Seat Back and/or Cushion

1. Remove the screws from the back of the seat back floor panel (Fig. 3). Lift the seat back out of the two bottom hooks.

2. To remove the seat cushion, push the seat cushion towards the rear of the car, and lift it up. Remove the seat cushion from the car.

3. Place the seat back into the bottom hooks attached to the seat back floor panel and install the screw in the back of the seat back floor panel.

4. Place the seat cushion into its respective mounting position, push the back seat cushion towards the rear of the car and down. The seat will lock into position.

Back Seat

1. Place the rear seat assembly in the down position.

2. Drive the pin from the hinge located on the bottom of the back seat.

3. Remove the bolts securing the rear seat to the floor pan and remove the seat from the car.

4. Install the bolts which secure the rear seat to the floor pan of the car.

5. Install the hinge pin in the hinge located on the bottom of the rear seat (Fig. 3).

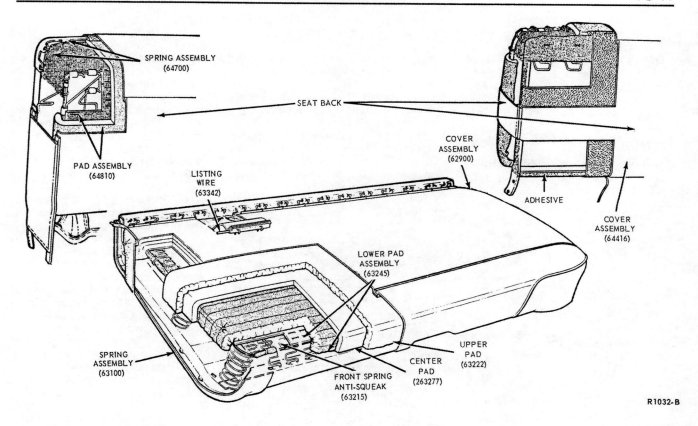

FIG. 2—Typical Seat Cushion Build-Up

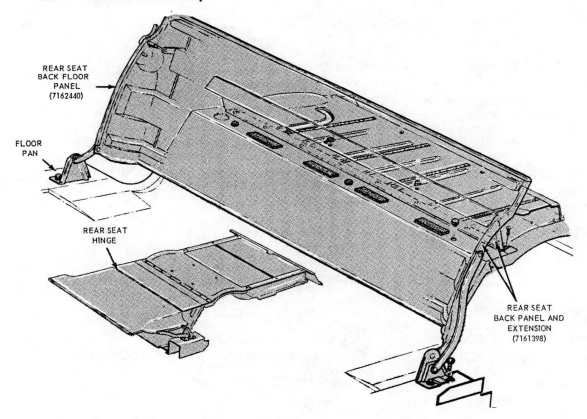

FIG. 3—Station Wagon Six-Passenger Seat Installation

2 RECLINING SEAT

DESCRIPTION AND OPERATION

The reclining seat mechanism consists of a seat actuator and control cable assembly and a seat adjusting handle. The seat actuator is located in the seat back. It is connected to the adjusting handle, located at the seat back right side pivot, by a control cable which is routed through the seat back (Fig. 4).

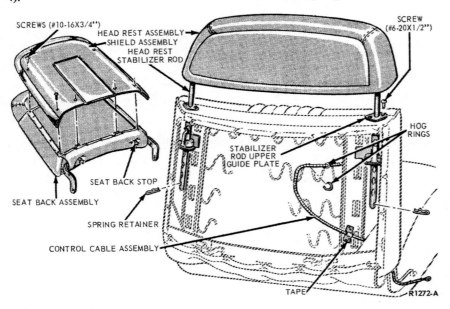

FIG. 4—Seat Back Shield and Headrest Assembly

The seat back reclining operation is controlled by the adjusting handle. When the handle is raised, the control cable releases a clutch in the seat actuator, allowing the seat back to recline. When the handle is released, the clutch engages and locks the actuator, thereby locking the seat back in position.

ADJUSTING ACTUATOR AND CABLE ASSEMBLY

REMOVAL

1. Remove the six seat back shield retaining screws and remove the seat back shield.
2. Remove the spring retainer from the lower ends of the headrest stabilizer rods and remove the headrest.
3. Remove the adjusting handle spring retainer and pull the handle off its shaft. Remove the speed clip which retains the control cable end to the adjusting handle (Fig. 5) and disengage the control cable end to

the adjusting handle (Fig. 4) and disengage the control cable from the adjusting handle.

4. Unsnap the pivot side outer cover from the pivot side outer cover retainer (Fig. 5).
5. Remove the pivot side outer cover retainer attaching nuts (Fig. 5) and rotate the retainer clockwise sufficiently to gain access to the cable retaining clips.

6. Loosen the two retainer clip screws and disengage the control cable from the seat back pivot (Fig. 5).
7. Remove the headrest stabilizer rod upper right guide plate retaining screws (Fig. 4) and remove the guide plate.
8. Remove the seat back stops (Fig. 4).
9. Cut the hog rings from the seat lower flap.
10. Remove the cotter pins and remove the hinge retaining pins from the seat back hinges.
11. Remove the roll pin from the actuator cylinder assembly at the hinge and remove the seat back assembly from the car.
12. Place the seat back assembly on a bench. Straighten the trim retaining tabs. Cut the hog rings at the top of the seat back trim and pull the trim cover away far enough to expose the actuator cylinder.
13. Remove the clevis pin from the upper actuator rod. Remove the hog rings which retain the cable assembly to the springs and remove the actuator assembly from the seat back.

INSTALLATION

1. Position the actuator assembly on the seat back spring assembly mounting brackets and insert the clevis pin in the upper actuator assembly rod. Install the self locking pin on the clevis pin. **The metal spacer located between the control cable**

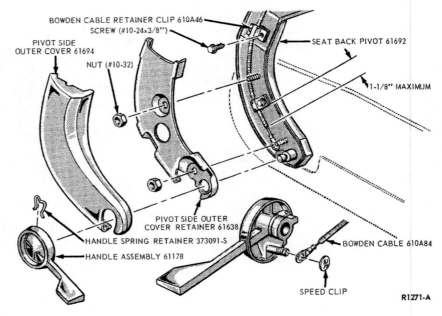

FIG. 5—Seat Adjusting Handle and Side Pivot—Disassembled

mounting bracket and the actuator lower mounting hole extends the over-all length of the actuator to provide for ease of installation. The spacer must remain intact during installation of the actuator.

2. With the actuator lower hole properly aligned with the mounting bracket, insert the retaining pin from the open side of the hole. If a new actuator assembly is being installed, the metal spacer will be driven out of the hole.

3. Position the cable assembly to the springs and install the two retaining hog rings.

4. Position the seat back trim over the tabs. Bend the tabs down and install new trim retaining hog rings.

5. Install the headrest stabilizer rod upper guide plate.

6. Position the seat back assembly to the seat cushion hinge assembly and install the roll pin which retains the lower actuator rod to the seat hinge.

7. Install the seat back hinge retaining pins and cotter pins.

8. Install new hog rings to retain the trim cover bottom flap.

9. Install the seat back stops.

10. Install the control cable under two retaining clamps on the seat back pivot.

11. Position the control cable end on the adjusting handle and install the speed clip cable retainer.

12. Install the pivot side outer cover retainer.

13. Install the adjusting handle on the adjusting handle shaft.

14. Adjust the control cable, if necessary, and tighten the cable clamps.

15. Install the pivot side outer cover.

16. Position the headrest on the seat back assembly and install the headrest stabilizer rod lower spring retainers.

17. Position the seat back shield on the seat back and install the seat back shield retaining screws.

ADJUSTING HANDLE ACTUATOR CABLE

REMOVAL

1. Remove the six seat back shield retaining screws and remove the seat back shield.

2. Remove the spring retainers from the lower ends of the headrest stabilizer rods and remove the headrest.

3. Remove the adjusting handle spring retainer and pull the handle

off its shaft. Remove the speed clip which retains the control cable end to the adjusting handle (Fig. 5) and disengage the control cable from the adjusting handle.

4. Unsnap the pivot side outer cover from the pivot side outer cover retainer (Fig. 5).

5. Remove the pivot side outer cover retainer attaching nuts (Fig. 5) and rotate the retainer clockwise sufficiently to gain access to the cable retaining clips.

6. Loosen the two retainer clip screws and disengage the control cable from the seat back pivot (Fig. 5).

7. Remove the headrest stabilizer rod upper right guide plate retaining screws (Fig. 4) and remove the guide plate.

8. Remove the seat back stops (Fig. 4).

9. Cut the hog rings from the seat back lower flap.

10. Remove the cotter pins and remove the hinge retaining pins from the seat back hinges.

11. Remove the roll pin from the actuator cylinder assembly at the hinge and remove the seat back assembly from the car.

12. Place the seat back assembly on a bench. Straighten the trim retaining tabs. Cut the hog rings at the top of the seat back trim and pull the trim cover away far enough to expose the actuator cylinder.

13. Remove the hog rings which retain the cable assembly to the springs.

14. Remove the actuator-to-cable release clip (Fig. 6).

15. Open the split end of the cable release pin and remove the cable (Fig. 6).

16. Manually disengage the actuator clutch by forcing the release pin from right to left and retain the pin in the open position by inserting the blade of a screwdriver (Fig. 6, View A) in the exposed slot to the right of the pin.

17. Remove and discard the cable release pin.

INSTALLATION

1. Install a new cable release pin and remove the screwdriver which is used to hold the clutch open.

2. Position the new cable into the release pin and bend the release pin slot closed.

3. Install the cable release clip (Fig. 6).

4. Position the cable to the seat spring elements and retain it with two hog rings.

5. Position the seat back trim over the tabs. Bend the tabs down and install new trim retaining hog rings.

6. Install the headrest stabilizer rod upper guide plates.

7. Position the seat back assembly to the seat cushion hinge assembly and install the roll pin which retains the lower actuator rod to the seat hinge.

8. Install the seat back hinge retaining pins and cotter pins.

9. Install new hog rings to retain

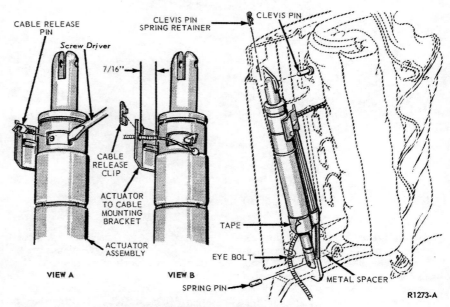

FIG. 6—Seat Actuator and Control Cable Assembly

the trim cover bottom flap.

10. Install the seat back stops.

11. Install the control cable under the two retaining clamps on the seat back pivot.

12. Position the control cable end on the adjusting handle and install the speed clip cable retainer.

13. Install the pivot side outer cover retainer.

14. Install the adjusting handle on the adjusting handle shaft.

15. Adjust the control cable, if necessary, and tighten the cable clamps.

16. Install pivot side outer cover.

17. Position the headrest on the seat back assembly and install the headrest stabilizer rod lower spring retainers.

18. Position the seat back shield on the seat back and install the seat back shield retaining screws.

3 SIX-WAY POWER SEAT

DESCRIPTION AND OPERATION

The six-way power seat (Fig. 7) ward switch controls the vertical movement, or tilt, of the front por- relay with the exception of horizontal movement, which is controlled

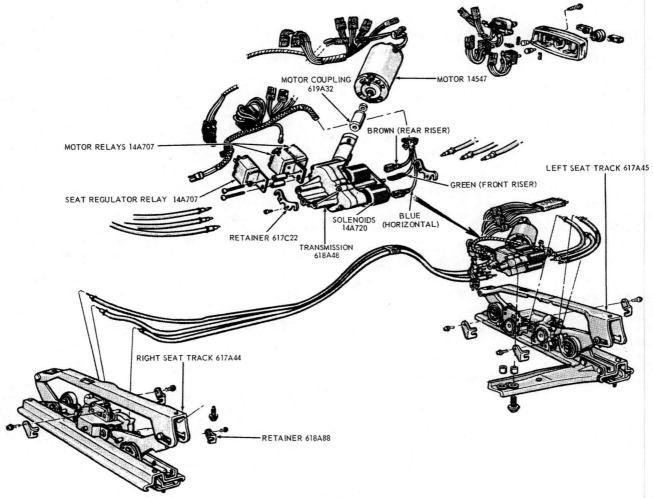

FIG. 7—Six-Way Power Seat—Disassembled

R 1305–A

provides horizontal, vertical and tilting adjustments. The seat is driven by a single motor through a transmission and six flexible drive cables encased in housings.

The control switches are mounted on the seat left side shield. The for- tion of the seat. The rear switch controls the vertical movement, or tilt of the rear portion of the seat. The center switch controls both horizontal and vertical movement of the seat. These switches control the operation of three solenoids through a directly by the switch.

The solenoids engage the transmission gears, transmitting driving power to the respective driven mechanisms of the seat through drive cables. The rear solenoid (brown wire) energizes the seat rear vertical drive assemblies. The lower front solenoid (green wire) energizes the front vertical drive assemblies. The horizontal seat movement is operated by the top front (blue wire) solenoid.

Both the control and power circuits are protected by a common 20-ampere circuit breaker mounted on the starting motor relay.

DIAGNOSIS AND TESTING

DIAGNOSIS GUIDE

Motor Does Not Operate

1. Transmission locked.
2. Defective motor.
3. Defective circuit breaker.
4. Open circuit.
5. Defective seat control switch.
6. Defective motor relay(s).

Motor Operates——No Seat Movement

1. Defective coupling.
2. Solenoids inoperative.
3. Open circuits.

No Vertical Operation—Tilt O.K.

1. Defective seat regulator relay.
2. Defective seat control switch.
3. Open circuit.

No Horizontal Operation

1. Defective solenoid.
2. Defective seat control switch.
3. Open circuit or loose wires.

No Tilt Front or Rear—Vertical Operation O.K.

1. Defective seat control switch.
2. Defective switch relay.
3. Open circuit.

TESTING

Seat Regulator Relay

If the seat tilts but has no vertical operation, substitute a known good seat regulator relay in place of the suspected relay and check the vertical operation.

Coupling

Check the transmission input shaft to determine if it rotates when the seat control switch is actuated. If it does not rotate and the motor is operating, replace the coupling.

Solenoid

Actuate the seat control switch and check for solenoid operation. An audible click will be heard when the solenoid is energized. If no click is heard, check for voltage at the solenoid using the solenoid frame as a ground. If voltage is available, replace the solenoid. If no voltage is available, check for voltage using a good ground. If voltage is available, ground the solenoid and check its operation. If the solenoid does not function, replace it.

Open Circuit

When checking for an open circuit, start the test at the point which is electrically the farthest from the source of power and work towards the source.

To check for an open circuit, check for voltage at each end of the wire with a test light (including splices and connectors). If voltage is available only at one end, the wire is open.

Switch

Substitute a known good switch in place of a suspected defective switch.

Motor

Check for voltage at the motor. If voltage is available, and the motor does not operate, replace the motor.

Transmission

If the transmission input shaft cannot be rotated (solenoids not energized), the transmission is locked and must be replaced. If the shaft rotates, the transmission is not locked.

Circuit Breaker

Actuate the seat control switch and listen for the solenoid(s) to click. If no click is heard, check for voltage at the input and output terminals of the circuit breaker. If voltage is available at only one terminal, the circuit breaker is defective. If voltage is available at both terminals, the circuit breaker is good. If no voltage is available at the circuit breaker, check for an open circuit between the circuit breaker and the starting motor relay battery terminal.

Motor Relays

If the motor does not operate, one or both motor relays could be defective or the relay connector terminal blocks are reversed.

If one or both relays are suspected to be defective, substitute known good relays in place of the suspected relay(s) and check the motor operation. The relay case must be grounded for relay operation.

One relay can be identified by a daub of green paint or by the number stamped on the relay. The other relay is identified only by the number stamped on the mounting bracket. The relay identified by the green paint (Number C5AB-14A707-E) should be connected to the connector with a red-yellow wire, a yellow wire, and a green-white wire. The other relay (Number C5AB-14A707-B) should be connected to the connector with a black-white, a red wire, and 2 red-yellow wires. If these wire connectors are not connected to the correct relay, the motor will be inoperative.

REMOVAL AND INSTALLATION

Seat and/or Seat Track

1. Raise the car and remove 2 seat track-to-floor pan retaining nuts from each side.
2. Lower the car and disconnect the wires at the connector near the tunnel.
3. Lift the seat up to disengage the seat track studs from the floor pan and remove the seat and seat track assembly from the car.
4. Place the seat upside down on a clean bench and disconnect the switch wires at the connectors.
5. Remove 2 bolts attaching each track to the seat frame and remove the track assembly from the seat.
6. Position the track assembly to the seat frame and install the attaching bolts.
7. Connect the switch wires to the track assembly at the connectors.
8. Position the seat track in the car and connect the wires at the connector.
9. Install the seat track to floor pan retaining nuts and torque the nuts to 12 to 25 ft-lbs.

Motor

1. Disconnect the seat motor wires at the multiple connector.
2. Remove 2 motor retaining nuts and remove the motor and drive coupling from the rear side of the seat.
3. Position the drive coupling on the motor shaft and position the motor and coupling to the seat track transmission.
4. Install the motor retaining nuts and connect the motor wires at the connector. Then, check the seat operation.

Transmission and Solenoids

1. Remove the seat and seat track assembly from the car and place it upside down on a clean bench.

2. Remove the cable housing retainers from both sides of the transmission (Fig. 7).

3. Remove the left track to seat frame attaching bolts and disconnect the switch wires at the connectors. Then, remove the left track, transmission, motor, and relays as an assembly from the seat frame.

4. Remove the transmission to bracket attaching bolts and separate the transmission from the cable housings and cables.

5. Disconnect the wires from the solenoids and remove the motor and coupling and the relays from the transmission.

6. Position the motor and drive coupling to the transmission and install the 2 retaining nuts.

7. Position the relays to the transmission and install the 2 attaching bolts.

8. Connect the wires to the solenoids (Fig. 7).

9. Position the transmission to the left drive cables and install the cable retainer.

10. Install the two transmission to bracket attaching bolts.

11. Insert the right drive cables into the transmission and install the retainer.

12. Position the left track to the seat frame and install the attaching bolts. Then, install the seat and seat track assembly in the car.

Cable and/or Housing—Right Side

1. Remove the seat and seat track assembly from the car and place it upside down on a clean bench.

2. Remove the cable housing retainer (Fig. 7) from the right side of the transmission and from the track.

3. Remove the right track to seat frame attaching bolts and separate the track and cables from the transmission. Then, remove the cable housing and/or cable from the track.

4. Position the cable housing and/or cable to the track and install the housing retainer.

5. Check to be sure that the right and left tracks are in the same position. Then, position the track, cable housings and cables to the transmission and install the retainer.

6. Position the track to the seat frame and install the two attaching bolts.

7. Install the seat and seat track assembly in the car.

Cable and/or Housing—Left Side

1. Remove the seat and seat track assembly from the car and place it upside down on a clean bench.

2. Remove the cable housing retainer (Fig. 7) from the left side of the transmission and from the left track.

3. Remove the left track to seat frame attaching bolts.

4. Remove the transmission to bracket attaching bolts and pull the track and cables away from the transmission. Then, remove the cable housing and/or cable from the track.

5. Position the cable housing and/or cable to the track and install the housing retainer.

6. Check to be sure that the right and left tracks are in the same position. Then, position the track, cable housings, and cables to the transmission and install the retainer.

7. Install the transmission to bracket attaching bolts and the track to seat frame attaching bolts.

8. Install the seat and seat track assembly in the car.

Seat Track—Right Side

1. Remove the seat and seat track assembly from the car and place it upside down on a clean bench.

2. Remove the cable housing retainers from the three cables connected to the right seat track (Fig. 7).

3. Remove the right track to seat frame attaching bolts; separate the cable housings and cables from the track and remove the track.

4. Operate the left track to the full up and full rearward position.

5. Manually operate the right track to the full up and full rearward position so that the 2 tracks are in the same position.

6. Position the cable housings and cables to the right track and install the cable retainers.

7. Position the right track to the seat frame and install the attaching bolts.

8. Install the seat and seat track assembly in the car.

Seat Track—Left Side

1. Remove the seat and seat track assembly from the car and place it upside down on a clean work bench.

2. Remove the cable housing retainers from the three cables connected to the left seat track (Fig. 7).

3. Remove the left track to seat frame attaching bolts.

4. Remove the two transmission to bracket attaching bolts (Fig. 7) and remove the left track.

5. Operate the right track to the full up and full rearward position.

6. Manually operate the left track to the full up and full rearward position so that the 2 tracks are in the same position.

7. Position the cable housings and cables to the left track and install the cable retainers.

8. Install the transmission to bracket attaching bolts.

9. Install the track to seat frame attaching bolts and install the seat and seat track assembly in the car.

PART 18-3   CONVERTIBLE TOP

1 CARE OF TOP FABRIC

Proper care of the top material will reduce the possibility of water stains, mildew, or shrinkage. Do not stack the top if it is damp. Always use the convertible top vinyl boot to keep the top material clean, dry, and in position when the top is stacked.

The rear window slide fastener should be lubricated at least once a year with stainless stick lubricant such as Door Ease.

Use the top compartment behind the rear seat back only for storage of the top. The storage of other items not only interferes with the proper operation of the top, but may also damage or stain the top material.

The vinyl top may be washed each time the car is washed. Clean the material with FoMoCo Interior Trim Cleaner and a scrub brush. For an extremely soiled top, use an abrasive cleaner sparingly. Be sure to rinse the top thoroughly with clean water during and after washing.

Do not use a cleaning fluid that is not recommended for vinyl material because damage to the top may result.

The vinyl coating becomes tacky at approximately 180°F. Therefore, when making paint repairs, be sure to protect the top material from heat.

2 OPERATION OF THE TOP

TO LOWER THE TOP

With the vehicle standing still, proceed as follows:

1. Make certain that the folding top stowage compartment area is not restricted as a result of objects stowed either in or beneath the stowage compartment.
2. Rotate the right and left sunvisors downward.
3. Disengage the right and left header clamps located in the front side rails. **To avoid cutting the top material or creating difficult boot installation, always close the handles after releasing the No. 1 bow from the windshield header.**
4. Actuate the folding top control switch located on the instrument panel until the top is in the fully stowed position.
5. Remove the dust hood (boot) from its protective case in the luggage compartment. Position the boot over the folded top and engage all snap fasteners.

Under no circumstances, should the folding top be operated while any of the following conditions prevail:

While the vehicle is in motion.

With the dust hood (boot) stowed in the folding top stowage compartment.

With objects either in or beneath the folding compartment.

With the back curtain window unzipped and hanging by the assist strap.

With the back curtain window unzipped and resting on the rear seat back moulding.

While the top material is wet.

The above practices can result in damage to the top material and/or mechanism, broken back curtain window glass and/or folding top material shrinkage. The dust hood is normally kept in its own protective envelope in the luggage compartment when not in use.

TO RAISE THE TOP

With the vehicle standing still, proceed as follows:

1. Lower both door and quarter windows.
2. Rotate the right and left sunvisors downward.
3. Remove the dust hood (boot); place it in its protective case in the luggage compartment.
4. Actuate the folding top control switch located on the instrument panel; immediately before the No. 1 bow dowel pins enter their respective striker plates, release the switch and open the header clamps in the right and left front side rails. Continue to raise the top until the No. 1 bow comes to rest properly on the windshield header. Close both header clamps making certain that the toggle hoods are fully engaged with their respective catches.

Under certain weather conditions it may be necessary to grasp the side rail directly above the approximate center of the door glass and pull down while clamping the No. 1 bow at the header.

5. Close the door and quarter windows and rotate the sunvisors as desired.

TO LOWER THE BACK CURTAIN WINDOW

1. Make certain that the folding top stowage compartment area is not restricted as a result of objects stowed either in or beneath the stow-

age compartment.

2. Disengage the back curtain window zipper completely.

3. Unsnap the assist strap from the No. 4 bow and carefully stow the window back of the rear seat back, making certain that the assembly lays free in the bottom of the folding top stowage compartment.

To prevent back curtain window glass breakage never operate the vehicle with the window unzippered and hanging by the assist strap or, unzippered and resting on the rear seat back mouldings.

TO RAISE THE BACK CURTAIN WINDOW

1. Engage the back curtain win-

dow assist strap snap fastener to the No. 4 bow.

2. Fully engage the zipper pilot (leading pin on lower half of zipper) in the zipper slide and zip the window closed.

Periodically lubricate the zipper with Door-Ease stick lubricant or bees' wax for ease of operation.

3 TROUBLE DIAGNOSIS

**CONVERTIBLE TOP
TROUBLE DIAGNOSIS GUIDE**

MALFUNCTION	PROBABLE CAUSE	CORRECTIVE ACTION
1 WATER LEAK AT WINDSHIELD HEADER	(a) Front side rail weatherstrip and/or retainer improperly installed. (b) Windshield header seal assembly misaligned or folded under the No. 1 bow. (c) Windshield header moulding dimpled excessively at the attaching screw holes. (d) Windshield header moulding sections improperly installed causing a void in the No. 1 bow weatherstrip. (e) Header clamp toggle hooks improperly adjusted.	(a) Repair or replace as necessary. (b) Correct header seal installation as necessary. (c) Remove the moulding and smooth out dimples. (d) Correct moulding installation as necessary. (e) Loosen header clamp Allen screw and adjust toggle hoods in or out as necessary. Retighten Allen screws.
2 WATER LEAK ABOVE DOOR AND/OR QUARTER WINDOWS	(a) Door or quarter glass improperly adjusted. (b) Side rail sag or overcrown causing a poor seal between top edge of glass and side rail weatherstrip. (c) Side rail weatherstrip improperly adjusted.	(a) Refer to Part 17-3 for window adjustment. (b) Refer to side rail crown adjustment and/or side rail to door glass adjustment under Section 4. (c) Refer to side rail weatherstrip adjustment under Section 4.
3 WATER LEAK IN LUGGAGE COMPARTMENT UPPER BACK PANEL AND DRAIN TROUGH AREA	(a) Inadequate weld sealer along pinch weld flange under belt moulding.	(a) Remove moulding and tape pinch weld flange. Seal pinch weld flange to belt moulding attaching nuts. Check for exposed or unused holes in the drain trough. To accomplish this, loosen the belt center and side tacking strips. Seal all holes including threaded holes for the tacking strip attaching screws. **Never back off on a tacking strip attaching screws as water will follow past the threads.** Make certain that the coach joints (weld joints), in the drain trough are adequately sealed.
4 DOWEL PINS FALL SHORT OF STRIKER PLATE CAUSING DIFFICULTY IN CLAMPING HEADER	(a) Top operated with door and/or quarter windows raised. (b) Front side rail hinge stop screw improperly adjusted causing the side rail to overcrown. (c) Body opening excessive.	(a) Door and quarter windows must always be lowered when raising the top to prevent interference. (b) Adjust either or both hinge stop screws as necessary. (c) Re-shim body bolts and spacers as necessary.

CONVERTIBLE TOP TROUBLE DIAGNOSIS GUIDE (Continued)

MALFUNCTION	PROBABLE CAUSE	CORRECTIVE ACTION
4 DOWEL PINS FALL SHORT OF STRIKER PLATE CAUSING DIFFICULTY IN CLAMPING HEADER (Continued)	(d) Balance link eccentric improperly adjusted.	(d) Refer to side rail to door glass adjustment under Section 4.
5 DIFFICULT TO ENGAGE HEADER CLAMPS	(a) Top operated with door and/or quarter windows raised. (b) Header clamp toggle hooks improperly adjusted. (c) Front side hinge stop screw improperly adjusted. (d) Front side rail weatherstrip improperly installed. (e) Body opening excessive.	(a) Door and quarter windows must always be lowered when raising the top to prevent interference. (b) Refer to toggle clamp hook and dowel adjustment under Section 4. (c) Refer to side rail crown adjustment under Section 4. (d) The front side rail weatherstrip must be installed so the metal insert portion of the weatherstrip corresponds with the No. 1 bow outer contour. (e) Re-shim body bolts and spacers as required.
6 FOLDING TOP STACKS TOO HIGH	(a) Bulky objects either in or beneath the folding compartment. (b) Rear curtain window resting on rear seat back moulding. (c) Dust hood (boot) attached to rear seat back moulding causing an obstruction between the rear curtain window and the rear seat back moulding. (d) Lower end of balance link improperly adjusted on the serrated attaching plate. (e) Restriction in the hinging action of either cylinder. (f) Side rail interferes with quarter trim panel.	(a) Remove foreign objects from top compartment area. (b) Top should never be operated unless rear curtain window is either fully zippered or, lowered and stowed behind the rear seat back. (c) Remove dust hood and stow in the envelope provided. (d) Refer to Side Rail Adjustment in The Stacked Position under Section 4. (e) Check for cause and correct as necessary. When this condition is noted, check for a bent cylinder rod. Repair or replace cylinder. (f) Improperly installed trim panel. Check and correct trim panel installation.
7 REAR CURTAIN WINDOW GLASS BREAKAGE	(a) Obstruction either in or under the folding compartment. (b) Folding top lowered with rear curtain window assembly unzippered and hanging on the No. 4 bow by the assist strap. (c) Folding top lowered with rear curtain window disengaged and resting on rear seat back moulding.	(a) Correct restriction as necessary. (b) Top should never be operated in this manner. (c) Top should never be operated in this manner.
8 TOP FAILS TO OPERATE	(a) Electrical circuit faulty. (b) Hydraulic system faulty.	(a) Check electrical circuit as described in Section 5. (b) Check hydraulic system as described in Section 5.
9 TOP OPERATES TOO SLOW	(a) Kink in the hydraulic lines. (b) Leak in the hydraulic system. (c) Excessive air in the hydraulic system.	(a) Repair or replace as necessary. (b) Correct as necessary. (c) Bleed system as described in Section 5.

4 CONVERTIBLE TOP ADJUSTMENTS

TOP STACK ADJUSTMENTS

LATERAL ADJUSTMENT

The stack to main pivot mounting is adjustable inboard—outboard to obtain the designed 9/32-inch dimension between the rear side rail and

3. Move the main pivot mounting side to side as necessary to obtain a 9/32-inch clearance between the outer edge of the rear side rail and the inner flange of the quarter belt moulding (Fig. 2).

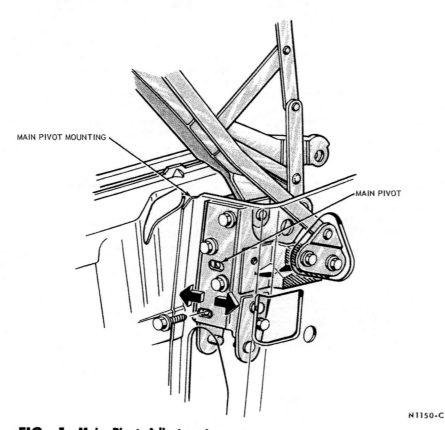

FIG. 1—Main Pivot Adjustment

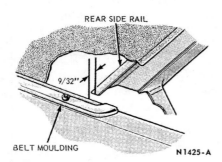

FIG. 2—Top Side Rail-To-Body Clearance

belt moulding (Figs. 1 and 2).

To adjust, proceed as follows:

1. Clamp the No. 1 bow to the windshield header.

2. Loosen the main pivot mounting attaching bolts on one side of the body (Fig. 1).

4. After a 9/32-inch clearance is obtained, tighten the attaching bolts.

5. Adjust the opposite side of the top in the same manner.

SIDE RAIL ADJUSTMENT IN STACKED POSITION

The balance link lower attaching plate is adjustable to permit maximum lowering of the side rail in the stacked position (Fig. 3).

To adjust, proceed as follows:

Loosen the adjuster bracket retaining bolts (Fig. 3) and move the bracket as necessary to lower the stacking height. Then, tighten the adjuster bracket retaining bolts.

It may be necessary to re-adjust the balance link upper eccentric as outlined under Side Rail to Door Glass Adjustment.

SIDE RAIL TO DOOR GLASS ADJUSTMENT

The balance link upper attachment incorporates an eccentric to obtain the required seal between the side rail weatherstrip and door glass (Fig. 4).

To adjust, proceed as follows:

1. With the top in the raised position, loosen the eccentric lock nut (Fig. 4) and rotate the eccentric pin to obtain a 3/8-inch clearance between the door glass frame and the front and center side rails (Fig. 5). This dimension increases 9/16-inch along the quarter window radius.

2. Hold the eccentric pin to prevent it from turning and tighten the lock nut.

SIDE RAIL CROWN ADJUSTMENT

The front to center side rail hinge incorporates an adjusting screw to control the side rail crown. This adjustment also permits improved dowel pin to striker plate entry.

To adjust, proceed as follows:

Raise the top to the mid-open position and turn the adjusting screw located in the front face of the rear half of the side rail hinge as necessary to obtain a constant dimension between the side rail and door glass when the top is clamped to the header.

TOP MATERIAL SAG ADJUSTMENT

The No. 3 bow to side rail attaching bracket incorporates an elongated vertical slot to reduce excessive top material sag between bows. The permissable sag between bows is ½ inch.

Adjustment is accomplished by loosening the No. 3 bow to side rail bracket attachment and raising each side of the bow. Maximum adjustment is approximately ¼ inch. Retighten the nut to retain the adjustment.

DOOR WINDOW TO TOP MATERIAL CLEARANCE

The No. 2 bow to side rail attaching bracket also incorporates an elongated vertical slot to permit up and down adjustment of the bow to obtain the specified clearance between the top edge material and the door window line (Fig. 6).

Adjustment is accomplished in the

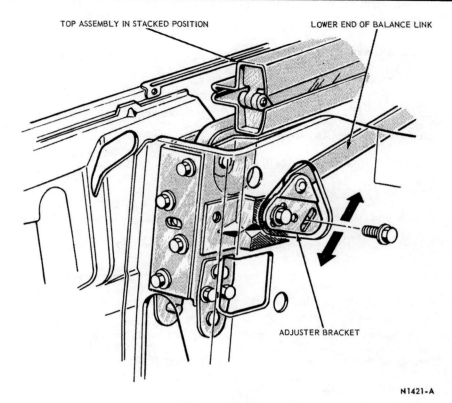

TOP ASSEMBLY IN STACKED POSITION   LOWER END OF BALANCE LINK

ADJUSTER BRACKET

N1421-A

FIG. 3—Side Rail Stacked Height Adjustment

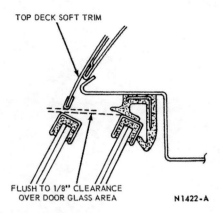

TOP DECK SOFT TRIM

FLUSH TO 1/8" CLEARANCE
OVER DOOR GLASS AREA

N1422-A

FIG. 6—Top Material to Door Window Clearance

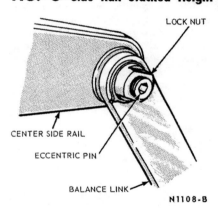

LOCK NUT

CENTER SIDE RAIL
ECCENTRIC PIN
BALANCE LINK

N1108-B

FIG. 4—Balance Link Eccentric Adjustment

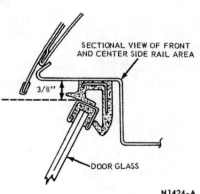

SECTIONAL VIEW OF FRONT
AND CENTER SIDE RAIL AREA

3/8"

DOOR GLASS

N1424-A

FIG. 5—Side Rail to Door Glass Clearance

pull must be felt as the card is pulled out. Both toggle clamps need not be adjusted unless necessary.

2. Release the toggle clamps, loosen the locking screw (Fig. 7), and thread the toggle hook in or out until adequate sealing pressure is applied at the header weatherstrip. Tighten the toggle clamp locking screw after adjustment. Excessive tightening is detrimental to a good seal.

3. The No. 1 bow dowel pins are adjustable inboard and outboard to obtain proper relationship of the No. 1 bow to the windshield header (Fig. 7). Loosen the dowel pin lock nut and adjust the dowel pin inboard or outboard as necessary (Fig. 7). Tighten the lock nut.

SIDE RAIL WEATHERSTRIP ADJUSTMENT

The center and rear side rail weatherstrips are adjustable fore-and-aft to obtain an interference fit between weatherstrip sections (Fig. 8).

To adjust, proceed as follows:

The center and rear side rail weatherstrips are adjustable fore-and-aft (Fig. 8) to provide a water

same manner as the No. 3 bow.

The specified clearance between the top material to door window is flush to ⅛-inch clearance.

TOGGLE CLAMP HOOK AND DOWEL ADJUSTMENT

The header clamp toggle hooks are adjustable up or down to obtain adequate windshield header seal (Fig. 7).

To adjust, proceed as follows:

1. To determine which side is not sealing, check the weatherstrip between the No. 1 bow and the header with a 3 by 5-inch card. A reasonable

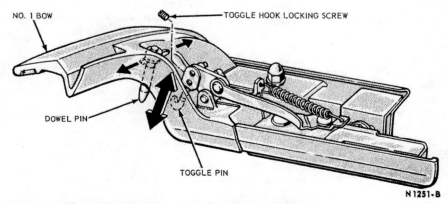

NO. 1 BOW   TOGGLE HOOK LOCKING SCREW
DOWEL PIN
TOGGLE PIN
N1251-B

FIG. 7—Toggle Clamp Hook and Dowel Adjustment

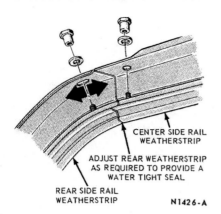

CENTER SIDE RAIL
WEATHERSTRIP

ADJUST REAR WEATHERSTRIP
AS REQUIRED TO PROVIDE A
WATER TIGHT SEAL

REAR SIDE RAIL
WEATHERSTRIP

N1426-A

**FIG. 8—Side Rail
Weatherstrip Adjustment**

tight seal at the rear break joint. To obtain a water tight seal between the front and center weatherstrips, trim the rear end of the front weatherstrip as required. **Any in-or-out adjustment that is required to insure an adequate seal between the glass frames and the weatherstrips must be accomplished by repositioning the**

glass angle (Group 17).

NO. 1 BOW ADJUSTMENT

The No. 1 bow can be adjusted fore-and-aft at each front side rail. However, this adjustment is used in production prior to trimming the top. No attempt should be made to alter this setting with the top material attached to the No. 1 bow.

5 HYDRAULIC SYSTEM

FLUID LEVEL IN RESERVOIR

1. Remove the rear seat cushion and seat back assembly.
2. Place absorbent cloth below the reservoir filler plug.
3. Remove the filler plug and check the fluid level. It should be level with the bottom of the filler plug hole. If fluid appears excessively low, check for leaks or restrictions in the hydraulic lines, loose or broken fittings and/or damaged cylinders.

If the system is faulty, repair or replace as necessary and bleed the system as described below.

BLEEDING SYSTEM

1. Lower the door and quarter windows.
2. Remove the filler plug from the reservoir and fill to the bottom of the filler plug hole with type A transmission fluid.
3. With the filler plug installed

by one or two threads, and engine running, cycle the top a sufficient number of times to adequately purge the system of air pockets. Excessive air will be noted in the transparent lines. Replenish the reservoir as necessary during the bleeding operation. Fill to the proper level and tighten the filler plug. **When cycling the top, make certain that the cylinders have freedom of movement in both the inner quarter panel structure and quarter trim panels.**

6 ELECTRICAL SYSTEM

BATTERY CHARGE

The battery should be fully charged before making any electrical checks because a partially discharged battery will cause slow motor and pump operation.

CURRENT DRAW

To check the current draw in the top operating circuit, disconnect the black wire at the circuit breaker (located on the starter relay), and connect an ammeter *in series* in the circuit. Operate the top control switch and note the ammeter readings. The current draw should be 28 amperes maximum while operating, and 40 to 50 amperes stalled, with a voltage reading of 12.3 volts. Current is excess of 75 amperes indicates a frozen pump or cylinder or a mechanical obstruction. Low amperage with the motor running and no top movement indicates a defective pump

or low fluid level in the reservoir.

TOP CONTROL SWITCH

1. Connect one terminal of a test lamp to the black (feed) wire of the top control switch, and ground the other lead. If the test lamp does not light, there is an open or short circuit between the battery and the switch or a bad circuit breaker.
2. If there is voltage to the switch, connect a jumper wire between the black (feed) wire and the red wire, and then between the black wire and yellow wire. If the top motor operates, the switch is faulty and must be replaced.

CIRCUIT BREAKER

If there is no voltage at the top control switch, connect a jumper wire across the terminals of the circuit breaker (located on the starter relay) and operate the switch. If the top motor operates, the circuit

breaker is faulty and must be replaced. If there is no voltage at the circuit breaker, check the black wire from the circuit breaker to the starter relay.

SWITCH-TO-MOTOR WIRES

Disconnect the yellow and the red switch-to-motor leads at the junction block near the motor. Connect a test lamp between the yellow wire and a ground, and check by operating the top control switch to raise the top. Connect the test lamp between the red wire and a ground, and check by operating the switch to lower the top. If the test lamp does not light in either case, the wire from the junction block is open or shorted.

MOTOR

Check the operation of the motor by connecting first one motor lead, and then the other, directly to the battery positive terminal. If the motor operates in either case, but will not operate when hooked into the wiring harness, check the wiring harness again for shorted or open circuits. If the motor will not work when hooked directly to the battery, check the black (ground) wire from the motor. If the motor still does not work, it must be replaced.

TOP CONTROL SWITCH

FORD

1. Disconnect negative (ground) cable from the battery.
2. Remove the set screw from the top control switch knob.
3. Remove the bezel nut and spacer and pull the switch and rear spacer from the switch opening.
4. Disconnect the switch wires and remove the switch and rear spacer.
5. Connect the switch wires and install the rear spacer on the switch.
6. Position the switch in the instrument panel opening and install the spacer and bezel nut.
7. Install the knob on the switch.
8. Connect the ground cable to the negative battery cable.

MERCURY

1. Disconnect negative (ground) cable from the battery.
2. Remove the set screw from the top control switch knob.
3. Remove 4 screws attaching the left access panel to the underside of the instrument panel, and remove the access panel.
4. Remove the bezel nut and pull the switch from the switch opening.
5. Disconnect the switch wires and remove the switch.
6. Connect the switch wires and position the switch in the instrument panel opening.
7. Install the bezel nut on the switch.
8. Install the switch knob.
9. Install the instrument panel lower left access cover.
10. Connect the ground cable to negative battery terminal.

7 REPAIR AND REPLACEMENT OF THE PUMP, CYLINDER AND MOTOR ASSEMBLIES

MOTOR AND PUMP

A pump repair kit and a reservoir repair kit are available for service.

REMOVAL

1. Operate the top to the fully raised position.
2. Remove the rear seat cushion and seat back.
3. Disconnect the motor leads and the ground wire.
4. Vent the reservoir by removing the filler plug, and then re-install the filler plug. **The reservoir must be vented in order to equalize the pressure. This lessens the possibility of fluid spraying on the trim and paint when the hoses are disconnected.**
5. Place absorbent cloths beneath the hose connections, disconnect the hoses, and then plug the open fittings and lines.
6. Remove the retaining nuts and washers and remove the motor and pump assembly from the floor pan. Exercise care to prevent loss of the rubber grommets.

DISASSEMBLY

1. Remove the filler plug, and drain the fluid from the reservoir.
2. Scribe lines on the reservoir and pump body for re-assembly purposes.
3. Remove the center bolt from the reservoir cover (Fig. 9), and remove the reservoir and seal at the end of the reservoir.
4. Remove the mounting bolts

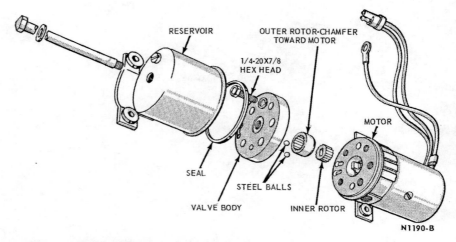

FIG. 9—Motor and Pump Disassembled

that retain the valve body to the pump body.
5. Place a cloth under the assembly, and carefully remove the valve body. Exercise care not to lose the 2 check balls.
6. Remove both rotors from the motor and pump assembly.

ASSEMBLY

Use all the parts contained in the pump repair kit when assembling the pump or reservoir.
1. Install the inner rotor on the armature shaft.
2. Install the outer rotor over the inner rotor.
3. Place the check balls in the pump body channels.

4. Install the valve body on the pump body.
5. Install the valve body mounting bolts.
6. Install the seal on the valve body (Fig. 9).
7. Install a new seal on the center bolt, and install the reservoir on the valve body, using the lines previously scribed as guides.

INSTALLATION

1. Remove the plugs from the lines and fittings, and connect the lines to the pump. Use cloths to absorb any fluid that leaks out of the lines or the pump.
2. Install the assembly on the floor pan, making sure that the rubber grommets are in the proper posi-

tion on the mounting brackets and that the ground wire is grounded under one of the retaining nuts.

3. Connect the motor lead wires at the connector.

4. Fill the system with type A transmission fluid and bleed the system as described in Section 5—Bleeding System.

TOP LIFT CYLINDER

1. Remove the rear seat cushion and seat back.

2. Remove the quarter trim panel.

3. Remove the locking pin, washers, and clevis pin from the lift cylinder rod (Fig. 10).

4. Remove 3 bolts attaching the cylinder pivot bracket side to the main pivots (Fig. 10), and remove the bracket side and bushings.

5. Lower the lift cylinder; disconnect and plug the hydraulic lines from the cylinder and remove the cylinders. Use absorbent rags to catch any fluid that leaks out during this operation.

6. Unplug and connect the hydraulic lines to the lift cylinder.

7. Position the lift cylinder, bushings, and the pivot bracket side to the main pivot, and install the 3 attaching bolts (Fig. 10).

8. Position the lift cylinder rod and bushings to the top linkage and install the clevis pin, washers, and locking pin (Fig. 10).

9. Add fluid to the reservoir and, with the filler plug loose, operate the top two or three times to bleed any air from the system. Then, with the top in the raised position, add fluid to the reservoir. The fluid level should not be less than ¼-inch below the filler plug opening.

10. Install the quarter trim panel, and rear seat back and seat cushion.

FRONT HOLD DOWN CLAMP

REMOVAL

1. Partially raise the convertible top.

2. Remove the side rail weatherstrip retainer nuts and screws and place it to the side.

3. Disconnect the handle return spring and remove the roll pin retaining clamp handle pivot pin by using a drift punch.

4. Remove the screws securing the clamp pivot bracket.

5. Remove the handle pivot pin and washers and remove the clamp from the top assembly.

INSTALLATION

1. Position the hold down clamp into the top assembly and install the handle pivot pin, washers, and roll pin.

2. Install the screws which secure the clamp to the pivot bracket.

3. Install the handle return spring, place the side rail weatherstrip into position and install the retainer nuts and screws.

4. Lower the convertible top to the windshield header and adjust the toggle clamp.

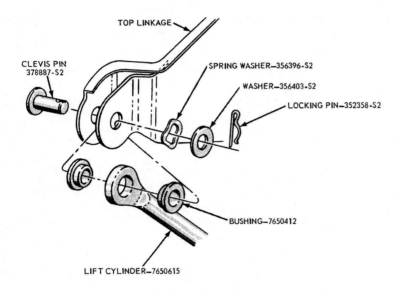

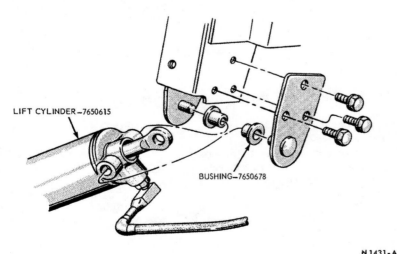

N 1431-A

FIG. 10—Folding Top Lift Cylinder Installation

8 FOLDING TOP TRIM REPLACEMENT

BACK CURTAIN WINDOW AND ZIPPER

REMOVAL

Protect the upper back panel, luggage compartment door and both quarter panels with suitable coverings. **Trim markings referred to should be made with tailors crayon or equivalent for ease of removal.**

1. Partially raise the convertible top.

2. Disengage the folding top compartment rear trim retainer springs at the support wire and the luggage compartment door hinge mounting brackets.

3. Disengage the compartment trim from the belt center and side front tacking strips.

4. Remove the back curtain tacking strip attaching screws.

5. Disengage the zipper and the assist strap and remove the back curtain assembly.

6. Mark the back curtain lower trim material along the lower edge of the belt center tacking strip and remove the tacking strip.

If it is necessary to replace the upper half of the zipper assembly, proceed with steps 7 through 12 to remove and steps 1 through 8 to install. If the upper half of the zipper does not require replacement, proceed to step 9 under Installation.

7. Remove the No. 4 bow outside moulding end tips, moulding and moulding retainer. Carefully detach the top material from the No. 4 bow.

8. Remove both side rail coat hanger hooks and install the two fabricated bow alignment gauges (Figs. 11 and 12). Retain each gauge with a No. 8-18 x 1 ¼-inch pan-head screw and washer (Fig. 12).

9. Remove both belt side front tacking strip attaching screws.

10. Remove rear side rail weatherstrips and pull the cemented quarter deck flap loose at each rear side rail.

11. Fold the top trim assembly to one side sufficiently to expose the No. 4 bow. Mark the bow to indicate the top back stay webbing location (both sides). Also mark the No. 4 bow at both ends of the zipper elastic material.

12. Detach the top back stay webbing and the upper half of the zipper assembly.

INSTALLATION

1. Carefully position the new upper half of the zipper assembly on the No. 4 bow; the edge of the material should be flush with the front edge of the No. 4 bow tacking strip. Working from the center outboard, stretch and secure the assembly with staples. **Both ends of the elastic must correspond with the marks on the No. 4 bow (step 11).**

2. Position the top back stay webbing on the No. 4 bow and secure each with staples.

3. Position the top material on the No. 4 bow and secure it with staples.

4. Install a narrow strip of tape over the staples and install the No. 4 bow outside moulding retainer, moulding and end tips.

5. Install both belt side front tacking strip attaching screws.

6. Cement the quarter deck flaps to each rear side rail.

7. Install both side rail weatherstrips and adjust as necessary.

8. Remove the bow locating gauges and install the coat hanger hooks.

9. Trim off the selvage edge of the old back curtain material that extends below the tacking strip. Refer to the mark made in Step 6 under Removal.

10. Using the old back curtain window assembly as a template, mark the new curtain to indicate the lower edge of the tacking strip. Also mark the tacking strip attaching hole locations. Remove the old back curtain assembly and cut out the tacking strip attaching holes in the new curtain only. **Do not cut off the selvage edge of the new back curtain window assembly.**

11. Center the new back curtain assembly on the belt center tacking strip. Locate the aligning mark across the lower edge of the material with the lower edge of the tacking strip and secure it with staples.

12. Fasten the back curtain assist strap to the No. 4 bow and engage the two zipper halves.

13. Install the belt center tacking strip attaching screws.

14. Install the top compartment trim to the belt tacking strips.

15. Install the two retainer springs between the trim compartment support wire and the luggage compartment door hinge mounting brackets.

TOP COMPARTMENT TRIM

REMOVAL

1. Disengage the compartment trim support wire retaining springs from the luggage compartment door hinge mounting bracket.

2. Remove the compartment rear trim assembly to belt tacking strip plastic drive pins.

3. Remove the compartment rear trim assembly to rear seat back strainer flange attaching screws.

4. Remove the compartment trim support wire and discard the old compartment trim assembly.

INSTALLATION

1. Insert the support wire through the retaining sleeve of the new compartment trim assembly.

2. Position the compartment trim assembly and install the attaching screws (No. 8-18 x ½-inch flat head) across the rear seat back strainer.

3. Drill sixteen $7/64$-inch holes through the compartment trim stiffener corresponding to the existing holes in the tacking strips. After each hole is drilled, re-insert the plastic drive pin.

4. Install the two support wire retaining springs.

CONVERTIBLE TOP FABRIC

Protect the upper back panel, luggage compartment door, and both quarter panels with suitable coverings. **Trim markings referred to should be made with tailors crayon or equivalent for ease of removal.**

Fabricate two bow locating gauges to the dimensions illustrated in Fig. 11.

REMOVAL

1. Disconnect the two retainer springs at the folding top compartment trim support wire and the luggage compartment door hinge mounting bracket (Fig. 13).

2. Disconnect the folding top compartment trim from the belt tacking strips (Fig. 13).

3. Remove all the belt tacking strip attaching screws. Unzip the rear curtain window and remove the window with the center tacking strip attached.

4. Before disconnecting the top quarter deck material from the belt side front tacking strips, mark the material in the following areas:
Mark the quarter deck material

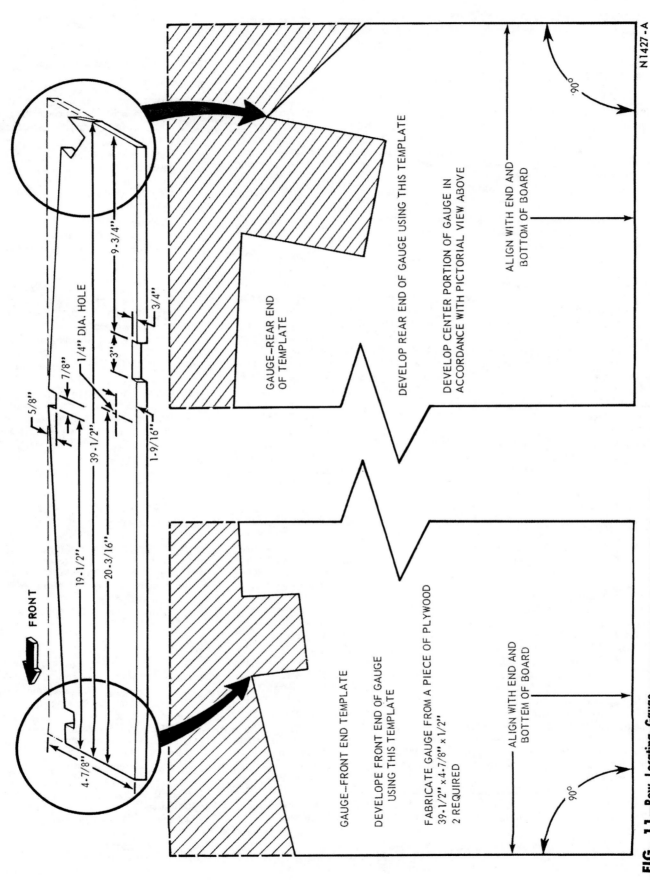

FRONT

5/8"

7/8"

1/4" DIA. HOLE

9-3/4"

3/4"

3"

39-1/2"

1-9/16"

19-1/2"

20-3/16"

4-7/8"

N1427-A

90°

ALIGN WITH END AND
BOTTOM OF BOARD

GAUGE—REAR END
OF TEMPLATE

DEVELOP REAR END OF GAUGE USING THIS TEMPLATE

DEVELOP CENTER PORTION OF GAUGE IN
ACCORDANCE WITH PICTORIAL VIEW ABOVE

90°

ALIGN WITH END AND
BOTTOM OF BOARD

GAUGE—FRONT END TEMPLATE

DEVELOPE FRONT END OF GAUGE
USING THIS TEMPLATE

FABRICATE GAUGE FROM A PIECE OF PLYWOOD
39-1/2" x 4-7/8" x 1/2"
2 REQUIRED

FIG. 11—Bow Locating Gauge

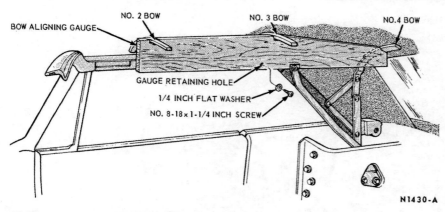

FIG. 12—Bow Locating Gauge Installation

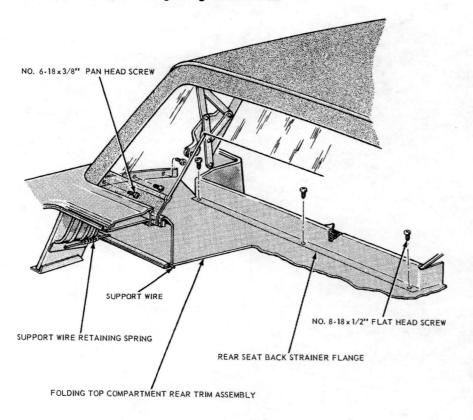

FIG. 13—Top Compartment Trim Installation

along the lower edge of the tacking strips (Fig. 14).

5. Remove the top quarter deck material from the belt side front tacking strips.

6. Lower the top and remove the weatherstrip retainer from the No. 1 bow. Remove the front side weatherstrip attaching nuts from both front side rails and remove the weatherstrip.

7. Remove the windshield header seal assembly and the top material from the No. 1 bow (Fig. 14).

8. Remove the rear side rail

weatherstrips. Loosen the top quarter material flaps that are cemented to the front and rear side rails.

9. Remove the top material hold down cables from the front side rail key hole slot after removing the slot retainer. Pull the cables rearward until each is removed from the retaining sleeve.

10. Raise the top and clamp the No. 1 bow to the header. Remove both side rail coat hanger hooks.

11. Install the two fabricated gauges for aligning the No. 2, 3 and 4 bows. Align the ¼-inch hole in

the wooden gauge with the coat hanger hook hole in the side rail and secure each gauge to the side rail with a No. 8-18 x 1 ¼-inch pan-head screw and washer (Fig. 12).

12. Remove the No. 2 and No. 3 bow listing retainer screws and remove both retainers from the listings (Fig. 14).

13. Remove the No. 4 bow outside moulding end tips, moulding, and moulding retainer.

14. Detach the top material from the No. 4 bow and place the assembly on a bench.

15. Trim off the selvage edge from the **old top** quarter deck material that extended below the tacking strips. Refer to Step 4 above.

INSTALLATION

1. Using the old top assembly as a template, mark the new top quarter deck to indicate the lower edge of the tacking strips. Also mark the tacking strip attaching holes. Cut out the belt side front tacking strip hole locations in the new top only. **Do not trim off the selvage edge.**

2. Fold the top center deck material to locate and mark a fore-and aft centerline at the No. 4 bow area. A corresponding center mark is provided on the upper surface of the No. 4 bow.

3. Align the belt side front tacking strip with the aligning marks on the top quarter deck (Fig. 14) and retain it with staples.

4. Position the top trim assembly on the folding top stack. Center the material on the No. 4 bow, making certain that the short outboard bond seam (Fig. 14) is also centered fore-and-aft on the No. 4 bow. Secure the material to the bow with staples.

5. Insert the two retainers in the No. 2 and No. 3 bow listings (Fig. 14).

6. Route the quarter deck retaining cables through the hold-down sleeves in the top material. Insert each cable through its respective front side rail keyhole slot and retain it with the keyhole retainer.

7. Install the belt tacking strip attaching screws loosely, approximately ¼-inch from bottoming.

8. Pull the top trim material forward over the No. 1 bow until the No. 2 and No. 3 bow listings are centered over their respective bows. While maintaining tension on the top trim, place a pencil mark on the outer surface of the trim material along the forward edge of the No. 1 bow.

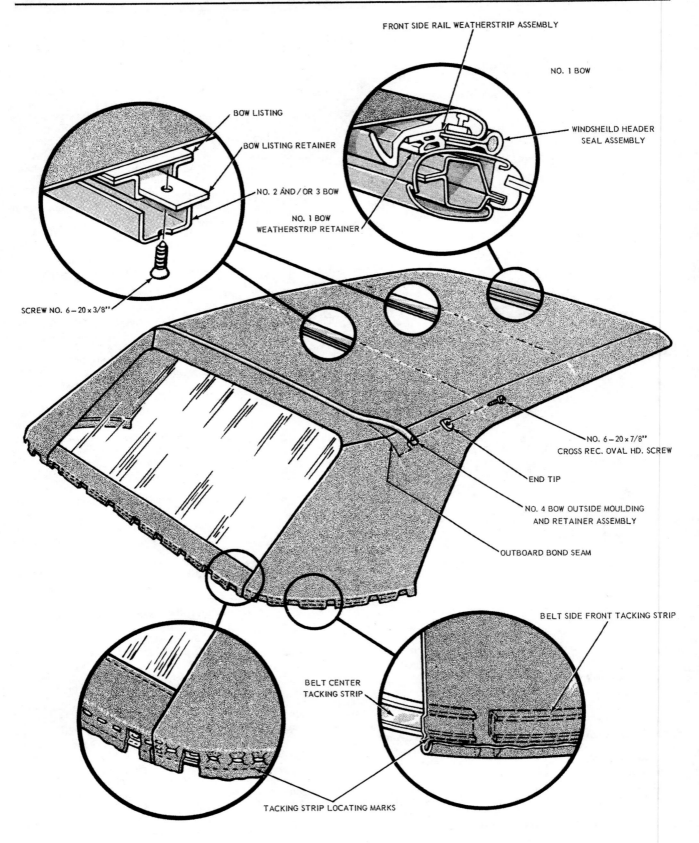

FRONT SIDE RAIL WEATHERSTRIP ASSEMBLY

NO. 1 BOW

WINDSHEILD HEADER
SEAL ASSEMBLY

BOW LISTING

BOW LISTING RETAINER

NO. 2 AND / OR 3 BOW

NO. 1 BOW
WEATHERSTRIP RETAINER

SCREW NO. 6 — 20 x 3/8''

NO. 6 — 20 x 7/8''
CROSS REC. OVAL HD. SCREW

END TIP

NO. 4 BOW OUTSIDE MOULDING
AND RETAINER ASSEMBLY

OUTBOARD BOND SEAM

BELT SIDE FRONT TACKING STRIP

BELT CENTER
TACKING STRIP

TACKING STRIP LOCATING MARKS

N 1429-A

FIG. 14—Fold Top Fabric Installation

9. Remove the two bow aligning gauges and install the coat hanger hooks.

10. Fold the front edge of the top material back from the No. 1 bow. Disengage the No. 1 bow from the windshield header and prop it up one foot above the header.

11. Apply trim cement C2AZ-19C 525-A across the lower front surface of the No. 1 bow and tacking strip and a like amount of cement to the adjacent inner surface of the top material.

12. *Lower the* No. 1 bow on the windshield header. **Do not latch the clamps.** With the top material properly centered on the No. 1 bow, start at the outer front corners and alternately pull the material forward to the pencil aligning mark. Make certain that all wrinkles are removed, then, fold and cement the material to the underside of the bow.

13. Position the windshield header seal assembly to the No. 1 bow and secure the seal and top material with staples. Trim off the excess top material.

14. Cement the front and rear flaps to each side rail. Pierce holes in the flaps for weatherstrip attachments.

15. Install the front side rail weatherstrip and the No. 1 bow retainer.

16. Install the rear side rail weatherstrips. Adjust as required.

17. Install the back curtain window.

18. With the No. 1 bow clamped to the header, tighten all belt tacking strip attaching screws securely.

19. Attach the compartment trim to the belt tacking strips.

20. Attach the compartment trim to the rear seat back strainer flange.

21. Engage the compartment trim support wire to the luggage compartment door hinge bracket springs.

22. Install the No. 4 bow outside moulding retainer, moulding and the two end tips.

MAINTENANCE SCHEDULE

GROUP 19

THOUSANDS OF MILES OR NUMBER OF MONTHS, WHICHEVER OCCURS FIRST (Except Where Noted)		As Required	6	12	18	24	30	36	See Manual Page
ENGINE									
Change engine oil and filter①			X	X	X	X	X	X	20-1
Check engine oil level			At Fuel Stops						20-2
Replace fuel filter (427 engine only)								X	20-2
Replace fuel filter (except 427 engine)		X							20-2
Adjust carburetor—idle speed, idle mixture, and fast (cold) idle speed (automatic choke only)		X							20-2
Adjust accelerator pump lever			Seasonal						20-5
Clean carburetor air cleaner and filter (paper type filter only)①			X	X	X	X	X		20-6
Replace carburetor air cleaner filter	Paper①							X	20-6
	Plastic①				X		X	X	
Clean crankcase oil filler breather cap①			X	X	X	X	X	X	20-6
Clean emission system hoses, tubes, oil separator, fittings, carburetor spacer and replace emission control valve				X		X		X	20-6
Replace thermactor air pump filter if so equipped				X		X		X	20-7
Check engine accessory drive belts		X							20-7
Lubricate exhaust control valve (240 & 390 engines)		X							20-8
Lubricate exhaust control valve (427 engines only)			X	X	X	X	X	X	20-8
Valve tappet adjustment (mechanical) conventional— 427 Hi Performance, and 428-4V Police Interceptor engines only				X		X		X	20-8
Check ignition timing				X		X		X	20-8
Check distributor points and adjust		X							20-9
Check spark plugs		X							20-9
Replace engine coolant (Or every two years)								X	20-10
Check engine coolant level		X							20-10

① On engine items, more frequent intervals will be required if the vehicle is operated in extremely dusty areas for extended periods of idling or short runs which prevent the engine from reaching normal operating temperatures.

TRANSMISSION

		As Required	6	12	18	24	30	36	See Manual Page
Adjust automatic transmission band	Rear	X							
	Front							X	20-10
Check transmission oil level			X	X	X	X	X	X	20-12

CHASSIS

	As Required	6	12	18	24	30	36	See Manual Page
Check axle fluid level		X	X	X	X	X	X	20-13
Check clutch linkage adjustment (manual and overdrive)	X							20-13
Lubricate transmission linkage	X							20-14
Lubricate front suspension ball joints							X	20-14
Lubricate steering linkage							X	20-14
Lubricate steering column lower assembly—heavy duty column	X							20-14
Check steering gear (pre-load on manual gear)	X							20-14
Check power steering reservoir fluid level		X	X	X	X	X	X	20-15
Check brake master cylinder fluid level		X	X	X	X	X	X	20-15
Check brake lines and lining Clean and pack front wheel bearings						X		20-15
Check parking brake linkage and adjust if required	X							20-17
Check tire pressure	X							10-17
Inspect and cross-switch wheels and tires	X							20-17
Check front wheel alignment and linkage	X							20-17
Check battery fluid level	X							20-19
Check air conditioning system	Annually at Beginning of A/C Season							20-19

CONTINUED ON NEXT PAGE

THOUSANDS OF MILES OR NUMBER OF MONTHS, WHICHEVER OCCURS FIRST (Except Where Noted)	As Required	6	12	18	24	30	36	See Manual Page
BODY								
Lubricate hood latch and hinge pivots	X							20-19
Lubricate hood auxiliary catch	X							20-19
Lubricate door lock cylinders		X	X	X	X	X	X	20-19
Lubricate luggage compartment lock cylinder		X	X	X	X	X	X	20-19
Lubricate door hinge and hinge check	X							20-19
Lubricate luggage compartment hinge pivots	X							20-19
Lubricate tailgate lock cylinder		X	X	X	X	X	X	20-19
Lubricate tailgate support and hinges	X							20-20
Lubricate fuel filler door hinges	X							20-20
Lubricate weatherstrip and rubber seals and seat track	X							20-20
Clean body drain holes or examine dust valves for proper operation	X							20-20
Replace windshield wiper blades	X							20-20
Check convertible top operation	X							20-20
Check convertible top fluid level	X							20-20

MAINTENANCE OPERATIONS

GROUP 20

PART 20-1 MAINTENANCE OPERATIONS

1 ENGINE

CHANGE ENGINE OIL AND FILTER

1. Raise the car.
2. Remove the oil pan drain plug and allow the engine oil to drain into a container.
3. Place a drip pan under the filter. Unscrew the filter from the adapter fitting.

4. Coat the gasket on the filter with oil. Place the filter in position on the adapter fitting. Hand tighten the filter until the gasket contacts

the adapter face, then advance it ½ turn.

5. Replace the oil pan drain plug and tighten it securely.

6. Refill the crankcase with the proper amount and grade of oil.

7. Lower the car.

8. Operate the engine at fast idle, and check for oil leaks. If oil leaks are evident, perform the necessary repairs to correct the leakage.

CHECK ENGINE OIL LEVEL

Check the oil level dipstick to be sure it indicates the correct quantity of oil in the crankcase. Be sure the oil is clean.

REPLACE FUEL FILTER ELEMENT

1. Raise the car

2. Unscrew the filter housing from the fuel filter cover. Remove and discard the filter element and gasket.

3. Clean the filter housing in solvent.

4. Coat a new gasket with light engine oil and position the gasket on the filter housing. Position a new filter element over the spout on the cover. **Only a filter element displaying installation instructions should be used. Install the filter element according to the printed instructions on the element.**

5. Screw the filter housing onto the cover. Hand tighten the filter housing until the gasket makes contact with cover; then, advance it ⅛ turn.

6. Lower the car.

7. Start the engine and check for fuel leaks.

ADJUST CARBURETOR—IDLE SPEED, FAST (COLD) IDLE SPEED AND IDLE MIXTURE (AUTOMATIC CHOKE ONLY)

CARBURETOR INTER-CONNECTING LINKAGE ADJUSTMENT—HOLLEY CARBURETORS

The following procedure is required for adjusting the inter-carburetor *linkage* to achieve proper progressive opening of the primary throttle plates to obtain the correct *idle speed.*

The secondary throttles are vacuum operated and are inter-connected by a rubber hose, located between the two secondary diaphragm vacuum operating chambers (Fig. 1), to assure synchronous action of the secondary throttle plates (no adjustment is required).

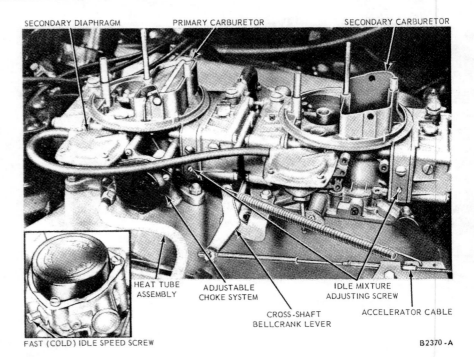

FAST (COLD) IDLE SPEED SCREW   B2370-A

FIG. 1—Holley Dual 4-V Carburetors—Left Side View

1. With the air cleaner removed, disconnect the inter-carburetor linkage at the front and rear carburetor primary throttle levers and at the bellcrank lever (Fig. 2). Disconnect the throttle control cable from the cross-shaft bellcrank lever.

2. Adjust the primary carburetor rod to a 4-³/₁₆ inch length (Fig. 2) from the center line of the hole to the center line of the bent end (operating centers).

3. Install the primary carburetor rod on the bellcrank lever and on the upper stud of the front carbu-retor lever (Fig. 2). Tighten the lock-nut and install the washers and re-tainer pins.

4. Move the bellcrank lever so that the front carburetor throttle is in the wide open position. Hold in this position.

5. Install the slotted end of the secondary carburetor rod on the throttle lever of the rear carburetor (Fig. 2).

6. Move the throttle lever of the rear carburetor to the wide open position; then, adjust the length of the secondary carburetor rod so that the

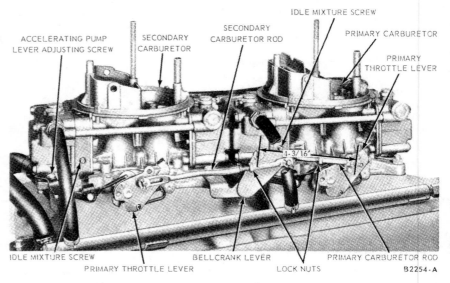

B2254-A

FIG. 2—Holley Dual 4-V Carburetors—Right Side View

hole in the rod at the bellcrank lever just engages the stud on the bellcrank lever (Fig. 2). Install the washers and retainer pins and tighten the locknut on the rod.

7. Open the throttle wide by operating the left side of the bellcrank assembly (on the intake manifold). Be sure the accelerator lever is engaged between the pin and the pad of the accelerator pedal (inside the car). Have someone depress the accelerator to the floor and while holding the carburetor linkage open, see if the accelerator rod pin will engage the bellcrank lever. Adjust as necessary.

8. Check the idle fuel mixture and idle speed adjustments. Adjust the carburetors as required. Refer to Idle Fuel Mixture and Idle (Hot Engine) Speed Adjustments (in this section) for the proper procedure.

IDLE FUEL MIXTURE AND IDLE (HOT ENGINE) SPEED ADJUSTMENTS

It is of utmost importance that the idle fuel system on 2-V and 4-V carburetors be balanced as closely as possible in order to obtain a satisfactory, stable, idle and fuel mixture adjustment. This is achieved by establishing initial idle speed and mixture adjustments before proceeding with the final idle speed and mixture adjustment, and the fast (cold engine) idle speed adjustment.

With the air cleaner removed, make the idle adjustments in the following sequence:

Initial Idle Speed and Fuel Mixture Adjustments—Ford Carburetors

Refer to Figs. 3 and 4 for views of the Ford 1-V carburetor idle fuel mixture and idle (hot engine) speed adjustment screws.

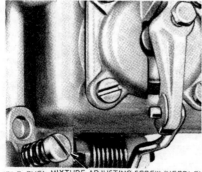

IDLE-FUEL MIXTURE ADJUSTING SCREW (NEEDLE)
B2395-A

FIG. 3—Idle Fuel Mixture Adjustment—Ford 1-V

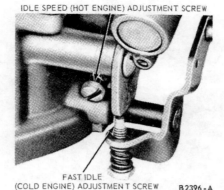

IDLE SPEED (HOT ENGINE) ADJUSTMENT SCREW

FAST IDLE (COLD ENGINE) ADJUSTMENT SCREW   B2396-A

FIG. 4—Idle Speed Adjustments—Ford 1-V

The idle fuel mixture and idle (hot engine) speed adjustment screws for the Ford 2-V and 4-V carburetors

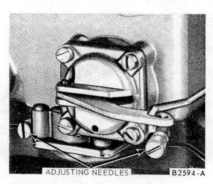

ADJUSTING NEEDLES   B2594-A

FIG. 5—Idle Fuel Mixture Adjustments—Typical for Ford 2-V or 4-V

are shown in Figs. 5 and 6.

1. Set the initial idle fuel mixture by turning the idle mixture screw(s) (needle) inward (clockwise) until lightly seated; then, turn the screw(s) outward (counterclockwise) the specified turns. **Do not turn the needle(s) tightly against their seat(s) as they may groove the end(s). If a needle is damaged, it must be replaced before a satisfactory fuel mixture can be obtained.**

2. Position the choke mechanism so that the choke plate is fully open. Seat the throttle plate in the throttle bore. **It may be necessary to back off on the dashpot (if so equipped) adjustment screw to seat the throttle plate in the throttle bore.** Set the idle speed adjustment screw to just make contact with the stop on the carburetor lower body (Ford 1-V) or throttle lever (Ford 2-V or 4-V), and turn the screw inward (clockwise) the specified turns.

Initial Idle Speed and Fuel Mixture Adjustments—Holley 4-V Carburetors

The idle fuel mixture is controlled by the idle fuel mixture adjusting screws (needles) located in the primary metering blocks of the carburetors (Figs. 1, 2, and 7). The idle (hot engine) speed adjusting screw location for each carburetor is shown in Fig. 7.

1. Initially set the idle mixture by turning the idle mixture screws inward until they are lightly seated; then turn the screws outward the specified turns. **Do not turn the**

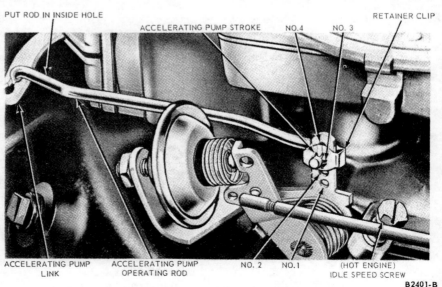

PUT ROD IN INSIDE HOLE   ACCELERATING PUMP STROKE   NO.4   NO.3   RETAINER CLIP

ACCELERATING PUMP LINK   ACCELERATING PUMP OPERATING ROD   NO.2   NO.1   (HOT ENGINE) IDLE SPEED SCREW   B2401-B

FIG. 6—Accelerating Pump Stroke and Idle (Hot Engine) Speed Adjustments—Typical for Ford 2-V and 4-V

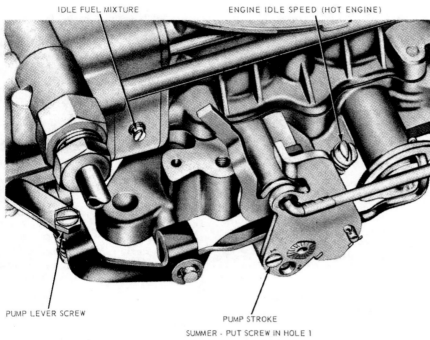

IDLE FUEL MIXTURE   ENGINE IDLE SPEED (HOT ENGINE)

PUMP LEVER SCREW

PUMP STROKE
SUMMER · PUT SCREW IN HOLE 1
WINTER · PUT SCREW IN HOLE 2

B2252- A

FIG. 7—Accelerating Pump, Idle Fuel Mixture and Idle (Hot Engine) Speed Adjustments—Holley Carburetors

needles tightly against the seat as this may groove the ends. If a needle is damaged, it must be replaced before a satisfactory fuel mixture can be obtained.

2. Turn the idle (hot engine) speed screw outward on each carburetor until the throttle plates close tight in the throttle bores. **It may be necessary to back the front carburetor fast (cold engine) idle adjusting screw (Fig. 1) to close the plates tight in the bores.** Set the idle speed adjustment screws to just make contact with the stops on the carburetor bodies and turn them inward the specified (Part 10-9) turns.

Final Idle (Hot Engine) Speed and Mixture Adjustments

The engine idle speed is adjusted to settings for a hot engine and a cold engine (fast idle speed during choke operation). All final idle speed and mixture adjustments must be made on a hot, normalized engine.

Refer to Figs. 1 through 7 for views of the idle fuel mixture and idle (hot engine) speed screws for the various carburetor applications.

1. Operate the engine until engine temperatures are stabilized. **On a car with an air conditioner, operate the engine for twenty minutes**

before setting the engine idle speed. The engine idle speed is adjusted with the air conditioner operating.

2. Position the transmission lever in neutral. Allow the throttle to drop back to the normal idle speed position. Attach a tachometer to the engine. Set the parking brake.

On cars equipped with a vacuum release parking brake, remove the vacuum line from the vacuum power unit of the automatic vacuum release parking brake assembly, and plug the vacuum line. Set the parking brake. **It is necessary to inactivate the vacuum power unit to keep the parking brake engaged when the engine is running during the adjustment procedures.**

3. Turn on the headlamps. **It is necessary to place the alternator under a load condition in this manner in order to obtain the specified engine idle speed during the adjustment procedure.**

4. **On a car with a manual-shift transmission, the engine idle speed is checked and adjusted with the gear shift lever in neutral position. On a car with an automatic transmission, the engine idle speed is checked and adjusted first with the transmission selector lever in the neutral position and adjusted with the transmission selector lever in the drive range position.** Adjust and

check the engine idle speed. **Be sure the dashpot (if so equipped) is not interfering with the throttle lever or the fast idle screw is not contacting the fast idle cam.**

On a carburetor equipped with a hot idle compensator, be sure the compensator is seated to allow for proper idle adjustment.

On a Ford carburetor, adjust the engine idle speed to specifications by turning the engine idle speed screw (Fig. 4 or 6) inward to increase the speed or outward to decrease the speed.

On the Holley carburetor, adjust the engine idle speed to specifications by turning each idle speed adjusting screw (Fig. 7) equally and alternately. **Turn the screws inward to increase the speed and outward to decrease the speed. Be sure the fast idle screw is not touching the fast idle cam when performing this adjustment.**

5. On a Ford carburetor, turn the idle mixture needle(s) (Figs. 3 and 5) inward until the engine rpm begins to drop, due to the lean mixture. **On cars equipped with a Thermactor exhaust emission system, turn the needle(s) outward ¼ turn. The outward adjustment of the idle fuel mixture needles is the final adjustment required.** On cars without the Thermactor system, turn the needle(s) outward until the rpm increases and begins to drop; then, turn the idle mixture needle(s) inward for maximum rpm and engine smoothness. **On Ford 2-V and 4-V carburetors, the needles should be turned evenly and alternately approximately the same amount. The final setting may vary about ½ turn difference between needles.**

On the Holley carburetors, adjust the idle fuel mixture by turning each idle mixture screw inward (Figs. 1, 2 and 7) evenly and alternately, starting with the front carburetor and finishing with the rear carburetor, until the engine rpm begins to drop (due to the lean mixture). Turn each screw outward until the engine rpm begins to drop (due to the rich mixture); then turn each screw inward for maximum engine rpm and smoothness. **Always favor a slightly rich idle fuel mixture.** Final adjustment of the idle fuel mixture screws should be within ⅛ turn of each other.

6. After the correct engine idle mixture has been obtained, **check the idle speed with the transmission selector lever in neutral and manu-**

ally opening and closing the throttle. Adjust the idle speed to specification, if required. (Adjustment to be made with headlights on.)

If the car is equipped with an automatic transmission, position the selector lever in drive range to check and adjust the idle speed to specification, if necessary.

The final engine idle speed may be varied to suit the conditions under which the car is to be operated.

9. Shut off the engine. Check the fast (cold engine) idle speed.

FAST (COLD ENGINE) IDLE SPEED ADJUSTMENT

On a Ford 1-V carburetor, the fast (cold engine) idle adjustment screw (Fig. 4) is located on the left side of the carburetor.

On a Ford 2-V and 4-V carburetor the fast (cold engine) idle adjustment screw (Fig. 8) is located on the right side of the carburetor.

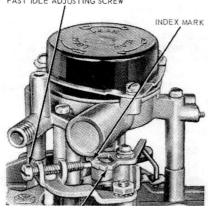

FAST IDLE ADJUSTING SCREW
INDEX MARK
FAST IDLE CAM
B2595-A

FIG. 8—Fast (Cold Engine) Idle Speed Adjustment—Ford 2-V and 4-V

On the Holley carburetor installation, the fast (cold engine) idle speed adjustment is performed on the front (primary) carburetor only. The fast idle speed screw is located on the left side of the front carburetor (Fig. 1).

The fast idle adjusting screw contacts one edge of the fast idle cam. The cam permits a faster engine idle speed for smoother running when the engine is cold during choke operation. As the choke plate is moved through its range of travel from the closed to the open position, the fast idle cam pick-up lever rotates the fast idle cam. Each position on the fast idle cam permits a slower idle rpm

as engine temperature rises and choking is reduced.

Make certain the idle (hot engine) speed and mixture is adjusted to specification before attempting to set the fast idle speed.

1. With the engine operating temperature normalized (hot), air cleaner removed and the tachometer attached, manually rotate the fast idle cam until the fast idle adjusting screw rests adjacent to the shoulder of the highest step (screw aligned with arrow mark) on the cam.

2. Start the engine, and turn the fast idle adjusting screw inward or outward as required to obtain the specified idle rpm.

3. Switch off the headlamps and the air conditioner (if so equipped). Remove the tachometer.

On a car equipped with a vacuum release parking brake, connect the vacuum line to the vacuum power unit of the automatic vacuum release parking brake assembly.

4. If the car is equipped with an automatic transmission, check the anti-stall dashpot for proper adjustment.

ANTI-STALL DASHPOT (IF SO EQUIPPED)

The anti-stall dashpot adjustment is made with the air cleaner removed from the car.

Ford 1-V

1. Adjust the throttle position to the hot idle setting. Turn the dashpot adjusting screw outward until it is clear of the dashpot plunger assembly (Fig. 9).

2. Turn the dashpot adjusting screw inward until it initially contacts the dashpot plunger assembly; then, turn the adjusting screw inward (clockwise) the specified (Part 10-9) number of turns against the dashpot diaphragm plunger assembly.

3. Check the accelerating pump lever and stroke for proper adjustment, if required. Install the air cleaner.

Ford 2-V and 4-V

1. With the engine idle speed and mixture properly adjusted, and the engine at normal operating temperature, loosen the anti-stall dashpot lock nut (Fig. 10).

2. Hold the throttle in the closed position and depress the plunger with a screwdriver blade. Check the clearance between the throttle lever and the plunger tip with a feeler

DASHPOT ADJUSTING SCREW
ADJUST THROTTLE TO HOT IDLE POSITION PRIOR TO ADJUSTING DASHPOT
B2397-A

FIG. 9—Anti-Stall Dashpot Adjustment—Ford 1-V

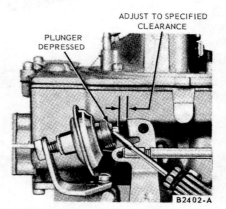

ADJUST TO SPECIFIED CLEARANCE
PLUNGER DEPRESSED
B2402-A

FIG. 10—Anti-Stall Dashpot Adjustment—Typical for Ford 2-V and 4-V

gauge of the specified clearance dimension. Turn the anti-stall dashpot in its bracket in a direction to provide the specified clearance between the tip of the plunger and the throttle lever. Tighten the locknut to secure the adjustment.

3. Check the accelerating pump stroke for proper adjustment, if required. Install the air cleaner assembly.

Adjust Accelerator Pump Lever—Ford 1-V

The pump stroke is controlled by changing location of the roll pin in the lever stop hole (Fig. 11).

1. For operation in ambient temperatures 50°F. and below, place

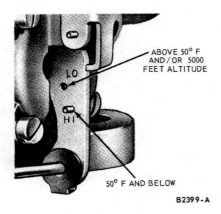

ABOVE 50° F
AND/OR 5000
FEET ALTITUDE

LO

HI

50° F AND BELOW

B2399-A

FIG. 11 — Accelerating Pump Stroke Adjustment — Ford 1-V

the roll pin in the lever hole marked HI (lower hole).

For best performance and economy at normal ambient temperatures and high altitude (above 50°F. and/or above 5,000 feet altitude), place the roll pin in the LO (upper hole) of the lever.

2. Check the vent valve for proper adjustment.

Ford 2-V and 4-V

The primary throttle shaft lever (overtravel lever) has 4 holes and the accelerating pump link has 2 holes (Fig. 6) to control the accelerating pump stroke for various ambient temperatures and operating conditions of the engine.

The accelerating pump operating rod should be in the specified hole in the over-travel lever and the inboard hole (hole closest to the pump plunger) in the accelerating pump link. (Fig. 6).

1. To release the rod from the retainer clip, press the tab end of the clip toward the rod; then, at the same time, press the rod away from the clip until it is disengaged.

2. Position the clip over the specified hole in the over-travel lever. Press the ends of the clip together and insert the operating rod through the clip and the over-travel lever. Release the clip to engage the rod.

Holley 4-V

To satisfy acceleration requirements in various climates, the accelerating pump discharge can be adjusted. The bottom hole (No. 2) in the cam provides a maximum pump discharge for extreme cold weather and the top hole (No. 1) provides the minimum pump discharge for warm weather operation (Fig. 7).

For summer operation, install the

adjustment screw in hole No. 1. For winter operation, install the adjustment screw in hole No. 2.

CLEAN CARBURETOR AIR CLEANER AND FILTER (PAPER-TYPE FILTER ONLY)

REMOVAL

1. Remove the wing nut(s) retaining the air cleaner assembly to the carburetor and the air duct (if equipped with air duct).

2. Remove the air cleaner assembly from the carburetor. **To prevent dirt from entering the carburetor, the filter element must never be removed when the air cleaner body is mounted on the carburetor.**

3. Remove the cover and filter element. Discard the air cleaner mounting gasket on the carburetor if it is excessively worn or damaged.

CLEAN FILTER ELEMENT

The filter element must never be cleaned with a solvent or cleaning solution. Also, oil must not be added to the surfaces of the filter element or air cleaner body.

There are two alternate procedures that can be used to clean the air filter element. One method is performed with the use of compressed air. The other is performed by tapping the element on a smooth horizontal surface.

Compressed Air Method. Direct a stream of compressed air through the element in the direction opposite that of the intake air flow, that is from the inside outward. **Extreme care must be exercised to prevent rupture of the element material.**

Tapping Method. Hold the element in a vertical position and tap it lightly against a smooth, horizontal surface to shake the dust and dirt out. **Do not deform the element or damage the gasket surfaces by tapping too hard.** Rotate the filter after each tap until the entire outer surface has been cleaned.

Inspection. Hold the filter in front of a back-up light and carefully inspect it for any splits or cracks. If the filter is split or cracked, replace it.

CLEAN BODY AND COVER

Clean the air cleaner body and cover with a solvent or compressed air. Wipe the air cleaner dry if a solvent is used. Inspect the air cleaner body and cover for distortion or damage at the gasket mating surfaces. Replace the cover or

body if they are damaged beyond repair.

INSTALLATION

1. Install a new air cleaner mounting gasket on the carburetor, if necessary. Install the air cleaner body on the carburetor so that the word FRONT faces the front of the car.

2. Place the element in the air cleaner body. **Make sure the element gasket is properly seated.** Install the cover and connect the air duct to the air cleaner (if equipped with air duct). Tighten the retaining wing nut(s).

REPLACE CARBURETOR AIR CLEANER FILTER

REMOVAL

1. Remove the wing nuts retaining the air cleaner assembly to the carburetor and the air duct (if equipped with air duct).

2. Remove the air cleaner assembly from the carburetor. **To prevent dirt from entering the carburetor, the filter element must never be removed when the air cleaner body is mounted on the carburetor.**

3. Remove the cover and filter element. Discard the filter element. Discard the air cleaner mounting gasket on the carburetor if it is excessively worn or damaged.

INSTALLATION

1. Install a new air cleaner mounting gasket on the carburetor, if necessary. Install the air cleaner body on the carburetor so that the word FRONT faces the front of the car.

2. Place the new element in the air cleaner body. **Make sure the element gasket is properly seated.** Install the cover and connect the air duct to the air cleaner (if equipped with air duct). Tighten the retaining wing nuts.

CLEAN CRANKCASE OIL FILLER BREATHER CAP

Wash the crankcase filler cap in solvent. **Do not oil the filter mesh.**

CLEAN EMISSION SYSTEM HOSES, TUBES, OIL SEPARATOR, FITTINGS, CARBURETOR SPACER, AND REPLACE EMISSION CONTROL VALVE

REMOVAL

1. Loosen or remove the hose clamps, and remove the vent hose (closed system only) from the air cleaner and oil filler tube breather cap. Remove the carburetor air cleaner.

2. Grasp the crankcase ventilation regulator valve (Fig. 12) and pull it

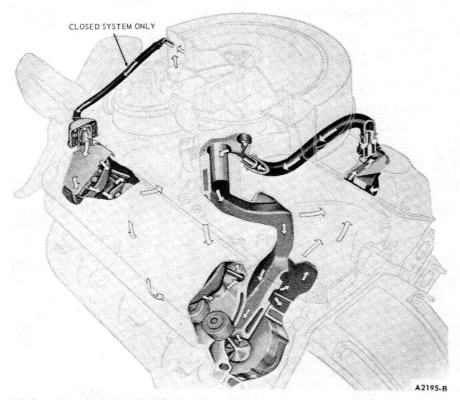

CLOSED SYSTEM ONLY

A2195-B

FIG. 12—Positive Crankcase Vent System

straight upward and out of the grommet in the right valve rocker arm cover.

3. Use a hose clamp tool to slide both hose clamps off the ends of the regulator valve inlet hose. Remove the inlet hose from the carburetor spacer, and separate the hose from the regulator valve.

CLEANING

Do not attempt to clean the crankcase ventilation regulator valve.

The oil filler tube breather cap, located on the valve rocker arm cover should be cleaned at the proper mileage interval. On open crankcase ventilation systems, remove the cap and wash it in a low-volatility, petroleum-base solvent. Probe the breather hole(s) to assure removal of any accumulated deposits. Shake the cap dry and install it. **Do not dry with compressed air as air pressure may damage the filter element.**

Clean the crankcase ventilation

system connection on the carburetor spacer or intake manifold (240 Six) by probing the inlet nipple with a flexible wire or bottle brush. Clean the fittings in the manifold with solvent.

Clean the rubber hoses with a low-volatility, petroleum-base solvent and dry with compressed air.

INSTALLATION

1. Install the inlet hose and hose clamp on the regulator valve. Install the inlet hose and hose clamp on the carburetor spacer inlet nipple or intake manifold fitting. Position the hose clamps.

2. Install the crankcase ventilation regulator valve in the right valve rocker arm cover. Be sure the grommet is properly seated around the regulator valve and valve rocker arm cover.

3. Install the air cleaner. Install the breather cap vent hose, and tighten or position the hose clamps.

REPLACE THERMACTOR AIR PUMP FILTER IF SO EQUIPPED

1. Remove the wing nut (Fig. 13) and air horn assembly. Remove the filter element from the air horn assembly.

2. Wipe the air horn assembly and air cleaner with a clean, dirt-free cloth to remove any accumulated dirt or foreign matter. Under extremely dirty conditions it may be necessary to wash both the air horn and body in low-volatility mineral spirits. Be sure the parts are dry before installing them.

3. **The filter element is not cleanable.** Place a new filter element on the air horn assembly. Position the assembled air horn and filter element in the air cleaner body. **Be sure the tang is fitted in the slot (Fig. 13).** Install the wing nut.

CHECK ENGINE ACCESSORY DRIVE BELTS

BELT TENSION

1. Install the belt tension tool on the drive belt (Fig. 14) and check the tension following the instructions of the tool manufacturer.

2. If adjustment is necessary, loosen the alternator mounting bolts and the alternator adjusting arm bolt. Move the alternator toward or away from the engine until the correct tension is obtained. Remove the gauge. Tighten the alternator adjusting arm bolt and the mounting bolts. Install the tension gauge and check the belt tension.

If the car is equipped with air conditioning:

Adjust the belt by repositioning the idler pulley if so equipped. Otherwise, follow this procedure.

1. Loosen the four compressor mounting bolts.

2. Adjust the belt tension by sliding the compressor towards the center of the car to decrease the tension, and towards the outside of the car to increase the tension.

3. Tighten the four mounting bolts to specification and check the belt tension.

If the car is equipped with power steering:

1. Loosen the mounting bolts incorporated on the front face of the pump cover plate (hub side) and the one nut at the rear.

2. Fix a $9/16$-inch open end wrench on the projecting $1/2$-inch boss and pry upward to correct tension. **Do not pry against the reservoir to obtain proper belt load as it can be deformed and cause a leak.**

3. Recheck the belt tension. When the tension has been correctly adjusted, tighten the bolts to specifications.

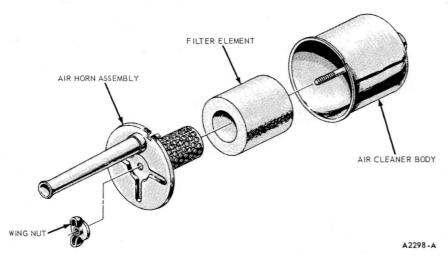

FILTER ELEMENT

AIR HORN ASSEMBLY

AIR CLEANER BODY

WING NUT

A2298-A

FIG. 13—Thermactor Exhaust Emission System Air Cleaner

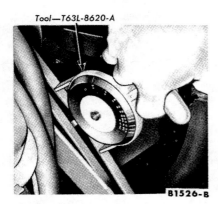

Tool—T63L-8620-A

B1526-B

FIG. 14—Checking Drive Belt Tension

DRIVE BELT REPLACEMENT

1. On a car with power steering, loosen the pump mounting bolts and remove the drive belt.

On a car with an air conditioner, remove the compressor drive belt.

2. Loosen the alternator mounting bolts and the alternator adjusting arm bolt. Move the alternator toward the engine. Remove the belt(s) from the alternator and crankshaft pulleys, and lift them over the fan.

3. Place the belt(s) over the fan. Insert the belt(s) in the water pump pulley, crankshaft pulley and alternator pulley grooves. Adjust the belt tension to specifications.

4. On a car *with an air conditioner*, install and adjust the compressor drive belt to specifications.

5. On a car with power steering, install the pump drive belt and tighten the pump mounting bolts. Adjust the drive belt tension to specifications. A half-inch boss has been incorporated on the front face of the pump cover plate so that a wrench

can be fitted to pry the pump and obtain proper belt tension.

LUBRICATE EXHAUST CONTROL VALVE (240, 390, AND 427 ENGINES)

Lubricate the shaft bushings with FoMoCo Exhaust Gas Control Valve Solvent (COAA-19A501-A) or a penetrating oil and graphite mixture, while operating the valve manually.

VALVE TAPPET ADJUSTMENT (MECHANICAL) CONVENTIONAL 427 HI-PERFORMANCE AND 428-4V POLICE INTERCEPTOR ENGINES ONLY

1. Be sure the engine is at normal operating temperature before attempting to set the valve lash.

2. Remove the air cleaner.

3. Remove the valve rocker arm covers and gaskets.

4. With the engine idling, set the valve lash (Fig. 15) using a step-

Step-Type Feeler Gauge   A1466-A

FIG. 15—Valve Lash Adjustment—Mechanical Valve Lifters

type feeler gauge only ("go" and "no go"). The final (hot) intake and

exhaust valve lash settings are listed in the Specifications Section.

For example, to obtain the correct setting if the valve is 0.019 inch, use a step-type feeler gauge of 0.018 inch ("go") and 0.020 inch ("no go"). The "go" step should enter, and the "no go" step should not enter. The resultant setting will be to the required setting (0.019 inch).

5. Install the valve rocker arm cover gaskets and covers.

6. Install the air cleaner.

CHECK IGNITION TIMING

TIMING MARK LOCATIONS

240 Six. The timing pointer (Fig. 16) has five timing marks ranging from top dead center (TDC) to 14°

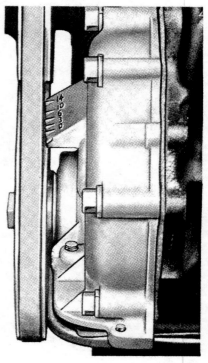

B1474-B

FIG. 16—240 Six Timing Marks

before top dead center (BTDC). The crankshaft pulley or damper has a timing notch. To adjust ignition timing, align the notch on the pulley or damper with the proper timing mark on the timing pointer.

V-8 Engines. The crankshaft damper for the 289 V-8 has five timing marks ranging from top dead center (TDC) to 12° before top dead center (BTDC).

The V-8 engines (Fig. 17 and Fig. 18) have timing marks ranging from top dead center (TDC) to

FIG. 17—V-8 Timing Marks (Except 289 Engine)

FIG. 18—289 V-8 Timing Marks

before top dead center (BTDC).

To adjust the ignition timing, align the pointer with the proper timing mark on the damper.

TIMING—ADJUSTMENT

To check and adjust the timing with a Rotunda 13-07 power timing light, proceed as follows:

1. Remove the plug wire from the number 1 spark plug.

2. Install the spark plug adaptor on the spark plug.

3. Connect the plug wire to the spark plug adaptor.

4. Clamp the timing light spark plug lead to the spark plug adaptor.

5. Connect the timing light battery leads to the battery terminals.

6. Disconnect the distributor vacuum line (if so equipped).

7. If necessary, clean and mark the timing marks.

8. Operate the engine below 550 rpm and point the timing light at the timing pointer.

9. If the timing is incorrect, loosen the distributor hold down bolt and rotate the distributor until the desired initial advance is obtained.

10. Tighten the distributor hold down bolt and check the timing again.

11. Turn off the engine.

12. Remove the timing light and connect the vacuum line.

CHECK AND ADJUST DISTRIBUTOR POINTS

Unsnap the distributor cap retaining clips, lift the distributor cap off the distributor housing, and position the cap out of the way (if necessary, remove the air cleaner and/or the high tension wire to gain access to the distributor).

Lift the rotor off the cam. Remove the dust cover (transistorized ignition).

INSPECTION

Replace the distributor point assembly if the contacts are badly burned or excessive metal transfer between the points is evident. Metal transfer is considered excessive when it equals or exceeds the gap setting.

REMOVAL

1. Remove the primary distributor-transistor lead and condenser wire (if equipped) from the breaker plate.

2. Remove the screw attaching the ground wire to the distributor point assembly.

3. Remove the screw nearest the distributor points, then remove the distributor point assembly.

INSTALLATION

1. When installing new distributor points, reverse the procedure for removal and make sure that the ground wire is attached to the distributor point assembly attaching screw which is furthest from the distributor points.

2. If the used points are serviceable, set the gap using a dwell meter.

To set the gap using a dwell meter:

Connect the dwell meter following the manufacturer's instructions.

NOTE: **In a car equipped with transistor ignition, make sure that the dwell meter is connected to the tachometer block rather than the coil.**

Operate the engine at idle speed and note the reading on the dwell meter.

Stop the engine and adjust the gap (decreasing the gap increases the dwell). Now check the dwell again.

Repeat this procedure until specified dwell is obtained.

If new points are installed, set the gap to specifications using a feeler gauge.

3. Install the dust cover (transistorized ignition).

4. Install the rotor. Install the distributor cap on the distributor housing and snap the retaining clips in place.

5. Install the air cleaner and/or the high tension lead if either was removed.

CHECK SPARK PLUGS

REMOVAL

1. Remove the wire from each spark plug by grasping the moulded cap of the wire only. **Do not pull on the wire because the wire connection inside the cap may become separated or the weather seal may be damaged.**

2. Clean the area around each spark plug port with compressed air, then remove the spark plugs.

3. Clean the plugs on a sand blast cleaner, following the manufacturer's instructions. **Do not prolong the use of the abrasive blast as it will erode the insulator.** Remove carbon and other deposits from the threads with a stiff wire brush. Any deposits will retard the heat flow from the plug to the cylinder head causing spark plug overheating and preignition.

4. Clean the electrode surfaces with a small file (Fig. 19). Dress the electrodes to secure flat parallel surfaces on both the center and side electrode.

5. After cleaning, examine the plug carefully for cracked or broken insulators, badly pitted electrodes, and other signs of failure. Replace as required.

ADJUSTMENT

Set the spark plug gap to specifications by bending the ground electrode (Fig. 20).

INSTALLATION

1. Install the spark plugs and torque each plug to 15-20 ft-lbs.

When a new spark plug is installed in a new replacement cylinder head, torque the plug to 20-30 ft-lbs.

2. Connect the spark plug wires. Push all weather seals into position.

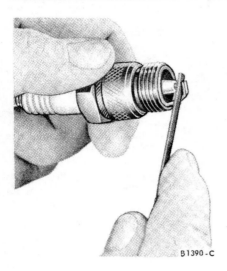

FIG. 19—Cleaning Plug Electrode

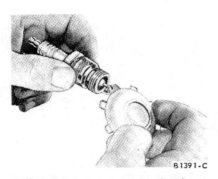

FIG. 20—Gapping Spark Plug

REPLACE ENGINE COOLANT

To drain the radiator, open the drain cock located at the bottom of the radiator. The cylinder block of the V-8 engines has a drain plug located on both sides of the block (Fig. 21). The Six Cylinder engines have one drain plug located at the right rear of the cylinder block.

To fill the cooling system, close the drain cocks or install the plugs

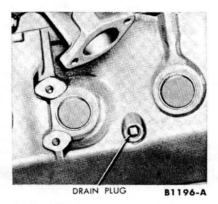

FIG. 21—Typical Cylinder Block Drain Plug

in the block and close the radiator drain cock. Fill the system to just below the filler neck of the radiator supply tank. Disconnect the heater outlet hose at the water pump to bleed or release trapped air in the system. When the coolant begins to escape, connect the heater outlet hose. Operate the engine until normal operating temperature has been reached. **After the initial fill, the coolant level will drop approximately one quart after the engine has been operated about 20 minutes at 2000 rpm. This is due to the displacement of entrapped air.** Add more coolant to fill the radiator supply tank, to 1 inch below the filler neck opening.

CHECK ENGINE COOLANT LEVEL

The coolant level should be kept below the filler neck.

2 TRANSMISSION

ADJUST AUTOMATIC TRANSMISSION BAND

CRUISE-O-MATIC FRONT BAND ADJUSTMENT

1. Drain the fluid from the transmission by removing the fluid filler tube. Use a clean drain can equipped with a fine meshscreen if the fluid is to be reused.
2. Remove the oil pan, then remove the fluid screen and clip from the transmission. Clean the inside of the oil pan. Remove all gasket material from oil pan and pan mounting face of case.
3. Loosen the front servo adjusting screw locknut two full turns.
4. Pull back on the actuating lever, then insert the Gauge Block, Tool 7225-C13-B, of front band adjusting Tool 7225-C, (Fig. 22) between the servo piston stem and adjusting screw.

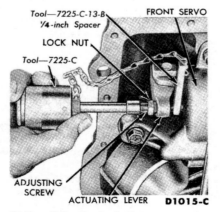

FIG. 22—Typical Front Band Adjustment

Tighten the adjusting screw until the wrench overruns. Back off the adjusting screw **exactly one complete turn,** then hold the adjusting screw stationary and tighten the locknut to specifications. Remove the gauge block. **Severe damage may result if the adjusting screw is not backed off exactly one complete turn.**

5. Install the transmission fluid screen. Install the pan, using a new gasket.
6. Connect the transmission fluid filler tube to the oil pan.
7. Refill the transmission to the **FULL** mark on the dipstick.
8. Start the engine and engage the transmission in each drive range to fill all fluid passages, then place the selector in the "P" position. *Check the fluid level* and add enough fluid to bring the level up to the **FULL** mark on the dipstick.

ALTERNATE FRONT BAND ADJUSTMENT PROCEDURE—(FORD TOOLS)

1. Disconnect the fluid filler tube from the oil pan, and drain the fluid from the transmission. **If the same fluid is to be used again in the transmission after the band adjustment, filter the fluid through a 100-mesh screen as it drains from the transmission. Re-use the fluid only if it is in good condition.**

2. Remove and thoroughly clean the oil pan and screen. Discard the oil pan gasket.

3. Loosen the front servo adjusting screw locknut two full turns with a $9/16$-inch wrench. Check the adjusting screw for free rotation in the actuating lever after the locknut is loosened, and free the screw if necessary.

4. Pull the adjusting screw end of the actuating lever away from the servo body, and insert the adjusting tool gauge block (Fig. 23) between

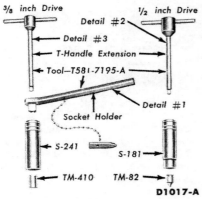

FIG. 23—Front and Rear Band Adjusting Tools

the servo piston stem and the adjusting screw.

5. Install the socket handle on the $9/16$-inch socket.

6. Insert the T-handle extension through the socket handle and socket, and install the screwdriver socket on the T-handle extension.

7. Place the tool on the adjusting screw so that the screwdriver socket engages the screw and the $9/16$-inch socket engages the locknut.

8. With a torque wrench on the T-handle extension, tighten the adjusting screw to 10 inch-pounds torque, and then back off the screw exactly one full turn. **Severe damage may result to the transmission if the adjusting screw is not backed off exactly one full turn.**

9. Hold the adjusting screw stationary, and torque the locknut to specification.

10. Remove the gauge block from the transmission.

11. Place a new gasket on the oil pan, and install the screen and pan on the transmission.

12. Connect the filler tube to the oil pan and tighten the fitting securely.

13. Fill the transmission with fluid.

REAR BAND ADJUSTMENT

1. Fold back the floor mat to expose the right side of the floor pan.

2. Remove the access hole cover from the floor pan. Remove all dirt from the adjusting screw threads, then oil the threads.

3. Loosen the rear band adjusting screw locknut with Tool 7195-C (Fig. 24). Using the "T" handle por-

FIG. 24—Rear Band Adjustment

tion of the tool, tighten the adjusting screw until the wrench overruns.

If the screw is found to be tighter than the wrench capacity (10 ft-lbs. torque), loosen the screw and re-tighten until the wrench overruns.

4. Back off the adjusting screw $1\frac{1}{2}$ turns. Hold the adjusting screw stationary, and tighten the adjusting screw locknut to specifications. **Severe damage may result if the adjusting screw is not backed off exactly $1\frac{1}{2}$ turns.**

ALTERNATE REAR BAND ADJUSTMENT PROCEDURE—(FORD TOOLS)

The tool shown in Fig. 23 may be used to adjust the rear band.

1. Place the socket holder on the $3/4$-inch socket (Fig. 23). Insert the T-handle extension through the handle and socket.

2. Place the $5/16$-inch 8-point socket on the extension. Place a torque wrench on the T-handle extension.

3. Insert the assembled tool in the access hole so that it engages the adjusting screw and the locknut.

4. Loosen the adjusting screw locknut.

5. Torque the adjusting screw to 10 foot-pounds.

6. Remove the torque wrench from the T-handle extension and back off the adjusting screw exactly $1\frac{1}{2}$ turns. **Severe damage may result to the transmission if the adjusting screw is not backed off exactly $1\frac{1}{2}$ turns.**

7. Hold the adjusting screw stationary, and tighten the locknut securely.

REAR BAND ADJUSTMENT WITH CONSOLE

Part of the console assembly will have to be removed to adjust the rear band.

1. Loosen the two forward screws that attach the glove compartment to the console panel.

2. Remove the gear shift lever knob.

3. Remove the four screws that attach the console finish panel casting to the console panel, and remove the casting (Fig. 25).

4. Remove the four bolts that secure the gear shift indicator to the support assembly.

5. Remove the twelve screws that attach the console panel mouldings to the console panel and remove the mouldings (Fig. 25).

6. Remove the eight screws that attach the console panel to the console support assembly.

7. Position the console panel out of the way and adjust the transmission rear band (Figs. 23 and 24).

8. Install the console panel and secure to the support assembly with eight screws.

9. Install the mouldings and the twelve attaching screws.

10. Secure the gear shift indicator with the four attaching bolts.

11. Install the console finish panel and secure with the four screws. Also tighten the two forward screws of the glove compartment.

12. Install the gear shift lever knob.

INTERMEDIATE BAND ADJUSTMENT

1. Clean all the dirt from the band adjusting screw area. Loosen the lock nut several turns.

2. With the tool shown in Fig. 26 tighten the adjusting screw until the tool handle clicks. The tool is a pre-

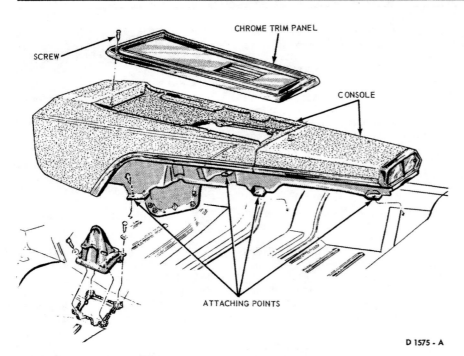

TOOL - T 59 P - 77370 - B

D 1597 - A

FIG. 28—Adjusting Intermediate Band

screw as shown in Fig. 28 until the wrench overruns, then back it off 1 turn. Tighten the adjustment screw lock nut to specification being careful not to disturb the adjustment screw setting.

5. Lower the car.

D 1575 - A

FIG. 25—Console Component Parts

Tool—T59P-77370-B or 7345

D1460-A

FIG. 26—Intermediate Band Adjustment

set torque wrench which clicks and overruns when the torque on the adjusting screw reaches 10 ft-lbs.

3. **Back off the adjusting screw exactly 1¾ turns.**

4. Hold the adjusting screw from turning and *torque* the locknut to specification.

C4 LOW-REVERSE BAND ADJUSTMENT

1. Clean all the dirt from the adjusting screw area. Loosen the lock nut several turns.

2. With the tools shown in Fig. 27, tighten the adjusting screw until the tool handle clicks. The tool is a

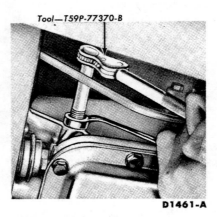

Tool—T59P-77370-B

D1461-A

FIG. 27—Low-Reverse Band Adjustment

preset torque wrench which clicks and overruns when the torque on the adjusting screw reaches 10 ft-lbs.

3. **Back off the adjusting screw exactly 3 full turns.**

4. Hold the adjusting screw from turning and torque the lock nut to specification.

C6 TRANSMISSION INTERMEDIATE BAND ADJUSTMENT

1. Raise the car on a hoist or jack stands.

2. Clean the threads of the intermediate band adjustment screw.

3. Loosen the adjustment screw lock nut.

4. Tighten the band adjustment

CHECK AUTOMATIC TRANSMISSION LEVEL

1. Make sure that the car is standing level. Then firmly apply the parking brake.

2. Run the engine at normal idle speed. If the transmission fluid is cold, run the engine at *fast idle* speed (about 1200 rpm) until the fluid reaches its normal operating temperature. When the fluid is warm, slow the engine down to normal idle speed.

3. On a Mercury equipped with a vacuum brake release, disconnect the release line and plug the end of the line; otherwise the parking brake will not hold with the transmission in any drive position.

4. Shift the selector lever through all positions, and place the lever at P. Do not turn off the engine during the fluid level checks.

5. Clean all dirt from the transmission fluid dipstick cap before removing the dipstick from the filler tube.

6. Pull the dipstick out of the tube, wipe it clean, and push it all the way back into the tube. Be sure it is properly seated.

7. Pull the dipstick out of the tube again, and check the fluid level. If necessary, add enough fluid to the transmission through the filler tube to raise the fluid level to the F (full) mark on the dipstick. **Do not over-**

fill the transmission. Install the dipstick, making sure it is fully seated in the tube.

8. Connect the vacuum brake release line if so equipped.

CHECK MANUAL SHIFT TRANSMISSION OIL LEVEL

1. Remove the filler plug from the side of the case.

2. If lubricant does not flow from the filler hole, fill the case with the specified lubricant until it is level with the lower edge of the filler hole.

3. Install the filler plug.

3 CHASSIS

CHECK AXLE FLUID LEVEL

The lubricant level should be maintained at the lower edge plug hole with the rear axle assembly in it's normal curb attitude. Use lubricant that meets Ford Specification ESW-M2C57-A on cars equipped with 240, 289 and 390 engines, (390 engines using only axle models WDC-AT, AV and BS).

Use ESA-M2C80-A axle lubricant for all 390 engines using axle model WDT and cars equipped with 410, 427 and 428 engines. Use ESW-M2C50-A lubricant for axles with locking differentials and add 1 oz. of

ESW-M2C58-A additive per pint of regular axle lube used.

CHECK CLUTCH LINKAGE ADJUSTMENT (MANUAL AND OVERDRIVE)

1. Disconnect the clutch return spring from the release lever.

2. Loosen the release lever rod locknut (Fig. 29) approximately three or four turns.

3. If there is no free travel, shorten the rod (by turning at square wrench area) until it is free of the clutch release lever.

4. Move the clutch release lever rearward until the release bearing lightly contacts the clutch pressure plate release fingers.

5. Adjust the rod length until the rod just contacts its seat in the release lever.

6. Using a feeler gauge, adjust the locknut to obtain approximately 0.206-inch clearance between the nut and the rod sleeve end.

7. Turn the rod at the square wrench area until the nut just contacts the rod sleeve end.

8. Tighten the locknut against the sleeve while holding the rod with a wrench.

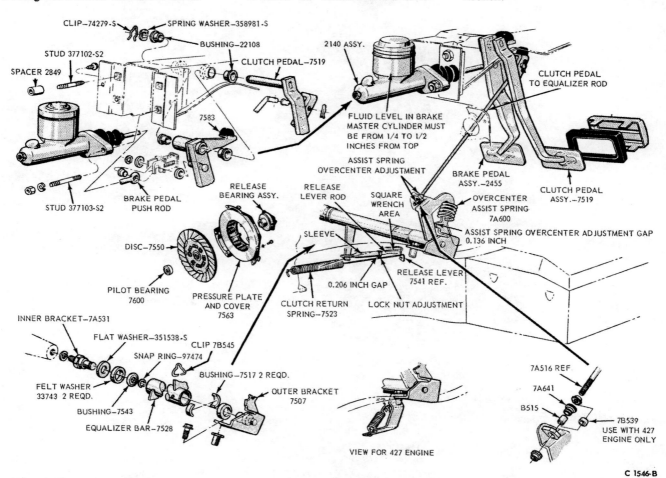

FIG. 29—Clutch Linkage

9. Install the clutch return spring.

10. Check the free travel at the pedal for conformance to specification. Re-adjust if necessary. As a final check, measure the free travel with the engine idling. This dimension should not be less than ½ inch.

11. Without disturbing the assist spring, lubricate each spring seat with C3VY-19586-A grease.

12. As a final check, measure the pedal free travel with the transmission in neutral and the engine running at about 3000 rpm. If the free travel at this speed is not a minimum of ½ inch, readjust the clutch pedal free travel. Otherwise, the release fingers may contact the release bearing continuously, resulting in premature bearing and clutch failure. Free travel must be exactly to specification.

INTERLOCK (OVERDRIVE MODELS ONLY)

Be sure that the clutch linkage is correctly adjusted before adjusting the interlock (Fig. 30).

3. Disconnect the rod from the interlock lever.

4. Loosen the interlock plate attaching screws. Move the interlock lever forward as far as possible to seat the interlock plate on the first and reverse speed shift lever pawl. Tighten the two attaching screws.

5. Adjust the length of the interlock rod so that it can be connected to the interlock lever while being held in the forward position. Connect the rod to the lever.

6. Shift the transmission into low and into neutral to check operation of the interlock. Readjust the interlock plate for snug fit if necessary.

7. Use COAZ-19584-A lubricant as required for the interlock linkage.

LUBRICATE AUTOMATIC TRANSMISSION KICKDOWN LINKAGE

Lubricate all pivot points in the kickdown linkage with SAE 10W engine oil.

age, trunnions and external shift mechanism (floor shift) as necessary. Use Lithium base grease (no Polyethelene).

LUBRICATE FRONT SUSPENSION BALL JOINTS

Wipe any accumulated dirt from around the lubrication plugs.

Remove the plugs and install lubrication fittings. Lubricate the ball joints and remove the lubrication fittings. Install the plugs.

LUBRICATE STEERING LINKAGE

Wipe any accumulated dirt from around the lubrication plugs.

Remove plugs and install fittings.

Apply the recommended lubricant to each steering linkage fitting with a pressure gun. Remove the fittings and replace the plugs.

CHECK STEERING GEAR PRELOAD OR OVER-CENTER MESH LOAD

MANUAL STEERING

1. Disconnect the Pitman arm from the steering arm-to-idler arm rod.

2. Loosen the nut which locks the sector adjusting screw (Fig. 31), and

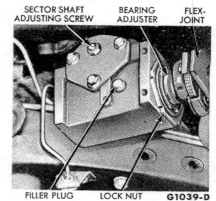

FIG. 31—Steering Gear Adjustments

turn the adjusting screw counterclockwise.

3. Measure the worm bearing preload by attaching an inch-pound torque wrench to the steering wheel nut (Fig. 32). With the steering wheel off center, read the pull required to rotate the input shaft approximately 1½ turns either side of *center. If the torque or preload is not within specification (Part 3-6) adjust as explained in the next step.*

4. Loosen the steering shaft bear-

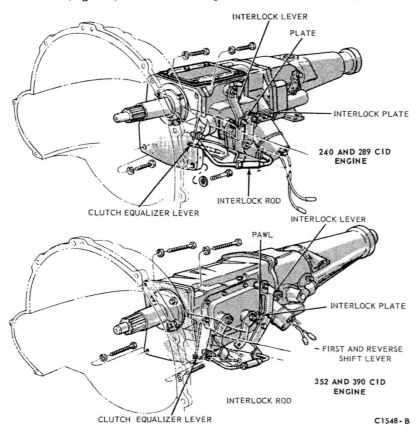

FIG. 30—Clutch Interlock Mechanism

1. Place the gearshift lever in the neutral position.

2. Loosen the adjustment locknut on the interlock rod.

LUBRICATE MANUAL TRANSMISSION SHIFT CONTROL AND LINKAGE

Clean and lubricate the shift link-

FIG. 32—Checking Preload—Typical

ing adjuster lock nut, and tighten or back off the bearing adjuster (Fig. 31) to bring the preload within the specified limits.

5. Tighten the steering shaft bearing adjuster lock nut, and recheck the preload.

6. Turn the steering wheel slowly to either stop. **Turn gently against the stop to avoid possible damage to the ball return guides.** Then rotate the wheel 2¾ turns to center the ball nut.

7. Turn the sector adjusting screw clockwise until the specified torque (Part 3-6) is necessary to rotate the worm past its center (high spot).

8. While holding the sector adjusting screw, tighten the locknut to specifications and recheck the backlash adjustment.

9. Connect the Pitman arm to the steering arm-to-idler arm rod.

POWER STEERING

1. Disconnect the Pitman arm from the sector shaft.

2. Disconnect the fluid return line at the reservoir. At the same time, cap the reservoir return line pipe.

3. Place the end of the return line in a clean container and cycle the steering wheel in both directions as required to discharge the fluid from the gear.

4. Remove the ornamental cover from the steering wheel hub and turn the steering wheel to 45° from the left stop.

5. Using an inch-pound torque wrench on the steering wheel nut, determine the torque required to rotate the shaft slowly through an approximate ⅛ turn from the 45° position.

6. Turn the steering gear back to center, then determine the torque required to rotate the shaft back and

forth across the center position. Loosen the adjuster nut, and turn the adjuster screw in (Fig. 33) until the

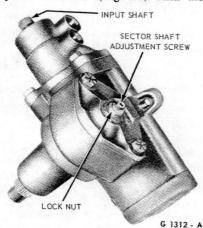

FIG. 33—Adjusting Mesh Load

reading is 8-9 in-lb greater than the torque 45° from the stop (max. 14 in-lb).

Tighten the lock nut while holding the screw in place.

7. Recheck the readings and replace the Pitman arm and steering wheel hub cover.

8. Connect the fluid return line to the reservoir and fill the reservoir with the specified lubricant to the proper level.

CHECK POWER STEERING RESERVOIR FLUID LEVEL

Run the engine until the fluid is at normal operating temperature. Then turn the steering wheel all the way to the left and right several times, and shut off the engine.

Check the fluid level in the power steering reservoir. The level must be at the full mark on the dipstick. On a pump with a straight filler tube the lubricant must be to the bottom of the filler tube. If the level is low, add enough automatic transmission fluid (C1AZ-19582-A) to raise the level to the F mark on the dip stick or to the bottom of the filler tube. **Do not overfill the reservoir.**

CHECK BRAKE MASTER CYLINDER FLUID LEVEL

1. Remove the filler cap from the master cylinder. The diaphragm which seals the master cylinder should come off with the cap.

2. Fill the reservoir to ⅜-inch from the top with the specified brake fluid.

3. Install the filler cap, making sure that the diaphragm is properly seated in the cap.

CHECK BRAKE LINES AND LINING

1. Raise all four wheels. Remove one of the front brake drums, and inspect the drum and the linings (the wheel bearings should be inspected at this time and repacked if necessary). **Do not let oil or grease touch the drum or the linings.** If the linings are worn to within 1/32 inch of the rivet heads, replace or reline both sets (primary and secondary) on the front or rear wheels. **Under no circumstances replace one lining only, or one wheel set.** Both front wheel sets or both rear wheel sets should be replaced whenever a respective lining or shoe is worn or damaged. If the drum braking surface is excessively scored, refinish it. The opposite wheel drum should be refinished an equal amount. The condition of the remaining front linings is usually about the same as that of the one inspected. The rear brake linings may also need replacing at the same time.

2. With the parking brakes in the fully released position, check the brake cables. The cable adjustment should be just tight enough to remove the slack. **Excessive tightening may pull the brake shoes off their anchors.**

3. Check all brake lines for leakage or physical damage and replace or repair as required.

4. Lower the car.

CLEAN AND PACK FRONT WHEEL BEARINGS

DRUM BRAKES

1. Raise the car until the wheel and tire clear the floor.

2. Remove the wheel cover or hub cap. Remove the grease cap from the hub. Remove the cotter pin, nut lock, adjusting nut, and flat washer from the spindle. Remove the outer bearing cone and roller assembly.

3. Pull the wheel, hub, and drum assembly off the wheel spindle.

4. Remove the grease retainer and the inner bearing cone and roller assembly from the hub with tool 1175AE.

5. Clean the lubricant off the inner and outer bearing cups with solvent and inspect the cups for scratches, pits, excessive wear, and other damage. If the cups are worn or damaged, remove them with a drift.

6. Soak a new grease retainer in light engine oil at least 30 minutes before installation. Thoroughly clean

the inner and outer bearing cones and rollers with solvent and dry them thoroughly. **Do not spin the bearings with compressed air.**

Inspect the cone and roller assemblies for wear or damage, and replace them if necessary. **The cone and roller assemblies and the bearing cups should be replaced as a unit if damage to either is encountered.**

7. Thoroughly clean the spindle and the inside of the hub with solvent to remove all old lubricant.

Cover the spindle with a clean cloth, and brush all loose dust and dirt from the brake assembly. **To prevent getting dirt on the spindle, carefully remove the cloth from the spindle.**

8. If the inner and/or outer bearing cup(s) were removed, install the replacement cup(s) in the hub with the proper tool. **Be sure to seat the cups properly in the hub.**

9. Pack the inside of the hub with specified wheel bearing grease. Add lubricant to the hub only until the grease is flush with the inside diameter of both bearing cups.

10. All old grease should be completely cleaned from the bearings before repacking them with new grease. Pack the bearing cone and roller assemblies with wheel bearing grease. A bearing packer is desirable for this operation. If a packer is not available, work as much lubricant as possible between the rollers and cages. Lubricate the cone surfaces with grease.

11. Place the inner bearing cone and roller assembly in the inner cup, and install the new grease retainer with the reverse end of the tool used in No. 8. **Be sure that the retainer is properly seated.**

12. Adjust the brake shoes as outlined in Part 2.

13. Install the wheel, hub, and drum assembly on the wheel spindle. **Keep the hub centered on the spindle to prevent damage to the grease retainer or the spindle threads.**

14. Install the outer bearing cone and roller assembly and the flat washer on the spindle, then install the adjusting nut.

15. While rotating the wheel, hub, and drum assembly, torque the adjusting nut to 17-25 ft-lbs to seat the bearings (Fig. 34).

16. Locate the nut lock on the adjusting nut so that the castellations on the lock are aligned with the cotter pin hole in the spindle.

17. Back off both the adjusting nut and the nut lock together until the next castellation on the nut lock

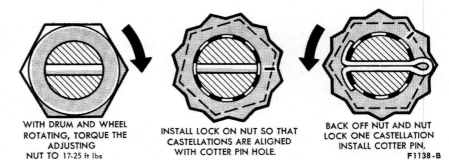

WITH DRUM AND WHEEL ROTATING, TORQUE THE ADJUSTING NUT TO 17-25 ft lbs

INSTALL LOCK ON NUT SO THAT CASTELLATIONS ARE ALIGNED WITH COTTER PIN HOLE.

BACK OFF NUT AND NUT LOCK ONE CASTELLATION INSTALL COTTER PIN.

F1138-B

FIG. 34—Front Wheel Bearing Adjustment

aligns with the cotter pin hole in the spindle.

18. Install a new cotter pin. Bend the ends of the cotter pin around the castellations of the nut lock to prevent interference with the radio static collector in the grease cap. Install the grease cap.

19. Install the wheel cover.

DISC BRAKES

1. Raise the car until the wheel and tire clear the floor.

2. Remove the wheel cover or hub cap from the wheel.

3. Remove the wheel and tire from the hub and rotor.

4. Remove 2 bolts and washers retaining the caliper to the spindle. Remove the caliper from the rotor and wire it to the underbody to prevent damage to the brake hose.

5. Remove the grease cap from the hub. Remove the cotter pin, nut lock, adjusting nut, and flat washer from the spindle. Remove the outer bearing cone and roller assembly.

6. Pull the hub and rotor assembly off the wheel spindle.

7. Remove the grease retainer and the inner bearing cone and roller assembly from the hub.

8. Clean the lubricant off the inner and outer bearing cups with solvent and inspect the cups for scratches, pits, excessive wear, and other damage. If the cups are worn or damaged, remove them with a drift.

9. Thoroughly clean the inner and outer bearing cones and rollers with solvent, and dry them thoroughly. Do not spin the bearings dry with compressed air.

Inspect the cones and rollers for wear or damage, and replace them if necessary. The cone and roller assemblies and the bearing cups should be replaced as a set if damage to either is encountered.

10. Thoroughly clean the spindle and the inside of the hub with solvent to remove all old lubricant.

Cover the spindle with a clean cloth, and brush all loose dust and dirt from the dust shield. **To prevent getting dirt on the spindle carefully remove the cloth from the spindle.**

11. If the inner and/or outer bearing cup(s) were removed, install the replacement cup(s) in the hub. **Be sure to seat the cups properly in the hub.**

12. Pack the inside of the hub with the specified wheel bearing grease. Add lubricant to the hub only until the grease is flush with the inside diameter of both bearing cups. **All old grease should be completely cleaned from the bearings before repacking with new grease.**

13. Pack the bearing cone and roller assemblies with wheel bearing grease. A bearing packer is desirable for this operation. If a packer is not available, work as much lubricant as possible between the rollers and cages. Lubricate the cone surfaces with grease.

14. **Place the inner bearing cone and roller assembly in the inner cup.** Apply a light film of grease to the grease retainer and install the new grease retainer. **Be sure the retainer is properly seated.**

15. Install the hub and rotor assembly on the wheel spindle. **Keep the hub centered on the spindle to prevent damage to the grease retainer or the spindle threads.**

16. Install the outer bearing cone and roller assembly and the flat washer on the spindle, then install the adjusting nut.

17. Adjust the wheel bearings as outlined in Section 2, and install a new cotter pin. Bend the ends of the cotter pin around the castellations of the nut lock to prevent interference with the radio static collector in the grease cap. Install the grease cap.

18. Install the caliper to the spindle and tighten the retaining bolts to specifications. Check for the correct flexible hose routing (Part 2).

19. Install the wheel and tire on the hub.

20. Install the wheel cover.

CHECK PARKING BRAKE LINKAGE AND ADJUST IF REQUIRED

Check the parking brake cables when the brakes are fully released. If the cables are loose, adjust them as follows:

1. Fully release the parking brake pedal.

2. Depress the parking brake pedal one notch from its normal released position.

3. Raise the car.

4. Turn the adjusting nut forward against the equalizer until a moderate drag is felt when turning the rear wheels.

5. Release the parking brake, and make sure that the brake shoes return to the fully released position.

CHECK TIRE PRESSURE

Check all tires for specified pressures (cold).

INSPECT AND CROSS-SWITCH WHEELS AND TIRES

Switch the tires according to Fig. 35.

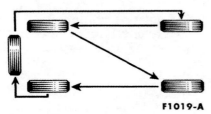

F1019-A

FIG. 35—Tire Cross Switching Diagram

Tighten the wheel nuts to specified torque.

CHECK FRONT WHEEL ALIGNMENT AND LINKAGE

Do not attempt to check and adjust front wheel alignment without first making a preliminary inspection of the front-end parts.

Check all the factors of front wheel alignment except the turning angle before making any adjustments. The turning angle should be checked only after caster, camber, and toe-in have been adjusted to specifications.

The front wheel alignment specifications are correct only when the car is at curb height. Before checking or adjusting the alignment factors the suspension alignment spacers must be installed to obtain the curb height.

EQUIPMENT INSTALLATION

Equipment used for front wheel alignment inspection must be accurate. Whenever possible, front wheel alignment checks should be performed on stationary wheel aligning equipment. In the absence of such equipment, portable equipment may be used and the work may be performed on a level floor. The floor area should be level within ¼ inch from front to rear of the car and within ⅛ inch from side to side. Alignment height spacers (Figs. 38 and 39) are used to check caster and camber. The spacers should be omitted when checking toe-in.

1. Check the runout of each front wheel and tire using a dial indicator against the rim outer band. If the runout exceeds ⅛ inch, correction may be made by rotating the wheel on the drum. When the minimum runout has been obtained, mark the point of greatest runout so the wheels can be positioned as shown in Fig. 36 when

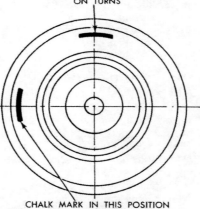

CHALK MARK IN THIS POSITION WHEN CHECKING TOE-IN AND TOE-OUT ON TURNS

CHALK MARK IN THIS POSITION WHEN CHECKING CASTER AND CAMBER

LOCATION OF POINT OF GREATEST LATERAL RUN-OUT ON FRONT WHEELS WHEN CHECKING ALIGNMENT FACTORS

F1215-A

FIG. 36—Front Wheel Position For Checking Alignment

checking the front end alignment. Hold a piece of chalk against the wheel rim or the tire sidewall while spinning the wheel. The chalk will mark the rim or tire at the point of greatest runout.

2. Drive the car in a straight line far enough to establish the straight-ahead position of the front wheels,

and then mark the steering wheel hub and the steering column collar (Fig. 37). **Do not adjust the steering wheel**

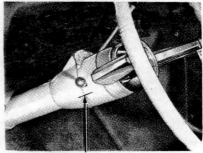

ALIGNMENT MARKS

F1267-B

FIG. 37—Straight Ahead Position Marks

spoke position at this time. If the front wheels are turned at any time during the inspection, align the marks to bring the wheels back to the straight-ahead position.

3. With the car in position for the front end alignment inspection and adjustment, install the suspension alignment spacers as follows to establish the curb height.

Lift the front of the car and position the alignment spacers between the suspension lower arm and the frame spring pocket as shown in Fig. 38.

Tool—T65P-3000-B or -C

F1271-A

FIG. 38—Alignment Spacer Installation—Front

Be sure the spacer pin is placed in the correct hole for the car being checked. The lower end of the alignment spacers should be placed over the head of the strut front attaching bolt. Remove the bumpers from the right and left rear side rails. Position the rear alignment spacers between the rear axle and the rear side rails as shown in Fig. 39.

Tool–T65P-3000-B or -C

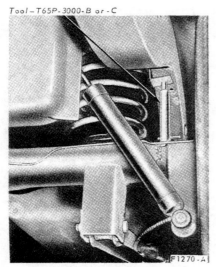

FIG. 39—Alignment Spacer Installation—Rear

4. Install the wheel alignment equipment on the car. Whichever type of equipment is used, follow the installation and inspection instructions provided by the equipment manufacturer.

CASTER

Check the caster angle at each front wheel.

The caster is the forward or rearward tilt of the top of the wheel spindle (Fig. 40). If the spindle tilts to the rear, caster is positive. If the spindle tilts to the front, caster is negative.

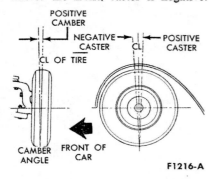

FIG. 40—Caster and Camber Angles

The correct caster angle, or tilt is specified in Part 3-6.

CAMBER

Check the camber angle at each front wheel.

Camber is the amount the front wheels are tilted at the top (Fig. 40). If a wheel tilts outward, camber is positive. If a wheel tilts inward, cam-

ber is negative. The correct camber angle, or outward (positive) tilt, is specified in Part 3-6.

TOE-IN

Alignment height spacers should not be used to check and adjust toe-in. Toe-in should only be checked and adjusted after the caster and camber have been adjusted to specifications.

Check the toe-in with the front wheels in the straight-ahead position. Measure the distance between the extreme front and also between the extreme rear of both front wheels. The difference between these two distances is the toe-in.

Correct toe-in, or inward pointing of both front wheels at the front, is specified in Part 3-6.

FRONT WHEEL TURNING ANGLE

When the inside wheel is turned 20°, the turning angle of the outside wheel should be as specified in Part 3-6. The turning angle cannot be adjusted directly, because it is a result of the combination of caster, camber, and toe-in adjustments and should, therefore, be measured only after these adjustments have been made. If the turning angle does not measure to specifications, check the spindle or other suspension parts for a bent condition.

CASTER AND CAMBER ADJUSTMENTS

After the front wheel alignment factors have been checked, make the necessary adjustments. **Do not attempt to adjust front wheel alignment by bending the suspension or steering parts.**

Caster and camber can be adjusted by loosening the bolts that attach the upper suspension arm inner shaft to the frame side rail, and moving the arm assembly in or out in the elongated bolt holes. Since any movement of the arm affects both caster and camber, **both** factors should be balanced against one another when making the adjustment.

Caster. To adjust caster, install the adjusting tool as shown in Fig. 41. Loosen both upper arm inner shaft retaining bolts, as required, and move either the front or rear of the shaft inboard or outboard as necessary to increase or decrease the caster angle. Then, tighten the bolt to retain the adjustment.

Camber. To adjust the camber, loosen both upper arm inner shaft retaining bolts as required, and move

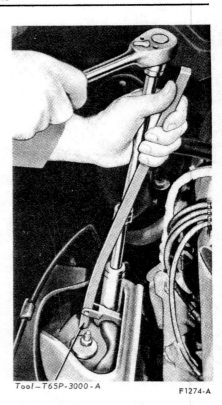

Tool–T65P-3000-A   F1274-A

FIG. 41—Adjusting Caster and Camber

both the front and rear ends of the shaft inboard or outboard as necessary with Tool-T65P-3000-A to increase or decrease the camber angle. Tighten the bolts and again check the caster and re-adjust if necessary. Then, remove the alignment spacers.

TOE-IN AND STEERING WHEEL SPOKE POSITION ADJUSTMENTS

Check the steering wheel spoke position when the front wheels are in the straight-ahead position. If the spokes are not in their normal position, they can be properly adjusted while toe-in is being adjusted.

1. Loosen the two clamp bolts on each spindle connecting rod sleeve (Fig. 42).

2. Adjust toe-in. If the steering wheel spokes are in their normal position, lengthen or shorten both rods equally to obtain correct toe-in (Fig. 42). If the steering wheel spokes are not in their normal position, make the necessary rod adjustments to obtain correct toe-in and steering wheel spoke alignment (Fig. 43).

3. Recheck toe-in and the steering wheel spoke position. If toe-in is correct and the steering wheel spokes are still not in their normal position, turn both connecting rod sleeves upward

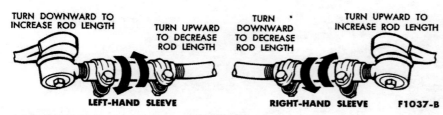

FIG. 42—Spindle Connecting Rod Adjustments

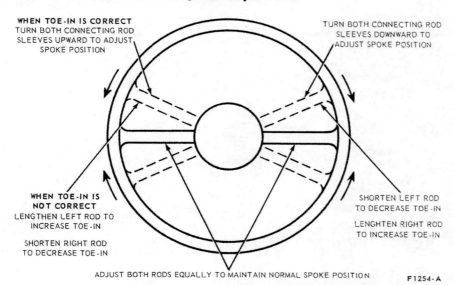

FIG. 43—Toe-In and Steering Wheel Spoke Alignment Adjustment

or downward the same number of turns to move the steering wheel spokes (Fig. 42).

4. When toe-in and the steering wheel spoke position are both correct, torque the clamp bolts on both connecting rod sleeves to specification.

The sleeve position should not be changed when the clamp bolts are tightened.

CHECK BATTERY FLUID LEVEL

The battery is mounted under the hood at the right front side of the engine compartment.

Keep the fluid in each battery cell up to the level of the ring in the bottom of the filler well. Generally, tap water may be added unless it has a high mineral content or has been stored in a metal container.

CHECK AIR CONDITIONING SYSTEM

A quick test of the refrigerant supply can be made by observing the flow of refrigerant through the sight glass (Fig. 44).

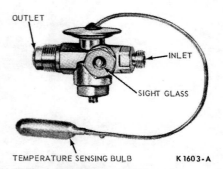

FIG. 44—Sight Glass

To check the refrigerant supply, place a large fan in front of the radiator to aid in cooling the engine. Set the servo control for maximum cooling and the blower on high. Operate the engine at 1300 rpm and observe the sight glass while the compressor is operating. There should be no bubbles in the sight glass after the start of the compressor. Bubbles will appear when the compressor starts but should clear after a few moments.

4 BODY

LUBRICATE HOOD LATCH AND HINGE PIVOTS

Apply Rotunda Polyethylene grease C4AZ-19584-B to all pivot points and to the striker plate as required to eliminate any binding condition (Fig. 45). Operate the latch mechanism several times to be sure that the lubricant has effectively worked in.

LUBRICATE HOOD AUXILIARY CATCH

Apply Rotunda Polyethylene grease C4AZ-19584-B to all pivot points as required to eliminate any binding conditions. Operate the catch several times to be sure that the lubricant has effectively worked in.

LUBRICATE DOOR LOCK CYLINDERS

Apply Rotunda Polyethylene grease C4AZ-19584-B sparingly through the key slot. Insert the key and operate the lock several times to be sure that the lubricant has effectively worked in.

LUBRICATE LUGGAGE COMPARTMENT LOCK CYLINDER

Apply Rotunda Polyethylene grease C4AZ-19584-B sparingly through the key slot. Insert the key and operate the lock several times to be sure that the lubricant has effectively worked in.

LUBRICATE DOOR HINGE AND HINGE CHECK

Apply the specified lubricant to the hinge pivot points as required to eliminate any binding condition. Open and close the door several times to be sure that the lubricant has effectively worked in.

LUBRICATE LUGGAGE COMPARTMENT HINGE PIVOTS

Apply the specified lubricant to the hinge pivot points as required. Open and close the luggage compartment several times to be sure that the hinge pivots do not bind.

LUBRICATE TAILGATE LOCK CYLINDER

Apply Rotunda Polyethylene

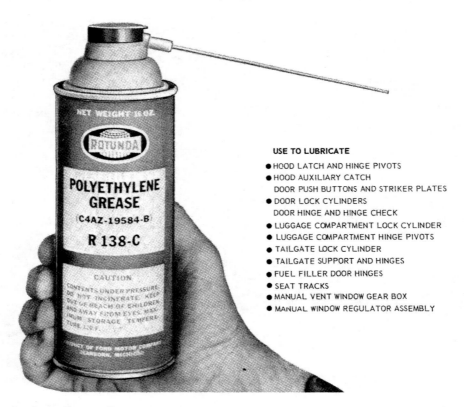

USE TO LUBRICATE

- HOOD LATCH AND HINGE PIVOTS
- HOOD AUXILIARY CATCH
  DOOR PUSH BUTTONS AND STRIKER PLATES
- DOOR LOCK CYLINDERS
  DOOR HINGE AND HINGE CHECK
- LUGGAGE COMPARTMENT LOCK CYLINDER
- LUGGAGE COMPARTMENT HINGE PIVOTS
- TAILGATE LOCK CYLINDER
- TAILGATE SUPPORT AND HINGES
- FUEL FILLER DOOR HINGES
- SEAT TRACKS
- MANUAL VENT WINDOW GEAR BOX
- MANUAL WINDOW REGULATOR ASSEMBLY

M 1113-A

FIG. 45 — Polyetheylene Grease Can

grease C4AZ-19584-B sparingly through the key slot. Insert the key and operate the lock several times to be sure that the lubricant has effectively worked in.

LUBRICATE TAILGATE SUPPORT AND HINGES

Apply Rotunda Polyethylene grease C4AZ-19584-B to all pivot and friction points to eliminate any binding conditions. Operate the tailgate several times to be sure that the lubricant has effectively worked in.

LUBRICATE FUEL FILLER DOOR HINGES

Apply Rotunda Polyethylene grease C4AZ-19584-B to the hinge pivot points as required to eliminate any binding condition. Open and close the door several times to be sure that the lubricant has effectively worked in.

LUBRICATE WEATHERSTRIP AND RUBBER SEALS

Use Silicone lubricant COAZ-19533-A-jelly or COAZ-19533-B-spray, as applicable, to lubricate

door weatherstrips to eliminate weatherstrip squeaks and make doors easier to close.

LUBRICATE SEAT TRACK

Apply Rotunda Polyethylene grease C4AZ-19584-B to the seat track slides, as required, for ease of operation.

CLEAN BODY DRAIN HOLES OR EXAMINE DUST VALVES FOR PROPER OPERATION

Make sure the drain holes in the doors, rocker panels and quarter panels are free from obstruction. Visually check the dust valves for proper sealing and draining operation.

REPLACE WINDSHIELD WIPER BLADES

Wiper blade replacement intervals will vary with the amount of use, type of weather, chemical reaction from road tars or salts and the age of the blades. Be sure that the windshield glass surface is not contaminated with oil, tree sap or other foreign sub-

stance which cannot be easily rubbed off.

Generally, if the wiper pattern across the glass is still uneven and streaked after these tests, replace the blades.

CHECK CONVERTIBLE TOP OPERATION

If convertible top operation becomes sluggish or slow, check the hydraulic reservoir fluid level. Fluid level should be approximately ¼ inch from the filler opening. The proper fluid for all cars is automatic transmission fluid.

CHECK CONVERTIBLE TOP FLUID LEVEL

1. Remove the rear seat and raise the top.
2. Place absorbent cloths below the filler plug.
3. Remove the filler plug, and check the fluid level. It should be level with the bottom edge of the hole.
4. If the level is low, check the system for leaks, adding hydraulic fluid as necessary (automatic transmission fluid).

LUBRICATION CHARTS AND SPECIFICATIONS

GROUP 21

LUBRICANT SPECIFICATIONS

ITEM	FORD PART NO.	PART NAME	FORD SPECIFICATION
Body Hinges	C4AZ-19584-A, R-138-B	Lifetime Body Grease	ESB-M1C105-A
Brake Master Cylinder	B7AZ-19542-A, R-103-A	Rotunda Heavy Duty Brake Fluid	SAE 70R3
Front Suspension Ball Joints and Steering Linkage	C1AZ-19590-B	FoMoCo Ball Joint Grease	ESA-M1C75-A
Front Wheel Bearings	C1AZ-19590-B	FoMoCo Wheel Bearing Grease	ESA-M1C75-A
Hood Latch & Safety Catch	C4AZ-19584-A, R-138-B	Lifetime Body Grease	ESB-M1C105-A
Lock Cylinders	B4A-19587-A	Rotunda Lock Lubricant	ESB-M2C20-A
Rear Axle-Limited Slip	C1AZ-19580-E or F	FoMoCo Hypoid Gear Lube	ESW-M2C50-A
Limited Slip Axles (use 1 oz. per pint of C1AZ-19580 E or F)	C1AA-19B546-A	Locking Differential Additive	ESW-M2C58-A
Rear Axle—All 240, 289 engines and 390 engines with axle model WDC-AT, AU and BS.	C2AZ-19580-D	FoMoCo Hypoid Gear Lube	ESW-M2C57-A
Rear Axle—All 410, 427, 428 engines and 390 engines with axle models WDT.	C6AZ-19580-A	FoMoCo Hypoid Gear Lube	ESA-M2C80-A
Steering Gear Housing (Manual)	C3AZ-19578-A	Lifetime Steering Gear Grease	ESW-M1C87-A
Steering—Power (Pump Reservoir)	C1AZ-19582-A, R-106-A	Rotunda Automatic Transmission Fluid	M2C33-D
Convertible Top Reservoir	C1AZ-19582-A, R-106-A	Rotunda Automatic Transmission Fluid	M2C33-D
Transmission (Automatic)	C1AZ-19582-A, R-106-A	Rotunda Automatic Transmission Fluid	M2C33-D
Transmission (Manual)	C3RZ-19C547-B	Rotunda Manual Transmission Lube	ESW-M2C83-A
Universal Joints	C1AZ-19586-B	FoMoCo Universal Lube	ESA-M1C57-A
Exhaust Heat Control Valve	C0AZ-19A501-A, R-149-A	Penetrating Lubricant	ESR-M99C50-A
Engine Crankcase Oil SAE 10W-20W-30 SAE 5W-10W-20 SAE 20W-30-40	C5AZ-19579-A, B or C R-10-D, E or F C5AZ-19579-D, E or F, R-10-D, E or F C5AZ-19579-G, H or J, R-10-G, H or J	Rotunda 6,000 Mile Motor Oil (MS Sequence tested SAE 10W-20W-30 above—10° F. to 90° F. SAE 5W-10W-20W for sustained temperatures below—10° F. SAE 20W-30-40 for temperatures above 90° F.	ESE-M2C101-A
Engine Oil Filter	C1AZ-6731-A, R1-A	Rotunda Oil Filter—6,000 mile type	

ENGINE CRANKCASE OILS

Use of SAE 10W-30 oil will provide the proper viscosity for all normal ranges of outside temperatures. For operation at sustained outside temperatures below −10°F. a 5W-20 oil should be used.

OIL QUALITY

Use only oils which have been tested and certified by the maker as satisfying automobile manufacturers specifications for Engines Operating Sequence Tests for Service M.S. Ford Motor Company specification covering these tests is ESE-M2C101-A. These tests are defined by ASTM committee D2 for section G-IV of

technical committee B and are published in the SAE Handbook.

These tests cover oil characteristics as follows:

Sequence I—Low Temperature Wear Prevention—(Cold Starts)

Sequence II — High Speed – High Temperature Wear Prevention

Sequence III—High Temperature Deposit Formation—(Varnish)

Sequence IV—Corrosion and Rust Prevention

Sequence V—Sludge Formation

If engine oils are used which do not meet these requirements, it will be necessary to change oil more frequently than every 6,000 miles. Ro-

tunda 6,000 Motor Oil meets these requirements.

If it is necessary to use an "MS" oil which is not certified by the marketer as having passed the Engine Operating Sequence Tests, the addition of Rotunda Oil Conditioner to the oil will satisfy the requirements.

OIL FILTER

Use of the right oil filter is also essential to good engine life and operation. For 6,000 mile filter change intervals, filters must meet Ford Specifications ES-COAE-6714-A. The genuine Rotunda Oil Filter meets this requirement.

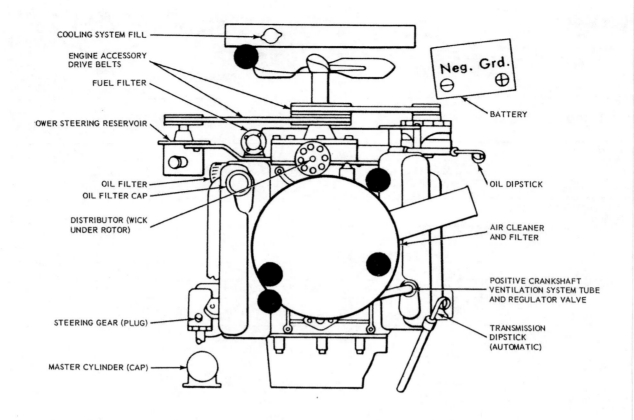

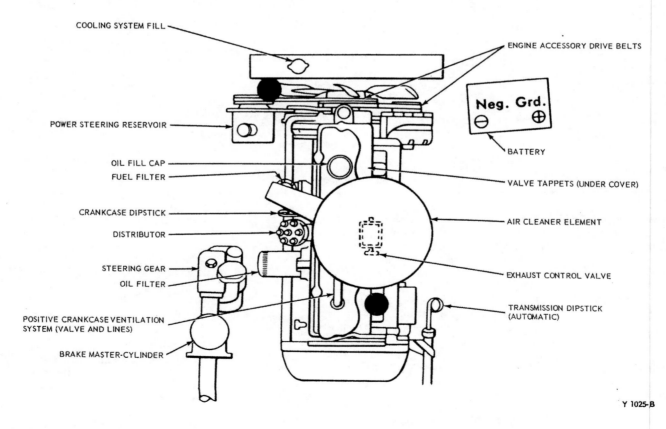

FIG. 1—Typical Lubrication Chart

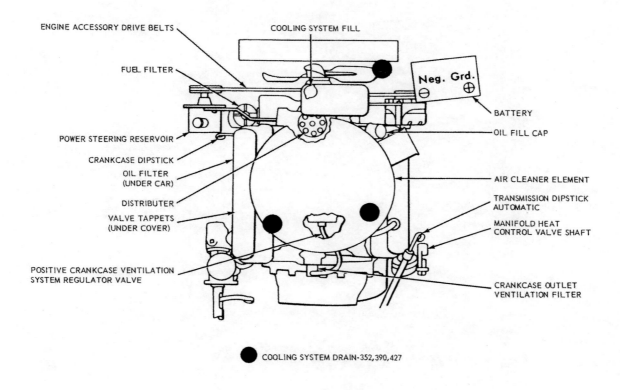

COOLING SYSTEM DRAIN-352,390,427

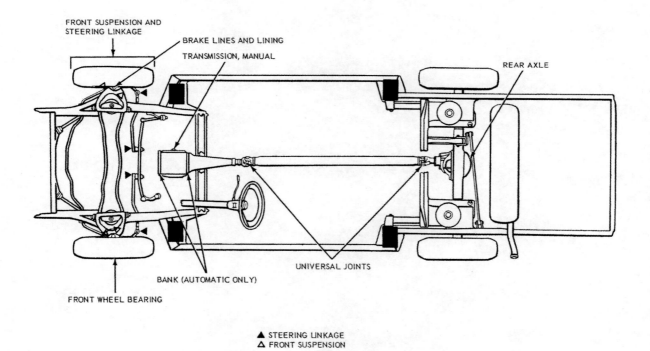

△ STEERING LINKAGE
△ FRONT SUSPENSION

Y 1002-B

FIG. 2—Typical Lubrication Chart

SCHEMATICS

GROUP 22

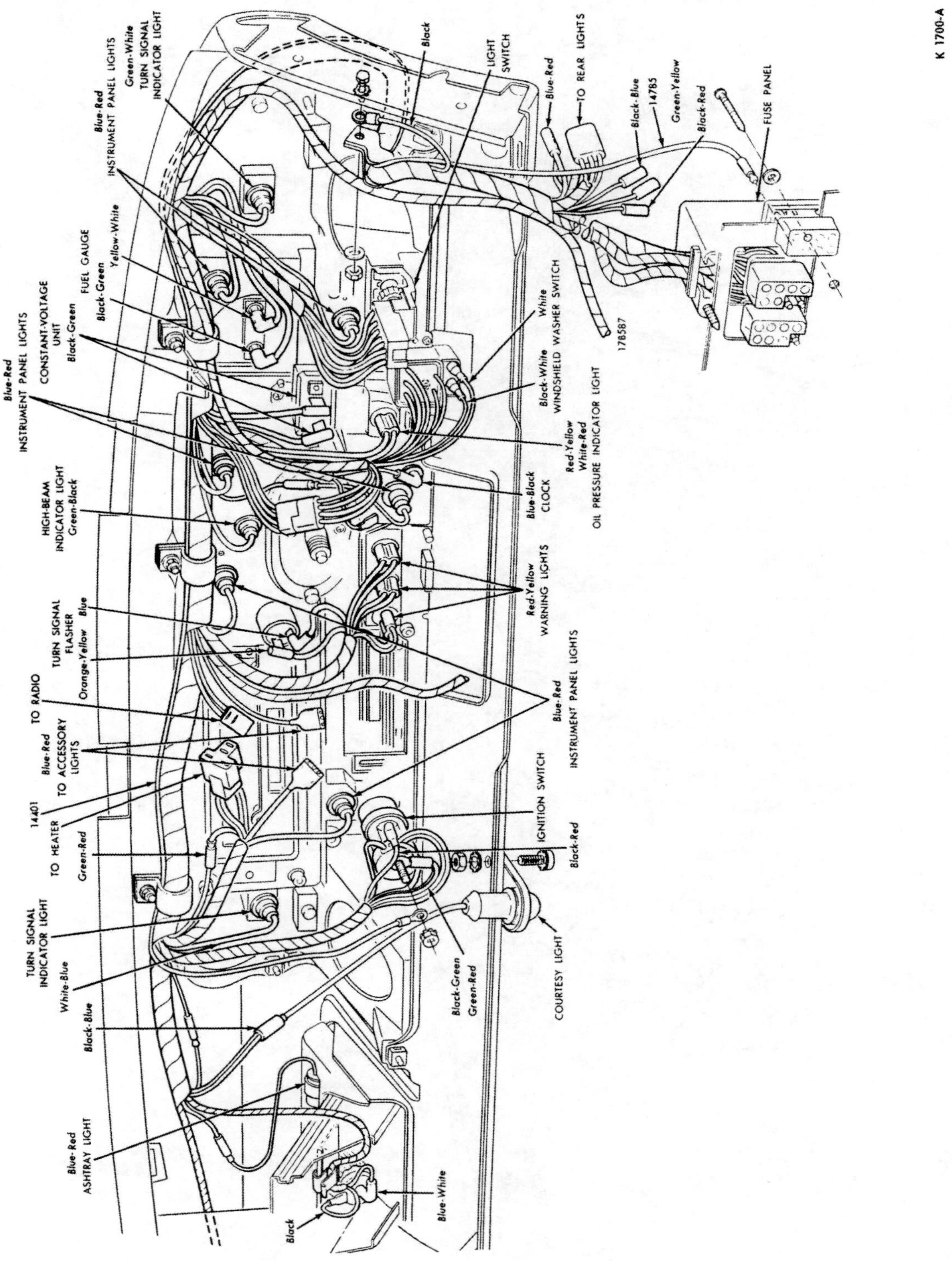

K 1700-A

Black

LIGHT SWITCH

Blue-Red

TO REAR LIGHTS

Blue-Red
Green-White
TURN SIGNAL
INDICATOR LIGHT

Blue-Red
INSTRUMENT PANEL LIGHTS

Black-Blue
14785
Green-Yellow
Black-Red

FUSE PANEL

Yellow-White

Black-Green

Fuel Gauge

Blue-Red
CONSTANT-VOLTAGE UNIT

Black-Green

Blue-Red
INSTRUMENT PANEL LIGHTS

White
WINDSHIELD WASHER SWITCH

Black-White

178587

HIGH-BEAM
INDICATOR LIGHT
Green-Black

Red-Yellow
White-Red
OIL PRESSURE INDICATOR LIGHT

Blue-Black
CLOCK

Red-Yellow
WARNING LIGHTS

TURN SIGNAL
FLASHER   Blue
Orange-Yellow

TO RADIO

Blue-Red

14401   Blue-Red
TO ACCESSORY LIGHTS

Blue-Red
INSTRUMENT PANEL LIGHTS

TO HEATER
Green-Red

IGNITION SWITCH

Black-Red

TURN SIGNAL
INDICATOR LIGHT

White-Blue

Black-Blue

Black-Green
Green-Red

COURTESY LIGHT

Blue-Red
ASHTRAY LIGHT

Blue-White

Black

FIG. 1—Instrument Panel—Ford

K 1701-A

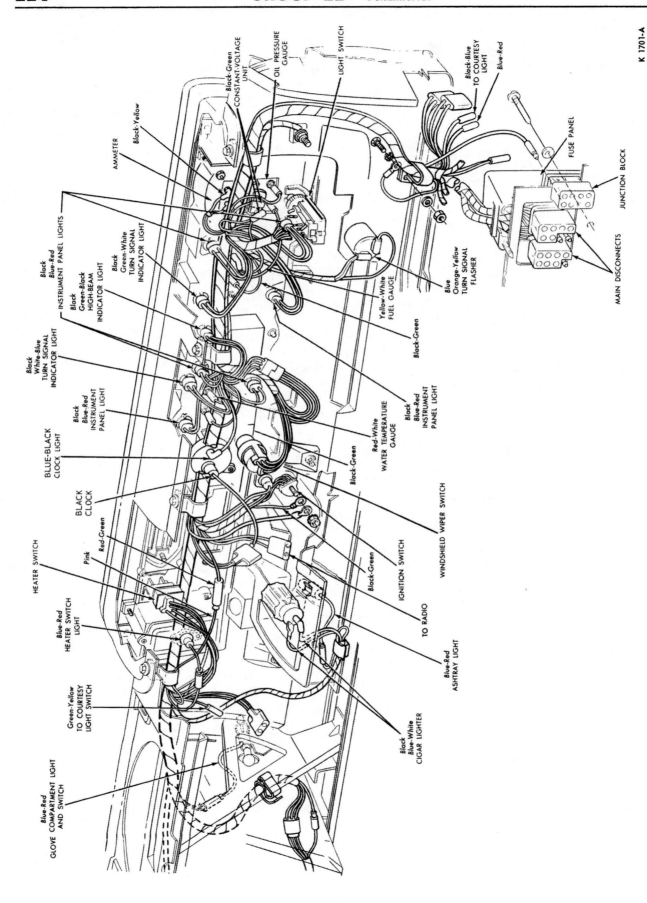

FIG. 2 – Instrument Panel—Mercury

AMMETER

Black-Green
CONSTANT-VOLTAGE
UNIT

OIL PRESSURE
GAUGE

LIGHT SWITCH

Black-Blue
TO COURTESY
LIGHT

Blue-Red

FUSE PANEL

JUNCTION BLOCK

MAIN DISCONNECTS

Black-Yellow

Black
Blue-Red
INSTRUMENT PANEL LIGHTS

Black
Green-Black HIGH-BEAM
INDICATOR LIGHT

Black
Green-White
TURN SIGNAL
INDICATOR LIGHT

Yellow-White
FUEL GAUGE

Blue
Orange-Yellow
TURN SIGNAL
FLASHER

Black-Green

Black
White-Blue
TURN SIGNAL
INDICATOR LIGHT

Black
Blue-Red
INSTRUMENT
PANEL LIGHT

BLUE-BLACK
CLOCK LIGHT

BLACK
CLOCK

Red-White
WATER TEMPERATURE
GAUGE

Black
Blue-Red INSTRUMENT
PANEL LIGHT

Black-Green

Black-Green

IGNITION SWITCH

WINDSHIELD WIPER SWITCH

HEATER SWITCH

Blue-Red
HEATER SWITCH
LIGHT

Pink

Red-Green

TO RADIO

Blue-Red
ASHTRAY LIGHT

Green-Yellow
TO COURTESY
LIGHT SWITCH

Blue-Red
GLOVE COMPARTMENT LIGHT
AND SWITCH

Black
Blue-White
CIGAR LIGHTER

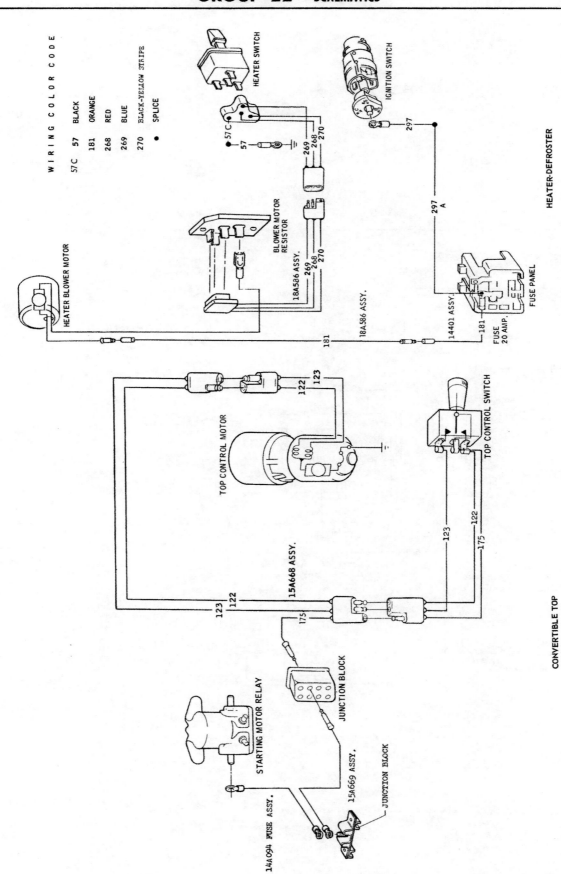

K 1702-A

WIRING COLOR CODE

57C 57 BLACK
181 ORANGE
268 RED
269 BLUE
270 BLACK-YELLOW STRIPE
•   SPLICE

HEATER SWITCH

IGNITION SWITCH

HEATER-DEFROSTER

HEATER BLOWER MOTOR

BLOWER MOTOR RESISTOR

18A586 ASSY.

18A586 ASSY.

FUSE PANEL

FUSE 20 AMP.

14401 ASSY.

TOP CONTROL MOTOR

TOP CONTROL SWITCH

15A668 ASSY.

JUNCTION BLOCK

JUNCTION BLOCK

15A669 ASSY.

STARTING MOTOR RELAY

14A094 FUSE ASSY.

CONVERTIBLE TOP

FIG. 3—Convertible Top, Heater and Defroster

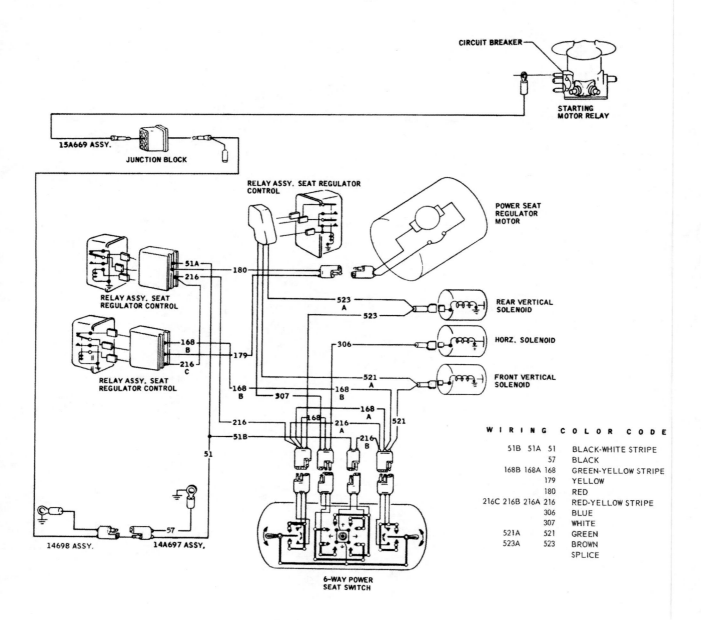

FIG. 4—6-Way Power Seat

CIRCUIT BREAKER

STARTING MOTOR RELAY

15A669 ASSY.

JUNCTION BLOCK

RELAY ASSY. SEAT REGULATOR CONTROL

POWER SEAT REGULATOR MOTOR

51A
216
180

RELAY ASSY. SEAT REGULATOR CONTROL

523 A
523

REAR VERTICAL SOLENOID

168 B
216 C

306

HORZ. SOLENOID

RELAY ASSY. SEAT REGULATOR CONTROL

179
521 A

FRONT VERTICAL SOLENOID

168 B
307
168 B

168 A
216 A
521

216
51B

216 A
216 B

51

57

14698 ASSY.

14A697 ASSY.

6-WAY POWER SEAT SWITCH

WIRING COLOR CODE

51B 51A 51		BLACK-WHITE STRIPE
	57	BLACK
168B 168A 168		GREEN-YELLOW STRIPE
	179	YELLOW
	180	RED
216C 216B 216A 216		RED-YELLOW STRIPE
	306	BLUE
	307	WHITE
521A	521	GREEN
523A	523	BROWN
		SPLICE

K 1703-A

K 1704-A

WIRING COLOR CODE

51A	51	BLACK-RED STRIPE
57B	57A	57	BLACK
	163	GRAY-ORANGE DOT ON ENDS
175	165	GRAY
170E	170B 170A	170	RED-BLUE STRIPE
170C		194	RED
317 170C		226	GRAY-YELLOW DOT ON ENDS
		227	GRAY-YELLOW DOT ON ENDS
	301A	301	RED-BROWN STRIPE
316	302A	302	YELLOW-BLUE STRIPE
	333	313	YELLOW-BLACK STRIPE
	334	314	RED-BLACK STRIPE
		319	YELLOW-VIOLET STRIPE
		320	RED-VIOLET STRIPE
		322	YELLOW-RED STRIPE
		323	RED-YELLOW STRIPE
938B 938A		938	BLACK-WHITE STRIPE
			SPLICE

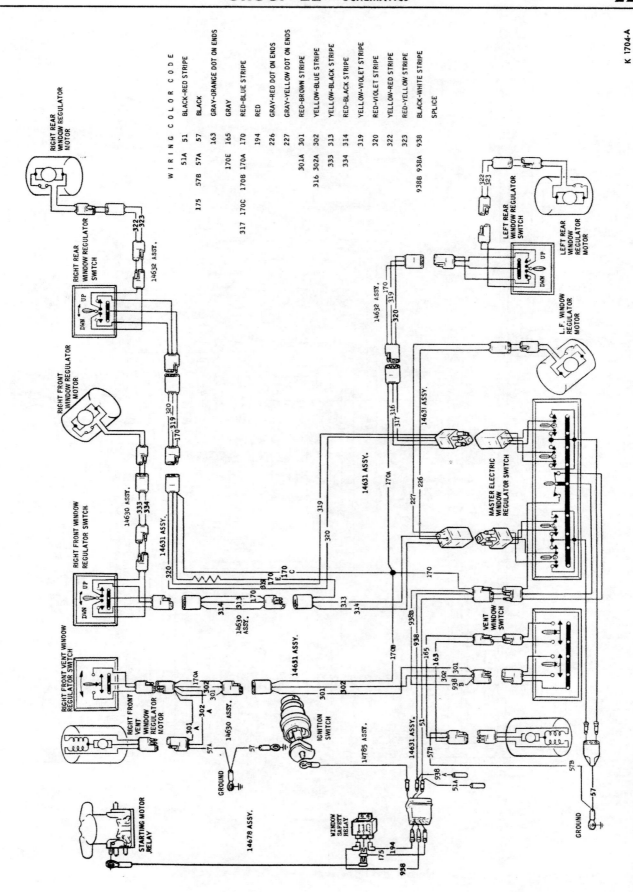

FIG. 5—Power Windows

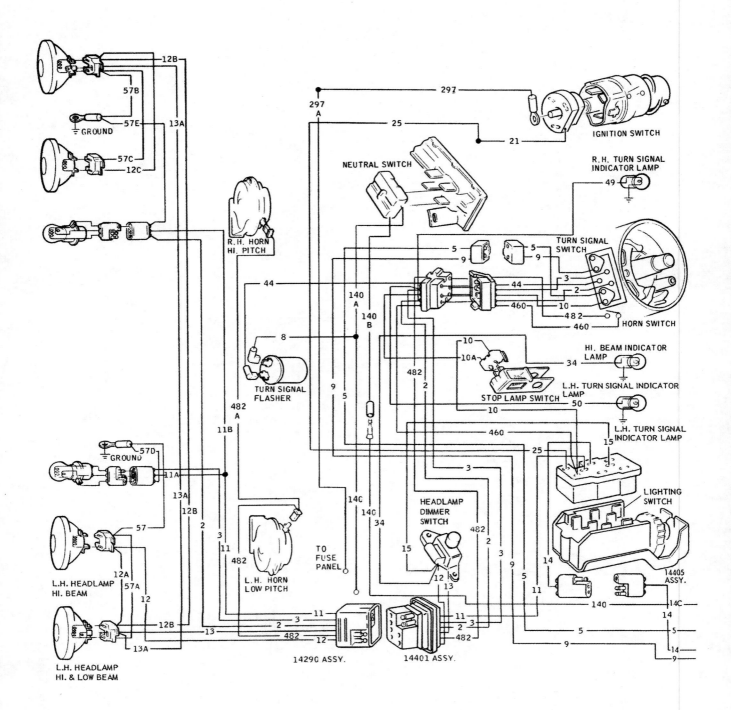

K 1705-A

FIG. 6—Ford Exterior Lighting, Turn Signals and Horns

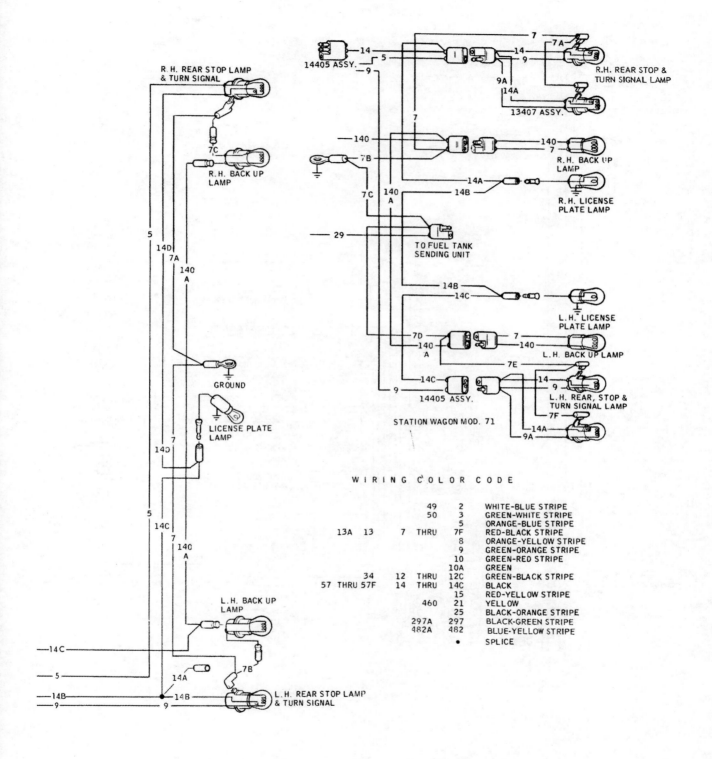

R.H. REAR STOP LAMP
& TURN SIGNAL

R.H. BACK UP
LAMP

5

14D

7A

140
A

GROUND

LICENSE PLATE
LAMP

14C

7

5

14C

7

140
A

L.H. BACK UP
LAMP

14C

5

14A

14B — 14B

9 — 9

7B

L.H. REAR STOP LAMP
& TURN SIGNAL

14405 ASSY.

14

5

9

7

7A

I

14

9

9A

14A

13407 ASSY.

7

R.H. REAR STOP &
TURN SIGNAL LAMP

140

7B

7C

140
A

29

140

140

7

R.H. BACK UP
LAMP

14A

14B

R.H. LICENSE
PLATE LAMP

TO FUEL TANK
SENDING UNIT

14B

14C

L.H. LICENSE
PLATE LAMP

7D

140
A

7

140

L.H. BACK UP LAMP

7E

14C

9

14405 ASSY.

14

9

7F

14A

9A

L.H. REAR, STOP &
TURN SIGNAL LAMP

STATION WAGON MOD. 71

WIRING COLOR CODE

	49	2	WHITE-BLUE STRIPE
	50	3	GREEN-WHITE STRIPE
		5	ORANGE-BLUE STRIPE
13A 13		7 THRU 7F	RED-BLACK STRIPE
		8	ORANGE-YELLOW STRIPE
		9	GREEN-ORANGE STRIPE
		10	GREEN-RED STRIPE
		10A	GREEN
	34	12 THRU 12C	GREEN-BLACK STRIPE
57 THRU 57F		14 THRU 14C	BLACK
		15	RED-YELLOW STRIPE
	460	21	YELLOW
		25	BLACK-ORANGE STRIPE
	297A	297	BLACK-GREEN STRIPE
	482A	482	BLUE-YELLOW STRIPE
	•		SPLICE

K 1705-A

FIG. 6—Ford Exterior Lighting, Turn Signals and Horns

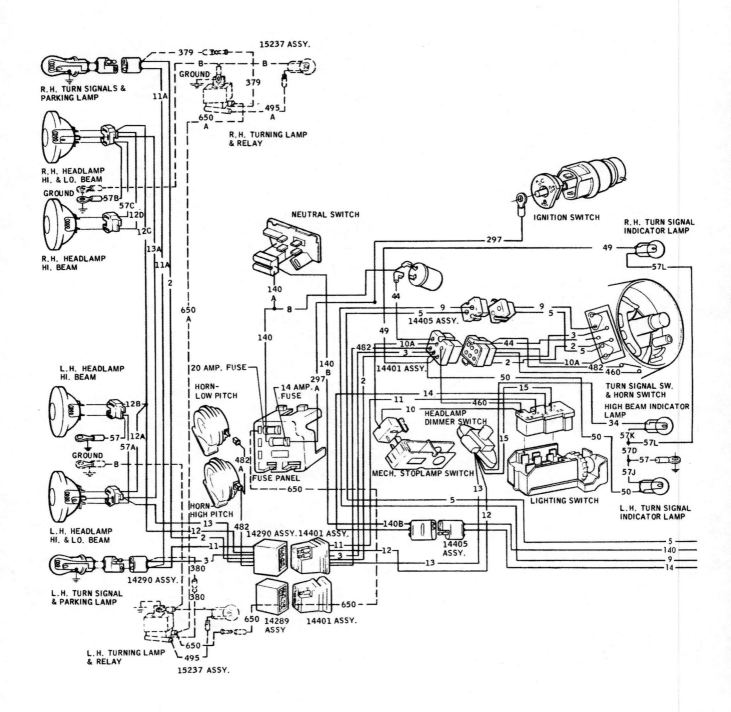

FIG. 7—Mercury Exterior Lighting, Turn Signals and Horns

K 1706-A

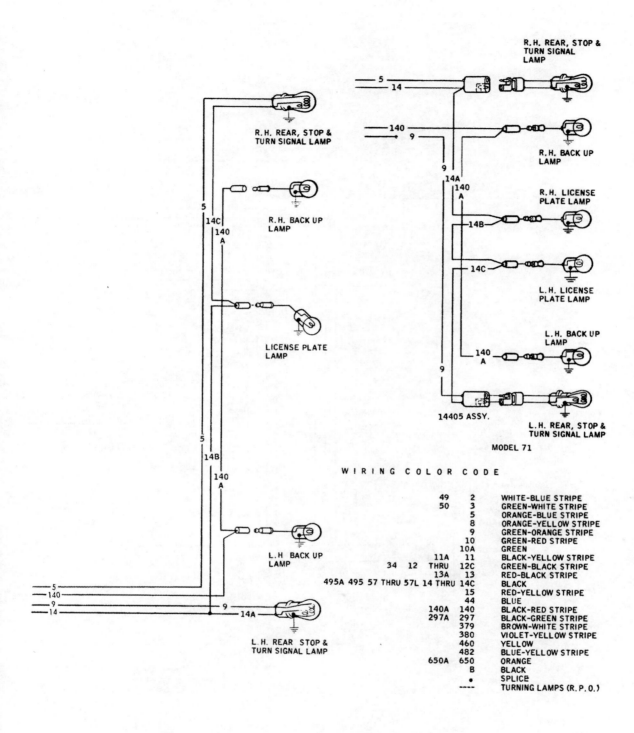

WIRING COLOR CODE

	49	2	WHITE-BLUE STRIPE
	50	3	GREEN-WHITE STRIPE
		5	ORANGE-BLUE STRIPE
		8	ORANGE-YELLOW STRIPE
		9	GREEN-ORANGE STRIPE
		10	GREEN-RED STRIPE
		10A	GREEN
		11A	11	BLACK-YELLOW STRIPE
34	12	THRU	12C	GREEN-BLACK STRIPE
		13A	13	RED-BLACK STRIPE
495A 495 57 THRU 57L	14 THRU	14C	BLACK
			15	RED-YELLOW STRIPE
			44	BLUE
		140A	140	BLACK-RED STRIPE
		297A	297	BLACK-GREEN STRIPE
			379	BROWN-WHITE STRIPE
			380	VIOLET-YELLOW STRIPE
			460	YELLOW
			482	BLUE-YELLOW STRIPE
		650A	650	ORANGE
			B	BLACK
			•	SPLICE
			----	TURNING LAMPS (R.P.O.)

K 1706-A

FIG. 7—Mercury Exterior Lighting, Turn Signals and Horns

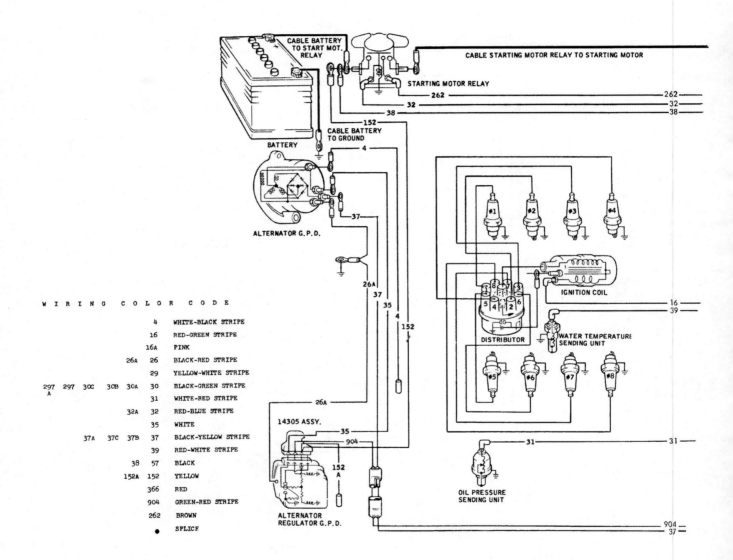

FIG. 8—Ignition, Starting, Charging and Gauges

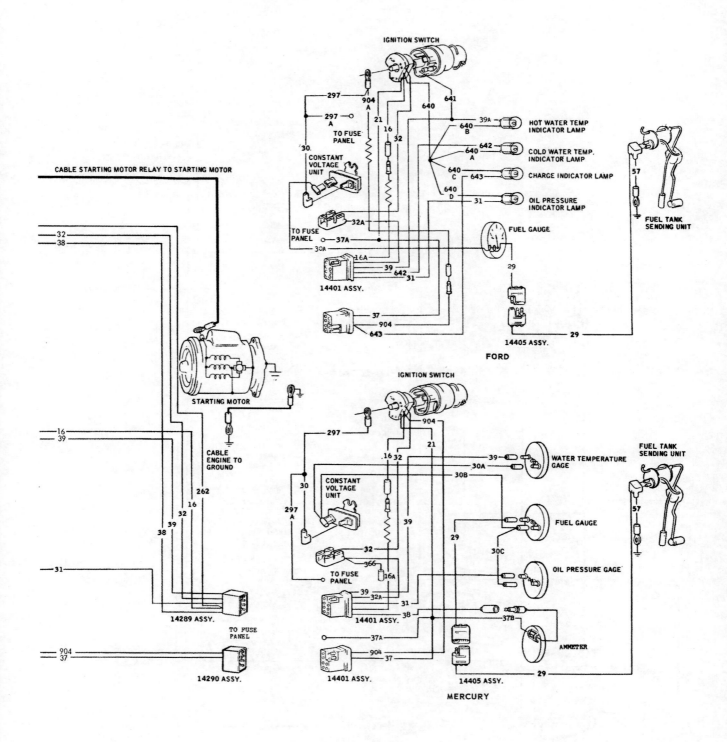

K 1707-A

FIG. 8—Ignition, Starting, Charging and Gauges

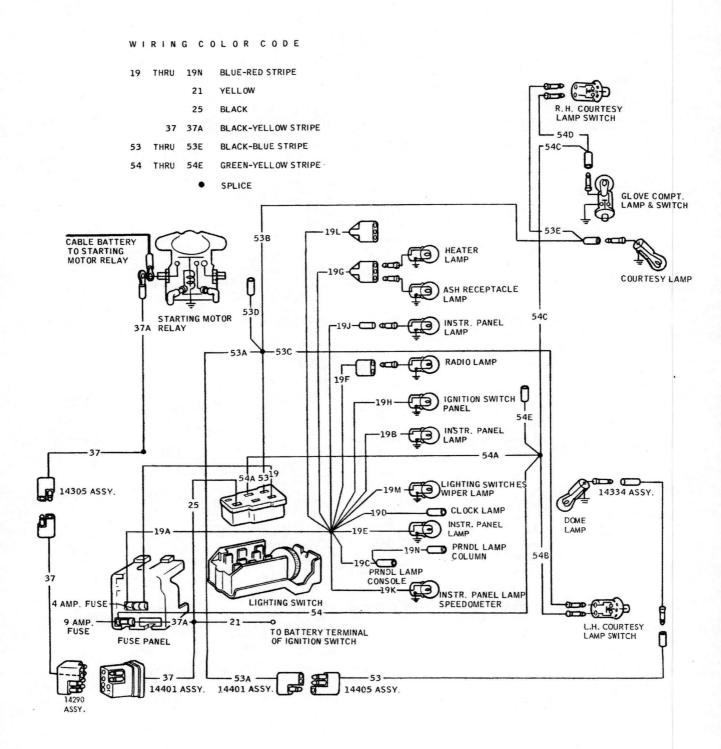

FIG. 9—Ford Interior Lighting

K 1708-A

K 1716-A

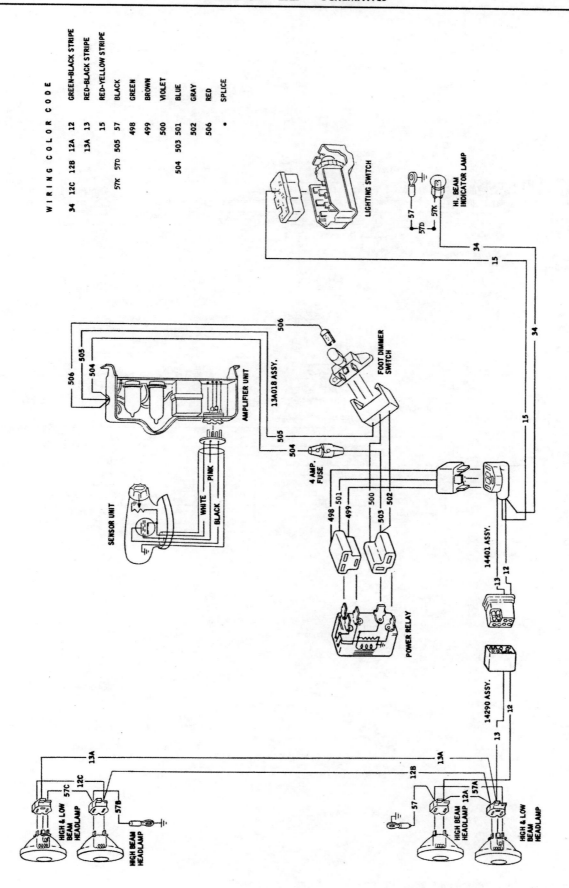

WIRING COLOR CODE

34	12C 12B 12A	12	GREEN-BLACK STRIPE
		13	RED-BLACK STRIPE
	13A	15	RED-YELLOW STRIPE
		57	BLACK
	57K 57D 505	498	GREEN
		499	BROWN
		500	VIOLET
	504 503 501	501	BLUE
		502	GRAY
		506	RED
		•	SPLICE

LIGHTING SWITCH

HI. BEAM INDICATOR LAMP

57

57D

57K

34

15

506

505

504

506

504

AMPLIFIER UNIT

13A018 ASSY.

FOOT DIMMER SWITCH

505

504

4 AMP. FUSE

SENSOR UNIT

WHITE
PINK
BLACK

498

501

499

500

503

502

POWER RELAY

14401 ASSY.

13

12

34

15

14290 ASSY.

13

12

13

12B

13A

57C

12C

57B

HIGH & LOW BEAM HEADLAMP

HIGH BEAM HEADLAMP

57

13A

57A

12A

HIGH & LOW BEAM HEADLAMP

HIGH & LOW BEAM HEADLAMP

FIG. 10—Mercury Interior Lighting

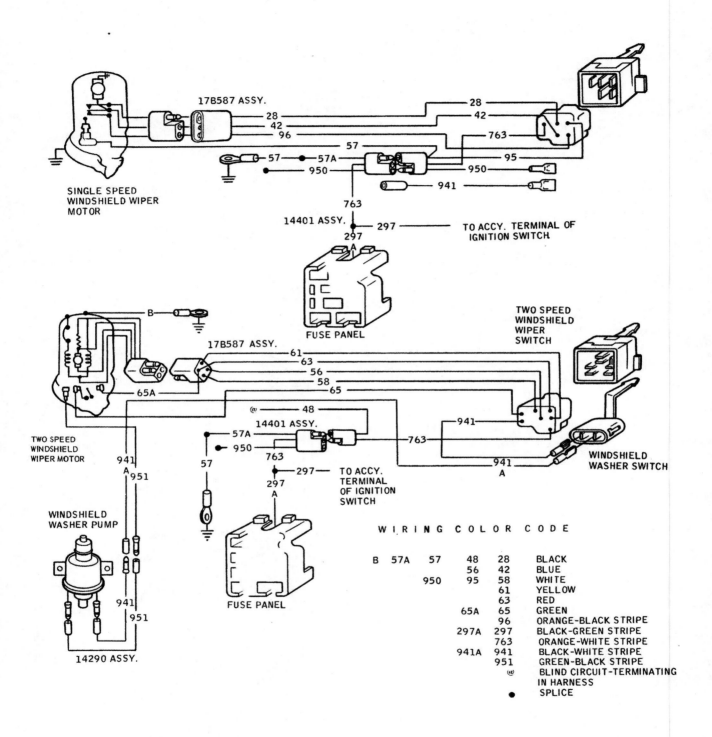

WIRING COLOR CODE

B	57A	57	48	28	BLACK
			56	42	BLUE
		950	95	58	WHITE
				61	YELLOW
				63	RED
			65A	65	GREEN
				96	ORANGE-BLACK STRIPE
			297A	297	BLACK-GREEN STRIPE
				763	ORANGE-WHITE STRIPE
			941A	941	BLACK-WHITE STRIPE
				951	GREEN-BLACK STRIPE
				@	BLIND CIRCUIT-TERMINATING IN HARNESS
				•	SPLICE

K 1710-A

FIG. 11—Ford Windshield Wiper and Washer—Single and Two Speed

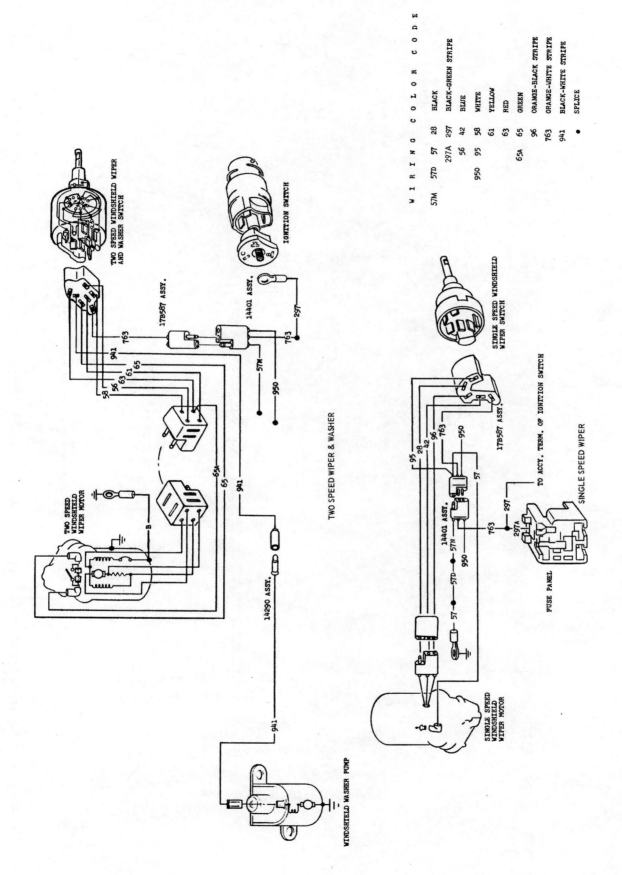

K 1711-A

WIRING COLOR CODE			
57M	57D	57	28	BLACK
		297A	297	BLACK-GREEN STRIPE
		56	42	BLUE
	950	95	58	WHITE
			61	YELLOW
			63	RED
			65	GREEN
		65A		
			96	ORANGE-BLACK STRIPE
			763	ORANGE-WHITE STRIPE
			941	BLACK-WHITE STRIPE
			•	SPLICE

FIG. 12 — Mercury Windshield Wiper and Washer — Single and Two Speed

K 1712-A

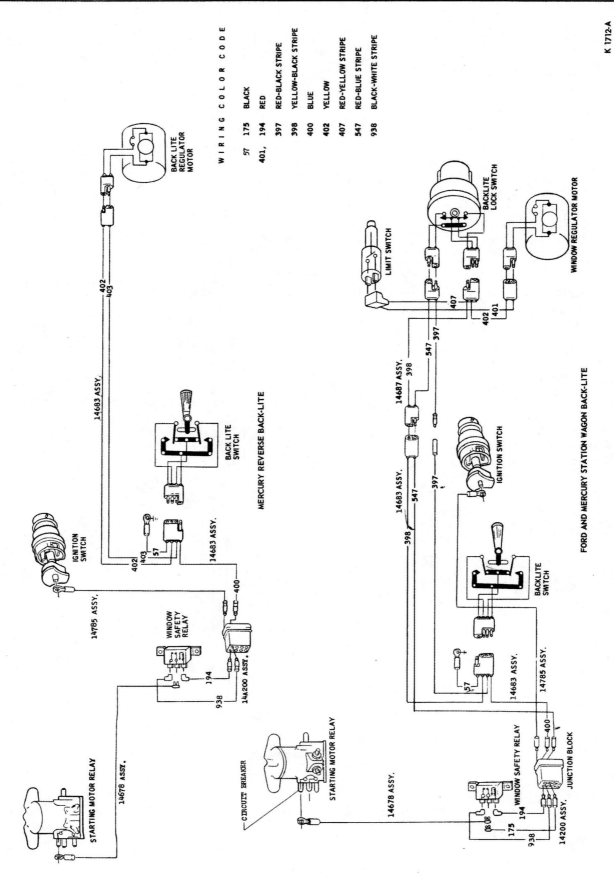

WIRING COLOR CODE

57	175	BLACK
401,	194	RED
	397	RED-BLACK STRIPE
	398	YELLOW-BLACK STRIPE
	400	BLUE
	402	YELLOW
	407	RED-YELLOW STRIPE
	547	RED-BLUE STRIPE
	938	BLACK-WHITE STRIPE

FIG. 13—Ford and Mercury Station Wagon Back-Lite and Mercury Reverse Back-Lite

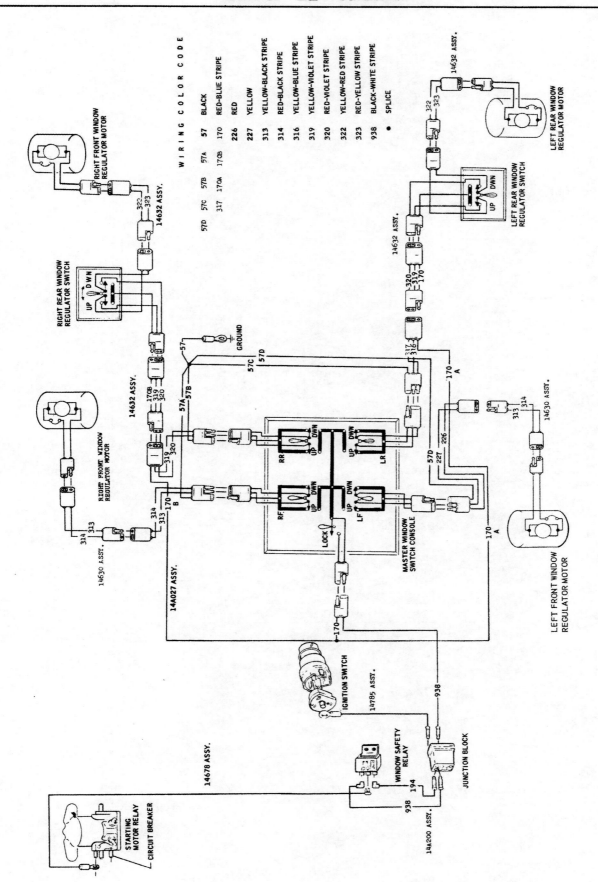

FIG. 14—Ford Power Windows—Console

K 1713-A

K 1714-A

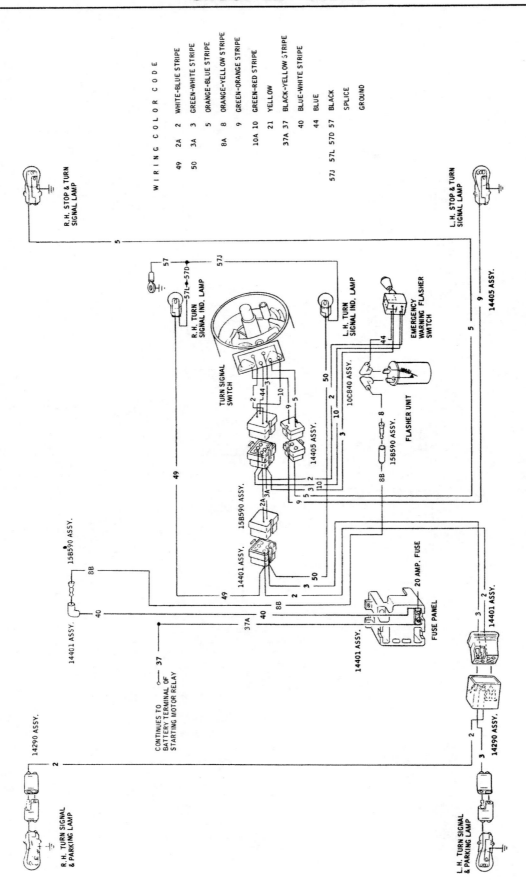

FIG. 15—Emergency Warning Flasher

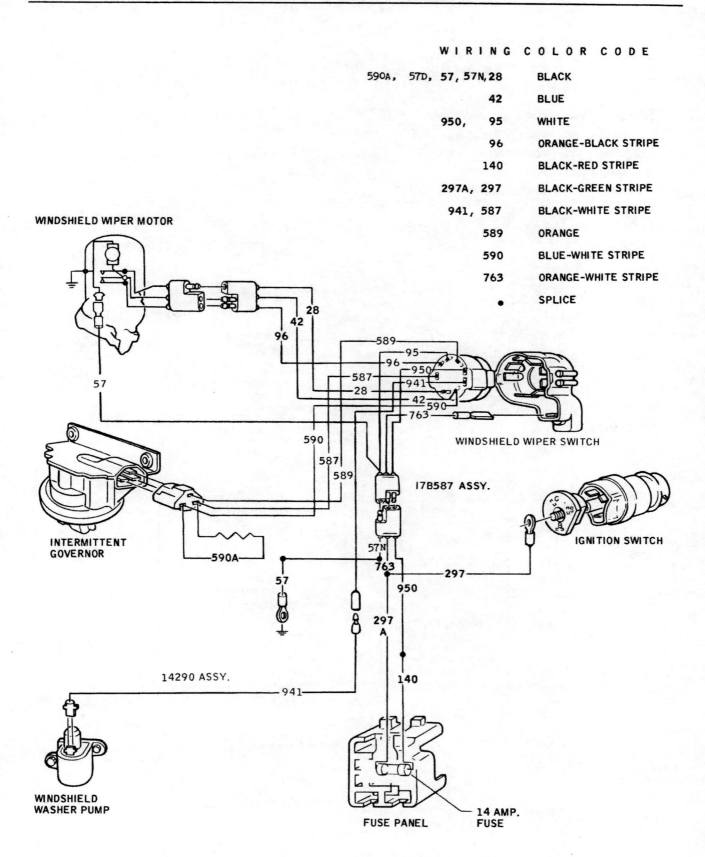

WIRING COLOR CODE

590A, 57D, 57, 57N, 28	BLACK
42	BLUE
950, 95	WHITE
96	ORANGE-BLACK STRIPE
140	BLACK-RED STRIPE
297A, 297	BLACK-GREEN STRIPE
941, 587	BLACK-WHITE STRIPE
589	ORANGE
590	BLUE-WHITE STRIPE
763	ORANGE-WHITE STRIPE
•	SPLICE

WINDSHIELD WIPER MOTOR

WINDSHIELD WIPER SWITCH

INTERMITTENT GOVERNOR

17B587 ASSY.

IGNITION SWITCH

14290 ASSY.

WINDSHIELD WASHER PUMP

FUSE PANEL

14 AMP. FUSE

FIG. 16—Mercury Intermittent Windshield Wiper and Washer

K 1715-A

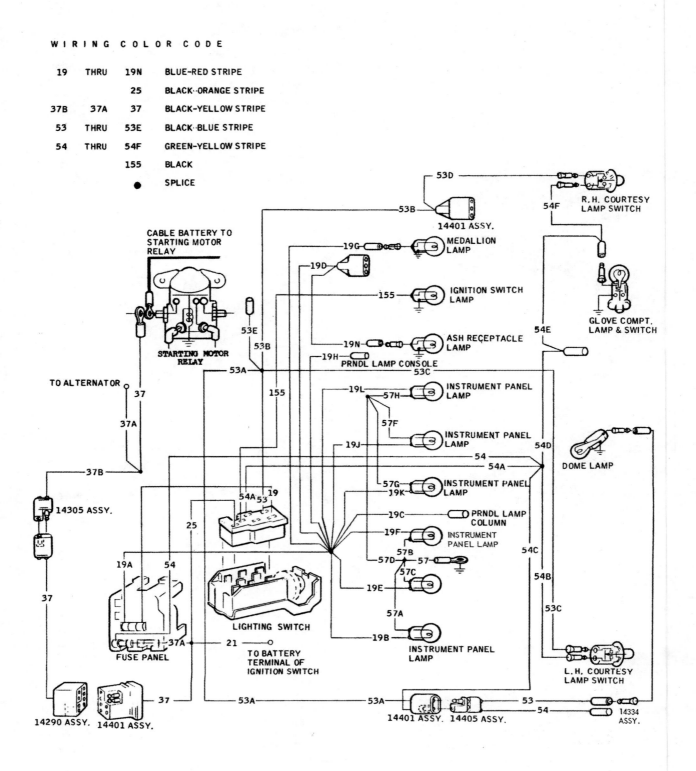

WIRING COLOR CODE

19	THRU	19N	BLUE-RED STRIPE
		25	BLACK-ORANGE STRIPE
37B	37A	37	BLACK-YELLOW STRIPE
53	THRU	53E	BLACK-BLUE STRIPE
54	THRU	54F	GREEN-YELLOW STRIPE
		155	BLACK
		●	SPLICE

53D
R.H. COURTESY LAMP SWITCH

53B
54F
14401 ASSY.

CABLE BATTERY TO STARTING MOTOR RELAY

19G   MEDALLION LAMP

19D

155   IGNITION SWITCH LAMP

GLOVE COMPT. LAMP & SWITCH

STARTING MOTOR RELAY

53E
53B

19N   ASH RECEPTACLE LAMP

54E

19H
PRNDL LAMP CONSOLE

53A
53C

TO ALTERNATOR   37

155

19L   57H   INSTRUMENT PANEL LAMP

37A

57F

INSTRUMENT PANEL LAMP

19J   54D

54
54A   DOME LAMP

37B

14305 ASSY.

57G   INSTRUMENT PANEL LAMP
19K

54A 53   19
25

19C   PRNDL LAMP COLUMN

19F   INSTRUMENT PANEL LAMP

54C

19A   54

57D   57B   57
57C
57A   19E

54B

53C

37

LIGHTING SWITCH

FUSE PANEL   37A   21   TO BATTERY TERMINAL OF IGNITION SWITCH

19B   INSTRUMENT PANEL LAMP

L.H. COURTESY LAMP SWITCH

14290 ASSY.   14401 ASSY.   37   53A   53A   14401 ASSY. 14405 ASSY.   53   54   14334 ASSY.

K 1709-A

FIG. 17—Mercury Automatic Headlight Dimmer